McGraw-Hill Electrical and Electronic Engineering Series
Frederick Emmons Terman, *Consulting Editor*
W. W. Harmon J. G. Truxal
Associate Consulting Editors

Electric Machinery

McGraw-Hill Electrical and Electronic Engineering Series

Frederick Emmons Terman, *Consulting Editor*

W. W. Harman and J. G. Truxal
Associate Consulting Editors

Bailey and Gault · Alternating-current Machinery
Beranek · Acoustics
Bruns and Saunders · Analysis of Feedback Control Systems
Cage · Theory and Application of Industrial Electronics
Cuccia · Harmonics, Sidebands, and Transients on Communication Engineering
Eastman · Fundamentals of Vacuum Tubes
Evans · Control-system Dynamics
Fitzgerald and Higginbotham · Basic Electrical Engineering
Fitzgerald and Kingsley · Electric Machinery
Geppert · Basic Electron Tubes
Glasford · Fundamentals of Television Engineering
Happell and Hesselberth · Engineering Electronics
Harman · Fundamentals of Electronic Motion
Hessler and Carey · Fundamentals of Electrical Engineering
Hill · Electronics in Engineering
Johnson · Transmission Lines and Networks
Kraus · Antennas
Kraus · Electromagnetics
LePage · Analysis of Alternating-current Circuits
LePage and Seely · General Network Analysis
Millman and Seely · Electronics
Millman and Taub · Pulse and Digital Circuits
Rogers · Introduction to Electric Fields
Rüdenberg · Transient Performance of Electric Power Systems
Seely · Electronic Engineering
Seely · Electron-tube Circuits
Seely · Radio Electronics
Siskind · Direct-current Machinery
Skilling · Electric Transmission Lines
Skilling · Transient Electric Currents
Spangenberg · Fundamentals of Electron Devices
Spangenberg · Vacuum Tubes
Stevenson · Elements of Power System Analysis
Storer · Passive Network Synthesis
Terman · Electronic and Radio Engineering
Terman and Pettit · Electronic Measurements
Thaler · Elements of Servomechanism Theory
Thaler and Brown · Servomechanism Analysis
Thompson · Alternating-current and Transient Circuit Analysis
Truxal · Automatic Feedback Control System Synthesis

ELECTRIC MACHINERY

AN INTEGRATED TREATMENT OF A-C AND D-C MACHINES

A. E. Fitzgerald, Sc.D.
Jackson and Moreland, Boston, Massachusetts;
formerly Associate Professor of Electrical Engineering,
Massachusetts Institute of Technology

Charles Kingsley, Jr., S.M.
Associate Professor of Electrical Engineering
Massachusetts Institute of Technology

New York Toronto London
McGRAW-HILL BOOK COMPANY, INC.
1952

ELECTRIC MACHINERY

Library of Congress Catalog Card Number: 51-12939

VII

THE MAPLE PRESS COMPANY, YORK, PA.

PREFACE

Recent years have seen very rapid and even spectacular developments in electric machinery, developments which have especially highlighted the versatility and controllability of electric motors and generators with their associated auxiliaries. These developments embrace both the large machines required to furnish the high powers and energies demanded by some industrial processes and the smaller electromagnetic devices which play essential roles in systems of machines. They make the machine and the vacuum tube companions in arms in meeting the exacting performance standards of modern industrial applications. They also make it necessary to regard the machine not simply as a static device grinding out an essentially constant number of kilowatts or revolutions per minute, but as a dynamic device capable of responding with precision to the spontaneous demands of the process being implemented. Moreover, they require unusual breadth of background and a high degree of mental alertness on the part of the engineers concerned with them.

These continuing developments create the need for new viewpoints and a new synthesis of machinery theory for use in undergraduate electrical-engineering courses. This book is the result of an intensive six-year program having these ends in view. To achieve the desired results, we consider it of first importance to present a *unified* theory of machinery whose methodology is closely related to that in other engineering fields. Thus, one object is to create in the student's mind not only a thoroughgoing picture of how machines work, but also the conviction that the underlying phenomena of torque and voltage production are the same in all types and that this sameness reflects directly into machine analysis. An additional object is to relate both the physical picture and the analysis to those in other fields—to view the machine as an amplifier, for example, or, more generally, as a circuit element for which prescribed properties are sought.

At the outset the rotating machine is regarded primarily as an electromechanical energy-conversion device complementing or competing with similar devices for the production or utilization of rotary or linear motion through the medium of magnetic and electric fields. Particular attention is given to torque and force production because of the relatively greater difficulty of visualization compared with voltage production. As a result, energy conversion in all of these devices is shown to be intimately related to the tendency of the stored field energy to change with motion and time. Machine operation is accordingly viewed in terms of the interaction between the magnetic fields of stator and rotor. This process leads to an early and integrated picture of the basic fundamentals common to all types and to the viewpoint that d-c, synchronous, and induction machines all represent special cases of applying the few common principles. The differences characterizing these special cases are, of course, also part of the picture. Detailed theories of performance follow from quantitative specifications of the mmf and flux-density waves for the various possible electric and magnetic configurations forming the specific machine types. By applying the concepts of interaction of the waves, the associated currents, voltages, torques, speeds, and other significant quantities are determined. Emphasis is given to performance features, limitations, and potentialities, and to the machine as a system element. Iron-core transformers form a natural part of the over-all study.

As the treatment proceeds, the notions of control, controllability, amplification, and related ideas are always influencing factors. These notions, as well as the treatment itself, culminate in an introductory study of the behavior of machines and systems of machines and control devices under dynamic conditions, presented in the last chapter. Such a study, coming in the senior year, offers unique opportunities for consolidation of the subject matter of a wide variety of courses. It also serves as a relatively simple but specific transition from the study of machinery to that of servomechanisms and feedback control methods.

The book presents more material than can be covered comprehensively in the usual two-semester sequence of courses devoted to d-c and a-c machinery. Moreover, the detailed content and order of subject matter in specific courses are naturally governed by local circumstances and the desires and enthusiasms of individual instructors. For these reasons, we have given particular attention to flexibility of use without loss of continuity. For example, Chaps. 8 and 12, dealing with somewhat advanced aspects of synchronous-machine theory and machine transients, are of interest primarily to students specializing in power applications, and these chapters may be omitted entirely in a general course. Some of the articles in other chapters may be omitted or assigned as collateral reading—for example, the articles in Chap. 4 dealing with harmonics, and the more advanced topics in the latter parts of Chaps. 9, 10, and 13. Some of the articles are subdivided into parts to aid in making assignments and to provide for further possibilities of omission of the more detailed or difficult aspects. For example, the part article, 3-9*d*, on commutator action in a-c machines may be omitted or postponed. These suggestions are by no means complete, and further possibilities for individual adaptations may be found readily by an experienced teacher of the subject.

The sequence in which the subject matter is studied likewise can be adapted to individual needs. For example, transformers may appropriately be studied at the beginning of the course or at any time prior to the study of polyphase induction machines in Chap. 9. The fact that transformers are treated in the Appendix does not indicate any intention on our part to minimize their importance. Rather, it is intended to emphasize flexibility in the teaching sequence.

Chapter 2, which correlates the basic concepts of rotating-machine theory with a broader viewpoint applying to electromechanical energy-conversion processes in general, is not a prerequisite to a study of the rest of the book. Some teachers may prefer to assign this chapter at or near the end of the course. Our own teaching experience indicates that study of it early in the course gives the student a better appreciation of the basic physical phenomena underlying the workings of rotating machines. He then realizes, before being immersed in the ramifications of rotating-machine theory, the intimate relationship of this theory with fundamental physics.

Chapter 3 and parts of Chap. 4, which present the unifying basic principles common to all types of rotating machines, should be studied before the more detailed aspects of d-c and a-c machines are taken up. Chapter 3 is the cornerstone for the structure of the rest of the book. But the sequence in which d-c, synchronous, and induction machines are studied in Chaps. 5 through 10 may be varied. The book can also be used for a one-semester course on a-c machines following a conventional d-c machinery course, with study of Chap. 3 serving to correlate and unify d-c and a-c machine theory.

During the planning and writing of this book, we have incurred indebtedness to many of our colleagues at the Massachusetts Institute of Technology. We wish especially to acknowledge the very real help of those who taught these courses with us during the developmental stages. We also wish to express appreciation for the forbearance of the hundreds of students who, during the same period, were exposed to trials and errors in all senses of the words.

A. E. Fitzgerald
Charles Kingsley, Jr.

Cambridge, Mass.
February, 1952

CONTENTS

CHAPTER 1

PHYSICAL ASPECTS OF ELECTROMECHANICAL ENERGY CONVERSION

THE general questions involved in the study of any group of technical devices are:

1. What do they look like?
2. How do they work?
3. What are the scientific and engineering problems associated with them?
4. What are their limitations and fields of usefulness, and how do they compare with competing devices?
5. How is detailed analysis of their performance carried out?

The object of this book is to answer these questions for the devices used in the interconversion of electrical and mechanical energy. Emphasis is given to the very common and very important electromagnetic rotating machine—the motors and generators encountered so often in everyday life. Attention is also devoted to broader aspects of electromechanical energy conversion, not only because of the importance of mechanisms other than the rotating machine, but also to gain proper perspective.

Attention is likewise given to the transformer, which, although not an electromechanical energy-conversion device, is an important auxiliary in the over-all problem of energy conversion. Moreover, in many respects its analytic details are closely related to those of motors and generators. The concepts of transformer behavior thus have the added feature of serving as an adjunct to the study of machines.

Strictly speaking, complete answers to any of the foregoing five questions depend upon study of the entire book. One may ask these questions at any of several technical levels; the more or less superficial answers appropriate for a layman are unsatisfactory to an engineer to an extent determined by his previous training. Probably the most difficult of the questions to answer is the second, dealing with how things work, for all the other answers are intimately dependent upon it. Ultimately the answer must go back to a natural phenomenon and an experimental law of nature. But a simple statement of the phenomenon or law by no means completes the picture. General correlation with related phenomena, the development of a number of alternate viewpoints, and integrated knowledge of the details linking the apparently simple physical bases with the sophisticated forms assumed by modern analytical theories all are essential to a profound grasp. The final objective is not only to provide intuitive familiarity with existing devices but also wherever possible to establish criteria by which proposed innovations may be judged.

Thus, the main object of the first three chapters is to examine how electromechanical energy-conversion devices work. This introductory chapter presents first a brief phenomenological survey of practical electromechanical energy-conversion means and then a preliminary view of the construction and basis of operation of common electromagnetic machines. It concludes with a short outline of how we shall go about the further examination of basic principles in the next two chapters and the detailed analytical studies of the subsequent chapters.

1-1. Electromechanical Energy Conversion. In general terms, an electromechanical energy-conversion device is a link between an electrical and a mechanical system. By appropriately coupling the two systems, it makes possible the conversion of energy from electrical to mechanical form or from mechanical to electrical form. In a device acting as a *generator*, the mechanical system delivers energy through the device to the electrical system; in a device acting as a *motor*, the electrical system delivers energy through the device to the mechanical system. The process is essentially reversible, although part of the energy is irreversibly converted to heat; any motor can be made to run as a generator, and any generator can be made to deliver mechanical power as a motor.

The coupling between the electrical and mechanical systems is through the medium of the fields of electric charges. Both electric and magnetic fields are in general present, and energy storage in these fields is inevitably associated with energy conversion. The energy in the coupling field of the device may change or tend to change during the energy-conversion process. In fact it may be said that the tendency for the energy in the coupling field to release itself and do work is the reason for the existence of coupling between the electrical and mechanical systems.

Electromechanical energy conversion accordingly depends on the existence in nature of phenomena interrelating magnetic and electric fields on the one hand and mechanical force and motion on the other. The principal phenomena utilized practically are the following:[1]

1. A mechanical force is exerted on a current-carrying conductor in a magnetic field, and between current-carrying circuits by means of their

[1] A survey of all known methods for conversion of energy to and from the electrical form is presented in L. W. Matsch and W. C. Brown, Electric Power Sources, *Elec. Eng.*, vol. 66, pp. 880–881, September, 1947.

magnetic fields. The energy-conversion process is reversible because a voltage is induced in a circuit undergoing motion in a magnetic field.

2. A mechanical force is exerted on ferromagnetic material tending to align it with or bring it into the position of the densest part of the magnetic field. When the magnetic field is created by a current-carrying coil, the energy-conversion process is reversible because motion of the material will cause a change in the flux linking the coil, and the change of flux linkages will induce a voltage in the coil.

3. A mechanical force is exerted on the plates of a charged capacitor and on dielectric material in an electric field; conversely, relative motion of the plates and the dielectric results in a change of either the charge or the voltage between the plates or both.

4. Certain crystals are slightly deformed when voltage gradients are applied in particular directions, and, conversely, when they are deformed, an electric charge appears. This phenomenon is known as the *piezoelectric effect.* Although the deformation of the crystal when voltage is applied is small, the associated mechanical force may be very large.

5. Most ferromagnetic materials show a very small deformation under the influence of a magnetic field, and, conversely, the magnetic properties are affected when the materials are strained mechanically. This phenomenon is called *magnetostriction.* As in the piezoelectric effect, the full elastic force of the material is available even though the changes in dimensions are small.

It is fortunate for the engineer that there is a variety of natural phenomena available for electromechanical energy conversion, for the versatility and range of applications of electrical methods are greatly increased thereby. The role of electricity is most apt to be that of an extremely versatile intermediary; although in the ultimate use of energy we seldom want it in electrical form, yet we often convert it to that form. Electrical energy can be transmitted and controlled with relative simplicity, reliability, and efficiency. A feeble source of electrical energy can be made to control a much larger source in a proportional manner so as to produce amplification. For these reasons, electrical techniques have found widespread applications in measurement and control of nonelectrical quantities. In a diesel-electric locomotive, for example, mechanical energy is available at the shaft of the diesel engine, and it is mechanical energy that is required at the axles. Yet electric generators and motors are interposed between these two points for the control and transmission of the energy; in effect, the conversion equipment permits the matching of the torque-speed characteristic of the diesel engine to the torque-speed characteristic required at the axle for optimum train operation. A host of similar examples can be mentioned, all ultimately involving the conversion of energy to or from the electrical form.

In their engineering applications, the foregoing five energy-conversion processes are supplementary rather than competitive. The most important from the point of view of the magnitude of energy involved is the rotating machine, utilizing the first and second phenomena. Electric motors range in size from midgets having a fraction of a watt output and used in instrument-type control mechanisms, up to giants of 65,000 hp used in pumping plants and steel mills. Electric generators with ratings above 100,000 kw are not unusual. By way of contrast, devices based on piezoelectric or magnetostrictive effects are limited to power levels below a few watts. Thus, according to Cady,[2] supplying 1 amp to a 100-watt lamp at a frequency of 60 cps would require 1,500 ft^2 of quartz-crystal area arranged in a pile about 10 ft high consisting of 1,500 thin layers 1 ft square and subjected to a pulsating force of 100 tons.

Another important class of electromechanical energy-conversion devices is formed by those producing translatory and vibratory motions. Translational devices in general may be based on application of any of the foregoing five phenomena. Among those using the first two phenomena are electromagnets, relays, and telephone receivers. It is in the field of translational and vibrational devices that the last three phenomena find their principal application, especially in devices for producing or detecting mechanical or acoustical vibration; examples are microphones, phonograph pickups, and driving systems for setting up supersonic vibrations. Operation of these devices at relatively low power levels is not a disadvantage, and considerations of dynamics, with emphasis on maximum power transfer and frequency-response characteristics, are highly favorable to them.

In this text we shall be primarily concerned with electromagnetic rotating machines, both the steady-state theory of the machines themselves and the dynamical theory of systems containing them. The machine is the best specific vehicle for illustrating the solution of energy-conversion problems. The size and cost elements alone in many motors and generators necessitate the most careful and thoroughgoing analysis. The luxury of true-to-life performance tests on the equivalent of breadboard setups can rarely be afforded—the engineer must be right the first time without the benefit of complete dress rehearsals. Thus no fruitful analytic avenue of approach can be overlooked. At the same time, we shall want to bear in mind that fuller perspective and deeper insight are gained by considering electromechanical energy conversion in a fairly broad sense, recognizing that all such devices have certain basic features in common.

[2] W. G. Cady, Nature and Use of Piezoelectricity, *Elec. Eng.*, vol. 66, pp. 758–762, August, 1947.

1-2. Rotating Machinery: Basis of Operation. In discussing and analyzing the operation of physical devices, more than one viewpoint can usually be adopted. The simplest viewpoint leads to quick, earthy understanding of certain specific features, but it is frequently a restricted one which does not fully reveal the general properties common to many similar devices. Most sophisticated and generalized viewpoints, usually evolved only after some experience with simpler approaches, highlight the general common properties and lead ultimately both to greater insight and to valuable criteria for optimum operation. In this article we shall discuss application of the first of the five phenomena listed in Art. 1-1, first from the simple viewpoint stated there, and then from a somewhat more general magnetic-field viewpoint.

a. The Blv, Bli Viewpoint. A more general statement of the fact that a voltage is induced in a conductor undergoing motion in a magnetic field is Faraday's law of electromagnetic induction, according to which an emf is induced in an electric circuit whenever the magnetic flux linking the circuit changes. The instantaneous emf e is given by

$$e = \frac{d\lambda}{dt} \tag{1-1}$$

where λ is the instantaneous value of flux linkage with the circuit and t is time.

Equation 1-1 is correct in any consistent system of units. In this text the rationalized mks system of units will be used in all theoretical derivations. In general when no units are given after a symbol or equation, mks units are to be understood; at times specific units are indicated either for emphasis or because the mks system is being departed from, as in expressing the output of a motor in horsepower.

For a winding in which all of the flux φ links all N turns of the winding, the flux linkage λ is $N\varphi$, and Eq. 1-1 may be written

$$e = N\frac{d\varphi}{dt} \tag{1-2}$$

Actually part of the magnetic field, usually a small portion in practical devices, is distributed throughout the space occupied by the turns of the winding and therefore links only a fraction of the turns. In computing the total linkage, proper account must be taken of the actual flux linking each turn. Equations 1-1 and 1-2 can be written interchangeably with the effect of the partial flux linkages included by defining the flux as

$$\varphi = \frac{\lambda}{N} \tag{1-3}$$

where φ is the average flux linkage per turn and can be visualized as an equivalent flux linking all N turns of the winding and taking into account partial flux linkages. In most practical devices having ferromagnetic cores, the effect of the partial linkages is relatively slight.

The Faraday law describes quantitatively the induction of voltages in electric rotating machines. Voltages are induced in windings or groups of coils by rotating these windings mechanically through a magnetic field or by mechanically rotating a magnetic field past the windings; by either method the flux linking a specific coil is changed periodically, and a voltage is generated. A sample coil is shown being wound in Fig. 1-1. A

FIG. 1-1. Armature coil being form-wound. (*Courtesy of General Electric Company.*)

group of such coils so interconnected that their induced voltages all make a positive contribution to the desired result is called an *armature winding*. The armature winding of a d-c machine is shown in Figs. 1-2 and 1-3; the armature is the rotating member of the machine, or the *rotor*. Figure 1-4 shows the armature winding of an a-c generator, *alternator*, or *synchronous generator*. Here the armature is the stationary member, or the *stator*.

These coils are wound on iron cores in order that the flux path through them may be as effective as possible. Because the armature iron is subjected to a varying magnetic flux, eddy currents will be induced in it; to minimize eddy-current loss, the armature iron is built up of thin laminations as illustrated in Fig. 1-5 for the armature of a d-c machine and in Fig. 1-6 for the armature of an alternator. The flux path is completed through the iron of the other machine member, and exciting coils or field windings are placed on that member to act as the primary sources of flux in the machine. Schematic diagrams showing the flux paths in a d-c machine and in a synchronous machine, respectively, are given in Figs. 1-7 and 1-8. The paths are indicated by dotted lines, of which path *abcda* is typical in both sketches. The field structure (stator) of a d-c machine is shown in

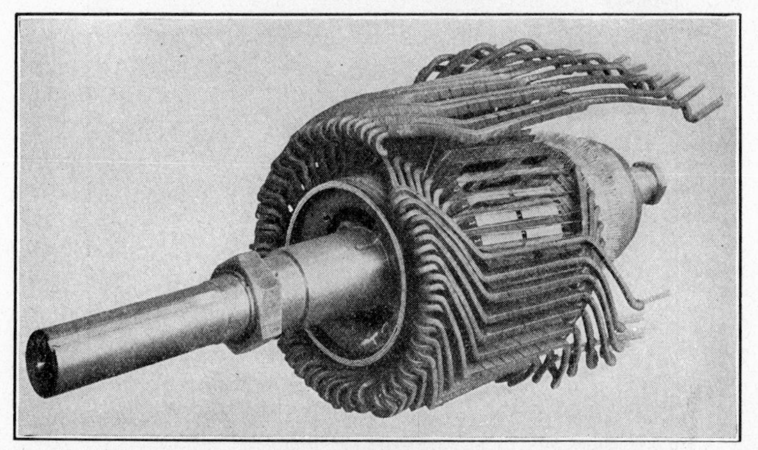

Fig. 1-2. Direct-current generator or motor armature in process of being wound. Each coil has one side placed in a slot bottom and the other side ready to be placed in a slot top. (*Courtesy of General Electric Company.*)

Fig. 1-9. One type of field structure (rotor) of a synchronous machine is shown in Fig. 1-10. The field windings in Figs. 1-7 to 1-10 are *concentrated windings* excited by direct current. Armature windings are almost invariably *distributed windings* with coils arranged around the entire

Fig. 1-3. Direct-current generator or motor armature nearing completion. Coils and some slot wedges are in place. Other slot wedges are ready to be driven into place. (*Courtesy of General Electric Company.*)

armature periphery for better utilization of space and material in the machine.

The radial distribution in the air gap of the flux created by the arma-

FIG. 1-4. Assembling armature coils in stator of turboalternator. The form-wound coils are fitted into the slots provided in the laminations. (*Courtesy of General Electric Company.*)

FIG. 1-5. Exploded view of the unwound armature of a 7.5-kw d-c machine. (*Courtesy of Allis-Chalmers Manufacturing Company.*)

Fig. 1-6. Assembling the stator iron of an alternator. Laminations are stacked on key bars welded to the frame. (*Courtesy of General Electric Company.*)

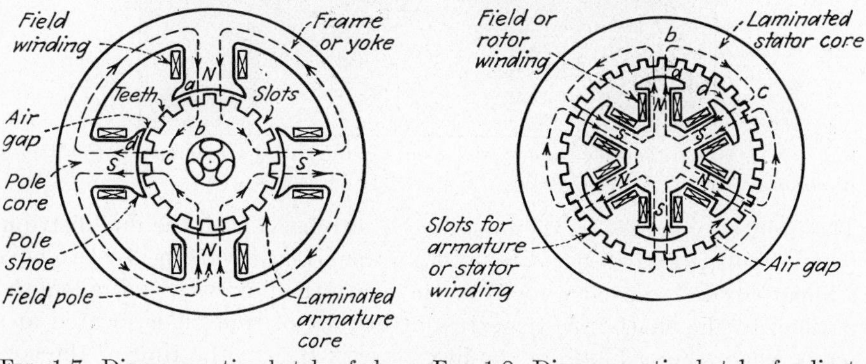

Fig. 1-7. Diagrammatic sketch of d-c machine.

Fig. 1-8. Diagrammatic sketch of salient-pole synchronous machine.

ture winding may be pictured by developing in the descriptive-geometry sense the cylinder forming the armature structure—*i.e.*, the cylinder is cut and laid out flat. The flux distribution for the d-c machine of Fig. 1-7 is shown in Fig. 1-11 with the effect of the armature slots on this distribution ignored. Only a two-dimensional plot need be used because the densities are the same for all points in the gap on a line parallel to the shaft of the machine, a statement which neglects the relatively minor effect of fringing flux at the ends of the rotor and stator. The ordinate of this curve at any point gives the flux density in the air gap at that point on the armature periphery. Thus, the flux densities which the armature conductors are sweeping through as the machine rotates can readily be seen. The analogous plot for a typical a-c machine will usually be more nearly sinusoidal. For most types of generators and motors in the steady state, the amplitude and shape of the air-gap flux distribution remain constant. Under these circumstances the only armature generated voltage results from mechanical motion of either the armature or the field.

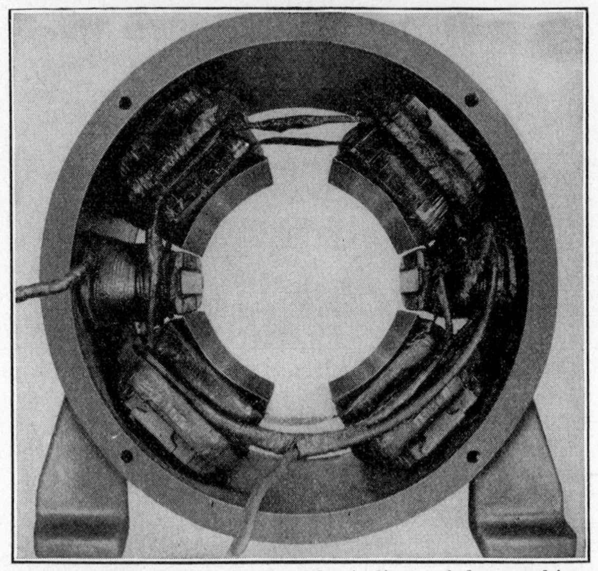

Fig. 1-9. Stator frame, field poles, and field windings of d-c machine. *(Courtesy of Westinghouse Electric Corporation.)*

The induced voltage can then readily be correlated with the flux distribution. Thus, consider any conductor on the armature of Fig. 1-11 to have a linear circumferential velocity v relative to the flux wave and a length l parallel to the shaft. At a particular instant of time, it is located at a point where the ordinate of the flux wave is $\boldsymbol{B}$. In the time dt the conductor sweeps out an area $lv\,dt$. The associated contribution made by motion of this conductor to the change in flux linking the armature circuit is $Blv\,dt$. In accordance with Eq. 1-1, the contribution of the conductor to the instantaneous armature generated voltage is

$$e = Blv \tag{1-4}$$

This emf is called a *speed voltage*. The instantaneous voltage for the entire armature winding may be computed by adding algebraically the

FIG. 1-10. General interior view of part of Boulder Dam hydroelectric station showing wound revolving field (suspended from two cranes) of 82,500-kva 16,500-volt 3-phase, 180-rpm 60-cps 40-pole water-wheel generator. (*Courtesy of General Electric Company.*)

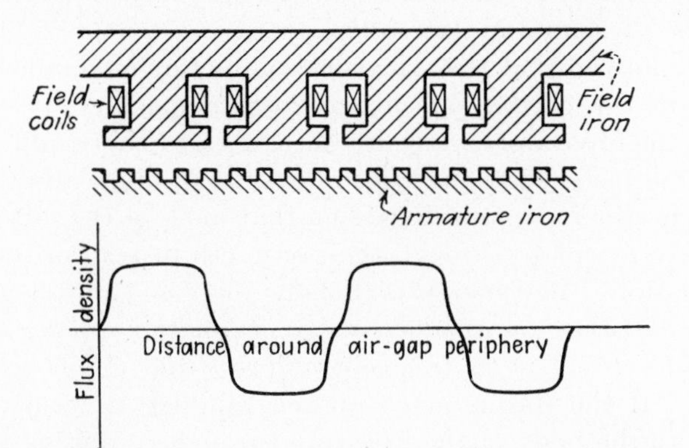

FIG. 1-11. Developed sketch of d-c machine structure showing the air-gap flux distribution.

voltages of all series conductors as computed by this equation. The *Blv* approach thus gives us one simple, systematic method of determining the rate of change of linkages with a winding when the changes are caused by mechanical motion alone. It is an approach which will be found useful in the subsequent analysis of rotating machines.

A complementary approach which will also be useful is based on the simple formulation of the fact that a mechanical force is exerted on a current-carrying conductor in a magnetic field. Quantitatively, the force on a straight section of conductor of length l perpendicular to a magnetic field of density B and carrying the current i is given by

$$f = Bli \tag{1-5}$$

When r is the radial distance from the center of the rotor shaft to the conductor, the associated torque is

$$T = Blri \tag{1-6}$$

The torque associated with the entire winding is the summation of the torques for the individual conductors or coil sides. Torque produced by such electromagnetic action is called *electromagnetic torque*. Electromagnetic torque, in association with rotation, gives rise to *electromagnetic power*, the torque, power, and speed being interrelated in the same manner as in ordinary mechanics.

Both Eqs. 1-5 and 1-6 are well-known expressions from elementary physics. Although at the moment they will be regarded as justified experimentally, consideration of the action and reaction associated with any type of energy conversion leads to the expectation that they are a natural consequence of conservation of energy and the *Blv* relation. This aspect will be presented in Art. 1-6*b*.

When it is noticed that the armature conductors are embedded in slots in Figs. 1-2 to 1-4, as they are in any normal machine, it is natural to ask whether the force and torque are the same as if the conductors were in the air gap and fastened to the armature surface. The question becomes particularly pertinent upon recognizing that most of the flux represented by the density B will go through the iron teeth instead of by way of the nonmagnetic slot. The answer is that the force and torque are the same either way; *but when the conductors are embedded in slots, the torque is exerted almost entirely on the iron core, and very little torque acts directly on the winding.* If the torque acted on the winding, it would have to be transmitted to the body of the iron core through compressive stresses in the insulation between the conductors and the sides of the slots; fortunately the insulation does not have to carry this mechanical load.[3]

[3] Description of an experiment verifying these conclusions may be found in J. H. Morecroft and A. Turner, Forces on Magnetically Shielded Conductors, *J. AIEE*,

From the *Blv*, *Bli* viewpoint, it follows that generator and motor operation is based on the physical reactions undergone by conductors located in a magnetic field. When there is relative motion between the flux and the conductor, a voltage is generated in the conductor; when the conductor carries current, a force is exerted on it. In line with this viewpoint, it will be noted that the machines whose details are presented in Figs. 1-1 to 1-11 consist essentially of two sets of windings, one set on the stator and one set on the rotor. The winding whose primary purpose is the production of flux is the field winding; that in which the voltage is to be induced is the armature winding.

An important fact which must be carefully noted is that generator and motor action go hand in hand in the windings of a rotating machine. Both motors and generators, when operating, have current-carrying conductors in a magnetic field, and the conductors and the flux are traveling at a definite speed relative to each other. Hence both a torque and a voltage of rotation are produced. In fact, within the windings themselves one could not distinguish between generation and motoring as the desired operational function without ascertaining the direction of power flow. Constructionally, generators and motors of the same type differ only in the details necessary for best adaptation of a machine for its intended service; any motor or generator may be used for energy conversion in either direction.

In a generator the resulting torque is a *counter torque* opposing rotation. It is the torque which the prime mover must overcome and is the mechanism through which greater electrical power output calls for greater mechanical power input. In a motor the rotational or speed voltage in the armature acts in opposition to the applied voltage and is termed a *counter emf*. All of these statements are specific tangible expressions of the reversibility which is characteristic of all electromechanical energy-conversion processes. One interesting application of this reversibility is in the electric braking of motor drives by causing the motor to act as a generator receiving mechanical energy from the moving parts and converting it to electrical energy which is dissipated in a resistor or pumped back into the power line. Thus, an electric locomotive on a downgrade may supply through two stages of conversion some of the energy required by another locomotive going upgrade.

It is naturally to be expected, then, that detailed analysis of generators and motors will be alike in their essentials. Examination of torque production in motors is at the same time examination of counter-torque production in generators; examination of emf production in generators is

vol. 48, pp. 25–27, January, 1929; analytic treatment based on electromagnetic field theory is given in B. Hague, "Electromagnetic Problems in Electrical Engineering," pp. 152–159, Oxford University Press, New York, 1929.

at the same time examination of counter-emf production in motors. These two examinations form the foundation of machinery analysis.

Example 1-1. The air-gap flux distribution in a somewhat idealized 2-pole machine has the rectangular waveform shown in Fig. 1-12. The flux per pole is 0.01 weber. The armature is rotating at a speed of 1,200 rpm.

The position of one armature coil at the instant when it is linking maximum flux is shown at ab. Half a revolution later, the coil is at $a'b'$, again linking maximum flux but in the opposite direction. There are four turns in the coil, and during this time it carries a steady current of 10.0 amp.

a. By direct application of Faraday's induction law, compute the coil voltage during this motion.

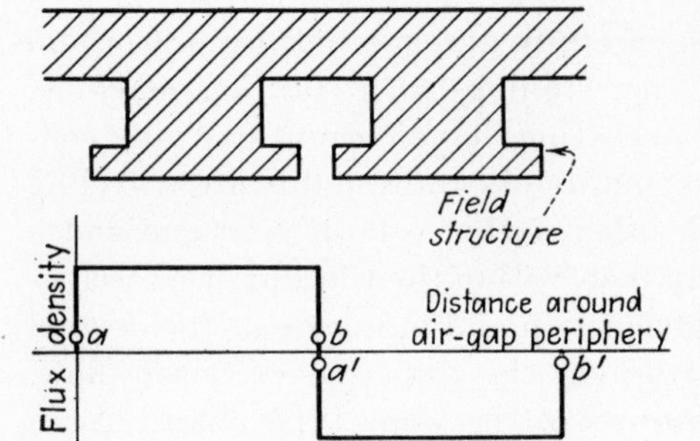

FIG. 1-12. Armature coil in rectangular flux distribution.

b. Compute the coil voltage by the Blv concept.

c. Compute the electrical power associated with this motion.

d. Determine the mechanical torque exerted on the armature by electromagnetic action.

e. Compute the mechanical power associated with *d*, and compare it with the power in *c*.

Solution. *a.* Because of the rectangular flux distribution and uniform speed of the armature, the flux linkages with the coil will change at a constant rate during this period. Halfway between ab and $a'b'$, for example, the net linkages will be zero, so that the flux linking the coil changes from the full flux per pole to zero in one-quarter of a revolution. From Eq. 1-1, the generated voltage is

$$e = \frac{d\lambda}{dt} = \frac{4 \times 0.01}{\frac{1}{4} \times (60/1200)} = 3.2 \text{ volts}$$

The instantaneous voltage is constant at this value during the half revolution.

b. When l is the axial length of the armature iron and r the radial distance from the center of the shaft to the air gap, the air-gap flux density is

$$B = \frac{\text{flux per pole}}{\text{area per pole}} = \frac{0.01}{\pi l r}$$

The linear velocity of the conductors is

$$v = \frac{1{,}200}{60} \times 2\pi r = 40\,\pi r$$

Since there are eight conductors involved in the two coil sides, the generated voltage, from Eq. 1-4, is

$$e = 8 \times \frac{0.01}{\pi l r} \times l \times 40\,\pi r = 3.2 \text{ volts}$$

c. The associated electrical power is

$$ei = 3.2 \times 10.0 = 32 \text{ watts}$$

d. The torque, computed from Eq. 1-6, is

$$T = 8 \times \frac{0.01}{\pi lr} \times lr \times 10.0 = \frac{0.8}{\pi} \text{ newton-m}$$

e. When torque and speed are given, power may be obtained from the relation

$$\begin{aligned} \text{Power} &= 2\pi T \times (\text{speed in rev/sec}) \\ &= 2\pi \times \frac{0.8}{\pi} \times \frac{1{,}200}{60} = 32 \text{ watts} \end{aligned}$$

The results here and in *c* are naturally equal, since both express the fact that electrical and mechanical energy are being interconverted at the rate of 32 watts.

Nowhere in this example has it been stated whether the machine is a generator or a motor. It may be either. If the generated voltage is of such polarity as to oppose the 10.0 amp, electrical power is absorbed, and the machine is acting as a motor. If the generated voltage is of such polarity as to aid the 10 amp, the machine is acting as a generator.

b. The Magnetic-field Viewpoint. A second viewpoint on electromechanical energy conversion through the medium of the magnetic field is to regard it as the result of two component magnetic fields trying to line up so that the center line of a north pole on one machine member is directly opposite the center line of a south pole on the other member. The component fields are created by the respective windings on the two members. Viewed physically, the process is the same as that by which two bar magnets, pivoted at their centers on the same shaft, line up so that their axes are parallel with unlike poles adjoining. This magnetic-field viewpoint is often a particularly helpful one for the examination of torque production in machines; it is also the one best suited to highlighting the basic features common to all electromechanical energy-conversion devices.

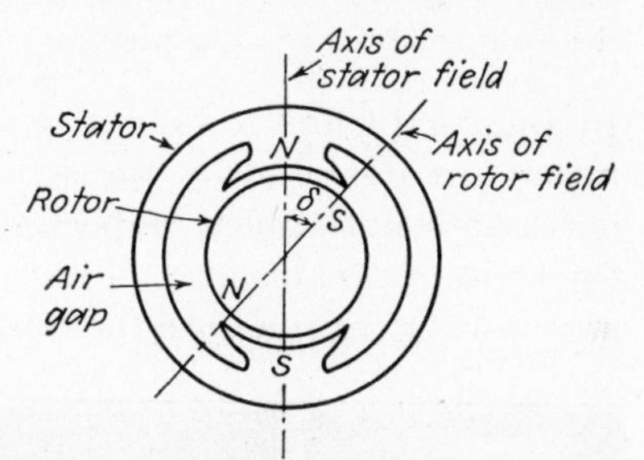

FIG. 1-13. Simplified 2-pole machine with salient stator poles. Axis of rotor field depends on electrical conditions in rotor windings.

Currents in the machine windings create magnetic flux in the air gap between the stator and the rotor, the flux path being completed through the stator and the rotor iron, as indicated in Figs. 1-7 and 1-8. This condition corresponds to the appearance of magnetic poles on both stator and rotor, the number of such poles depending on the specific winding design. These poles are shown schematically in Fig. 1-13 for a greatly simplified 2-pole machine. The field axes indicated here are the magnetic center lines of the several poles. The stator in Fig. 1-13 is shown with *salient poles* (*i.e.*, poles which stick out from the cylindrical surface) and the rotor with *nonsalient poles* (*i.e.*, a completely cylindrical surface), although practical machines may have nonsalient poles on either the rotor or stator or both. Figure 1-14 shows a similar machine with nonsalient poles on both rotor and stator; a practical example of such a machine is the *turbo-alternator* (*i.e.*, steam-turbine-driven a-c generator) whose stator is shown in Fig. 1-4 and whose cylindrical rotor is typified by Fig. 1-15. The axes of these fields do not necessarily remain fixed in space or with respect to the stator or rotor structure, a fact which is perhaps more easily visualized for the nonsalient structure of Fig. 1-14. In some machines the axes do remain fixed in space; in others, however, they rotate at a uniform angular velocity. In most of the machines which we shall study, the flux per pole remains constant for steady operating conditions.

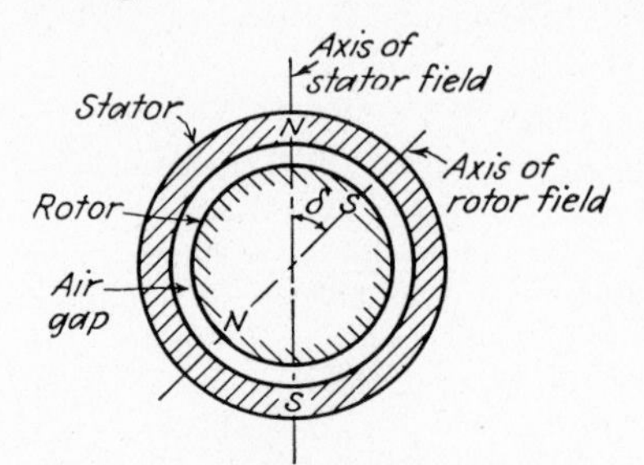

FIG. 1-14. Simplified 2-pole machine with nonsalient poles on rotor and stator. Axes of fields depend on electrical conditions in windings.

Torque is produced by interaction of the two component magnetic fields. In Figs. 1-13 and 1-14, for example, the north and south poles on the rotors are attracted by the south and north poles and repelled by the north and south poles, respectively, on the stator, resulting in a counterclockwise rotor torque. Notice that the same magnitude of electromagnetic torque acts on both the rotor and stator structures: the torque on the stator is simply transmitted through the frame of the machine to the foundation, since the stator is not free to rotate.

FIG. 1-15. Two-pole cylindrical rotor of 10,714-kva 7,500-kw 13.8-kv 3-phase 60-cps 3,600-rpm turboalternator. (*Courtesy of Allis-Chalmers Manufacturing Company.*)

The magnitude of the torque is proportional to the product of the field strengths. It is also a function of the angle δ between the field axes, varying in a 2-pole machine from zero at $\delta = 0°$ to a maximum at $\delta = 90°$

back to zero at $\delta = 180°$, and repeating this half cycle in the negative direction for the range 180 to 360°. For sinusoidal distribution of flux in the air gap (*i.e.*, flux density varying sinusoidally with distance around the air-gap periphery), the torque is shown in Chap. 3 to be proportional to the sine of the angle δ; this case is the usual one for a-c machines and gives qualitatively correct conclusions for d-c machines. The angle δ is commonly referred to as the *torque angle* or *power angle*.

Example 1-2. By using the concept of interaction between magnetic fields, show that electromagnetic torque cannot be obtained by using a 4-pole rotor in a 2-pole stator.

Solution. Consider the simplified motor of Fig. 1-16 with two poles on the stator and four on the rotor. The axes of the rotor field are at an arbitrary angle with the axis of the stator field. The two pairs of poles on the rotor have equal strengths in order to avoid unbalanced radial magnetic pull and the consequent poor bearing operation and tendency to vibrate.

On the N_1N_2 axis, pole N_1 is repelled by pole N and attracted by pole S, causing a counterclockwise torque. Pole N_2 is likewise repelled by N and attracted by S, causing an equal clockwise torque. Hence the net torque is zero. A similar situation exists on the S_1S_2 axis, so that no net electromagnetic torque is produced.

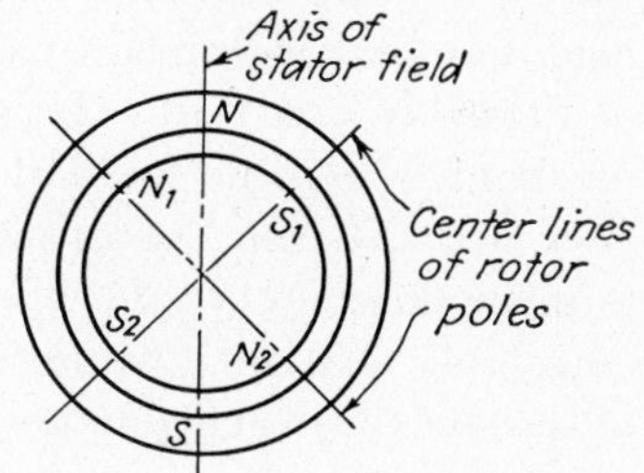

FIG. 1-16. Simplified machine with 2-pole stator and 4-pole rotor.

The same result is obtained by examination of any combination of unequal numbers of rotor and stator poles. Thus, the general conclusion is that *all rotating machines must have the same number of poles on the stator and on the rotor.* This conclusion applies equally well to generators, for if no counter torque is produced there can be no reaction on the mechanical driver and hence no energy conversion.

In motor and generator action, then, the magnetic fields tend to line up, pole to pole. When their complete alignment is prevented by the application of a mechanical torque to the rotor from a source of mechanical energy, mechanical to electrical energy conversion takes place: generator action is obtained. When, on the other hand, their complete alignment is prevented by the need to furnish torque to a mechanical shaft load, electrical to mechanical energy conversion takes place: motor action is obtained. The picture is one wherein the resultant magnetic field of the two windings acts as an intermediate seat of energy storage—energy which may flow either in the direction of electrical energy available at the armature terminals or in the direction of mechanical energy available at the shaft, depending on the circumstances dictated by the equipment connected to the armature terminals and to the shaft.

It is naturally to be expected that one quantitative formulation of this viewpoint will be in terms of the stored energy in the magnetic field. Such quantitative formulation is given in Chap. 2, where it is shown that electromagnetic torque can be evaluated as the rate of change of stored magnetic energy with angular motion of the rotor. Machinery analysis in these terms becomes the evaluation for specific machine configurations of the angular rate of change of stored magnetic energy as a function of winding voltages and currents and of shaft torques and speeds. Another and, for many purposes, more direct quantitative formulation, based essentially on the Faraday law and energy conservation, is given in Chap. 3. For the steady-state operation of the common electromagnetic rotating machines, the same end results are naturally obtained from the several alternative viewpoints; a certain degree of overlapping of these viewpoints may therefore be expected as additional specific details are unfolded.

One definite advantage of the field-energy viewpoint is that it permits combination of the first two of the five phenomena listed in Art. 1-1. Forces tending to align ferromagnetic material with the densest part of the field may play significant parts in machines having salient poles, like those of Figs. 1-8 and 1-10. Indeed, these forces form the principal operating mechanism in some small motors known as *reluctance motors*, and of course they are also the operating forces in many translational devices of the plunger-magnet type. Their presence in some rotating machines indicates only that the evaluation of magnetic energy should take cognizance of the specific iron geometry concerned. Moreover, the field-energy viewpoint provides the groundwork necessary to ultimate basic understanding of transient happenings in energy-conversion devices, in contrast to the simpler steady-state phenomena with which most of this book is concerned. Of still greater importance is the fact that evaluations in terms of field energy permit correlation and comparison of electromagnetic rotating machines with other types of electromechanical energy-conversion devices.

1-3. Electric Generators. We have seen that electric generators make direct application of the Faraday law that the voltage induced in a coil or winding is determined by the time rate of change of flux linkages with that winding. In both a-c and d-c generators the field winding, the primary source of flux, is excited from a d-c source: it carries a steady direct current and creates a constant flux in the air gap and iron of the machine. The armature winding is connected to the load requiring electric power. When either the armature or the field is rotated, the relative motion between the armature and the flux established by the field current causes the flux linking the armature winding to change periodically and hence results in voltage being induced in the armature winding.

More concrete ideas of generator action can be gained by discussing the armature induced voltages in very much simplified a-c and d-c generators. Such a discussion is the principal object of this article. Preliminary quantitative details are postponed until Chap. 3.

a. Synchronous Generators (Alternators). With rare exceptions, the armature winding of an alternator is on the stator, and the field winding is on the rotor with the field current conducted to it by means of *carbon brushes* bearing on *slip rings* or *collector rings.* Slip rings may be seen in Figs. 1-10 and 1-15. Constructional factors dictate this orientation of the two windings: the field current is usually much smaller than the armature current, and it is advantageous to have the light-current winding on the rotor and to avoid passing the heavy current through a sliding contact.

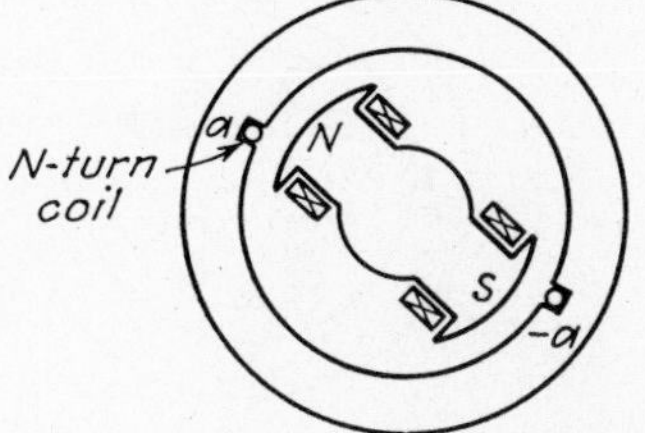

FIG. 1-17. Elementary 2-pole alternator with single armature coil.

An elementary alternator is shown in Fig. 1-17. A 2-pole machine is chosen, salient poles being shown for purposes of diagrammatic symbolism only. The armature winding, consisting of a single coil of N turns, is indicated by the two coil sides a and $-a$ placed at diametrically opposite points on the stator. The conductors forming these coil sides are parallel to the shaft of the machine. The rotor is turned at a constant speed n rpm by a source of mechanical energy connected to its shaft.

Now the object is to generate a sinusoidal alternating voltage in the armature coil. Consideration of the Blv equation, 1-4, shows that, for constant velocity v, the conductor-voltage waveform in time is the same as the flux-density waveform in space. Hence for the conductor voltage

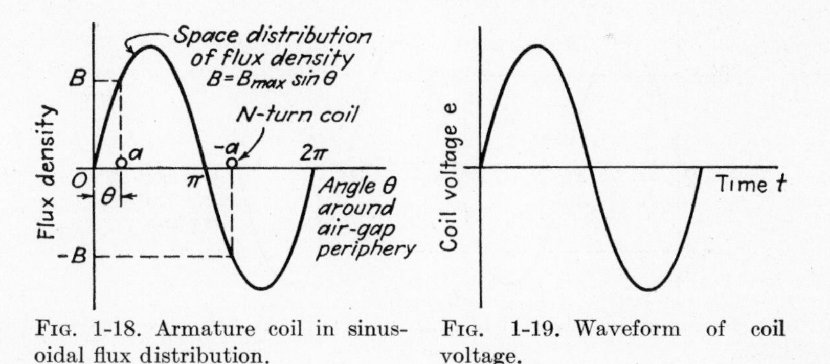

FIG. 1-18. Armature coil in sinusoidal flux distribution.

FIG. 1-19. Waveform of coil voltage.

to vary sinusoidally with time t, the flux density B must be a sinusoidal function of the space angle θ around the air-gap periphery. The angular variation of flux density around the air gap of practical alternators may be approximated reasonably closely by a sine wave, as shown in developed form in Fig. 1-18. As the rotor revolves, the flux waveform sweeps by the coil sides a and $-a$. The resulting coil voltage (Fig. 1-19) is evidently a function of the amplitude of the flux-density wave and the constant rotor speed.

The coil voltage passes through a complete cycle of values for each revolution of the 2-pole machine of Fig. 1-17. The period of the voltage wave is therefore $60/n$ sec, and its frequency is $n/60$ cps. Thus, a 2-pole alternator must revolve at 3,600 rpm to produce a 60-cps voltage.

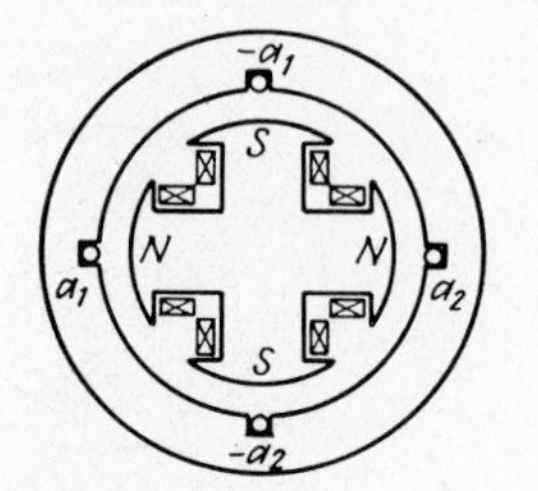

FIG. 1-20. Elementary 4-pole single-phase alternator.

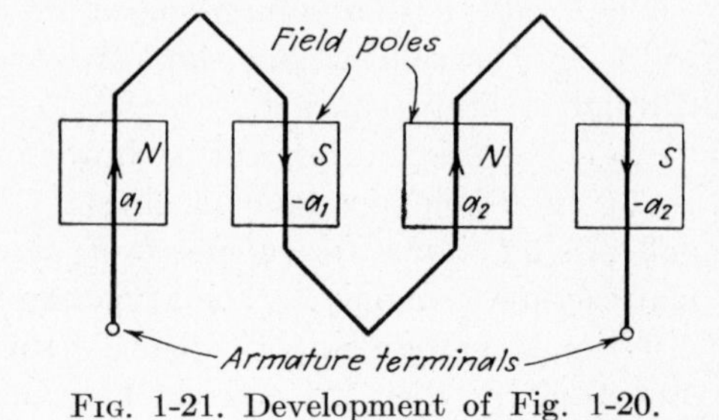

FIG. 1-21. Development of Fig. 1-20.

A great many synchronous machines have more than two poles. As a specific example, Fig. 1-20 shows the most elementary 4-pole single-phase alternator. The armature winding now consists of the two coils a_1, $-a_1$ and a_2, $-a_2$. These two coils are connected in series by their end connections, as shown in Fig. 1-21, which is a development of the winding with 1-turn coils. At the instant of time corresponding to that in Fig. 1-18, the relation of the four coil sides to the flux-density wave is that given by

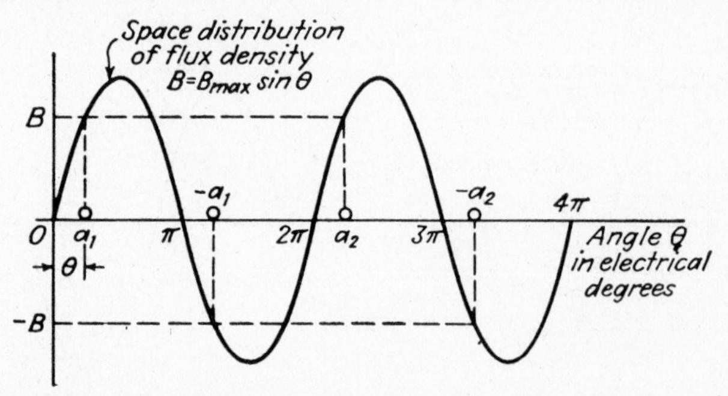

FIG. 1-22. Instantaneous position of armature coils with respect to sinusoidal flux distribution.

Fig. 1-22. When a machine has more than two poles, it is common during the early stages of a theoretical investigation to concentrate on a single pair of poles for simplicity and to recognize that the electric, magnetic, and mechanical conditions associated with every other pole pair are essentially repetitions of those for the pair under consideration. For this reason, it is usual to express angles in *electrical degrees* or *electrical radians* rather than in mechanical units. One pair of poles in a

p-pole machine is considered to span 360 electrical degrees or 2π electrical radians, whereas, of course, it requires the entire p poles to span 360 mechanical degrees or 2π mechanical radians. As a consequence,

$$\text{Angle in electrical units} = \frac{p}{2} \times (\text{angle in mechanical units}) \qquad (1\text{-}7)$$

Accordingly, each coil in Fig. 1-20 spans 180 electrical degrees or a half cycle on the flux wave, just as does the coil in Fig. 1-17. Such coils

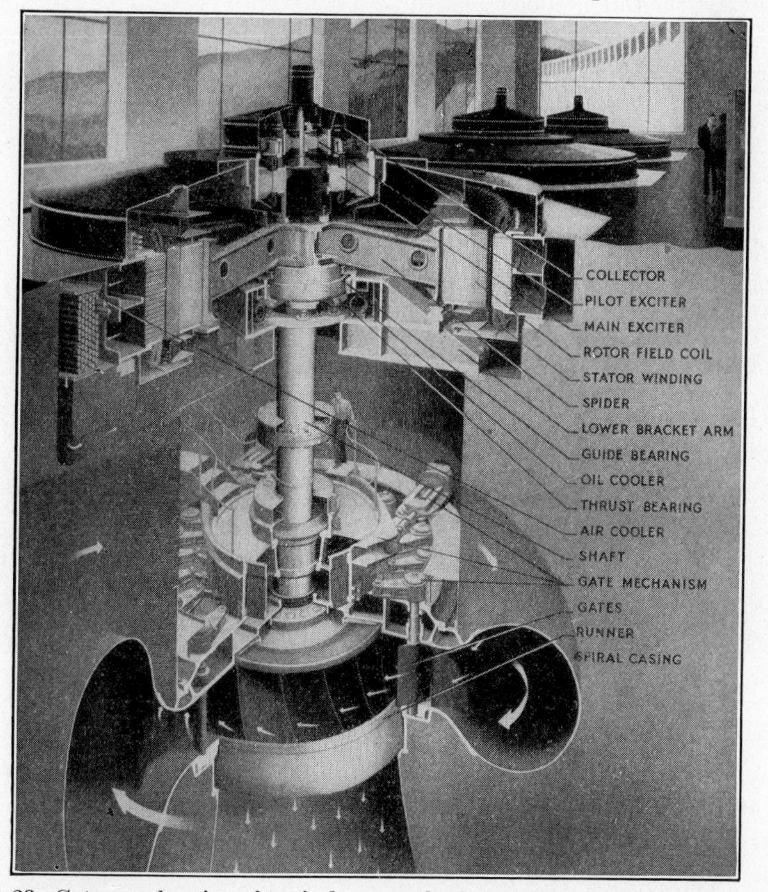

FIG. 1-23. Cutaway drawing of typical water-wheel generator. (*Courtesy of Westinghouse Electric Corporation.*)

are called *full-pitch coils*. The coil voltage of a p-pole machine passes through a complete cycle of values every time a pair of poles sweeps by, or $p/2$ times each revolution. The frequency of the voltage wave is therefore

$$f = \frac{p}{2}\,\frac{n}{60} \qquad \text{cps} \qquad (1\text{-}8)$$

The constructional reasons for some synchronous generators having salient-pole rotor structures and others having cylindrical rotor structures can be more fully appreciated with the aid of Eq. 1-8. Most power systems in the United States operate at a frequency of 60 cps. A salient-pole construction is characteristic of hydroelectric generators because hydraulic turbines operate at relatively low speeds, and, as a result, a relatively large number of poles are required to provide the desired frequency; the salient-pole construction is better adapted mechanically to this situation. Steam turbines, on the other hand, operate best at relatively high speeds, and turboalternators are commonly 2- or 4-pole cylindrical-rotor machines. A cutaway view of a representative hydroelectric generator is shown in Fig. 1-23. The external appearance of a modern turboalternator is shown in Fig. 1-24. A third type of prime mover now in use for a-c generators is the gas turbine. The generator construction is essentially the same as those for use with steam turbines. A gas-turbine power plant is illustrated in Fig. 1-25.

FIG. 1-24. External view of 40,000-kw 3,600-rpm alternator driven by a condensing tandem-compound steam turbine. (*Courtesy of Allis-Chalmers Manufacturing Company.*)

With very few exceptions, synchronous generators are 3-phase machines because of the advantages of 3-phase service for generation, transmission, and heavy-power utilization. For the production of a set of three voltages phase-displaced 120 electrical degrees in time, it follows that a minimum of three coils phase-displaced 120 electrical degrees in space must be

FIG. 1-25. Gas-turbine power plant. The cubicle is the 3,500-kw 3,600-rpm 60-cps alternator. The smaller machines in front of it are the exciter and starting motor. The gas turbine is in the rear. (*Courtesy of General Electric Company.*)

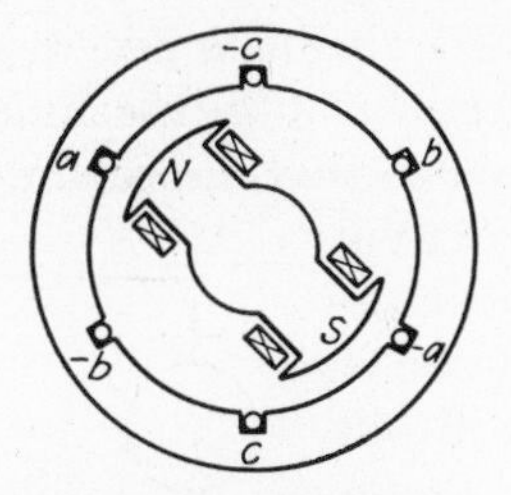

FIG. 1-26. Elementary 2-pole 3-phase alternator.

FIG. 1-27. Elementary 4-pole 3-phase alternator.

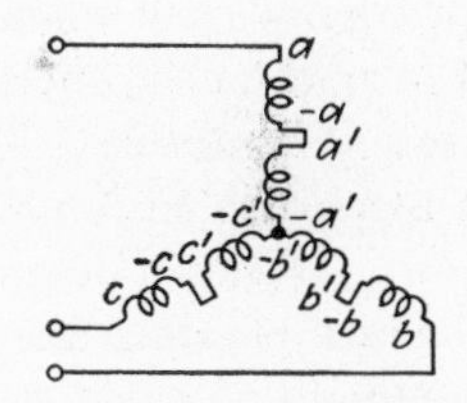

FIG. 1-28. Schematic diagram for Y connection of the winding in Fig. 1-27.

used. An elementary 3-phase 2-pole machine with one coil per phase is shown in Fig. 1-26. The three phases are designated by the letters a, b, and c. In an elementary 4-pole machine, two such sets of coils must be used, as illustrated in Fig. 1-27; in an elementary p-pole machine, $p/2$ such sets must be used. The two coils in each phase of Fig. 1-27 are connected in series so that their voltages aid, and the three phases may then be either Y- or Δ-connected. Figure 1-28 shows how the coils are interconnected to form a Y connection. Figure 1-29 gives the symbolic representation used in circuit diagrams where all three phases, as well as the d-c field circuit, are specifically shown; Fig. 1-30 gives the representation used in *single-line diagrams* of the a-c system (in which, for simplicity, only one of the three phases is shown specifically, the presence of the other two being understood). If desired, the alternator winding connection in Fig. 1-30 may be indicated by placing either a Y or a Δ in the circle for the alternator. All of the windings of Figs. 1-17, 1-20, 1-26, and 1-27 are full-pitch, concentrated windings because the two sides, such as a and $-a$, of any given coil are 180 electrical degrees or a full pole pitch apart, and because all the turns in any set are concentrated in one pair of slots. Practical alternator windings usually depart from both of these conditions in order to make the fullest use of construction materials and, as will be shown in Chap. 4, to make the terminal voltages conform more nearly to sinusoids. Exactly the same general principles that we have been discussing hold in the more practical cases.

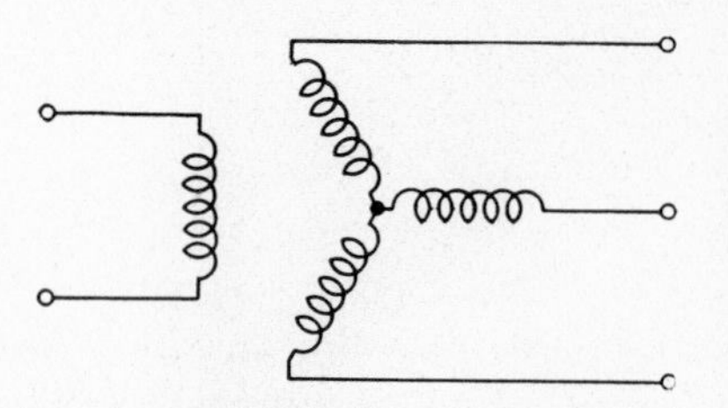

Fig. 1-29. Symbolic representation of Y-connected alternator.

When, as has been implied in the foregoing discussion, the flux is entirely that created by the d-c field winding, the corresponding voltage induced in the armature winding is called the *excitation voltage*. This voltage appears not only when the synchronous machine is acting as a generator, but also when the energy-conversion process is reversed and the machine is acting as a motor. The excitation voltage is equal to that appearing at the armature terminals only when the armature current is zero. When a definite armature current is present, the armature winding also creates a component flux wave in the air gap—a flux wave which, in accordance with the magnetic-field viewpoint, reacts with that created by the field winding to produce electromagnetic torque. The magnetic effect of the armature current will ultimately have to be taken into account in quantitative analysis of machine performance.

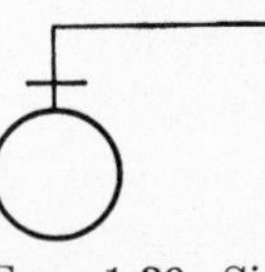

Fig. 1-30. Single-line representation of alternator.

The electromagnetic counter torque in alternators is basically the same as the motivating torque in the corresponding motors. Remarks on electromagnetic torque will therefore not be given separately here. Preliminary torque considerations are presented in Art. 1-4.

b. D-C Generators. The armature winding of a d-c generator is on the rotor with current conducted from it by means of carbon brushes, and the field winding is on the stator. The general appearance of an assembled d-c generator may be seen from Fig. 1-31. The machine is of the general construction sketched in Fig. 1-7.

A very elementary 2-pole d-c generator is shown in Fig. 1-32. The armature winding, consisting of a single full-pitch coil of N turns, is

FIG. 1-31. Direct-current generator, rated 600 kw, 240 volts, 900 rpm. Part of a synchronous motor-generator set with the driving motor rated 875 hp, 4,160 volts, 900 rpm, 3-phase, 60 cps. (*Courtesy of Allis-Chalmers Manufacturing Company.*)

indicated by the two coil sides a and $-a$ placed at diametrically opposite points on the rotor with the conductors parallel to the shaft of the machine. The rotor is normally turned at a constant speed by a source of mechanical energy connected to the shaft. As already mentioned, the air-gap flux distribution usually approximates a flat-topped wave rather than the sine wave found in alternators; the relative disposition at a particular instant of the two coil sides with respect to such a flux wave is that given in Fig. 1-33. Except for the waveforms, the situation is essentially the same as that for the elementary alternator presented in Fig. 1-18: in Fig. 1-33 the conductors are moving rather than the field, but it is *relative* motion that induces a voltage.

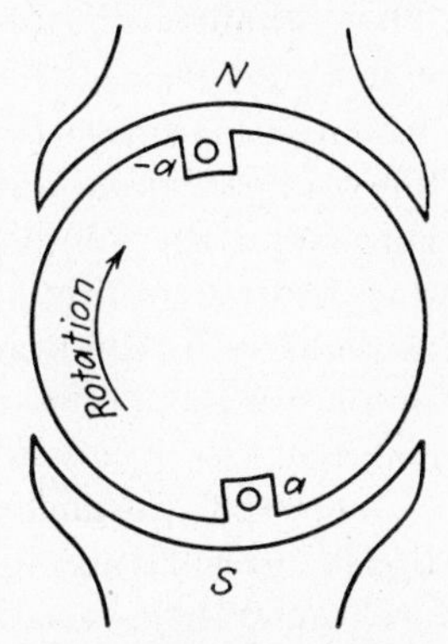

FIG. 1-32. Elementary d-c generator.

Although the ultimate purpose is the generation of a direct voltage, the voltage induced in an individual armature coil is an alternating voltage which, for constant machine speed, has the same waveform in time as the flux distribution of Fig. 1-33 has in space. The alternating waveform must therefore be rectified before the machine terminals are reached. This rectification is provided mechanically by means of a *commutator*, which is a cylinder formed of copper segments insulated from each other by mica and mounted on, but insulated from, the rotor shaft. Stationary carbon *brushes* held against the commutator surface connect the winding to the armature terminals of the machine. The commutator and brushes may readily be seen in Fig. 1-31. The necessity for commutation in order to obtain direct voltages and currents is the reason that the armatures of d-c machines are placed on the rotor.

For the elementary generator of Fig. 1-32, the commutator takes the form shown in Fig. 1-34. For the direction of rotation shown, the commutator at all times connects the coil side which is under the south pole to the positive brushes and that under the north pole to the negative brush. If the direction of rotation reverses, the polarity of the brushes reverses. The commutator provides full-wave rectification for the single armature coil, transforming the voltage waveform between brushes to that of Fig. 1-35 and making available a unidirectional voltage to the external circuit. The time-average value of this voltage is dependent upon the machine speed and the average ordinate of one-half cycle of the flux wave. The d-c winding of Fig. 1-34 is, of course, simplified to the point of being unrealistic in the practical sense, and it will be essential later to examine in detail the action of commutators and their influence on armature voltage.

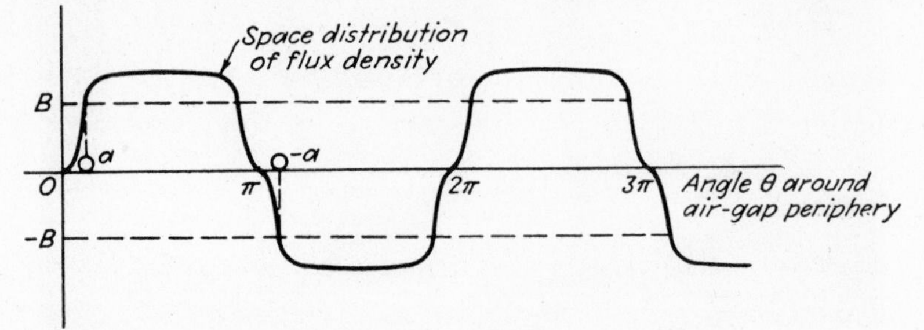

FIG. 1-33. Armature coil and flux waveform.

As in the alternator, the field winding of a d-c generator carries a steady direct current and must therefore be connected to a d-c source. Two general possibilities exist; the field winding may be connected to a d-c source which is electrically independent of the machine, resulting in a *separately excited generator;* or it may be recognized that the armature itself constitutes a d-c source capable of supplying electric power not only to the load on the machine but also to its own field winding, resulting in a *self-*

excited generator. In the latter case, residual magnetism must be present in the machine iron to get the self-excitation process started.

The symbolic connection diagram of a separately excited generator is given in Fig. 1-36. The required field current is a very small fraction of the armature current—of the order of 1 to 3 per cent in the average generator. A small amount of power in the field circuit of a separately

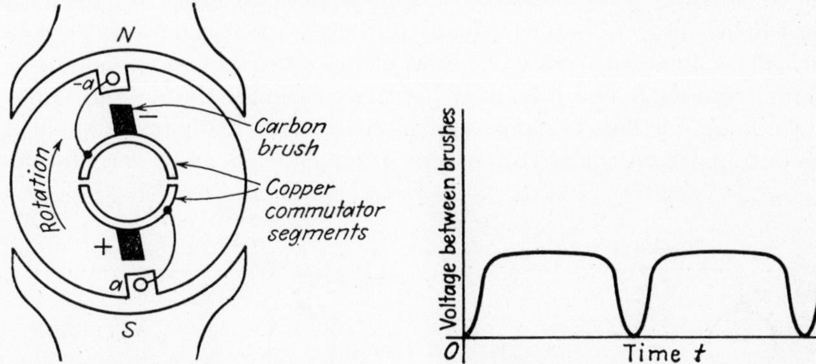

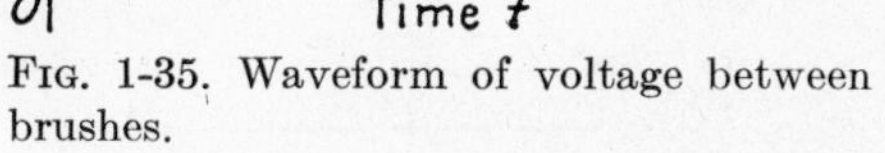

FIG. 1-34. Elementary d-c machine with commutator.

FIG. 1-35. Waveform of voltage between brushes.

excited generator may control a relatively large amount of power in the armature circuit: in effect, amplification is achieved by electrodynamic means. The simplest manner of achieving such control is through a rheostat in the field circuit. The rheostat controls the field current and hence the height of the flux-density wave; it follows that control of the

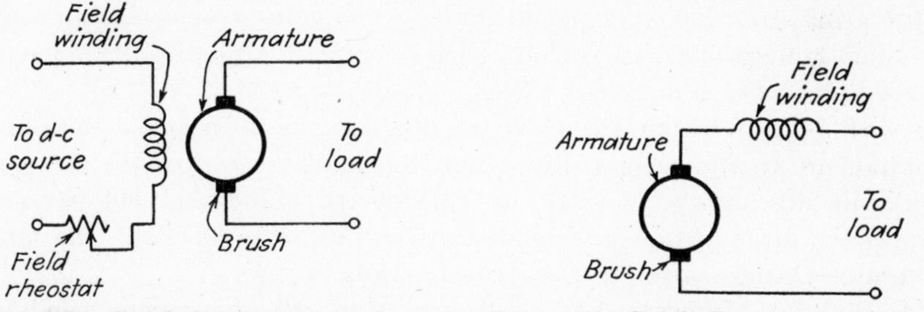

FIG. 1-36. Symbolic representation of separately excited d-c generator.

FIG. 1-37. Symbolic representation of series d-c generator.

generated voltage is thereby obtained. Separately excited generators are commonly used when control over the armature voltage and output is of especial importance.

The field windings of self-excited generators may be supplied in three different ways. The field may be connected in series with the armature (Fig. 1-37), resulting in a *series generator*. The field may be connected in shunt with the armature (Fig. 1-38), resulting in a *shunt generator*. Or the field may be in two sections (Fig. 1-39), one of which is connected in series and the other in shunt with the armature, resulting in a *compound generator*. The field current of a series generator is the same as the load current, so that the air-gap flux and hence the voltage vary widely with load. As a consequence, series generators are not very often used. The voltage of shunt generators drops off somewhat with load, but not in a manner which is objectionable for many purposes. Compound generators are normally connected so that the mmf of the series winding aids that of the shunt winding. The advantage is that, through the action of the series winding, the flux per pole can increase with load, resulting in a voltage output which is nearly constant or which even rises somewhat as

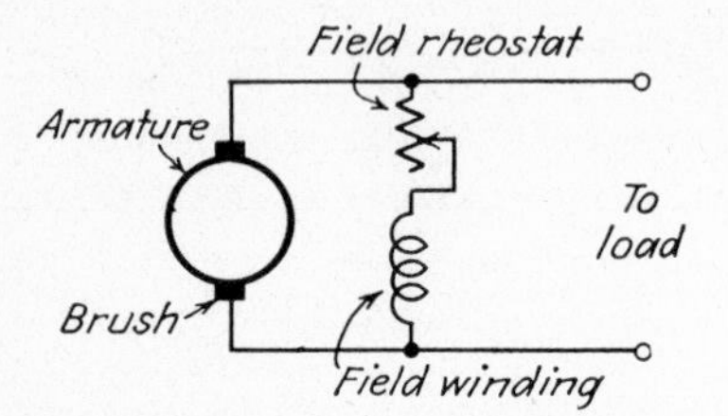

FIG. 1-38. Symbolic representation of shunt d-c generator.

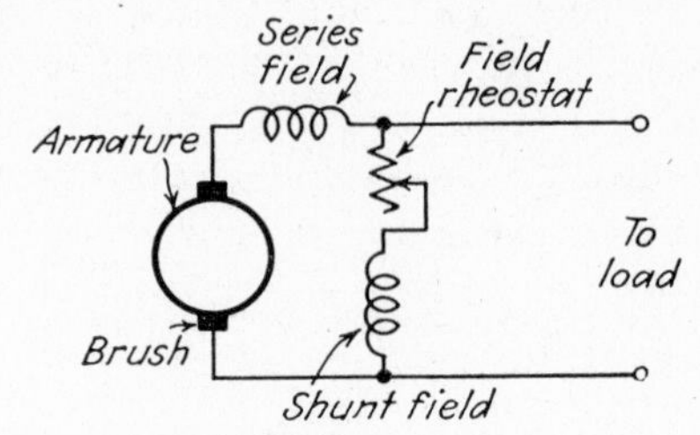

FIG. 1-39. Symbolic representation of compound d-c generator.

load increases. The shunt winding usually contains many turns of relatively small wire. The series winding, wound on the outside, consists of a few turns of comparatively heavy conductor because it must carry the full armature current of the machine. The voltage of both shunt and compound generators may be controlled over reasonable limits by means of rheostats in the shunt field.

As with a-c generators, the armature of a d-c generator also contributes a component to the air-gap flux when the machine is loaded, and this effect will ultimately have to be considered. Likewise, the electromagnetic counter torque in a loaded d-c generator is basically the same as the motivating torque in the corresponding motor.

1-4. Electric Motors. All of the five principal phenomena used for electromechanical energy conversion are reversible. We accordingly expect that any electric generator will have as a counterpart a corresponding type of electric motor; in fact, we realize that both voltage-producing and torque- or force-producing processes will go on simultaneously on an action and reaction basis within either a generator or a motor. The torque- or force-producing process in electromagnetic machinery can be discussed from the *Bli* viewpoint or, usually with greater satisfaction, in terms of the concept of interaction between rotor and stator component flux waves regarded as two magnetic fields tending to line up.

The essential parts of electric motors, like those of generators, include two sets of windings wound on, or embedded in slots in, iron cores. Motor action results when the effects of the currents in the two windings are such that a unidirectional torque is produced on the rotor and is of sufficient magnitude to overcome the opposition to rotation caused by the load on the motor shaft. Either or both windings may be excited by alternating or direct currents to form the commonly encountered varieties of practical electric motors. As illustrated in simple fashion by Example 1-2, the rotor and stator must be wound for the same number of poles to produce a successful motor.

When alternating current is supplied to one winding (the armature) and direct current to the other (the field), the motors are known as *synchronous motors* and are the counterparts of the synchronous generators considered in Art. 1-3*a*. As in these generators, the d-c winding of synchronous motors is almost invariably placed on the rotor. Since induced voltages as well as torques are associated with both motors and generators, we intuitively expect an induced counter emf in the armature winding of the motor similar to that in an alternator. Moreover, in order that the counter emf and the impressed armature voltage may enter into an appropriate Kirchhoff-law balance in the steady state, we may expect a relation between operating speed and impressed frequency not unlike that given by Eq. 1-8. In fact, we shall find in Chap. 3 that exactly this relation is obeyed. Synchronous motors therefore operate at an absolutely constant average speed determined by the number of poles and the impressed frequency. Significant departure from this speed, occasionally caused by electrical or mechanical disturbances, results in loss of motor action and shutdown of the machine.

The broad constructional features of general-purpose synchronous motors are much the same as for the synchronous generator sketched diagrammatically in Fig. 1-8. The rotor of Fig. 1-40 is that of a synchronous motor. A typical low-speed synchronous motor is shown in Fig. 1-41.

A second class of motors, the *d-c motor*, arises when direct current is supplied to both rotor and stator windings (*i.e.*, to both the armature and the field). The armature and field may be connected in series (Fig. 1-42*a*), resulting in a *series motor;* in parallel to the supply (Fig. 1-42*b*), resulting in a *shunt motor;* or one winding, the field or stator winding, may be in two sections, one of which is connected in series and the other in parallel with the armature (Fig. 1-42*c*), resulting in a *compound motor*. These three motors are, respectively, the counterparts of the three d-c generators shown schematically in Figs. 1-37 to 1-39. Direct-current

FIG. 1-40. Rotor of synchronous motor rated 600 hp, 2,200 volts, 3-phase, 60 cps, 720 rpm. The field winding is excited from a 250-volt d-c source through the slip rings in front of the rotor. The bar or cage winding in the pole faces is called an *amortisseur* or *damper winding* and is for starting by induction-motor action. (*Courtesy of Allis-Chalmers Manufacturing Company.*)

FIG. 1-41. Group of 350-hp 400-rpm 3-phase 60-cps 80 per cent power-factor synchronous motors driving Jordan refiners in a paper mill. (*Courtesy of Westinghouse Electric Corporation.*)

motors do not differ in general constructional features from d-c generators.

The outstanding applicational advantages of d-c motors will ultimately be shown to lie in the variety of performance characteristics offered by the possibilities of shunt, series, and compound excitation and in the relatively high degree of adaptability to control, both manual and automatic. To mention but one simple aspect: as load is added to the motor shaft, the series motor operates at speeds which decrease rapidly, the shunt motor at almost constant speed, and the compound motor with any degree of droop

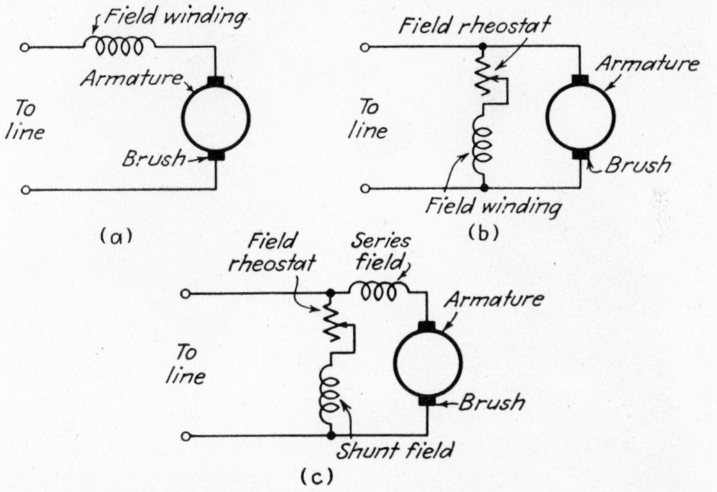

FIG. 1-42. Symbolic representation of (*a*) series, (*b*) shunt, and (*c*) compound d-c motors.

between these extremes, depending on the relative strengths of series and shunt fields.

The third variation on exciting motor stator and rotor windings is to supply alternating current to both windings. The most common example is the *induction motor*, in which alternating current is supplied directly to the stator and by induction (*i.e.*, transformer action) to the rotor. Although the induction motor is the most common of all motors, it has no direct equivalent in the generators considered in Art. 1-3; as will be seen when induction machines are analyzed in detail, induction-generator action is entirely possible, but the performance features are such that the machines are seldom used as generators. Another common illustration of this general type of motor is the *a-c series motor*, in which the two windings are connected in series so that the same alternating current exists in each.

In the induction motor, the stator winding (Fig. 1-43) is essentially the same as that of a synchronous motor. On the rotor, of which Fig. 1-44 is a sample, the winding is electrically closed on itself and very often has no external terminals; currents are induced in it by transformer action from the stator winding. The usual induction-motor characteristic is that the speed drops off slightly as load is added to its shaft, although variations in the degree of droop may be obtained. A typical induction motor is shown in Fig. 1-45.

There is thus a variety of motor types, all operating on the same basic principles but having in general different performance characteristics.

FIG. 1-43. Close-up of stator winding of 1,500-hp 2,300-volt 3-phase 60-cps 1,770-rpm squirrel-cage induction motor. (*Courtesy of Allis-Chalmers Manufacturing Company.*)

Counter torques in generators will, of course, be essential factors in generator action. Our detailed studies of motors and generators will accordingly consist in large measure of studies of torques and induced emfs. The physical processes of emf induction are usually comparatively easy to visualize. The physics of torque and force production in electrical equipment, however, is not so easy to grasp in a complete and satisfying manner. As a consequence, the greater part of Chaps. 2 and 3 is devoted to studies of how forces and torques are obtained, first in very simple mechanisms and later in the more sophisticated motors and generators.

FIG. 1-44. Rotor of 300-hp 2,300-volt 3-phase 60-cps 503-rpm squirrel-cage induction motor. (*Courtesy of Allis-Chalmers Manufacturing Company.*)

FIG. 1-45. Induction motor, rated 1,000 hp, 440 volts, 3-phase, 60 cps, 1,780 rpm, driving an air-conditioning compressor. (*Courtesy of Westinghouse Electric Corporation.*)

So far, the existence of forces and torques rests simply on statements of the *Bli* and magnetic-field viewpoints.

1-5. The Nature of Machinery Problems. As we begin to converge on more specific methods of machine analysis, we need to reflect momentarily on our objectives; what are the machine characteristics that we need to know, and to know in reasonably precise, quantitative form? The answer involves consideration of what, specifically, the machines are intended to do for us. Both motors and generators must play the role of very willing servants to the loads they are supplying with energy—and we wish, in so far as it is practically and economically feasible, to set up a situation wherein the master has every requirement spontaneously satisfied.

The power or torque supplied by an electric motor to the mechanical equipment driven is determined in a large degree by the requirements of the equipment. The motor must satisfy these requirements or quit trying (quitting usually takes the form of the motor being disconnected from the line by automatic circuit breakers because of the excessive currents associated with the motor's attempts to fulfill the requirements). The rotational speed at which these power or torque requirements are satisfied is an important factor determined by the characteristics of both motor and load: the operating speed is fixed by the point at which the power or torque that the motor can furnish electromagnetically is equal to the power or torque that the load can absorb mechanically. In Fig. 1-46, for instance, the solid curve is a plot of the operating speed of an induction motor as a function of its mechanical torque output. The dotted curve is a plot of the mechanical torque input required by a fan for various operating speeds. When the fan and motor are coupled, the operating point of the combination is at the intersection of these two curves—where what the motor can give is the same as what the fan can take.

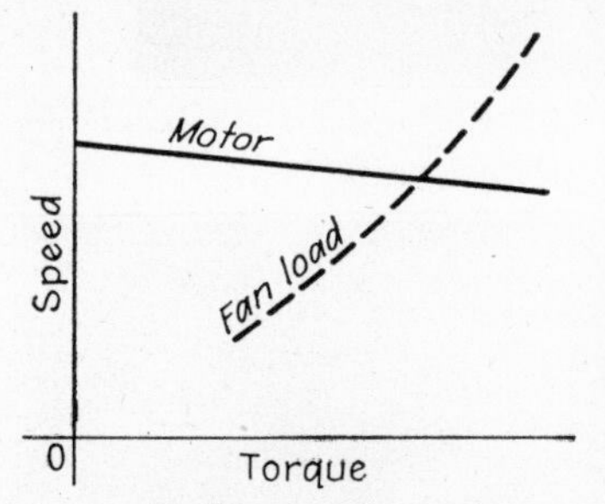

FIG. 1-46. Superposition of motor and load characteristics.

Motor power or torque requirements vary, of course, depending on conditions within the driven equipment. The requirements of some motor loads are satisfied by a speed which remains approximately constant as load varies; an ordinary hydraulic pump is an example. Others, like a phonograph turntable, require absolutely constant speed. Still others require a speed closely coordinated with another speed: the raising of both ends of a vertical lift bridge, for instance. The automatic direction of guns in accordance with data received from radar signals is a motor application where the instantaneous *position* of the driven equipment must be controlled accurately. Some motor applications, such as cranes and many traction-type drives, inherently demand low speeds and heavy torques at one end of the range and relatively high speeds and light torques at the other—a varying-speed characteristic, in other words. Others may require an adjustable-constant speed (*e.g.*, some machine-tool drives in which the speed of operation may require adjustment over a wide range but must always be carefully predetermined) or an adjustable-varying speed (a crane is again an example). In almost every application the torque which the motor is capable of supplying while starting, the maximum torque which it can furnish while running, and the current requirements are items of importance, and not infrequently of determining importance.

Many similar remarks can be made for generators. For example, the terminal voltage and power output of a generator are determined by the characteristics of both the generator and its load. Thus, the solid curve of Fig. 1-47 is a plot of the terminal voltage of a d-c shunt generator as a function of its electrical power output. The dotted curve is a plot of the electrical power input required by a load at various impressed voltages. When the load is connected to the generator terminals, the operating point of the combination is at the intersection of these two curves—where what the generator can give is the same as what the load can take. Often, as in the usual central station, the requirement is that terminal voltage shall remain substantially constant over a wide load range. Not infrequently, however, a motor is associated with its own individual generator in order to provide greater flexibility and more precise control. Then it may be desired that the terminal voltage vary with load in some particular fashion.

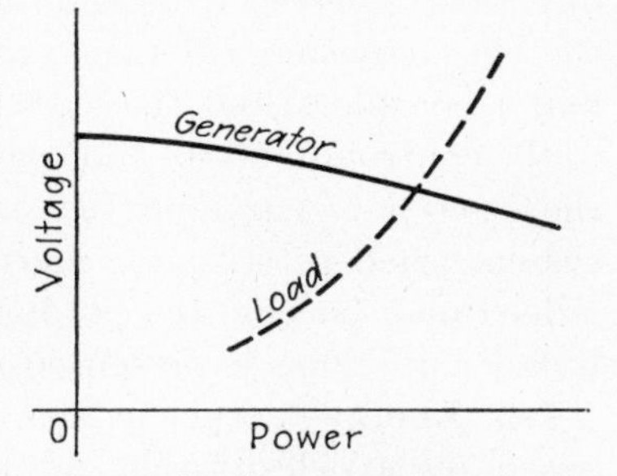

FIG. 1-47. Superposition of generator and load characteristics.

Among the features of outstanding importance, therefore, are the torque-speed characteristics of motors and the voltage-load characteristics of generators, together with knowledge of the limits between which these characteristics can be varied and ideas of how such variations may be obtained. Moreover, pertinent economic features are efficiency, power factor, comparative costs, and the effect of losses on the heating and rating of the machines. The direct object of our analysis of machinery is accordingly to study and compare these features for the various machine types, and the greater portion of this book is devoted to such study. Of course there are many important, interesting, and complex engineering problems associated with the design, development, and manufacturing of machines for which these studies are but the introduction; most such problems are beyond the scope of the book.[4]

[4] For a brief description of the influence of electrical, mechanical, and metallurgical developments on a typical modern machine, see Limits to 3600-rpm Generating Units Raised, *Westinghouse Engr.*, vol. 6, pp. 131–133, September, 1946.

To a considerable extent, this study is based on steady-state characteristics, for initial mastering of machine workings is most easily gained thereby. In an increasingly important class of applications in the field of automatic control, however, the emphasis is rather on the dynamic behavior of the complete electromechanical system of which the machine is one component. For example, it may be desired to control the speed or position of a shaft driving a load in accordance with some specified function of time or of some other variable. A typical industrial application is the accurate control of tension in a process involving the winding of long strips of material, such as paper, on a reel. Dynamic controls of astounding accuracy and rapidity of response have been developed: an example, previously mentioned, is the tracking of aircraft by radar, and the automatic pointing of antiaircraft weapons in accordance with the directions received from the radar signals. In applications of this kind, the electromechanical transient behavior of the system as a whole is a major consideration; the system should respond accurately and rapidly to the control function, and oscillations should die out quickly. Not only the electrical characteristics but also the mechanical properties of the system, such as stiffness, inertia, and friction, must be considered and indeed may become the predominant factors. An introduction to these broader problems is presented in the last three chapters.

1-6. Energy Balance in Electromechanical Energy Conversion. In the remaining articles of this chapter, we wish to approach more specifically the methods of machinery analysis by which the problems of the preceding article are solved. The actual analyses of the various machine types are carried out in the later chapters; the present preliminary approach culminates in a general outline (Art. 1-7) of how we embark on such analyses.

From our previous discussions, it is evident that we are primarily interested in the interrelations between torque, speed, generated voltage, and current. One revealing and generally useful method of attack is by means of the principle of conservation of energy. This principle will be applied first to the broad problem of electromechanical energy conversion as described in Art. 1-1, and then specifically to the more common electromagnetic rotating machines in the steady state.

a. Application to Electromechanical Energy Conversion in General. A general principle applicable to all problems in which mass is constant is the *principle of conservation of energy*, which states that energy is then neither created nor destroyed; it is simply changed in form. The application of this general principle offers a convenient means for finding the characteristic relationships which are inherent in electromechanical coupling. Electromechanical energy conversion involves energy in four forms, and the principle of conservation of energy leads to the following relation between these forms:

$$\begin{pmatrix}\text{Energy input}\\ \text{from electrical}\\ \text{source}\end{pmatrix} = \begin{pmatrix}\text{mechanical}\\ \text{energy}\\ \text{output}\end{pmatrix} + \begin{pmatrix}\text{increase in}\\ \text{energy stored}\\ \text{in coupling}\\ \text{field}\end{pmatrix} + \begin{pmatrix}\text{energy}\\ \text{converted}\\ \text{to heat}\end{pmatrix} \quad (1\text{-}9)$$

Equation 1-9 is applicable to all conversion devices; it is written so that the electrical and mechanical energy terms have positive values for motor action. The equation applies equally well to generator action: the electrical and mechanical energy terms then have negative values.

Irreversible conversion of energy to heat arises from three causes: part of the electrical energy is converted directly to heat in the resistances of the current paths, part of the mechanical energy developed within the device is absorbed in friction and windage and converted to heat, and part of the energy absorbed by the coupling field is converted to heat in magnetic core loss (for magnetic coupling) or dielectric loss (for electric coupling). If the energy losses in the electrical system, the mechanical system, and the coupling field are grouped with the corresponding terms in Eq. 1-9, the energy balance may be written in the following form:

$$\begin{pmatrix}\text{Electrical}\\ \text{energy input}\\ \text{minus resist-}\\ \text{ance losses}\end{pmatrix} = \begin{pmatrix}\text{mechanical}\\ \text{energy out-}\\ \text{put plus fric-}\\ \text{tion and wind-}\\ \text{age losses}\end{pmatrix} + \begin{pmatrix}\text{increase in}\\ \text{energy stored}\\ \text{in coupling}\\ \text{field plus as-}\\ \text{sociated losses}\end{pmatrix} \quad (1\text{-}10)$$

The left-hand side of Eq. 1-10 can be expressed in terms of the currents and voltages in the electric circuits of the coupling device. Consider, for example, the energy-conversion device shown schematically in Fig. 1-48. The differential energy input from the electrical source in time dt is $v_t i\,dt$, where v_t is the instantaneous terminal voltage and i is the instantaneous current. The energy loss in the resistance of the device is $i^2 r\,dt$, where r is the resistance. Hence the left-hand side of Eq. 1-10 is

$$dW_{\text{elec}} = v_t i\,dt - i^2 r\,dt \quad (1\text{-}11)$$

$$= (v_t - ir) i\,dt \quad (1\text{-}12)$$

where dW_{elec} is the net electrical energy input to the coupling device after resistance losses have been taken into account. For the coupling device to absorb energy from the electric circuit, the coupling field must produce a reaction in the circuit. This reaction is the counter emf indicated by the voltage e in Fig. 1-48. In electromagnetic rotating machinery, for example, it is a Faraday-law or *Blv* voltage. Reaction on the input is an essential part of the process of interconversion of energy between an electric circuit and any other medium. The coupling field may be likened to a reservoir of energy, releasing energy to the output system and being replenished through the reaction of the field on the input system. For the voltages to balance properly, the counter emf e must be

$$e = v_t - ir \tag{1-13}$$

Substitution of Eq. 1-13 in 1-12 gives

$$dW_{\text{elec}} = ei\,dt \tag{1-14}$$

If electrical energy is supplied to the coupling field from more than one circuit, the total electrical energy input is the sum of terms of the form of Eq. 1-14.

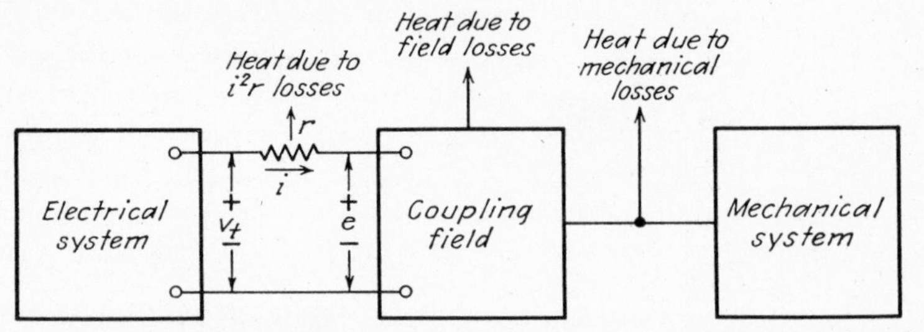

FIG. 1-48. General representation of electromechanical-energy-conversion device.

The first term on the right-hand side of Eq. 1-10 is the total energy converted to mechanical form, including both useful energy and friction and windage losses. This total mechanical energy is sometimes called the *internal mechanical energy;* it differs from the useful mechanical energy by the mechanical friction and windage losses caused by the motion of the mechanical parts of the energy-conversion device. The second term on the right-hand side of Eq. 1-10 is the total energy absorbed by the coupling field, including both stored energy and losses.

From the foregoing discussion, it should be evident that the resistances of the electric circuits and the friction and windage of the mechanical system, though always present, play no basic parts in the energy-conversion process. They can be accounted for as losses in the electrical and mechanical systems on the two sides of the coupling element, as indicated in block-diagram form in Fig. 1-48. The basic energy-conversion process is one involving the coupling field and its action and reaction on the electrical and mechanical systems. For motor action, the sum of the energy absorbed by the coupling field and the internal energy converted to mechanical form can always be equated to the internal electrical energy associated with the flow of electricity against the counter emf e caused by the coupling field. In differential form, Eq. 1-10 may be written

$$dW_{\text{elec}} = ei\,dt = dW_{\text{mech}} + dW_{\text{fld}} \tag{1-15}$$

where dW_{mech} is the differential internal mechanical energy and dW_{fld} is the differential energy absorbed by the coupling field including losses.

Equation 1-15 is the fundamental basis for analysis of energy-conversion devices. It is applied to a variety of such devices in Chap. 2. A restricted form applicable to common rotating machines in the steady state will now be presented.

b. Application to Constant-field-energy Electromagnetic Rotating Machines. The magnetic fields in many of the commonly used electromagnetic rotating machines—the d-c, synchronous, and polyphase induction machines already mentioned are examples—remain substantially constant in magnitude and spatial waveform when the machines are operating in the steady state. The magnetic field itself may revolve around the machine, as does the flux produced by the d-c field winding on the rotor of a synchronous machine when that rotor is turning, for instance; or one machine member may rotate through the stationary magnetic flux, as does the revolving armature of a d-c machine; but these statements merely mean that the flux density in an individual element of air or iron may change with time, not that the over-all flux-density wave is changing. Now the energy stored in a magnetic field is a function of the flux density at all points in space occupied by the field and is constant under the foregoing circumstances. These machines, when operating in the steady state, are therefore *constant-field-energy machines*. The stored magnetic energy increases from zero to a definite value while the machine is first excited and started from rest; it may change in value during the transient readjustment processes accompanying the transition from one steady operating condition to another; and it decreases to zero when the machine is shut down by disconnecting it from the electrical supply system. But during the analysis of any particular steady operating condition, it does not change.

This state of affairs suggests that the term dW_{fld} in Eq. 1-15 be considered zero. One further obstacle must be overcome, however: as indicated in Eq. 1-10, the term dW_{fld} includes losses associated with the magnetic field. From a rigorous viewpoint, both hysteresis and eddy currents have a direct bearing on the field-energy term. An approximation is ordinarily introduced here, one of only very minor practical importance. The approximation is to regard the hysteresis and eddy-current losses as playing no basic parts in the energy-conversion process and accordingly to divorce them from the dW_{fld} term. They are then classified in much the same manner as the i^2r and mechanical losses: their presence must be recognized, but they do not enter directly into the basic internal energy balance. Very frequently, hysteresis and eddy-current losses are combined with mechanical losses to form a category called *rotational losses.*

Under these circumstances, the differential field-energy term in Eq. 1-15 may be considered zero. The restricted form of the relation is then

$$dW_{\text{elec}} = ei\,dt = dW_{\text{mech}} \tag{1-16}$$

or

$$p_{\text{elec}} = ei = p_{\text{mech}} \tag{1-17}$$

where p_{elec} and p_{mech} are the instantaneous electric and mechanical powers. To recapitulate, the word *restricted* is used in presenting the foregoing relation because it is confined to constant-field-energy machines in the steady state with hysteresis and eddy-current phenomena accounted for simply as a debit term in the ultimate power bookkeeping.

Application of Eq. 1-16 or 1-17 to the elementary machines considered in Art. 1-2 lends greater insight to the theoretical basis of machine operation. Consider first an individual armature conductor. From the *Blv* equation, 1-4, the instantaneous electric power is *Blvi*. Mechanical power is torque times mechanical angular velocity, the latter being v/r when v is the peripheral speed and r the radius. Equation 1-17 then becomes

$$Blvi = T\frac{v}{r} \tag{1-18}$$

or

$$T = Blri \tag{1-19}$$

which is Eq. 1-6 obtained from Faraday's law and conservation of energy.

Now consider the entire armature winding, for which, by Eq. 1-1,

$$e = \frac{d\lambda}{dt} \tag{1-20}$$

so that

$$p_{\text{elec}} = ei = i\frac{d\lambda}{dt} \tag{1-21}$$

When ω is the angular velocity of the rotor in electrical radians per second for a p-pole machine,

$$p_{\text{mech}} = T\left(\frac{2}{p}\,\omega\right) \tag{1-22}$$

the factor $2/p$ appearing in order to convert ω to mechanical radians per second. The quantity ω may be replaced by $d\theta/dt$ when θ designates the instantaneous angular position (in electrical radians) of a point on the rotor with respect to a fixed reference. Equation 1-17 then becomes

$$i\frac{d\lambda}{dt} = T\frac{2}{p}\frac{d\theta}{dt} \tag{1-23}$$

or

$$T = \frac{p}{2}i\frac{d\lambda}{d\theta} \tag{1-24}$$

Equations 1-4 and 1-19 form the basis of a conductor-by-conductor approach to evaluation of generated voltage and electromagnetic torque, the approach being followed by summation over all conductors for the complete evaluation. Equations 1-20 and 1-24 view the entire winding, regarding generated voltage as the *time* rate of change of linkages and torque as the *angular* rate of change of linkages. The two groups of equations provide alternate methods of attack, leading, of course, to the same end results. As a matter of fact, a third possibility exists which is a convenient combination of the other two. Generated voltage for the entire winding can be evaluated on the basis of either Eq. 1-4 or Eq. 1-20. Substitution of this voltage in Eq. 1-17 then permits derivation of a torque expression for the entire winding. All three possibilities will be used in our analyses in later chapters.

Although it is not immediately and completely evident, Eq. 1-24 is a quantitative formulation of the magnetic-field viewpoint presented in Art. 1-2*b*. It says, in effect, that a current-carrying winding tends to line itself up with a magnetic field in such a position that a further differential change of position causes no further change of linkages with the winding—that is, such a position that $d\lambda/d\theta$ is zero. Further correlation with fundamental energy-conversion processes at the basic theoretical level is given in Chap. 2. Both the method of applying Eq. 1-24 to machines and its correlation with the magnetic-field viewpoint are considered in greater detail in Chap. 3.

1-7. Résumé. Outline of Machinery Analysis. Any electromechanical energy-conversion mechanism is a coupling device between the electrical and the mechanical systems utilizing the medium of a magnetic or an electric field. The field must react on the electrical system to produce a voltage and hence a current and on the mechanical system to produce a force or torque and hence linear or rotary motion. Generators and motors utilize the magnetic field as an intermediary and take advantage of Faraday's law of induction, *viz.*, that an induced voltage which is proportional to the time rate of change of flux linkages appears in a winding. Intimately associated with this effect, and related to it through the conservation-of-energy principle, is the production of a force on a current-carrying conductor in a magnetic field; the latter effect may alternatively be regarded as a force proportional to the angular rate of change of flux linkages with a winding. The two effects are present in both generators and motors, a statement which simply emphasizes the inherent reversibility of energy-conversion processes. The main distinction between generators and motors, therefore, is the direction of energy flow. The energy irreversibly converted to heat plays no basic role in the conversion process, although the presence of losses must be accounted for in the final formulation of performance theories.

Among the essential parts of almost every type of generator and motor are two sets of windings wound on, or embedded in slots in, iron cores. The primary function of one set, the field winding, is the establishment of a magnetic field in the machine. The other set, the armature winding, is the one in which the emf or counter emf of rotation is induced; currents in it are intimately related to the torque or counter torque produced. Thus, the words *field* and *armature* are functional descriptions of the windings; the words *stator* and *rotor* describe only their location. Structural considerations (and the necessity for commutation in d-c machines) determine the winding locations in individual machine types.

Three principal types of machines accordingly appear: synchronous machines, with direct current in one winding, the field winding, and alternating current available from or impressed at the terminals of the other winding; d-c machines, with direct current not only in the field winding but also available from or impressed on the terminals of the other winding; and induction machines (together with a-c commutator machines such as the a-c series motor), with alternating currents in both windings. All three types are capable of generator and motor action, but the last is rarely used commercially for generator action. Certain conditions must be satisfied for successful energy conversion, one of which is that magnetic fields produced by the two sets of windings must have the same number of poles. The action of specific machines can be examined from the Blv, Bli viewpoints or from the viewpoint of the component magnetic fields of the two sets of windings trying to align themselves. The fundamental operating principles of all electromagnetic rotating machines are thus essentially the same. As might be expected from inspection of the individual structural details and electrical interconnections, the details of analysis for synchronous, d-c, and induction machines will follow diverging branches on the basic trunk. The general strategy underlying analysis, however, is the same for all types.

The quantities of primary interest in machinery analysis are generated and terminal voltages, currents, torques, and speeds. The two basic relations for any machine are one for generated voltage in terms of flux density (or flux per pole) and speed, and one for electromagnetic torque in terms of flux density (or flux per pole) and current. With these two relations and the principles of electric-circuit theory and mechanics, any desired operating conditions can be quantitatively investigated. The general strategy of steady-state machinery analysis as it will be carried out in later chapters can be summarized briefly in the following four steps.

1. Obtain from Faraday's law (Eq. 1-1 or 1-4) an expression for generated emf or counter emf. This evaluation requires knowledge of the flux-density waveform in the machine and hence demands examination of the flux distribution.

2. Investigate and include factors causing difference between generated emf and terminal voltage under load. One such factor is resistance of the armature winding. Another condition which must be borne in mind is that the armature winding also creates a component magnetic field, and the flux-linkage bookkeeping must be complete in this respect to yield the correct terminal voltage. This effect may be included in the evaluation of emf in the first step, or it may be made part of the second step; analytical convenience is the deciding point. These factors are usually represented by the parameters of equivalent electric circuits. Their evaluation again requires knowledge of flux distribution, with emphasis on that for the armature.

The equivalent of the foregoing two steps, plus accounting for magnetic core losses, applies also to the transformer and constitutes the basis of its analysis.

3. Obtain an expression for electromagnetic torque or counter torque. In general, the relation may be established through any of four approaches:

a. The energy-conversion principle may be applied. When the rotational emf is evaluated in the first step, the electromagnetic power created by it in conjunction with the armature current may be formulated. This power may be equated to that created by the electromagnetic torque in conjunction with the speed, as in Eq. 1-17.

b. The *Bli* relation (Eq. 1-6) may be used for individual conductor torque, followed by summation over the entire armature winding. Knowledge of flux distribution is evidently required.

c. The torque may be evaluated from the angular rate of change of flux linkages with the armature winding by application of Eq. 1-24. Again knowledge of flux distribution is required.

d. The torque may be evaluated from field-energy considerations. This possibility is mentioned below to a further extent and is discussed in detail in Chap. 2.

4. Appropriately include machine losses. Ordinarily such inclusion is accomplished by taking account of i^2r losses in evaluating electric powers, and of mechanical losses together with hysteresis and eddy-current losses in evaluating mechanical powers.

Application of these steps is carried out in the studies of steady-state performance presented in Chaps. 3 to 11. Transformer analysis is presented in the Appendix. Transient and dynamic behavior of machines and systems of machines is investigated in Chaps. 12 and 13. Of course the presentation of analytical details must be supplemented by much more complete consideration of constructional and electrical features, flux-density waveforms, and physical pictures of machine happenings than is possible in the present introductory chapter. The general objective for each machine is to obtain equivalent circuits so that the techniques of circuit theory become available for the investigation of energy-conversion phenomena.

In general, all four methods listed for evaluation of electromagnetic torque may be applied to the basic machine types. While these methods all yield the same results, the processes of applying the methods lead to different degrees and shades of insight into machinery fundamentals. Expediency is also a consideration, for some methods may lead more directly to the desired results in a specific case. The first method leads directly and easily to a result but gives almost no insight into how torque is produced. It says, in effect, that if the machine works, a certain relation must be satisfied. The second method constitutes a more careful examination into the details of torque production in terms of the forces on current-carrying conductors in magnetic fields; as such, it answers more fully the question of how machines work. Since the torque relation (Eq. 1-6) is derivable from Faraday's law and energy conservation in constant-field-energy machines, the second method is the equivalent of the first, but it is applied at more nearly a basic level. This torque relation is readily applicable only to certain electromagnetic machines, however, and therefore the second method does not reveal the fundamental aspects common to all electromechanical energy-conversion devices or even those common to all electromagnetic forms of these devices. The third method has the advantage of demonstrating clearly and simply the torque-producing action common to all forms of rotating electromagnetic machines; it therefore forms the basis of the more detailed examination of rotating-machinery concepts in Chap. 3.

The fourth method is the most fundamental of the approaches but also the most difficult to apply. It is based on use of Eq. 1-15, a relation applicable to all electromechanical energy-conversion devices. In somewhat restricted form, it leads to Eq. 1-24, on which the third method is based, and to the magnetic-field viewpoint of Art. 1-2*b*; it therefore naturally has areas in common with the second and third methods. Because of its greater generality, the fourth method requires appreciably more in the way of introductory background than has been given in this chapter. To furnish this background, to illustrate its applications and implications, and by these means to bring out the common aspects of energy-conversion problems are the objects of Chap. 2.

CHAPTER 2

ELECTROMECHANICAL-ENERGY-CONVERSION PRINCIPLES

All electromechanical-energy-conversion devices have certain basic features in common. The moving-coil telephone receiver, for example, behaves according to the same basic physical laws which govern the behavior of a 100,000-kw electric generator. The purpose of this chapter is to describe the physical principles of electromechanical energy conversion in general terms, to develop a basic theory from which the mechanical forces produced by magnetic and electrostatic fields can be determined, and to compare the potentialities of magnetic and electrostatic fields as force-producing media. Although the steady-state theory of rotating machines is developed on a simplified basis in subsequent chapters, the study of this chapter should give the three-dimensional perspective of binocular vision to the reader's outlook on machine theory, by providing a background against which the subsequent details can be viewed.

The method of attack has already been discussed in Art. 1-6*a*. As shown in Eq. 1-15, application of the principle of conservation of energy to the electromechanical-energy-conversion process leads to the basic differential equation

$$dW_{\text{elec}} = dW_{\text{fld}} + dW_{\text{mech}} \tag{2-1}$$

where dW_{elec} is the net electrical energy input after copper losses have been accounted for, dW_{fld} is the differential energy absorbed by the coupling field, and dW_{mech} is the net internal energy converted to mechanical form including mechanical losses. This equation is written so that the electrical and mechanical energy terms have positive values for motor action. It applies equally well to generator action: the electrical and mechanical energy terms then have negative values. This equation, together with Faraday's law for induced voltage, is the foundation on which the whole structure of this chapter is laid. The procedure involves two steps: (1) Obtain an expression for the energy stored in the coupling field in terms of the magnetic or electric conditions and parameters which are functions of the configuration of the mechanical parts. (2) Then investigate how the electrical and field energy terms are affected by mechanical motion. The mechanical energy is then obtainable from Eq. 2-1. Both magnetic and electrostatic fields are considered and compared, with emphasis on the former because of its predominant importance.

2-1. Singly Excited Magnetic Systems. Consider first a singly excited magnetic system, *i.e.*, a system comprising a single exciting coil and its associated magnetic circuit, as indicated schematically in Fig. 2-1. According to Faraday's law of electromagnetic induction, an emf is induced in an electric circuit whenever the magnetic flux linking the circuit changes. The emf is proportional to the time rate of change of the flux linkage, and its direction is such as to tend to induce a current which would prevent the flux from changing. Thus if the current and flux are increasing, the emf induced in the coil is in a direction to oppose the current, as shown by the + and − signs associated with the emf e in Fig. 2-1. When the flux is increasing, the time derivative $d\lambda/dt$ of the flux linkage is positive, and hence the instantaneous value of the counter emf e is given by

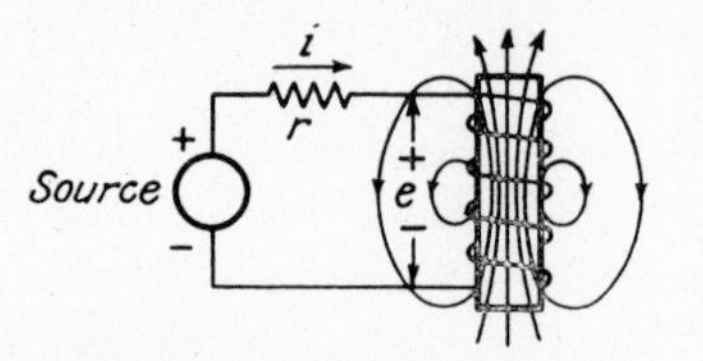

FIG. 2-1. Elementary singly excited magnetic system.

$$e = +\frac{d\lambda}{dt} \tag{2-2}$$

This equation is, of course, correct in any consistent system of units. In this text, the units are generally those of the rationalized mks system.

If all of the flux φ linked all N turns of the coil, as it would if the flux were all confined to a magnetic core, the flux linkage would be $N\varphi$, and the counter emf would be

$$e = +N\frac{d\varphi}{dt} \tag{2-3}$$

Actually part of the magnetic field is distributed throughout the space occupied by the turns of the winding and therefore links only a fraction of the turns. The effect of the partial flux linkages can be taken into account by defining an equivalent value of the flux as in Eq. 1-3.

As shown in Art. 1-6*a*, the differential energy dW_{elec} supplied by the electrical source in time dt (after copper loss in the coil has been accounted for) is

$$dW_{\text{elec}} = ei\,dt \tag{2-4}$$

where i is the instantaneous current from the source. From Eqs. 2-2 and 2-3,

$$dW_{\text{elec}} = i\,d\lambda = Ni\,d\varphi = \mathfrak{F}\,d\varphi \tag{2-5}$$

where $\mathfrak{F} \equiv Ni$ and is the mmf of the coil in ampere-turns.

Equation 2-5 shows that a change in flux linking a circuit is associated with flow of electrical energy in the circuit. What happens to this energy depends on what it is that caused the change in flux. The tracing of this energy flow is the subject of the rest of this article.

a. Energy in the Magnetic Field. The field energy can be determined from the energy supplied by the source in establishing the field. Mechanical forces on the core and coil are created by the field, but if there is no mechanical motion of the core or coil, no mechanical work is done. Later in this article we shall consider what happens when mechanical motion is allowed to take place. For the present, consider the energy interchanges for a *fixed* configuration of the core and coil. Under these circumstances Eq. 2-1 reduces to

$$dW_{\text{elec}} = dW_{\text{fld}} + 0 \tag{2-6}$$

and from Eq. 2-5,

$$dW_{\text{fld}} = i\,d\lambda = \mathfrak{F}\,d\varphi \tag{2-7}$$

That is, when no mechanical motion takes place, the electrical energy input $i\,d\lambda$ associated with a change in flux is absorbed by the field.

The energy absorbed by the field in changing the flux linkage from λ_1 to λ_2, or the flux from φ_1 to φ_2, is

$$\Delta W_{\text{fld}} = \int_{\lambda_1}^{\lambda_2} i\,d\lambda = \int_{\varphi_1}^{\varphi_2} \mathfrak{F}\,d\varphi \tag{2-8}$$

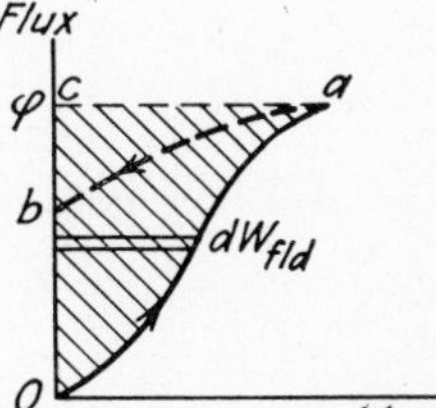

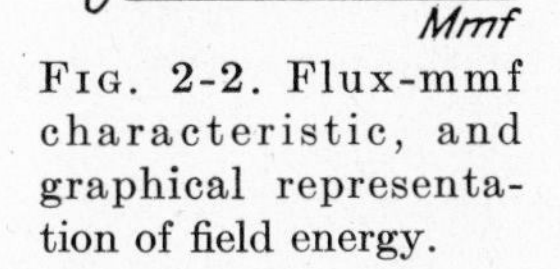
FIG. 2-2. Flux-mmf characteristic, and graphical representation of field energy.

If the initial flux is zero, the energy absorbed by the field when flux linkage λ, or flux φ, is established is

$$W_{\text{fld}} = \int_0^{\lambda} i\,d\lambda = \int_0^{\varphi} \mathfrak{F}\,d\varphi \tag{2-9}$$

In these equations, the flux is a function of the mmf, the relation between them depending on the geometry of the coil and magnetic circuit, and the magnetic properties of the core material. If the magnetic circuit contains ferromagnetic material, the relation will be more or less nonlinear, as in the rising curve *Oa* of Fig. 2-2, and the integrations in Eqs. 2-8 and 2-9 must then be performed graphically. Because of hysteresis and eddy currents, the relation between flux and mmf is not single-valued. The falling curve is indicated by the broken line *ab* in Fig. 2-2. When the mmf is reduced to zero, only a part of the energy that was absorbed by the field during the build-up process is returned to the circuit, the energy returned being given by area *abc*. Some energy remains stored in the kinetic energy associated with the spinning electrons producing the residual flux, and some has been dissipated in the core losses caused by hysteresis and eddy currents. The net energy absorbed during the build-up and build-down process *Oab* is the area *OabO* in Fig. 2-2. If the time rate of change is sufficiently slow so that the effects of eddy currents can be neglected, the flux-current characteristics *Oa* and *ab* become the rising and falling magnetization curves. Under cyclic conditions, the hysteresis loss can be evaluated from the area of a closed hysteresis loop.

Most electromagnetic-energy-conversion devices contain air gaps in series with the magnetic circuit, and usually most of the mmf is required to overcome the air-gap reluctance. Most of the energy is then stored in the air gap and is returned to the circuit when the field is reduced. Because of the simplicity of the resulting relations, magnetic nonlinearity and core losses are often neglected in the analysis of practical devices. The final results of such approximate analyses can, if necessary, be corrected for the effects of these neglected factors by semiempirical methods.

When core loss is ignored, the energy absorbed by the field is stored and will be returned to the circuit when the flux is reduced to zero. When the flux and mmf are directly proportional, as in air, the energy stored in the field is, from Eq. 2-9,

$$W_{\text{fld}} = \tfrac{1}{2} i\lambda = \tfrac{1}{2}\mathfrak{F}\varphi \tag{2-10}$$

The stored energy can also be expressed in terms of the *reluctance*, defined as

$$\mathfrak{R} \equiv \frac{\mathfrak{F}}{\varphi} \tag{2-11}$$

or the *permeance*, defined as

$$\mathfrak{P} \equiv \frac{\varphi}{\mathfrak{F}} = \frac{1}{\mathfrak{R}} \tag{2-12}$$

With nonlinearity and hysteresis neglected, the reluctance and permeance are constant, and the stored energy is

$$W_{\text{fld}} = \tfrac{1}{2}\mathfrak{R}\varphi^2 = \tfrac{1}{2}\mathfrak{P}\mathfrak{F}^2 \tag{2-13}$$

The *self-inductance* L of the coil in henrys is defined as the flux linkage in weber-turns per ampere, or

$$L \equiv \frac{\lambda}{i} \tag{2-14}$$

and is constant if the reluctance is constant. Substitution of this relation in Eq. 2-10 gives the familiar expression for energy stored in the field of a constant inductance; thus

$$W_{\text{fld}} = \tfrac{1}{2}Li^2 \tag{2-15}$$

The energy associated with the field is distributed throughout the space occupied by the field. For a magnetic medium with constant permeability and no losses, the energy density is assumed to be

$$w_{\text{fld}} = \frac{1}{2}\mathcal{H}\mathcal{B} = \frac{1}{2}\mu\mathcal{H}^2 = \frac{1}{2}\frac{\mathcal{B}^2}{\mu} \tag{2-16}$$

where w_{fld} is the magnetic stored energy density in joules per cubic meter at a point where the magnetic field intensity is $\mathcal{H}$ amp-turns/m, the flux density is $\mathcal{B}$ webers/m^2, and the permeability is μ in rationalized mks units. Equation 2-16 follows from Eq. 2-10, because $\mathcal{H}$ is the mmf per unit length and $\mathcal{B}$ is the flux per unit area.

In the foregoing discussion the field-energy relations have been expressed in three ways, and it is appropriate to comment briefly on the three viewpoints. In Eq. 2-16 the magnetic stored energy is expressed in terms of the specific or per-unit-volume properties of the magnetic field. This viewpoint is that of the designer. He thinks in terms of properties of materials and field intensities, stress intensities, flow densities, and like concepts. He then builds up the geometrical form and arrangement of any specific device from a knowledge of what he can do with unit volume of the available materials. In Eq. 2-15, the field energy is expressed in terms of current and inductance, familiar and useful concepts, particularly when nonlinearity is unimportant. The viewpoint here is that of the circuit analyst. Except for difficulties in taking into account nonlinearity, the theory of the operating characteristics of most electromagnetic-energy-conversion devices can be developed on the basis of assuming the device to be a circuit element with time-varying inductance parameters. This viewpoint, however, gives very little insight into the internal phenomena and gives no conception of physical size. In Eqs. 2-7 to 2-13, the field energy is expressed in terms of the whole field. The viewpoint here is somewhere between the other two. The expressions readily can be translated into the language of either the designer or the circuit analyst. In this text all three viewpoints will be taken at various times.

b. Mechanical Work. Up to the present we have considered the energy interchanges between the electric circuit and the magnetic field for a fixed configuration of the mechanical parts. The interchange of energy between an electrical system and a mechanical system is possible when the energy in the coupling field is influenced by the configuration of the mechanical elements.

As a simple example, consider the relay attracting the iron armature in Fig. 2-3*a*. The magnetization curves of the magnetic circuit for the open and closed positions of the armature are shown in Fig. 2-3*b*. Suppose the switch *S* is closed and the armature is held forcibly in the open position until the current in the coil has settled down to its final steady-state value. The corresponding operating point for the magnetic circuit is the point *a* (Fig. 2-3*b*). Now let the armature be released. It will move under the influence of the magnetic force of attraction and eventually will stop in the closed position. After the transients have disappeared, the final operating point is at b in Fig. 2-3b.

During the transient period while the armature is moving, the flux is increasing, and a counter emf is induced in the coil. This emf depends on how fast the armature moves. If it moves very slowly, the induced emf is negligible; the current then stays substantially constant, and the flux-mmf locus during the transient period approaches the vertical dotted line ab in Fig. 2-3b. On the other hand, if the motion is very fast, it will have taken place before the flux has changed appreciably; the flux-mmf locus while the armature is moving then approaches the horizontal dotted line aa', and after the motion is all over the flux and mmf rise

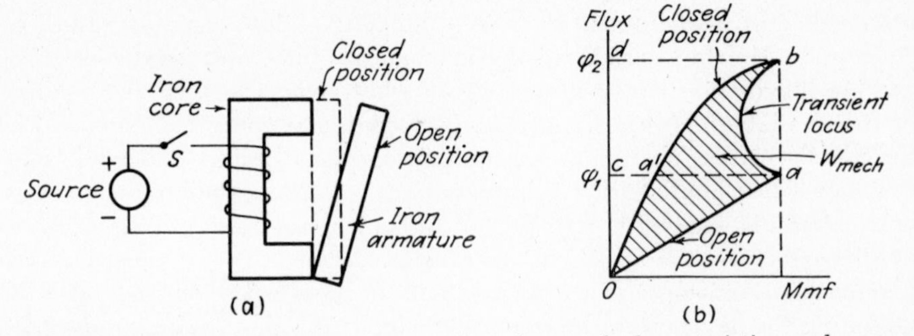

Fig. 2-3. (a) Relay, and (b) corresponding flux-mmf characteristics and energy relations.

along the magnetization curve $a'b$. The complete solution for the transient condition is complicated and involves the inertia and frictional forces of the mechanical system as well as the transient behavior of the electrical system. We shall not go any further into these details. Rather, we shall assume that the flux-mmf locus during the transient period is known and lies somewhere between the two limits described above, as shown by the curve ab in Fig. 2-3b.

Consider the significance of the various areas in Fig. 2-3b. Area $OacO$ to the left of the original magnetization curve represents the energy abstracted from the electrical source and absorbed by the magnetic field during the initial excitation of the coil while the armature is in the open position. For simplicity, neglect hysteresis and eddy currents. This energy then is stored in the magnetic field. After the armature has moved into the closed position, the energy stored in the field is represented by the area $ObdO$ to the left of the final magnetization curve. Consequently the increase in energy stored in the field is

$$\Delta W_{\text{fld}} = ObdO - OacO \tag{2-17}$$

While the armature is moving, the flux is increasing from φ_1 to φ_2, and an emf is induced in the coil. The corresponding energy abstracted from the source during this time is, from Eq. 2-5,

$$W_{\text{elec}} = \int_{\varphi_1}^{\varphi_2} \mathfrak{F}\, d\varphi = \text{area } cabdc \tag{2-18}$$

Substitution of Eqs. 2-17 and 2-18 in the energy-balance equation, 2-1, gives

$$W_{\text{elec}} = \Delta W_{\text{fld}} + W_{\text{mech}} \tag{2-19}$$

$$\text{Area } cabdc = ObdO - OacO + W_{\text{mech}} \tag{2-20}$$

whence

$$W_{\text{mech}} = OacO + cabdc - ObdO = OabdO - ObdO \tag{2-21}$$

$$= OabO \tag{2-22}$$

This important relation shows that the energy converted to mechanical form equals the area included by the original and final magnetization curves and the flux-mmf locus during motion, as shown by the cross-hatched area in Fig. 2-3*b*. Any singly excited magnetic system whose magnetization curve is affected by the relative position of its parts is a potential electromechanical-energy-conversion device.

c. Mechanical Forces, Linear Analysis. The magnitude and direction of the mechanical forces on any part of a magnetic system can be determined by considering what would happen to the energy balance if the part in question were allowed to move an infinitesimal distance dx in the direction of the magnetic force f acting upon it. With core losses and nonlinearities neglected, the energy relations can be described in terms of linear parameters—inductance, reluctance, or permeance, as in Eqs. 2-13 and 2-15. These parameters are functions of the geometry of the core and coil, and of the magnetic properties of the core material. For example, the inductance of the coil and the reluctance of the magnetic circuit in Fig. 2-3*a* depend on the configuration of the core and coil. The most important factors are the length and cross-sectional area of the air gap.

Although the relations which will be derived below have a very broad significance, it may be helpful initially to consider a simple specific case such as the relay of Fig. 2-3*a*. The magnetic force of attraction acting on the armature can be determined by considering the effect on the energy balance if the air gap shortened a differential amount dx. Mechanical work $f\,dx$ would then be done by the magnetic force of attraction f. At the same time the reluctance of the magnetic circuit and the inductance of the coil would change. The current and flux also may change because of the induced transients described in Art. 2-1*b*.

The effects of the differential motion dx on the energy balance (Eq. 2-1) can be accounted for conveniently in terms of the resulting differential changes in the flux and reluctance. In accordance with Eq. 2-5, the differential electrical energy input is

$$dW_{\text{elec}} = F\,d\phi \tag{2-23}$$

where F and ϕ are the values of mmf and flux at the operating condition and $d\phi$ is the differential change in flux resulting from the differential displacement dx. In accordance with Eq. 2-13, the field energy is

$$W_{\text{fld}} = \tfrac{1}{2}\mathcal{R}\phi^2 \tag{2-24}$$

Both $\mathcal{R}$ and ϕ are variables and consequently for differential changes

$$dW_{\text{fld}} = \tfrac{1}{2}\phi^2\,d\mathcal{R} + \mathcal{R}\phi\,d\phi \tag{2-25}$$

But $\mathcal{R}\phi = F$, and therefore

$$dW_{\text{fld}} = \tfrac{1}{2}\phi^2\,d\mathcal{R} + F\,d\phi \tag{2-26}$$

Substitution of Eqs. 2-23 and 2-26 in the basic energy equation, 2-1, gives

$$F\,d\phi = \tfrac{1}{2}\phi^2\,d\mathcal{R} + F\,d\phi + dW_{\text{mech}} \tag{2-27}$$

Therefore

$$dW_{\text{mech}} = f\,dx = -\tfrac{1}{2}\phi^2\,d\mathcal{R} \tag{2-28}$$

or

$$f = -\frac{1}{2}\phi^2\frac{d\mathcal{R}}{dx} \tag{2-29}$$

Note that the electrical energy input $F\,d\phi$ on the left-hand side of Eq. 2-27 is balanced by an identical term accounting for that part of the change in field energy caused by the change in flux. These terms have no effect on the mechanical force, which therefore is independent of the differential change in flux. The force depends solely on the value of the flux and on the space rate of change of the reluctance. These equations therefore show that a *change in flux* involves energy transmission between the field and the *electrical* system, whereas a *change in reluctance* involves an interchange of energy between the field and the *mechanical* system. Equation 2-29 shows that because of the flux in the system *forces are set up which tend to decrease the reluctance and move the mechanical parts toward the configuration of minimum reluctance.*

In a singly excited magnetic system containing iron elements, it is the configuration of the iron elements which principally affects the reluctance. Most of the force then acts directly on these iron elements. In the normal type of energy-conversion device, most of the force which is available to do useful work acts on iron bodies mounted to allow the desired type of motion. In such a device, there is normally a single force or torque which is involved in the desired energy conversion. There are also forces acting to produce stresses within the iron members. These stresses cause strains which modify the shape of the members in a manner to reduce the reluctance. This phenomenon is known as *magnetostriction*. The result of the internal stresses in an alternating field is vibration, which is usually undesirable since it causes noise.

There are also forces acting directly on the exciting coil. In accordance with the general principle, these forces tend to move the coil as a rigid body into the position on the magnetic circuit where the reluctance is a minimum and also tend to deform it by compressing it axially and expanding it in cross-sectional area of flux path. A coil wound on a rectangular form, for example, tends to deform into a circle. The shape and position of the exciting coil on an iron magnetic circuit usually have relatively little effect on the reluctance. Consequently, under normal conditions the forces acting directly on the exciting coil are much smaller than those acting on the iron members. Under abnormal conditions, however, such as short circuits on large power apparatus, the forces on the coil may be extremely large.

Other useful forms of the force equation can be derived from Eq. 2-29. In terms of mmf and permeance

$$f = +\frac{1}{2}F^2\frac{d\mathcal{P}}{dx} \tag{2-30}$$

In terms of flux and mmf,

$$f = -\frac{1}{2}\phi\left(\frac{\partial F}{\partial x}\right)_{\phi=\text{const}} \tag{2-31}$$

where $\partial F/\partial x$ is the partial derivative of mmf with respect to x at constant flux. Alternatively

$$f = +\frac{1}{2}F\left(\frac{\partial \phi}{\partial x}\right)_{F=\text{const}} \tag{2-32}$$

where $\partial\phi/\partial x$ is the partial derivative of flux with respect to x at constant mmf. In terms of current and inductance

$$f = +\frac{1}{2}i^2\frac{dL}{dx} \tag{2-33}$$

The force is thus seen to act in a direction to increase the permeance, decrease the mmf at constant flux, increase the flux at constant mmf, or increase the inductance.

The force can also be expressed in terms of the rates of change of field energy with respect to displacement. Thus, from Eqs. 2-13 and 2-29,

$$f = -\left(\frac{\partial W_{\text{fld}}}{\partial x}\right)_{\phi=\text{const}} \tag{2-34}$$

We have already seen in the discussion of Eq. 2-27 that differential changes in flux have no bearing on the mechanical force, because for differentials the electrical energy input $F\,d\phi$ is balanced by an identical field-energy increment. Since the force is independent of $d\phi$, an expression for the force can be obtained by considering what would happen if the flux were constant. Equation 2-34 simply states that if the displacement dx were to take place at constant flux the electrical energy input $F\,d\phi$ in Eq. 2-27 would be zero and the mechanical work done would be at the expense of the energy stored in the magnetic field. The force therefore equals the rate, with respect to motion, at which energy can be abstracted from the field at constant flux.

Also note that, from Eqs. 2-15 and 2-33,

$$f = +\left(\frac{\partial W_{\text{fld}}}{\partial x}\right)_{i=\text{const}} \tag{2-35}$$

Study of Eq. 2-35 reveals some interesting and useful facts. The equation shows that if a displacement occurs with the current kept constant, the mechanical work $f\,dx$ equals the increment in field energy dW_{fld}. Thus for a linear system at constant current, half of the electrical energy input goes toward increasing the energy stored in the field; the other half is delivered as mechanical work. The mechanical work done by the magnetic force equals the increase in field energy at constant current, or the force equals the rate of increase of field energy with respect to x at constant current.

Equation 2-34 is applicable to nonlinear as well as linear systems. Equation 2-35, however, is restricted to linear systems. We shall find it to be a useful unifying principle which applies also to linear multiply excited systems.

Although the simple relay of Fig. 2-3*a* has been used as an illustration of magnetic forces, it should be clearly understood that the relations which have been derived in this article have a very broad significance. Consider any singly excited magnetic system, one part of which is movable as a rigid body with respect to the other parts. In general, the movable part will be acted upon by magnetic translational forces and rotational torques tending to move it toward the position of minimum reluctance. The value of the component magnetic force acting in any direction on any part can be determined by imagining the part in question to be given a differential displacement in the desired direction, say dx, and evaluating the corresponding derivatives in any of the preceding force equations. Torque can be determined by giving the part a differential angular displacement $d\theta$ in the desired direction and finding the corresponding derivatives with respect to the angle θ.

Example 2-1. Derive expressions for the force of attraction between two parallel plane faces of high-permeability ferromagnetic material with flux passing normally between them, as shown in Fig. 2-4. Neglect fringing.

Solution. The force relations readily can be derived in terms of the air-gap reluctance, the air-gap permeance, or the air-gap field energy. The first approach will be chosen here.

The reluctance $\mathcal{R}_{ag}$ of the air gap is

$$\mathcal{R}_{ag} = \frac{g}{\mu_0 A} \tag{2-36}$$

where g is the air-gap length, A is the area of each surface, and μ_0 is the permeability of air. Differentiation with respect to x (Fig. 2-4) gives

$$\frac{d\mathcal{R}_{ag}}{dx} = \frac{1}{\mu_0 A}\frac{dg}{dx} = -\frac{1}{\mu_0 A} \tag{2-37}$$

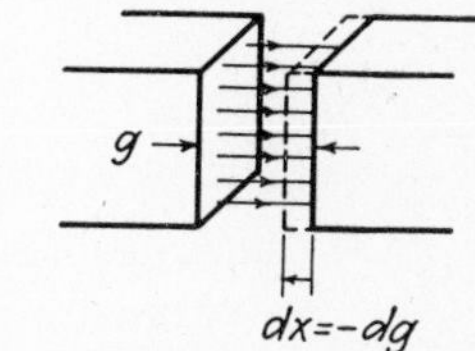

FIG. 2-4. Air gap with parallel faces, Example 2-1.

since dx is a negative increment in gap length. Substitution of Eq. 2-37 in Eq. 2-29 gives

$$f = +\frac{\phi_{ag}^2}{2\mu_0 A} \tag{2-38}$$

where ϕ_{ag} is the air-gap flux. In rationalized mks units the force is in newtons. An alternative form is

$$f = +\frac{B_{ag}^2 A}{2\mu_0} \tag{2-39}$$

where B_{ag} is the air-gap flux density and equals ϕ_{ag}/A.

Example 2-2. The magnetic circuit shown in Fig. 2-5 is made of cast steel. The rotor is free to turn about a vertical axis. The dimensions are shown in the figure.

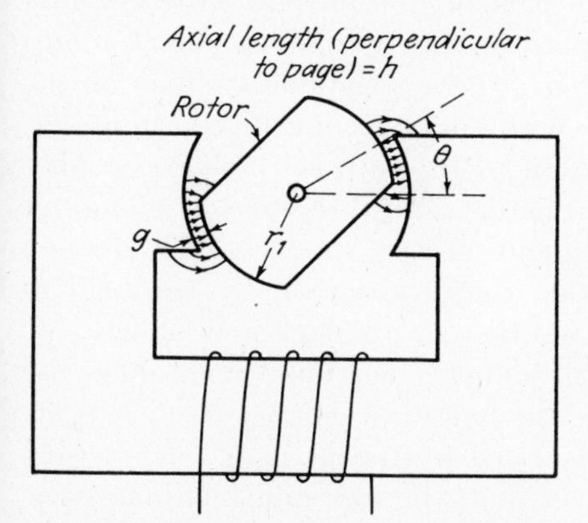

FIG. 2-5. Magnetic system for Example 2-2.

a. Derive an expression in mks rationalized units for the torque acting on the rotor in terms of the dimensions and the mmf consumed by the two air gaps. Neglect the effects of fringing.

b. The maximum flux density in the overlapping portions of the air gaps is limited to approximately 130 kilolines/in.², because of saturation in the steel. Compute the maximum torque in inch-pounds for the following dimensions: $r_1 = 1.00$ in.; $h = 1.00$ in.; $g = 0.10$ in.

Solution. In a manner paralleling Example 2-1, the torque can be derived from the derivative of air-gap reluctance, of air-gap permeance, or of field energy. This time the last approach will be used.

a. The field-energy density is $B_{ag}^2/2\mu_0$ (Eq. 2-16), and the volume of the two overlapping air gaps is $2gh(r_1 + 0.5g)\theta$. Consequently the field energy is

$$W_{ag} = \frac{B_{ag}^2 gh(r_1 + 0.5g)\theta}{\mu_0} \tag{2-40}$$

At constant mmf, B_{ag} is constant, and therefore differentiation of Eq. 2-40 with respect to θ at constant mmf, in accordance with Eq. 2-35, gives for the torque

$$T = \frac{B_{ag}^2(r_1 + 0.5g)gh}{\mu_0} \tag{2-41}$$

b. Convert the flux density and dimensions to mks units.

$$\begin{aligned} B_{ag} &= \frac{130{,}000}{6.45} \times 10^4 \times 10^{-8} = 2.02 \text{ webers/m}^2 \\ g &= 0.1 \times 2.54 \times 10^{-2} = 0.00254 \text{ m} \\ h &= r_1 = 1.00 \times 2.54 \times 10^{-2} = 0.0254 \text{ m} \\ \mu_0 &= 4\pi \times 10^{-7} \end{aligned}$$

Substitution of these numerical values in Eq. 2-41 gives

$$\begin{aligned} T &= 5.56 \text{ newton-m} \\ &= 5.56 \times 0.738 \times 12 = 49.3 \text{ in.-lb} \end{aligned}$$

d. Effects of Nonlinearity. The evaluation of the term in Eq. 2-1 representing the change in field energy becomes complicated when hysteresis and magnetic saturation are considered. Graphical methods of computation based on the energy diagram of Fig. 2-3*b* must then be used. In other words, we can study what would happen to the areas in Fig. 2-3*b* if the motion were shrunk to an infinitesimal. Eddy currents need not be considered in the problem of determining the force under d-c conditions, since their effects are proportional to the time rate of change of flux. The displacement dx given to the moving part for the purpose of evaluating the force may be considered to take place so slowly that stationary conditions always prevail. Eddy currents may have a significant effect on the energy balance in devices operating with time-varying fluxes, however, and should then be taken into account. In contrast, hysteresis phenomena are dependent on magnetic history and direction of change of magnetic condition but are independent of the time rate of change. Hysteresis will therefore influence the energy absorbed by the field in going from one stationary state to another, no matter how slowly the change is made, and consequently will influence the force even under d-c conditions. Under cyclic conditions, the hysteresis energy loss per cycle can be evaluated from the area of a closed hysteresis loop. Hysteresis effects will be neglected here, however, and the flux-mmf characteristic will be assumed to be nonlinear but single-valued.[1] The customary pro-

[1] For other treatments of the same problem, see L. V. Bewley, "Two-dimensional Fields in Electrical Engineering," pp. 189–191, The Macmillan Company, New York, 1948; V. Karapetoff, Mechanical Forces between Electric Currents and Saturated Magnetic Fields, *Trans. AIEE*, vol. 46, pp. 563–569, 1927; R. E. Doherty and R. H. Park, Mechanical Forces between Electric Circuits, *Trans. AIEE*, vol. 45, pp. 240–250, 1926. For discussion of the effects of hysteresis, see H. C. Roters, "Electromagnetic Devices," pp. 32–35, 73–77, 199–201, John Wiley & Sons, Inc., New York, 1941.

cedure in problems involving noncyclic mmfs is to use the mean magnetization curve drawn through the tips of a family of symmetrical hysteresis loops and giving an average relation, approximately midway between the rising and falling magnetization curves—a reasonable approximation when the exact magnetic history is unknown. The purpose of the following discussion is not so much to derive an accurate method of calculation as it is to show why the relatively simple relations derived on the basis of linearity, as in Art. 2-1*c*, usually are capable of giving fairly accurate results.

Considerable care must be taken with the notation. As in Art. 2-1*c*, let ϕ and F be the particular values of flux and mmf for which the force is to be determined. Let φ and $\mathfrak{F}$ be variable values of flux and mmf, the relation between them being the magnetization curve *Oa* in Fig. 2-6, *a* being the operating point. Now let the movable part take a displacement dx in the direction in which it is desired to find the component magnetic force. The mmf $\mathfrak{F}$ is a function of both flux and geometry, and therefore the effect of the displacement will be to change the magnetization curve to a new curve *Ob* in Fig. 2-6. For any value of flux φ, the horizontal distance $d\mathfrak{F}$ between the two curves is a function of the flux and equals the partial differential of mmf with respect to displacement; *i.e.*,

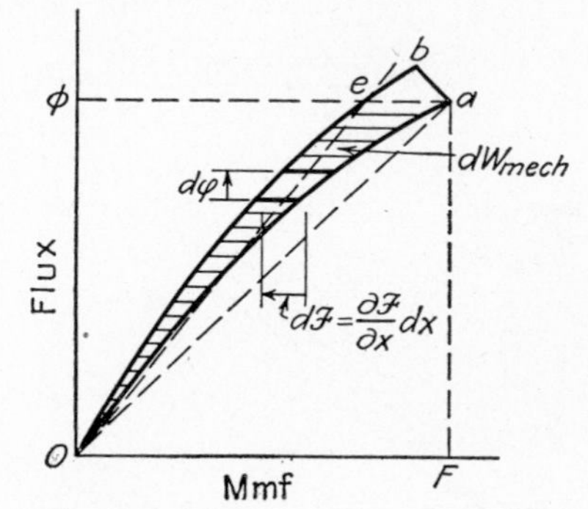

FIG. 2-6. Nonlinear flux-mmf characteristics and differential energy relations.

$$d\mathfrak{F} = \frac{\partial \mathfrak{F}}{\partial x}\,dx \tag{2-42}$$

The movable part of the magnetic circuit tends to move under the influence of the magnetic force in such a direction as to decrease the reluctance, and accordingly the new magnetization curve *Ob* is drawn to the left of the original curve in Fig. 2-6. Let the operating flux also change from ϕ to $\phi + d\phi$. The new operating point is *b* in Fig. 2-6.

It is shown in Art. 2-1*b* that the mechanical work done is equal to the area *OabO* enclosed by the original and final magnetization curves and the flux-mmf locus during motion. When the motion is shrunk to an infinitesimal dx, as in Fig. 2-6, the area *OabO* becomes an infinitesimal and the mechanical work becomes $f\,dx$.

The size of the area *OaeO* between the two magnetization curves in Fig. 2-6 is the integration of the differential parallelograms of height $d\varphi$ and base $d\mathfrak{F}$, or

$$\text{Size of area } OaeO = \int_0^\phi d\mathfrak{F}\, d\varphi = \int^\phi \frac{\partial \mathfrak{F}}{\partial x}\, dx\, d\varphi \tag{2-43}$$

The area of the triangle abe is an infinitesimal of the second order, and therefore area $OaeO$ approaches area $OabO$ when dx approaches zero. In the limit these areas are exactly equal. The integrals in Eq. 2-43 represent algebraically the *increase* in field energy that would be caused by an increment $d\mathfrak{F}$ in mmf. But the force acts in a direction to decrease the mmf. Consequently the energy abstracted from the field and converted into mechanical work is the negative of these integrals, or

$$f\, dx = -\int_0^\phi \frac{\partial \mathfrak{F}}{\partial x}\, dx\, d\varphi \tag{2-44}$$

Since dx is a constant in the integration, it can be taken outside of the integral, and division of both sides of Eq. 2-44 by dx then gives

$$f = -\int_0^\phi \frac{\partial \mathfrak{F}}{\partial x}\, d\varphi \tag{2-45}$$

The negative sign shows that the magnetic force acts in a direction to *decrease the reluctance* and transfer energy from the field to the mechanical system, as in Eqs. 2-29, 2-31, and 2-34.

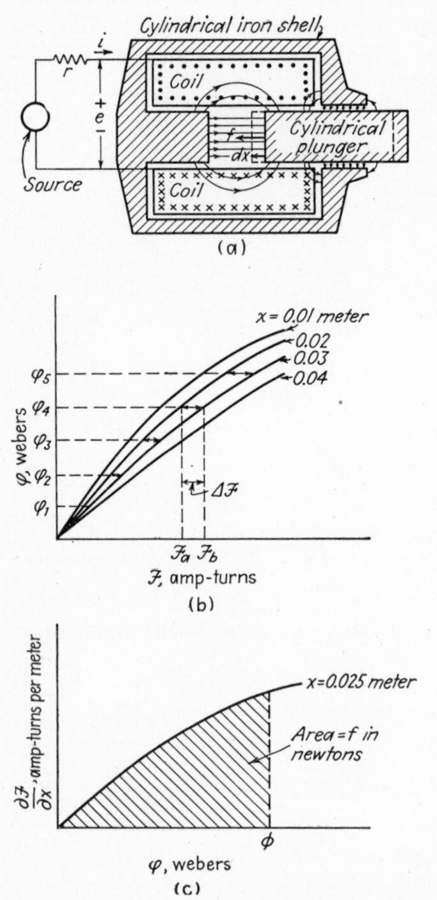

FIG. 2-7. (*a*) Cylindrical plunger magnet. (*b*) Family of magnetization curves. (*c*) Graphical integration for determining the force, Example 2-3.

Example 2-3. The force can be determined by finding values of $\partial\mathfrak{F}/\partial x$ from a family of magnetization curves, plotting these values against flux with x as a parameter, and graphically performing the integration of Eq. 2-45. For example, suppose a family of magnetization curves are taken on the plunger magnet of Fig. 2-7*a*, with the plunger held in a fixed position for each curve. Moving-iron magnetic devices of this type are used for producing a relatively large force acting through a relatively short distance.[2] Four typical curves are shown in Fig. 2-7*b*, where x is the spacing between the faces of the movable cylindrical plunger and the

[2] For an extensive treatment of a wide variety of moving-iron devices see H. C. Roters, "Electromagnetic Devices," John Wiley & Sons, Inc., New York, 1941.

fixed cylindrical core, in meters. The problem is: Find the force for a particular value ϕ of the flux and a spacing $x = 0.025$ m.

Solution. At a given value of flux, say φ_4, the increment in mmf when x varies from 0.02 to 0.03 m (Fig. 2-7*b*) is $\Delta\mathfrak{F} = \mathfrak{F}_b - \mathfrak{F}_a$ amp-turns, and the corresponding increment in x is $\Delta x = 0.01$ m. The average value of x over this internal is 0.025 m. If the horizontal spacings between the curves at any given value of flux are fairly uniform, $\Delta\mathfrak{F}/\Delta x$ is a close approximation to $\partial\mathfrak{F}/\partial x$ at $\varphi = \varphi_4$ and $x = 0.025$ m. By choosing several values of flux and determining the corresponding increments in mmf between the curves for $x = 0.02$ and $x = 0.03$, as indicated in Fig. 2-7*b*, data can be obtained for a curve of $\partial\mathfrak{F}/\partial x$ as a function of φ for $x = 0.025$ m, as shown in Fig. 2-7*c*. In accordance with Eq. 2-45, the force for a value of flux ϕ and a gap of 0.025 m equals the crosshatched area in Fig. 2-7*c* and acts in a direction to shorten the gap.

The procedure described above is fairly complicated and laborious. Fortunately, however, the much simpler relations derived on the basis of linearity usually give satisfactory results when properly applied, even though the magnetic circuit may be saturated. This fact can now be appreciated from a reexamination of the energy balance in the light of what has been shown in the preceding discussion.

Assume that the distribution of flux throughout the magnetic material and in the leakage field is unchanged when the movable part is given a displacement dx and the flux is held constant. This condition usually is approximately met in singly excited systems, except when the saturation or the magnetic leakage is abnormally high. Also assume that the volume of magnetic material in the field is constant. Then the only changes in magnetic conditions caused by the displacement dx occur in the immediate vicinity of the variable air gap, whose reluctance is independent of the flux. The problem then reduces to one involving changes in only the linear portion of the field. All the force relations which have previously been derived in Art. 2-1*c* for the linear case therefore apply within the limitations of the assumptions. Thus Eqs. 2-29, 2-30, 2-34, and 2-35 may be written in terms of the air-gap flux, the magnetic potential difference between the faces of the air gap, the air-gap reluctance, the air-gap permeance, and the magnetic energy stored in the air gap. The problem then reduces to the calculation of conditions in the air gap, which in turn can be computed from dimensions.[3]

Alternatively, within the limits of the assumptions stated at the beginning of the preceding paragraph, the force can be expressed in terms of the parameters of the complete magnetic circuit, just as if it were a linear magnetic circuit. For example, on the basis of the assumptions, the increment in mmf $d\mathfrak{F}$ in Fig. 2-6 is proportional to the flux φ, and therefore the crosshatched area *OaeO* between the two magnetization curves equals the area of the triangle *OaeO* whose slant sides are the dashed

[3] For methods of computing the permeance of a number of air-gap configurations and force formulas for a number of particular cases, see the reference cited in footnote 2.

straight lines Oa and Oe in Fig. 2-6. For an infinitesimal displacement dx, the cross-hatched area $OaeO$ equals area $OabO$, which in turn equals the mechanical work $f\,dx$. Consequently, within the limits of the assumptions,

$$f\,dx = -\frac{1}{2}\phi\,dF = -\frac{1}{2}\phi\frac{\partial F}{\partial x}\,dx \tag{2-46}$$

or

$$f = -\frac{1}{2}\phi\left(\frac{\partial F}{\partial x}\right)_{\phi=\text{const}} \tag{2-47}$$

where ϕ and F are the particular values of flux and mmf at the operating point. Compare with Eq. 2-31. All the other force relations for the linear case also apply. For example, in terms of the coil current and inductance,

$$f = +\frac{1}{2}i^2\left(\frac{\partial L}{\partial x}\right)_{\phi=\text{const}} \tag{2-48}$$

where L is the inductance at the operating point and is a function of the operating flux ϕ. This relation is useful when it is desired to determine the force from measurement of the parameters of the exciting winding.

The representation of a device involving nonlinear magnetic characteristics by means of equivalent parameters whose values are adjusted to take into account saturation at any specified operating point, and which can be considered constant for small changes, is a commonly used artifice in the analysis of nonlinear devices. It will be used frequently in subsequent work. The representation of a nonlinear moving-iron device by an equivalent inductance, as in Eq. 2-48, is a simple example.

Although nonlinearity does not enter directly into these approximate force equations, it should not be forgotten that saturation often may have an important indirect effect on the force produced by a specified coil current, since the air-gap flux and mmf, and the equivalent inductance, will be determined by the magnetic characteristics of the entire magnetic circuit.

Although the discussion of this article is based on the magnetic field produced by a current-carrying coil, the final results show that the force depends primarily on energy changes at the variable air gap and is independent of the source of the field. Force equations in terms of conditions at the air gap therefore apply equally well when the field is produced by permanent magnets.

In some devices, such as the plunger magnet of Fig. 2-7a, the motion of the movable part results in a change in the volume of magnetic material in the field, and consequently the field energy available for mechanical work when the air-gap volume is reduced is diminished by the energy required to magnetize the additional volume of magnetic material. For example, if A is the cross-sectional area of the cylindrical plunger in Fig. 2-7a, the effect of the motion dx is to replace a volume $A\ dx$ of air by an equal volume of plunger. The energy dW_p required to magnetize the additional volume of plunger can be expressed as

$$dW_p = A\ dx \int_0^{B_p} \mathcal{H}_p\ d\mathcal{B}_p \tag{2-49}$$

where the integral is the energy absorbed per cubic meter of plunger material in establishing a flux density B_p in the plunger corresponding to the operating flux and can be evaluated graphically from the area between the rising $\mathcal{BH}$ curve and the flux-density axis, in a manner similar to that indicated in Fig. 2-2. Since force is the rate of change of energy with respect to displacement, the usually small amount to be subtracted from the force is

$$\text{Loss of force} = \frac{dW_p}{dx} = A \int_0^{B_p} \mathcal{H}_p\ d\mathcal{B}_p \tag{2-50}$$

Example 2-4. Estimate the order of magnitude of the error in the force on the plunger of Fig. 2-7a caused by neglecting the change in volume of magnetic material in the field.

Solution. Fairly crude approximations can be made since only a rough estimate is required. Consequently the plunger will be treated as if it had constant permeability μ_p, and the value of permeability will be taken conservatively low. Fringing in the air gap also will be neglected. The flux density in the plunger than equals that in the air gap, namely, B_{ag}. Allowing the plunger to move replaces a volume $A\ dx$ of air in which the energy density is $B_{ag}^2/2\mu_0$ by an equal volume of plunger in which the energy density is $B_{ag}^2/2\mu_p$. If the displacement is considered to take place at constant flux, the energy released from the field is available to do mechanical work, whence

$$f\ dx = \left(\frac{B_{ag}^2}{2\mu_0} - \frac{B_{ag}^2}{2\mu_p}\right) A\ dx \tag{2-51}$$

or

$$f = \frac{B_{ag}^2 A}{2\mu_0}\left(1 - \frac{1}{\mu_p/\mu_0}\right) \tag{2-52}$$

where μ_p/μ_0 is the permeability of the plunger relative to air.

Soft-steel castings and mild cold-rolled steel, for example, have relative permeabilities greater than 500 over the range from about 10 to 80 kilolines/in.^{2} For such materials, therefore, the loss of force caused by the energy absorbed by the plunger is only about $\frac{1}{500}$, or 0.2 per cent, of the force created by the air-gap field over a wide range of flux densities. The loss of force is appreciable only in cases where the forces and flux densities are low.

2-2. Reluctance Torque in Rotating Machines. Advantage has been taken of the simplicity of the variable-reluctance principle in a wide variety of devices for producing mechanical force or torque. Some of them, such as lifting magnets and magnetic chucks, are required merely to hold a piece of ferromagnetic material; others, such as iron-core solenoids, relays, and contactors, are required to exert a force through a specified distance; still others, such as iron-vane instruments, are required to produce a rotational torque against a restraining spring so that the deflection of a pointer is indicative of the steady-state value of the current or voltage of the circuit to which they are connected; with others, such as moving-iron telephone receivers and the electromagnets used for controlling the operation of hydraulic motors in servomechanisms, the force or torque should be very nearly proportional to an electrical signal, and the dynamic response should be as rapid as possible. In all the above devices the motion is through a limited range.

The variable-reluctance principle can also be applied for producing continuous rotation of a shaft, and the result, the *single-phase a-c reluctance motor*, is one of the simplest forms of electric motor. This motor is of the *synchronous* type; *i.e.*, it operates at a speed proportional to the frequency of the applied voltage. The commonest application of such motors is in driving electric clocks and other timing devices since their speed is constant when they are operated from a source whose frequency is constant. The theory of the electromagnetic type of reluctance motor is developed in this article, and an analogous type of electrostatic single-phase synchronous motor is described in Art. 2-5.

Although the analysis is devoted specifically to the simple single-phase motor, its broad significance should be borne in mind. Thus similar phenomena may be present in any rotating machine whose magnetic circuit is of such a form that its reluctance depends on the relative angular position of its stationary and moving parts. For example, reluctance torque is a significant component of the torque produced by a salient-pole synchronous machine of the type shown in Fig. 1-40.

The principal constructional features of one form of single-phase reluctance motor are shown in Fig. 2-8*a*. The essential feature is that the rotor be shaped so that the reluctance of the magnetic circuit depends on the angular position of the rotor. Thus in Fig. 2-8*a*, the reluctance $\mathcal{R}$ is a periodic function of the angle θ_o between the long axis of the rotor and the axis of the stator poles, as indicated in Fig. 2-8*b*. The reluctance has a minimum value $\mathcal{R}_d$, called the *direct-axis reluctance*, when the axis of the rotor is directly in line with the axis of the stator poles ($\theta_o = 0, \pi, 2\pi, \ldots$), and a maximum value $\mathcal{R}_q$, called the *quadrature-axis reluctance*, when the axis of the rotor is at right angles to the axis of the stator poles ($\theta_o = \pi/2, 3\pi/2, \ldots$). The exciting winding is connected to a source of single-phase alternating voltage. The flux therefore is also alternating, as shown by the curve φ in Fig. 2-8*b*. In accordance with the rotational equivalent of Eq. 2-29

$$T = -\frac{1}{2}\varphi^2 \frac{d\mathcal{R}}{d\theta_o} \tag{2-53}$$

where T is the instantaneous torque acting in the direction to increase the angle θ_o. The corresponding curves of φ^2 and $d\mathcal{R}/d\theta_o$ are shown in Fig.

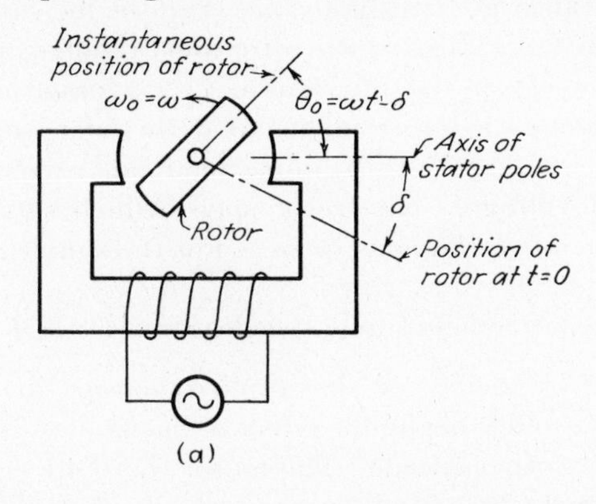

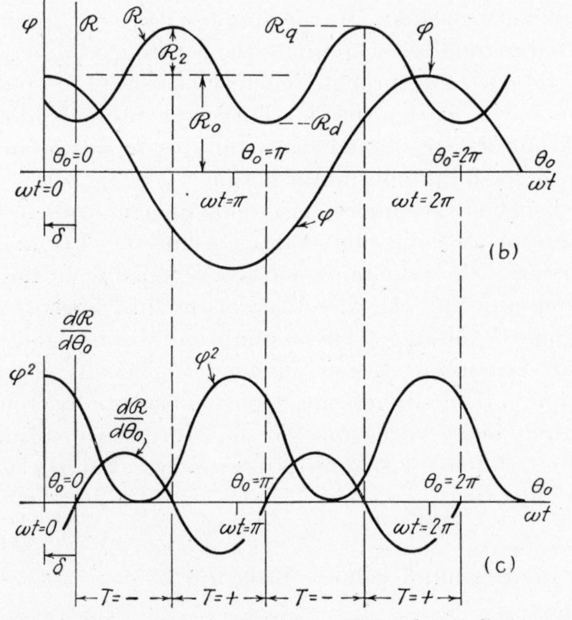

FIG. 2-8. (*a*) Elementary reluctance motor. (*b*) and (*c*) Corresponding flux and reluctance variations.

2-8*c*. From Eq. 2-53, the direction of the torque is determined by the sign of $d\mathcal{R}/d\theta_o$. It is positive while the reluctance is decreasing.

Examination of Eq. 2-53 and Fig. 2-8*c* shows that if the speed of the rotor and the phase relation between the reluctance variation and the flux wave are such that the average square of the flux is greater while the reluctance is decreasing than it is while the reluctance is increasing, the average torque acts in the direction to increase θ_o and thereby to keep the rotor revolving. To meet these requirements, the rotor speed must be such that the reluctance goes through one cycle of its variation in each half cycle of the flux wave; that is, the rotor must revolve one-half a revolution in one-half a cycle of the flux wave. Its average angular velocity in radians per second therefore must equal the time angular velocity ω of the flux wave, whence the rotor must make one revolution for each cycle of the applied voltage. The rotor speed which satisfies these requirements is known as *synchronous speed*. For the simple reluctance motor of Fig. 2-8*a*,

$$\text{Synchronous speed in rev/sec} = f \tag{2-54}$$

where f is the frequency of the applied voltage in cycles per second. Except for the usually negligible effect of harmonics, no average torque is produced at any other speed. The motor therefore is not self-starting, a limitation characteristic of all types of synchronous motors. It must be started by auxiliary means. In the simplest types of clock motors, the motor is started manually by spinning the rotor at or above synchronous speed; as the rotor coasts through synchronous speed it "pulls into step" and continues to run at this speed. Large synchronous motors and self-starting clock motors are started electrically by means of auxiliary windings which produce induction-motor action.

The basic theory of the single-phase reluctance motor can be developed on the assumption of sinusoidal variations of the flux and reluctance. Actually, of course, the reluctance variation depends on the geometry of the magnetic circuit, and the waveform of the flux depends on the waveform of the applied voltage. The assumption of sinusoidal waveforms is made primarily because of its convenience; it is usually also a fairly realistic assumption. If the waveforms depart substantially from sine waves, the flux and reluctance variations can be expressed in terms of Fourier series, but this refinement seldom is necessary. Let the instantaneous value φ of the flux be

$$\varphi = \phi_{max} \cos \omega t \tag{2-55}$$

where ϕ_{max} is its maximum value. From Eq. 2-55

$$\varphi^2 = \phi_{max}^2 \cos^2 \omega t = \tfrac{1}{2}\phi_{max}^2(1 + \cos 2\omega t) \tag{2-56}$$

Most electromechanical energy-conversion devices are designed so that the resistances of the windings are as small as possible. If the voltage drop due to the winding resistance is negligible, the flux must vary in such a manner as to induce a counter emf e equal to the voltage v_t applied to the winding. For sinusoidal variations, substitution of Eq. 2-55 in Faraday's law gives

$$e = N \frac{d\varphi}{dt} = -N\omega\phi_{\max} \sin \omega t \tag{2-57}$$

whence the relation between the rms value of the counter emf in volts and the maximum value of the flux in webers is

$$E_{\mathrm{rms}} = \frac{2\pi}{\sqrt{2}} fN\phi_{\max} = 4.44fN\phi_{\max} \tag{2-58}$$

This relation is already familiar to students who have studied transformer theory. Thus when a sinusoidally varying voltage is impressed on a winding whose resistance is negligible, a sinusoidally varying flux must be established whose maximum value $\phi_{\max}$ satisfies Eq. 2-58. The applied voltage and the induced counter emf are then equal, and Kirchhoff's law is satisfied.

The instantaneous value $\mathcal{R}$ of the reluctance is a function of the instantaneous angle θ_o. Inspection of the reluctance curve in Fig. 2-8*b* shows that if a sinusoidal variation is assumed, the reluctance can be expressed as

$$\mathcal{R} = \tfrac{1}{2}(\mathcal{R}_q + \mathcal{R}_d) - \tfrac{1}{2}(\mathcal{R}_q - \mathcal{R}_d) \cos 2\theta_o \tag{2-59}$$

Differentiation of Eq. 2-59 gives

$$\frac{d\mathcal{R}}{d\theta_o} = (\mathcal{R}_q - \mathcal{R}_d) \sin 2\theta_o \tag{2-60}$$

Assume that the rotor has been started by some auxiliary means and is running at a constant angular velocity of ω_o rad/sec. Actually, the instantaneous torque pulsates, and therefore the instantaneous speed is not absolutely constant. The inertias of the rotor and its mechanical load, however, maintain substantially constant speed. If the effects of the torque pulsations are neglected, the instantaneous position of the rotor is

$$\theta_o = \omega_o t - \delta \tag{2-61}$$

where δ is its instantaneous position at zero time when the flux is passing through its maximum value. For convenience, δ is taken as a *lag* angle, as indicated in Fig. 2-8*a*.

Substitution of Eq. 2-61 in Eq. 2-60 gives

$$\frac{d\mathcal{R}}{d\theta_o} = (\mathcal{R}_q - \mathcal{R}_d) \sin (2\omega_o t - 2\delta) \tag{2-62}$$

and substitution of Eqs. 2-56 and 2-62 in the basic torque relation (Eq. 2-53) then gives

$$T = -\tfrac{1}{4} \phi_{\max}^2 (\mathcal{R}_q - \mathcal{R}_d)[\sin (2\omega_o t - 2\delta) + \sin (2\omega_o t - 2\delta) \cos 2\omega t] \tag{2-63}$$

By use of the trigonometric identity

$$\sin \alpha \cos \beta = \tfrac{1}{2} \sin (\alpha + \beta) + \tfrac{1}{2} \sin (\alpha - \beta) \tag{2-64}$$

the torque expression becomes

$$T = -\tfrac{1}{4}\phi_{\max}^2 (\mathcal{R}_q - \mathcal{R}_d) \{\sin (2\omega_o t - 2\delta) + \tfrac{1}{2} \sin [2(\omega_o + \omega)t - 2\delta] + \tfrac{1}{2} \sin [2(\omega_o - \omega)t - 2\delta]\} \tag{2-65}$$

When the shaft angular velocity ω_o is not equal to the time angular velocity ω of the flux wave, the three sine terms in Eq. 2-65 are functions of time, and the average value of each of them over a complete

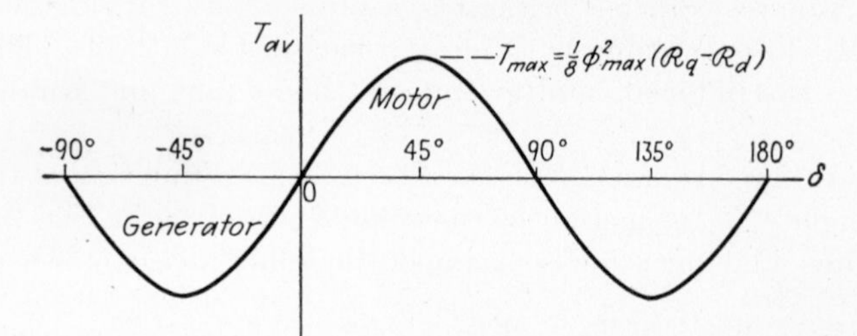

FIG. 2-9. Torque-angle characteristic of a reluctance motor.

cycle is zero. Therefore no average torque is developed. However, if ω_o equals ω, the torque becomes

$$T = -\tfrac{1}{4}\phi_{\max}^2 (\mathcal{R}_q - \mathcal{R}_d) [\sin (2\omega t - 2\delta) + \tfrac{1}{2} \sin (4\omega t - 2\delta) + \tfrac{1}{2} \sin (-2\delta)] \tag{2-66}$$

The first two sine terms are functions of time, and therefore their average values are zero. They represent pulsating components of the torque of twice and four times line frequency. The last sine term is independent of time. The average value T_{av} of the torque therefore is

$$T_{av} = +\tfrac{1}{8}\phi_{\max}^2(\mathcal{R}_q - \mathcal{R}_d) \sin 2\delta \tag{2-67}$$

Equation 2-67 is characteristic of the reluctance torque in all synchronous motors, whether they be of the simple single-phase type described here or of the more complicated form met in large polyphase salient-pole synchronous machines described in Chap. 8. If the applied voltage and frequency are constant and the resistance drop is negligible, $\phi_{\max}$ must be constant, as given by Eq. 2-58. The reluctances $\mathcal{R}_q$ and $\mathcal{R}_d$ depend primarily on the configuration of the magnetic circuit. Thus the rotor phase angle δ is the only variable on the right-hand side of Eq. 2-67. The relation between the average torque developed by the motor and the angle δ is shown in Fig. 2-9. The phase angle δ adjusts itself so that the electromagnetic torque T_{av} developed by the motor equals the torque required to drive the mechanical load connected to its shaft plus the torque required to overcome rotational losses in the motor. For this reason the rotor angle δ is often called the *torque angle.* If the load torque increases, the motor momentarily slows down, thereby increasing the lag angle δ until sufficient electromagnetic torque is developed to carry the increased load. After the brief transient required for adjustment of the torque angle δ, operation is resumed at synchronous speed. Note that the maximum value of the average electromagnetic torque the motor can develop occurs when δ equals 45° and is

$$T_{\max} = \tfrac{1}{8}\phi_{\max}^2(\mathcal{R}_q - \mathcal{R}_d) \tag{2-68}$$

The motor stalls if a mechanical load is applied that requires a torque exceeding this value.

As with any electromechanical-energy-conversion device, the process is essentially reversible. If mechanical power is supplied to the shaft, the rotor advances in phase; *i.e.*, the angle δ becomes negative. The average electromagnetic torque changes sign and therefore represents mechanical power absorbed and converted into electrical power, as shown by the portion of the torque-angle characteristic to the left of the origin in Fig. 2-9. As with motor action, there is a definite limit to the mechanical power that can be absorbed, occurring when $\delta = -45°$. Any further increase in driving torque causes overspeeding and loss of synchronism.

Example 2-5. When the rotor of a reluctance motor like that shown in Fig. 2-8*a* is in the direct-axis position, the inductance of its exciting winding is $L_d = 1.00$ henry. When the rotor is in the quadrature-axis position, the inductance is $L_q = 0.50$ henry. The exciting winding has $N = 1{,}000$ turns. Determine approximately the maximum torque that the motor can develop with 115 volts at 60 cps applied to its exciting winding.

Solution. According to Eq. 2-58,

$$\phi_{\max} = \frac{115}{(4.44)(1{,}000)(60)} = 4.32 \times 10^{-4} \text{ weber}$$

From the definition of inductance

$$L = \frac{N\phi}{I} = \frac{N^2\phi}{NI} = \frac{N^2}{\mathcal{R}} \tag{2-69}$$

or

$$\mathcal{R} = \frac{N^2}{L} \tag{2-70}$$

whence

$$\mathcal{R}_q = \frac{10^6}{0.50} = 2.00 \times 10^6 \text{ mks units}$$

$$\mathcal{R}_d = \frac{10^6}{1.00} = 1.00 \times 10^6 \text{ mks units}$$

Substitution of numerical values in Eq. 2-68 then gives

$$T_{\max} = \tfrac{1}{8}(4.32)^2(10^{-8})(2.00 - 1.00)(10^6) = 2.34 \times 10^{-2} \text{ newton-m}$$

In English units of a convenient size (inch-ounces),

$$T_{\max} = (2.34)(10^{-2})(0.738)(16)(12) = 3.31 \text{ in.-oz.}$$

2-3. Multiply Excited Magnetic Systems. Except for the simple moving-iron mechanisms discussed in Arts. 2-1 and 2-2, most electromechanical-energy-conversion devices of the magnetic type are provided with several windings arranged in two groups. One group of windings is mounted on a stationary member and the other group on a movable member. The tendency for the magnetic field energy to change when one group of windings moves with respect to the other group gives rise to mechanical forces. The theory of numerous types of energy-conversion devices, including most rotating machines, is based on this general principle. The various types differ only as to number of windings, their physical arrangement, and the manner of connecting the windings to the external electric circuits.

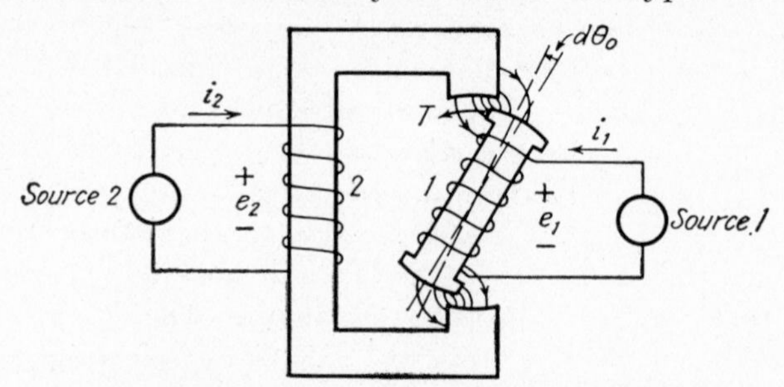

FIG. 2-10. Elementary multiply excited magnetic system.

The simplest type of such a device, analysis of which will serve to demonstrate the basic principles underlying the action of all of them, consists of two magnetically coupled windings connected to two separate electrical sources as shown in Fig. 2-10. Winding 1 is mounted on a rotor which can be rotated with respect to the stator on which winding 2 is mounted. Both stator and rotor cores are made of magnetic material. The energy in the magnetic field is influenced by the relative positions of the stator and rotor, and equal and opposite mechanical torques act on the two members in much the same manner as two permanent magnets react on each other. The component magnetic fields of stator and rotor tend to align themselves.

The torque can be determined by a line of reasoning identical to that used in the analysis of singly excited systems in Art. 2-1. Imagine the rotor to be allowed to move through a differential angular displacement $d\theta_o$ in the direction of the magnetic torque T acting upon it.

Mechanical work $T\,d\theta_o$ watt-sec will be done by the magnetic field. In general, the flux linkages with the windings may be changed, and counter emfs e_1 and e_2 will be induced in them. Energy will be abstracted from the two electrical sources. The field energy also may be changed. As in Eq. 2-1, the energy balance is

$$dW_{\text{elec}} = T\,d\theta_o + dW_{\text{fld}} \tag{2-71}$$

The differential energy dW_{elec} abstracted from the two sources is

$$dW_{\text{elec}} = e_1 i_1\,dt + e_2 i_2\,dt \tag{2-72}$$

Since the counter emf e_1 is

$$e_1 = +\frac{d\lambda_1}{dt} \tag{2-73}$$

the differential energy abstracted from source 1 is

$$e_1 i_1\,dt = i_1\,d\lambda_1 \tag{2-74}$$

where λ_1 is the flux linkage with winding 1 produced by the combined effect of the currents i_1 and i_2. Compare with Eq. 2-5. Similarly, the differential energy abstracted from source 2 is

$$e_2 i_2\,dt = i_2\,d\lambda_2 \tag{2-75}$$

where λ_2 is the resultant flux linkage with winding 2. Then, from Eq. 2-72

$$dW_{\text{elec}} = i_1\,d\lambda_1 + i_2\,d\lambda_2 \tag{2-76}$$

In order to continue the analysis, the field energy must be related to the energy abstracted from the electrical sources. The exact relations, including nonlinearity and hysteresis, are quite unwieldy; fortunately, since most of the field energy is stored in the air gaps, satisfactory results usually can be obtained by use of linear approximations. If magnetic nonlinearity is neglected, the superposition principle can be applied, and the flux linkages can be expressed in terms of the components that would be produced by each current acting alone. The energy relations then can be expressed conveniently in terms of the self- and mutual inductances L_{11}, L_{22}, and M_{12} of the windings. Thus the resultant flux linkage λ_1 with winding 1 can be expressed as

$$\lambda_1 = L_{11} i_1 + M_{12} i_2 \tag{2-77}$$

Similarly the resultant flux linkage λ_2 with winding 2 is

$$\lambda_2 = L_{22} i_2 + M_{12} i_1 \tag{2-78}$$

In a linear system the mutual-inductance coefficients as viewed from either of two circuits are equal; that is, M_{12} in Eq. 2-77 is identical to

M_{12} in Eq. 2-78. In these equations the relative directions of the self- and mutual flux linkages are accounted for by the algebraic sign of the mutual inductance. Thus the mutual inductance is a positive quantity if positive currents in the two windings produce self- and mutual fluxes in the same direction; otherwise it is a negative quantity.

An expression for the energy stored in the magnetic field can be obtained by considering the energy supplied by the sources in establishing the currents i_1 and i_2. If no motion takes place during the process, no mechanical work is done, and all of the energy supplied by the sources goes into storage in the field. Under these conditions

$$dW_{\text{fld}} = dW_{\text{elec}} = i_1\, d\lambda_1 + i_2\, d\lambda_2 \tag{2-79}$$

For fixed configuration the inductances are constant. Differentiation of Eqs. 2-77 and 2-78 and substitution of the results in Eq. 2-79 then gives

$$dW_{\text{fld}} = i_1 L_{11}\, di_1 + i_2 L_{22}\, di_2 + M_{12}(i_1 di_2 + i_2\, di_1) \tag{2-80}$$

But $i_1\, di_2 + i_2\, di_1$ is the differential $d(i_1 i_2)$ of the product of the currents. Consequently

$$dW_{\text{fld}} = L_{11} i_1\, di_1 + L_{22} i_2\, di_2 + M_{12}\, d(i_1 i_2) \tag{2-81}$$

and the field energy corresponding to currents i_1 and i_2 is

$$W_{\text{fld}} = L_{11} \int_0^{i_1} i_1\, di_1 + L_{22} \int_0^{i_2} i_2\, di_2 + M_{12} \int_0^{i_1 i_2} d(i_1 i_2) \tag{2-82}$$

$$= \tfrac{1}{2} L_{11} i_1^2 + \tfrac{1}{2} L_{22} i_2^2 + M_{12} i_1 i_2 \tag{2-83}$$

If the field is produced by currents in more than two circuits, the equation for the field energy in terms of the self- and mutual inductances can be obtained by an identical reasoning process. With three circuits, for example, the result is

$$W_{\text{fld}} = \tfrac{1}{2} L_{11} i_1^2 + \tfrac{1}{2} L_{22} i_2^2 + \tfrac{1}{2} L_{33} i_3^2 + M_{12} i_1 i_2 + M_{23} i_2 i_3 + M_{31} i_3 i_1 \tag{2-84}$$

The differential changes in the electrical and field energy resulting from a differential angular displacement $d\theta_o$ can now be expressed in terms of the inductances and currents, and the mechanical torque T can then be found from Eq. 2-71. In general, all the inductance parameters may be functions of the rotor position. In evaluating the field energy for a *fixed* configuration, as in Eqs. 2-79 to 2-83, the inductances were constants; they must now be considered as *variables*, however, because we are allowing the configuration to change. In fact it is these changes of inductance with configuration which account for the mechanical energy output. The currents also may change because of the effects of induced transients. Differential changes in the currents, however, have no effect on the mechanical forces, since the forces depend solely on the values of the currents and the geometrical configuration. For the sake of completeness, however, the effects of differential changes in the currents are included in the following analysis.

Differentiation of Eqs. 2-77 and 2-78 with respect to the inductances and currents and substitution of the results in Eq. 2-76 gives for the electrical energy input

$$dW_{elec} = L_{11}i_1\,di_1 + M_{12}i_1\,di_2 + i_1^2\,dL_{11} + i_1i_2\,dM_{12} + L_{22}i_2\,di_2 + M_{12}i_2\,di_1 + i_2^2\,dL_{22} + i_1i_2\,dM_{12} \tag{2-85}$$

Similarly from Eq. 2-83 the increment in field energy is

$$dW_{fld} = L_{11}i_1\,di_1 + \tfrac{1}{2}i_1^2\,dL_{11} + L_{22}i_2\,di_2 + \tfrac{1}{2}i_2^2\,dL_{22} + M_{12}i_1\,di_2 + M_{12}i_2\,di_1 + i_1i_2\,dM_{12} \tag{2-86}$$

When Eqs. 2-85 and 2-86 are substituted in Eq. 2-71, the four terms $L_{11}i_1\,di_1 + L_{22}i_2\,di_2 + M_{12}i_1\,di_2 + M_{12}i_2\,di_1$ expressing the electrical-energy input caused by the current increments di_1 and di_2 are balanced by identical terms expressing the corresponding increments in field energy. These terms therefore cancel. In other words, differential changes in the currents have no effect on the mechanical forces. Substitution of the remaining terms in Eq. 2-71 gives

$$i_1^2\,dL_{11} + i_2^2\,dL_{22} + 2i_1i_2\,dM_{12} = \tfrac{1}{2}i_1^2\,dL_{11} + \tfrac{1}{2}i_2^2\,dL_{22} + i_1i_2\,dM_{12} + T\,d\theta_o \tag{2-87}$$

whence

$$T = \frac{1}{2}i_1^2\frac{dL_{11}}{d\theta_o} + \frac{1}{2}i_2^2\frac{dL_{22}}{d\theta_o} + i_1i_2\frac{dM_{12}}{d\theta_o} \tag{2-88}$$

The translational equivalent of Eq. 2-88 is obtained if torque T is replaced by translational force f and angular displacement $d\theta_o$ by linear displacement dx in the direction of the force. The extension of Eq. 2-88 to a situation involving several circuits whose self- and mutual inductances depend upon the angular position of some member should be obvious from consideration of the line of reasoning followed in the derivation of Eq. 2-88. For example, with three circuits,

$$T = \frac{1}{2}i_1^2\frac{dL_{11}}{d\theta_o} + \frac{1}{2}i_2^2\frac{dL_{22}}{d\theta_o} + \frac{1}{2}i_3^2\frac{dL_{33}}{d\theta_o} + i_1i_2\frac{dM_{12}}{d\theta_o} + i_2i_3\frac{dM_{23}}{d\theta_o} + i_3i_1\frac{dM_{31}}{d\theta_o} \tag{2-89}$$

Examination of Eq. 2-87 shows that the sum of the three terms on the right-hand side expressing the increment in field energy at constant currents is half of the left-hand side expressing the electrical energy input at constant currents. The other half of the electrical energy input at constant currents therefore is delivered as mechanical energy. The increment in field energy at constant currents therefore equals the mechanical energy delivered; hence the torque or force equals the rate of increase of field energy with respect to motion at constant current;

$$T = + \left(\frac{\partial W_{\text{fld}}}{\partial \theta_o} \right)_{\text{currents = const}} \tag{2-90}$$

In Art. 2-1*c* this relation has been found to apply to linear singly excited systems. (See Eq. 2-35.) For a linear system, Eq. 2-90 simply says that mechanical forces and torques act on the magnetic material and conductors in such a direction as to increase the field energy at constant currents.

When the magnetic circuit contains iron, the terms involving the angular rates of change of the self-inductances in Eq. 2-88 are the reluctance torques that have previously been discussed in Arts. 2-1 and 2-2 in connection with singly excited systems. They express the fact that the field due to one current acting alone produces forces on magnetic material tending to move it so as to reduce the reluctance of the magnetic circuit. Thus, if both stator and rotor cores in Fig. 2-10 are made of magnetic material, the field due to either current acting alone tends to move the rotor into a vertical position.

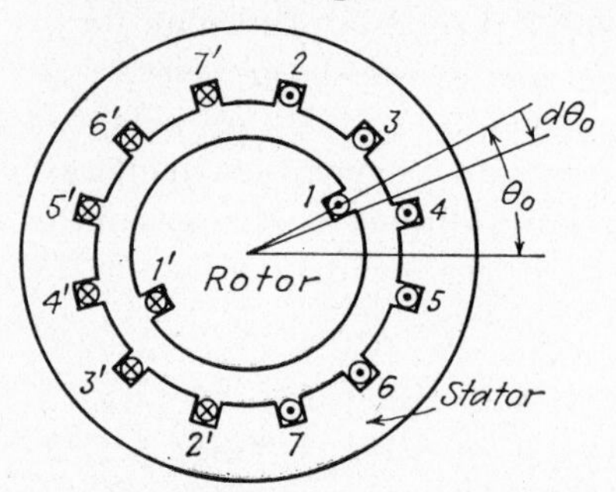

FIG. 2-11. Elementary cylindrical-rotor machine.

The terms involving the angular rates of change of the mutual inductances express the torques due to the interaction of the magnetic field of one current with that of another. These terms merely say that the magnetic fields of stator and rotor tend to line up. These are the principal torques in a large class of rotating machines.

a. Torque in Uniform-air-gap Machines. Consider the simple device shown in Fig. 2-11 consisting of a cylindrical steel rotor core mounted concentrically inside a hollow cylindrical steel stator core. The rotor carries a single winding 1-1′ placed in a pair of diametrically opposite slots shown in cross section in the figure. The stator carries a number of windings 2-2′, 3-3′, etc., arranged in slots around the inside periphery of the stator core, and shown in cross section. The dots and crosses on the cross sections of the windings represent the heads and tails of arrows pointing in the positive directions of the currents. The arrangement is not unlike that of a 2-pole turboalternator.

Except for the effect of the slots, the air gap is uniform, and the reluctance of the magnetic circuit is independent of the angular position θ_o of the rotor. Consequently, with slots neglected, the self-inductances of the windings are independent of θ_o, and the reluctance torques are zero. Furthermore, the mutual inductances between the various pairs of stator windings are independent of θ_o. Therefore Eq. 2-89 reduces to

$$T = i_1 \left(i_2 \frac{dM_{12}}{d\theta_o} + i_3 \frac{dM_{13}}{d\theta_o} + \cdots \right) \tag{2-91}$$

In terms of flux linkages,

$$i_2 M_{12} = \lambda_{12} \qquad i_3 M_{13} = \lambda_{13} \qquad \cdots \tag{2-92}$$

where λ_{12}, for example, is the flux linkage with winding 1 produced by the current in winding 2. The flux linkage λ_{1s} with the rotor winding 1 produced by the *combined* effect of *all* the currents in the stator windings is

$$\lambda_{1s} = i_2 M_{12} + i_3 M_{13} + \cdots \tag{2-93}$$

Differentiation of Eq. 2-93 with the currents constant gives

$$\frac{\partial \lambda_{1s}}{\partial \theta_o} = i_2 \frac{dM_{12}}{d\theta_o} + i_3 \frac{dM_{13}}{d\theta_o} + \cdots \tag{2-94}$$

and by substitution in Eq. 2-91

$$T = i_1 \left(\frac{\partial \lambda_{1s}}{\partial \theta_o} \right)_{\text{currents} = \text{const}} \tag{2-95}$$

If the flux linkage λ_{1s} in Eq. 2-95 is divided by the number of turns N_1 in the rotor winding,

$$T = N_1 i_1 \frac{\partial}{\partial \theta_o} \frac{\lambda_{1s}}{N_1} = F_1 \frac{\partial \phi_{1s}}{\partial \theta_o} \tag{2-96}$$

where $N_1 i_1 = F_1$ is the rotor mmf and $\lambda_{1s}/N_1 = \phi_{1s}$ is the flux linking the rotor winding produced by the stator mmf.

Equation 2-96 expresses the torque as the interaction of the mmf of the rotor winding with the magnetic field produced by the stator currents. A simple qualitative picture of this interaction can be obtained from consideration of the component fields produced by the stator and rotor currents. Figure 2-12*a* shows the general character of the field produced by the rotor current in the device of Fig. 2-11. Since the permeability of steel is much greater than that of air, the flux lines enter and leave the stator and rotor surfaces very nearly perpendicularly, and except in the vicinity of the slot openings, the direction of the air-gap field is very nearly radial. For the positive direction of the rotor current shown in the figure, the right-hand-screw relation between the positive directions of flux and of the current producing it shows that the rotor current produces north magnetic polarity at the lower right-hand surface of the rotor and south magnetic polarity along the diametrically opposite rotor surface, as indicated by the letters N_r and S_r in Fig. 2-12*c*. Figure 2-12*b* shows the general character of the field produced by the stator currents. The flux density at the rotor surface varies around its circumference in a manner dependent on the mmfs of the stator coils and the way in which the coils are distributed. For the positive directions shown in Fig. 2-12*b*, the stator currents produce north magnetic polarity along the upper air-gap surface of the stator and south polarity along its lower air-gap surface as indicated by N_s and S_s in Fig. 2-12*c*. The torque can be regarded as the attraction between opposite magnetic poles of stator and rotor and

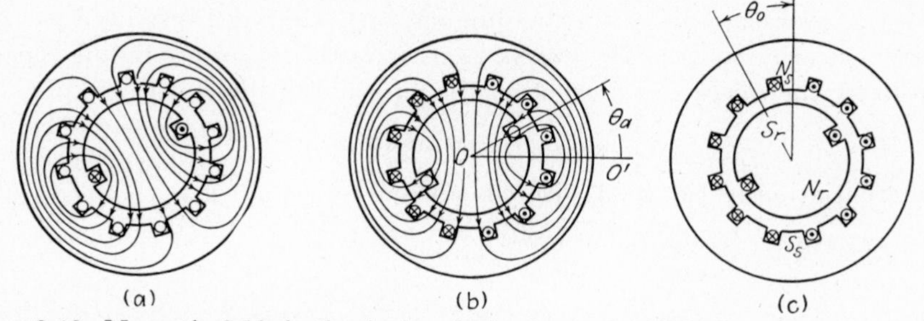

FIG. 2-12. Magnetic fields in the device of Fig. 2-11. (*a*) Field due to rotor current; (*b*) field due to stator currents; (*c*) magnetic polarities of stator and rotor.

acts to tend to reduce the angle θ_o, bringing the stator and rotor fields into alignment.

b. Torque in Terms of Air-gap Flux Density. An exact evaluation of the flux linkages in even so simple a device as that of Fig. 2-11 is a magnetic-field problem of great complexity. It is a hopeless task to include rigorously the nonlinear magnetic characteristics of the iron of actual rotating machines. Even the assumption of constant permeability does not simplify the situation sufficiently. Because the permeability of iron is at least several hundred times that of air, however, the flux distribution in the air gap is closely what it would be if the iron had infinite permeability. Even so, the determination of an accurate field map is no simple matter, because of the effects of the slots. Analyses of the problem have been made by both analytical and graphical flux-plotting methods, but only relatively simple configurations are directly susceptible to analytical solution.[4] The need for simplifying assumptions is thus distinctly evident.

[4] For analytical attacks on the problem see, for example, L. V. Bewley, "Two-dimensional Fields in Electrical Engineering," The Macmillan Company, New York, 1948; B. Hague, "Electromagnetic Problems in Electrical Engineering," Oxford University Press, New York, 1929. Bewley also discusses graphical methods.

In the analysis of rotating machines, the actual machine is often considered to be replaced by an idealized equivalent one with negligible slot openings and with infinitely permeable iron. The advantage of the idealized machine is that its air-gap field can readily be visualized. The air-gap length of the equivalent machine is adjusted to account for the effect on the air-gap reluctance caused by the slot openings in the actual machine, and an allowance is made for the mmf required by the iron in the actual machine, the latter being computed as a magnetic-circuit problem. Such an equivalent machine preserves the principal features of the actual machine, though obviously the two differ in so far as effects caused directly by the presence of slot openings are concerned. It probably does not require too great a stretch of the imagination to see

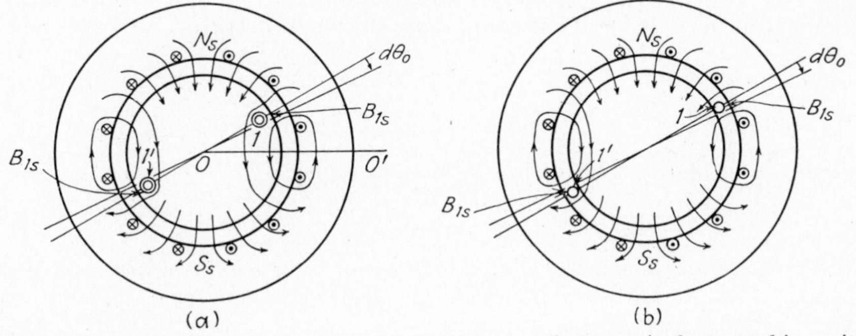

FIG. 2-13. (a) Idealized uniform-air-gap machine, and (b) equivalent machine with rotor coil in the air gap.

that, aside from the effect on the air-gap reluctance, secondary effects of the slot openings usually are not very great. The thought process is one compounded from logic and intuition and justified by experimental checks.

As a means for introducing some useful concepts, consider the device shown in Fig. 2-13a, an idealization of the device of Fig. 2-11. The rotor winding 1-1′ is embedded in slots whose openings at the air gap are of negligible width. The iron is assumed to have infinite permeability. The magnetic field produced by the stator currents then enters and leaves the rotor surface in a radial direction. Its distribution around the circumference depends on the mmfs of the stator coils and the way in which the stator coils are distributed. The general character of this field is shown in Fig. 2-13a for a 2-pole arrangement. To avoid complicating the figure, only a few of the flux lines are shown completely. If the stator slot openings also are of negligible width, the reluctance torques will be zero.

A simple and useful expression for the torque acting on the rotor can now be obtained by expressing the angular rate of change of rotor flux linkages in terms of the air-gap flux density. Let the flux density of the stator field at the rotor surface over coil side 1 be B_{1s}. The two poles of the stator field are assumed to be alike in flux distribution except for the difference in polarity; the flux density over coil side 1′ therefore has the same absolute value but is opposite in direction. Consider the change in rotor linkages resulting from an angular displacement $d\theta_o$ of the rotor. Associated with $d\theta_o$ is an element of rotor surface area $lr\, d\theta_o$ and an increment of flux $B_{1s}lr\, d\theta_o$ at each rotor coil side, where l is the axial length of the rotor and r is its radius. If fringing flux at the ends of the rotor is neglected, the increment $d\phi_{1s}$ in flux linking the rotor resulting from $d\theta_o$ displacement of the two coil sides is

$$d\phi_{1s} = 2B_{1s}lr\, d\theta_o \tag{2-97}$$

The partial derivative of rotor linkages at constant stator currents therefore is

$$\frac{\partial \lambda_{1s}}{\partial \theta_o} = 2B_{1s}lrN_1 \tag{2-98}$$

Substitution of Eq. 2-98 in Eq. 2-95 then gives

$$T = 2B_{1s}lrN_1i_1 \tag{2-99}$$

The direction of the torque is such as to tend to bring the stator and rotor fields into alignment.

Before proceeding further, compare this result with the expression for the torque acting on a similar N_1-turn coil of length l and radius r placed just outside of the rotor surface and directly in the air gap, as shown by the coil sides 1-1′ in Fig. 2-13*b*. From the *Bli* equation, 1-5, it can be seen that the force on each coil side is $B_{1s}lN_1i_1$. The torque on the coil is

$$T = 2B_{1s}lrN_1i_1 \tag{2-100}$$

The same result could, of course, have been obtained from the angular rate of change of linkages (Eq. 2-95). This result is identical with Eq. 2-99 for the torque acting on the rotor with the embedded coil of Fig. 2-13*a*, an identity which really is not surprising because, after all, the increment in flux linkage resulting from an angular displacement $d\theta_o$ of the rotor with the embedded coil is the same as the increment in flux linkage for the same angular displacement of the coil in the air gap.

For the idealized smooth-air-gap machine, therefore, the torque is the same as it would be if the embedded coils were lifted out of their slots and placed directly in the air-gap field. The torque can be computed as if it were the sum of *Bli* forces on the conductors.

An important point should be noted, however: when the conductors are located in the air gap, the torque is exerted directly on them; but *when the conductors are embedded in slots, as in practically all rotating machines, the torque is almost entirely exerted on the rotor core and very little torque acts directly on the windings.* To show that the torque is exerted on the rotor core, suppose that the rotor winding in Fig. 2-13*a* could be given a differential angular displacement $d\theta_o$ still remaining within its slots, but without moving the rotor core. Very little change in the flux linkage λ_{1s} would be produced because very little flux penetrates into the slots where the conductors are placed. Therefore Eq. 2-95 shows that only a small torque acts directly on the winding. On the other hand, if the rotor winding were held stationary and the rotor core were given a differential displacement $d\theta_o$, the change in flux linkage with the rotor winding would be practically the same as when winding and core move together as a rigid body. Therefore almost all of the torque is exerted directly on the rotor core. If the torque acted on the winding, it would have to be transmitted to the body of the rotor through compressive stresses in the insulation between the conductors and the sides of the slots. Fortunately the insulation does not have to carry this mechanical load. The windings merely serve as the sources of the mmfs producing the interacting magnetic fields.

c. Speed and Transformer Voltages. Up to this point we have concerned ourselves with the mechanism by which mechanical force or torque is produced electrically. Continuous flow of power between a mechanical and an electrical system, rather than merely the production of a static force or torque, requires continuous motion such as rotation of a shaft. Rotation of a winding with respect to a magnetic field generates an emf in the winding. The product of the current in the winding and the emf is electrical power, and the product of the torque and the angular velocity is mechanical power. A necessary counterpart to the study of torque in rotating machines therefore is a study of the generation of emfs in windings rotating with respect to magnetic fields.

The voltage generated in a winding equals the time rate of change of the flux linkages produced by the combined effect of all the currents. For the simple two-winding device of Fig. 2-10 with the shaft rotating at an angular velocity ω_o and the currents varying with time, differentiation of Eqs. 2-77 and 2-78 gives

$$e_1 = L_{11}\frac{di_1}{dt} + M_{12}\frac{di_2}{dt} + i_1\frac{dL_{11}}{dt} + i_2\frac{dM_{12}}{dt} \qquad (2\text{-}101)$$

$$e_2 = L_{22}\frac{di_2}{dt} + M_{12}\frac{di_1}{dt} + i_2\frac{dL_{22}}{dt} + i_1\frac{dM_{12}}{dt} \qquad (2\text{-}102)$$

The positive directions of the voltages and currents are shown in Fig. 2-10. These internally generated voltages e_1 and e_2 differ from the terminal voltages by the resistance drops in the windings.

The first two terms on the right-hand side of Eqs. 2-101 and 2-102 are the component voltages generated by the time variations of the currents and are identical to the voltages that would be generated by induction if the rotor were stationary at its instantaneous angular position θ_o. These voltages are of the same nature as the voltages induced in a static transformer winding and are therefore commonly called *transformer voltages.* Denoting them by e_{1T} and e_{2T},

$$e_{1T} \equiv L_{11} \frac{di_1}{dt} + M_{12} \frac{di_2}{dt} \tag{2-103}$$

$$e_{2T} \equiv L_{22} \frac{di_2}{dt} + M_{12} \frac{di_1}{dt} \tag{2-104}$$

The first term on the right-hand side of these equations is the reactive voltage drop due to the self-inductance of the winding. The second is the voltage induced in the winding under consideration by transformer action from the other winding.

The third and fourth terms on the right-hand side of Eqs. 2-101 and 2-102 arise when the inductances are functions of the angular position of the rotor and the rotor is revolving. They are commonly called *speed voltages.* Denoting them by e_{1S} and e_{2S},

$$e_{1S} = i_1 \frac{dL_{11}}{dt} + i_2 \frac{dM_{12}}{dt} \tag{2-105}$$

$$= \left(i_1 \frac{dL_{11}}{d\theta_o} + i_2 \frac{dM_{12}}{d\theta_o} \right) \frac{d\theta_o}{dt} \tag{2-106}$$

$$= \left(i_1 \frac{dL_{11}}{d\theta_o} + i_2 \frac{dM_{12}}{d\theta_o} \right) \omega_o \tag{2-107}$$

and similarly

$$e_{2S} = \left(i_2 \frac{dL_{22}}{d\theta_o} + i_1 \frac{dM_{12}}{d\theta_o} \right) \omega_o \tag{2-108}$$

where $d\theta_o/dt$ is the angular velocity ω_o of the rotor. The first term inside the parentheses in Eqs. 2-107 and 2-108 arises only when the self-inductances vary with the angular position of the rotor. The second term is the voltage induced in the winding by its rotation with respect to the magnetic field of the other winding. The resultant generated voltages are then

$$e_1 = e_{1T} + e_{1S} \tag{2-109}$$

$$e_2 = e_{2T} + e_{2S} \tag{2-110}$$

Examination of the power flow associated with these component voltages gives further insight into the energy-conversion process. The instantaneous electrical power input (after copper losses have been accounted for) is

$$p_{\text{elec}} = e_1 i_1 + e_2 i_2 \tag{2-111}$$

$$= e_{1T} i_1 + e_{2T} i_2 + e_{1S} i_1 + e_{2S} i_2 \tag{2-112}$$

From Eqs. 2-107 and 2-108, the third and fourth terms on the right-hand side of Eq. 2-112 can be expressed as

$$e_{1S} i_1 + e_{2S} i_2 = \left(i_1^2 \frac{dL_{11}}{d\theta_o} + i_2^2 \frac{dL_{22}}{d\theta_o} + 2 i_1 i_2 \frac{dM_{12}}{d\theta_o} \right) \omega_o \tag{2-113}$$

Comparison with Eq. 2-88 shows that the group of terms in parentheses equals twice the instantaneous torque T, whence

$$\tfrac{1}{2}(e_{1S} i_1 + e_{2S} i_2) = T\omega_o = p_{\text{mech}} \tag{2-114}$$

where p_{mech} is the instantaneous mechanical power developed, or

$$T = \frac{1}{2\omega_o}(e_{1S} i_1 + e_{2S} i_2) \tag{2-115}$$

Equation 2-114 shows that the instantaneous mechanical power equals half the power corresponding to the speed voltages. The rest of the electrical power input goes to increasing the energy stored in the coupling field; *i.e.*, the instantaneous power input to the field is

$$p_{\text{fld}} = p_{\text{elec}} - p_{\text{mech}} \tag{2-116}$$

$$= e_{1T} i_1 + e_{2T} i_2 + \tfrac{1}{2}(e_{1S} i_1 + e_{2S} i_2) \tag{2-117}$$

The transformer voltages have no direct effect on the mechanical power, a fairly obvious fact when one recalls that these voltages are not concerned with the motion associated with mechanical power.

The speed and transformer voltages can also be expressed in terms of the air-gap flux density. Consider the idealized device of Fig. 2-13*a* when its rotor is revolving with an angular velocity ω_o and its stator currents are varying with time. The total rate of change of rotor linkages then is the sum of three components: (1) the rate of change of the component linkages produced by the rotor current, $L_{11}\, di_1/dt$; (2) the rate of change caused by the time variation of the inducing field produced by the stator currents, $M_{12}\, di_2/dt + M_{13}\, di_3/dt + \cdots$; and (3) the rate of change caused by angular motion of the rotor in this inducing field. The first and second components are transformer voltages. The third component is the speed voltage e_{1S} generated in the rotor by its rotation in the stator field. It can be expressed as

$$e_{1S} = \frac{\partial \lambda_{1S}}{\partial \theta_o}\frac{d\theta_o}{dt} = \frac{\partial \lambda_{1S}}{\partial \theta_o}\omega_o \tag{2-118}$$

where λ_{1s} is the flux linkage with the rotor winding produced by the combined effect of all the stator currents.

The partial derivative $\partial\lambda_{1s}/\partial\theta_o$ expresses the rate at which rotor linkages would vary with angle if the rotor currents and inducing field were constant in time. It can be expressed in terms of the flux density B_{1s} in the air gap at a rotor coil side, as in Eq. 2-98. Substitution of Eq. 2-98 in Eq. 2-118 gives

$$e_{1S} = 2N_1B_{1s}lr\omega_o \tag{2-119}$$

where N_1 is the number of turns in the rotor winding and l and r are, respectively, the axial length and radius of the rotor.

An alternative form can be obtained through recognition that $r\omega_o$ is the linear velocity v of the surface of the rotor; thus

$$e_{1S} = 2N_1B_{1s}lv \tag{2-120}$$

This emf is the same as the voltage that would be generated in the air-gap coil of Fig. 2-13*b* according to the "cutting-of-flux" concept (Eq. 1-4). For the idealized smooth-air-gap machine, the speed voltage is thus the same as it would be if the embedded conductors were lifted out of their slots and placed directly in the air-gap field.

Example 2-6. Consider that the flux-density wave produced by the stator currents at the rotor surface in Fig. 2-13*a* is a stationary sinusoidal function of the space angle θ and that the stator currents vary sinusoidally with time. The rotor is revolving in this field. This situation is very similar to that existing in the air gap of a single-phase a-c motor.

Derive an expression for the voltage generated in the single-coil rotor winding of Fig. 2-13*a*. The rotor circuit is open. Identify the speed and transformer components of this voltage.

Solution. The air-gap flux-density distribution is a standing wave, stationary in space and pulsating sinusoidally with time. It can be expressed as

$$B_s = B_{s\ \max} \sin \omega t \sin \theta \tag{2-121}$$

where $B_{s\ \max}$ is the flux density on the rotor surface opposite the center of a stator pole at a moment when the stator current has its instantaneous maximum value, ω is the angular frequency $2\pi f$ of the stator currents, and θ is the space angle measured from an axis perpendicular to the stator-pole axis. Zero time is chosen as the instant when the instantaneous stator current is zero.

Let the angular position of the rotor coil side 1 at zero time be α, and let the angular velocity of the rotor be ω_0 rad/sec. The angular position θ_0 of the rotor at time t then is

$$\theta_0 = \omega_0 t + \alpha \tag{2-122}$$

as shown in Fig. 2-14, which is a development, in the descriptive-geometry sense, of Fig. 2-13*a* obtained by cutting the rotor along the radius OO' and rolling it out flat. The flux-density wave at the same instant is also shown.

Associated with the differential angle $d\theta$ is an element of rotor surface area $lr\,d\theta$ and an element of flux

$$B_s lr\,d\theta = lrB_{s\ \max} \sin \omega t \sin \theta\,d\theta \tag{2-123}$$

crossing the rotor surface, where l and r are, respectively, the axial length and radius of the rotor. The flux linkage λ_{1s} with the N_1-turn rotor winding then is

$$\lambda_{1s} = N_1 \int_{\theta_0}^{\pi+\theta_0} lrB_{s\,\max} \sin \omega t \sin \theta \, d\theta \tag{2-124}$$

$$= 2N_1B_{s\,\max}\, lr \sin \omega t \cos \theta_0 \tag{2-125}$$

The voltage e_1 induced in the rotor winding is found by differentiating Eq. 2-125 with respect to time, remembering that $d\theta_0/dt = \omega_0$; thus

$$e_1 = (-2N_1B_{s\,\max}\, lr \sin \omega t \sin \theta_0)\omega_0 + (2N_1B_{s\,\max}\, lr \cos \theta_0 \cos \omega t)\omega \tag{2-126}$$

The first term on the right-hand side of Eq. 2-126 is the speed voltage e_{1S} generated by motion of the rotor winding with respect to the stator field. This term can be

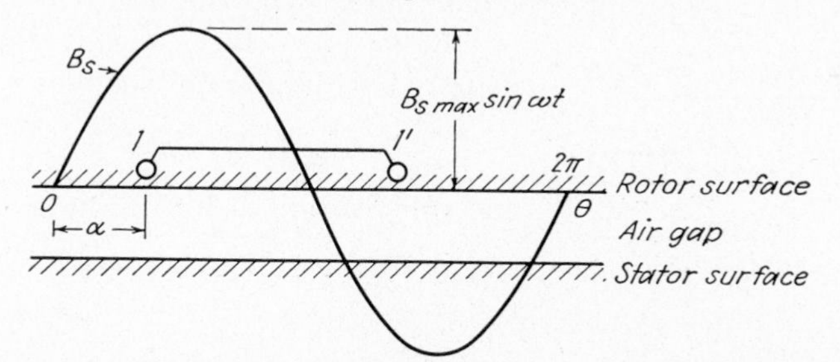

FIG. 2-14. Rotor coil in a pulsating magnetic field, Example 2-6.

simplified through noting in Eq. 2-121 that $B_{s\,\max} \sin \omega t \sin \theta_0$ is the instantaneous flux density B_{1s} over coil side 1; thus

$$e_{1S} = -2N_1B_{1s}lr\omega_0 \tag{2-127}$$

a result in agreement with Eq. 2-119 (except for sign, a detail which depends on the assumed positive directions). The second term on the right-hand side of Eq. 2-126 is the result of the time rate of change of the stator field, as if the rotor were stationary at position θ_0. It is the transformer voltage e_{1T}; thus

$$e_{1T} = 2\omega N_1B_{s\,\max}lr \cos \theta_0 \cos \omega t \tag{2-128}$$

2-4. The Electrostatic Field as a Coupling Medium. The electrostatic field can be treated in a manner paralleling the foregoing discussion of the magnetic field, and similar energy relations will be obtained. First we shall obtain expressions for the energy stored in the field; then we shall see what happens to the energy balance when the charged bodies are allowed to move under the influence of the mechanical forces created by the field.

For these purposes consider the electrostatic field of the simple capacitor shown in Fig. 2-15. If the current is i, the differential electrical energy supplied to the capacitor in time dt is

$$dW_{\text{elec}} = ei\,dt = e\,dq \tag{2-129}$$

where e is the instantaneous counter emf due to the charge q on the capacitor and $i\,dt = dq$ is the differential charge dq added to the capacitor. If no mechanical motion takes place, no mechanical work is done, and the energy supplied by the source is absorbed by the field For a fixed configuration, the differential energy input to the field is

$$dW_{\text{fld}} = dW_{\text{elec}} = e\,dq \tag{2-130}$$

According to Gauss' theorem, the total electrostatic flux crossing a closed surface is proportional to the charge enclosed, and in rationalized mks units the constant of proportionality is unity. The total electrostatic flux ψ passing through a closed surface surrounding the positively charged condenser plate equals the charge $+q$. This flux leaves the surface of the positive plate and terminates on the negative charge $-q$ on the surface of the negatively charged plate. For differential changes,

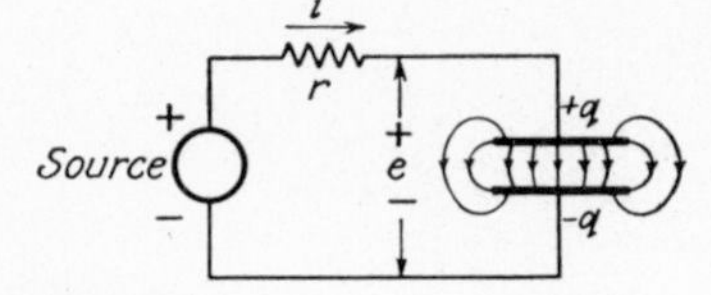

FIG. 2-15. Charged capacitor.

$$d\psi = dq \tag{2-131}$$

and substitution in Eq. 2-130 gives

$$dW_{\text{fld}} = e\,d\psi \tag{2-132}$$

Note the similarity between Eq. 2-132 and Eq. 2-7.

The energy absorbed in establishing from zero a charge q or an electric flux ψ is

$$W_{\text{fld}} = \int_0^q e\,dq = \int_0^\psi e\,d\psi \tag{2-133}$$

Compare with Eq. 2-9. If the permittivity (capacitivity) of the dielectric material in the space occupied by the field is constant and dielectric losses are zero, the charge and flux are proportional to the emf e and

$$W_{\text{fld}} = \tfrac{1}{2}eq = \tfrac{1}{2}e\psi \tag{2-134}$$

Compare with Eq. 2-10. The capacitance C of the condenser in farads is defined as

$$C \equiv \frac{q}{e} \tag{2-135}$$

and is constant if the permittivity is constant. Substitution of Eq. 2-135 in Eq. 2-134 gives the familiar expression for energy stored in a capacitance; thus

$$W_{\text{fld}} = \tfrac{1}{2}Ce^2 \tag{2-136}$$

Compare with Eq. 2-15.

The density w_{fld} of energy stored in an electrostatic field in a linear loss-less dielectric can be expressed as

$$w_{\text{fld}} = \frac{1}{2}\,\mathcal{E}\mathcal{D} = \frac{1}{2}\,\epsilon\mathcal{E}^2 = \frac{1}{2}\,\frac{\mathcal{D}^2}{\epsilon} \tag{2-137}$$

in joules per cubic meter at a point where the electric field intensity is $\mathcal{E}$ volts/m, the electrostatic flux density or displacement is $\mathfrak{D}$ coulombs/m^2, and the permittivity is ϵ. Compare with Eq. 2-16. In the rationalized mks system, the permittivity of free space ϵ_0 is

$$\epsilon_0 = 8.85 \times 10^{-12} \text{ coulomb}^2/\text{newton-m}^2 \tag{2-138}$$

Relations for the mechanical forces created by the electrostatic field can now be obtained by methods exactly similar to those used in treating the magnetic field in Art. 2-1*c*. For example, suppose the plates of the capacitor in Fig. 2-15 are allowed to move closer together a differential distance dx under the influence of the force of attraction f between the oppositely charged plates. Mechanical work $f\,dx$ is then done by the field. The capacitance will change, and also the voltage between the plates and the charges on them may change. From Eq. 2-135 for differential changes

$$dq = C\,de + e\,dC \tag{2-139}$$

Substitution of Eq. 2-139 in Eq. 2-129 gives for the energy supplied by the source

$$dW_{\text{elec}} = Ce\,de + e^2\,dC \tag{2-140}$$

Differentiation of Eq. 2-136 gives for the increment in field energy

$$dW_{\text{fld}} = Ce\,de + \tfrac{1}{2}e^2\,dC \tag{2-141}$$

Substitution of Eqs. 2-140 and 2-141 in the energy-balance equation, 2-1, then gives

$$f\,dx = \tfrac{1}{2}e^2\,dC \tag{2-142}$$

or

$$f = +\frac{1}{2}e^2\frac{dC}{dx} \tag{2-143}$$

The force acts in a direction to increase the capacitance. Compare with Eq. 2-33. Alternative expressions readily can be derived in terms of charge and voltage, or of field energy. For example

$$f = -\frac{1}{2}q\frac{\partial e}{\partial x} = -\left(\frac{\partial W_{\text{fld}}}{\partial x}\right)_{q=\text{const}} \tag{2-144}$$

$$f = +\frac{1}{2}e\frac{\partial q}{\partial x} = +\left(\frac{\partial W_{\text{fld}}}{\partial x}\right)_{e=\text{const}} \tag{2-145}$$

Compare with Eqs. 2-31 and 2-34 and with 2-32 and 2-35. The force acts in a direction to decrease the voltage and field energy at constant charge, or to increase the charge and field energy at constant voltage.

Although the capacitor of Fig. 2-15 has been used as a simple illustration, these equations give the force in the direction of dx on any body whose position influences the field.

2-5. Single-phase Electrostatic Synchronous Machine. An electrostatic synchronous machine of the variable-capacitance type[5] analogous to the magnetic variable-reluctance synchronous machine of Art. 2-2 is shown in Fig. 2-16. It is essentially a variable capacitance of the parallel-plate interleaving type whose rotor is free to rotate continuously. A high-voltage single-phase a-c source is connected across the stator and rotor. The rotor preferably should be grounded. As shown subsequently, high potential gradients are necessary in electrostatic devices to

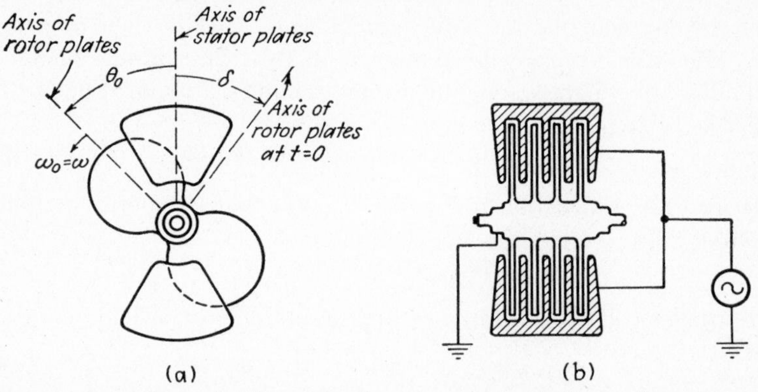

FIG. 2-16. (a) End view and (b) cross section of an electrostatic synchronous machine.

obtain mechanical forces of the same order of magnitude as those which can be obtained in magnetic devices of comparable size. Air at atmospheric pressure will not withstand such potential gradients, but high vacuum is a much superior insulating medium.

By analogy with Eq. 2-143, the instantaneous electrostatic torque T acting on a system whose capacitance C depends on the angular position θ of its parts is

$$T = +\frac{1}{2} e^2 \frac{dC}{d\theta} \tag{2-146}$$

where e is the instantaneous voltage. In Fig. 2-16, the capacitance C is a periodic function of the angle θ_o. If the plates are shaped so that the capacitance varies sinusoidally between maximum and minimum

[5] An analysis of this and a number of other types of electrostatic variable-capacitance rotating machines is the subject of the doctorate thesis by J. G. Trump, "Vacuum Electrostatic Engineering," Massachusetts Institute of Technology, Cambridge, Mass., 1933. For a brief survey of the potentialities of electrostatic machinery, see J. G. Trump, Electrostatic Sources of Electric Power, *Elec. Eng.*, vol. 66, No. 6, pp. 525–534, June, 1947.

values C_{max} and C_{min},

$$C = \tfrac{1}{2}(C_{max} + C_{min}) + \tfrac{1}{2}(C_{max} - C_{min}) \cos 2\theta_o \tag{2-147}$$

If the applied voltage is sinusoidal,

$$e = E_{max} \cos \omega t \tag{2-148}$$

where E_{max} is its maximum value and zero time is chosen at the peak of the voltage wave. If the speed of the rotor is ω_o rad/sec, and its instantaneous angular position at zero time is δ rad behind the position of maximum capacitance,

$$\theta_o = \omega_o t - \delta \tag{2-149}$$

If ω_o and δ are such that in each half cycle of the voltage wave the average square of the voltage is greater while the capacitance is increasing than it is while the capacitance is decreasing, average torque is developed in the direction to increase θ_o and thereby to keep the rotor revolving.

The analysis parallels that of the magnetic-reluctance motor. The synchronous speed ω_o equals the time angular velocity ω of the voltage wave. The average torque is

$$T_{av} = \tfrac{1}{8}E^2_{max}(C_{max} - C_{min}) \sin 2\delta \tag{2-150}$$

Compare with Eq. 2-67. The machine has all the operating characteristics of the magnetic type of reluctance motor.

In spite of the simplicity of electrostatic phenomena, the practical applications of electrostatic machines to date have been only as low-power high-voltage generators of the belt type, producing high constant potentials for X rays and nuclear research. No practical applications of the variable-capacitance type of machine have been made up to the present, although an experimental model has been built and tested. Some of the reasons for the preponderance of electromagnetic machinery are discussed in the following article.

2-6. Comparison of Electromagnetic and Electrostatic Machinery. In order to produce electrically a mechanical force between two rigid bodies, a concentration of energy must exist in the region between them. The energy storage can be in either a magnetic or an electrostatic field. Comparatively speaking, electromagnetic machines are high-current devices, while electrostatic machines are high-voltage devices. The availability of inexpensive materials with satisfactory magnetic, electrical, and mechanical properties, such as silicon-steel core materials and copper conductors, has made possible the enormous development of electromagnetic devices. On the other hand, no satisfactory means are available for insulating the potential gradients necessary to store energy electrostatically with densities equal to those that can be concentrated in the magnetic field in an air gap between two iron surfaces.

For purposes of obtaining a numerical comparison, consider the essentially uniform fields produced in the two simple cases shown in Fig. 2-17. As in Eq. 2-39, the expression for the magnetic force of attraction between the two parallel plane faces of ferromagnetic material shown in Fig. 2-17*a* is

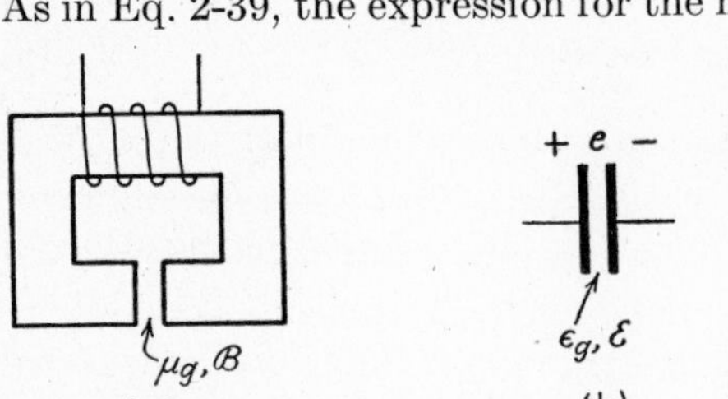

FIG. 2-17. Elementary magnetic and electrostatic systems for comparison of energy relations.

$$f_{\text{mag}} = \frac{1}{2}\frac{\mathcal{B}^2 A}{\mu_g} \tag{2-151}$$

where $\mathcal{B}$ is the flux density in the air gap, A is the area of each face, and μ_g is the permeability of the medium in the gap in rationalized units. The permeability of the ferromagnetic material is assumed to be high compared with μ_g. The force per unit area of gap faces is

$$\frac{f_{\text{mag}}}{A} = \frac{1}{2}\frac{\mathcal{B}^2}{\mu_g} \tag{2-152}$$

The corresponding expression for the electrostatic force of attraction per unit area acting on each of the two parallel charged plates (Fig. 2-17*b*) is

$$\frac{f_{\text{elec}}}{A} = \frac{1}{2}\frac{\mathfrak{D}^2}{\epsilon_g} = \frac{1}{2}\epsilon_g \mathcal{E}^2 \tag{2-153}$$

In Eq. 2-153, $\mathfrak{D}$ is the electrostatic flux density in the gap and equals the charge density on the plates, $\mathcal{E}$ is the corresponding electric field intensity, and ϵ_g is the permittivity of the medium in the gap in rationalized units.

With magnetically operated devices the flux density that can be produced in an air gap depends primarily on the characteristics of the ferromagnetic material in the other parts of the magnetic circuit. For example, the commercially available grades of silicon steel used in the cores of rotating machines have their maximum permeabilities at flux densities of about 0.6 weber/m² (about 40 kilolines/in.²), and the "knee" of the magnetization curve—*i.e.*, the region where the permeability decreases rapidly with increasing magnetizing force—is in the range from about 1.1 to 1.4 webers/m² (about 70 to 90 kilolines/in.²). Although it is theoretically possible to raise the flux density indefinitely by increasing the mmf of the exciting winding, it becomes uneconomical to do so, since for flux densities in the iron portion of the magnetic circuit much above the knee of the magnetization curve the power required by the exciting winding increases much more rapidly than the flux density in the gap.

It is a simple matter to produce flux densities in an air gap of the order of 1 weber/m² (64.5 kilolines/in.²). At this flux density,

$$\frac{f_{\text{mag}}}{A} = \frac{1}{2} \times \frac{1^2}{4\pi \times 10^{-7}} = 3.98 \times 10^5 \text{ newtons/m}^2 \qquad (2\text{-}154)$$

or the magnetic stored energy density equals 3.98×10^5 watt-sec/m³. In English units, this force intensity is 57.7 psi. This force is the order of magnitude of the intensity of radial magnetic force between the iron stator and rotor surfaces in rotating machines.

The charge concentration needed to produce electrostatically force intensities comparable with those which can be produced magnetically results in potential gradients which are extremely difficult to insulate. For example, air at atmospheric pressure will withstand a maximum potential gradient of approximately 30,000 volts/cm, or 3×10^6 volts/m. Its permittivity in rationalized mks units is 8.85×10^{-12}. From Eq. 2-153, the maximum force intensity that can be obtained between the plates in Fig. 2-17*b* with air as the insulating medium is

$$\frac{f_{\text{elec}}}{A} = \frac{1}{2} \times 8.85 \times 10^{-12} \times 9 \times 10^{12} = 39.8 \text{ newtons/m}^2 \qquad (2\text{-}155)$$

or the maximum density at which energy can be stored electrostatically in air at atmospheric pressure is about 40 watt-sec/m³. In English units, this force intensity is 0.00577 psi.

Considerably higher potential gradients can be insulated if high vacuum or certain gases under pressures of several atmospheres are used as the insulating medium. High vacuum is preferable for rotating machinery, since windage loss then is negligible. Breakdown in vacuum is not solely dependent on potential gradient but is also a function of the total voltage between electrodes. It appears possible that cathode gradients of several million volts per centimeter may be insulated, even at the intermediate and high voltages that would be required in power machinery. If the gradient could be raised to 3×10^8 volts/m, the electrostatic force intensity would be 57.7 psi, the same as the magnetic force intensity at a magnetic flux density of 1 weber/m². Such potential gradients would be necessary for development of electrostatic rotating machines of compactness comparable with electromagnetic machines. If such vacuum-insulated machines could be built, they would have the advantages over electromagnetic machines of no windage loss, no magnetic core loss, very little dielectric loss, and very small I^2R loss. Their efficiencies therefore would be very high. They would probably be confined to high-voltage high-power applications.

2-7. Résumé. Magnetic and electrostatic fields are seats of energy storage. Whenever the energy in the field is influenced by the configuration of the mechanical parts constituting the boundaries of the field, mechanical forces are created which tend to move the mechanical elements so that energy is transmitted from the field to the mechanical system.

Maxwell drew a useful analogy between the energy-storage phenomena in a magnetic or electrostatic field and the corresponding stress-strain energy stored in a stretched elastic medium. He pictured the fields as equivalent to a state of tension along the directions of the flux lines, as with stretched elastic bands, an analogy which can be put into exact mathematical form. Although this picture is probably only an analogy arising because of the mathematical similarity between the theories of electromagnetic-field phenomena and stretched elastic media and does not purport to attribute identity to the mechanisms underlying the two classes of phenomena, nevertheless the picture of abstract field phenomena in terms of the tangible elastic medium may be helpful, even though in the last analysis the exact mechanism of elasticity may be no more clearly understood than the field phenomena. The attraction between iron surfaces in a magnetic field and the attraction between charged condenser plates, for example, may readily be visualized in terms of the elastic-band analogy.

The force relations can readily be formulated from the conservation-of-energy principle. The singly excited magnetic system is considered first in Art. 2-1, by means of a thought process which analyzes what would happen if the mechanical parts were allowed to move a differential distance under the influence of the mechanical forces set up by the field. The result is the basic relation, Eq. 2-29, which shows that the forces tend to produce the configuration of minimum reluctance.

The magnetic forces which tend to move rigid bodies into the positions of minimum reluctance are used to advantage in a wide variety of moving-iron devices consisting of an exciting coil wound on a magnetic circuit, part of which is movable. Most of the force acts between the fixed and movable iron members, since the reluctance of such a magnetic circuit is determined primarily by the air gap between these members. Forces also act directly on the exciting coil which tend to move it into the position of minimum reluctance and to deform it into the shape for minimum reluctance; *i.e.*, the deforming forces tend to compress the coil axially, to deform it into a circle, and to expand it radially. Under normal conditions, however, the forces acting directly on the exciting coil are small. These forces may, however, become exceedingly important under abnormal conditions such as short circuits on large power apparatus.

If magnetic nonlinearity is neglected, the force or torque acting on any part of a singly excited magnetic system readily can be expressed in terms of the space rate of change of reluctance, permeance, or inductance, as in

Eq. 2-29, 2-30, or 2-33. The force or torque acts in a direction to decrease the reluctance, to increase the permeance, and to increase the self-inductance. Alternatively, the force or torque can be expressed in terms of the partial space derivatives of mmf, of flux, or of field energy, as in Eq. 2-31, 2-32, 2-34, or 2-35; the force or torque acts in a direction to decrease the mmf and field energy at constant flux, or to increase the flux and field energy at constant mmf. Analogous expressions for the electrostatic field are given in Eqs. 2-143 to 2-145.

In Art. 2-1*d* the effects of magnetic nonlinearity are examined, and a graphical method of analysis is developed. Fortunately, however, most of the field energy usually is stored in the air gap of a moving-iron device, and therefore the linear analysis of Art. 2-1*c* usually gives satisfactory results.

In rotating machines, the variable-reluctance effect is a potential producer of torque whenever the configuration of the magnetic circuit is such that the reluctance depends on the angular position of the rotor. The basic relation is Eq. 2-53 in which the instantaneous torque is proportional to the square of the flux and the angular rate of decrease of reluctance. If the flux is a periodic function of time, as when alternating voltage is impressed on the exciting winding, and if the rotor is revolving so that the average square of the flux is greater while the reluctance is decreasing than it is while the reluctance is increasing, average torque will be produced in a direction to sustain rotation, as shown in Art. 2-2. Since the square of the flux goes through a cycle of its variation in a half cycle of the flux wave, the speed of the rotor must be such that the reluctance variation goes through a cycle of its variation in a half cycle of the flux wave. This is the only speed at which average torque is produced and is known as synchronous speed. The machine is a synchronous machine of the reluctance type. It accommodates itself to changes in shaft torque by adjusting the phase relation between the flux-squared wave and the reluctance variation, as shown in Eq. 2-67. For this reason the phase angle δ in Eq. 2-67 is known as the torque angle. For motor action, the reluctance variation lags behind the flux-squared wave; for generator action, it leads. The average torque is proportional to $\sin 2\delta$, as in Eq. 2-67. Its maximum value occurs when δ equals 45° and is given by Eq. 2-68.

An analogous type of synchronous machine using the electrostatic field as the energy-conversion medium is described in Art. 2-5, and the potentialities of magnetic and electrostatic fields for electromechanical coupling are compared in Art. 2-6. A comparison of the two types of devices can be made by comparing the density with which energy can be stored in the coupling fields. It is shown that potential gradients of about 3 million volts per centimeter are required to store energy in an electrostatic field at a density comparable with that which can easily be attained in a magnetic field. Electrostatic machines will be unable to compete with magnetic machines unless the problem of insulating such potential gradients can be solved satisfactorily.

Most electromechanical energy-conversion devices, including nearly all rotating machines, are provided with several windings, and the useful torque or force is produced by the interaction of the magnetic fields of the two groups. Investigation of the basic theory of these multiply excited magnetic systems is the subject of Art. 2-3. We have seen that the effects of nonlinearity usually are of secondary importance when air gaps are present, and therefore multiply excited systems usually can be treated on a linear basis. The torque acting on the simple device of Fig. 2-10 can then readily be expressed in terms of the angular rates of change of the self- and mutual inductances, as in Eqs. 2-88 and 2-89, or in terms of the angular rate of increase of field energy at constant currents, as in Eq. 2-90. In Eqs. 2-88 and 2-89, the terms involving the angular derivatives of the self-inductances are recognized as the reluctance torques of Art. 2-1*c*. They merely say that the field due to one current acting alone produces forces on magnetic material tending to move it so as to reduce the reluctance of the magnetic circuit. The terms involving the angular derivatives of the mutual inductances express the torques produced by the interaction of the magnetic field of one current with that of another. These terms merely say that the magnetic fields of stator and rotor tend to line up in the same direction. Since these are the principal torques in most rotating machines and in many other devices, our investigation now narrows down to a study of these mutual torques, as in Art. 2-3*a*. For this study, the rather simple device of Figs. 2-11 and 2-12 is chosen, because it incorporates many of the principal features of rotating machines without all of their complexities. The torque acting on the rotor of Fig. 2-11 then can be expressed concisely in terms of the angular rate of change of rotor flux linkages at constant stator currents, as in Eq. 2-95.

Even with so simple a device as that of Fig. 2-11, an exact evaluation of the angular rate of change of rotor flux linkages is no simple matter. Even when the permeability of the iron is assumed to be infinite, the effects of slot openings cause complications. The need for further simplification is evident, a need which becomes increasingly imperative in subsequent chapters when actual machines are considered. Thus arises the picture of the idealized smooth-air-gap machine of Fig. 2-13*a*. The torque on the rotor of the idealized machine then can readily be expressed in terms of the air-gap flux density as in Eq. 2-99, a result which is the same as the torque computed from the *Bli* forces on the conductors of a coil placed directly in the air-gap field, as in Fig. 2-13*b*. This important distinction should be remembered, however: when the coil is embedded in slots, as in Fig. 2-13*a*, the torque acts directly on the rotor core and not on the coil.

Through Art. 2-3*b*, the discussion has been almost wholly concerned with the production of *mechanical* force; the counterpart of this problem is the production of *electromotive* force. Mechanical force or torque is a *space* rate of change of flux linkages; electromotive force is a *time* rate of change. If the field through which the rotor of Fig. 2-13*a* moves is simultaneously varying with time, the total time derivative of flux linkages is the sum of two partial derivatives, one caused by the motion of the rotor and the other caused by the variation of the amplitude of the field. The former is the speed voltage and, in a uniform-air-gap machine, is equivalent to a Blv voltage generated by "cutting of flux," as in the equivalent air-gap coil of Fig. 2-13*b*. The speed voltage and the torque taken together constitute the action-reaction mechanism by which the coupling field calls for input to supply output. The latter voltage component is the transformer voltage; it has no direct effect on the electromechanical energy-conversion process since it has nothing to do with mechanical motion.

This chapter has been concerned with basic principles applying, in the main, to a wide variety of electromechanical energy-conversion devices. Basically rotating machines and moving-coil telephones, for example, work in the same way. It is not surprising, however, to find that their more detailed theories begin to follow diverging courses, primarily because different characteristics are important, and their sizes and structural features (designed to bring out the desired characteristics) are necessarily entirely different. The remainder of this text is devoted almost entirely to the development of the rotating-machine aspects of electromechanical energy conversion. The rotating machine is a fairly complicated conglomeration of electric and magnetic circuits. Although the steady-state theory of rotating machines is developed on a somewhat simplified and more restricted basis in subsequent chapters, the fairly searching analyses of simple devices in this chapter should serve to give the reader a sense of perspective and a feeling of confidence that he knows how electromagnetic machinery "works."

PROBLEMS

2-1. The time constant L/R of the field winding of a 10-kw 1,150-rpm d-c shunt generator is 0.15 sec. At normal operating conditions, the copper loss in its field winding is 350 watts. Compute the energy stored in its magnetic field, in watt-seconds, at normal operating conditions.

2-2. The cylindrical iron-clad solenoid magnet shown in Fig. 2-18 is used for tripping circuit breakers, operating valves, and in other applications in which a relatively large force is applied to a member which moves a relatively small distance. When the coil current is zero, the plunger drops against a stop such that the gap g is

0.50 in. When the coil is energized by a direct current of sufficient magnitude, the plunger is raised until it hits another stop set so that g is 0.10 in. The plunger is supported so that it can move freely in the axial direction. The air gap between the shell and the plunger can be assumed to be uniform and 0.01 in. long. For the purposes of this problem neglect magnetic leakage and fringing in the air gaps. The exciting coil has 1,000 turns and carries a constant current of 3.0 amp.

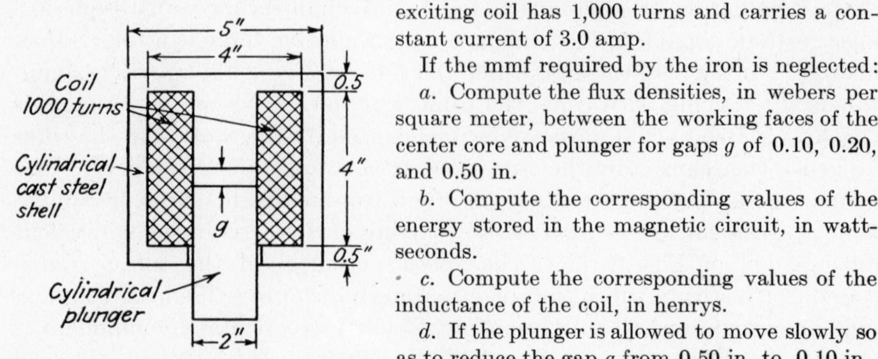

FIG. 2-18. Plunger magnet for Probs. 2-2, 2-3, and 2-4.

If the mmf required by the iron is neglected:

a. Compute the flux densities, in webers per square meter, between the working faces of the center core and plunger for gaps g of 0.10, 0.20, and 0.50 in.

b. Compute the corresponding values of the energy stored in the magnetic circuit, in watt-seconds.

c. Compute the corresponding values of the inductance of the coil, in henrys.

d. If the plunger is allowed to move slowly so as to reduce the gap g from 0.50 in. to 0.10 in., how much mechanical work will be done by the plunger, in watt-seconds? In foot-pounds?

e. For the conditions of *d* how much energy will be supplied by the electrical source (in excess of copper loss)?

f. Find a numerical expression for the inductance in henrys as a function of the gap length g in meters.

g. Find a numerical expression for the energy stored in the magnetic field, in watt-seconds, as a function of the gap length g in meters.

2-3. For the plunger magnet of Prob. 2-2, find an expression for the force acting on the plunger, in newtons, as a function of the plunger displacement g in meters by each of the following methods:

a. From part *f* of Prob. 2-2.

b. From part *g* of Prob. 2-2.

c. Plot a curve of force in newtons as a function of g in meters.

d. From the area under this force-displacement curve, compute the work done by the plunger when it moves slowly so as to reduce the gap g from 0.50 in. to 0.10 in. Compare with the result of Prob. 2-2, part *d*.

e. If, instead of moving slowly, the plunger moves very rapidly, what will be the effect on the force-distance curve? On the mechanical work done? Under these circumstances can the coil current remain constant, and if not, what will happen to it?

2-4. Data for the magnetization curve of the iron portion of the magnetic circuit of the plunger magnet of Prob. 2-2 are given below:

Flux, kilolines	100	150	200	240	250	260	270	275
Mmf, amp-turns	60	95	150	250	305	425	600	725

Plot magnetization curves for the complete magnetic circuit (flux in webers vs. total mmf in ampere-turns) for the following conditions:

a. Gap g = 0.50 in.

b. Gap g = 0.10 in.

c. From these curves find graphically the work done by the plunger if it is allowed to move slowly from $g = 0.50$ in. to $g = 0.10$ in. while the coil carries a constant current of 3.0 amp. Compare with the result of Prob. 2-2, part *d*.

d. Also find the energy supplied by the electrical source (in excess of copper loss). Compare with results of part *c* and of Prob. 2-2, part *e*.

2-5. Figure 2-19 shows in cross section a plunger magnet in which the cylindrical plunger is free to move vertically in brass guide rings which center it in the two air gaps. (The permeability of brass is the same as that of air.) Stops keep the plunger within the confines of the upper gap. The length of the plunger is 10 in.

a. Derive an expression for the magnetic force f tending to lift the plunger, in terms of the coil mmf F, the dimensions r, g, and l expressed as symbols, and the position x of the top of the plunger. Use rationalized mks units. Neglect leakage, fringing, and reluctance of the flux paths in the steel. The ratio g/r is sufficiently small so that approximations may be made with respect to the air gaps.

b. Sketch the static force-stroke curves for constant coil mmf.

c. Compute the numerical value of the force in pounds at $x = 1.00$ in. for the dimensions shown and with a coil mmf of 1,000 amp-turns.

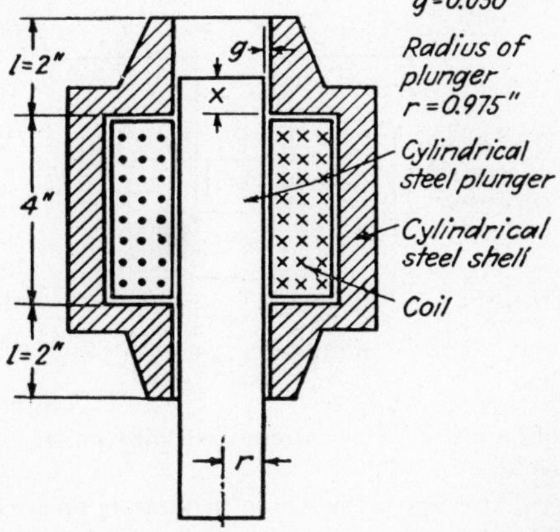

FIG. 2-19. Plunger magnet for Prob. 2-5.

2-6. Solve Prob. 2-5 if the plunger is 6 in. long. Other dimensions are given in Fig. 2-19. For part *c* compute the force at $x = 0.25$ in. with a coil mmf of 2,000 amp-turns.

2-7. The armature and field structures of a simplified 2-pole d-c machine are shown in the end view (*a*) and cross section (*b*) in Fig. 2-20. Because of an error in

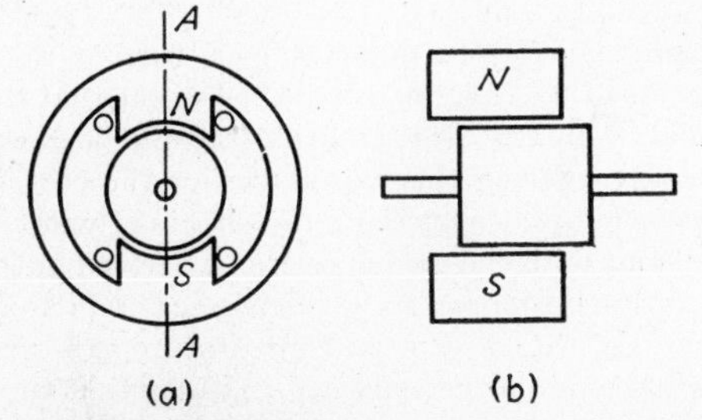

FIG. 2-20. Simplified d-c machine, Prob. 2-7.

assembly, the armature core is displaced 0.5 in. in an axial direction from its correct position. Other numerical data are as follows:

Length of each air gap = 0.10 in.
Diameter of armature = 10.0 in.
Air-gap flux density = 50 kilolines/in.^{2}
Angle subtended by each pole shoe = 100°

The air-gap length can be considered constant under the pole shoes, and the armature can be considered as a smooth cylinder.

Find the axial force in pounds tending to center the armature.

2-8. Figure 2-21 shows the general nature of the slot-leakage flux produced by current i in a rectangular conductor embedded in a rectangular slot in iron. Assume that the slot-leakage flux φ_s goes straight across the slot in the region between the top of the conductor and the top of the slot.

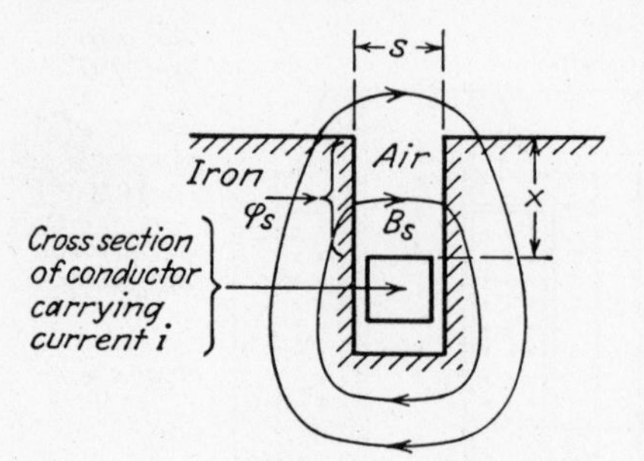

FIG. 2-21. Conductor in slot, Prob. 2-8.

a. Derive an expression for the flux density B_s in the region between the top of the conductor and the top of the slot.

b. Derive an expression for the slot-leakage flux φ_s crossing the slot above the conductor, in terms of the height x of the slot above the conductor, the slot width s, and the embedded length l perpendicular to the paper.

c. Derive an expression for the force f created by this magnetic field on a conductor of length l. Use rationalized mks units. In what direction does this force act on the conductor?

d. Compute the force in pounds on a conductor 1.0 ft long in a slot 1.0 in. wide when the current in the conductor is 1,000 amp.

2-9. Assume that the reluctance variation in a single-phase reluctance motor (Fig. 2-8*a*) is as shown in Fig. 2-22 and that the flux varies sinusoidally with time. The rotor is revolving at synchronous speed.

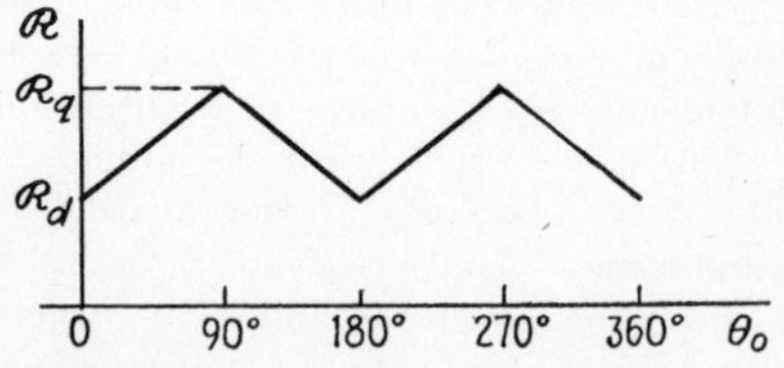

FIG. 2-22. Reluctance variation for Prob. 2-9.

a. Sketch curves of the instantaneous torque as a function of time for values of the torque angle $\delta = 0°, 30°, 45°$.

b. Derive an expression for the average torque in terms of ϕ_{max}, $\mathcal{R}_d$, $\mathcal{R}_q$, and δ.

2-10. Derive an expression for the instantaneous current taken by a single-phase reluctance motor in terms of ϕ_{max}, $\mathcal{R}_q$, $\mathcal{R}_d$, and δ. Assume that the flux and reluctance variations are sinusoidal, as in Fig. 2-8*b*, and that the effects of core loss and magnetic nonlinearity are negligible. Using this expression for the current, derive an expression for the average power input, neglecting the effects of winding resistance. Show that the result is consistent with the torque relations derived in the text.

2-11. Express the torque developed by a single-phase reluctance motor in terms of the impressed voltage V_t, the direct- and quadrature-axis reactances X_d and X_q, the torque angle δ, and the angular velocity ω_o. Assume that the winding resistance is negligible and that the flux and reluctance variations are sinusoidal. The direct- and quadrature-axis reactances are, respectively, the reactances of the winding when the rotor axis is in line with, and when it is in quadrature with, the axis of the stator poles.

2-12. Two coils have self- and mutual inductances in henrys as functions of a displacement x in meters as follows:

$$L_{11} = 1 + x$$
$$L_{22} = 2(1 + x)$$
$$M_{12} = 1 - x$$

The resistances are negligible.

a. For constant currents $I_1 = +10.0$ amp and $i_2 = -5.0$ amp, compute the mechanical work done in increasing x from 0 to $+1.0$ m.

b. Does the force developed in part *a* tend to increase or decrease x?

c. During the motion of part *a*, how much energy is supplied by source 1? By source 2?

d. Compute the average value of the force developed for $x = 0.50$ m when coil 2 is short-circuited and a sinusoidal voltage of 377 volts rms at 60 cps is applied to coil 1.

2-13. The self-inductances L_{11} and L_{22} and the absolute value of the mutual inductance M_{12} of the device shown in Fig. 2-10 are given in the table below for two angular positions θ_o of the rotor, where θ_o is measured from a horizontal reference axis to the axis of the rotor:

θ_o	L_{11}	L_{22}	M_{12}
45°	0.60	1.10	0.30
75°	1.00	2.00	1.00

The inductances are given in henrys and may be assumed to vary linearly with θ_o over the range $45° < \theta_o < 75°$.

For each of the following cases, compute the electromagnetic torque in newton-meters when the rotor is stationary at an angular position $\theta_o = 60°$ (approximately the position shown in Fig. 2-10), and state whether this torque tends to turn the rotor in a clockwise or counterclockwise direction.

a. $i_1 = 10.0$ amp, $i_2 = 0$.

b. $i_1 = 0$, $i_2 = 10.0$ amp.

c. $i_1 = 10.0$ amp, and $i_2 = 10.0$ amp in arrow directions (Fig. 2-10).

d. $i_1 = 10.0$ amp in arrow direction, and $i_2 = 10.0$ amp in reverse direction.

e. $I_1 = 10.0$ amp rms value of sinusoidal alternating current, with coil 2 short-circuited. In this case the resistance of coil 2 may be neglected, and it is the time average of the torque which is wanted.

2-14. Consider a rotating machine having two windings, one on the stator and one on the rotor. The windings are distributed in such a way that when the rotor revolves the mutual inductance between stator and rotor windings varies as the cosine of the angle between their magnetic axes. The maximum value of the mutual inductance is M. The air gap is uniform so that the self-inductances L_{11} and L_{22} of stator and rotor can be considered to be constant, independent of the angular position of the rotor. The shaft is coupled to a device which can be made to absorb or deliver mechanical torque over a wide range of speeds.

This machine can be connected and operated in several ways. For example, suppose the rotor is excited with direct current and the stator is connected to a single-phase 60-cps system which can either absorb or deliver power. The machine then has the basic features of an idealized single-phase synchronous machine.

a. Describe the nature of the torque developed by the machine as the speed is varied by control of the device connected to its shaft.

b. Is there a synchronous speed?

c. If so, how many rpm?

d. Is average torque developed at any other speed?

e. Derive an expression for the average torque in terms of the d-c rotor current, the rms value of the 60-cps stator current (assumed sinusoidal in waveform), the maximum value M of the mutual inductance between stator and rotor, and any other variables which you need.

f. Under the assumed conditions of sinusoidal variation of mutual inductance, sinusoidal stator current, and constant d-c rotor current, what can you say regarding the waveforms of the voltages at the stator and rotor terminals?

g. What would you expect regarding waveforms if the rotor were excited from a low-impedance source, such as a storage battery?

2-15. Suppose the stator and rotor windings of the machine of Prob. 2-14 are connected in series and energized from a 60-cps source. For convenience, the current can be considered sinusoidal.

a. What is the nature of the torque produced when the rotor is stationary?

b. Is a starting torque produced?

c. Is there a synchronous speed? If so, how many rpm?

d. Derive an expression for the average torque in terms of the rms current I, the maximum value M of the mutual inductance, and any other variables which you may need.

2-16. Two windings, one mounted on a stator and the other on a rotor, have self- and mutual inductances as given below:

$$L_{11} = 2.20 \text{ henrys} \qquad L_{22} = 1.00 \text{ henry}$$
$$M_{12} = 1.414 \cos \theta_o \text{ henrys}$$

where θ_0 is the angle between the axes of the windings. The resistances of the windings may be neglected.

Winding 2 is short-circuited, and the current in winding 1 as a function of time is $i_1 = 14.14 \sin \omega t$.

a. If the rotor is stationary, derive an expression for the numerical value, in newton-meters, of the instantaneous torque on the rotor in terms of the angle θ_o.

b. Compute the average torque in newton-meters when $\theta_o = 45°$.

c. If the rotor is allowed to move, will it rotate continuously, or will it tend to come to rest? If the latter, at what value of θ_o?

2-17. Figure 2-23 shows in cross section a machine having a rotor winding ff and two identical stator windings aa and bb. The self-inductance of each stator winding is L_{aa} henrys and of the rotor winding is L_{ff} henrys. The air gap is uniform. The stator windings are in quadrature. The mutual inductance between a stator winding and the rotor winding depends on the angular position θ_o of the rotor and may be assumed to be

$$M_{af} = M \cos \theta_o \qquad M_{bf} = M \sin \theta_o$$

where M is the maximum value of the mutual inductance. The resistance of each stator winding is r_a ohms.

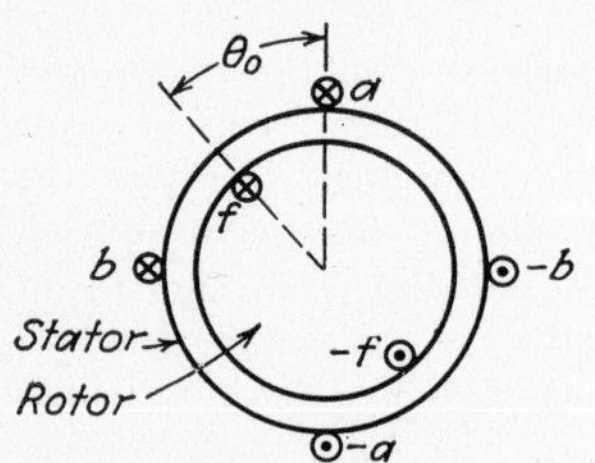

FIG. 2-23. Elementary cylindrical-rotor 2-phase synchronous machine, Prob. 2-17.

a. Derive a general expression for the torque T in terms of the angle θ_o, the inductance constants, and the instantaneous currents i_a, i_b, and i_f. Does this expression apply at standstill? When the rotor is revolving?

b. Suppose the rotor is stationary and constant direct currents $I_a = 5$ amp, $I_b = 5$ amp, $I_f = 10$ amp are supplied to the windings in the directions indicated by the dots and crosses in Fig. 2-23. If the rotor is allowed to move, will it rotate continuously or will it tend to come to rest? If the latter, at what value of θ_o?

c. The rotor winding is now excited by a constant direct current I_f, and the stator windings carry balanced 2-phase currents

$$i_a = \sqrt{2}\, I_a \cos \omega t \qquad i_b = \sqrt{2}\, I_a \sin \omega t$$

The rotor is revolving at synchronous speed so that its instantaneous angular position θ_o is given by $\theta_o = \omega t - \delta$, where δ is a phase angle describing the position of the rotor at $t = 0$. The machine is an elementary 2-phase synchronous machine. Derive an expression for the torque under these conditions. Describe its nature.

d. Under the conditions of part *c*, derive an expression for the instantaneous terminal voltages of stator phases *a* and *b*.

2-18. Figure 2-24 shows in cross section a machine having two identical stator windings *aa* and *bb* arranged in quadrature on a laminated steel core. The salient-pole rotor is made of steel and carries a winding *f* connected to slip rings. The machine is an elementary 2-phase salient-pole synchronous machine.

Because of the nonuniform air gap, the self- and mutual inductances of the stator windings are functions of the angular position θ_o of the rotor, as follows;

$$L_{aa} = L_0 + L_2 \cos 2\theta_o$$
$$L_{bb} = L_0 - L_2 \cos 2\theta_o$$
$$M_{ab} = L_2 \sin 2\theta_o$$

where L_0 and L_2 are positive constants. The mutual inductances between the rotor and the stator windings are functions of θ_o as follows:

$$M_{af} = M \cos \theta_o \qquad M_{bf} = M \sin \theta_o$$

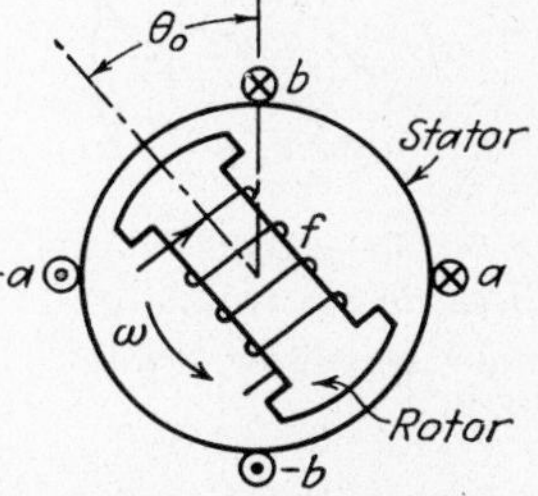

FIG. 2-24. Elementary salient-pole 2-phase synchronous machine, Prob. 2-18.

where M is a positive constant. The self-inductance L_{ff} of the rotor winding is constant, independent of θ_o.

The rotor (or field) winding *f* is excited with direct current I_f, and the stator windings are connected to a balanced 2-phase voltage source. The currents in the stator windings are

$$i_a = \sqrt{2}\, I_a \cos \omega t \qquad i_b = \sqrt{2}\, I_a \sin \omega t$$

The rotor is revolving at synchronous speed so that its instantaneous angular position is given by

$$\theta_o = \omega t - \delta$$

where δ is a phase angle describing the position of the rotor at $t = 0$.

a. Derive an expression for the electromagnetic torque acting on the rotor. Describe its nature.

b. Can the machine be operated as a motor? As a generator? Explain.

c. Will the machine continue to run if the field current I_f is reduced to zero? If so, give an expression for the torque, and a physical explanation.

2-19. Show that, if the stator windings of the idealized machine of Fig. 2-13 are arranged so that the flux-density wave in the air gap is sinusoidally distributed around the periphery of the rotor, the torque can be expressed as

$$T = \Phi_s F_1 \sin \delta$$

where Φ_s is the flux per pole produced by the stator currents, F_1 is the rotor mmf, and δ is the angle between the axes of the stator and rotor fields.

A very similar equation, modified to fit multipolar machines with distributed windings on both stator and rotor, forms the basis for the analytical treatment of rotating machines in Chap. 3.

2-20. Figure 2-25 shows a 2-pole rotor revolving inside a smooth stator which carries a coil of 100 turns. The rotor produces a sinusoidal space distribution of flux at the stator surface, the peak value of the flux-density wave being 0.80 weber/m^2 when the current in the rotor is 10 amp. The magnetic circuit is linear. The inside diameter of the stator is 0.10 m, and its axial length is 0.10 m. The rotor is driven at a speed of 60 rev/sec.

a. The rotor is excited by a direct current of 10 amp. Taking zero time as the instant when the axis of the rotor is vertical, find the expression for the instantaneous voltage generated in the open-circuited stator coil.

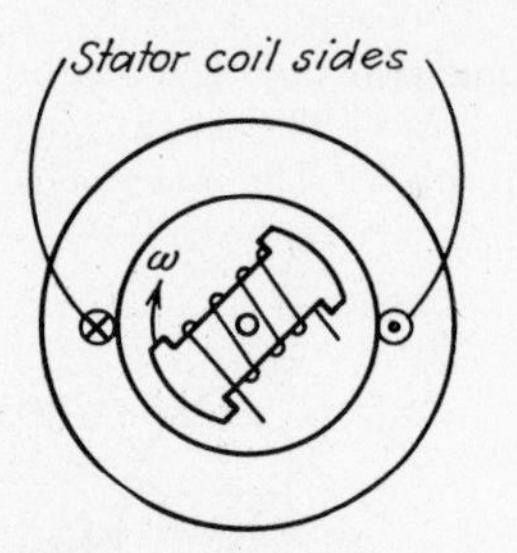

FIG. 2-25. Elementary generator, Prob. 2-20.

b. The rotor is now excited by a 60-cps sinusoidal alternating current whose rms value is 7.07 amp. Consequently, the rotor current reverses every half revolution; it is timed to go through zero whenever the axis of the rotor is vertical. Taking zero time as the instant when the axis of the rotor is vertical, find the expression for the instantaneous voltage generated in the open-circuited stator coil.

This scheme is sometimes suggested as a d-c generator without a commutator, the thought being that if alternate half cycles of the alternating voltage generated in part *a* are reversed by reversal of the polarity of the field (rotor) winding, then a pulsating direct voltage will be generated in the stator. Explain whether this invention will work as described.

2-21. Consider a single-phase electrostatic synchronous machine of the type shown in Fig. 2-16. The purpose of this problem is to investigate some of the physical proportions of such a machine designed to develop 1 hp at 3,600 rpm with 60-cps applied voltages. Several operating voltages will be considered, and both air and vacuum insulation will be investigated. The following assumptions can be made:

1. The applied voltages vary sinusoidally.
2. The plates are shaped so that the capacitance varies sinusoidally with rotor angle, the minimum capacitance being negligibly small.
3. For mechanical reasons, the minimum permissible clearance between stator and rotor plates will be taken (more or less arbitrarily) as 0.1 cm.
4. Edge effects will be neglected, and the potential gradients between stator and rotor plates will be considered to be uniform. The maximum permissible potential gradients will be taken as 10 kv/cm in air and 1,000 kv/cm in vacuum. These values allow a factor of safety of about 3 for edge effects.

The following results are to be computed:

a. Determine the maximum value of the capacitance for operation at an rms voltage of 115 volts.

b. Determine the corresponding total rotor surface area.

c. If one face of each of the approximately circular surfaces constituting half of each rotor plate in Fig. 2-16 has a surface area of 200 cm^2, how many rotor plates will be required?

d. Roughly what would be the diameter of the rotor?

e. If each stator and rotor plate had a thickness of 0.1 cm (determine by mechanical considerations), how long would the motor be? (Do not be surprised if you arrive at a monstrosity!)

f. Determine the minimum rms voltage which would take full advantage of the maximum permissible potential gradient in air. For this operating voltage, repeat the calculations called for in *a* to *e*.

g. Determine the minimum rms voltage which would take full advantage of the maximum permissible potential gradient in vacuum. For this operating voltage, repeat the calculations called for in *a* to *e*.

CHAPTER 3

BASIC CONCEPTS OF MACHINE PERFORMANCE

THE object of this chapter is to apply the fundamental principles of Chap. 1 to rotating machinery. The viewpoint adopted is essentially that of magnetic fields trying to align themselves and, in the process, producing torques and voltages. Torque is accordingly evaluated from Eq. 1-24 by the third of the four methods outlined in Art. 1-7.

The important analytical results are formulations for torque (Eq. 3-22) and for induced voltage (Eqs. 3-36 and 3-38). These expressions are specific forms which may be directly applied to the steady-state analysis of all forms of rotating machines, as illustrated in the later chapters. In addition to their analytical value, they provide essential background for physical examination of the workings of various machine types. Thus, at the conclusion of the chapter the reader should have more definite physical notions of how machines operate, plus a springboard for the subsequent detailed analysis.

3-1. Armature Windings as Current Sheets. Most armatures have distributed windings—*i.e.*, windings which are spread over a number of slots around the periphery of the machine, as sketched in developed form in Fig. 3-1. For final, detailed evaluation of torque or voltage in a specific machine, the exact layout of this winding and the nature of the currents in it must be known. For a general examination of torque and voltage production, however, the nature and disposition of the windings need not be completely specified. In fact, the more complete specifications which must be fulfilled for optimum production of torque or voltage follow from the results of such an examination rather than constitute a set of necessary premises to it.

For purposes of torque evaluation, it is assumed that the winding of Fig. 3-1 is very finely distributed—in other words, that the armature contains a great number of inductors uniformly distributed around its surface and with a very small angular distance between adjacent inductors. Such an idealized winding is the equivalent of a *current sheet*, or surface distribution of current wrapped around the armature. To visualize such a current sheet, imagine a very thin strip of conducting material to cover the cylindrical surface of the armature. Imagine further that the strip carries current parallel to the shaft in one direction over parts of the armature surface and in the other direction over the remaining parts. Figure 3-2 shows such current sheets diagrammatically for a 2-pole and 4-pole winding with the currents and their directions symbolized by the crosshatched areas. The uniform height of these areas in Fig. 3-2 indicates a uniform surface distribution of current or the same current magnitude per unit angle anywhere around the circumference. Uniform angular current density as shown here is only a particular example chosen for illustrative purposes.

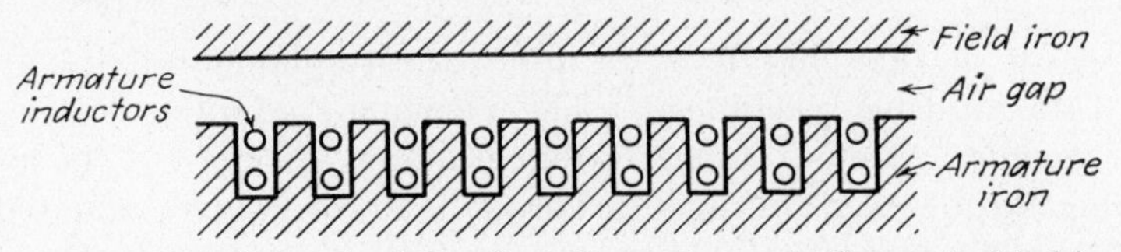

Fig. 3-1. Developed sketch of distributed armature winding embedded in slots.

The nature of the magnetic field produced by a current sheet can be illustrated by means of this special case of uniform current density. For the 2-pole machine of Fig. 3-2a, assume that the iron presents a smooth, cylindrical surface on both sides of the air gap and, further, that the iron has infinite permeability. The mmf of the current sheet is then available solely for forcing flux across the reluctance of the uniform air gap. The uniform current sheet with the associated iron surfaces is shown in developed form in Fig. 3-3a. From the symmetry of the structure, it is evident that the flux density in the air gap at angle θ will be

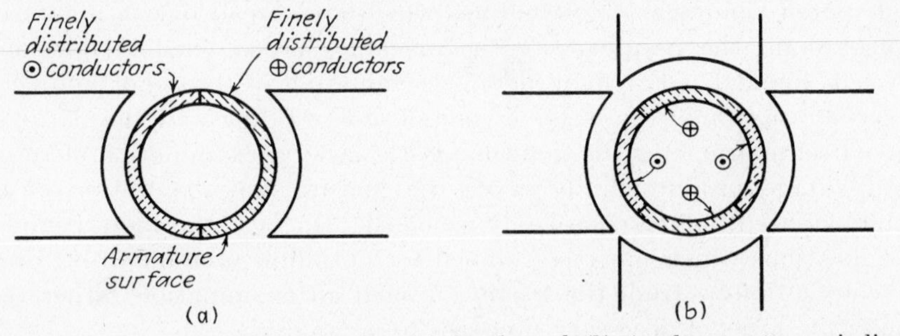

Fig. 3-2. Current sheets representing (a) 2-pole and (b) 4-pole armature windings.

the same in magnitude as that of angle $\theta + \pi$, but the fields are in the opposite directions. Recall that, in rationalized mks units, the mmf acting on any path is equal to the total current enclosed by the path. At the outset choose specifically the path *abcd* (Fig. 3-3b), crossing the gap at the angles π and 2π. With uniform angular current density J amp/rad, the mmf for path *abcd* is πJ. The magnitude of the magnetic potential difference across the gap at each of the angles π and 2π is $\pi J/2$. A plot of the magnetic potential difference for various points along the

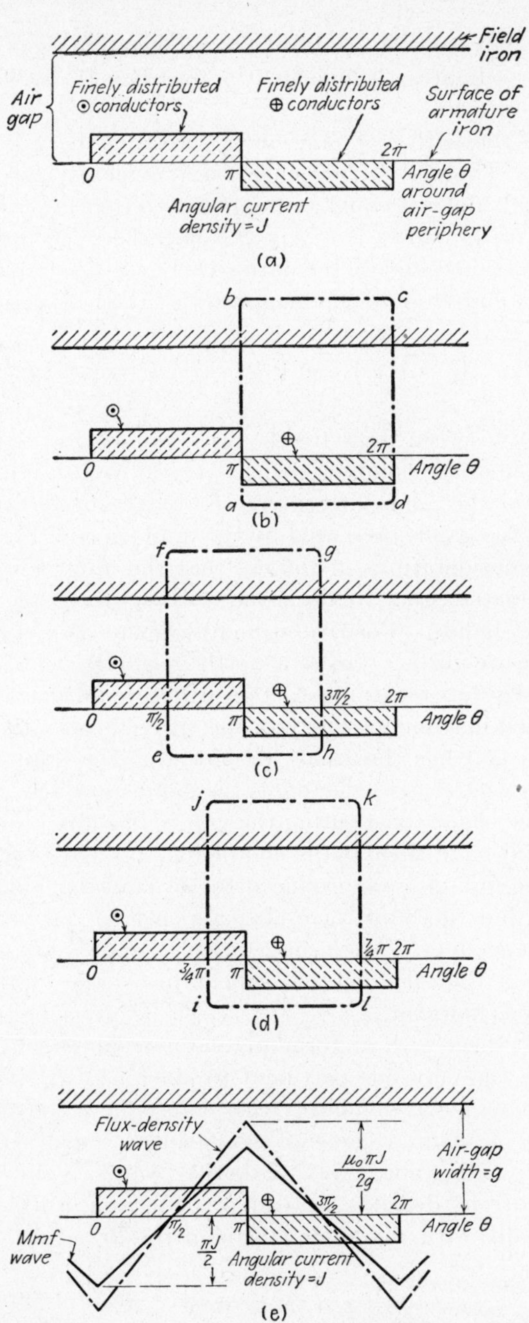

FIG. 3-3. Uniform current sheet, with several mmf paths and associated mmf and flux-density waves.

air gap is called an *mmf wave*. Positive and negative signs are associated with the mmf ordinates to indicate whether flux is leaving or entering the armature surface.

Next choose the path *efgh* (Fig. 3-3*c*), crossing the gap at the angles $\pi/2$ and $3\pi/2$. The net current enclosed is evidently zero, for the current between $\pi/2$ and π is equal and opposite to that between π and $3\pi/2$. The ordinates of the mmf wave at $\pi/2$ and $3\pi/2$ are accordingly zero.

For a third instance, choose the path *ijkl* (Fig. 3-3*d*), crossing the gap at the angles $3\pi/4$ and $7\pi/4$. The magnitude of the net current enclosed is

$$\left(\frac{7\pi}{4} - \pi\right)J - \left(\pi - \frac{3\pi}{4}\right)J = \frac{\pi}{2}J \tag{3-1}$$

a value midway between those for the other two paths. The ordinate of the mmf wave at these points is then $(\pi/4)J$ in magnitude.

A summary of the mmf pattern created by the uniform current sheet at all points in the gap is presented by the mmf wave of Fig. 3-3*e*. From the foregoing considerations, it follows that the mmf wave is a triangle with peak ordinates equal to $\pi J/2$ and with zeros at the mid-points of the two current bands. Positive ordinates denote flux entering the gap from the armature surface (as at a north magnetic pole), and negative ordinates denote flux returning to the armature surface from the gap. For the idealized machine of Fig. 3-3, the space flux-density distribution in the uniform gap has the same waveform as the mmf but ordinates differing by the factor μ_0/g, where g is the gap length and μ_0 the permeability of the free space constituting the gap. The flux lines cross the air gap radially and have their paths completed through the armature and field iron. The flux density produced by an mmf wave depends on the air-gap length, but the mmf wave depends only on the current distribution and is independent of the iron geometry. The mmf wave would be the same even if the machine had salient poles; the flux-density wave would be altered, however.

But a current sheet with uniform angular current density in each band is by no means the only one pertinent to machine analysis. For many purposes, in fact, a current sheet with sinusoidal variation of angular current density is of more general significance. Such a current sheet, with the corresponding mmf and flux-density waves, is shown in Fig. 3-4. The angular current density, instead of being uniform as in Fig. 3-3, varies sinusoidally with the angle θ around the armature circumference and is given by

$$J = J_{\text{peak}} \sin \theta \tag{3-2}$$

where J_{peak} is the amplitude of the sinusoid, occurring at $\theta = \pi/2$. (We shall frequently be discussing and sketching sinusoidal distributions of angular current density J, mmf F, and flux density B. In an attempt to emphasize the fact that these are sine waves in *space*, in contrast to sine waves in *time*, the subscript *peak* will be used to denote the amplitude of the quantity to which it is attached.) The net current in any one band (that between $\theta = 0$ and $\theta = \pi$, for example), obtained by integration over the armature surface occupied by that band, is

$$\int_0^\pi J\, d\theta = \int_0^\pi J_{\text{peak}} \sin\theta\, d\theta = 2J_{\text{peak}} \tag{3-3}$$

By repetition of the process associated with Fig. 3-3, the mmf wave is seen to be sinusoidal with its positive peak occurring at $\theta = \pi$. The

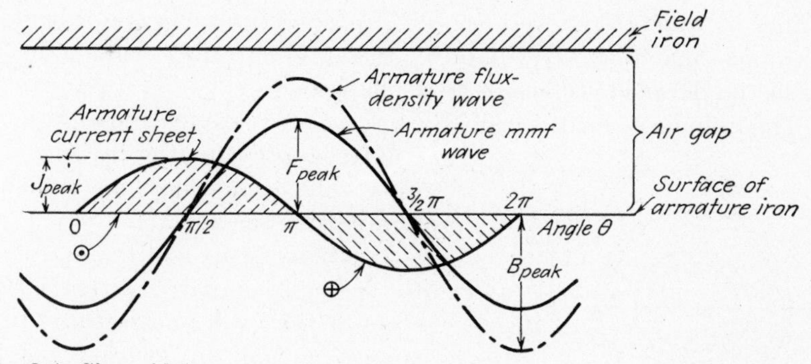

FIG. 3-4. Sinusoidal current sheet and associated mmf and flux-density waves.

mmf amplitude is half the net current in one band, the factor of ½ appearing because this current must force the flux both across the air gap and back again. That is,

$$F_{\text{peak}} = \tfrac{1}{2} \int_0^\pi J_{\text{peak}} \sin\theta\, d\theta = J_{\text{peak}} \tag{3-4}$$

and the mmf acting across the air gap at any point θ is

$$F = F_{\text{peak}} \sin\left(\theta - \frac{\pi}{2}\right) \tag{3-5}$$

As before, the flux-density wave is obtained by multiplying the ordinates of the mmf wave by μ_0/g.

For general examinations of torque production in rotating machines, the armature winding can be represented by a current sheet or by its corresponding mmf wave. Torque evaluation then becomes a study of the interaction of the current sheet or mmf wave with the resultant flux density existing in the air gap. Thus the viewpoint of energy conversion as the result of magnetic fields trying to align themselves begins to assume a more tangible form. The interaction with a sinusoidal current sheet will be seen to be of fundamental importance in the next three articles.

3-2. Torque in Electric Machines. To study the quantities which are of importance in the production of torque, consider the simplified machine of Fig. 3-5. The presence of windings is indicated on both the stator and rotor, and it makes no difference for analytical purposes which is the armature and which the field winding. The flux lines shown in the sketch correspond to those in a 2-pole machine; until a result is obtained, attention will be centered on the 2-pole case, after which generalization to the p-pole machine will be given. Five sets of idealizing assumptions will be made in order to facilitate the analysis:

1. The machine is considered to have a uniform air gap. Reluctance torques, discussed in Art. 2-2, thus do not enter the picture. For those machines in which they are a significant factor (notably the salient-pole synchronous machine; see Chap. 8), reluctance torques will be incorporated in the detailed studies of later chapters.

2. The influence of saturation, hysteresis, and eddy currents in the iron will be ignored for the present. The iron will accordingly be taken as infinitely permeable.

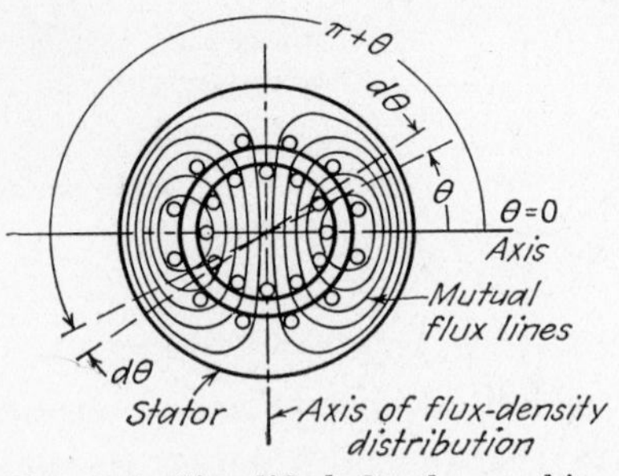

FIG. 3-5. Simplified 2-pole machine, showing mutual-flux lines.

3. The air-gap width g is assumed to be small compared with the diameters of the rotor and stator. In discussing air-gap flux density, one then need recognize no difference between that at the rotor surface, that at the stator surface, or that at any intermediate radial distance in the gap. Fringing of flux at the ends of the rotor and stator iron will also be ignored.

4. The air-gap flux density B will be considered to vary sinusoidally around the air-gap periphery, as shown by the sine wave of flux density in the developed diagram of Fig. 3-6. The angle θ is a space angle measured in electrical units with the origin arbitrarily placed at the zero crossing of the flux-density wave. The position of the zero crossing in general depends on electrical conditions within the windings. The peaks of the flux-density wave correspond to the labeling *axis of flux-density distribution* in Fig. 3-5, and the two halves of the sine wave correspond to two poles.

It may appear technically presumptuous at this point to consider sinusoidally distributed flux density in view of the lack of other detailed specifications. Such consideration is based on singling out the space fundamental component of whatever distribution may actually exist and drawing tentative conclusions with all space harmonics neglected. Thus, one obviously neglected factor is the effect of the slots shown in Fig. 3-1 but not even indicated in Fig. 3-5 in spite of the fact that they will introduce harmonics into the flux wave. One makes the mental note to examine the orders of magnitude and the effects of these harmonics at a later time. As a matter of fact, it will be found that the normal situation in actual a-c machines is purposely made to correspond closely to sinusoidal flux distribution and that the size and influence of harmonics are minimized. It will also be found that torque in normal d-c machines is independent of the flux distribution as long as the distribution is the same before each pole except, of course, for the difference between a north and south pole. No significant qualitative errors occur in either d-c or a-c cases.

5. The armature will be represented by a sinusoidal current sheet with its associated sinusoidal mmf wave, both shown in Fig. 3-6. The mmf

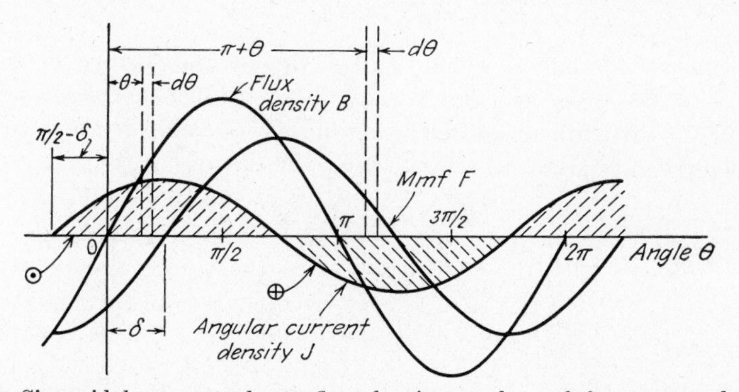

FIG. 3-6. Sinusoidal current sheet, flux density, and mmf for torque derivation.

wave is given an arbitrary space displacement of δ rad from the flux-density wave; the sinusoid representing the current sheet leads that for the mmf wave by $\pi/2$ rad and hence is displaced by the angle $(\pi/2) - \delta$ from the flux-density wave.

The assumption of a sinusoidal current sheet and mmf wave requires remarks similar to those accompanying the assumed sinusoidal distribution of flux density. Once again the fundamental component is being singled out, and the effects of harmonics remain to be examined later; once again the assumption will be found to be reasonably realistic for actual a-c machines, and special attention will be given later to the distribution in d-c machines; once again no significant qualitative errors occur in any case.

With these premises established, our procedure will be to use Eq. 1-24 to evaluate the torque increment contributed by differential portions of the current sheet, and then to sum all such increments by integration over the entire current sheet to obtain the total torque. In Fig. 3-6, the air-gap flux density B at any angle θ around the circumference is

$$B = B_{peak} \sin \theta \tag{3-6}$$

where B_{peak} is the amplitude. The angular current density at the angle θ is

$$J = J_{peak} \sin \left(\theta + \frac{\pi}{2} - \delta \right) = J_{peak} \cos (\theta - \delta) \tag{3-7}$$

where J_{peak} is the amplitude of the current-density wave. The magnetic potential difference across the air gap, or ordinate of the mmf wave, is

$$F = F_{peak} \sin (\theta - \delta) \tag{3-8}$$

and, from Eq. 3-4, the mmf amplitude F_{peak} is

$$F_{peak} = J_{peak} \tag{3-9}$$

Now select two angle increments $d\theta$ on the air-gap surface at the angles θ and $\pi + \theta$ (see Figs. 3-5 and 3-6). These surface increments form an elementary 1-turn full-pitch coil (*i.e.*, one whose sides are one pole pitch or 180 electrical degrees apart) carrying the current

$$i = J\, d\theta = J_{peak} \cos (\theta - \delta)\, d\theta \tag{3-10}$$

The flux linkages with the elementary coil are

$$\lambda = \int_{\theta}^{\pi+\theta} Blr\, d\theta \tag{3-11}$$

where l and r are, respectively, the axial length of the machine iron and its radius at the air gap. By use of Eq. 3-6, the flux linkages become

$$\lambda = \int_{\theta}^{\pi+\theta} B_{peak} lr \sin \theta\, d\theta \tag{3-12}$$

$$= 2B_{peak} lr \cos \theta \tag{3-13}$$

The angular rate of change of linkages with the elementary coil is

$$\frac{d\lambda}{d\theta} = -2B_{peak} lr \sin \theta \tag{3-14}$$

i.e., if the coil should move, the flux linking it would change at this rate.

From Eq. 1-24 written for the 2-pole case, electromagnetic torque is given by

$$T = i \frac{d\lambda}{d\theta} \tag{3-15}$$

The torque increment associated with the elementary coil is therefore, by substitution of Eqs. 3-10 and 3-14,

$$dT = -2J_{peak} B_{peak} lr \cos (\theta - \delta) \sin \theta\, d\theta \tag{3-16}$$

The total torque is the sum of all such increments, which can be obtained by integration over any angular interval of π rad, say that from 0 to π. Torque is then

$$T = -2J_{\text{peak}}B_{\text{peak}}lr \int_0^\pi \cos(\theta - \delta) \sin\theta \, d\theta \tag{3-17}$$

$$= -\pi J_{\text{peak}}B_{\text{peak}}lr \sin\delta \tag{3-18}$$

or, by use of Eq. 3-9,

$$T = -\pi F_{\text{peak}}B_{\text{peak}}lr \sin\delta \tag{3-19}$$

The negative sign in these torque expressions indicates that the torque acts in a direction to decrease the displacement angle δ between the flux-density and mmf waves when, as was done in Fig. 3-6, positive values of B and F are taken so that they correspond to flux crossing the air gap in the same direction. The winding member producing the mmf then tends toward the left in Fig. 3-6, and the other member tends toward the right. The negative sign may be dropped, and the direction of electromagnetic torque for both motors and generators may be conveniently determined from the fact that the torque tends to line up the rotor and stator fields so that the component fluxes cross the air gap in the same direction.

Equations 3-18 and 3-19 give the total torque for a 2-pole machine. For a multipolar machine, they give the torque per pair of poles when the angle δ is measured in electrical units; the total torque for a p-pole machine is then, with the minus sign dropped,

$$T = \pi \frac{p}{2} F_{\text{peak}}B_{\text{peak}}lr \sin\delta \tag{3-20}$$

Alternative forms arise when it is recognized that the flux per pole is

$$\Phi = \int_0^\pi lr \frac{2}{p} B_{\text{peak}} \sin\theta \, d\theta = \frac{4}{p} lrB_{\text{peak}} \tag{3-21}$$

Use of Eq. 3-21 in 3-20 yields

$$T = \frac{\pi}{2}\left(\frac{p}{2}\right)^2 F_{\text{peak}}\Phi \sin\delta \tag{3-22}$$

In much of our future work, Eq. 3-22 will be the preferred form, for it is often expeditious to think in terms of flux per pole and amplitude of the mmf wave. The torque will be exerted on both the rotor and stator structures and will cause rotation of whichever member is free to move. For torque evaluation, therefore, the mmf F_{peak} may be taken as that of the rotor or the stator winding as convenience may dictate.

3-3. Interpretation of Torque Equations. The torque equation 3-22 is of special value for the conceptual insight which it can give to the electromagnetic production of torque and hence to electromechanical energy conversion. Qualitatively, it immediately lends pertinence to the viewpoint of torque as produced by interaction between the magnetic fields of the stator and rotor currents. Quantitatively, it indicates that, under the assumed sinusoidal conditions, the torque is proportional to the amplitude of the flux-density wave, the amplitude of the mmf wave, and the sine of the angle δ between their axes. This angle is commonly called the *torque angle.* It is indicated in the schematic diagram of Fig. 3-7.

The quantitative indications furnish valuable guides for the evolution of successful motor types and valuable criteria for judging the potential worth of newly proposed variations. For example, they may readily be used to show whether, in a specific case, a steady or time-varying

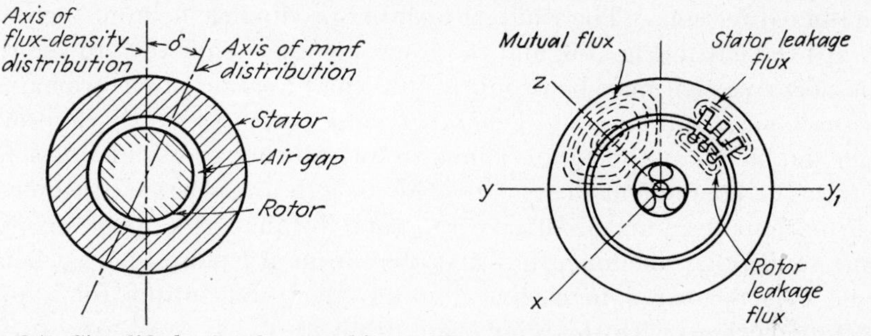

FIG. 3-7. Simplified 2-pole machine, showing torque angle.

FIG. 3-8. Mutual- and leakage-flux paths in typical machine.

torque is produced. They also form one basis of performance analysis. Together with the assumptions back of them, they emphasize the fact that flux-density and mmf waveforms in electric machines must be carefully studied, for it is through the medium of these waves that the torque equations are applied to practical machines whose construction features require departure from the assumed ideal conditions.

As an example of the nature of the flux involved in the torque equations, Fig. 3-8 shows the principal flux lines in a particular type of rotating machine. Most of the flux produced by the rotor and stator windings (roughly 90 per cent or more in typical machines) crosses the air gap and links both windings; this flux is termed the *mutual flux.* Small percentages of the flux, however, do not cross the gap but link only the rotor winding or only the stator winding; these are, respectively, the *rotor leakage flux* and the *stator leakage flux.* It is only the mutual flux which is of direct concern in torque evaluation, and the flux-density waveform of Fig. 3-6 is that of the mutual flux. The leakage fluxes do not enter directly into torque production. The situation in this respect may be expressed in the following rough, physical manner: Since the stator leakage flux does not link the rotor winding, the winding does not know of that leakage flux's existence, and hence the rotor mmf cannot react with the stator leakage flux to produce torque; and a similar statement can be made with regard to rotor leakage flux and stator mmf. As will be shown in Chap. 4, time rates of change of the stator and rotor leakage flux linkages do affect machine performance by virtue of the voltages they induce in their own windings. This effect, however, is an auxiliary one rather than a fundamental part of torque production. In any machine, therefore, the primary function of the field winding is to establish the mutual flux wave, and that of the armature is to establish the mmf wave.

But the armature mmf, acting as it does on the magnetic circuit traversed by the mutual flux, may affect both the magnitude and the

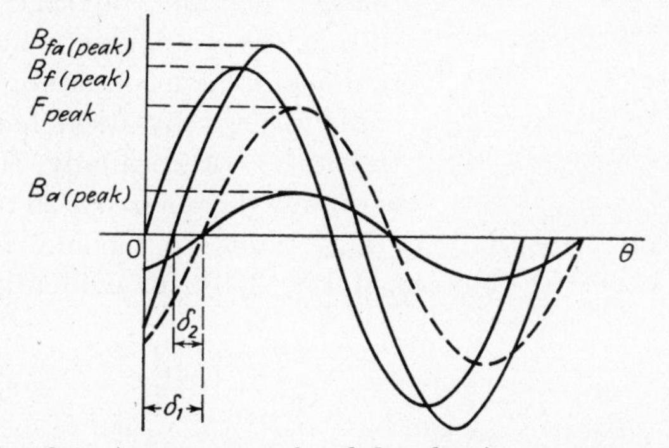

FIG. 3-9. Armature mmf and flux-density components.

distribution of the flux. As a consequence, the following question naturally arises: By the flux density B_{peak} or flux per pole Φ in the torque equations, do we mean those which would be created by the field winding acting alone or those existing with the field and armature windings simultaneously excited? The answer is that, under the idealizing assumptions of the preceding article, we may use either provided we use the corresponding value of the angle δ.

To justify this answer, recall that the air gap of the machine is assumed of uniform width and the iron of infinite permeability. The machine then constitutes a uniform linear magnetic circuit, and superposition may be used. The solid curve of amplitude $B_{f(\text{peak})}$ in Fig. 3-9 is the spatial flux-density distribution caused by the field winding acting alone. The dotted curve of amplitude F_{peak} is the armature-mmf wave; acting alone, it produces the flux-density wave of amplitude $B_{a(\text{peak})}$ in space phase with the mmf wave. The wave $B_{fa(\text{peak})}$ is the sum of the $B_{f(\text{peak})}$ and $B_{a(\text{peak})}$ waves and represents the flux distribution existing with field and armature mmfs simultaneously present. Addition of these sine waves may be carried out conveniently by means of a vector diagram, just as addition of the familiar sinusoidal currents or voltages of a-c circuit theory is commonly carried out vectorially. Such vector addition is illustrated in Fig. 3-10. (One should not lose sight of the fact that the sine waves being added in Figs. 3-9 and 3-10 are space distributions plotted with angle around the air-gap periphery as abscissas. On the other hand, the usual sinusoidal currents and voltages of a-c circuit theory are plotted with time or an angle directly dependent on time as abscissas. Since vector diagrams are simply convenient artifices for adding sine waves having the same mathematical period, vector addition is not restricted to variations with time.)

Now in view of the sin δ term in the torque equations, the $B_{a(\text{peak})}$ and armature-mmf waves, being in space phase, cannot interact to produce torque—a statement which physically is the equivalent of saying that an iron-cored reactor by itself has no tendency to rotate. Accordingly, the same result is obtained from Eq. 3-20 by substituting $B_{f(\text{peak})}$, F_{peak}, and δ_1 or $B_{fa(\text{peak})}$, F_{peak}, and δ_2. Geometric justification follows from the vector diagram of Fig. 3-10, for evidently

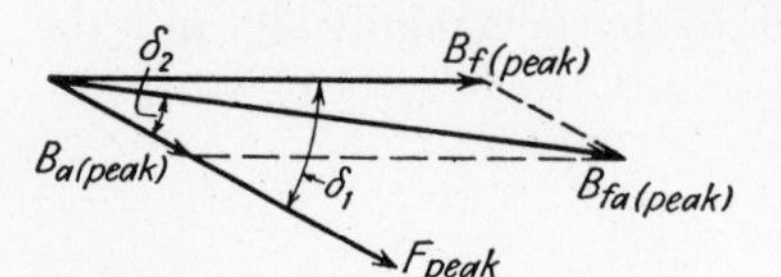

FIG. 3-10. Vector addition of flux-density waves.

$$B_{f(\text{peak})} \sin \delta_1 = B_{fa(\text{peak})} \sin \delta_2 \tag{3-23}$$

and hence

$$B_{f(\text{peak})}F_{\text{peak}} \sin \delta_1 = B_{fa(\text{peak})}F_{\text{peak}} \sin \delta_2 \tag{3-24}$$

Ability to reason in terms of either $B_{f(\text{peak})}$ or $B_{fa(\text{peak})}$ is a great convenience in deducing the properties of machines.

If the effects of magnetic saturation in the iron were not neglected in the foregoing argument, linear superposition of flux densities could not be used. More nearly correctly in such a case, the flux density resulting from the combined action of field and armature mmf should be used. Saturation also affects the harmonic content of the flux wave. As a matter of fact, it will be found that many of the concepts of machine analysis are based on the assumptions of negligible saturation or infinite permeability of the iron. Correction for the effects of these assumptions in practical cases is made on a basis compounded from logic and empiricism.

One further remark may be made concerning the torque equations and the thought process leading up to them. There is no restriction that the current sheet, mmf wave, or flux-density wave need remain stationary in space. They may remain stationary, or they may rotate around the air gap. In the synchronous machine, for example, the flux wave produced by the field winding revolves in the air gap as the entire rotor structure revolves. If the armature current sheet and mmf wave revolve similarly, a continuous torque may be produced by the efforts of the stator and rotor fields to align themselves in accordance with the torque equations.

3-4. Optimum Conditions for Production of Motor Torque. Preliminary considerations which must be satisfied for successful electrical-to-mechanical energy conversion may readily be derived from the form of the torque equation and the concept of interaction between flux-density and mmf waves. As already indicated in Art. 1-4, three general possibilities exist for the production of these waves in an electric motor:

1. Alternating currents may be supplied to both the stator and rotor windings. The most common example is the induction motor, in which alternating current is supplied directly to the stator and by induction (*i.e.*, transformer action) to the rotor. Another common illustration is the a-c series motor, in which the two windings are connected in series so that the same alternating current exists in each.

2. Alternating current may be supplied to one winding (the armature) and direct current to the other (the field). Motors so excited are synchronous motors.

3. Direct current may be supplied to both rotor and stator windings, resulting in a d-c motor.

For best motor action, it must be recognized that the rotor torque should act in the same direction at all times and should preferably be a steady torque rather than a time-varying torque. By reference to the torque equations, it will be seen that the torque angle δ should remain constant with time. Consequently, for the production of a steady, unidirectional torque, *the axis of the flux-density distribution and the axis of the armature-mmf distribution must remain fixed in space relative to each other.* In Fig. 3-7, for example, if one axis is stationary, the other axis must be stationary; if one axis rotates, the other axis must rotate in the same direction at the same speed. Since torque is proportional to the product of the wave amplitudes, *best operation results if the flux per pole and the armature mmf per pole do not fluctuate with time.* Otherwise torque pulsations are produced which may cause undesirable vibration of the motor and the equipment driven. In some motor types (the single-phase a-c series motor, for example), the field strengths must unavoidably vary in magnitude sinusoidally with time. The time variations of mmf and flux density in such cases must be as nearly in phase as possible (in the series motor they are exactly in phase) in order to produce the greatest possible net torque in the forward direction per unit of current input to the motor. As a matter of fact, the torque of a motor with single-phase a-c supply must inevitably be a pulsating torque because of the pulsations in instantaneous electric power inherent in a single-phase circuit.

Several corollaries pertaining to specific motor types follow from these considerations plus the fact that the rotor winding must rotate at a definite speed. Consider, for example, a motor like that of Fig. 1-7 with direct current supplied to both rotor and stator. The field of the stator winding is obviously stationary in space. Consequently, the field of the rotor must be rendered stationary in space despite rotation of the rotor winding. As will be shown in Art. 3-9, this action is accomplished by means of the commutator.

Consider next the case of a motor with direct current supplied to the rotor winding, as in the synchronous motor, of which Fig. 1-8 is typical. The rotor is then the equivalent of a set of rotating d-c electromagnets, and the field of the rotor revolves in space at the same speed as the rotor itself. The field of the stator must therefore revolve at precisely the same speed. As will be shown in Art. 3-6, such a rotating field may be obtained electrically by the appropriate design of polyphase a-c winding. An alternative statement of this speed situation is that the speed of the rotor must be precisely equal to the speed of the rotating stator field, the latter being determined by the supply frequency and the number of poles.

A third variation consists in a motor with polyphase a-c winding on both stator and rotor, as will be found in the polyphase induction motor. Each of these polyphase windings produces a rotating field. The rotor field then revolves at a speed of n_2 *with respect to the rotor structure itself*, and superposed on it is the mechanical rotation of the rotor structure at the speed n. The rotor field thus revolves in space at a speed $n + n_2$, n_2 being considered positive if it is in the same direction as n. In order that the axes of stator and rotor fields be stationary relative to each other, the stator field must rotate in space at a speed of

$$n_1 = n + n_2 \tag{3-25}$$

It is thus evident that there is a variety of methods for the production of motor torque and hence a variety of motor types, all operating on the same principle but having in general different performance characteristics. Counter torques similarly produced in generators will, of course, influence their action. Before investigating the general nature of these characteristics and influences, it will be appropriate to examine voltage conditions within the windings.

3-5. Voltages Generated in Electric Machines. Study of the voltages induced in any of the windings placed on armatures of machines resolves into study of the voltage induced in a single coil of those windings, followed by addition of the individual coil voltages in the manner dictated by the specific interconnection of coils forming the complete winding. Such a single coil of N turns is indicated by the two *coil sides* a and $-a$ in Fig. 3-11. The coil spans a full 180 electrical degrees or a complete pole pitch and hence is a full-pitch coil. For simplicity, a 2-pole machine is indicated, salient poles being chosen for purposes of diagrammatic symbolism only. This simple winding is developed in Fig. 3-12, and the spatial flux-density wave is shown superimposed. Flux density is assumed to be sinusoidally distributed. The general nature of the induced voltage has already been discussed in Art. 1-3. The voltage magnitude will now be determined by means of the Faraday law (Eq. 1-1).

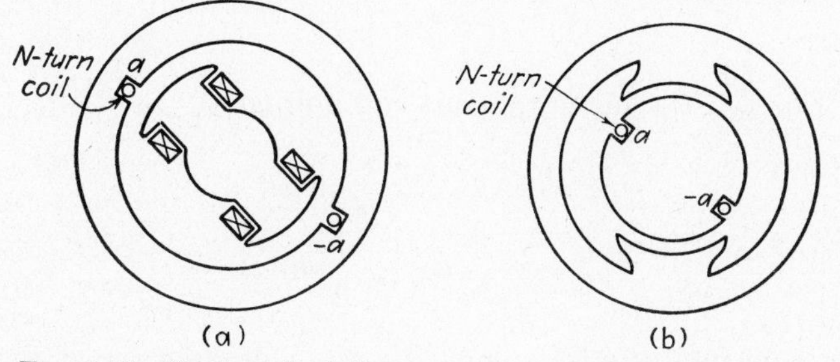

FIG. 3-11. Single coil of N turns on (a) stator and (b) rotor.

The element of flux linkages contributed by the angle element $d\theta$ at the air-gap periphery is

$$d\lambda = NBlr\frac{2}{p}\,d\theta = NB_{\text{peak}}lr\frac{2}{p}\sin\theta\,d\theta \tag{3-26}$$

l being the axial length of coil side embedded in iron, r the coil radius, p the number of poles, and B_{peak} the amplitude of the flux-density wave. The factor $2/p$ appears because angle θ is measured in electrical units. At the instant of time when the displacement of coil side a is α electrical radians from the zero crossing of the flux-density wave, the total flux linkages with the coil are

$$\lambda = NB_{\text{peak}}lr\frac{2}{p}\int_{\alpha}^{\pi+\alpha}\sin\theta\,d\theta \tag{3-27}$$

$$= NB_{\text{peak}}lr\frac{4}{p}\cos\alpha \tag{3-28}$$

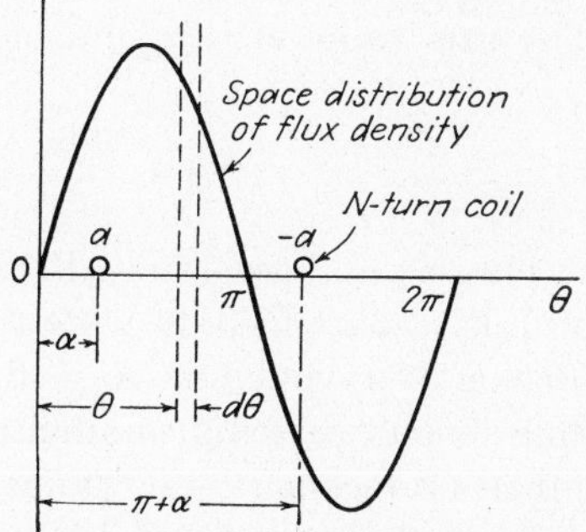

FIG. 3-12. Developed diagram of N-turn coil in sinusoidal flux distribution.

Now if the relative speed of the coil and the flux-density wave is ω electrical radians per second, we have

$$\alpha = \omega t \tag{3-29}$$

t being time in seconds arbitrarily reckoned as zero when coil side a is at the origin in Fig. 3-12. In terms of relative speed n in rpm,

$$\omega = 2\pi \frac{p}{2} \frac{n}{60} \tag{3-30}$$

since the angle α passes through 2π electrical radians for every pair of poles swept through.

The flux linkages then become

$$\lambda = NB_{\text{peak}} lr \frac{4}{p} \cos \omega t \tag{3-31}$$

and from Eq. 1-1, the instantaneous coil voltage is

$$e = \omega NB_{\text{peak}} lr \frac{4}{p} \sin \omega t \tag{3-32}$$

$$= 2\pi f NB_{\text{peak}} lr \frac{4}{p} \sin \omega t \tag{3-33}$$

In the last equation, the frequency f of the voltage wave is given by

$$f = \frac{\omega}{2\pi} = \frac{p}{2} \frac{n}{60} \qquad \text{cps} \tag{3-34}$$

Equation 3-33 can be put in somewhat more convenient and compact form by recognizing from Eq. 3-21 that $B_{\text{peak}} lr(4/p)$ is the flux per pole Φ; thus,

$$e = 2\pi f N\Phi \sin \omega t \tag{3-35}$$

The rms value of this sinusoidal voltage is

$$E = \frac{2\pi}{\sqrt{2}} fN\Phi = 4.44 fN\Phi \tag{3-36}$$

Those who have studied transformer theory will recognize the identity of Eqs. 3-35 and 3-36 with the corresponding emf equations of a transformer (see Appendix A). Relative motion of a coil and a fixed spatial flux-density distribution in a rotating machine produces the same voltage effect as does a time-varying flux density in association with stationary coils in a transformer. In studying machine voltages, we frequently concern ourselves with the distribution of flux density and mmf *in space* for the reason that these space distributions, in conjunction with rotation, profoundly influence the variations *in time* of emf and currents in the windings. Rotation, in effect, introduces the time element and transforms a space distribution of flux density into a time variation of voltage.

The voltage induced in the single coil of Fig. 3-11*a* is, of course, a single-phase voltage. For the production of a set of 3-phase voltages, it follows that three coils phase-displaced 120 electrical degrees in space must be used. The dispositions of armature coils in elementary 3-phase machines have already been shown in Figs. 1-26 to 1-28. For these more complex cases, Eq. 3-36 gives the rms voltage per phase when N is the total series turns per phase. All of these windings are full-pitch concentrated windings because the two sides, such as a and $-a$, of any given coil are 180 electrical degrees apart and because all the turns of that coil are concentrated in one pair of slots. For other than concentrated full-pitch windings a reduction factor must be applied to Eq. 3-36 to obtain the voltage (see Art. 4-1). Exactly the same principles hold, however, provided the coils considered here are regarded as equivalent full-pitch concentrated coils replacing whatever winding layout is actually used.

From Eq. 3-35 it is evident that, even if the ultimate purpose is the generation of a direct voltage, the voltage induced in an armature coil is an alternating voltage. The alternating waveform must therefore be rectified. Mechanical rectification is provided by the commutator, the device already referred to in Art. 3-4 for keeping the field of the rotor stationary in space and described in elementary form in Art. 1-3*b*. For the single coil of Fig. 3-11*b*, the commutator provides full-wave rectification. With the continued assumption of sinusoidal flux distribution, the voltage waveform between brushes is transformed to that of Fig. 3-13. The average or d-c value of the voltage between brushes is

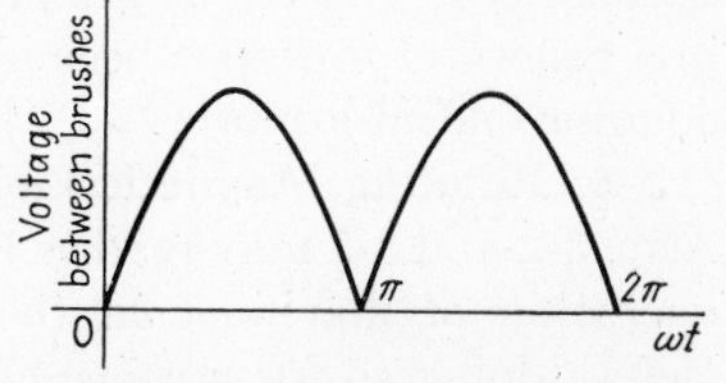

FIG. 3-13. Commutated voltage waveform for elementary d-c generator.

$$E_a = \frac{1}{\pi} \int_0^\pi 2\pi f N\Phi \sin \omega t \, d(\omega t) = 4fN\Phi \tag{3-37}$$

It is usually more convenient in the d-c case to express the voltage E_a in terms of the speed n in rpm instead of the frequency f of the coil voltage. Substitution of Eq. 3-34 in 3-37 yields

$$E_a = 2p\Phi N \frac{n}{60} \tag{3-38}$$

The 1-coil d-c winding implied here is, of course, simplified to the point of being unrealistic in the practical sense, and it will be essential later to examine in detail the action of commutators and their influence on the voltage and mmf of the associated windings. Actually, Eq. 3-38 gives correct results for the more practical d-c windings as well, provided that N be taken as the total number of turns in series between armature terminals.

For all of the voltage equations developed in this article, a question arises, as it did in the torque case, concerning what value of flux or flux density to use in view of the fact that armature mmf influences flux conditions in the machine. Should the flux or flux density corresponding to the field excitation alone be used, or should that corresponding to the combined effect of field and armature mmf be used? The answer depends on the method of analysis to be chosen for handling the other details of the particular problem; in all methods, however, the influence of the armature mmf must be included. The most usual method in d-c cases is to use the flux corresponding to the resultant mmf; the calculated voltage then differs from the terminal voltages by only the armature resistance drop. The same method is frequently adopted in a-c cases, except that account must also be taken of the armature leakage flux when the armature carries current.

The nature of the armature mmf must therefore be studied, not only because of its role in the production of torque in a motor or counter torque in a generator, but also because of its influence on emf in a generator and counter emf in a motor.

3-6. Rotating Magnetic Fields. The torque and voltage principles of Arts. 3-2 and 3-5 may readily be applied to qualitative examination of the operation of machines in the light of the criteria stated in Art. 3-4. Before doing so for a-c machines, however, it is necessary to study the nature of the mmf and magnetic field produced by a winding in which the currents are time-varying. In particular, we shall study the mmf patterns of a 3-phase winding representing an idealization of those found on the stator of 3-phase induction and synchronous machines. Very elementary versions of such windings are shown diagrammatically in Figs. 1-26 and 1-27. Once again attention will be focused on a 2-pole machine or upon one pair of poles of the more general p-pole winding. Events will be presented from the viewpoint of an observer stationary with respect to the winding; *i.e.*, if the winding is on the stator, events will be viewed from the stator.

Ideally, the 3-phase winding may be considered composed of three superimposed sinusoidal current sheets, each sheet being like the one shown in Fig. 3-4 or 3-6, and each sheet being associated with one phase of the machine. The windings must be so placed that the sinusoids representing the three component current sheets are displaced from each other by 120 electrical degrees in space around the air-gap circumference. The three component sinusoidal mmf waves produced by the sheets are accordingly displaced by 120 electrical degrees in space from each other also.

But each phase of the winding is excited by an alternating current which varies in magnitude sinusoidally with time. The current density everywhere on the corresponding component current sheet, as well as all ordinates on the corresponding component mmf wave, therefore also vary in magnitude sinusoidally with time. For example, a sinusoidal variation with time for current i_a in phase a is shown in Fig. 3-14. At time t_1, when i_a is a positive maximum, the space distributions of the component current sheet and mmf produced by phase a are shown in Fig. 3-15a. At time t_2, when i_a is a positive half maximum, the same space distributions are shown in Fig. 3-15b. These distributions have not shifted in space because the winding is stationary with respect to the observer; all of the ordinates are only half the corresponding values in Fig. 3-15a, however. Similarly at time t_3, when i_a is a negative half maximum, the space distributions are shown in Fig. 3-15c. Again the waves have not shifted in space position, but the ordinates are the opposite of those in Fig. 3-15b because the current i_a has reversed. Thus, when the winding is excited by alternating current, the component current sheet and mmf distribution for each individual phase form pulsating standing waves in space, with the pulsations following the sinusoidal variations of the phase current.

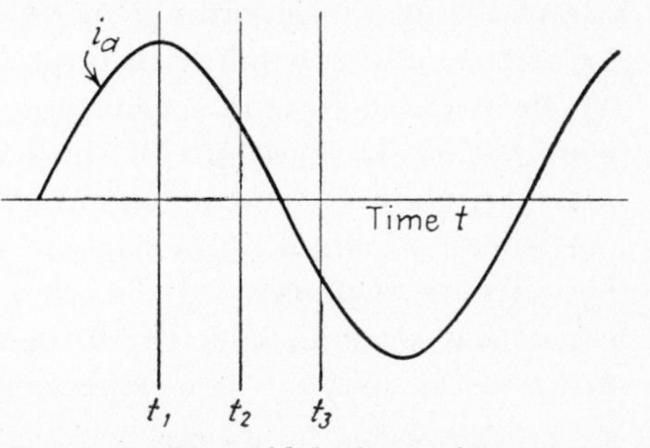

FIG. 3-14. Sinusoidal alternating current.

The net results for a 3-phase winding may be obtained by appropriate superposition of the components produced by the individual phases. This superposition will first be carried out pictorially and then by analytic means. To avoid unduly confusing the sketches, only the mmf waves will be drawn, the current sheets being omitted.

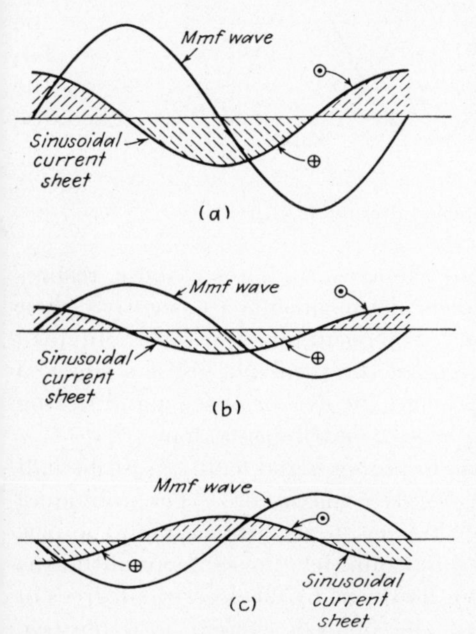

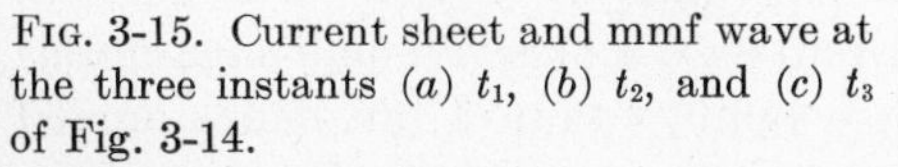

FIG. 3-15. Current sheet and mmf wave at the three instants (a) t_1, (b) t_2, and (c) t_3 of Fig. 3-14.

When the winding is excited by balanced 3-phase currents, the instantaneous phase currents vary with time in the manner shown in Fig. 3-16. The three current amplitudes are equal, and the sinusoids are displaced 120 electrical degrees in time; the time-phase sequence in Fig. 3-16 is abc. The distributions of air-gap mmf in space around the machine circumference at the three instants of time t_1, t_2, and t_3 are given in Fig. 3-17. The three sketches are, in effect, snapshots of the component and resultant mmfs taken at three separate times. The labeling *Axis of phase a, b, or c* locates the maximum ordinate of the component-mmf wave for the phase. By virtue of the winding disposition, these three axes are displaced by 120 electrical degrees in space from each other, the space-phase sequence being *abc*. The locations of three equivalent coils producing the mmf waves are shown by the small circles a and $-a$, b and $-b$, and c and $-c$.

At the first instant t_1, the current in phase a is a positive maximum, and the currents in phases b and c are a negative half maximum. The corresponding space distribution of the mmf contributions for each phase are shown in Fig. 3-17a. The component mmfs for phases b and c are drawn

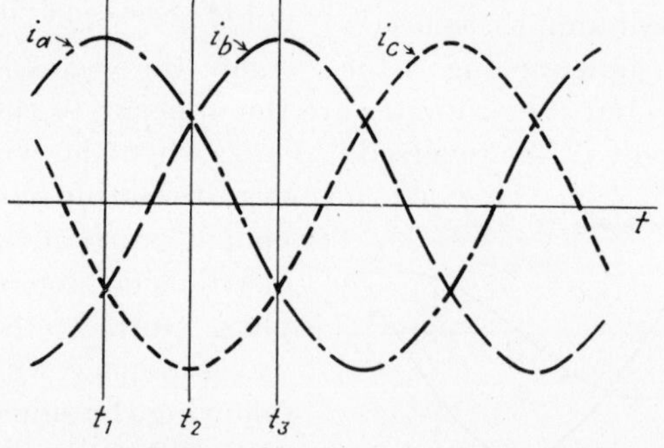

FIG. 3-16. Balanced 3-phase alternating currents.

with their negative half waves about the axes of phases b and c, respectively, because these two instantaneous phase currents are negative; their amplitudes are half that for phase a. The resultant-mmf wave, obtained by adding the individual contributions of the three phases, is a sinusoid with its positive half wave centered about the axis of phase a and having an amplitude $\frac{3}{2}$ times that of the phase-a contribution alone.

At the later instant t_2, the currents in phases a and b are a positive half maximum, and that in phase c is a negative maximum. The individual mmf components (Fig. 3-17b) have changed in accordance with the new instantaneous currents, but the resultant mmf has the same amplitude as at t_1. It has now moved to the right, however, by 60 electrical degrees in space. Similarly, at time t_3 (when the phase-b current is a positive maximum and the phase-a and -c currents are a negative half maximum) the same resultant-mmf distribution is again obtained, but it has moved 60 electrical degrees still farther to the right (see Fig. 3-17c). As time passes, then, the resultant-mmf wave retains its form and amplitude but shifts progressively along the winding. This shift corresponds to a field rotating uniformly around the circumference of the air gap. Results

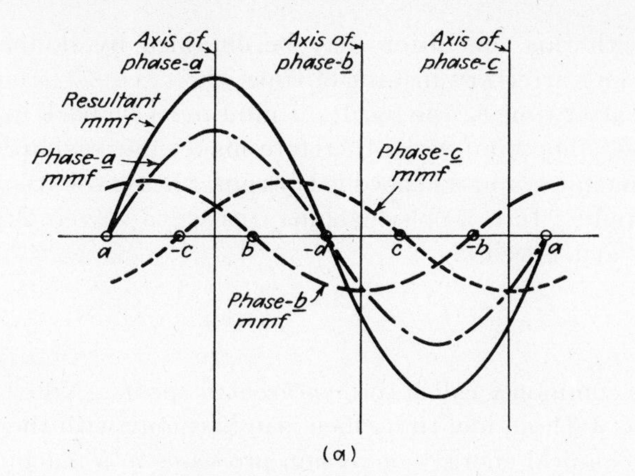

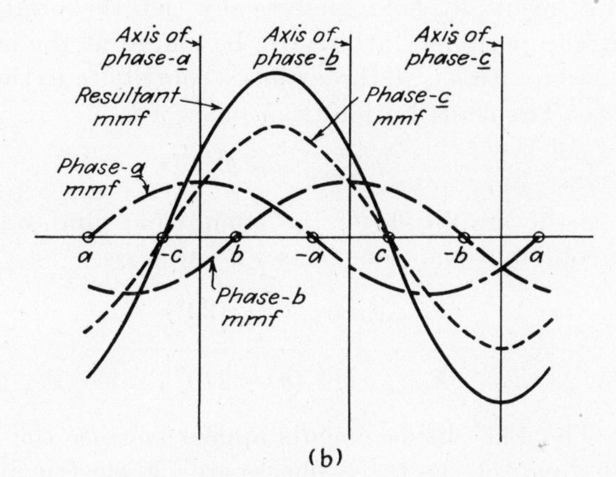

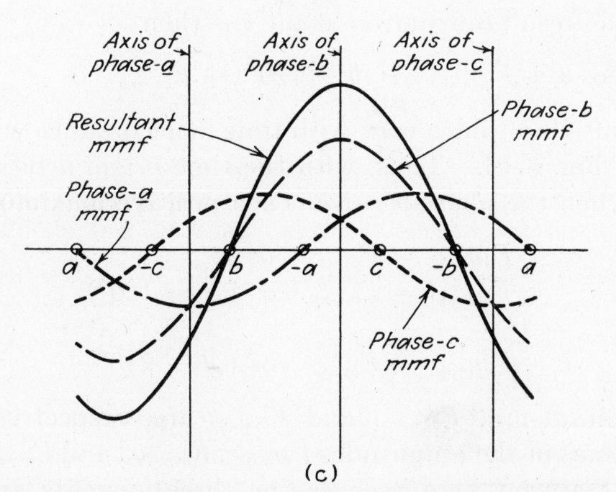

FIG. 3-17. Component and resultant mmf distributions caused by currents of Fig. 3-16 in 3-phase armature winding. Diagram (*a*) is for time t_1, Fig. 3-16; (*b*) for time t_2; (*c*) for time t_3.

consistent with this conclusion may be obtained by sketching the distribution at any arbitrary instant of time.

One cycle after time t_1, the resultant mmf must be back in the position of Fig. 3-17*a*. The mmf wave therefore makes one revolution per cycle in a 2-pole machine, and its speed is $60f$ rpm, f being the frequency of the winding current. In a p-pole machine, the wave travels $2/p$ revolution per cycle, or at a speed of

$$n = \frac{120f}{p} \qquad \text{rpm} \tag{3-39}$$

This speed is commonly called the *synchronous speed*. Note that Eq. 3-39 is the same as 3-34, an identity which is in harmony with the reversibility of electromechanical energy-conversion processes in a machine.

To study the resultant field analytically, let the origin for angle θ around the air-gap periphery arbitrarily be placed at the axis of phase a (Fig. 3-17). At any time t, all three phases contribute to the air-gap mmf at any point θ. The contribution from phase a is

$$F_{a(\text{peak})} \cos \theta$$

where $F_{a(\text{peak})}$ is the amplitude of the component-mmf wave at time t. Similarly, the contributions from phases b and c are

$$F_{b(\text{peak})} \cos (\theta - 120°)$$

and

$$F_{c(\text{peak})} \cos (\theta - 240°)$$

respectively. The 120° displacements appear because the machine is so wound that the axes of the three phases are 120 electrical degrees apart in space. The resultant mmf at point θ is then

$$F_\theta = F_{a(\text{peak})} \cos \theta + F_{b(\text{peak})} \cos (\theta - 120°) + F_{c(\text{peak})} \cos (\theta - 240°) \tag{3-40}$$

But the mmf amplitudes vary with time in accordance with the current variations of Fig. 3-16. Thus, with the time origin arbitrarily taken at the instant when the phase-a current is a positive maximum,

$$F_{a(\text{peak})} = F_{a(\text{max})} \cos \omega t \tag{3-41}$$
$$F_{b(\text{peak})} = F_{b(\text{max})} \cos (\omega t - 120°) \tag{3-42}$$

and

$$F_{c(\text{peak})} = F_{c(\text{max})} \cos (\omega t - 240°) \tag{3-43}$$

The quantities $F_{a(\text{max})}$, $F_{b(\text{max})}$, and $F_{c(\text{max})}$ are, respectively, the time-maximum values of the amplitudes $F_{a(\text{peak})}$, $F_{b(\text{peak})}$, and $F_{c(\text{peak})}$. The 120° displacements appear here because the three currents are 120° phase-displaced in time. Since the currents in the three phases are balanced and therefore of equal amplitude, the three amplitudes $F_{a(\text{max})}$, $F_{b(\text{max})}$, and

$F_{c(\max)}$ are also equal and the symbol $F_{\max}$ may be used for all three. Equation 3-40 accordingly becomes

$$F_\theta = F_{\max} \cos \theta \cos \omega t + F_{\max} \cos (\theta - 120°) \cos (\omega t - 120°) + F_{\max} \cos (\theta - 240°) \cos (\omega t - 240°) \quad (3\text{-}44)$$

Each of the three components on the right-hand side of Eq. 3-44 is a pulsating standing wave like that described by Fig. 3-15. In each term the trigonometric function of θ defines the space distribution as a stationary sinusoid, and the trigonometric function of t indicates that the amplitudes pulsate with time. The first of the three terms expresses the phase-a component shown in Fig. 3-17; the second and third terms express, respectively, the phase-b and -c components also shown in Fig. 3-17.

By use of the trigonometric transformation

$$\cos \alpha \cos \beta = \tfrac{1}{2} \cos (\alpha - \beta) + \tfrac{1}{2} \cos (\alpha + \beta) \quad (3\text{-}45)$$

each of the components in Eq. 3-44 can be expressed as cosine functions of sum and difference angles. Thus,

$$\begin{aligned} F_\theta = {} & \tfrac{1}{2}F_{\max} \cos (\theta - \omega t) + \tfrac{1}{2}F_{\max} \cos (\theta + \omega t) \\ & + \tfrac{1}{2}F_{\max} \cos (\theta - \omega t) + \tfrac{1}{2}F_{\max} \cos (\theta + \omega t - 240°) \\ & + \tfrac{1}{2}F_{\max} \cos (\theta - \omega t) + \tfrac{1}{2}F_{\max} \cos (\theta + \omega t - 480°) \end{aligned} \quad (3\text{-}46)$$

Now the three cosine terms involving the angles $\theta + \omega t$, $\theta + \omega t - 240°$, and $\theta + \omega t - 480°$ are three equal sinusoids displaced in phase by 120°. (Note that a lag angle of 480° is equivalent to a lag angle of $480 - 360 = 120$ deg.) Their sum is therefore zero, and Eq. 3-46 reduces to

$$F_\theta = \tfrac{3}{2}F_{\max} \cos (\theta - \omega t) \quad (3\text{-}47)$$

which is the desired expression for the resultant-mmf wave.

The wave described by Eq. 3-47 is a sinusoidal function of the space angle θ. It has a constant amplitude and a space-phase angle ωt which is a linear function of time. The angle ωt provides rotation of the entire wave around the air gap at the constant angular velocity ω. Thus, at a fixed time t_x, the wave is a sinusoid in space with its positive peak displaced ωt_x electrical radians from the fixed point on the winding which is the origin for θ; at a later instant t_y, the positive peak of the same wave is displaced ωt_y from the origin, and the wave has moved $\omega(t_y - t_x)$ around the gap. At $t = 0$, the current in phase a is a maximum, and the positive peak of the resultant-mmf wave is located at the axis of phase a as shown in Fig. 3-17a; one-third of a cycle later, the current in phase b is a maximum, and the positive peak is located at the axis of phase b as shown in Fig. 3-17c; and so on. The result is therefore entirely consistent with that pictured in Fig. 3-17. The angular velocity of the wave is $\omega = 2\pi f$ electrical radians per second. Since πp electrical radians corresponds to one revolution in a p-pole machine, the rotational speed of the wave is $2f/p$ rev/sec, or $120f/p$ rpm, a result which is the same as Eq. 3-39.

In general, it may be shown that a rotating field of constant amplitude will be produced by a q-phase winding excited by balanced q-phase currents when the respective phases are wound $2\pi/q$ electrical radians apart in space. The constant amplitude will equal $q/2$ times the maximum contribution of any one phase, and the speed of the wave is given by Eq. 3-39.

Under the idealizing assumptions established at the beginning of Art. 3-2, the mmf waves may readily be translated into their corresponding flux-density waves. The relation between flux density and mmf is established by the air gap alone and is

$$B = \frac{\mu_0 F}{g} \tag{3-48}$$

g being the gap length and μ_0 the permeability, $4\pi \times 10^{-7}$ in the rationalized mks system, of the free space constituting the gap.

Under these circumstances, the symbol F may be replaced by the symbol B for flux density in all the equations of this article. Moreover, the waves of Fig. 3-17 may be given the alternative designation *flux distribution*. A polyphase winding excited by balanced polyphase currents is thus seen to produce the same general effect as spinning a permanent magnet about an axis perpendicular to the magnet, or as the rotation of d-c-excited field poles.

3-7. Polyphase Induction Machines. For a first qualitative application of the torque, voltage, and mmf principles which have been developed, the polyphase induction machine will be chosen. As indicated in Art. 3-4, the induction motor is one in which alternating current is supplied to the stator directly and to the rotor by induction or transformer action from the stator. The stator winding is of the type discussed in the preceding article. When excited from a polyphase source, it will produce a component field in the air gap rotating at synchronous speed as given by Eq. 3-39. This speed will be designated as n_1, the speed of the stator field with respect to the stator, in the following discussion. Consider the rotor winding to be of the same type, wound for the same number of poles, but with the terminals short-circuited.

a. Motor Starting Conditions. First the rotor will be assumed at standstill and magnetic-field conditions examined to determine whether a starting torque is produced. With the rotor stationary, the relative speed of stator field and rotor conductors is n_1. A rotor voltage is therefore induced whose frequency, determined by Eq. 3-34, is equal to the stator or line frequency. The voltage magnitude is determined by Eq. 3-36, and the accompanying rotor currents are determined by the voltage magnitude and the rotor impedance. Since the rotor is wound for the same number of poles as the stator, the component fields produced by these rotor currents will also revolve at the speed n_1 with respect to the stationary rotor. Rotor and stator component fields are therefore stationary with respect to each other in space, and a starting torque is produced. The magnitude of the torque is determined by the torque equation, 3-22; the value of the torque angle δ depends on the rotor-circuit constants, a dependence discussed in Art. 3-7*c* below. If this magnitude is sufficient to overcome the opposition to rotation created by the shaft load, the motor will come up to its operating speed. The operating speed can never equal the synchronous speed of the stator field, however, for the rotor conductors would then be stationary with respect to this field, and no voltage would be induced in them.

Those who are familiar with transformer theory will recognize that, with the rotor stationary, as at the instant of starting, the motor is the equivalent of a short-circuited polyphase transformer with an air gap in the magnetic circuit. The rotor current causes a compensating current in the stator winding, an effect the same as that of the secondary current in a transformer. The resultant of the stator and rotor component fields in the air gap induces a stator voltage in accordance with Eq. 3-36. This induced stator voltage is a counter emf and differs from the stator terminal voltage by the drop in the *stator leakage impedance*. Moreover, the impedance limiting the magnitude of the rotor current is the *rotor leakage impedance* when the rotor voltage is taken as that induced by the resultant air-gap flux. It will therefore not be surprising to find the equivalent circuit of an induction motor at starting to be identical with that of a short-circuited transformer; impedances may be reflected from one side to the other by using the square of the effective turns ratio just as in the transformer.

b. Motor Running Conditions. To determine how rotation is sustained, consider the rotor to be turning at the steady mechanical speed n rpm in the forward direction (*i.e.*, in the same direction as the rotating stator field). The rotor is then traveling at a speed $n_1 - n$ rpm in the backward direction with respect to the rotating stator field, or the *slip* of the rotor is $n_1 - n$ rpm. Slip is more usually expressed as a fraction of synchronous speed; *i.e.*,

$$s = \frac{n_1 - n}{n_1} \tag{3-49}$$

or

$$n = n_1(1 - s) \tag{3-50}$$

In accordance with Eq. 3-34, this relative motion of magnetic field and rotor winding causes voltages of frequency equal to sf, called *slip frequency*, to be induced in the rotor. The accompanying rotor currents are determined by the magnitudes of the voltages and the rotor impedance at slip frequency. Since the frequency of these currents is now only the fraction s of what it was with the rotor stationary, the component rotor field set up by them will travel *with respect to the rotor structure* at only the fraction s of its former speed; in other words, it will travel at $n_2 = sn_1$ rpm in the forward direction with respect to the rotor. But superimposed on this rotation is the mechanical rotation of the rotor at n rpm. The speed of the rotor field in space is the sum of these two speeds and equals

$$sn_1 + n, \text{ or } sn_1 + n_1(1 - s), \text{ or } n_1$$

The stator and rotor fields are therefore stationary with respect to each other, torque is produced in accordance with Eq. 3-22, and rotation is maintained. Such a torque, which exists at any mechanical speed n other than synchronous speed, is called an *asynchronous torque*.

Example 3-1. The stator of a 3-phase 6-pole 60-cps induction motor is connected to the 3-phase 60-cps mains. For each of the following conditions, (1) at the instant of starting, (2) when the rotor mechanical speed is one-third synchronous speed, and (3) when the rotor is operating at a slip of 3 per cent, give the rotor frequency and the following speeds in rpm:

a. Speed of stator field with respect to stator
b. Speed of stator field with respect to rotor
c. Speed of rotor field with respect to rotor
d. Speed of rotor field with respect to stator
e. Speed of rotor field with respect to stator field

Solution. The results, summarized in the following table, follow from straightforward application of Eqs. 3-34, 3-39, 3-49, and 3-50, together with the principles just discussed:

Condition	Rotor frequency, cps	Speed *a*	Speed *b*	Speed *c*	Speed *d*	Speed *e*
1	60	1,200	1,200	1,200	1,200	0
2	40	1,200	800	800	1,200	0
3	1.8	1,200	36	36	1,200	0

The direct transformer equivalence of the induction motor with stationary rotor is seen to be altered in one important respect when the rotor revolves: frequency conversion or frequency transformation is added. A given frequency f on the stator is converted to the frequency sf on the rotor, and conversely. These facts are often used to change system frequencies in electric power systems. To an observer on the rotor, the phenomena appear different in nature from those at starting only in that the rotating field in the air gap is sweeping by him at a slower rate, corresponding to the reduced frequency sf. The impedance limiting the magnitude of rotor current is still the rotor leakage impedance, but it is now the value at slip frequency. To an observer on the stator, the phenomena do not appear at all different in nature from those at starting. This observer's evidence of the presence of the rotor is a rotor component field traveling at synchronous speed, just as it was at starting. The rotor current therefore continues to cause a compensating current at stator frequency in the stator winding. The resultant air-gap field continues to induce a stator voltage in accordance with Eq. 3-36. This induced stator

FIG. 3-18. Wound rotor for 3-phase induction motor. (*Courtesy of General Electric Company.*)

voltage is still a counter emf differing from the stator terminal voltage by the drop in the stator leakage impedance. It will therefore not be surprising to find the equivalent circuit of an induction motor under running conditions closely resembling that of a transformer; the effect of rotation must be included in reflecting impedances from one side to the other, however.

c. Reactions of the Rotor; Squirrel-cage Rotors. Motors having a rotor winding similar to that on the stator (or so-called *phase-wound* or *coil-wound rotor*) are referred to as *wound-rotor motors.* On a wound rotor, the terminal of each rotor phase is connected to a *slip ring* or *collector ring* on the shaft. Carbon brushes bearing on these rings make the rotor terminals available at points external to the motor so that additional resistance may be inserted in the rotor circuit if desired. When no external resistance is desired, the brushes are simply short-circuited. A typical wound rotor is shown in Fig. 3-18.

A second and widely used construction is the *squirrel-cage rotor* with a winding consisting of conducting bars embedded in slots in the rotor iron and short-circuited at each end by conducting *end rings.* A diagrammatic sketch of such a winding is given in Fig. 3-19; most practical squirrel-cage rotors have more bars than shown here, and the bars frequently are skewed somewhat. A cutaway view of a squirrel-cage rotor is given in Fig. 3-20. In the larger squirrel-cage motors, the rotor bars are circular or rectangular copper conductors, usually bare, welded or brazed to copper end rings. In the smaller motors, the bars and end rings are often aluminum cast directly in the slots in one piece. The extreme simplicity and ruggedness of the squirrel-cage construction are outstanding advantages of the induction motor.

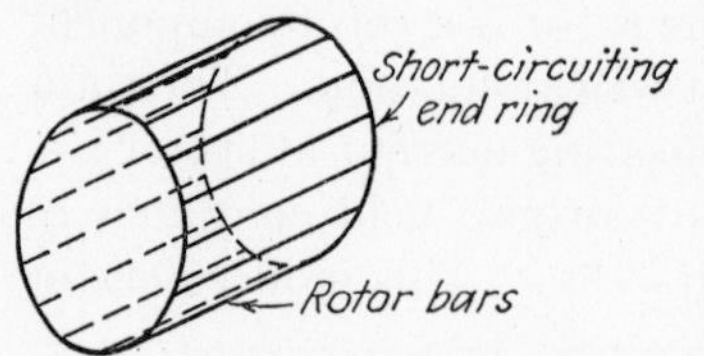

FIG. 3-19. Diagrammatic sketch of squirrel-cage rotor.

A squirrel-cage rotor may be used with any induction-motor stator which it will fit mechanically (a statement which neglects possible harmful effects of harmonics in the mmf and flux waves), for the number of rotor poles is always equal to the number of poles in the inducing field and hence equal to the number on the stator. This equality is simply in accordance with Lenz' law, whereby the directions of the instantaneous bar currents are such as to oppose the changing flux linkages causing them. For these linkages to be opposed, the rotor-mmf wave must have the same number of poles as the stator component flux wave.

The space-phase displacement δ between this rotor-mmf wave and the air-gap flux-density wave has an important bearing on motor performance

FIG. 3-20. Squirrel-cage rotor (one-third cut away) with cast-aluminum cage winding and integrally cast fans for 3-phase induction motor. Cross section of rotor conductor may be seen in upper part of rotor. (*Courtesy of General Electric Company.*)

because it enters the torque equation, 3-22. Factors influencing δ may be determined by study of a simplified coil-wound rotor winding like that on the stator in Figs. 1-26 and 3-17, or the equivalent cage winding of Fig. 3-21. A development of such an idealized winding is given in Fig. 3-22. The flux-density wave is moving to the right at slip speed with respect to the winding and, in Fig. 3-22*a*, is shown in the position for maximum instantaneous voltage in phase *a*. If rotor leakage reactance is very small compared with rotor resistance (which is very nearly the case at the small slips corresponding to normal operation), the phase-a current will also be a maximum. As shown in Art. 3-6 and Fig. 3-17a, the rotor-mmf wave will then be centered on phase a. It is so shown in Fig. 3-22a. The displacement angle or torque angle δ under these conditions is at its optimum value of 90° ($\sin \delta = 1$ in Eq. 3-22).

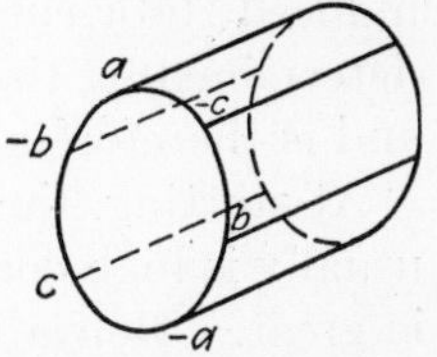

FIG. 3-21. Equivalent cage winding for induction motor.

If the rotor leakage reactance is appreciable, however, the phase-a current lags the induced voltage by the power-factor angle θ_2 of the leakage impedance. The phase-a current will not be a maximum until a correspondingly later time. The rotor-mmf wave will then not be centered on phase a until the flux wave has traveled θ_2 degrees farther down the gap, as shown in Fig. 3-22b. The angle δ is now $90° + \theta_2$. In general, therefore, the torque angle of an induction motor is

$$\delta = 90° + \theta_2 \tag{3-51}$$

It departs from the optimum value by the power-factor angle of the rotor leakage impedance at slip frequency. If desired, the term $\sin \delta$ in Eq. 3-22 may be replaced by $\cos \theta_2$ for an induction motor. The electromagnetic rotor torque is directed toward the right in Fig. 3-22, or in the direction of the rotating flux wave.

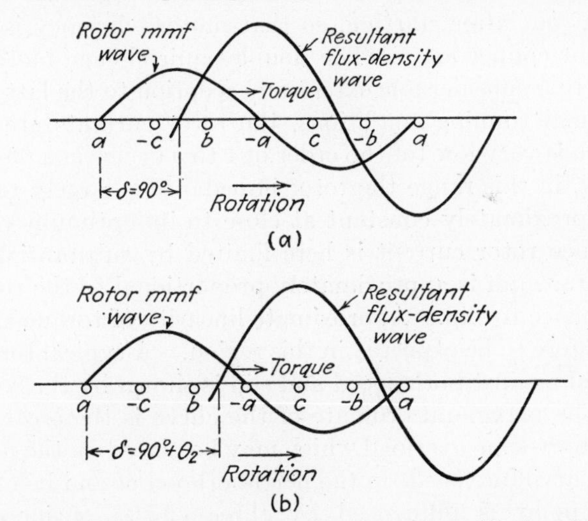

FIG. 3-22. Developed rotor winding of induction motor with flux-density and mmf waves in their relative positions for (a) zero and (b) nonzero rotor leakage reactance.

d. Motor Performance. Three of the important operating characteristics of any motor are the starting torque, the maximum possible torque which may be obtained, and the torque-speed curve showing the behavior of the motor under changing load. The general nature of these characteristics may be deduced from the torque equation, 3-22, with the equivalence of the term sin δ and rotor power factor borne in mind. Recall that the amplitude F_{max} of the rotor-mmf wave is determined by the induced rotor current. Recognize also that the air-gap flux Φ is largely determined by the impressed stator voltage, in accordance with Eq. 3-36, and is therefore approximately constant.

At starting, the rotor currents are at stator frequency, rotor reactance usually is high compared with resistance, and the departure of δ from 90° is great. Hence the starting torque per unit of current usually is relatively low. One of the purposes of the wound-rotor motor is to enable the insertion of external resistance in the rotor circuit at starting, thereby improving rotor power factor, bringing δ nearer its optimum value, and increasing the starting torque per unit of current. Starting torque will not increase indefinitely with rotor resistance, however, for beyond a certain point increased rotor impedance and hence lower rotor field strength will more than overcome the effect of improved power factor. Similar results may be achieved with a cage rotor by increasing the bar or end-ring resistances, a step having the disadvantage that the resistance cannot be cut out after starting, so that motor efficiency is lowered by increased rotor copper loss. (The double-squirrel-cage motor described in Chap. 9 is to a considerable extent an exception to the last statement.)

Under normal running conditions, the rotor currents are at slip frequency, which is very low (of the order of 1 to 5 cycles in a 60-cps motor). Consequently, in this range the rotor impedance is largely resistive, and δ remains approximately constant at close to its optimum value of 90°. Moreover, since rotor current is here limited by substantially only the resistance, rotor mmf is approximately proportional to the rotor induced voltage and hence to slip. Approximate linearity of torque as a function of slip is therefore to be expected in this region. A typical torque characteristic plotted against both speed and slip is shown by the solid curve in Fig. 3-23. The maximum ordinate of the curve is the *breakdown torque* limiting the short-time overload which may be placed on the motor. The shape of the curve for speeds in the neighborhood of and below the maximum-torque point is influenced by three effects of increasing slip: increased rotor voltage and thus a tendency to increase rotor current and mmf; increased rotor impedance and thus a tendency to decrease rotor current and mmf; and decreased rotor power factor and hence decreased torque angle. Mathematical investigation is necessary to assess the various factors.

The squirrel-cage motor is substantially a constant-speed motor having about 5 per cent drop in speed from no load to full load. Speed variation may be obtained by using a wound-rotor motor and inserting external resistance in the rotor circuit. In the normal operating range, the external resistance simply increases the rotor impedance, necessitating a higher slip for a desired rotor mmf and torque. The influence of increased rotor resistance on the torque-speed characteristic is shown by the dotted curves in Fig. 3-23. Variation of starting torque with rotor resistance may be seen from these curves by noting the variation of the zero-speed ordinates.

e. Generator Action. A specific example of the reversibility of electromechanical energy conversion, as well as of the basic similarity of phenomena in generators and motors, is offered by the polyphase induction

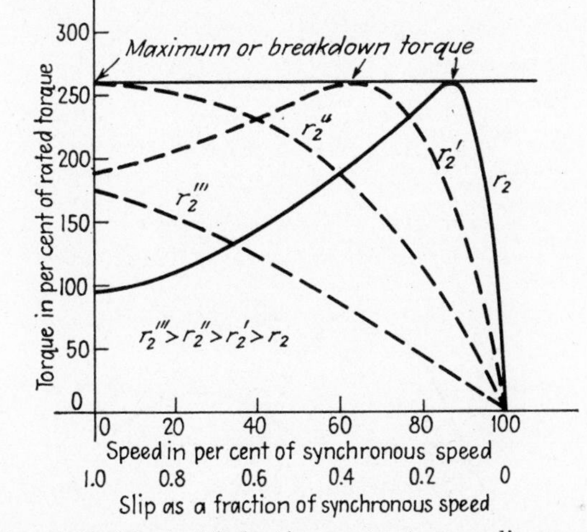

Fig. 3-23. Typical induction motor torque-slip curves.

machine. When operating below synchronous speed, it can act only as a motor; when driven above synchronous speed, however, it is capable of acting as a generator.

Induction-generator action may be examined by means of Fig. 3-24, which is the counterpart of Fig. 3-22. Relative directions of motion are indicated by the arrows inserted between parts *a* and *b* of Fig. 3-24; numerical values of speed are shown for the particular case of a 6-pole 60-cps machine whose rotor is driven mechanically at 1,300 rpm. In Fig. 3-24*a*, as in Fig. 3-22*a*, the flux-density wave is shown in the position for maximum instantaneous voltage in phase *a*, but the induced rotor voltage directions in the two cases are opposite because of the oppositely directed relative motions of flux and rotor conductors. With negligible rotor reactance, the phase-*a* current is also a maximum, and the rotor-mmf wave is centered on phase *a*. In the generator, the rotor-mmf wave is of polarity opposite to that in the motor because of the opposite induced voltage and hence current directions. The torque angle δ is therefore $-90°$. The electromagnetic rotor torque is directed toward the left in Fig. 3-24.

When rotor leakage reactance is appreciable, the rotor-mmf wave will not be centered on phase a until the flux wave has traveled θ_2 degrees

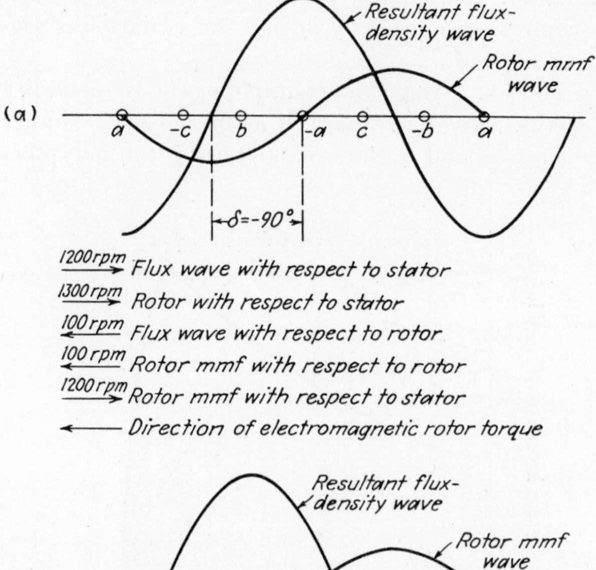

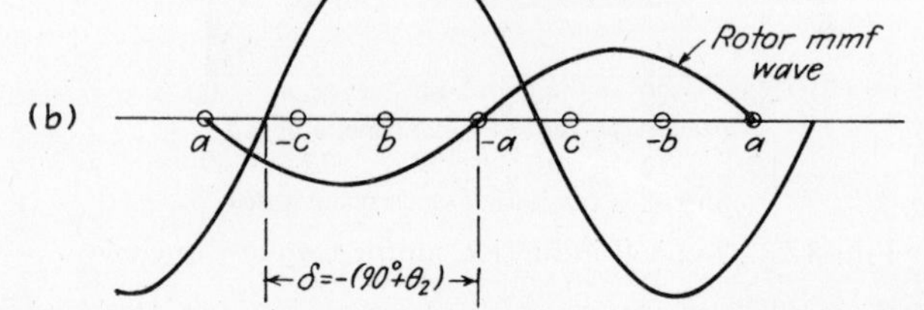

FIG. 3-24. Developed rotor winding of induction generator with flux-density and mmf waves in their relative positions for (a) zero and (b) nonzero rotor leakage reactance.

farther down the gap relative to the rotor. This travel is toward the left in Fig. 3-24*b* instead of the right as in Fig. 3-22*b*. The torque angle is now

$$\delta = -(90° + \theta_2) \tag{3-52}$$

For a generator, then, the electromagnetic torque on the rotor is in the direction opposite to the rotation of the flux wave in space. It is a steady torque because rotor and stator fields are stationary relative to each other. In order to keep the rotor revolving in the same direction as the flux wave, an opposite mechanical torque must be applied. The nature of the torque-slip characteristic in the generator region is illustrated by Fig. 3-25, in which the same general influences determine the shape of the curve as in the motor case. If the machine were connected to an a-c system capable of either absorbing or supplying power, it would supply power to that system when it was driven above synchronous speed. If the mechanical torque were removed, it would slow down under the influence of the counter electromagnetic torque until the situation of Fig. 3-24 became that of Fig. 3-22—*i.e.*, until the direction of the electromagnetic torque reversed. Steady operation as a motor would then follow, with the electromagnetic torque just sufficient to overcome the losses associated with rotation.

Examination of induction-generator action is of value for the theoretical insight it gives to motor and generator operation. It is of little practical importance, however, for induction generators are rarely used

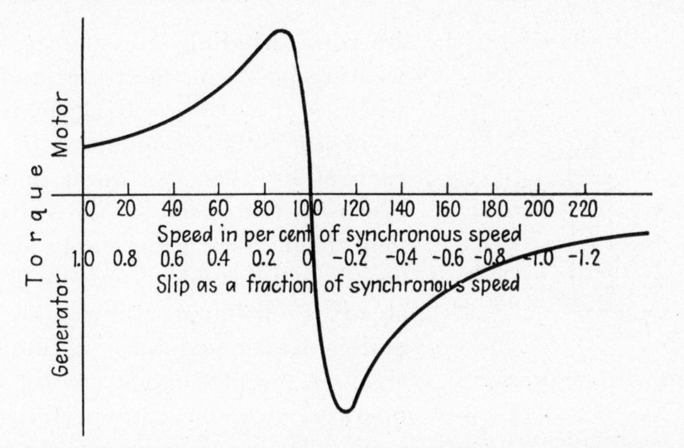

Fig. 3-25. Induction-machine torque-slip curve in both motor and generator region.

for primary electromechanical energy conversion. When they are so used, other types of a-c generators are required to operate in parallel, both to establish the frequency and to supply the excitation needed to set up the flux in the induction generators. In general, the over-all economics of mechanical-to-electrical energy conversion are such that the induction generator is in a poor competitive position compared to the synchronous generator.

Example 3-2. A 6-pole 3-phase wound-rotor induction machine is driven by another machine on its shaft at 900 rpm. The rotor is connected to a 3-phase 60-cps system. Describe the magnetic field within the induction machine and the nature of the voltage, if any, produced at the stator terminals.

Solution. The rotor winding will produce a field, assumed sinusoidally distributed in space, which, in accordance with Eq. 3-39, will rotate at a speed of 1,200 rpm with respect to the rotor. If the mechanical rotation of the rotor is in the same direction, this field will rotate with a speed of 1,200 + 900, or 2,100 rpm with respect to the stator. From Eq. 3-34, a sinusoidal voltage at 105 cps will be induced in the stator.

If the mechanical rotation of the rotor is in the opposite direction, the field will rotate with a speed of 1,200 − 900, or 300, rpm with respect to the stator. From Eq. 3-34, a sinusoidal voltage at 15 cps will be induced in the stator.

This example illustrates the general principle of the *induction frequency converter*.

3-8. Polyphase Synchronous Machines. As indicated in Art. 3-4, the synchronous motor is one in which alternating current is supplied to one winding, the armature winding, and direct current to the other winding, the field winding; the synchronous generator is, of course, similar, with alternating current obtained from the armature winding. Direct-current excitation for the field is frequently supplied from a small d-c generator, called an *exciter*, which is often mounted on the same shaft as the synchronous machine. The armature or stator winding is of the type discussed in Art. 3-6. When carrying polyphase currents, it will produce a component field in the air gap rotating at synchronous speed as given by Eq. 3-39.

The field produced by the d-c rotor winding is evidently stationary with respect to the rotor and revolves with it. For the rotating fields of stator and rotor to be stationary with respect to each other, then, the rotor must turn at precisely the speed of the stator component field—*i.e.*, at precisely synchronous speed. Only under this condition can a steady, continuous torque be produced and synchronous-motor action be effective. A synchronous motor therefore operates at a constant speed regardless of load. An electromagnetic torque of this nature, having a steady value at only one speed, is called a *synchronous torque*.

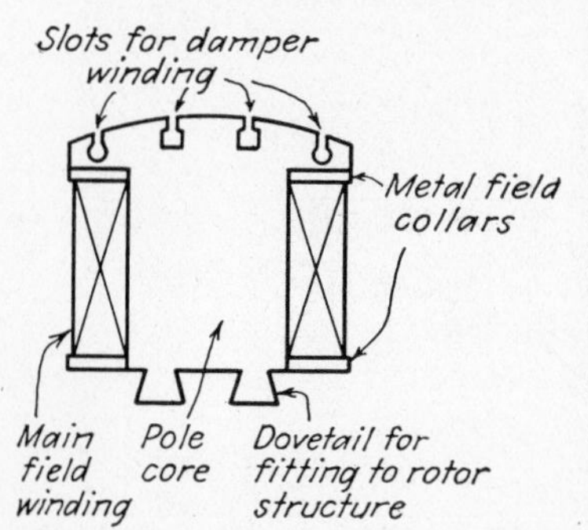

FIG. 3-26. Diagrammatic cross section of salient pole of synchronous motor.

With the rotor stationary, as in a synchronous motor at starting, the rotating stator field is traveling at synchronous speed with respect to the rotor field, and the torque varies sinusoidally with time, reversing during each cycle. Hence a synchronous motor per se has no net starting torque. To make the motor self-starting, a squirrel-cage winding, called an *amortisseur* or *damper winding*, is inserted in the rotor pole faces, as shown diagrammatically in Fig. 3-26 and pictorially in Fig. 3-27. The rotor then comes up almost to synchronous speed by induction-motor action with the field winding unexcited. When the field winding is energized, the rotor and stator fields are still not quite stationary with respect to each other but move at a slow relative speed equal to the slip speed of the induction-motor action—perhaps at about 5 to 10 rpm, for example. The synchronous torque still varies sinusoidally but at only a very low frequency, equal to slip frequency. If the load and inertia are not too great, the positive half cycle of synchronous torque lasts long enough to raise the rotor speed from slip speed to synchronous speed, in other words, to *pull the rotor into synchronism.* Actually, in critical cases, it may require the cumulative effect of several successive positive half cycles to cause synchronous speed to be reached; the motor is then said to have pulled in after *slipping a number of poles.*

Behavior of a synchronous motor under running conditions can readily be visualized in terms of the torque equation, 3-22. Let the mmf be that of the d-c rotor winding, and recognize that in normal operation the direct current in this winding remains constant. Recognize also that the air-gap flux Φ is largely determined by the impressed stator voltage, in accordance with Eq. 3-36, and is therefore sensibly constant. Variation in the torque requirements of the load must consequently be taken care of by variation of the torque angle δ. At no load, the torque is just sufficient to overcome losses associated with rotation, and δ is very small.

FIG. 3-27. Salient rotor pole of synchronous motor showing damper bars and field coil. (*Courtesy of Westinghouse Electric Corporation.*)

With a light shaft load, only a relatively small additional electromagnetic torque is required, and δ is still small. When more shaft load is added, the rotor must drop back in space phase with respect to the rotating flux wave just enough so that δ assumes the value required to supply the necessary torque. The readjustment process is actually a dynamic one accompanied by a temporary decrease in the instantaneous mechanical speed of the rotor and a damped mechanical oscillation of the rotor about its new space-phase position. In a practical machine, some changes in the amplitudes of the resultant-flux-density and mmf waves may also occur because of factors (such as saturation and leakage-impedance drop) neglected in the present argument. The adjustment of the rotor to its new phase position following a load change may be observed experimentally in the laboratory by viewing the machine rotor with stroboscopic light having a flashing frequency which causes the rotor to appear stationary when it is turning at its normal synchronous speed.

When δ becomes 90°, the maximum possible torque or power, called *pull-out torque* or *pull-out power*, for a fixed terminal voltage and field current is reached. If the load requirements exceed this value, the motor slows down under the influence of the excess shaft torque, and synchronous-motor action is lost because rotor and stator fields are no longer stationary with respect to each other. Under these conditions, the motor is usually disconnected from the line by the action of automatic circuit breakers. This phenomenon is known as *pulling out of step* or *losing synchronism.* Pull-out torque limits the short-time overload that may be placed on the motor.

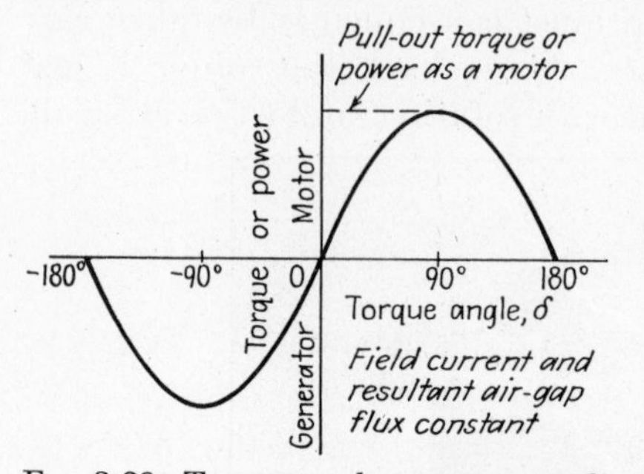

FIG. 3-28. Torque-angle or power-angle curve of synchronous machine.

Variation of synchronous torque with torque angle, as dictated by Eq. 3-22, is shown in the *torque-angle curve* of Fig. 3-28. For an idealized machine operating at constant field current and constant resultant air-gap flux, the variation of torque with torque angle is sinusoidal. Increase of either field current or terminal voltage causes the amplitude of the curve to be increased. Since the operating speed is constant and power and torque are therefore proportional, this curve may alternatively be plotted as a *power-angle curve* with electromagnetic power as ordinates and torque angle as abscissas.

Example 3-3. Suppose that the stator as well as the rotor of a synchronous motor is suspended in bearings so that it can rotate. Let the stator be connected to a 3-phase source and caused to rotate in a backward direction at synchronous speed while the rotor remains stationary. The rotor is excited by direct current.

a. Describe the action as a brake is applied to the stator structure, bringing it to rest.

b. What torque must be exerted by the brake in order to hold the stator at rest?

Solution. a. The stator component field rotates at synchronous speed in the forward direction with respect to the stator structure. On this rotation is superimposed the mechanical rotation of the stator. Before braking, therefore, the stator component field is stationary in space with respect to the rotor component field, so that rotation is maintained by synchronous-motor action.

When the brake is applied, the mechanical speed of the stator decreases. The stator component field, still rotating at synchronous speed with respect to the stator structure, then travels forward in space at a speed equal to the difference between synchronous speed and the mechanical speed of the stator. Synchronous torque causes the rotor structure to travel forward at the same speed in order that rotor and stator component fields shall remain stationary relative to each other. When the stator structure is brought to rest, the rotor is traveling forward at synchronous speed. Thus, full synchronous torque up to the pull-out value is available for starting the load on the rotor shaft.

b. A torque equal to the electromagnetic torque is exerted on both the rotor and stator structures. In the ideal case with friction, windage, and core losses negligible, the brake torque must equal the electromagnetic torque, which in turn must equal the mechanical torque supplied by the shaft to the load.

This example outlines the principles of the so-called *super-synchronous motor* used for some paper- and cement-mill drives where the starting duty is especially severe.

As in the induction motor, the electromagnetic torque in a synchronous motor is exerted in the same direction as the flux wave is rotating. As in the induction generator, the electromagnetic torque on the rotor of a synchronous generator is in the direction opposite to the rotation of the flux wave. It is a steady torque because rotor and stator fields are stationary relative to each other, the generator being driven at synchronous speed by the applied mechanical torque of a prime mover. Because of the reversal of the electromagnetic torque, the angle δ must be of the opposite sign to that in the motor case. The interrelation of generator and motor action and the associated influence on torque angle are illustrated in Fig. 3-28, where generator action is represented by merely extending the motor curve into the negative region. If the synchronous machine were connected to an a-c system capable of either absorbing or supplying power, it would supply power to that system when it was driven so that the rotor mmf was ahead of the flux wave. If the mechanical torque were removed, the rotor would drop back in space phase under the influence of the counter electromagnetic torque until the direction of this electromagnetic torque reversed. Steady operation as a motor would then follow, with the electromagnetic torque just sufficient to overcome rotational losses. The readjustment process would be attended by temporary changes of short duration in instantaneous speed, and usually by small damped oscillations, or *hunting*, about the new equilibrium position.

One of the important characteristics of a generator is the variation of terminal voltage with load. The terminal voltage differs from the generated voltage (Eq. 3-36) by the drop in the winding impedance. To predict the variation in terminal voltage at constant field current, the component flux created by the field winding alone may be used for Φ in Eq. 3-36. Flux Φ and armature induced voltage E then remain constant, and the effect of armature mmf is included by assigning the appropriate reactance to the machine. Typical results for several load power factors are indicated in Fig. 3-29. Voltage variation is affected not only by active-power output but also by power factor or by reactive-power output. The results indicated in Fig. 3-29 are in accord with those which might be predicted from simple a-c circuit theory for transmission of power and reactive power through an inductive circuit element with fixed sending-end voltage. In many practical cases, the generator is equipped with an automatic voltage regulator which alters the field current so that rated terminal voltage is maintained as load changes. The generator-plus-regulator characteristic then becomes that of Fig. 3-30.

The modern 3-phase synchronous generator is the invariable choice for bulk conversion of mechanical to electrical energy. Even though a substantial portion of all electrical energy is utilized as direct current,

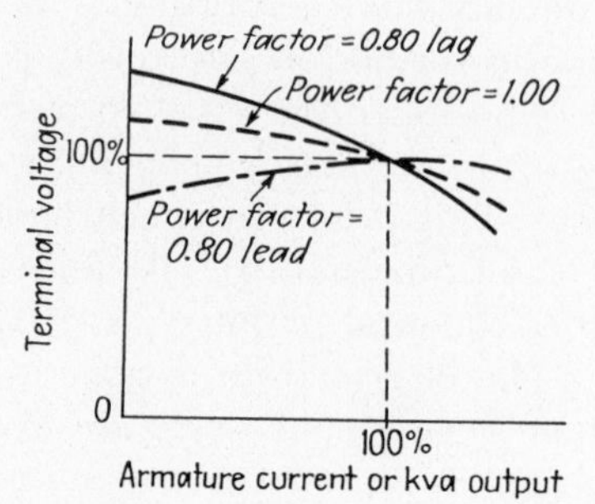

FIG. 3-29. Terminal-voltage variation with load at constant field current for synchronous generator.

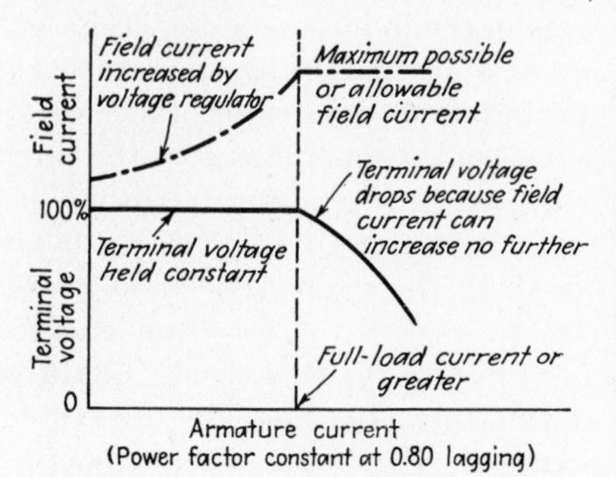

FIG. 3-30. Characteristics of a voltage-regulated synchronous generator.

economy usually dictates that the primary, or first, mechanical-to-electrical conversion, together with transmission to the utilization center, be in terms of alternating current; rectification to direct current, if required, is then performed at or near the consumption point.

3-9. Commutator Action. Before examining the performance of d-c machines, it is necessary to investigate means of rendering the rotor field stationary in space despite rotation of the rotor winding, as indicated in Art. 3-4; it is also necessary to investigate rectification of the a-c waveform in the rotor coils to direct current at the rotor or armature terminals, as indicated in Art. 3-5. Since these two functions are performed through the agency of one device, the commutator, this investigation becomes a study of commutator action.

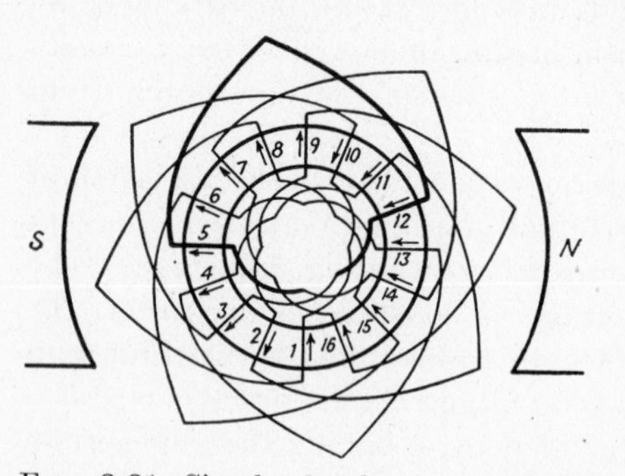

FIG. 3-31. Simple 2-pole d-c machine armature.

a. Effect on Current and Rotor Field. The general nature of the armature winding of a 2-pole d-c machine is shown diagrammatically in Fig. 3-31, a sketch which is more nearly representative of practical windings than is that of Fig. 1-34 for an elementary 1-coil armature. To show the details of the winding and its interconnections more fully, a representation roughly approximating a conical projection is used. The cylindrical armature is distorted into the shape of a truncated cone with the base of the cone away from the reader and the tip of the cone toward him. The numbered radial lines are the *armature inductors,* which, on the actual cylindrical armature, are directed essentially parallel to the shaft of the machine. Arrows next to these radial lines indicate actual or assumed

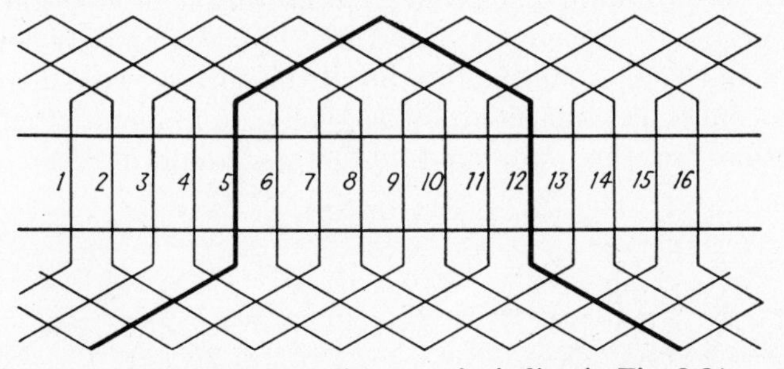

Fig. 3-32. Developed diagram of winding in Fig. 3-31.

current directions in the inductors; arrows radially outward denote current directed away from the reader into the plane of the paper, and arrows radially inward denote current directed out of the plane of the paper. The curved lines interconnecting the inductors are the *back* and *front connections;* the front connections are those near the center of the sketch. Two inductors approximately 180 electrical degrees apart in this winding, with their back connection, form a discrete coil like that shown by the heavy line including inductors 5 and 12. The individual coils are interconnected by means of the front connections to form a winding which closes on itself. The corresponding developed wiring diagram is given in Fig. 3-32. In neither of these two figures are the connections from the winding itself to the external armature circuit shown, for one object of this article is to develop these connections. Otherwise, the two diagrams are typical of d-c armatures except that, for simplicity, fewer than the usual number of inductors are shown.

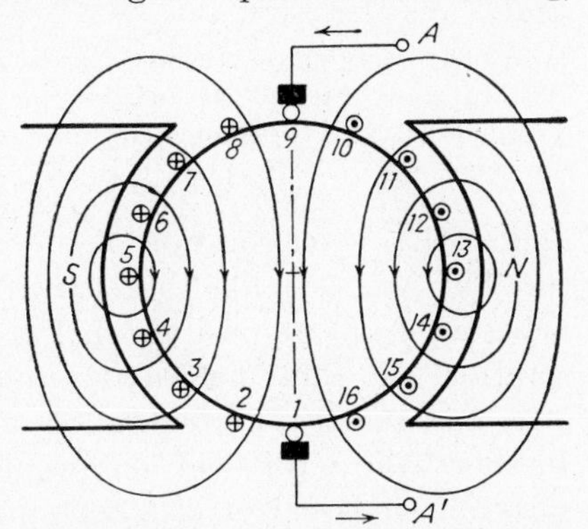

Fig. 3-33. Sectional sketch of winding in Fig. 3-31.

The nature of the problem encountered in rendering the rotor field stationary despite rotation of the rotor may be appreciated with the aid of Fig. 3-33. The winding in this sketch is the same as that in the conical projection of Fig. 3-31, and the assumed current directions are the same.

Direct current is introduced into the winding by way of terminals A and A', and assumed current directions at one instant of time are indicated for the inductors forming the coil sides. At this instant, the armature flux lines are as sketched in Fig. 3-33, and the armature winding is the equivalent of a single coil whose axis is vertical. The axis of the magnetic field produced by it is therefore displaced from that of the stator field by 90°, the optimum displacement angle for the production of electromagnetic torque. If terminals A and A' were permanently connected to inductors 9 and 1 (as would be the case if the current were introduced by way of two slip rings connected, respectively, to inductors 9 and 1), current directions in the numbered inductors would forever remain as

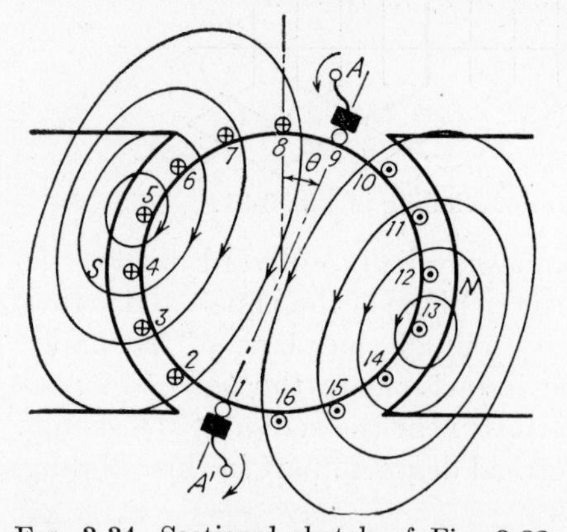

Fig. 3-34. Sectional sketch of Fig. 3-33 after rotation through the angle θ with terminals A and A' connected through slip rings.

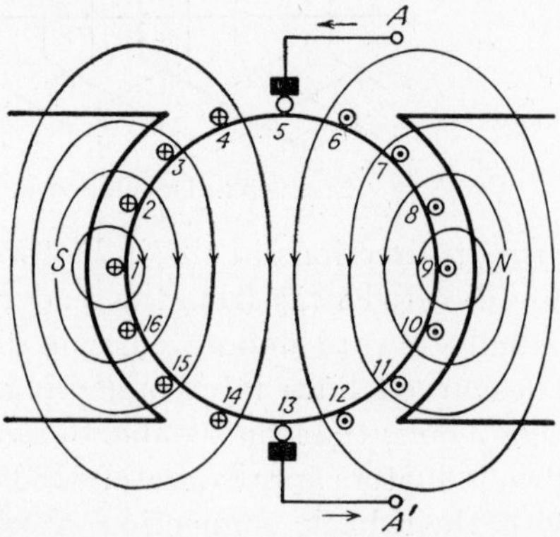

Fig. 3-35. Sectional sketch of Fig. 3-33 after rotation through 90° with terminals A and A' connected through a commutator.

indicated. After rotation of the armature through θ degrees, the armature flux would be like that shown in Fig. 3-34, with its axis displaced by θ degrees from its position in Fig. 3-33. After one-eighth revolution of rotation, the rotor field axis would be 45° from that of the stator, and after one-quarter of a revolution it would coincide with that of the stator. In short, the rotor field axis would rotate with the rotor. The desired situation one-quarter of a revolution (clockwise) later is that shown in Fig. 3-35. Here the axis of the rotor field occupies the same space position as in Fig. 3-33. Study of the two sketches leads to the conclusion that, in general, the current direction in a coil must be reversed as it passes through the center of the interpolar space, or *neutral plane*. In other words, terminals A and A' should not be connected to fixed points on the armature winding but should be connected successively to those two points which are passing through the neutral plane—to 9 and 1 in Fig. 3-33, to 8 and 16 a little later, to 7 and 15 still later, to 6 and 14 next, and to 5 and 13 in Fig. 3-35. This switching problem is solved by means of the commutator, a cylinder formed of copper segments insulated from each other by mica and mounted on, but insulated from, the rotor shaft. One commutator segment is used for each rotor coil. A partly assembled commutator is shown in Fig. 3-36. Stationary carbon brushes held against the commutator surface connect the winding to the terminals A and A'. These terminals are thereby connected at any instant to

FIG. 3-36. Assembling commutator bars and insulation on vee ring during construction of a commutator for 1,200-kw 525-volt 750-rpm shunt-wound d-c generator. (*Courtesy of Allis-Chalmers Manufacturing Company.*)

inductors occupying a particular position in space, rather than being permanently tied to a specific set of inductors.

For further examination of commutator action, Fig. 3-37 gives a detailed wiring diagram of the armature in Fig. 3-33; this winding is also the one of Fig. 3-31, but the commutator segments and brushes have now been added. To show the details of the winding and commutator connections more fully, a representation approximating a conical projection is used once more. The circular segments near the center are the commutator segments. The two shaded blocks bearing on two of the commutator segments are the carbon brushes, which are stationary. The brushes actually bear on the outer surface of the commutator, although they are here shown on the inner surface to avoid confusing the drawing. The electrical position of these brushes is shown by the shaded rectangles in Fig. 3-33.

There are two possible paths through the armature for current entering at brush A, one through inductors 2, 11, 4, 13, 6, 15, 8, and 1, and the other through inductors 9, 16, 7, 14, 5, 12, 3, and 10. The resulting current directions shown in Fig. 3-37 are then in agreement with those in Fig. 3-33. The resulting electromagnetic torque causes clockwise rotation. One-quarter of a revolution later, as shown in Fig. 3-38, the two paths between brushes are inductors 14, 7, 16, 9, 2, 11, 4, and 13 and inductors 5, 12, 3, 10, 1, 8, 15, and 6. Current directions are in agreement with the desired directions in Fig. 3-35, and the rotor field is still displaced

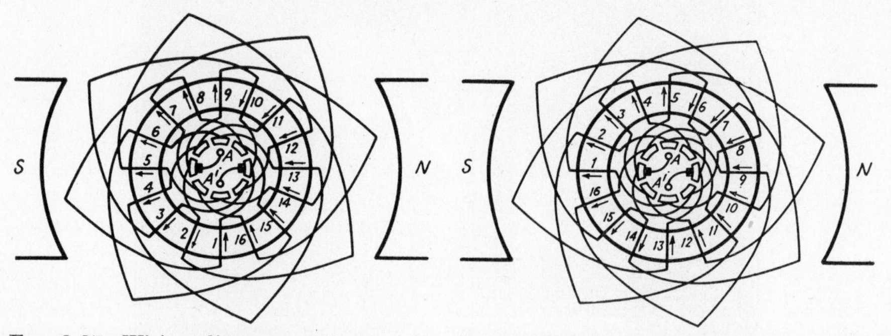

FIG. 3-37. Wiring diagram of 2-pole armature in Fig. 3-31 with commutator segments and brushes added.

FIG. 3-38. The winding of Fig. 3-37 after rotation through 90°.

90° from the stator field. The same conclusion may be reached by redrawing the figures at any arbitrary later instant.

If the brush axis were shifted 22.5° clockwise in Fig. 3-33, so that their electrical position corresponded to inductors 10 and 2, the axis of the rotor field would be similarly shifted. It would then depart from the optimum value of 90° by 22.5°, but it would remain stationary in the new position. In a practical winding with many more inductors and commutator segments, the shift in rotor field axis corresponds to the shift of the brush axis in electrical degrees. The 90° position shown in Figs. 3-37 and 3-38 is the normal position, however. For d-c machines, then, it may be concluded that *regardless of rotation of the rotor, the commutator will fix the rotor field axis along a stationary line in space determined by the brush axis.* Crudely stated, the commutator takes out the effect of armature rotation as far as the armature field is concerned.

b. Effect on Voltage. Rectification of the alternating waveform of voltage induced in the armature coils may also be seen from the foregoing figures. If the armature of Fig. 3-38 is considered as that of a generator given counterclockwise rotation by a prime mover, the arrows indicate the directions of voltage rise or of current when the generator is loaded. The voltage between brushes is the sum of the individual inductor voltages in either of the two parallel paths through the winding, as indicated schematically in Fig. 3-39*a*, less the resistance drop. The inductors in any one path all contribute voltages in the same direction. Conditions one-quarter of a revolution later, as shown in Fig. 3-37 and indicated schematically in Fig. 3-39*b*, are the same, inductors being regrouped in the parallel paths as they pass from under one stator pole to the other.

It is oversimplification to regard the commutator as having one function, rectification, in a generator, and another function, rendering the rotor field stationary, in a motor. Because generator and motor action go hand in hand in the armature winding, the commutator must perform both functions in each machine. The counter torque in a generator is then a steady, unidirectional torque, and the counter emf in a motor is a direct voltage. Moreover, the two functions are really one, for the switching of inductors required for a stationary rotor field is inherently the same switching required for rectification.

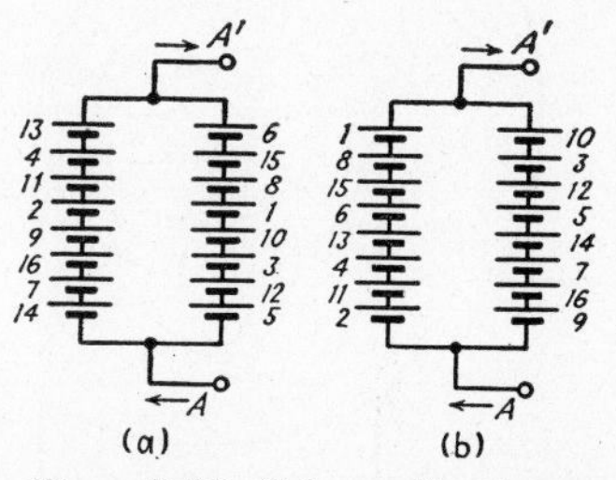

FIG. 3-39. Schematic representation of the individual inductor voltages in the winding of (*a*) Fig. 3-38 and (*b*) Fig. 3-37 for counterclockwise rotation of the armature.

c. Multipolar Windings. When a machine has more than two poles, there are two possible methods of interconnecting the inductors and commutator segments to form the complete winding: inductors associated with each pair of adjacent poles may be formed into two parallel groups, yielding an armature with as many parallel paths as there are poles; or all the inductors on the armature may be formed into only two groups or parallel paths, with half of the total inductors connected in series in each group. These two possibilities are illustrated for an elementary 4-pole machine in Figs. 3-40 and 3-41. Arrows show the directions of voltage rise for counterclockwise rotation. In both cases, one brush per path or group is necessary, so that the former connection requires as many brushes as there are poles, while the latter requires only two brushes.

The winding of Fig. 3-40 is known as a *parallel* or *lap winding,* the latter designation arising from the fact that the course of any one parallel path laps back on itself. The grouping of the inductors into parallel paths is shown schematically in Fig. 3-42 for the instant for which Fig. 3-40 is drawn. Inductors 7 and 12 do not appear in this grouping because the coil which they form is short-circuited by the upper positive brush at this time—*i.e.*, it is undergoing commutation, with the inductors in transition between two armature groups. Both of these inductors are in the interpolar space in a region of zero or very low flux density.

The winding of Fig. 3-41 is known as a *series* or *wave winding*, the latter designation arising from the fact that the course of a parallel path moves through the winding in a wavelike progression. The grouping of the

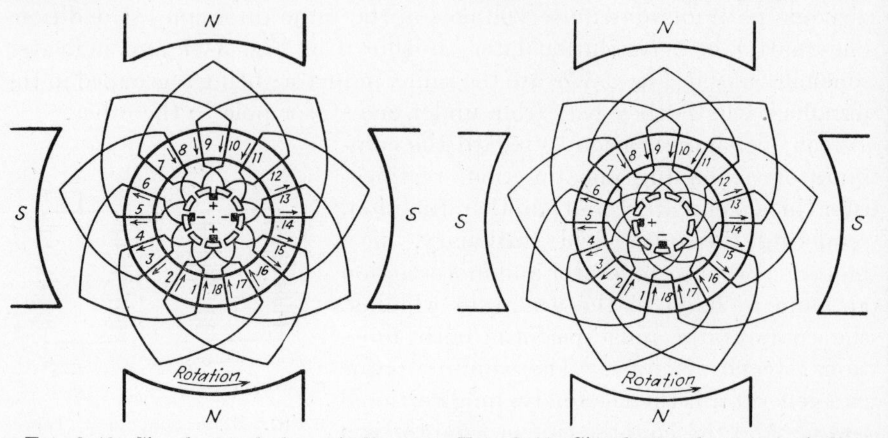

FIG. 3-40. Simple 4-pole lap winding. FIG. 3-41. Simple 4-pole wave winding.

inductors into two parallel paths is shown schematically in Fig. 3-43 for the instant for which Fig. 3-41 is drawn. Inductors 7 and 12 appear as excess in one of the paths and are shown separately in Fig. 3-43. These two inductors, being in a region of very low or zero flux density, do not contribute appreciably to voltage unbalance in the parallel paths; in a

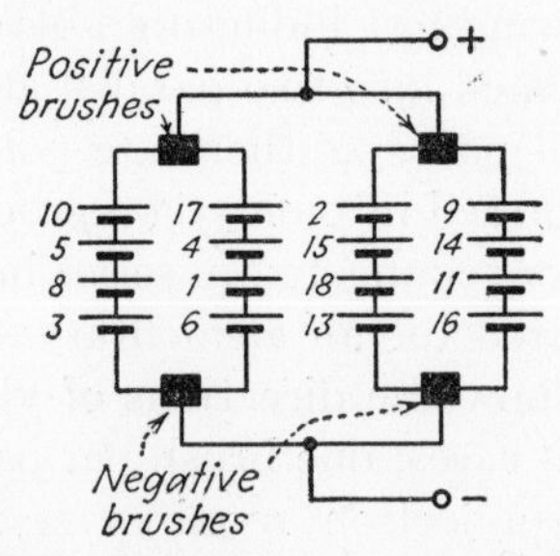

FIG. 3-42. Schematic representation of the individual inductor voltages in the winding of Fig. 3-40.

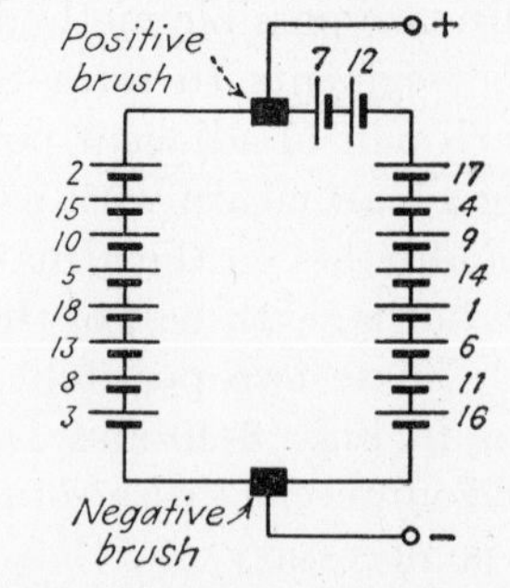

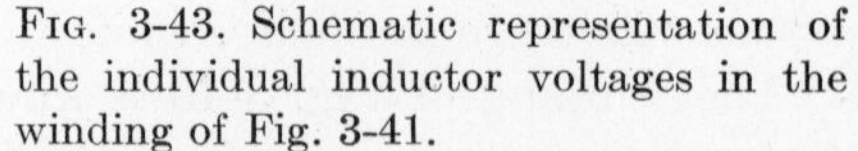
FIG. 3-43. Schematic representation of the individual inductor voltages in the winding of Fig. 3-41.

winding with a much greater number of inductors, the unbalance is negligible. Only two brushes are necessary, and only two are shown in Fig. 3-41. With a large number of armature inductors, however, it becomes practicable to insert additional brushes. Points 360 electrical degrees apart on the windings are at the same potential and therefore may be connected together; consequently, brushes may be added at these points and connected in parallel with existing brushes of the same polarity. As a result, a number of brushes equal to the number of poles is usually used on a wave winding in order to minimize the current per brush contact. These additional brushes do not increase the number of parallel paths, which remains at two regardless of the number of poles or brushes.

Comparison of Figs. 3-40 and 3-41 shows that the principal difference in geometric appearance of the lap and wave winding lies in the manner of making the front connections to the commutator segments. This difference is illustrated in Fig. 3-44, which also shows that the armature coils may consist of two or more turns, and that the coil side may therefore contain two or more inductors. Usually there are two coil sides in each slot, one below the other, with the winding so arranged that any coil has one side in the top of a slot and the other in the bottom of another slot. Thus, in the winding diagrams the odd-numbered coil sides may be considered to lie in the tops of the slots and the even-numbered in the bottom.

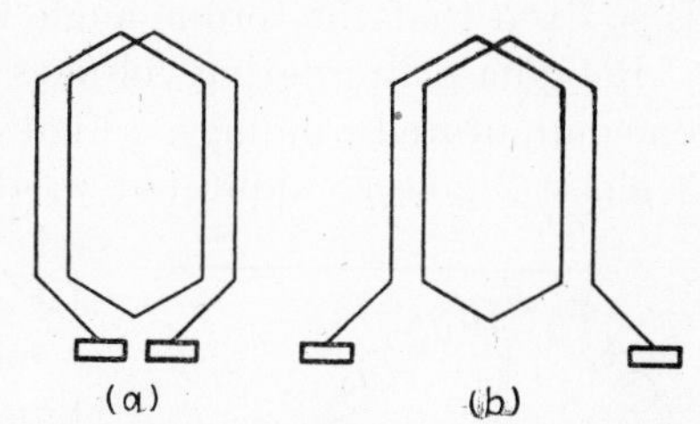

FIG. 3-44. Connections of armature coil to commutator segments in (a) lap winding and (b) wave winding.

One of the more obvious advantages of multipolar windings is that the coil-end connections are relatively shorter. Of the two types, the lap winding is better suited to heavier currents because of the greater number of parallel paths, and the wave winding is better suited to higher voltages because of the greater number of inductors in series per path. Except for heavy-current machines, the wave winding is the more commonly used.

d. Commutator Action in A-C Machines. Insight into the role of the commutator may be reinforced by considering its action when the windings discussed in the foregoing parts of this article are employed in machines having at least one winding excited by alternating current. At the same time, possibilities appear for types of a-c machines not considered heretofore.

If an alternating voltage is applied to the brushes of Figs. 3-33 and 3-37, for example, the situation within the winding is essentially similar to that discussed for these windings except that the arrow directions for current reverse whenever the current in the external circuit reverses. The instantaneous current facing a fixed point in space in the air gap varies along with the external current. The rotor field axis still remains fixed as determined by the brushes, but the rotor mmf varies in magnitude sinusoidally with time. No average torque is produced if the stator winding is excited by direct current, for then the instantaneous torque varies sinusoidally along with the rotor mmf. If the axis of the stator field remains fixed but its magnitude varies sinusoidally in time with a component in time phase with the variation in rotor field, average torque is produced. In the a-c series motor referred to in Art. 3-4, the rotor has a commutated winding, and the stator and rotor excitations are provided by the same current because the two windings are connected in series. The time variations are therefore in phase; the brush position is so fixed that the torque angle is 90°.

Polyphase alternating voltages may also be obtained from or impressed on commutated windings. Figure 3-45 presents a schematic diagram of a 3-phase 2-pole commutated winding. Each curl may be regarded as a coil connected to other coils in the manner of Fig. 3-37 with the coil terminals connected to commutator segments; a multipolar machine may be either lap- or wave-wound. From the a-c viewpoint, the winding is simply a Δ-connected 3-phase winding. For simplicity, commutator segments are not shown, but the electrical positions of three brushes 120 electrical degrees apart are indicated at A, B, and C. Three permanent taps, a, b, and c, are also shown, and they are to be regarded as brought out from the rotor through slip rings. They are added to provide a contrast between the effects of commutators and slip rings.

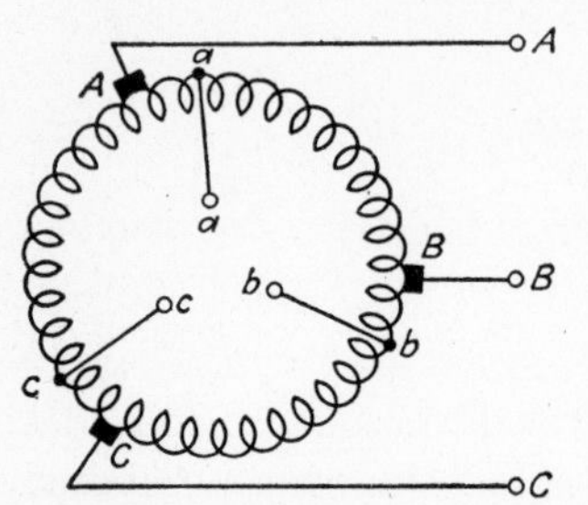

FIG. 3-45. Three-phase 2-pole armature winding with commutator and slip rings.

Consider first that this winding is used in conjunction with a d-c-excited stator producing a stationary flux wave. Alternating voltages of frequency given by Eq. 3-34 are generated in the coils, and 3-phase voltages of this frequency appear between slip rings a, b, and c just as in any synchronous generator. Direct voltages appear between brushes A, B, and C just as in any d-c generator.

Consider now that the winding is used in conjunction with a polyphase-excited stator winding like that of Fig. 3-17. The stator field is rotating in space at synchronous speed, determined by the stator frequency in accordance with Eq. 3-39. The voltages generated in the rotor coils are of slip frequency (as in the rotor of an induction motor), which, of course, depends on the rotor speed. Three-phase voltages of this frequency appear between slip rings a, b, and c just as at the slip rings of a wound-rotor induction motor. The voltages appearing between brushes A, B, and C, however, are 3-phase voltages whose frequency is equal to that of the stator regardless of the speed of the rotor. This conclusion may be verified by noting the positions in space of the group of rotor coils between any two brushes (A and B, for example) for a finely distributed winding. At any and all instants, there is a rotor coil in each of the possible positions around this portion of the periphery. The identity of the coil in any one position changes as the rotor revolves and one coil is replaced by another; but the resultant effect, in this respect, is like that of a group of coils fixed in space. The position of the group is determined only by the position of the brushes and is entirely independent of rotation of the rotor. The voltage between the two brushes is of the same frequency as if the rotor were stationary and must therefore equal the stator frequency. The magnitude of the voltage does depend on rotor speed, however. It is zero at synchronous speed.

A similar contrast exists between the influence of slip rings and commutator on the speed of the rotor-mmf wave. If 3-phase currents are introduced through slip rings a, b, and c, the rotor-mmf wave will rotate with respect to the rotor itself at synchronous speed as given by Eq. 3-39. On this speed must be superposed the mechanical speed of the rotor, so that the speed of the rotor-mmf wave in space is definitely a function of the rotor mechanical speed. With 3-phase currents introduced through brushes A, B, and C, however, the speed of the rotor-mmf wave in space is equal to synchronous speed regardless of rotor rotation This last conclusion again follows from the fact that the coils between any two brushes occupy a fixed position in space. At any and all instants, the groups AB, BC, and CA constitute three phase groups like coils a, b, and c in Fig. 3-17. Regardless of the mechanical speed of the rotor, the speed of the rotor-mmf wave in space is the same as though the rotor were stationary.

The general effect of commutating a rotor winding, then, is that *the frequency of the rotor generated voltage as viewed from the brushes and the speed of the rotor mmf wave in space are independent of rotor mechanical speed and are equal, respectively, to those existing with the rotor stationary.* For complete generality, zero frequency should be regarded as a d-c case. With slip rings, on the other hand, both the frequency of the rotor generated voltage and the speed of the rotor-mmf wave in space are dependent on rotor speed: they may be obtained by superposing the effects of rotation on the rotor-stationary values, due regard being paid to signs. The contrast is like that of viewing a machine rotor by light from a stroboscope whose flashing frequency is continuously adjusted so that the rotor appears stationary in spite of rotation, and viewing it by ordinary light which makes the speed effect very obvious—the commutator is a sort of stroboscope by which the external circuit views the rotor winding.

There is a large variety of a-c machines, many of them rather uncommon, which make use of commutated windings. The general operating characteristics of the commutator machine depend upon the manner in which the connections are made to the stator and rotor windings through slip rings and brushes on the commutator and upon the frequency, magnitude, and relative phase of the terminal voltages. The many possible combinations permit a great variety in the operating characteristics.

Example 3-4. Figure 3-46 is a schematic diagram of a 2-pole machine with a d-c excited stator producing a field which is stationary in space. The rotor winding is of the same type as that of Fig. 3-45 and is commutated, with two brushes, A and B, located in the neutral plane. There are also three slip rings a, b, and c, permanently tapped to the winding at points 120 electrical degrees apart.

List the ways in which this machine may be operated.

Solution. The machine may be made to perform a total of seven different functions. When the slip rings are ignored, the machine may be operated as (1) a conventional d-c generator or (2) a conventional d-c motor.

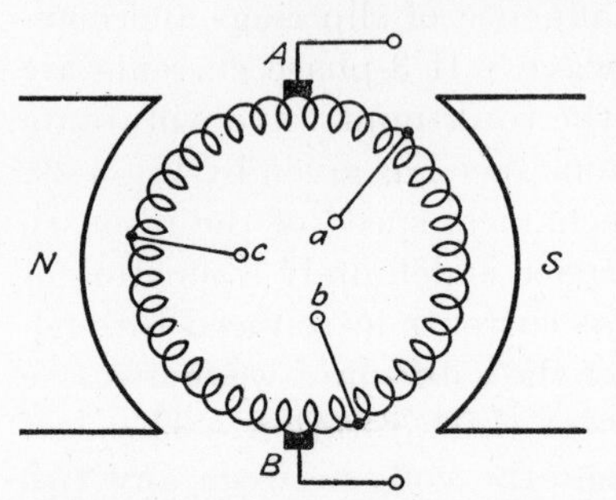

FIG. 3-46. Commutated 3-phase winding for Example 3-4.

When the brushes are ignored, the machine may be operated as (3) a 3-phase synchronous generator or (4) a 3-phase synchronous motor. In the latter case, damper windings would usually be provided in the pole faces for starting.

The machine may be operated as (5), a *double-current generator* delivering direct current through the commutator and simultaneously delivering 3-phase alternating current through the slip rings. The current in any armature coil is then a combination of the contributions of the direct current and the alternating current.

The machine may (6) receive 3-phase power through the slip rings and deliver d-c power through the brushes. When so operated, it is called a *synchronous converter*. Such machines are the equivalent of synchronous motors when viewed from the slip rings and d-c generators when viewed from the brushes. Synchronous converters, at one time widely installed for conversion from alternating to direct current, are now obsolescent and becoming superseded by mercury-arc rectifiers and ignitrons because of economic considerations. As in the synchronous motor, damper windings would normally be provided in the pole faces for starting from the a-c end.

Finally, the machine may be operated as (7) an *inverted converter* or *inverter*, receiving d-c power through the brushes and delivering 3-phase power through the slip rings. Such machines have a tendency to race under certain conditions and are not used practically. When inversion is required, as in aircraft with some a-c equipment but with a d-c power supply, a motor-generator set ordinarily is used.

Two combinations which have not been listed are supplying single-phase alternating current to the brushes and supplying direct current to the slip rings. In the former case, the rotor field axis is fixed in space, but the rotor mmf varies sinusoidally in magnitude; in the latter case, the rotor field axis rotates with the rotor. In neither case will average torque be produced.

3-10. D-C Machines. The basic factors determining the behavior of d-c machines differ in two important respects from those in the induction and synchronous machines examined previously: the torque angle is fixed by the brush axis, normally at the optimum value of 90°; and, as viewed from the brushes, the d-c values of generated emf and terminal voltage differ only by the voltage drop in the armature resistance. Variation of electromagnetic torque is therefore determined only by variation of the rotor and stator field strengths, and the variations in generated or terminal voltage may readily be traced from similar considerations. Variation of rotor and stator field strength with changing load depends on the method of connecting the field or stator circuit. For a d-c motor, the three possibilities mentioned in Art. 1-4 are illustrated in Fig. 1-42.

In the shunt motor the stator or field current is determined by the impressed voltage and the field resistance and is independent of motor load. The flux per stator pole is then very nearly constant in normal operation. (It may decrease slightly with load because of a usually small demagnetizing effect of increased armature current.) Consequently, increased torque must be accompanied by a very nearly proportional increase in armature mmf and armature current and hence by a small decrease in counter emf to allow this increased current through the small armature resistance. Since counter emf is determined by flux and speed in accordance with Eq. 3-38, the speed must drop slightly. Like the squirrel-cage induction motor, the shunt motor is substantially a constant-speed motor having about 5 per cent drop in speed from no load to full load. A typical speed-load characteristic is shown by the solid curve in Fig. 3-47. Starting torque and maximum torque are limited by the armature current that can be commutated successfully.

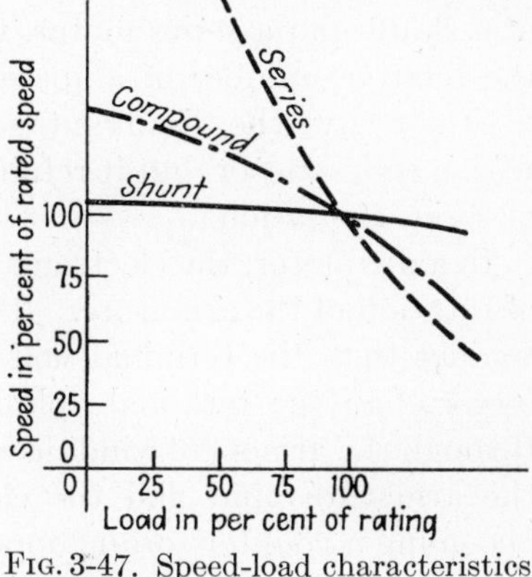

FIG. 3-47. Speed-load characteristics of d-c motors.

An outstanding advantage of the shunt motor is ease of speed control. With a rheostat in the shunt-field circuit, the field current and flux per pole may be varied at will, and variation of flux causes the inverse variation of speed to maintain counter emf approximately equal to the impressed terminal voltage. A maximum speed range of about 4 or 5 to 1 may be obtained by this method, the limitation again being commutating conditions. By variation of the impressed armature voltage, very wide speed ranges may be obtained.

In the series motor increase in load is accompanied by increases in the armature current and mmf and the stator field flux (provided the iron is not completely saturated). Because flux increases with load, speed must drop in order to maintain the balance between impressed voltage and counter emf; moreover, the increase in armature current caused by increased torque is smaller than in the shunt motor because of the increased flux. The series motor is therefore a varying-speed motor with a markedly drooping speed-load characteristic of the type shown dotted in Fig. 3-47. For applications requiring heavy torque overloads, this characteristic is particularly advantageous because the corresponding power overloads are held to more reasonable values by the associated speed drops. Very favorable starting characteristics also result from the increase in flux with increased armature current.

In the compound motor the series field may be connected either *cumulatively*, so that its mmf adds to that of the shunt field, or *differentially*, so that it opposes. The differential connection is very rarely used. As shown by the dashed curve in Fig. 3-47, a cumulatively compounded motor will have a speed-load characteristic intermediate between those of a shunt and a series motor, the drop of speed with load depending on the relative number of ampere-turns in the shunt and series fields. It does not have the disadvantage of very high light-load speed associated with a series motor, but it retains to a considerable degree the advantages of series excitation.

In a d-c motor, the electromagnetic torque is, of course, in the direction of rotation of the armature. The voltage E_a generated in the armature is smaller than the terminal voltage. For operation as a generator, E_a is larger than the terminal voltage, and the relative direction of current through the armature winding is reversed. Because of this reversal, both the armature mmf and the electromagnetic torque reverse, the latter becoming a counter torque opposing rotation. If the machine were connected to a d-c system capable of either absorbing or supplying power, it would supply power to that system when it was driven so that the generated voltage E_a exceeded the terminal voltage. If the mechanical torque were removed, the armature would slow down under the influence of the counter electromagnetic torque until E_a became smaller than the terminal voltage. Reversal of the electromagnetic torque and steady operation as a motor would follow, with the electromagnetic torque just sufficient to overcome rotational losses.

Any of the three excitation methods may also be used for generation. Such generators are called *self-excited generators* and require residual magnetism in the iron core for the initial appearance of voltage. In addition, the field may be *separately excited* from an external d-c source. Typical load-voltage characteristics for these four types of d-c generators are shown in Fig. 3-48; the general shapes of these curves may be deduced by the same type of reasoning as used above for motors, constant-speed prime movers being assumed. Because constant-voltage power systems are the rule, series generators are very seldom used. The compound characteristic of Fig. 3-48 is for an *overcompounded generator*, one in which the series field is strong enough so that the full-load voltage is greater than the no-load voltage. Normally, an overcompounded generator is operated with its no-load voltage set at the rated value and hence with a greater full-load voltage, the increment compensating for increased resistance drop in the feeder between the generator terminals and the load. If the series field is so adjusted that full-load and no-load voltages are equal, the generator is *flat-compounded;* if the full-load voltage is lower, it is *undercompounded.*

3-11. Résumé. A retrospective view of the high lights of this chapter may be obtained by considering the following question: How might the basic rotating machines and their variants have evolved from the few fundamental magnetic considerations of the earlier chapters?

A theorist, setting out to develop on paper some of the basic machine types which are so common today, might start with the notion of magnetic fields and conductors or turns interacting to produce voltages and, if the conductors or turns carry current, forces. These notions might be formulated in several different ways; the specific formulations chosen here are those between voltage and time rate of change of flux linkages, and between torque and angular rate of change of linkages. Reflection upon the features common to these two formulations, especially in view of the energy-conservation principle, leads to the expectation that whenever a motor is developed, a generator will also have been developed, and conversely.

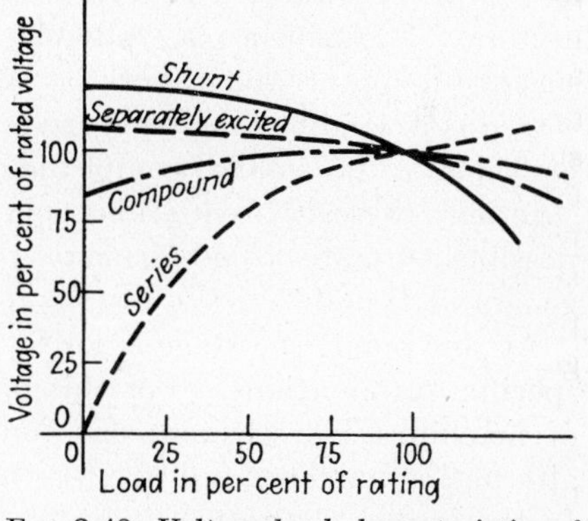

FIG. 3-48. Voltage-load characteristics of d-c generators.

At the outset, the nature of the windings and of their interconnections with each other and to the external circuits is nebulous. Equally nebulous is the nature of the flux-density distribution. Since something definite must be assumed in order to launch an investigation of possibilities, sinusoidal air-gap flux density and a sinusoidal armature current sheet, or, what amounts to the same thing, sinusoidal armature-mmf distribution, are chosen as heuristic assumptions. Back of this choice lies the feeling, born of experience with Fourier series, that the ultimate results will be of value regardless of the actual distributions which are finally used in practical machines. Back of this choice also lies the intuitive conviction that close conformity with these assumptions will ultimately be found in those machines which are to produce or operate on sinusoidal voltages and currents. A note is made to investigate the influence of the neglected harmonics at a later time, however. (A partial examination of harmonics is made in the next chapter, where it will be found that, while normally small, they may become decided nuisances unless care is used to minimize them in a-c machines. Modifications based on more nearly the actual current sheet and mmf distribution in d-c machines are also included there.)

On this basis, the electromagnetic-torque equation is obtained. By showing torque to depend on the product of the amplitudes of the mmf and flux-density waves and on the sine of the space angle between their axes, it leads to the important conclusion that stator and rotor fields must be stationary relative to each other for the production of a steady unidirectional torque. This conclusion applies not only to motors, but also to the production of a steady unidirectional counter torque in generators. It furnishes a valuable criterion for recognizing potentially successful motor and generator types. The equation for voltage generated in a winding, likewise based on sinusoidal flux distribution in space, provides a necessary complement to the torque equation. Taken together, these two equations, plus simple circuit considerations, make possible estimates of performance of the potentially successful motor and generator types.

At this point, the stage is set for more explicit specifications and more specific examinations. For this purpose, two important general classes of machines are selected: one for the production or use of polyphase alternating current, and one for the production or use of direct current. In the former class, two types are selected: the induction machine, with alternating current in both rotor and stator windings; and the synchronous machine, with direct current in one winding, usually the rotor, and alternating current in the other. The d-c machine, with direct current in both windings, completes the possible combinations. The possibility of many variants on these types is acknowledged, but attention is confined to the main line of development, at the same time recognizing that such development will furnish guiding principles for later examination of any proposed variant.

Winding configurations then begin to take on more definite form. For example, the 120° time-phase displacement of 3-phase voltages suggests 120-electrical-degree space-phase displacement of the coils or coil groups in the respective phases of a 3-phase winding. Upon investigation, it is found that such a winding produces a field of constant amplitude which rotates at a speed determined by the number of poles and the frequency. Thus, polyphase induction and synchronous machines involve the interaction of rotor and stator fields revolving synchronously in the air gap. Direct-current machines, on the other hand, involve the interaction of rotor and stator fields which are stationary in space, but otherwise act in accordance with the same basic principles. The necessity of a switching device, the commutator, in a d-c machine is recognized in order that the rotor field may be stationary in spite of rotor rotation and in order to convert the a-c waveforms in the armature coils into direct current at the machine terminals. It is found that, in general, the effect of commutating a rotor winding is that the frequency of the rotor generated voltage and the speed of the rotor-mmf wave in space are independent of rotor mechanical speed and are equal, respectively, to those existing with the rotor stationary; zero frequency is here regarded as the d-c case.

Then follow qualitative examinations of important performance features of these machines—examinations whose results definitely signify the development of energy-conversion devices with a range of desirable operating characteristics. With reference to motor action under changing load, for example, the induction machine is found to operate normally at substantially constant speed, the synchronous machine at absolutely constant speed, and the d-c machine ranging from substantially constant to widely varying speed, depending on the field-circuit connections. An outstanding advantage of the d-c shunt motor is found in its adaptability to adjustable-speed service. In fact, the feeling begins to arise that commutator machines may be readily adapted to adjustable- and varying-speed service, whereas machines associated with a rotating field will be inherently better suited to operation at speeds close to that of the field. This feeling is heightened by the fact that the commutator, in effect, removes the influence of mechanical rotation of the rotor as far as the rotor field is concerned.

Characteristic similarities are also noted. It is entirely natural, for instance, to find that the induction motor possesses essentially the same torque-speed curve in the normal operating range as the shunt motor at constant field current. In the normal operating range of small slips, the torque angle of the induction motor is close to 90° and varies but little with load; for the shunt motor, the torque angle is fixed at 90° by the brush axis. In both motors, the air-gap flux density remains approximately constant. In both motors, therefore, the amplitude of the rotor mmf must increase about in proportion to the torque, and the rotors must slow down to permit the associated increase in rotor current through the rotor resistance. Since the internal processes are practically identical, it would be surprising if the external characteristics were not also similar.

At this point in the evolution, the main line of development exhibits, at least in theory, every chance of success. The next steps are to examine the premises more closely, especially as regards waveforms of flux density and mmf in the light of the more definite and practical form now being taken on by the winding arrangements; to make such modifications as appear necessary; and to lay the foundations for and carry out detailed analyses of performance. These steps are the subjects of the following chapters.

Although logical, the foregoing synthesis is an artificial one compounded from hindsight. The true, historical development, with its economic motivations and many experimental trials and errors, is completely ignored. As but one example of the part played by experiment, the idea of the squirrel-cage rotor was first investigated on a test floor by cutting the end connections of a wound rotor, scraping the insulation clear, and soldering them together to form a winding short-circuited at the ends of each conductor. Also ignored are improvements in the properties of materials and in production methods, factors which account to a considerable extent for whatever over-all degree of perfection is found in modern machines.

PROBLEMS

3-1. The object of this problem is to illustrate how the armature windings of certain machines (*i.e.*, d-c machines) may be approximately represented by uniform current sheets, with the degree of correspondence growing better as the winding is distributed in a greater number of slots around the armature periphery. For this purpose, consider an armature with 8 slots uniformly distributed over 360 electrical degrees or one pair of poles. The air gap is of uniform width, the slot openings are very small, and the reluctance of the iron is negligible.

Lay out 360 electrical degrees of the armature with its slots in developed form in the manner of Fig. 3-1, and number the slots 1 to 8 from left to right. The winding consists of 8 single-turn coils, each carrying a direct current of 10 amp. Coil sides which may be placed in slots 1 to 4 carry current directed into the paper; those which may be placed in slots 5 to 8 carry current out of the paper.

a. Consider that all eight coils are placed with one side in slot 1 and the other in slot 5. The remaining slots are empty. Draw the rectangular mmf wave produced by these coils.

b. Next consider that four coils have one side in slot 1 and the other in slot 5, while the remaining four have one side in slot 3 and the other in slot 7. Draw the component rectangular mmf waves produced by each group of coils, and superimpose the components to give the resultant-mmf wave.

c. Now consider that two coils are placed in slots 1 and 5, two in 2 and 6, two in 3 and 7, and two in 4 and 8. Again superimpose the component rectangular waves to produce the resultant wave. Note that the task can be systematized and simplified by recognizing that the mmf wave is symmetrical about its axis and takes a step at each slot which is definitely related to the number of ampere-conductors in the slot.

d. Let the armature now consist of 16 slots per 360 electrical degrees with one coil side in each slot. Draw the resultant-mmf wave.

e. Approximate each of the resultant waves of *a* to *d* by isosceles triangles, noting that the representation grows better as the winding is more finely distributed.

f. Evaluate the uniform angular current density in amperes per radian which will produce each of the triangular waves in *e*.

3-2. An alternative approximate representation of the mmf waves in Prob. 3-1 is obtained by the use of sinusoids. For this purpose, only the fundamental component of the rectangular mmf wave produced by each individual coil is retained (as we shall see in Chap 4, the harmonics may be included in other ways in machine theory).

Repeat parts *a* to *d* of Prob. 3-1 on this sinusoidal basis, noting that the amplitude of the fundamental component of a rectangular wave is $4/\pi$ times the height of the wave. In parts *a* and *b*, draw both the component sine waves for coil groups in the same slots and the resultant sine wave; in parts *c* and *d*, draw only the resultant waves. Recognize that phase-displaced sine waves in space may be added by using vector artifices similar to those for sine waves in time.

Evaluate the amplitude in amperes per radian for the sinusoidal current sheets which will produce the four resultant-mmf waves.

3-3. A 2-pole machine has a uniform smooth air gap of radial width g. The axial length of the rotor and stator iron is l, and end effects may be neglected. The rotor diameter is D, where $D \gg g$. The rotor and stator iron may be considered to have very high permeability compared with that of the air gap. The rotor and stator windings produce mmf waves which are sinusoidally distributed in space around the air gap and are given by

$$F_1 = F_{1(\text{peak})} \sin (\theta + \delta)$$

and

$$F_2 = F_{2(\text{peak})} \sin \theta$$

respectively, where θ and δ have the same meaning as in Art. 3-2.

a. Derive an expression for the stored energy in the magnetic field of the machine.

b. Recognize that electromagnetic torque can be taken as the angular rate of change of stored energy and that this rate may be evaluated with mmf considered constant. On this basis, derive the torque equation, 3-22, for the p-pole machine from the result obtained in *a*.

3-4. The armature-mmf and air-gap flux-density waves in a d-c machine are sometimes represented by an isosceles triangle of amplitude F_A and a rectangle of height B, respectively. Consider that the zero crossings of these waves are displaced by the electrical angle δ.

a. Derive an expression for torque in terms of F_A, the flux per pole Φ, the angle δ, and the number of poles p.

b. Reduce the expression in *a* to the form appropriate for a d-c machine with the brushes in their normal position, $\delta = \pi/2$.

c. Determine the percentage error which would be caused by using only the fundamental components of the triangular mmf and rectangular flux density in obtaining the torque in *b*. The flux per pole Φ is to be taken as that corresponding to the fundamental component of flux density.

d. As an alternate to *b*, the rectangular flux-density wave is to be replaced by a sinusoid having the same flux per pole Φ. Only the fundamental component of the triangular mmf wave is to be used. Determine the percentage error in evaluating the torque in *b*.

3-5. Work parts *a* and *b* of Prob. 3-4 with the air-gap flux-density wave represented by a sinusoid of amplitude $B_{(\text{peak})}$. The armature-mmf wave is still an isosceles triangle of amplitude F_A.

3-6. The following mmf and flux-density distributions are found in the air gaps of rotating machines: (1) mmf due to the rotor currents, (2) mmf due to the stator currents, (3) resultant mmf, (4) flux density due to the rotor currents, (5) flux density due to the stator currents, (6) resultant flux density. For uniform-air-gap machines, sinusoidal distributions of the mmf and flux-density waves are a reasonable assumption. If, also, all of the reluctance is assumed to be in the air gap, show that Eq. 3-22 can be written in terms of the following quantities, and identify the angle in each case:

a. Quantities 1 and 5
b. Quantities 2 and 4
c. Quantities 1 and 6
d. Quantities 1 and 2

3-7. In Example 1-2 it is shown on a simple physical basis that electromagnetic torque cannot be obtained by using a 4-pole rotor in a 2-pole stator. The generalization of this conclusion is that all rotating machines must have the same number of poles on stator and rotor. To reach the same conclusion on an analytical basis, consider that the function of one machine member is to produce a sinusoidal flux-density distribution having $2m$ poles,

$$B = B_{(\text{peak})} \sin m\theta$$

Consider that the function of the other is to produce a sinusoidal current sheet and an associated sinusoidal mmf distribution having $2n$ poles,

$$F = F_{(\text{peak})} \sin n(\theta - \delta)$$

In both of these expressions, θ and δ are measured in mechanical units.

By paralleling the general process leading to Eq. 3-22, evaluate the torque in terms of the component flux density and mmf, and show that it is zero unless $m = n$.

3-8. A small experimental 3-phase 4-pole alternator has the full-pitch concentrated Y-connected armature winding shown diagrammatically in Figs. 1-27 and 1-28. Each coil (that represented by coil sides a and $-a$, for example) has 2 turns, and all the turns in any one phase are connected in series. The flux per pole is 25.0 megalines and is sinusoidally distributed in space. The rotor is driven at 1,800 rpm.

a. Determine the rms generated voltage to neutral.

b. Determine the rms generated voltage between lines.

c. Consider an *abc* phase order, and take zero time at the instant when the flux linkages with phase a are a maximum. Write a consistent set of time equations for the three phase voltages from terminals a, b, and c to neutral.

d. Under the conditions of *c*, write a consistent set of time equations for the three voltages between lines a and b, b and c, and c and a.

3-9. The derivation of Eq. 3-38 for the average emf E_a in an N-turn coil on a d-c machine armature is based on sinusoidal flux distribution. Obtain the corresponding expression for the case of rectangular distribution of the air-gap flux.

3-10. Equation 3-35 for the instantaneous voltage generated in an N-turn coil is based on a flux wave of constant amplitude sinusoidally distributed in space and rotating at a uniform speed with respect to the coil. It applies to the normal 3-phase machine operating under balanced conditions. A different type of situation may arise in single-phase motor analysis, however. The air-gap flux density may be considered to vary sinusoidally in space around the periphery, but the wave does not rotate. Since the flux is produced by an alternating current which varies sinusoidally with time at the angular frequency ω, the amplitude of the flux wave also varies sinusoidally with time. The N-turn coil on the rotor revolves at the steady speed n.

Investigate the nature of the generated coil voltage under these conditions. In particular, show that it consists of two components, one whose amplitude is proportional to the angular velocity ω of the current in the field winding, and one whose amplitude is proportional to the speed n of the armature. The former component is called a *transformer voltage;* the latter, a *speed voltage.*

3-11. Draw approximately to scale in the manner of Fig. 3-17 the stator flux distributions for a 2-pole 3-phase induction or synchronous machine at the following instants of time:

a. When the current in phase *b* is zero.

b. An arbitrarily chosen instant not corresponding to zero or maximum current in any phase.

Show the contribution from each of the three phases as well as the total stator flux distribution.

3-12. Draw approximately to scale the stator flux distribution corresponding to the three given in Fig. 3-17 but for the reverse phase sequence—*i.e.*, with the applied voltages reaching their time maxima in *cba* order instead of *abc* order.

3-13. Draw approximately to scale the counterpart of Fig. 3-17 for the windings of *a* and *b*:

a. One consisting of 2 coils 90° apart in space with impressed voltages which are equal in magnitude but phase displaced 90° in time. Such a winding would be used in a 2-pole motor for 3-wire 2-phase service.

b. One consisting of 4 coils 90° apart in space with impressed voltages which are equal in magnitude but phase-displaced 90° in time. Such a winding would be used in a 4-phase motor.

c. If the supply frequency in *b* is 60 cps, what is the synchronous speed?

d. Can the resultant fields in *a* and *b* be distinguished from that of a 3-phase winding?

e. State the effect on the field in *a* if the two voltages are only about 80° phase-displaced in time. This situation arises during the starting of some single-phase induction motors.

3-14. In a balanced 2-phase machine, the two windings are displaced 90 electrical degrees in space and the currents in the two windings are phase-displaced 90 electrical degrees in time. For such a machine, carry out the process leading up to an equation such as 3-47 for the rotating mmf wave. Accompany the derivation with interpretive comments, and include sketches like those of Figs. 3-16 and 3-17.

3-15. The following statements are made in Art. 3-6 just after deriving and discussing Eq. 3-47: "In general it may be shown that a rotating field of constant amplitude will be produced by a q-phase winding excited by balanced q-phase currents when the respective phases are wound $2\pi/q$ electrical radians apart in space. The constant amplitude will equal $q/2$ times the maximum contribution of any one phase, and the speed of the wave is given by Eq. 3-39."

Prove these statements.

3-16. A 3-phase induction motor runs at almost 1,200 rpm at no load and 1,140 rpm at full load when supplied with power from a 60-cps 3-phase line.

a. How many poles has the motor?

b. What is the per cent slip at full load?

c. What is the corresponding frequency of the rotor voltages?

d. What is the corresponding speed of (1) the rotor field with respect to the rotor? (2) Of the rotor field with respect to the stator? (3) Of the rotor field with respect to the stator field?

e. What speed would the rotor have at a slip of 10 per cent?

f. What is the rotor frequency at this speed?

g. Repeat part *d* for a slip of 10 per cent.

3-17. An Electropult (see *Westinghouse Engr.*, September, 1946, p. 161) based on the induction-motor principle may be used for launching heavily loaded airplanes from short runways. It consists of a launching car riding on a long track. The track is a developed squirrel-cage winding, and the launching car, which is 12 ft long, $3\frac{1}{2}$ ft wide, and only $5\frac{1}{2}$ in. high, has a developed 3-phase 8-pole winding. The center-line distance between adjacent poles is $\frac{12}{8} = 1\frac{1}{2}$ ft. Power at 60 cps is fed to the car from arms extending through slots to rails below ground level. The car develops 10,000 hp and can launch an airplane in as little as 4 sec over a 340-ft run.

a. What is the synchronous speed in miles per hour?

b. Will the car reach this speed? Explain your answer.

c. To what slip frequency does a car speed of 75 mph correspond?

d. The resistance of the bars in the squirrel-cage track winding diminishes from a maximum at the start of the runway to a minimum where the airplane leaves the runway. Explain the purpose and the effect of this construction.

e. As soon as the airplane is launched, direct current is applied to the 3-phase winding. Explain what the effect of this would be.

3-18. An induction-motor stator has a 4-pole 3-phase winding which is connected to a 60-cps balanced 3-phase source. The rotor has a 4-pole 2-phase winding which is short-circuited at the slip rings.

a. Is there a starting torque?

b. At 1,200 rpm what is the frequency of rotor emfs?

c. The resultant sinusoidal flux per pole is 0.04 weber, and the rotor leakage-reactance-to-resistance ratio is 4.0 at 60 cps and varies linearly with rotor frequency. What is the amplitude of the rotor-mmf wave required to produce a torque of 50 newton-m at 1,200 rpm?

3-19. Describe the effect on the normal torque-speed characteristic of an induction motor produced by:

a. Halving the applied voltage with normal frequency

b. Halving both the applied voltage and frequency

Sketch the associated torque-speed characteristics in their approximate relative positions with respect to the normal one. Neglect the effects of stator resistance and leakage reactance.

3-20. A polyphase wound-rotor induction motor with some external resistance added to the rotor circuit is loaded by a brake so that it runs at a speed of n rpm and produces a torque of T_1 newton-m. Then the added resistance is cut out so that the motor runs with the rotor slip rings short-circuited. The resistance and leakage reactance of the stator may be ignored.

a. If the load is now adjusted so that the motor still runs at a speed of n rpm, state whether the following quantities have increased or decreased from their values when the motor was running with added rotor resistance: torque, torque angle δ, rotor mmf.

b. If the load is now adjusted so that the motor torque is T_1, describe what happens to the rotor mmf and the torque angle δ compared with their initial values.

3-21. A 10-hp 220-volt 3-phase 6-pole 60-cps wound-rotor induction motor has a rotor resistance of 0.2 ohm per phase and a rotor leakage reactance of 0.6 ohm per phase at 60 cps.

The total flux per pole is 0.025 weber. With a certain shaft load, the torque required to start the load and the rotor is 30 lb-ft.

a. What is the minimum amplitude of the rotor-mmf wave in order for the motor to start?

b. If the amplitude of the rotor-mmf wave is 250 amp-turns, how much resistance must be added to each rotor phase in order that sufficient torque be developed to start the motor?

3-22. A 3-phase induction-motor stator is wound for 6 poles. Assuming that all of the following rotors will fit mechanically, state which ones will produce motor action with this stator:

a. Four-pole 3-phase wound rotor

b. Four-pole 4-phase wound rotor

c. Six-pole 3-phase wound rotor
d. Six-pole 4-phase wound rotor
e. Squirrel-cage rotor
f. Six-pole rotor excited from a d-c source

3-23. The stator of an unloaded 3-phase 6-pole wound-rotor induction motor is connected to a 60-cps source; the rotor is connected to a 25-cps source.

a. Is a starting torque produced?

b. At what speed will steady-state motor action result? There are two possible answers, depending on circumstances in a particular case.

c. What determines the one of the two speeds in *b* at which the motor will operate in a specific case?

d. Suppose now that the rotor supply frequency is varied over the range zero to 25 cps. Sketch curves showing motor speed in rpm as a function of rotor frequency, interpreting zero frequency as direct current.

e. What changes are made in the foregoing answers if the motor is fully loaded instead of unloaded?

3-24. A 3-phase 8-pole Y-connected 60-cps synchronous alternator has 100 armature turns per phase which may be assumed to be formed into concentrated full-pitch coils. The machine is delivering 20 kw of power to a balanced 3-phase system having 550 volts line to line. Under this condition, the mmf wave due to the field poles alone produces a peak value of sinusoidal mmf at the center of the poles equal to 1,000 amp-turns. The armature winding has negligible resistance and leakage reactance.

a. What is the resultant sinusoidal air-gap flux per pole in webers?

b. What is the angle between the field poles and the resultant flux wave?

3-25. A synchronous motor with its stator connected to a balanced polyphase source is operating at 1.00 power factor and constant load torque equal to one-half of its full-load value. State which way (in the direction of rotation or counter to the direction of rotation) the rotor will move relative to the resultant air-gap flux-density wave as the field current is increased.

3-26. A synchronous motor fed from constant-voltage mains is supplying a constant-torque load. The effects of losses and of the leakage reactance of the armature may be ignored. The field current is initially adjusted so that the motor is operating at unity power factor. Describe with reasons the effect of decreasing the field current on the following quantities:

a. The magnitude of the resultant flux wave

b. The component of armature current in phase with the voltage

c. The space phase angle δ between the armature mmf and the resultant flux wave

3-27. A 100-hp 3-phase synchronous motor is operating from constant-voltage mains at full load with a power factor of 0.80 leading. The operator slowly decreases the motor field current with the intention of ultimately making it zero. No other changes are made. Describe briefly the significant happenings as field current is decreased.

3-28. Electrical power is to be supplied to a 3-phase 25-cps system from a 3-phase 60-cps system through a motor-generator set consisting of two directly coupled synchronous machines.

a. What is the minimum number of poles which the motor may have?

b. What is the minimum number of poles which the generator may have?

c. At what speed in rpm will the set specified in *a* and *b* operate?

3-29. Figure 3-49 shows a 3-phase wound-rotor induction machine whose shaft is rigidly coupled to the shaft of a 3-phase synchronous motor. The terminals of the

3-phase rotor winding of the induction machine are brought out to slip rings as shown. The induction machine is driven by the synchronous motor at the proper speed and in the proper direction of rotation so that 3-phase 120-cps voltages are available at the slip rings. The induction machine has a 6-pole stator winding.

a. How many poles must the rotor winding of the induction machine have?

b. If the stator field in the induction machine rotates in a clockwise direction, what must be the direction of rotation of its rotor?

c. What must be the speed in rpm?

d. How many poles must the synchronous motor have?

3-30. The system shown in Fig. 3-49 is used to convert balanced 60-cps voltages to other frequencies. The synchronous motor has 2 poles and drives the interconnecting shaft in the clockwise direction. The induction machine has 12 poles, and its stator windings are connected to the lines to produce a counterclockwise rotating field (in the opposite direction to the synchronous motor). The machine has a wound rotor whose terminals are brought out through slip rings.

a. At what speed does the motor run?

b. What is the frequency of the rotor voltages in the induction machine?

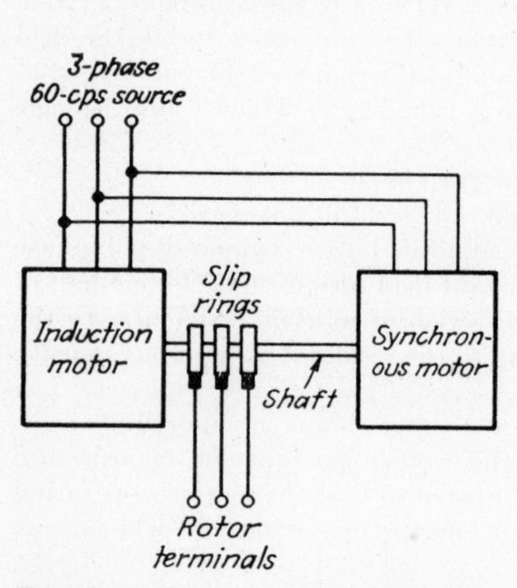

FIG. 3-49. Interconnected induction and synchronous motors for Probs. 3-29 and 3-30.

FIG. 3-50. Direct-current armature winding for Prob. 3-31.

3-31. For the winding diagram of the armature of a d-c machine shown in Fig. 3-50, determine:

a. Number of poles

b. Whether lap or wave

c. Number of brushes

d. Number of circuits in parallel

The winding diagram shows only 1 turn per coil. How many turns and what flux per pole would be necessary to generate 110 volts at 1,750 rpm when the flux is approximately 500 kilolines per pole?

3-32. The armature of the machine shown in Fig. 3-46 is fed with 60-cps current through slip rings *a*, *b*, *c*. The field is excited with direct current. The armature revolves as a synchronous machine at 3,600 rpm. What frequency would you expect at the brushes *A* and *B* if they revolve in the same direction as the armature at (*a*)

3,600, (*b*) 2,400, (*c*) 1,200, and (*d*) zero rpm? If the brushes revolve in the opposite direction?

Answer the above questions in case the armature is fed with 60-cps current but that it revolves at a speed of 2,400 rpm while the d-c field structure rotates in the opposite direction at 1,200 rpm.

3-33. *a.* Compare the effect on the speed of a d-c shunt motor of varying the line voltage with that of varying only the armature terminal voltage, so that the field current remains fixed.

b. Compare both of these effects with that of varying only the shunt-field current, the armature terminal voltage remaining fixed.

3-34. State approximately how the armature current and speed of a d-c shunt motor would be affected by each of the following changes in the operating conditions:

a. Halving the armature terminal voltage, the field current and load torque remaining constant.

b. Halving the armature terminal voltage, the field current and horsepower output remaining constant.

c. Doubling the field flux, the armature terminal voltage and load torque remaining constant.

d. Halving both the field flux and armature terminal voltage, the horsepower output remaining constant.

e. Halving the armature terminal voltage, the field flux remaining constant and the load torque varying as the square of the speed.

In each case, only brief quantitative statements of the order of magnitude of the changes are desired, *e.g.*, "speed approximately doubled."

3-35. Write a brief technical discussion on the feasibility of operating (*a*) shunt, (*b*) series, and (*c*) compound motors from a single-phase a-c line. Do not concern yourself at this time with such aspects as obtaining sparkless commutation and the effects of hysteresis and eddy-current losses on operation.

CHAPTER 4

INTRODUCTION TO MACHINE ANALYSIS

THE preliminary study of machine workings and potentialities in the preceding chapter is based upon idealized machines, the principal idealizing assumptions being the five sets outlined at the beginning of Art. 3-2. On the other hand, the detailed studies of specific machine types presented in the chapters immediately following this one must be based on close representations of actual conditions found in practical, everyday motors and generators. Between these two stages of theoretical development must come a reconciliation of the ideal to the practical, which is the primary object of the present chapter.

The most important steps in achieving this object are examinations of induced-voltage, flux-density, and mmf waveforms as created by realistic windings. Careful attention must be paid to the effects of departures from the sinusoids assumed in Chap. 3 and to means for minimizing the departures and effects when they are found to be harmful. In the last respect, some degree of divergence begins to appear between the detailed theories of a-c and of d-c machines, divergence largely arising from the presence of commutated windings in d-c machines. More specifically, it is found that in the common, well-designed a-c machines the effects of the departures from sinusoids are quite small under normal running conditions; performance analyses may accordingly be based directly on the principles discussed in Chap. 3. For d-c machines, however, it is found that the armature mmf is more faithfully represented by a triangle and that the specific distribution of the flux per pole over the armature circumference does not usually affect the analytical results. Revised voltage and torque equations are presented in recognition of these facts.

When combined with the ideas already developed, these examinations yield a small group of relations between machine quantities upon which subsequent study of performance characteristics is founded. These relations are Eqs. 4-14 and 4-47 for induced voltage and electromagnetic torque in a-c machines and Eqs. 4-38 and 4-56 for the same quantities in d-c machines. Consideration must also be given to such items as the techniques for handling saturation and of including losses and their effects.

4-1. Polyphase Machines—Generated Voltages. Two of the important factors to be considered in bridging the gap between simple windings and practical windings are the most economical use of space and material in the machine and the minimizing of effects of the hitherto neglected harmonics. More complex and satisfying winding arrangements are readily derived from these considerations and may be examined in terms of Eq. 3-36, which gives the voltage induced in a single coil of N turns by a rotating field with a sinusoidal space distribution. A new element, however, is the addition of individual coil or conductor voltages to give the voltage of a phase group. Such addition of fundamental-frequency voltages is the subject of this article. Consideration of the influence on the voltage of space harmonics in the flux distribution is postponed until Art. 4-6.

a. Distributed Fractional-pitch Windings. One practical disadvantage of the simple concentrated windings of Fig. 1-26 is that a goodly portion of the stator inner surface is not effectively utilized. In both cases, one slot per pole is devoted to each phase. Inspection of these figures leads to the idea of cutting additional slots between those already present and devoting two or more successive slots per pole to each phase, thereby obtaining a winding in which the coil sides of any phase are distributed over portions of the stator surface. The 120° displacement between phases of a 3-phase machine must, of course, be maintained. Distributing a winding in this manner will also be found to decrease the harmonic content of the voltage and mmf waves.

Such a distributed winding is illustrated in Fig. 4-1 for a 3-phase 2-pole machine. This case retains all the features of a more general one with any integral number of phases, poles, and slots per pole per phase. At the same time, a *double-layer winding* is shown, rather than the *single-layer winding* of Fig. 1-26. Double-layer windings usually lead to simpler end connections and to a machine which is more economical to manufacture and are found in all machines except some small motors below 10 hp in size. Generally, one side of a coil, such as a_1, is placed in the bottom of a slot, and the other side, $-a_1$, is placed in the top of another slot. Coil sides such as a_1 and a_3 or a_2 and a_4 which are in adjacent slots and associated with the same phase constitute a *phase belt.* All phase belts are alike when an integral number of slots per pole per phase are used, and for the normal machine the peripheral angle subtended by a phase belt is 60 electrical degrees for a 3-phase machine and 90 electrical degrees for a 2-phase machine.

Individual coils in Fig. 4-1 all span a full pole pitch or 180 electrical degrees; accordingly, the winding is a *full-pitch winding.* Suppose now that all coil sides in the tops of the slots are shifted one slot counterclockwise, as in Fig. 4-2. Any coil, such as a_1, $-a_1$, then spans only $5/6$ of a pole pitch or $(5/6)(180) = 150$ electrical degrees, and the winding is a *fractional-pitch* or *chorded winding.* Similar shifting by two slots yields a

⅔-pitch winding, and so forth. Phase groupings are now intermingled, for some slots contain coil sides in phase a and b, a and c, and b and c. Individual phase groups, such as that formed by a_1, a_2, a_3, a_4 on one side and $-a_1$, $-a_2$, $-a_3$, $-a_4$ on the other, are still displaced by 120 electrical degrees from the groups in other phases so that 3-phase voltages are produced. Besides the minor feature of shortening the end connections, fractional-pitch windings will be found to decrease the harmonic content of both the voltage and mmf waves.

The end connections between the coil sides are normally in a region of negligible flux density, and hence altering them does not significantly

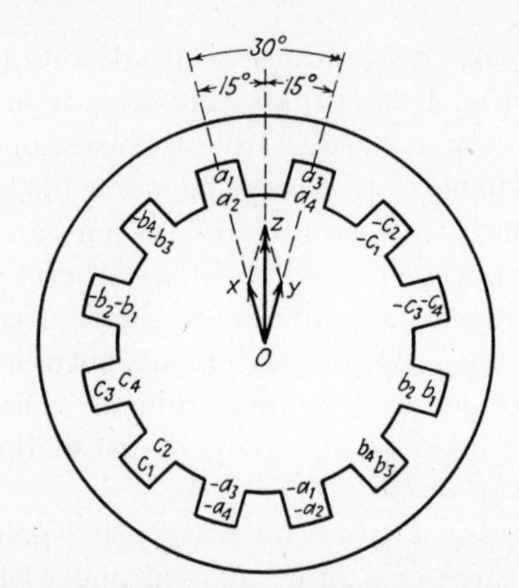

FIG. 4-1. Distributed 3-phase 2-pole full-pitch armature winding with voltage vector diagram.

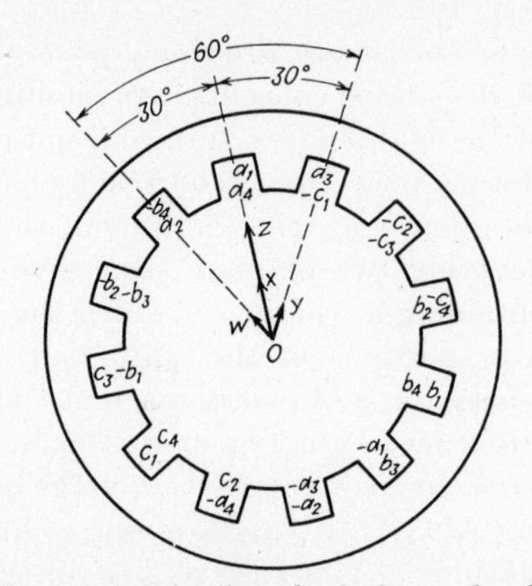

FIG. 4-2. Distributed 3-phase 2-pole fractional-pitch armature winding with voltage vector diagram.

affect the mutual flux linkages of the winding. Allocation of coil sides in slots is then the factor determining the generated voltages, and only that allocation need be specified in Figs. 4-1 and 4-2. The only requisite is that all coil sides in a phase be included in the interconnection in such a manner that individual voltages shall make a positive contribution to the total. The practical consequence is that end connections can be made according to the dictates of manufacturing simplicity; the theoretical consequence is that, when computational advantages result, the coil sides in a phase may be combined in an arbitrary fashion to form equivalent coils.

One sacrifice is made in using the distributed and fractional-pitch windings of Figs. 4-1 and 4-2 compared with the concentrated full-pitch windings of Fig. 1-26: for the same number of turns per phase, the generated voltage is lower. The harmonics are, in general, lowered by an appreciably greater factor, however, and the total number of turns which can be accommodated on a fixed iron geometry is increased. The effect of distributing the winding in Fig. 4-1 is that the voltages of coils a_1 and a_2 are not in phase with those of coils a_3 and a_4. Thus, the voltage of coils a_1 and a_2 may be represented by vector OX in Fig. 4-1, and that of coils a_3 and a_4 by the vector OY. The time phase displacement between these two voltages is the same as the electrical angle between adjacent slots, so that OX and OY coincide with the center lines of adjacent slots. The resultant vector OZ for phase a is obviously smaller than the arithmetic sum of OX and OY.

In addition, the effect of fractional pitch in Fig. 4-2 is that a coil links a smaller portion of the total pole flux than if it were a full-pitch coil. This effect may be superimposed on that of distributing the winding by regarding coil sides a_2 and $-a_1$ as an equivalent coil with the vector voltage OW (Fig. 4-2), coil sides a_1, a_4, $-a_2$, and $-a_3$ as two equivalent coils with the vector voltage OX (twice the length of OW), and coil sides a_3 and $-a_4$ as an equivalent coil with the vector voltage OY. The resultant vector OZ for phase a is obviously smaller than the arithmetic sum of OW, OX, and OY and is also smaller than OZ in Fig. 4-1.

The combination of these two effects may be included in a *winding factor* k_w to be used as a reduction factor in Eq. 3-36. Thus, the generated voltage per phase is

$$E = 4.44 k_w f N_{ph} \Phi \tag{4-1}$$

where N_{ph} is the total turns in series per phase and k_w inserts the departure from the concentrated full-pitch case. For a 3-phase machine, Eq. 4-1 yields the line-to-line voltage for a Δ-connected winding and the line-to-neutral voltage for a Y-connected winding. As in any balanced Y connection, the line-to-line voltage of the latter winding is $\sqrt{3}$ times the line-to-neutral voltage.

Example 4-1. A 3-phase 6-pole a-c machine has a full-pitch winding distributed in 36 slots. Determine the winding factor k_w.

Solution. Since the winding has $36/(6 \times 3) = 2$ slots per pole per phase, the situation facing any pair of poles is that of Fig. 4-1 and the vector diagram inserted there applies. Consider vectors OX and OY each to be two units long. Then,

$$OZ = 2 \cos 15° + 2 \cos 15° = 3.863$$

The arithmetic sum of OX and OY is four units; hence

$$k_w = \frac{3.863}{4} = 0.966$$

Example 4-2. The winding of Example 4-1 is replaced by one having a ⅚ pitch. Find the new winding factor k_w.

Solution. The vector diagram in Fig. 4-2 now applies. Consider vectors OW and OY to be one unit long and OX to be two units long. Then,

$$OZ = (1) \cos 30° + 2 + (1) \cos 30° = 3.732$$

and the winding factor is

$$k_w = \frac{3.732}{4} = 0.933$$

By comparison with Example 4-1, the generated voltage of this winding is seen to be reduced by a factor of 0.966 because of its distribution in more than 1 slot per pole per phase and by an additional factor of

$$\frac{0.933}{0.966} = 0.966$$

because of use of 5⁄6 pitch. Equality of the two factors is a coincidence in this case and is of no significance.

b. Breadth and Pitch Factors. By considering separately the effects of distributing and of chording the winding, reduction factors may be obtained in generalized form convenient for quantitative analysis. The

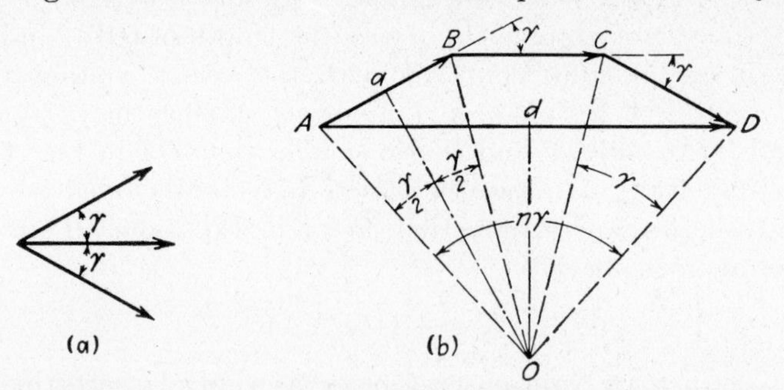

FIG. 4-3. (*a*) Voltage vectors in a distributed winding, and (*b*) addition of these vectors.

effect of distributing the winding in n slots per phase belt is to yield n voltage vectors phase-displaced by the electrical angle γ between slots, γ being equal to 180 electrical degrees divided by the number of slots per pole. Such a group of vectors is shown in Fig. 4-3*a* and, in a more convenient form for addition, again in Fig. 4-3*b*. Each vector AB, BC, and CD is the chord of a circle with center at O and subtends the angle γ at the center. The vector sum AD subtends the angle $n\gamma$, which, as noted previously, is 60 electrical degrees for the normal uniformly distributed 3-phase machine and 90 electrical degrees for the corresponding 2-phase machine. From triangles OAa and OAd, respectively,

$$OA = \frac{Aa}{\sin(\gamma/2)} = \frac{AB}{2\sin(\gamma/2)} \tag{4-2}$$

$$OA = \frac{Ad}{\sin(n\gamma/2)} = \frac{AD}{2\sin(n\gamma/2)} \tag{4-3}$$

Equating these two values of OA yields

$$AD = AB\,\frac{\sin(n\gamma/2)}{\sin(\gamma/2)} \tag{4-4}$$

But the arithmetic sum of the vectors is $n(AB)$. Consequently the reduction factor arising from distributing the winding is

$$k_b = \frac{AD}{n(AB)} = \frac{\sin (n\gamma/2)}{n \sin (\gamma/2)} \tag{4-5}$$

The factor k_b is called the *breadth factor* of the winding.

The effect of chording on the coil voltage may be obtained by a modification of the approach leading to Eq. 3-36. The basic sketch of Fig. 3-12 is redrawn in Fig. 4-4 with coil side $-a$ only ρ electrical degrees from side a instead of a full 180°. The integration in Eq. 3-27 for flux linkages is now performed between the limits α and $\rho + \alpha$; thus,

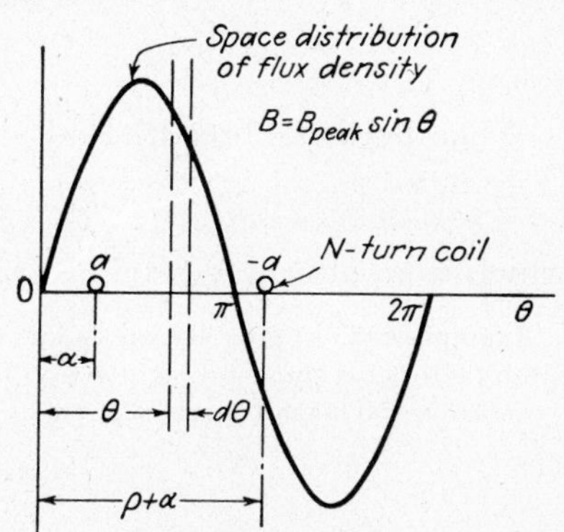

FIG. 4-4. Fractional-pitch coil in sinusoidal field.

$$\lambda = NB_{\text{peak}}lr \frac{2}{p} \int_{\alpha}^{\rho+\alpha} \sin \theta \, d\theta \tag{4-6}$$

$$= NB_{\text{peak}}lr \frac{2}{p} [\cos \alpha - \cos (\alpha + \rho)] \tag{4-7}$$

or, with α replaced by ωt in accordance with Eq. 3-29,

$$\lambda = NB_{\text{peak}}lr \frac{2}{p} [\cos \omega t - \cos (\omega t + \rho)] \tag{4-8}$$

The addition of cosine waves required in the brackets of Eq. 4-8 may be performed vectorially as indicated in Fig. 4-5, from which it follows that

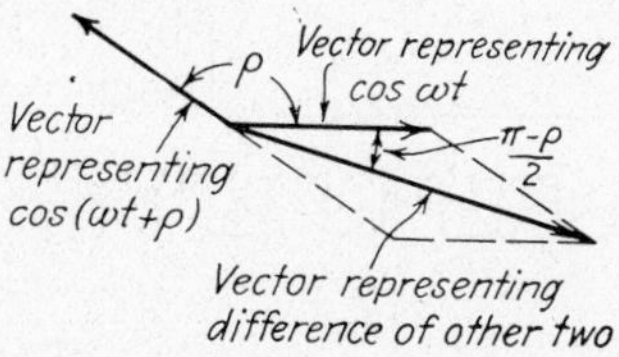

FIG. 4-5. Vector addition for fractional-pitch coil.

$$\cos \omega t - \cos (\omega t + \rho) = 2 \cos \frac{\pi - \rho}{2} \cos \left(\omega t - \frac{\pi - \rho}{2} \right) \tag{4-9}$$

a result which may also be obtained directly from the terms in Eq. 4-8 by the appropriate trigonometric transformations. The flux linkages are then

$$\lambda = NB_{\text{peak}}lr \frac{4}{p} \cos \frac{\pi - \rho}{2} \cos \left(\omega t - \frac{\pi - \rho}{2} \right) \tag{4-10}$$

and the instantaneous voltage, corresponding to Eq. 3-35, is

$$e = \omega NB_{\text{peak}}lr \frac{4}{p} \cos \frac{\pi - \rho}{2} \sin \left(\omega t - \frac{\pi - \rho}{2} \right) \tag{4-11}$$

The phase angle $(\pi - \rho)/2$ in Eq. 4-11 merely indicates that the instantaneous voltage is no longer zero when α in Fig. 4-4 is zero. The factor $\cos (\pi - \rho)/2$ is an amplitude-reduction factor, however, so that the rms voltage of Eq. 3-36 is modified to

$$E = 4.44 k_p f N_{ph} \Phi \tag{4-12}$$

where the *pitch factor* k_p is

$$k_p = \cos \frac{\pi - \rho}{2} \tag{4-13}$$

When both the breadth and pitch factors apply, the rms voltage is

$$E = 4.44 k_b k_p f N_{ph} \Phi \tag{4-14}$$

which is an alternate form of Eq. 4-1.

Example 4-3. Using the methods of Eqs. 4-5 and 4-13, determine the breadth and pitch factors for the winding of Example 4-2, and compare the results.

Solution. The slot angle γ is 180/(3 × 2), or 30°. Hence

$$k_b = \frac{\sin 30^\circ}{2 \sin 15^\circ} = 0.966$$

The coil pitch ρ is $\frac{5}{6} \times 180$, or 150°. Hence

$$k_p = \cos \tfrac{1}{2}(180^\circ - 150^\circ) = 0.966$$

Naturally these values equal the corresponding ones of Example 4-2.

c. Correlation with Blv Concept. The foregoing discussion of generated voltages, as well as those in Chap. 3, are expressed in terms of the voltage of a complete coil as determined by the time rate of change of linkages

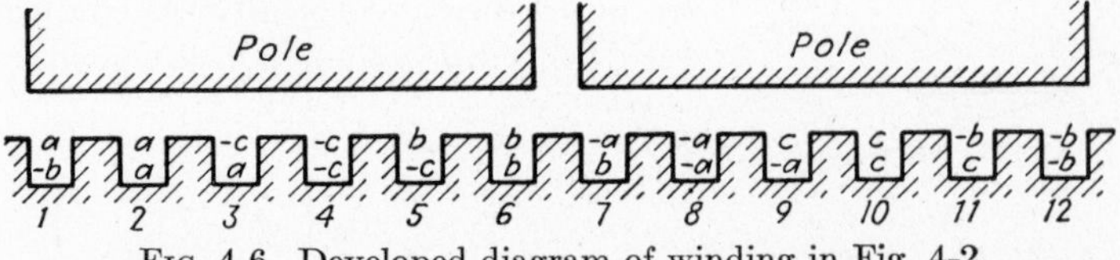

FIG. 4-6. Developed diagram of winding in Fig. 4-2.

with that coil. As pointed out in Art. 1-2, identical results may be obtained by using the *Blv* concept for the voltage of individual conductors forming the coil sides. The amplitude of the instantaneous voltage in Eq. 3-35 is readily obtainable from the *Blv* concept, as is the amplitude in Eq. 4-11 when the pitch factor is added. Use of this concept permits a restatement of the roles of the breadth and pitch factor which may be helpful by furnishing an alternate viewpoint.

A redrawing of Fig. 4-2 in developed form is presented in Fig. 4-6. Numerical subscripts identifying the specific coils are omitted since the end connections are immaterial as long as each conductor makes a positive contribution to the total. The slot at the left is the one through which the dotted extension of vector OW goes in Fig. 4-2. Each of the conductors in Fig. 4-6 has a Blv voltage induced in it, and the time-phase displacement of these voltages is the same as the space-phase displacement of the corresponding conductors in electrical degrees. The role of the breadth factor for any phase, such as a, may now be regarded as that of adding vectorially the voltages of the phase-a conductors in the tops of the slots, for such addition is performed by vector diagrams like that of Fig. 4-3. The role of the pitch factor similarly may be regarded as that of incorporating in this sum the voltages of conductors in the bottoms of the slots, for such addition is performed by vector diagrams exactly like that of Fig. 4-5.

Thus, the pitch and breadth factors merely systematize addition by turning it into multiplication; coil-by-coil or conductor-by-conductor addition of voltages is the basis of determining the multiplying factors, depending on whether the change-of-linkages or the Blv viewpoint is chosen.

Example 4-4. Consider that a Blv computation for the winding of Examples 4-2 and 4-3, and of Fig. 4-6, shows unity rms voltage to be induced in each coil side. By complex-number addition, determine the net rms induced voltage in each phase.

Solution. Let phase a be the particular phase selected, and arbitrarily choose the voltage of coil side a in slot 1, Fig. 4-6, as the reference vector. The phase-a voltages in the several pertinent slots are then as follows:

$$\begin{aligned}
&\text{Slot 1:} && 1.00\underline{/0^\circ} &&= 1.00 + j0\\
&\text{Slot 2:} && 2.00\underline{/30^\circ} &&= 1.73 + j1.00\\
&\text{Slot 3:} && 1.00\underline{/60^\circ} &&= 0.500 + j0.866\\
&\text{Slot 7:} && -1.00\underline{/180^\circ} &&= 1.00 + j0\\
&\text{Slot 8:} && -2.00\underline{/210^\circ} &&= 1.73 + j1.00\\
&\text{Slot 9:} && -1.00\underline{/240^\circ} &&= 0.500 + j0.866
\end{aligned}$$

The 30° time-phase displacement between coil-side voltages in adjacent slots coincides with the electrical angle between slots. The assumption that slot-2 voltages lead the slot-1 voltage is equivalent to considering motion of the magnetic field from right to left in Fig. 4-6. The minus signs added for slots 7, 8, and 9 represent the fact that it is the *difference* of two coil-side voltages which forms the voltage of the equivalent coil.

Vector addition of these six voltages gives $6.46 + j3.73 = 7.46\underline{/30^\circ}$ for the resultant value. The winding factor is evidently

$$k_w = \frac{7.46}{8} = 0.933$$

In most machines, the space distribution of air-gap flux density departs appreciably from a sine wave. Then Eqs. 4-1 and 4-14 yield the fundamental-frequency component of voltage when the flux per pole Φ is evaluated from the space-fundamental component of the flux distribution. For a complete investigation, each harmonic component must be examined separately by generally similar methods, methods which are given in detail in Art. 4-6. It is shown there that the use of distributed fractional-pitch windings, together with a few other possible expedients, greatly reduces the harmonic-voltage magnitudes in comparison to the fundamental. In normal practical machines, these harmonics are seldom troublesome to other than the designers of the machines, who must make sure that they are not excessive.

4-2. Polyphase Machines—Magnetic Fields. Distribution of a winding in several slots per pole per phase and the use of fractional-pitch coils influence not only the emf generated in the winding but also the magnetic field produced by it. The procedure in evaluating this influence is first to examine the mmf wave produced by single full-pitch concentrated coils and then to devise methods for adding the waves for individual coils to give the resultant wave for the entire winding. In adding these components, it will be found that the process is not unlike the one for adding coil voltages: pitch, breadth, and winding factors play substantially the same roles in each case. Primary emphasis is given to the space-fundamental components of mmf distributions, with harmonics and their effects postponed to later articles.

a. MMF Waves: Concentrated Full-pitch Windings. The windings of any generator or motor consist of discrete coils distributed around the air-gap circumference. To study the magnetic field produced, consider first the simple rotor and stator structure of Fig. 4-7 with a single concentrated coil of N turns. The air gap is of uniform radial width g, considered small in comparison with the air-gap diameter. The reluctance of the iron portions of the magnetic circuit is negligible, and the effect of the two slots on the magnetic field is ignored. Fringing of flux at the two end surfaces of the rotor and stator iron is also ignored.

A current in the coil will then cause a uniform radial magnetic field in the gap. The spatial flux-density distribution is indicated by the dotted curve of circular form in the undeveloped machine of Fig. 4-7a and by the dotted rectangular curve in the developed machine of Fig. 4-7b. With a steady direct current in the coil, these dotted waves are *space waves* which are stationary with respect to the coil. With a-c excitation, they become pulsating standing waves with respect to the coil. For sinusoidal a-c excitation, the height of these curves from their zero lines varies sinusoidally with time; with an rms current I, the time-maximum value of the height is

$$B_{\text{coil (max)}} = \frac{\sqrt{2}\, NI\mu_0}{2g} \tag{4-15}$$

with μ_0 the gap permeability. A difference of magnetic potential is concurrently established between any point on the stator and the point radially opposite on the rotor. The wave representing the variations of magnetic potential difference around the air-gap circumference is of exactly the same shape as the wave of flux distribution. The time-maximum height of the magnetic-potential-difference wave for the N-turn coil is

$$F_{\text{coil(max)}} = \frac{N}{2}(\sqrt{2}\,I) \qquad \text{amp-turns} \tag{4-16}$$

Our attention is to be confined to the space-fundamental component, shown by the sine wave in Fig. 4-7*b*. The Fourier-series representation

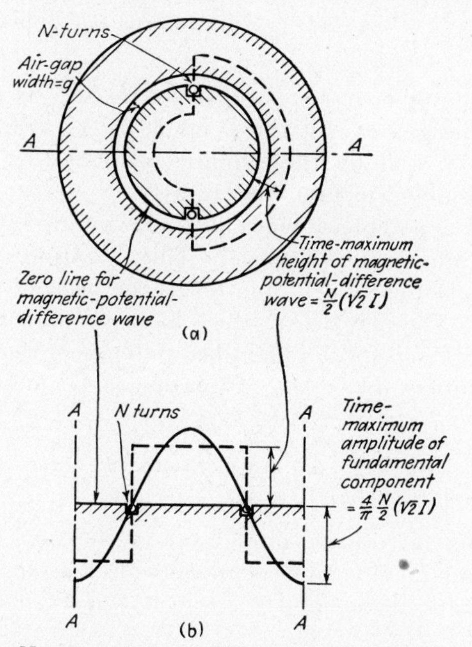

FIG. 4-7. (*a*) Single N-turn coil in uniform-air-gap machine, and (*b*) associated rectangular flux distribution with its fundamental component.

of a wave whose height y at any point x is a rectangular function of x with amplitude Y is

$$y = \frac{4}{\pi}\left(Y \sin x + \frac{Y}{3} \sin 3x + \frac{Y}{5} \sin 5x + \cdots\right) \tag{4-17}$$

in which the fundamental component is the first term on the right-hand side. It follows from Eq. 4-16 that the time-maximum amplitude of the space-fundamental component of the mmf wave is

$$F_{\text{coil(max)1}} = \frac{4}{\pi}\frac{N}{2}(\sqrt{2}\,I) \qquad \text{amp-turns} \tag{4-18}$$

Equation 4-18 is based on a 2-pole single-phase concentrated winding. For a p-pole single-phase concentrated winding having N turns, N/p turns are associated with each pole, and the time-maximum amplitude of the spatial mmf wave becomes

$$\frac{4}{\pi}\frac{N}{p}(\sqrt{2}\,I) \qquad \text{amp-turns per pole} \tag{4-19}$$

For a polyphase concentrated winding, the amplitude for one phase becomes

$$\frac{4}{\pi}\frac{N_{ph}}{p}(\sqrt{2}\,I) \qquad \text{amp-turns per pole} \tag{4-20}$$

where N_{ph} is the number of series turns per phase. It is this last amplitude which is designated by the symbols $F_{a(\max)}$, $F_{b(\max)}$, or $F_{c(\max)}$ in Eqs. 3-41 to 3-43, and by the common symbol $F_{\max}$ in the balanced 3-phase case considered in Eqs. 3-44 to 3-47.

Each phase of a polyphase concentrated winding creates such a pulsating standing mmf wave in space. This situation is essentially that depicted by Figs. 3-15 and 3-17 and forms the basis of the analysis leading to Eq. 3-47. The new detail which has been added is that the wave amplitudes are now specifically identified in terms of the number of turns, current, and number of poles. Equation 3-47 may accordingly be rewritten

$$F_\theta = \frac{3}{2}\frac{4}{\pi}\frac{N_{ph}}{p}(\sqrt{2}\,I)\cos(\theta - \omega t) \tag{4-21}$$

We see, then, that a rotating mmf wave of constant amplitude is produced by the fundamental mmf components in a 3-phase machine. The amplitude of the resultant-mmf wave in a 3-phase machine in ampere-turns per pole is

$$F_A = \frac{3}{2}\frac{4}{\pi}\frac{N_{ph}}{p}(\sqrt{2}\,I) = 0.90\,\frac{3N_{ph}}{p}\,I \tag{4-22}$$

Similarly, it may be shown that for a q-phase machine, the amplitude is

$$F_A = \frac{q}{2}\frac{4}{\pi}\frac{N_{ph}}{p}(\sqrt{2}\,I) = 0.90\,\frac{qN_{ph}}{p}\,I \tag{4-23}$$

In Eqs. 4-22 and 4-23, I is the rms current per phase. The equations include only the fundamental component of the actual distribution and apply to concentrated full-pitch windings with balanced excitation.

b. MMF Waves: Distributed Fractional-pitch Windings. When the coils in each phase of a winding are distributed among several slots per pole, the resultant space-fundamental mmf may be obtained by superposition from the preceding simpler considerations for a concentrated winding. The effect of distribution may be seen from Fig. 4-8, which is a reproduction of the 3-phase 2-pole full-pitch winding with two slots per pole per phase given in Fig. 4-1. Coils a_1 and a_2, b_1 and b_2, and c_1 and c_2 by themselves constitute the equivalent of a 3-phase 2-pole concentrated winding like that of Fig. 1-26 because they form three sets of coils excited by polyphase currents and mechanically displaced 120° from each other. They therefore produce a rotating space-fundamental mmf like that shown in Fig. 3-17 and described by Eq. 3-47; the amplitude of this contribution is given by Eq. 4-22 when N_{ph} is taken as the sum of the series turns in coils a_1 and a_2 only. Similarly, coils a_3 and a_4, b_3 and b_4, and c_3 and c_4 produce another identical mmf wave, but one which is phase-displaced in space by the slot angle γ from the former wave. The resultant fundamental mmf wave for the winding may be obtained by adding these two sinusoidal contributions.

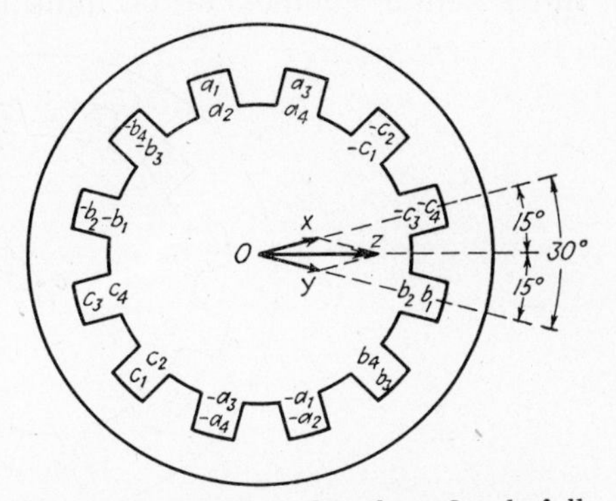

FIG. 4-8. Distributed 3-phase 2-pole full-pitch armature winding with mmf vector diagram.

The contribution from the $a_1a_2b_1b_2c_1c_2$ coils may be represented by the vector OX in Fig. 4-8. Such vector representation is appropriate because the waveforms concerned are sinusoidal, and vector diagrams are simply convenient means for adding sine waves. These are space sinusoids, however, not time sinusoids. Vector OX is drawn in the space position of the mmf peak for an instant of time when the current in phase a is a maximum. The length of OX is proportional to the number of turns in the associated coils. Similarly, the contribution from the $a_3a_4b_3b_4c_3c_4$ coils may be represented by the vector OY. Accordingly, the vector OZ represents the resultant mmf wave. Just as in the corresponding voltage diagram, the resultant mmf is seen to be smaller than if the same number of turns per phase were concentrated in one slot per pole.

In like manner, mmf vectors can be drawn for fractional-pitch windings as illustrated in Fig. 4-9, which is a reproduction of the 3-phase 2-pole 5/6-pitch winding with two slots per pole per phase given in Fig. 4-2. Vector OW represents the contribution for the equivalent coils formed by conductors a_2 and $-a_1$, b_2 and $-b_1$, and c_2 and $-c_1$; OX for a_1a_4 and $-a_3 - a_2$, b_1b_4 and $-b_3 - b_2$, and c_1c_4 and $-c_3 - c_2$; and OY for a_3 and $-a_4$, b_3 and $-b_4$, and c_3 and $-c_4$. The resultant vector OZ is, of course, smaller than the algebraic sum of the individual contributions and is also smaller than OZ in Fig. 4-8.

By comparison with Figs. 4-1 and 4-2, these vector diagrams may be seen to be identical with those for generated voltages. It therefore follows that the pitch and breadth factors previously developed may be applied directly to the determination of resultant mmf. Thus, for a distributed fractional-pitch polyphase winding, the amplitude of the space-fundamental component of mmf may be obtained by using $k_b k_p N_{ph}$

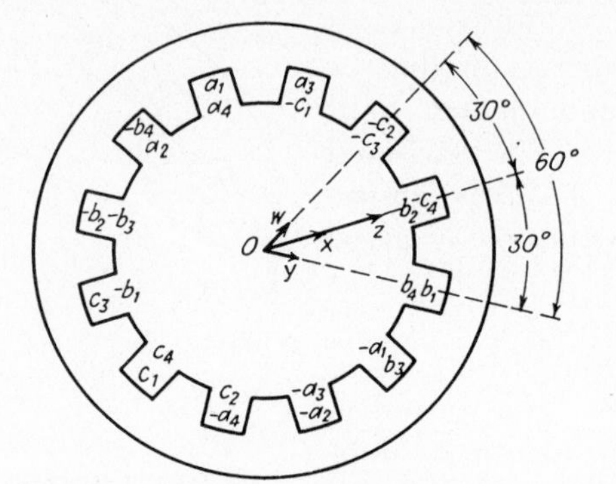

FIG. 4-9. Distributed 3-phase 2-pole fractional-pitch armature winding with mmf vector diagram.

instead of simply N_{ph} in Eqs. 4-22 and 4-23. These equations then become

$$F_A = \frac{3}{2}\frac{4}{\pi}\frac{k_b k_p N_{ph}}{p}(\sqrt{2}\,I) = 0.90\,\frac{3k_b k_p N_{ph}}{p}\,I \qquad \text{amp-turns per pole} \tag{4-24}$$

for a 3-phase machine and

$$F_A = \frac{q}{2}\frac{4}{\pi}\frac{k_b k_p N_{ph}}{p}(\sqrt{2}\,I) = 0.90\,\frac{qk_b k_p N_{ph}}{p}\,I \qquad \text{amp-turns per pole} \tag{4-25}$$

for a q-phase machine, where F_A is in ampere-turns per pole.

4-3. D-C Machines—Generated Voltages. In the preceding two articles, definite steps are taken toward the reconciliation of the voltage and mmf waveforms in practical a-c windings with those in the idealized versions adopted for study in Chap. 3. Similar steps must now be taken for d-c machines.

The resultant spatial flux-density distribution in which the armature coils of a d-c machine rotate usually has the general form shown in Fig. 4-10. It departs very appreciably from the sine wave assumed in obtaining the elementary generated-voltage equation, 3-38, and the departure must be recognized in obtaining a revised voltage expression. Inspection of this distribution shows that the voltage of an individual coil will vary with time because of the space variation of flux density. By virtue of the commutator action, however, it will always make a positive contribution to the voltage between brushes when the brushes are in their proper position. Because of the time variation of the coil voltage, the output voltage between brushes will not have an absolutely steady value but will contain a small ripple, called *commutator ripple*, about a steady average value. When only a few armature coils and slots per pole are used, the ripple may indeed not be small; an extreme ripple, shown in Fig. 3-13, arises from the use of only a single armature coil. For the

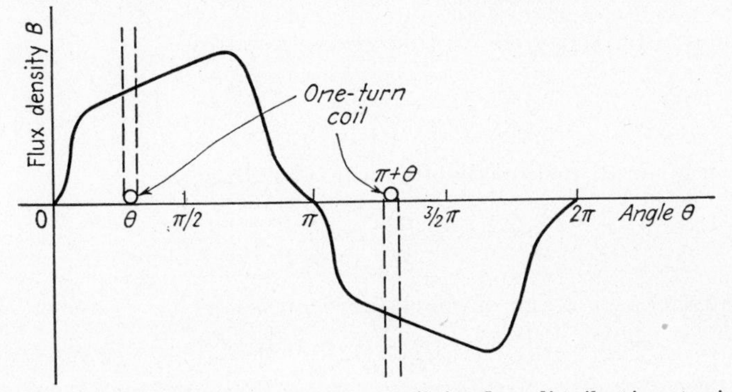

FIG. 4-10. Full-pitch single-turn armature coil in flux distribution typical of d-c machines.

large number of coils distributed over the armature surface of a practical machine, however, the ripple may be ignored for most purposes. It is then the *average value* of the coil voltage that constitutes its significant contribution to the armature generated emf. The armature emf can be evaluated by adding the average voltage contributions of all the coils in series between brushes. Algebraic rather than vector addition is, of course, appropriate, because it is the d-c or average value of coil voltage which is being added.

Consider, then, a single full-pitch 1-turn coil (Fig. 4-10) at the instant when it is subtending the electrical angle θ to $\theta + \pi$ in a p-pole machine. For simplicity, only two of the p poles are indicated. The origin for the angle θ around the air-gap periphery is taken at the zero crossing of the resultant flux-density wave. The flux-density wave may have any constant shape which is finite, continuous, and single-valued and has half-cycle symmetry; *i.e.*, the value of flux density at the angle $\theta + \pi$ is the negative of the value at θ. The flux linkages with the coil are

$$\lambda = lr \int_{\theta}^{\theta+\pi} B_\theta \frac{2}{p}\, d\theta \tag{4-26}$$

l and r being the axial length and radius of the coil, respectively. If the coil is displaced by an angle $d\theta$, the value of these linkages changes to an extent determined by the flux in the angle increments $d\theta$ at θ and $\theta + \pi$. The change at θ in flux linking the coil is proportional to $-B_\theta\, d\theta$; the corresponding change at $\theta + \pi$ is $+B_{\theta+\pi}\, d\theta$. The net change in flux linkages is then

$$d\lambda = lr \frac{2}{p} (-B_\theta\, d\theta + B_{\theta+\pi}\, d\theta) \tag{4-27}$$

But, because of the half-cycle symmetry of the flux wave,

$$B_{\theta+\pi} = -B_\theta \tag{4-28}$$

The angular rate of change of linkages is therefore

$$\frac{d\lambda}{d\theta} = -2lr \frac{2}{p} B_\theta \tag{4-29}$$

Since, in general, instantaneous induced voltage is

$$e = \frac{d\lambda}{dt} = \frac{d\lambda}{d\theta}\frac{d\theta}{dt} \tag{4-30}$$

the instantaneous voltage of the 1-turn coil is

$$e_{\text{turn}} = 2lr \frac{2}{p} B_\theta \frac{d\theta}{dt} \tag{4-31}$$

with the minus sign omitted, since the positive direction of emf can be determined, when needed, by Lenz' law. The angular velocity $d\theta/dt$ is related to the speed n in rpm by the expression

$$\frac{d\theta}{dt} = \frac{2\pi n}{60}\frac{p}{2} \tag{4-32}$$

for the p-pole machine. Hence,

$$e_{\text{turn}} = 4\pi \frac{n}{60} lrB_\theta \tag{4-33}$$

With the brushes in the neutral position (*i.e.*, located so they are connected to inductors at $\theta = 0$ and $\theta = \pi$ in Fig. 4-10), the contribution of the coil to the average induced voltage of the armature is equal to the average value of e_{turn} over the time required for the left-hand side of the coil to rotate from $\theta = 0$ to $\theta = \pi$. Thus,

$$E_{a(\text{turn})} = \frac{1}{\pi}\int_0^\pi e_{\text{turn}}\, d\theta \tag{4-34}$$

$$= 4\frac{n}{60}\int_0^\pi B_\theta lr\, d\theta \tag{4-35}$$

The integral in Eq. 4-35 can be evaluated from the fact that it differs from the flux per pole Φ in a p-pole machine by the factor $2/p$; that is,

$$\Phi = \int_0^\pi B_\theta lr \frac{2}{p}\, d\theta \tag{4-36}$$

so that

$$E_{a(\text{turn})} = 2p\Phi \frac{n}{60} \tag{4-37}$$

If the brushes were not in the neutral position, the average of e_{turn} would not be taken over the interval $\theta = 0$ to $\theta = \pi$, but over the interval subtended by the actual brush position. With the brushes in their normal neutral position, the average voltage per armature coil is dependent on the flux per pole but is independent of its space distribution around the air gap. Equation 4-37 is accordingly consistent with Eq. 3-38, developed on the basis of sinusoidal flux distribution.

When there is a total of Z inductors in the armature winding, there are $Z/2$ turns, each of which is making the contribution given by Eq. 4-37 to the average voltage. With a parallel paths through the armature (see Art. 3-9*c*, and note that $a = 2$ for a wave winding and $a = p$ for a lap winding), only $1/a$ of these turns are in series between positive and negative brushes. There are then $Z/2a$ series turns between brushes, and the resultant average value of armature generated voltage is

$$E_a = p\Phi \frac{Z}{a} \frac{n}{60} \tag{4-38}$$

Since the quantities p, Z, and a are determined by design and remain constant for a specific machine, Eq. 4-38 is frequently written as

$$E_a = k_E \Phi n \tag{4-39}$$

where

$$k_E = \frac{p}{60} \frac{Z}{a} \tag{4-40}$$

Summation of the individual inductor voltages by multiplying the voltage per inductor by the number of series inductors is equivalent to saying that all inductors at all times make a positive contribution to the resultant emf. This equivalence in turn involves the assumptions that the brushes are in the neutral position, that the armature coils are full-pitch coils, and that the effect on the resultant voltage of short-circuiting one or more coils by the brushes during commutation is negligible. Either a shift of the brushes from the neutral position or the use of short-pitch coils will cause the voltage contribution of inductors to be negative during the portion of the revolution when they are near the center of the interpolar space. For the small brush shifts which may occasionally be encountered or the small angles by which the armature coils may fall short of full-pitch coils, the number of inductors so involved at any instant of time is relatively small. Moreover, the inductors at this instant are in the region of very low flux density associated with the interpolar space, so that their voltage contribution during this period is relatively very small. As far as commutation is concerned, the time during which a given coil is short-circuited by the brushes is relatively small and again corresponds to the interpolar region of low flux density. The end result is that Eq. 4-38 gives an induced voltage which may be slightly high but which will be well within the range of engineering accuracy for all normal machines. Actually, the effect of brush shift can be incorporated, if desired, by reinterpretation of the flux per pole Φ. Lastly, it may be pointed out that all these effects are appropriately included when k_E is determined from tests on the particular machine.

The same result can be obtained by direct application of the *Blv* concept for voltage in terms of the value of flux density being swept through by the conductor; this alternative process will not be repeated here. Either process shows the armature generated voltage E_a to be directly dependent on the flux per pole Φ but to be independent of its distribution as long as the brushes are in their proper position. Moreover, when Φ is taken as the resultant flux per pole determined by both field and armature mmf, all of the time-varying flux linkages with the active armature turns are included. The armature terminal voltage under load then differs from E_a only by the resistance drop in the armature winding and brushes.

Example 4-5. The wave-wound armature of a 250-volt 1,750-rpm 4-pole d-c machine has 37 slots with 6 coil sides per slot and 2 turns per coil. The average length of 1 turn is 30 in., and the armature conductor has a resistance of 1.0 ohm per 1,000 ft.

a. Find the resultant flux per pole required to produce a generated emf equal to the rated voltage at rated speed.

b. Determine the resistance of the armature winding.

c. Consider that the machine is driven at rated speed and acting as a generator with an armature current of 40 amp. The voltage drop in the brushes and brush contacts equals 2.0 volts total. To what value must the resultant flux be adjusted for the armature terminal voltage to equal the rated value?

d. If the speed of the prime mover should drop to 1,600 rpm, with conditions otherwise as in *c*, to what value must the resultant flux be readjusted for the armature terminal voltage again to equal the rated value?

e. Consider that the machine is acting as a motor with rated armature terminal voltage and an armature current of 40 amp. The brush and brush-contact drop is still 2.0 volts. To what value must the resultant flux be adjusted for the motor speed to equal 1,500 rpm?

Solution. *a.* The total number of armature inductors is

$$Z = 37 \times 6 \times 2 = 444$$

Equation 4-38 then yields

$$250 = 4\Phi \times \frac{444}{2} \times \frac{1,750}{60}$$

or

$$\Phi = 0.00965 \text{ weber, or } 965,000 \text{ lines per pole}$$

b. There are a total of $Z/2 = 222$ turns on the armature, 111 of which are in each of the two parallel paths between the positive and negative terminals. The resistance of one parallel path is

$$111 \times \frac{30}{12} \times \frac{1}{1,000} = 0.28 \text{ ohm}$$

The resistance of the armature winding between terminals is then 0.28/2, or 0.14 ohm.

c. Under these conditions, E_a must be higher than the armature terminal voltage by the amount of the drop in the winding and brushes; *i.e.*,

$$E_a = 250 + 2 + 40 \times 0.14 = 257.6 \text{ volts}$$

Hence,

$$\Phi = 0.00965 \times \frac{257.6}{250} = 0.00993 \text{ weber}$$

d. The voltage E_a must still be 257.6 volts. From Eq. 4-39, the flux must be increased to

$$\Phi = 0.00993 \times \frac{1,750}{1,600} = 0.0109 \text{ weber}$$

e. Under these conditions, E_a must be lower than the armature terminal voltage by the amount of the drop in the winding and brushes; *i.e.*,

$$E_a = 250 - 2 - 40 \times 0.14 = 242.4 \text{ volts}$$

In order that this voltage may be generated at a speed of 1,500 rpm, the flux per pole must be

$$\Phi = 0.00965 \times \frac{242.4}{250} \times \frac{1,750}{1,500} = 0.0109 \text{ weber}$$

4-4. D-C Machines—Magnetic Fields. The brushes on a d-c machine are normally so positioned around the commutator that they are connected directly to inductors in the neutral plane or interpolar space. All active armature inductors carry equal currents, and the currents have one direction for all inductors under a north field pole and the opposite direction for all inductors under a south field pole. These directions remain the same regardless of the speed of rotation: as a particular inductor passes from under a north field pole to under a south field pole, the current direction in it is changed by the commutator action. It becomes an easy matter to examine the mmf produced by the armature winding, for rotation of the winding can be essentially ignored.

Since the armature inductors under any field pole are uniformly distributed over the armature surface and all carry the same current in the same direction, representation by a current sheet with uniform angular current density suggests itself. Thus, a 2-pole d-c winding may be represented in the manner of Fig. 4-11, and a 4-pole winding in the manner of Fig. 4-12. This representation becomes more and more nearly an exact one as the number of slots and inductors becomes very large. As shown by Fig. 3-3 and its accompanying discussion, the associated armature-mmf wave is a triangular wave whose peak value is $\pi J/2$

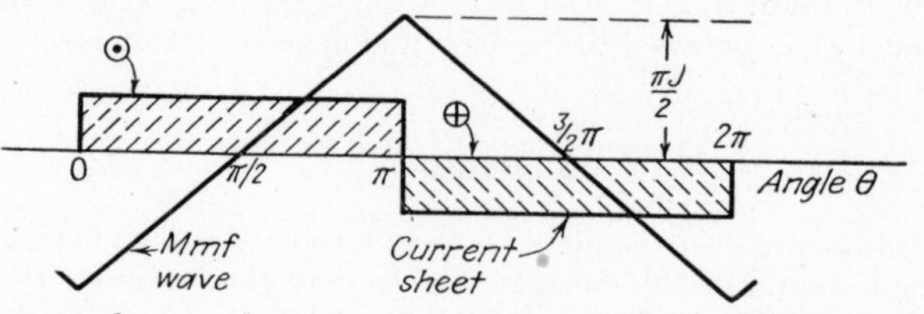

FIG. 4-11. Current sheet and mmf wave for 2-pole finely distributed d-c armature winding.

amp-turns per pole when J is the angular current density in amperes per electrical radian.

The angular current density can be evaluated by equating the number of ampere-conductors under a pole in the actual winding to the number of ampere-conductors under a pole in the current sheet. For a winding with Z inductors, a parallel paths, p poles, and carrying the armature current I_a, the current per inductor is I_a/a. The number of armature inductors under a pole at any time is Z/p. The number of ampere-conductors per pole is then $(Z/p)\,(I_a/a)$. In the uniform current sheet,

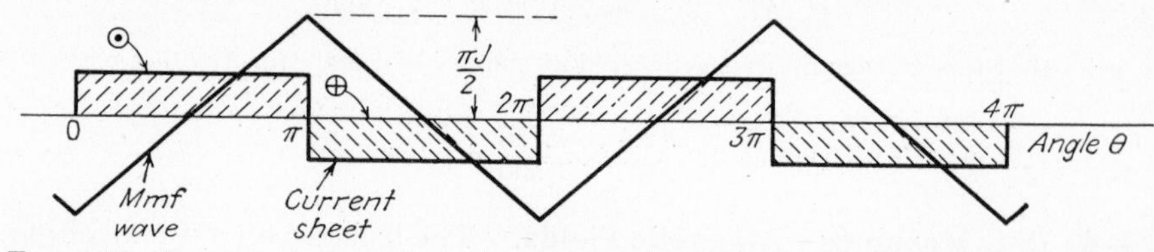

FIG. 4-12. Current sheet and mmf wave for 4-pole finely distributed d-c armature winding.

the total current under a pole is πJ, and the sheet is the equivalent of one large conductor. For the magnetic effects to be equivalent,

$$\pi J = \frac{Z}{p}\frac{I_a}{a} \tag{4-41}$$

or

$$J = \frac{Z}{\pi p}\frac{I_a}{a} \qquad \text{amp/elec rad} \tag{4-42}$$

In accordance with Fig. 3-3e, the peak amplitude of the associated triangular mmf wave is

$$F_A = \frac{\pi J}{2} = \frac{Z}{2p}\frac{I_a}{a} \qquad \text{amp-turns per pole} \tag{4-43}$$

In our subsequent reexamination of torque in d-c machines, it turns out to be a simple matter to deal directly with the triangular mmf wave and the uniform current sheet. Accordingly, it is unnecessary to single out fundamental components or harmonics for individual treatment. In this respect, the analysis of d-c machines with their commutated windings is less ramified than for a-c machines.

4-5. Modified Torque Equations. With more specific relations for armature mmf and generated voltage available, we are in a position to reexamine the basic torque equation, 3-22. Such reexamination is carried out first for polyphase a-c machines and then for d-c machines. The results are summarizing equations for electromagnetic torque in forms which are most convenient for subsequent detailed analysis of individual machine types. The development for d-c machines incorporates the representation of the armature winding by an equivalent uniform current sheet.

a. Polyphase A-C Machines. The basic torque equation, 3-22, may be modified by replacing Φ by its value from Eq. 4-14 and F_{peak} by the mmf amplitude in Eq. 4-25. Thus, for the entire machine

$$T = \frac{\pi}{2}\left(\frac{p}{2}\right)^2 F_A\Phi \sin \delta \tag{4-44}$$

$$= \frac{\pi}{8} p^2 \left[\frac{E}{(2\pi/\sqrt{2})k_b k_p f N_{ph}}\right]\left(\frac{2\sqrt{2}}{\pi}\frac{qk_bk_pN_{ph}}{p} I\right) \sin \delta \tag{4-45}$$

$$= \frac{p}{4\pi f} qEI \sin \delta \tag{4-46}$$

Now, as illustrated by the discussion of Art. 3-7*c* and *e*, the term sin δ, referring to the space angle between the flux-density wave and the mmf or magnetic-potential-difference wave, may be replaced by the term cos θ, referring to the time angle between the E and I vectors, provided care is ultimately used in evaluating the direction of the torque. A brief recapitulation of this reasoning in more general terms is the following: The mmf wave is centered on a particular phase at the instant when the current in that phase is a maximum; the flux wave is centered on that phase at an instant 90 electrical degrees in time away from that when the generated voltage is a maximum; the space angle δ between the waves and the time angle θ between the E and I vectors therefore differ by 90°; and sin δ may be replaced by cos θ.

Equation 4-46 may therefore be written

$$T = \frac{p}{4\pi f} qEI \cos \theta \tag{4-47}$$

In this equation, the term $4\pi f/p = 2\omega/p$ is the mechanical angular velocity of the field with respect to the winding. Moreover, the term $qEI \cos \theta$ is the average power in the q-phase winding. Equation 4-47 therefore characterizes the energy-conversion process simply by equating average mechanical and electrical power in the steady state. If the generated power is positive, the electromagnetic torque is in the same direction as the relative velocity ω of the magnetic field with respect to the winding; if the generated power is negative, the electromagnetic torque is opposite to the direction of the relative velocity ω. Equation 4-47 might have been written directly from energy-conservation principles together with the fact that the average rate of energy storage in the magnetic field is zero in the steady state; in other words, it might have been written by direct application of the first of the four methods of torque evaluation outlined in Art. 1-7. It may also be obtained readily from the *Blv* and *Bli* concepts discussed in Art. 1-2*a*. The disadvantage of confining oneself to writing it directly from energy conservation is that it then says, in effect, *if* the machine works, these relations must be satisfied. It gives no physical idea of *how* the machine works, what criteria for successful operation must be satisfied, or what varied possibilities exist for developing successful machine types. The approach by way of basic electromagnetic principles and the torque equation, 3-22, or any of its other forms is much more fruitful in these respects. In view of the assumptions and idealizations which have been necessary in following this approach, it is reassuring to find an outward indication of basic soundness in that conservation of energy is still satisfied in the present results.

The principal advantages of Eq. 4-47 from the computational viewpoint are twofold. In the first place, a method of power bookkeeping is immediately suggested for the determination of some machine characteristics. Such a method would be based on the equality between mechanical or electrical power input and electrical or mechanical output, respectively, plus losses. Equation 4-47 and its associated relations form convenient links between power and other machine quantities. Second, the fact that it involves only circuit quantities and not field quantities makes it more directly applicable to analysis of the machine by an equivalent circuit.

b. D-C Machines. A revised version of the basic torque equation must be obtained in order to fit the triangular mmf wave created by d-c armatures. The procedure is very like that leading to Eq. 3-22, but the flux-density, armature mmf, and armature current sheet are no longer sine waves. The basic relation once more is Eq. 1-24 for electromagnetic torque T in a p-pole machine in terms of angular rate of change of flux linkages $d\lambda/d\theta$ and current i, namely,

$$T = \frac{p}{2} i \frac{d\lambda}{d\theta} \tag{4-48}$$

As in the derivation of Eq. 3-22, attention will first be confined to the 2-pole case.

Consider, then, a machine for which the space distributions of resultant flux density and armature mmf are as shown in Fig. 4-13. The origin is taken at the zero crossing of the flux-density wave, and the mmf wave is displaced from it by the angle δ. The sign convention for both the flux-density and mmf wave is consistent with the convention of considering the flux positive when it leaves the armature surface as from a

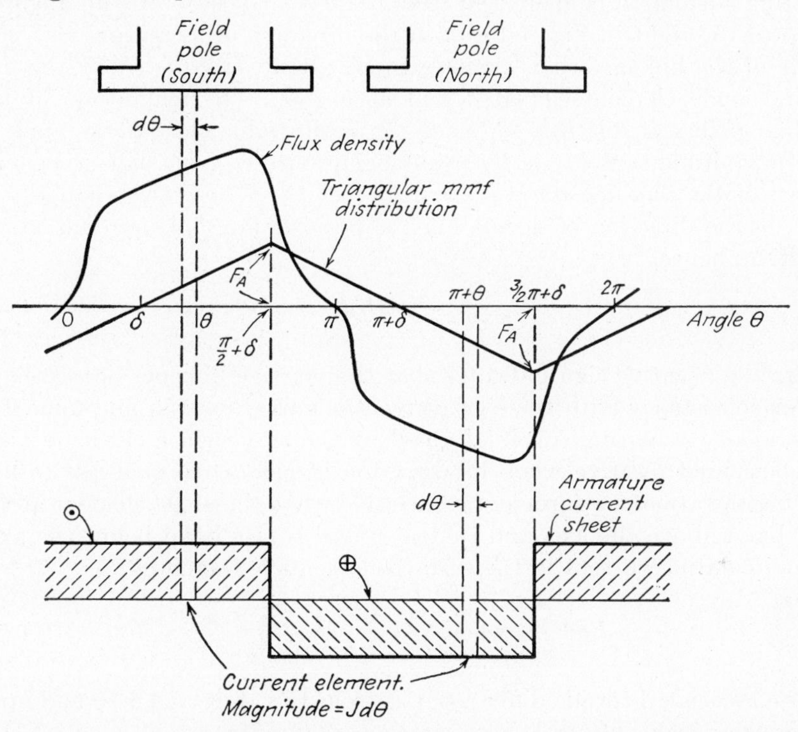

FIG. 4-13. Flux density, mmf, and current sheet for typical d-c machine with finely distributed armature winding.

north magnetic pole on the armature. The flux-density wave may have any constant shape which is finite, continuous, and single-valued and has half-cycle symmetry. The mmf wave is triangular with its amplitude given by Eq. 4-43. The current sheet producing it has the uniform angular surface current density given by Eq. 4-42.

Figure 4-13 shows two current elements contained in the angles $d\theta$ located π electrical radians apart in the current sheet; one current element is at the angle θ, and the other is at the angle $\theta + \pi$. The two elements contain equal and opposite currents of magnitude $J\,d\theta$ and thus form a circulating current or are the equivalent of a 1-turn full-pitch coil carrying this current. The torque dT contributed by these current elements will first be evaluated, and then the total torque T will be found by integrating so as to include all such elements on the armature.

The total flux linking this circulating current is

$$\lambda = \int_{\theta}^{\theta+\pi} Blr\, d\theta \tag{4-49}$$

To find the angular rate of change of these linkages, imagine the circulating current to be displaced from its present position by an angle $d\theta$ (toward the right in Fig. 4-13, or in the direction of increasing θ). The value of the linkages then changes to an extent determined by the flux in the angle elements $d\theta$ at θ and at $\theta + \pi$. The magnitude of the change of flux at θ is $B_\theta lr\, d\theta$, where B_θ is the value of B at the angle θ. The magnitude at $\theta + \pi$ is $B_{\theta+\pi}lr\, d\theta$, or, by virtue of the half-cycle symmetry of the flux-density wave, again $B_\theta lr\, d\theta$. These two changes are both in the direction of decreasing the positive flux linkages and so are additive; hence,

$$\frac{d\lambda}{d\theta} = -2B_\theta lr \tag{4-50}$$

where the negative sign indicates that the positive linkages decrease.

For consistency with the sign conventions used for flux and mmf, the equivalent circulating current formed by the two surface elements must be considered positive when its direction is such as to give rise to flux leaving the armature surface, *i.e.*, positive when the angle element at θ is in a band above the axis and that at $\theta + \pi$ is in a band below the axis. The circulating current in the surface elements is therefore

$$J\, d\theta \qquad \text{when } \delta - \frac{\pi}{2} < \theta < \delta + \frac{\pi}{2} \tag{4-51}$$

The associated torque differential is, from Eqs. 4-48 and 4-50 and upon recognizing that only two poles are concerned so far,

$$dT = -J(2lr)B_\theta\, d\theta \qquad \text{when } \delta - \frac{\pi}{2} < \theta < \delta + \frac{\pi}{2} \tag{4-52}$$

The total torque for a p-pole machine, found by integration over the angle from $\delta - (\pi/2)$ to $\delta + (\pi/2)$ so as to include all the current sheet, and multiplication by the number of pole pairs, is then

$$T = -pJ \int_{\delta-(\pi/2)}^{\delta+(\pi/2)} B_\theta lr\, d\theta = -\frac{p^2}{2} J \int_{\delta-(\pi/2)}^{\delta+(\pi/2)} B_\theta lr \frac{2}{p}\, d\theta \tag{4-53}$$

The development can be carried no further than Eq. 4-53 in terms of the general displacement angle δ. In normal operation of a d-c machine, however, the brushes are placed in the neutral plane, and $\delta = \pi/2$. The integral in Eq. 4-53 then becomes the flux per pole Φ. Consequently, the torque for a machine with brushes on the neutral is

$$T = -\frac{p^2}{2} J\Phi \tag{4-54}$$

By virtue of Eq. 4-43, the torque may also be written

$$T = -\frac{p^2}{\pi} F_A\Phi \tag{4-55}$$

This expression for the electromagnetic torque is essentially a formulation of the magnetic-field viewpoint, which, as stated in Art. 1-2*b*, regards torque as the result of magnetic fields trying to line up so that a north magnetic pole on one machine member is directly opposite a south pole on the other member. The minus sign in Eq. 4-55 is also in accord with this viewpoint; it shows that the torque acts in the direction tending to make δ smaller than 90°—in other words, so that the positive halves of the two waves in Fig. 4-13 tend to pull together, corresponding to a north pole on the rotor trying to line up with a south pole on the stator.

When it is remembered that the electromagnetic torque acts in the direction tending to line up stator and rotor fields, the minus sign may be dropped in Eqs. 4-54 and 4-55 and the resulting relations regarded as ones for torque magnitude only. By another combination of Eqs. 4-42 and 4-54, the torque can be put in the form

$$T = \frac{p}{2\pi}\frac{Z}{a}\Phi I_a \qquad \text{newton-m} \tag{4-56}$$

where the minus sign has been dropped. Flux Φ is measured in webers and armature current I_a in amperes. Since the number of poles p, armature inductors Z, and parallel paths a are design constants which remain fixed for any specific machine, Eq. 4-56 is often written as

$$T = k_T\Phi I_a \qquad \text{newton-m} \tag{4-57}$$

where

$$k_T = \frac{p}{2\pi}\frac{Z}{a} \tag{4-58}$$

Alternatively,

$$T = 0.738\frac{p}{2\pi}\frac{Z}{a}\Phi I_a = k'_T\Phi I_a \qquad \text{lb-ft} \tag{4-59}$$

where

$$k'_T = 0.738\frac{p}{2\pi}\frac{Z}{a} \tag{4-60}$$

The analysis leading to Eqs. 4-56 to 4-60 clearly shows the electromagnetic torque of a d-c machine, like the armature generated voltage investigated in Art. 4-3, to depend only on the flux per pole and not on its distribution as long as the brushes are in their normal neutral position. No separate examination of harmonic effects is required, and detailed analyses of steady-state performance may therefore be based on Eqs. 4-38 for voltage and 4-56 for torque. These equations may be combined to yield a single relation characterizing the energy-conversion process by the equality of mechanical and electrical power, as was done in Art. 4-5*a* for polyphase machines. Thus, substitution of the value of Φ from Eq. 4-38 in Eq. 4-56 gives

$$T = \frac{60}{2\pi n} E_a I_a = \frac{1}{\omega_o} E_a I_a \tag{4-61}$$

where ω_o is the angular velocity of the shaft. Equation 4-61 for d-c machines is exactly equivalent to Eq. 4-47 for a-c machines. All of the concluding remarks in the last two paragraphs of Art. 4-5*a* may therefore be repeated here for d-c machines with reference to Eq. 4-61.

4-6. Generated Voltage Harmonics. For d-c machines, the generated-voltage equation, 4-38, takes appropriate cognizance of whatever flux distribution may be found in an actual machine as long as the brushes are in their proper position. For a-c machines, however, the generated-voltage equation, 4-14, takes cognizance of only fundamental-frequency components. Harmonics in the generated voltage of a-c machines are studied in this article. The techniques are very like those of Art. 4-1 except that they are applied term by term to the higher frequency components.

a. Voltage Harmonics in Polyphase Machines. Spatial flux-density distributions in the air gaps of machines are never pure sinusoids. Several factors intimately related to limitations of mechanical construction enter into the departure from a sinusoid. The flux distribution of the exciting or field winding acting alone can be made only approximately sinusoidal, as illustrated by Fig. 4-14 for a synchronous machine. Also, when the machine is loaded, both the armature and field or stator and rotor mmfs play a part in determining the resultant air-gap flux, a fact which may give rise to further distortion. Pronounced effects of this nature may be found in salient-pole machines because of wide differences in air-gap geometry in the polar and interpolar axes. Possible saturation of local regions of the iron may also contribute to distortion. Moreover, the slots for embedding the windings in the rotor and stator iron will affect the flux distribution for both unloaded and loaded machines, effects which are ignored in Fig. 4-14. For the present, attention will be confined to flux distributions whose spatial waveforms retain their shape while they rotate with respect to the armature winding. Conformity to this restriction is most nearly achieved by the flux created by the d-c field winding of a synchronous machine, and then only when the effect of slots is ignored.

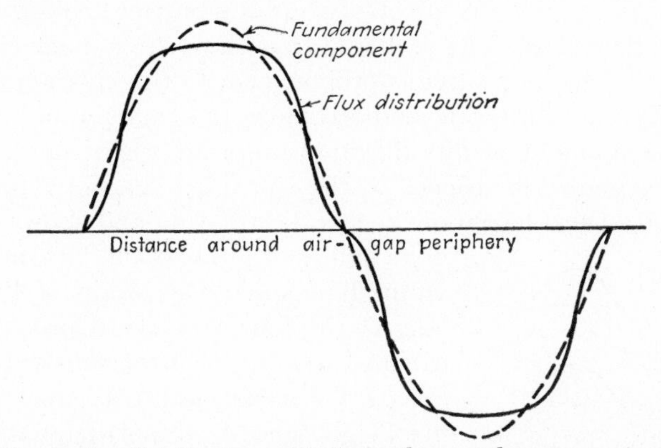

FIG. 4-14. Air-gap flux distribution, with its fundamental component, created by main field winding in a synchronous machine.

Neglect of harmonics is the equivalent of regarding the fundamental components, shown dotted in Fig. 4-14, as sufficiently good representations of the actual distributions. Analysis based on sinusoids, however, may be applied not only to the fundamental but also to each of the harmonics to obtain results more nearly consistent with the actual waveform. These harmonics become factors of potential importance when it is recognized that, in accordance with the Blv equation with velocity v constant, the time waveform of the voltage generated in a coil side is identical with the space waveform of flux-density distribution. When the total voltage of all the coil sides forming an entire phase is viewed, however, it may be found that the harmonic voltages are greatly decreased in comparison with the fundamental.

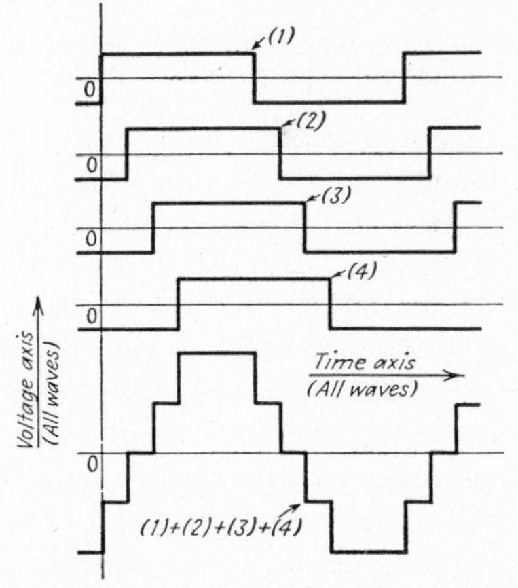

FIG. 4-15. Individual coil-voltage waveforms in a distributed a-c armature winding, and the resulting waveform for the coil group.

The effect of distributing the winding may be seen pictorially in Fig. 4-15, which is drawn for a machine with full-pitch coils distributed in four slots per pole per phase. The flux distribution is assumed to be rectangular; accordingly, the coil-voltage waveforms (1), (2), (3), and

(4) are likewise rectangular. The four voltages are displaced in time by the electrical angle between slots. As a result, the waveform of their sum is much more nearly sinusoidal than that of the individual component, and the harmonic content is correspondingly lowered.

To observe pictorially the effect of chording on the voltage waveform of a coil, note from Eqs. 3-31 and 3-33 that the voltage induced in a coil by a sinusoidal space-flux wave is proportional to the maximum value of the flux linkages with the coil, and recognize that maximum linkages for a sinusoidal component of flux distribution occur when the coil is symmetrically disposed with respect to the sinusoid. Figure 4-16 is drawn specifically for a third harmonic in flux distribution and shows coils with four values of pitch at the instant of maximum linkages. The value of linkages in any of the four sketches is proportional to the net area between the sine wave and the axis. For a full-pitch coil, this value is at its height and is proportional to the area under a full half cycle. For a ⅚-pitch coil, it is noticeably lower. For a ⅔-pitch coil, the value is zero and will remain zero regardless of the relative position of coil and flux wave. For a ½-pitch coil, the value is the same as for the ⅚ pitch coil but is reversed in sign, indicating a reversal of the third-harmonic voltage. During the decrease in coil pitch, the fundamental linkages also decrease, of course, but not nearly in the same proportion. Thus, by appropriate choice of coil pitch, the third harmonic of coil voltage can be reduced by any desired amount and can be made zero by use of a ⅔ pitch. Similarly, the fifth harmonic can be made zero by a ⅘ pitch, the seventh by a 6/7 pitch, etc. From the *Blv* viewpoint, these statements are the equivalent of saying that the harmonic voltage in the two coil sides can be phase-displaced by a desired amount, so that, for any individual harmonic, their sum can be reduced by a desired factor.

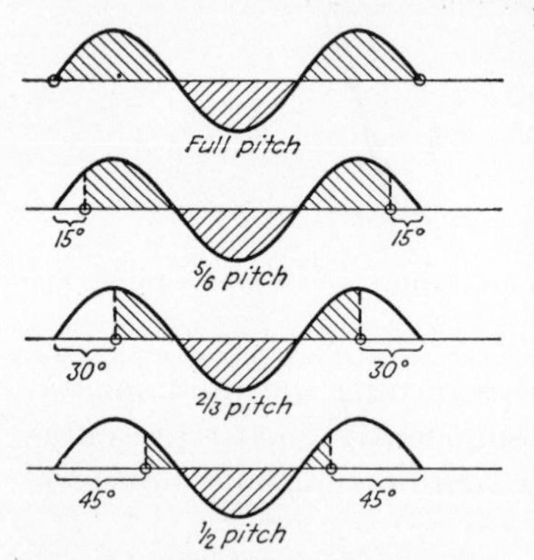

FIG. 4-16. Third-harmonic flux linking a full-pitch and several fractional-pitch coils. All angles are measured on the fundamental scale.

The magnitudes of the harmonic voltages in a distributed fractional-pitch winding may be computed readily. The phase displacement created by a slot angle of γ electrical degrees on the fundamental scale becomes $h\gamma$ for the hth harmonic on the harmonic scale; likewise, the pitch angle ρ electrical degrees on the fundamental scale becomes $h\rho$ on the harmonic scale. The breadth, pitch, and winding factors then become

$$k_{bh} = \frac{\sin (nh\gamma/2)}{n \sin (h\gamma/2)} \tag{4-62}$$

$$k_{ph} = \cos \frac{h(\pi - \rho)}{2} \tag{4-63}$$

and

$$k_{wh} = k_{bh}k_{ph} \tag{4-64}$$

for the hth harmonic. Ordinarily, only odd harmonics are involved because in a normal machine the flux-distribution curve possesses half-cycle symmetry. The rms value of the harmonic generated voltage, corresponding to that of Eq. 4-14, is usually expressed in terms of the hth harmonic flux Φ_h per hth-harmonic pole as

$$E_h = 4.44k_{bh}k_{ph}hfN_{ph}\Phi_h \tag{4-65}$$

f still being the fundamental frequency and the added factor h appearing because the number of hth-harmonic poles traversed per revolution is h times the number of fundamental poles traversed.

Example 4-6. In Examples 4-2 and 4-3, breadth, pitch, and winding factors for the emf fundamental are computed for a 3-phase 6-pole a-c machine having a 5/6-pitch winding distributed in 36 slots. Consider now that the flux-density distribution is to be rectangular and that account is to be taken of harmonics up to and including the seventh. Compare the relative magnitudes of emf harmonics with those of the flux-density harmonics.

Solution. Breadth, pitch, and winding factors, obtained from Eqs. 4-62, 4-63, and 4-64, are as follows:

Factor	$h = 1$	$h = 3$	$h = 5$	$h = 7$
k_{bh}	0.966	0.707	0.259	−0.259
k_{ph}	0.966	0.707	0.259	−0.259
k_{wh}	0.933	0.500	0.067	0.067
k_{wh}/k_{w1}	1	0.536	0.072	0.072

The ratio k_{wh}/k_{w1} indicates the relative attenuation of the harmonics compared with the fundamental.

The hth-harmonic flux per hth-harmonic pole is a function of the amplitude $B_{(\text{peak})h}$ of the hth flux-density harmonic and of the area of the hth-harmonic pole, the latter being $1/h$ of the area of a fundamental pole. That is,

$$\frac{\Phi_h}{\Phi_1} = \frac{B_{(\text{peak})h}}{hB_{(\text{peak})1}} \tag{4-66}$$

The generated-voltage ratio is, from Eq. 4-65,

$$\frac{E_h}{E_1} = \frac{hk_{bh}k_{ph}\Phi_h}{k_{b1}k_{p1}\Phi_1} = \frac{k_{wh}B_{(\text{peak})h}}{k_{w1}B_{(\text{peak})1}} \tag{4-67}$$

The ratio $B_{(peak)h}/B_{(peak)1}$ is given by the Fourier series for a rectangular wave, Eq. 4-17. The resulting comparison of flux- and voltage-harmonic ratios is as follows:

Ratio	$h = 1$	$h = 3$	$h = 5$	$h = 7$
$B_{(peak)h}/B_{(peak)1}$	1	0.333	0.200	0.143
E_h/E_1	1	0.179	0.014	0.010

Example 4-7. Show that for a q-phase machine the harmonic breadth and pitch factors will be the same as those for the fundamental when the order of the harmonic is given by

$$h = 2S_p \pm 1$$

where S_p is the number of slots per pole.

Solution. Refer to Fig. 4-3, and recall that breadth factor provides a means of adding a group of equal vectors displaced from each other by a definite angle. The displacement of the fundamentals is

$$\frac{180°}{S_p} = \gamma$$

The displacement of the harmonic vectors of order $2S_p \pm 1$ is

$$(2S_p \pm 1)\frac{180°}{S_p} = 360° \pm \frac{180°}{S_p} = 360° \pm \gamma$$

Now n equal vectors whose displacement from each other is $360° \pm \gamma$ will obviously have the same ratio of magnitude of vector sum to arithmetic sum as will n equal vectors whose displacement is γ. Hence the breadth factors are the same.

Similarly, refer to Fig. 4-5, and recall that pitch factor merely provides a means of adding two equal vectors displaced by a definite angle. The displacement of the fundamentals is

$$\rho = m\gamma = m\frac{180°}{S_p}$$

where m is an integer. This equation states, in effect, that the two sides of a coil must be placed in slots and hence displaced by some multiple of the angle between slots. The displacement of harmonic vectors of order $2S_p \pm 1$ is

$$(2S_p \pm 1)m\frac{180°}{S_p} = m(360°) \pm m\frac{180°}{S_p} = m(360°) \pm \rho$$

Now two equal vectors whose displacement is $m(360°) \pm \rho$ will obviously have the same ratio of magnitude of vector sum to arithmetic sum as will two equal vectors whose displacement is ρ. Hence the pitch factors are the same.

These harmonics are known as *slot* or *tooth harmonics*. They may be among the most troublesome because their magnitudes relative to the fundamental are not reduced by the breadth and pitch factors as are those of other harmonics. Reduction of tooth harmonics by means of skewing is discussed in Art. 4-8.

b. Fractional-slot Windings. All of the polyphase windings considered thus far have had an integral number of slots per pole per phase and have therefore been *integral-slot windings.* As a result, the appearance of the winding before each pole is the same. See Fig. 4-6, for example, noting that the array of letter designations for coil sides is the same for each pole except for the minus signs. Note also that in the upper row of coil sides those labeled $-a$ follow precisely 180 electrical degrees after those labeled a and that the same situation obtains in the lower row.

An ingenious and useful method of reducing harmonic content is found in *fractional-slot windings,* where the number of slots per pole per phase is not an integer. This method is especially valuable in low-speed machines, where, because of the many poles required, there is room for only a very few slots per pole, and hence the normal distribution factor cannot be counted on for significant reduction of harmonics. Also, use of a fractional-slot winding provides an additional degree of freedom in the choice of punchings for the iron core and thus may lead to a more economical machine by permitting the use of punchings for which tools

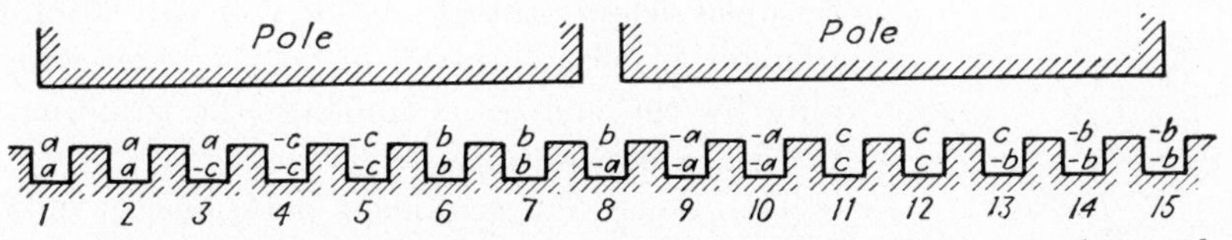

FIG. 4-17. Developed diagram of 3-phase winding with $2\frac{1}{2}$ slots per pole per phase.

are already available An example of a 3-phase winding having $2\frac{1}{2}$ slots per pole per phase is given in Fig. 4-17 Note here that the appearance of the winding before each pole is not the same. When more than two poles are used, however, the appearance before every pair of poles will be the same as for the pair shown here, so that two poles constitute a repeatable section for this particular example. The pitch of the winding is seven slots; hence the lower row starting in slot 8 is a repetition of the upper row with the sign changed. Three-phase voltages are produced because any one phase-a group is displaced 120 electrical degrees from the corresponding phase-b and phase-c groups.

As far as reduction of harmonics is concerned, the essential difference between the windings of Figs. 4-6 and 4-17 is that, in the latter, the coil sides labeled $-a$ in the upper row (or in the lower row) do not follow precisely 180 electrical degrees after those labeled a. In Fig. 4-17, they follow 192° after. Vectors representing the phase-a fundamental voltages in the upper coil sides are shown in Fig. 4-18a, where the numerical designations are those of the slots in Fig. 4-17. When vectors 9 and 10 are reversed preparatory to adding them to the others, the diagram becomes that of Fig. 4-18b. But this diagram is the equivalent of one which would be drawn for determining the distribution factor of an integral-slot winding with a significantly greater number of slots per pole per phase. The modified breadth factor k'_b, equal to the ratio of the vector sum to the algebraic sum in Fig. 4-18*b*, is 0.957. In a similar manner, the diagram of Fig. 4-19 may be constructed for third-harmonic voltages, leading to a modified breadth factor k'_{b3} of 0.647. In fact, all

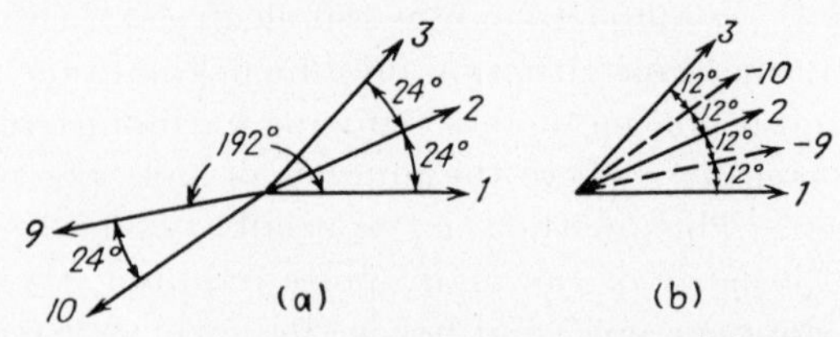

FIG. 4-18. Addition of fundamental voltages in phase *a* of the winding in Fig. 4-17.

of the modified breadth factors k'_{bh} for this winding are the same as the breadth factors for an integral-slot winding with five slots per pole per phase. Thus, the advantages of a more finely distributed winding are retained despite the availability of only a limited number of slots. Pitch factors are determined only by the coil pitch and are the same as for integral-slot windings.

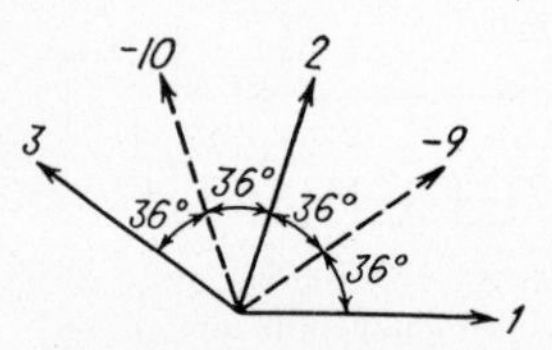

FIG. 4-19. Addition of third-harmonic voltages in phase *a* of the winding in Fig. 4-17.

The fact that balanced polyphase windings are required restricts the combinations of slot and pole numbers which may be used successfully in fractional-slot windings. Each proposed winding may be examined for balance, and the winding factors may be computed by the vector-diagram method illustrated in the preceding paragraph.

c. Three-phase Line-to-line Voltages. Additional influence on terminal-voltage waveform is exerted by the manner of interconnecting coil groups to form a polyphase machine. This influence may be illustrated by considering a 3-phase Y-connected machine (Fig. 4-20). For a flux distribution given by

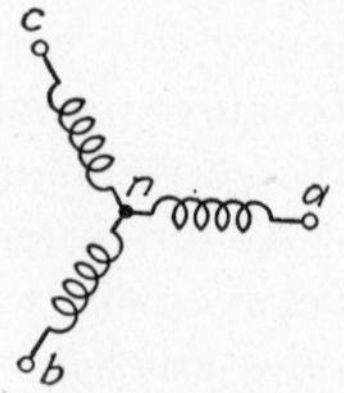

$$B = B_{(\text{peak})1} \sin x + B_{(\text{peak})3} \sin (3x + \alpha_3) + B_{(\text{peak})5} \sin (5x + \alpha_5) + \cdots \tag{4-68}$$

the phase-*a* voltage may be written as

$$e_{an} = \sqrt{2}\, E_1 \sin \omega t + \sqrt{2}\, E_3 \sin (3\omega t + \theta_3) + \sqrt{2}\, E_5 \sin (5\omega t + \theta_5) + \cdots \tag{4-69}$$

FIG. 4-20. Three-phase Y-connected armature.

The angles $\theta_3, \theta_5, \ldots, \theta_h$ are the phase angles of the harmonics with respect to the fundamental. In Eq. 4-69, the voltage e_{an} is the amount by which the potential of terminal *a* exceeds that of the neutral *n*; in general any voltage symbol with such a double subscript is to be interpreted as the amount by which the potential of the point specified by the first subscript exceeds that of the point specified by the second subscript. The time origin in Eq. 4-69 is arbitrarily placed at the zero of the fundamental component of e_{an}. The rms voltages $E_1, E_3, E_5, \ldots, E_h$ are given by Eq. 4-65. For an *abc* phase order of fundamental voltages, the voltages of phases *b* and *c* are

$$e_{bn} = \sqrt{2}\,E_1 \sin(\omega t - 120°) + \sqrt{2}\,E_3 \sin(3\omega t + \theta_3 - 3 \times 120°) + \sqrt{2}\,E_5 \sin(5\omega t + \theta_5 - 5 \times 120°) + \cdots \tag{4-70}$$

and

$$e_{cn} = \sqrt{2}\,E_1 \sin(\omega t + 120°) + \sqrt{2}\,E_3 \sin(3\omega t + \theta_3 + 3 \times 120°) + \sqrt{2}\,E_5 \sin(5\omega t + \theta_5 + 5 \times 120°) + \cdots \tag{4-71}$$

When the numerical phase angles are reduced to their smallest equivalent angles, Eqs. 4-70 and 4-71 may be rewritten

$$e_{bn} = \sqrt{2}\,E_1 \sin(\omega t - 120°) + \sqrt{2}\,E_3 \sin(3\omega t + \theta_3) + \sqrt{2}\,E_5 \sin(5\omega t + \theta_5 + 120°) + \cdots \tag{4-72}$$

and

$$e_{cn} = \sqrt{2}\,E_1 \sin(\omega t + 120°) + \sqrt{2}\,E_3 \sin(3\omega t + \theta_3) + \sqrt{2}\,E_5 \sin(5\omega t + \theta_5 - 120°) + \cdots \tag{4-73}$$

Vector diagrams showing the line-to-neutral voltages E_{an}, E_{bn}, and E_{cn} for the fundamental, third harmonic, and fifth harmonic are given in

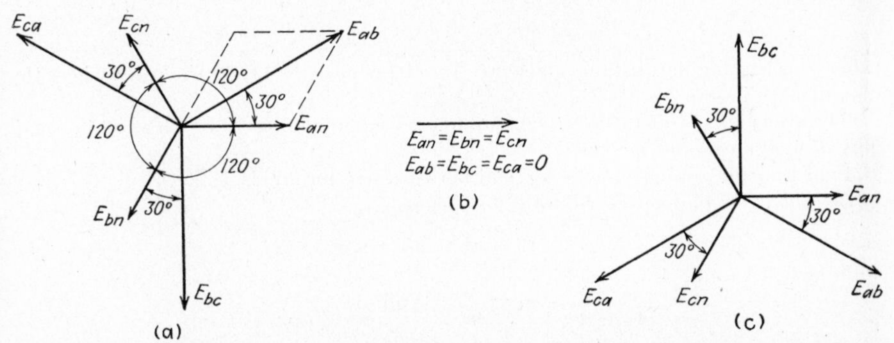

FIG. 4-21. Line-to-neutral and line-to-line voltages for (*a*) fundamental components, (*b*) third harmonics, and (*c*) fifth harmonics in Y-connected alternator.

Fig. 4-21. Notice that the third-harmonic line-to-neutral voltages are all in phase and that the fifth-harmonic voltages are of opposite phase order to the fundamental.

The line-to-line voltage e_{ab} is

$$e_{ab} = e_{an} + e_{nb} = e_{an} - e_{bn} \tag{4-74}$$

The vector construction yielding the fundamental line-to-line voltage E_{ab} is shown in Fig. 4-21*a*. In like manner, the other fundamental and harmonic line-to-line voltages are found to be as indicated in Figs. 4-21*b* and 4-21*c*. Since the third-harmonic line-to-neutral voltages are in time phase, their differences are zero, and no third-harmonic components appear in the line-to-line voltages. The same conclusion holds for all harmonics whose orders are multiples of 3. The waveform of the line-to-line voltages is thus seen to differ from that of the line-to-neutral voltages. Moreover, since the rms value E of a voltage containing a fundamental whose rms value is E_1 and harmonics whose rms values are E_3, E_5, etc., is given by

$$E = \sqrt{E_1^2 + E_3^2 + E_5^2 + \cdots} \tag{4-75}$$

the rms line-to-line voltage will differ somewhat from $\sqrt{3}$ times the rms line-to-neutral voltage when the latter contains triple harmonics.

If a Δ connection is used instead of a Y connection, the third-harmonic voltages around the closed Δ are in phase, and a third-harmonic circulating current exists in the winding. No third-harmonic components exist in the line-to-line voltage, however, the third-harmonic generated voltages being compensated by the impedance drop caused by the circulating current.

Example 4-8. The armature of a 3-phase Y-connected 60-cps 8-pole alternator has 24 slots per pole. The coil pitch is 5/6, and there are 4 series turns in each coil. The flux-density variation in the air gap is given by

$$B_\theta = B_{(\text{peak})1}(\sin\theta + 0.35 \sin 3\theta - 0.40 \sin 5\theta)$$

where θ is the angular distance in electrical radians measured from the point where the flux density is zero.

The alternator is operating at synchronous speed, unloaded, and with a total air-gap flux of 4.80 megalines per pole.

Find the rms voltages per phase and between line terminals.

Solution. If Φ_0 denotes the total flux per pole,

$$\Phi_0 = \Phi_1 + \Phi_3 + \Phi_5$$

and, as in Example 4-6,

$$\Phi_0 = \Phi_1 + \frac{0.35}{3}\Phi_1 - \frac{0.40}{5}\Phi_1 = 1.037\Phi_1$$

Since $\Phi_0 = 4.80$ megalines,

$$\Phi_1 = 4.63 \qquad \Phi_3 = 0.540 \qquad \Phi_5 = 0.370$$

The angle between slots is $^{180}/_{24} = 7.5$ electrical degrees, and there are $n = 8$ slots per pole per phase. The pitch angle $\rho = 150°$. From Eqs. 4-62 and 4-63, the corresponding breadth and pitch factors are

$$k_{b1} = 0.956 \qquad k_{b3} = 0.641 \qquad k_{b5} = 0.195$$
$$k_{p1} = 0.966 \qquad k_{p3} = 0.707 \qquad k_{p5} = 0.259$$

From Eq. 4-65, the rms phase voltages are

$$E_1 = 2{,}910 \text{ volts} \qquad E_3 = 501 \text{ volts} \qquad E_5 = 63.6 \text{ volts}$$

From Eq. 4-75, the rms line-to-neutral and line-to-line voltages are, respectively,

$$E_{an} = \sqrt{(2{,}910)^2 + (501)^2 + (63.6)^2} = 2{,}954 \text{ volts}$$

and

$$E_{bc} = \sqrt{3}\sqrt{(2{,}910)^2 + (63.6)^2} = 5{,}040 \text{ volts}$$

4-7. MMF Harmonics. Just as it is desirable to examine generated-voltage harmonics and means of minimizing them in order to obtain a complete and satisfying picture of machine operation, so it is also desirable to examine the mmf harmonics and their effects. These harmonics not only affect generated voltage through their influence on machine fluxes but may also affect electromagnetic torque through the dependence of torque on mmf space waveform. Magnetomotive-force waveforms will be studied in some detail in this article, first for polyphase machines, and then for d-c machines.

a. MMF Harmonics in Three-phase Machines. The present examination will be based specifically on the harmonics produced by a 3-phase integral-slot winding in a idealized machine like that in Art. 4-2. In building up the result from the rectangular mmf wave produced by a single coil, attention will be directed toward the harmonic components. In particular, the hth harmonic will be singled out to illustrate the procedure in a harmonic-by-harmonic examination.

Expression 4-20 gives the time-maximum amplitude of the space-fundamental mmf for one phase in a p-pole machine with a concentrated full-pitch winding having N_{ph} series turns per pole. By virtue of the Fourier series given in Eq. 4-17, the corresponding equation for the hth harmonic of the rectangular space distribution is

$$F_{(\max)h} = \frac{4}{\pi}\frac{1}{h}\frac{N_{ph}}{p}(\sqrt{2}\,I) \text{ amp-turns per pole} \tag{4-76}$$

Notice in Eq. 4-17 that no even harmonics are involved, so that h is restricted to odd integers. By analogy with Eq. 3-44, the instantaneous value of the hth-harmonic resultant mmf for all three phases at point θ in space is

$$F_{\theta h} = F_{(\max)h}[\cos h\theta \cos \omega t + \cos (h\theta - h \times 120°) \cos (\omega t - 120°) + \cos (h\theta - h \times 240°) \cos (\omega t - 240°)] \tag{4-77}$$

The factor h appears in space terms like $h\theta - h \times 120°$ because Eq. 4-77 is concerned with the h-order space harmonics; it does not appear in time terms like $\omega t - 120°$ because the waveform of the current is sinusoidal in time.

For specific values of h, the bracketed term in Eq. 4-77 can be simplified for interpretation by the same trigonometric transformation used for Eq. 3-47. Thus, for $h = 3$ or any multiple of 3, the bracketed term becomes zero. There are therefore no triple harmonics in the resultant mmf of a balanced 3-phase winding.

For $h = 7$, 13, or any odd number one more than a multiple of 3, the bracketed term becomes $\frac{3}{2} \cos (h\theta - \omega t)$. Interpreted in the same manner as Eq. 3-47, this result describes a field of constant amplitude rotating in the same direction as the fundamental but, because of the factor h preceding the angle θ, at only $1/h$ of the speed of the fundamental.

For $h = 5$, 11, or any odd number two more than a multiple of 3, the bracketed term becomes $\frac{3}{2} \cos (h\theta + \omega t)$. The interpretation now is a field of constant amplitude rotating at $1/h$ the speed of the fundamental but, because of the plus sign before ωt, rotating in the opposite direction.

For distributed fractional-pitch windings, mmf vectors like those of Figs. 4-8 and 4-9 may be drawn for the harmonics, the difference being that space displacement angles between harmonic vectors are h times those between corresponding fundamental vectors. Harmonic breadth and pitch factors may be used to determine the resultant mmf, the situation being once more identical with that for generated voltages. Accordingly, the amplitude of the hth harmonic mmf of a 3-phase integral-slot winding in ampere-turns per pole is

$$F_{Ah} = \frac{3}{2} \frac{4}{\pi} \frac{1}{h} \frac{k_{bh} k_{ph} N_{ph}}{p} \sqrt{2}\, I = 0.90 \frac{3 k_{bh} k_{ph} N_{ph}}{hp} I \tag{4-78}$$

where h must be odd and not a multiple of 3. Harmonic breadth and pitch factors k_{bh} and k_{ph}, given by Eqs. 4-62 and 4-63, exert the same influence toward minimizing mmf harmonics as they do toward generated-voltage harmonics.

b. MMFS in D-C Machines. In our revised study of torque production in d-c machines (Art. 4-3*b*), the armature is represented by an equivalent uniform current sheet with its associated triangular mmf wave. For a complete and satisfying picture, we are accordingly interested in any departures of the actual mmf waveform from a triangle.

The simple 2-pole d-c armature of Figs. 3-31 to 3-33 may be used for examination of the armature mmf. It is shown in developed form in Fig. 4-22*a* with the appropriate current directions indicated. The mmf wave, shown by the stepped curve of Fig. 4-22*b*, may be plotted under the assumptions of uniform air gap, no reluctance in the iron, and negligible effect of slots. Thus, recognize that the increment in mmf at each slot is equal to the number of ampere-conductors in the slot. Accordingly, start around the winding circumference at any point on it, drawing horizontal lines between slots and inserting the appropriate vertical step at each slot; when a complete cycle has been traversed, the axis of symmetry of the resulting wave gives the zero line for the plot. Positive ordinates denote flux lines leaving those points on the armature surface as though they were north magnetic poles. With the armature current constant, the wave is the same at all instants of time. The peak-to-peak height of the curve must equal the number of

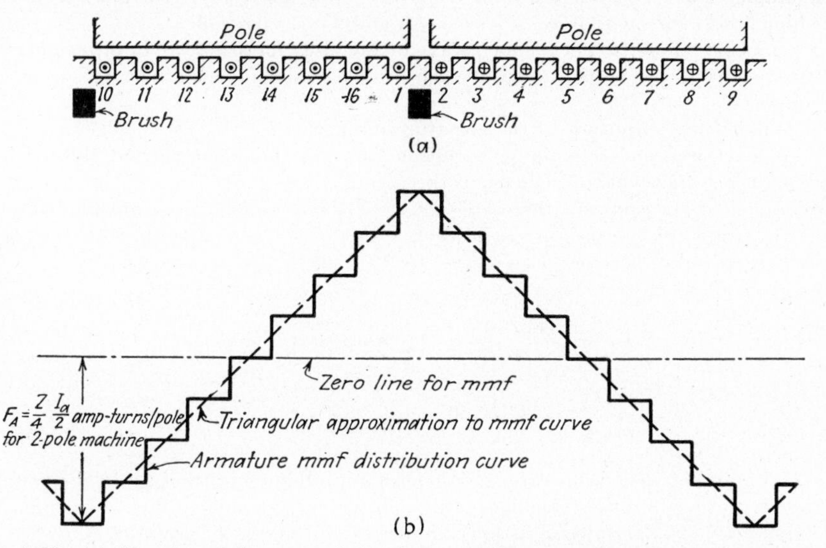

FIG. 4-22. (*a*) Developed diagram of simple 2-pole d-c armature winding, and (*b*) the corresponding mmf wave.

ampere-conductors under one pole, and the amplitude F_A of the curve is half this value. Consequently, for a 2-pole machine,

$$F_A = \frac{Z}{4}\frac{I_a}{2} \qquad \text{amp-turns per pole} \tag{4-79}$$

where Z is the total number of inductors in the winding and I_a is the armature current. Current I_a is divided by 2 because there are two parallel paths through a 2-pole armature. For a p-pole machine,

$$F_A = \frac{Z}{2p}\frac{I_a}{a} \qquad \text{amp-turns per pole} \tag{4-80}$$

where a is the number of parallel paths through the armature. This value is the same as that given by Eq. 4-43, obtained on the basis of a uniform current sheet.

The effects of the armature mmf on the resultant air-gap flux are often referred to as *armature-reaction effects*. Armature mmf causes the air-gap flux and its distribution in a loaded d-c machine to be different from that in the same machine with the same field current but with no armature current; the armature mmf increases the flux under one half of a field pole and decreases it under the other half. This distorting effect of armature reaction has some important practical consequences which must be considered fully in detailed studies of d-c machine performance and limitations.

Example 4-9. The wave-wound armature of a 250-volt 1,750-rpm 4-pole d-c machine has 37 slots with 6 coil sides per slot and 2 turns per coil.

a. In a plot similar to the stepped wave of Fig. 4-22 for armature mmf, what must be the height of the vertical step at each armature slot for an armature current of 40 amp?

b. What is the amplitude of the armature mmf wave?

c. When the armature winding is replaced by an equivalent current sheet, what must be the surface current density of the sheet?

Solution. a. In each slot there are $6 \times 2 = 12$ inductors. Since a wave winding has two parallel paths, the current in each inductor is $^{40}\!/_2 = 20$ amp. At each slot, therefore, the mmf increases or decreases by $12 \times 20 = 240$ amp-turns.

b. From Eq. 4-80, with $Z = 37 \times 6 \times 2 = 444$ total inductors,

$$F_A = \frac{444}{2 \times 4} \frac{40}{2} = 1{,}110 \text{ amp-turns per pole}$$

c. From Eq. 4-42,

$$J = \frac{444 \times 40}{\pi \times 4 \times 2} = 707 \text{ amp/elec rad}$$

or 12.35 amp per electrical degree. For an 8.5-in.-diameter armature (which would be about normal for this machine), this density corresponds to $707 \times 4\pi/8.5\pi$, or 333 amp per inch of peripheral distance around the surface of the armature.

4-8. The Effect of Harmonics. For d-c machines, the torque and voltage equations are based on mmf and flux-density distributions which are very close to the ones actually existing. The corresponding equations for a-c machines, however, are based on only the fundamental-frequency components. An examination of harmonic effects in a-c machines is accordingly appropriate before the latter equations are applied to detailed analysis.

From the parts of the preceding two articles dealing with polyphase machines, a general picture can be obtained of the orders of magnitude and nature of the departure from sine waves in both the flux and mmf distributions. The principles developed in Chap. 3 may be applied to the important harmonics to appraise their influence on performance features. Such an appraisal leads to the conclusion that harmonics have only a minor effect in a well-designed machine under normal operating conditions.

The harmonics of largest magnitude are those of low order—the fifth and seventh in a 3-phase machine, for example—and the *tooth* or *slot harmonics* whose order for a 3-phase machine is given by (see Example 4-7)

$$h = 2S_p \pm 1 \tag{4-81}$$

where S_p is the number of slots per pole. The low-order harmonics are important because their amplitude is usually significant in comparison with that of the fundamental. We have seen, however, that these harmonics may be reduced to very small proportions by proper chording and distribution of the winding. The tooth harmonics are important because their amplitudes relative to the fundamental cannot be reduced by chording or distributing the winding. This importance may be enhanced by the effect of the slot openings, neglected in our previous considerations, in offering air-gap permeance variations which accentuate these particular fields in comparison to others.

Skewing of the rotor slots is usually an effective means of reducing trouble from tooth harmonics. The effects of skewing on the harmonic

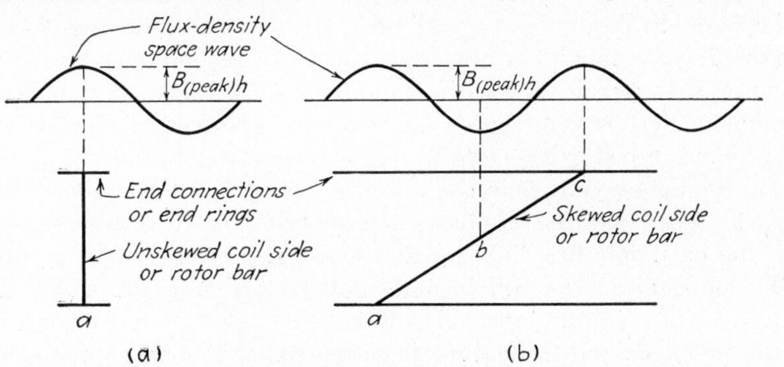

FIG. 4-23. Harmonic flux wave cut by (*a*) unskewed rotor bar and (*b*) skewed rotor bar.

voltage induced in a coil side or rotor bar may be seen qualitatively from the simple diagram of Fig. 4-23, which shows a single conductor or bar of the winding and a harmonic flux-density wave at one instant of time. In Fig. 4-23*a* with the bar unskewed, the entire bar *ac* lies in the flux density $B_{(\text{peak})h}$, and the induced voltage, in accordance with the *Blv* concept, is proportional to $B_{(\text{peak})h}$. In Fig. 4-23*b*, however, the bar is so skewed that it covers an entire cycle of values of the flux-density wave. A voltage induced in one element of length of the bar is accordingly canceled by an equal and opposite voltage in another element lying in an equal and opposite flux density; and this conclusion applies regardless of the instantaneous relative positions of bar and flux wave. No current exists in the rotor winding as a result of this flux harmonic: the harmonic has therefore been completely *skewed out*. A different amount of skew will, of course, only partially nullify the influence of the harmonic, but the result will generally be a significant reduction. The effect of skewing may thus be seen to be not unlike that of distributing the winding: distributing spreads the *phase group* of coil sides or bars over an appreciable portion of the flux wave; skewing spreads the *individual coil sides or* *bars* over an appreciable portion; both expedients bring vector rather than algebraic addition into play as a harmonic-reducing means. The usual amount of skewing used practically is of the order of magnitude of one slot pitch.

The most important effects of flux and mmf harmonics, all of which are disadvantageous, are four in number: introduction of harmonics into the generated voltage, interaction of rotor and stator harmonics to produce *parasitic torques*, the introduction of vibration, and, closely allied to the third, the introduction of noise. Harmonic fluxes also add somewhat to machine losses through the production of relatively high-frequency core losses, notably in the teeth and pole faces.

The first effect is of concern principally in synchronous generators and is illustrated in Examples 4-6 and 4-8. Harmonics in the armature mmf do not directly cause harmonics in the terminal voltage, but they do influence the magnitude of the fundamental voltage. Since the hth-harmonic armature mmf sets up a field with hp poles rotating at $1/h$ of synchronous speed with respect to the armature, it induces a fundamental-frequency voltage in the winding rather than a harmonic voltage. The voltage so induced is phase-displaced 90 electrical degrees in time from the harmonic flux linkages and hence from the current giving rise to the harmonics. As will be indicated in Art. 4-9, the effect of this induced voltage on the terminal voltage is included by means of a reactance drop considered to be directly proportional to armature current.

Minimizing the last three effects listed above is apt to be a particularly severe problem in squirrel-cage induction motors because the combination of the stator-mmf harmonics and their reaction on the squirrel-cage rotor acts as a rich source of varied harmonics on both sides of the air gap. The cause and nature of parasitic torques, for example, can be examined by recalling that sinusoidal mmf and flux-density waves interact to produce average torque in accordance with Eq. 3-22 when the two waves have the same number of poles and are stationary with respect to each other in space. If the two waves are stationary relative to each other for any rotor speed, an asynchronous torque like the main torque in an induction motor is produced. If they are stationary for only one rotor speed, a synchronous torque like that in a synchronous motor is produced at that speed only.

The torque-slip curve showing the variation of asynchronous torque produced by two interacting harmonic components is similar to that of Fig. 3-25 for the fundamentals, although the condition of constant terminal voltage does not apply to the harmonics. Figure 3-25 is redrawn in Fig. 4-24 and extended over a greater range of slips. Slip in Fig. 4-24 must be evaluated with respect to the speed of the harmonic, not the speed of the fundamental wave. The seventh mmf harmonic in a p-pole motor, for example, produces a field with $7p$ poles rotating at $\frac{1}{7}$ of the speed of the fundamental field and in the same direction. Its effect is therefore like that of a small $7p$-pole motor coupled to the same shaft as the main motor and is shown in Fig. 4-25. Notice that the seventh-harmonic contribution to torque is of possible significance only at low motor speeds and not at all for the normal running speeds. If the

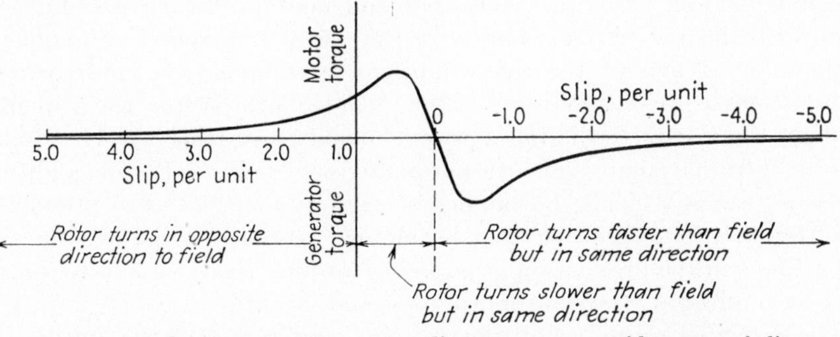

FIG. 4-24. Induction-machine torque-slip curve over a wide range of slips.

seventh harmonic were large, however, the starting performance of the motor would be seriously affected, and the motor might run at a low speed in the neighborhood of $\frac{6}{7}$ slip (about $\frac{1}{7}$ of normal speed) instead of coming up to its normal operating speed at a very low slip. Such a phenomenon is known as *asynchronous crawling* and must clearly be avoided for the motor to render satisfactory service.

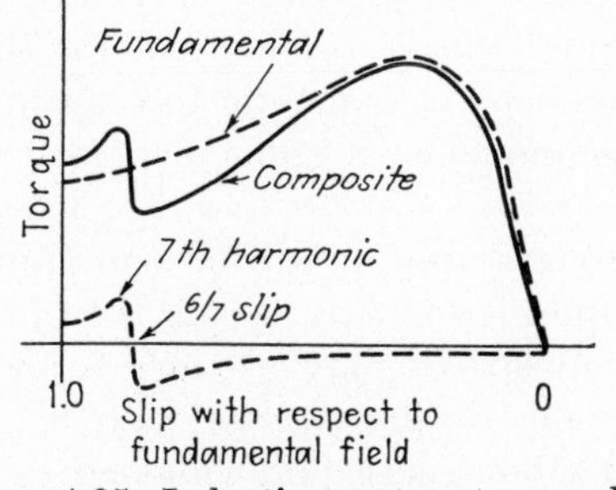

FIG. 4-25. Induction-motor torque-slip curve with asynchronous cusp created by seventh-harmonic flux.

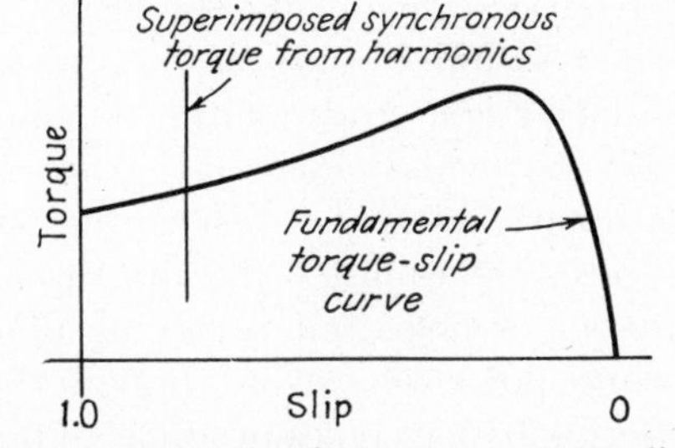

FIG. 4-26. Induction-motor torque-slip curve with superimposed synchronous torque created by harmonic flux.

Stator and rotor harmonics interacting to produce synchronous torques may give rise to similar harmful effects, as shown in the torque-slip curve of Fig. 4-26. Again the rotor may crawl at a low subsynchronous speed instead of reaching normal operating speed, and the phenomenon this time is referred to as *synchronous crawling*. If a pair or a series of pairs of such harmonics interlock at zero speed, the motor may not start at all, even without load; such a motor is said to exhibit a *locking torque, dead point,* or *cogging effect.* An unwisely chosen combination of rotor and stator slots, resulting in the presence of both synchronous and asynchronous cusps, may give rise to a torque-speed curve which is indeed very rough in the low-speed region.

Full appreciation of the possibilities of occurrence of synchronous crawling, as well as of the vibration- and noise-producing possibilities, requires realization of the richness of the motor as a source of magnetic harmonics. When a rotor cage winding is acted upon by a fundamental, fifth-harmonic, seventh-harmonic, etc., field from the stator, the principal fields produced by the induced rotor currents are, respectively, fundamental, fifth-harmonic, seventh-harmonic, etc., fields. But in addition to these principal fields, harmonics of each of them are also produced, resulting in a long series of rotor harmonics. Besides being of potential importance in the production of parasitic torques, these rotor waves may be very important contributors to noise and vibration.

The principal source of air-borne noise is vibration of the stator and rotor structures under the influence of magnetic forces causing the structures to distort periodically with time; the machine, in other words, acts as a giant magnetic loud-speaker. In general, study of motor noise involves study of the magnetic forces and of the mechanical response of the structures to these forces. The magnetic forces concerned now include the radial forces on the stator and rotor iron at the air gap—forces like those discussed in Art. 2-1 whose magnitudes are proportional to the square of the flux density. In this respect, study of vibration and noise supplements the study of normal torque production, for the former includes study of the radial component of magnetic force, while the latter is a study of the tangential component. Confinement of the study to fields which have the same number of poles and which are stationary relative to each other is no longer appropriate in examining vibration and noise. To cite three examples, two fields having the same number of poles but revolving at different speeds may produce serious torque pulsations even though the average torque is zero; two fields differing by two poles produce an unbalanced magnetic pull whose effect is like that of a mechanical unbalance of the rotor; and either a single 2-pole field by itself or a combination of two fields differing by four poles tends to distort the parts into a rotating ellipse. All such possibilities must be carefully examined as potential sources of trouble to ensure vibration- and noise-free machines.

In addition to reduction by means of the pitch and breadth factors and by skewing, the harmful effects of harmonics are avoided by careful choice of the combination of numbers of stator and rotor slots. Proposed combinations are studied to determine the significant rotor and stator harmonics and to single out those which may interact to produce harmful effects. The part played by harmonics is thus that of a potential nuisance which must be eliminated, but it is a part to which careful attention must be devoted.[1]

4-9. Leakage Reactance. Analysis of machine performance on the basis of the induced-voltage and electromagnetic-torque relations clearly involves quantitative specifications of the magnetic field within the machine. Although the resultant magnetic field is decidedly more complicated in a machine than in a transformer because of the more complex copper and iron geometries involved, the same general principles of analysis are applied. The resultant field is considered to consist of three components: the *mutual flux* which links both the rotor and stator windings, the *stator leakage field* linking only the stator winding and created by the stator current, and the *rotor leakage field* linking only the rotor winding and created by the rotor current. These three fields, of course, possess the characteristic common to all components in any physical system: they do not exist by themselves as individual physical entities when both windings are excited; then only the resultant field truly exists in the machine. If the field is mapped with only the rotor winding excited, flux lines can be clearly recognized and labeled as either rotor leakage flux or mutual flux. Similarly, if the field is mapped with only the stator winding excited, flux lines can be clearly recognized and labeled as either stator leakage flux or mutual flux. But if the resultant field of the combined mmf is then mapped, none of the previously labeled lines will appear explicitly, for they will have lost their identity as a result of the merging of the two causes represented by rotor and stator mmf. Appreciable analytical simplification results from reasoning in terms of the component fields, however, so that the resultant field is rarely mapped and rarely appears explicitly in machine analysis. The application of superposition implicit in such reasoning carries with it the restriction that the component fields be evaluated using the iron permeabilities corresponding to the resultant field. Fortunately, however, this restriction is not serious,

[1] The following is a selection from the literature on harmonics, parasitic torques, vibration, and noise in machinery: F. T. Chapman, "A Study of the Induction Motor," Chaps. VII and XII, John Wiley & Sons, Inc., New York, 1930; B. Hague, The Mathematical Treatment of the MMF of Armature Windings, *J. IEE*, vol. 55, p. 489, 1917; Q. Graham, The MMF of Polyphase Windings, *Trans. AIEE*, vol. 56, p. 118, 1927; G. Kron, Induction Motor Slot Combinations, *Trans. AIEE*, vol. 50, p. 757, 1931; E. E. Dreese, Synchronous Motor Effects in Induction Machines, *Trans. AIEE*, vol. 49, p. 1033, 1930; Q. Graham, Dead Points in Squirrel-cage Motors, *Trans. AIEE*, vol. 49, p. 637, 1940; L. E. Hildebrand, Quiet Induction Motors, *Trans. AIEE*, vol. 49, p. 848, 1930; W. J. Morrill, Harmonic Theory of Noise in Induction Motors, *Trans. AIEE*, vol. 59, p. 474, 1940; P. L. Alger, "The Nature of Polyphase Induction Machines," John Wiley & Sons, Inc., New York, 1951.

for the leakage-flux paths are largely in air, and the leakage flux does not seriously influence saturation in the main flux path.

It is the mutual flux to which attention has been largely confined thus far. The leakage field of a winding in a uniform-air-gap machine does not contribute to the torque associated with that winding for, from the viewpoint of the torque equation, 3-22, the torque angle δ for this component field is zero. Nevertheless leakage fields do influence the characteristics of the energy-conversion devices. Thus, the voltage induced by changing leakage-flux linkages may enter directly into the determination of the voltage E, current I, or phase angle θ for use in Eq. 4-47 when these quantities are found from other stated conditions of machine operation.

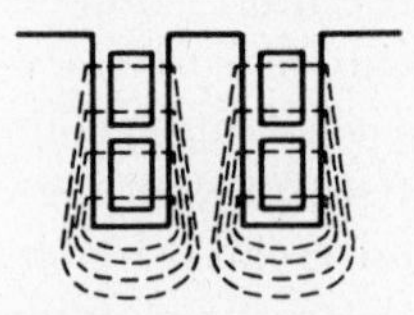

Fig. 4-27. Slot-leakage flux.

As in the transformer, the effect of the changing leakage-flux linkages of a winding is incorporated analytically by ascribing to the winding a *leakage inductance*, equal to the number of leakage-flux linkages per unit of current in it, and a corresponding *leakage reactance.* Among the important contributors to leakage reactance are slot-leakage flux, coil-end-leakage flux, and harmonic fluxes. The *slot-leakage flux,* as indicated in Fig. 4-27, is assumed to cross the slot and complete its path in the iron of the teeth and core; its linkages are associated with the portion of the conductor embedded in the slots. Evidently a deep, narrow slot will have higher leakage than a shallow, broad one. Also the slot-leakage flux may contribute to nonuniform current distribution over the cross

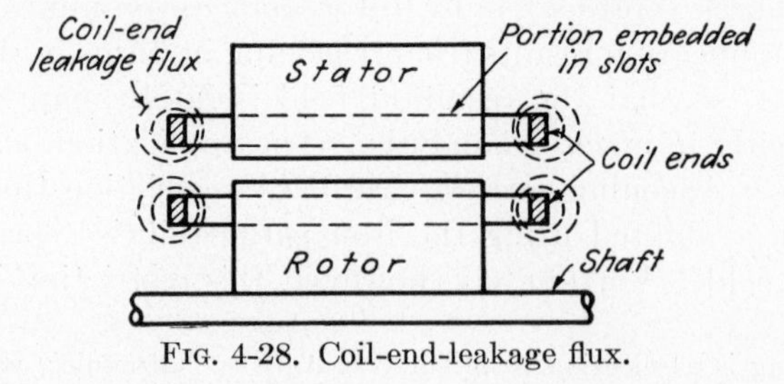

Fig. 4-28. Coil-end-leakage flux.

section of the conductors. The nature of the *coil-end-leakage flux,* associated with the end turns or portion of the conductor not embedded in slots, is indicated diagrammatically in Fig. 4-28. Nonsynchronously rotating harmonic fluxes are included in the leakage reactance because their paths are also largely in air and because, as pointed out in Art. 4-8, the voltage induced by them is of fundamental frequency and, like any reactive voltage, is phase-displaced 90° from the current associated with it. The effects of harmonics are therefore seen to be incorporated in steady-state a-c-machine theory in two ways: voltage effects are included as part of the leakage-reactance drop, and parasitic-torque, noise, and vibration effects are included in separate studies to ensure the production of machines which are trouble-free in these respects.

The leakage reactance of a winding is affected by the layout of the winding.[2] It is smaller for a distributed winding than for a concentrated winding and smaller for a fractional pitch than for a full pitch. All windings, of course, create leakage flux whether they carry an alternating or a direct current. In d-c windings such as the field windings of synchronous or d-c machines, leakage fluxes induce no voltage in the steady state, so that the corresponding leakage inductances or reactances do not enter into the associated analyses. For problems involving machine transients, however, leakage inductances form a pertinent concept for these windings as well as for a-c windings.

4-10. The Treatment of Saturation. Both electromagnetic torque and generated voltage in all machines depend on rates of change of flux linkages with the windings of the machines, the torque on the angular rate of change, and the voltage on the time rate of change. For specified mmfs in the windings, the fluxes depend on the reluctances of the iron portions of the magnetic circuits as well as of the air gaps. Saturation may therefore appreciably influence the characteristics of the machines. Another aspect of saturation, a more subtle one and one more difficult to evaluate without experimental and theoretical comparisons, concerns its influence on the basic premises from which the analytic approach to machinery is developed. Specifically, all relations for mmf are based on negligible reluctance in the iron. When these relations are applied to practical machines with varying degrees of saturation in the iron, the actual machine is, in effect, replaced for these considerations by an equivalent machine: one whose iron has negligible reluctance but whose air-gap length is increased by an amount sufficient to absorb the magnetic-potential drop in the iron of the actual machine. Although it is rarely made explicitly, such replacement occurs implicitly whenever the previously developed mmf equations are used in conjunction with values of flux or flux density which are determined with due consideration of the reluctance of the iron. Incidentally, the effects of air-gap nonuniformities such as slots and ventilating ducts are also incorporated through the medium of an equivalent smooth gap, a replacement which, in contrast to that above, is made explicitly during magnetic-circuit computations for the machine structure. Thus, serious efforts are made to reproduce the magnetic conditions at the air gap correctly, and the computed per-

[2] For methods of computing leakage reactances, see P. L. Alger, The Calculation of the Armature Reactances of Synchronous Machines, *Trans. AIEE*, vol. 47, p. 493, 1928; L. A. Kilgore, Calculation of Synchronous Machine Constants, *Trans. AIEE*, vol. 50, p. 1201, 1931.

formance of machines is based largely on those conditions. Final assurance of the legitimacy of the approach must, of course, be the pragmatic one given by close experimental checks.

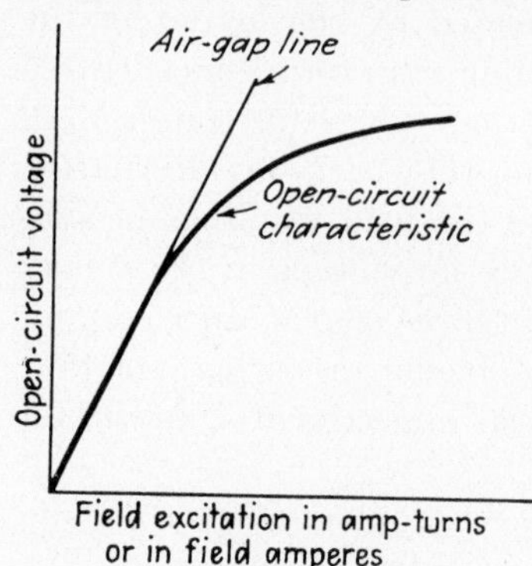

FIG. 4-29. Typical open-circuit characteristic and air-gap line.

Magnetic-circuit data essential to the handling of saturation are given by the *open-circuit characteristic, magnetization curve*, or *saturation curve*. An example is shown in Fig. 4-29. Basically, this characteristic is the magnetization curve for the particular iron and air geometry of the machine under consideration. Frequently the abscissa is plotted in terms of field current or magnetizing current instead of mmf in ampere-turns. It is also recognized that the generated voltage with zero armature current is directly proportional to the flux when the speed is constant. For convenience in use, then, open-circuit terminal voltage is plotted on the ordinate scale rather than air-gap flux per pole, and the entire curve is drawn for a stated fixed speed, usually rated speed. The straight line tangent to the lower portion of the curve is the *air-gap line* indicating very closely the mmf required to overcome the reluctance of the air gap. If it were not for the effects of saturation, the air-gap line and open-circuit characteristic would coincide, so that the departure of the curve from the air-gap line is an indication of the degree of saturation present. In a normal machine, the ratio at rated voltage of the total mmf to that required by the air gap alone usually is between 1.1 and 1.25.

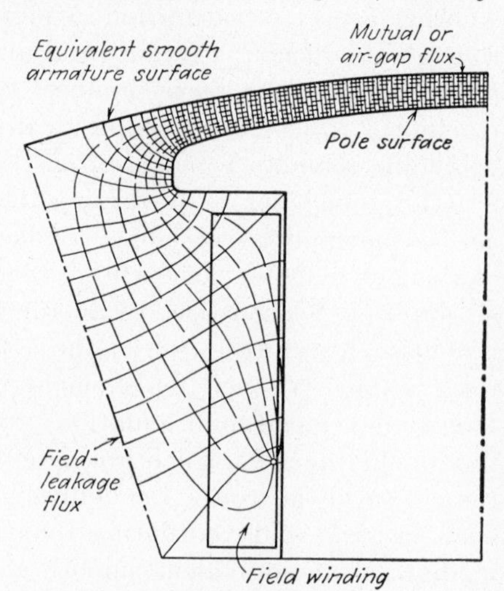

FIG. 4-30. Distribution of flux around a salient pole. The solid lines are flux lines; the dotted lines are loci of equal magnetic potential.

The open-circuit characteristic may be calculated from design data by magnetic-circuit methods, often guided by flux mapping. A small sample map of the flux distribution around the pole of a salient-pole machine is given in Fig. 4-30. The distribution of air-gap flux found by means of this map, together with the fundamental- and third-harmonic components, are shown in Fig. 4-31. The map is drawn on the basis of infinite permeability in the iron and for a smooth armature surface with the air-gap width increased to compensate for the effect of armature slots on the flux per pole. Slot effects may be studied separately on either an analytical or a graphical basis. The influence of a slot on an otherwise uniform field is indicated graphically in Figs. 4-32 and 4-33. Note that in Fig. 4-32 the scale to which the field is mapped increases

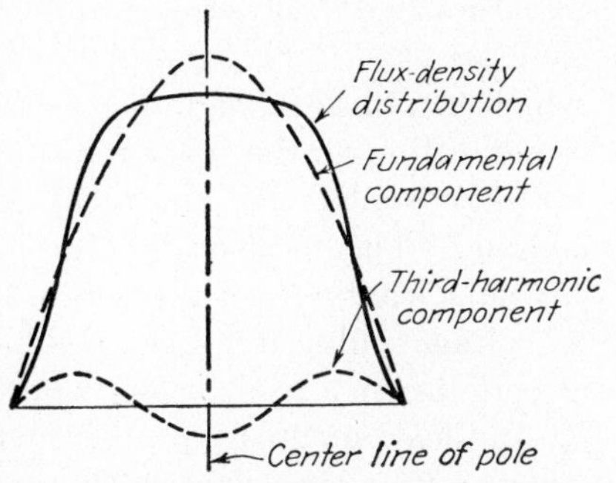

FIG. 4-31. Flux-density wave corresponding to Fig. 4-30, with its fundamental and third-harmonic components.

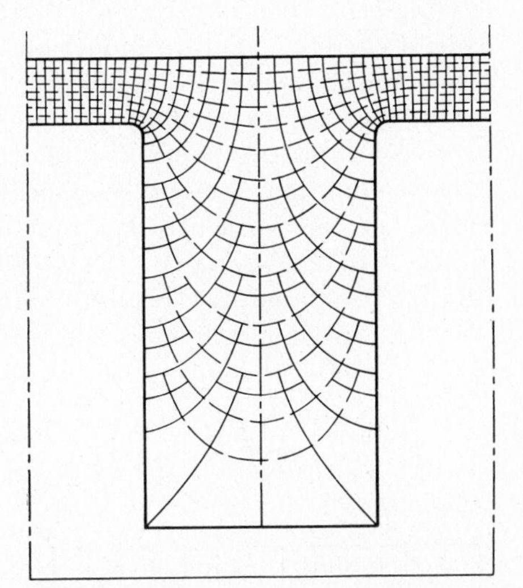

FIG. 4-32. Distribution of flux in a slot. The solid lines are flux lines; the dotted lines are loci of equal magnetic potential.

at locations where a flux line is drawn only up to a point where it crosses an equipotential line. When this change is borne in mind, it is seen that the flux density in the slot is far lower than in the tooth. The general

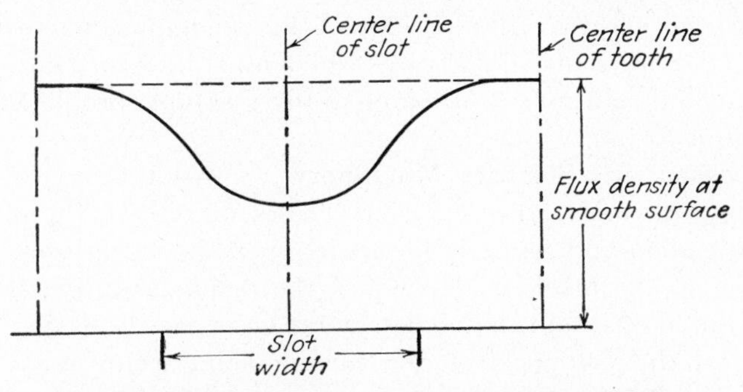

FIG. 4-33. Effect of a slot on the air-gap flux density.

nature of the flux-density wave with slot effects superimposed is shown in Fig. 4-34. Slot effects are indicated in a pronounced form here because of the use of only a few relatively wide slots per pole. Flux maps of the type indicated in Figs. 4-30 and 4-32 yield precise, quantitative results, for they are graphical solutions of Laplace's equation for the assumed boundary conditions.[3]

If the machine is an existing one, the magnetization curve is most commonly determined by operating it as an unloaded generator and reading the values of terminal voltage corresponding to a series of values of field current. For an induction motor, the technique used for transformers may be adapted: the motor is operated at or close to synchronous speed, and values of magnetizing current are obtained for a series of values of impressed stator voltage.

Determination of electromagnetic conditions within these energy-conversion devices evidently has much in common with the same problem in iron-core transformers. Magnetomotive forces of the rotor and stator windings combine to a resultant mmf which establishes the mutual flux in much the same fashion as in a transformer, although the space relation of the component mmfs must be given careful consideration in a rotating machine. The induced voltage in a machine winding closely resembles the voltage induced by the resultant core flux in a transformer winding, and leakage fluxes are handled in about the same way, although the leakage fluxes of machine windings carrying direct currents do not enter directly into determination of performance. Such resemblance is naturally to be expected, for both transformers and machines consist of two or more electric circuits coupled by a common magnetic circuit. Many of the stratagems and artifices which must be resorted to in order to obtain practical solutions to fundamentally insoluble problems are therefore common to the two devices.

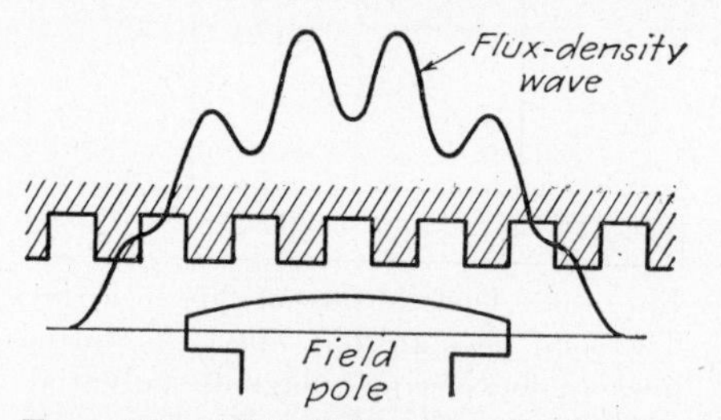

FIG. 4-34. Main-field flux distribution with slot effects superimposed. Slot effects are exaggerated because of showing only a few wide slots per pole.

4-11. Losses in Electric Machinery. Consideration of machine losses is important for three reasons: losses determine the efficiency of the machine and appreciably influence its operating cost; losses determine the heating of the machine and hence the rating or power output that may be obtained without undue deterioration of the insulation because of heating; and the voltage drops or current components associated with supplying the losses must be properly accounted for in machine repre-

[3] For detailed accounts of flux-mapping methods for electrical machinery, see A. R. Stevenson and R. H. Park, Graphical Determination of Magnetic Fields, *Trans. AIEE*, vol. 46, p. 112, 1927; R. W. Wieseman, Graphical Determination of Magnetic Fields, *Trans. AIEE*, vol. 46, p. 141, 1927.

Figures 4-30 to 4-33 are adapted from figures appearing in these references.

sentation. Machine efficiency, like that of any energy-transforming device, is given by

$$\text{Efficiency} = \frac{\text{output}}{\text{input}} \tag{4-82}$$

which can also be expressed as

$$\text{Efficiency} = \frac{\text{input} - \text{losses}}{\text{input}} = 1 - \frac{\text{losses}}{\text{input}} \tag{4-83}$$

$$= \frac{\text{output}}{\text{output} + \text{losses}} \tag{4-84}$$

Rotating machines in general operate efficiently except at light loads. The full-load efficiency of average motors, for example, is in the neighborhood of 74 per cent for 1-hp size, 89 per cent for 50-hp, 93 per cent for 500-hp, and 97 per cent for 5,000 hp. The efficiency of slow-speed motors is usually lower than that of high-speed motors, the total spread being 3 or 4 per cent.

The forms given by Eqs. 4-83 and 4-84 are often used for electric machines, for their efficiency is most commonly determined by measurement of losses instead of by directly measuring the input and output under load. Loss measurements have the advantage of convenience and economy and of yielding more accurate and precise values of efficiency because a given percentage error in measuring losses causes only about one-tenth of that percentage error in the efficiency. Efficiencies determined from loss measurements can be used in comparing competing machines provided that exactly the same methods of measurement and computation are used in each case. For this reason, the various losses and the conditions for their measurement are precisely defined by the American Standards Association (ASA). The following discussion of individual losses incorporates many of these provisions as given in *Bulletin* C50-1943, American Standards for Rotating Electrical Machinery, although no attempt is made to present all the details to be found in that bulletin:

1. *Copper losses*, or I^2R losses, are, of course, found in all the windings of the machine. By convention, these losses are computed on the basis of the d-c resistances of the winding at 75°C. Actually the I^2R loss depends on the effective resistance of the winding under the operating frequency and flux conditions. The increment in loss represented by the difference between d-c and effective resistances is included with stray-load losses, discussed below. In the field circuits of synchronous and d-c machines, only the losses in the field winding are charged against the machine; the I^2R loss in the rheostat controlling the field current and all losses in external sources supplying the excitation are charged against the

plant of which the machine is a part. Closely associated with I^2R loss is the *brush-contact loss* at slip rings and commutators. By convention, this loss is normally neglected for induction and synchronous machines, and for industrial-type d-c machines the voltage drop at the brushes is regarded as constant at 2 volts total when carbon and graphite brushes with shunts (pigtails) are used.

2. *Mechanical losses* consist of brush and bearing friction, windage, and the power required to circulate the air through the machine and ventilating system, if one is provided, whether by self-contained or external fans (except for the power required to force air through long or restricted ducts external to the machine). Friction and windage losses may be measured by determining the input to the machine running at the proper speed but unloaded and unexcited. Frequently they are lumped with core loss and determined at the same time.

3. *Open-circuit,* or *no-load, core loss* consists of the hysteresis and eddy-current losses arising from changing flux densities in the iron of the machine with only the main exciting winding energized. In d-c and synchronous machines, these losses are confined largely to the armature iron, although the flux pulsations arising from slot openings will cause losses in the field iron as well, particularly in the pole shoes or surfaces of the field iron. In induction machines, the losses are confined largely to the stator iron. Open-circuit core loss may be found by measuring the input to the machine when it is operating unloaded at rated speed or frequency and under the appropriate flux or voltage conditions, and deducting the friction and windage loss and, if the machine is self-driven during the test, the no-load armature copper loss (no-load stator copper loss for an induction motor). Usually data are taken for a curve of core loss as a function of armature voltage in the neighborhood of rated voltage. The core loss under load is then considered to be the value at a voltage equal to rated voltage corrected for armature ohmic-resistance drop under load (a vectorial correction for an a-c machine). For induction motors, however, this correction is dispensed with, and the core loss at rated voltage is used. For efficiency determination alone, there is no need to segregate open-circuit core loss and friction and windage loss; the sum of these two losses is termed the *no-load rotational loss.*

Eddy-current loss is dependent on the squares of the flux density, frequency, and thickness of laminations. Under normal machine conditions, it may be expressed to a sufficiently close approximation as

$$P_e = K_e(B_{\max} f \tau)^2 \tag{4-85}$$

where τ is the lamination thickness, $B_{\max}$ the maximum flux density, f the frequency, and K_e a proportionality constant whose value depends on the units used, the volume of iron, and the resistivity of the iron. Variation of hysteresis loss can be expressed in equation form only on an empirical basis. The most commonly used relation is

$$P_h = K_h f B_{\max}^n \tag{4-86}$$

where K_h is a proportionality constant dependent on the characteristics and volume of iron and the units used, and the exponent n ranges from 1.5 to 2.5 with a value of 2.0 often used for estimating purposes in machines. In both Eqs. 4-85 and 4-86, frequency may be replaced by speed and flux density by the appropriate voltage when the proportionality constants are changed accordingly. Such replacements are implied when the core-loss tests are made at rated speed and the appropriate voltage.

When the machine is loaded, the space distribution of flux density is significantly changed by the mmf of the load currents. The actual core losses increase noticeably. For example, the mmf harmonics previously discussed cause appreciable losses in the iron near the air-gap surfaces. The total increment in core loss is classified as part of the stray load loss.

4. *Stray load loss* consists of the losses arising from nonuniform current distribution in the copper and the additional core losses produced in the iron by distortion of the magnetic flux by the load current. It is a difficult loss to determine accurately. By convention it is taken as 1.0 per cent of the output for d-c machines. For synchronous machines it may be found from a short-circuit test as described in Chap. 7. For induction motors use may be made of a d-c excitation test which will not be described in this text.[4]

Study of the foregoing classification of the various losses in a machine, together with the associated test methods, shows it to have a few features which, from a fundamental viewpoint, are somewhat artificial. Illustrations are offered by the division of iron losses into no-load core loss and an increment which appears under load, the division of copper losses into ohmic I^2R losses and an increment created by nonuniform current distribution, and the lumping of these two increments in the scavenger-like stray-load-loss category. These features are dictated by ease of testing and justified by the fact that the principal motivation behind the standard classification is the determination of the total losses and a value of efficiency suitable for economic comparison of machines and at the same time as nearly equal to the actual efficiency as possible.

[4] For complete descriptions of all accepted methods of measuring machine losses, the following AIEE Standards should be consulted:

Test Code for Polyphase Induction Machines, No. 500, August, 1937.

Test Code for Direct-current Machines, No. 501, July, 1941.

Test Code for Polyphase Synchronous Machines, No. 503, July, 1945.

See also C. W. Ricker and C. E. Tucker, "Electrical Engineering Laboratory Experiments," 4th ed., McGraw-Hill Book Company, Inc., New York, 1940.

Because of this seeming dominance of efficiency aspects, it may be appropriate to emphasize once more that losses play more than a bookkeeping type of part in machine operation.

In a generator, for example, components of mechanical input torque to the shaft are obviously required to supply copper and iron losses as well as friction and windage losses and the generator output. These losses may therefore be appreciable factors in the damping of electrical and mechanical transients in the machine. Components of the stray load loss, although they may be individually only a fraction of a per cent of the output, may be of first importance in the design of the machine. Thus rotor heating is usually the limiting factor in the design of large high-speed alternators, and the components of stray loss on the surface of the rotor structure are of great importance because they directly affect the dimensions of an alternator of given output. Of more direct concern in the theoretical aspects previously presented is the influence of hysteresis and eddy currents in causing flux to lag behind mmf. This influence is the same as that causing the flux in a transformer to lag the exciting current by an angle depending on the ratio of the hysteresis and eddy-current losses to the magnetizing volt-amperes. In similar fashion, there is a small angle of lag between the rotating mmf waves of Arts. 3-6 and 4-2 and the corresponding component flux-density waves. Associated with this influence is a torque on magnetic material in a rotating field, a torque proportional to the hysteresis and eddy-current losses in the material. Although the torque accompanying these losses is relatively small in normal machines, direct use of it is made in one type of small motor, the hysteresis motor.

Example 4-10. A 3-phase 60-cps 550-volt 8-pole 50-hp squirrel-cage induction motor has a full-load efficiency of 89.0 per cent. It is operated at full load 8 hr/day during 300 days of the year. For computations of fixed charges, the interest rate is taken as 5 per cent per year, and the useful life of the equipment is regarded as 10 years. The incremental cost of electric power is 1.0 cent per kilowatthour.

How much is a 1.0 per cent improvement in full-load efficiency worth under these conditions?

Solution. This example offers a simplified illustration of some of the factors involved in economic comparison of competing equipment and in estimating costs in engineering. For such analyses the total cost of equipment is divided into fixed cost and operating cost.

Fixed cost is the cost of *owning* the equipment and is based on the initial capital expenditure. It includes interest (or the amount the initial expenditure might have earned if invested in some other manner), taxes, insurance, and depreciation and obsolescence (a charge made so that the equipment may be replaced by its equivalent when it or the process in which it is involved becomes obsolete or no longer serviceable). In this example depreciation charges will be estimated by the so-called *straight-line method; i.e.*, based on an estimated life of 10 years, a charge of 10 per cent of the initial investment will be made each year. With taxes and insurance neglected for present purposes, the annual fixed charge is then 15 per cent of the initial investment.

Operating cost is the cost of *running* the equipment and includes the cost of expendable items, such as power, and the cost of maintenance, supervision, and labor. In this example the yearly operating costs of two motors with different efficiencies differ only by the cost of the difference in losses.

By use of Eq. 4-84,

$$\text{Losses} = 50 \times 746 \times \frac{1.00 - 0.89}{0.89} = 4{,}610 \text{ watts}$$

for an efficiency of 89 per cent, and

$$\text{Losses} = 50 \times 746 \times \frac{1.00 - 0.90}{0.90} = 4{,}150 \text{ watts}$$

for an efficiency of 90 per cent. The yearly saving in operating cost is then

$$\frac{4{,}610 - 4{,}150}{1{,}000} \times 8 \times 300 \times 0.01 = \$11$$

Since operating costs are decreased by $11 per year, annual fixed costs may be increased by not more than this amount. The annual fixed costs are

$$FC_{0.89} = 0.15 \times (\text{initial cost})_{0.89}$$

and

$$FC_{0.90} = 0.15 \times (\text{initial cost})_{0.90}$$

The yearly difference in fixed costs is therefore

$$0.15(\text{initial cost differential}) = \$11$$

or

$$\text{Initial cost differential} = \$73.30$$

Consequently a 1.0 per cent improvement in efficiency is worth $73.30 under these circumstances. If such an improvement can be obtained by an expenditure of less than $73.30, it should be obtained; if, however, it requires a greater expenditure, the idea should be discarded.

4-12. Rating and Heating. One of the most important factors in the design and operation of electric machines is the relation between the life of the insulation and operating temperature of the machine. Organic insulating materials suffer definite thermal aging or thermal decomposition which is primarily a function of time and temperature and which ultimately leads to charring, brittleness, and loss of mechanical durability and dielectric strength. A rough rule of thumb indicative of the thermal instability of organic insulating materials is that for each additional 8 to 10°C temperature rise, the time to failure of the insulation is halved. Consequently, definite maximum allowable temperature rises for machine insulation are specified by the ASA, American Institute of Electrical Engineers (AIEE), and National Electrical Manufacturers Association (NEMA). The temperature rise resulting from the losses considered in the previous article is therefore an important and frequently a determining factor in the rating of a machine. It is not the only factor, however; maximum torque, starting torque and starting current, efficiency, and power factor are all typical of performance features which must meet definite requirements. These features, rather than temperature rise, will sometimes control the amount of material used in a machine of given rating, as in many open and semienclosed types of general-purpose motors.

For purposes of establishing temperature limits, insulating materials are classified according to their composition. The three classes of chief interest for machines are defined as follows:[5]

Class A insulation consists of (1) cotton, silk, paper, and similar organic materials when either impregnated or immersed in a liquid dielectric; (2) molded and laminated materials with cellulose filler, phenolic resins, and other resins of similar properties; (3) films and sheets of cellulose acetate and other cellulose derivatives of similar properties; and (4) varnishes (enamel) as applied to conductors.

Class B insulation consists of mica, asbestos, fiberglass, and similar inorganic materials in built-up form with organic binding substances. A small proportion of Class A materials may be used for structural purposes only.

Class H insulation consists of (1) mica, asbestos, fiberglass, and similar inorganic materials in built-up form with binding substances composed of silicone compounds, or materials with equivalent properties; (2) silicone compounds in rubbery or resinous forms, or materials with equivalent properties. A minute portion of Class A materials may be had only where essential for structural purposes during manufacture.

Recommended values of "hottest-spot" temperatures, established as a benchmark in arriving at more detailed permissible temperature rises for specific machine parts, are as follows for these three classes of insulation:

Class A: 105°C
Class B: 130°C
Class H: 180°C

Since the limiting ambient temperature is normally taken as 40°C, these values correspond to temperature rises of 65, 90, and 140°C at the hottest point in the machine.

To indicate the general nature and orders of magnitude of standard specifications for allowable temperature rises, the limits for various parts of selected motors are given in Table 4-1. The principal exception to application of these temperature limits is aircraft equipment, where insulation life approaching that in industrial equipment is not required and where, in consequence, higher temperatures are allowed. In the second column of the table, the term *general-purpose motor* refers to any motor of 200 hp or less and 450 rpm or more, having a continuous rating and designed, listed, or offered in standard ratings for use without restriction to a particular application. In contrast, a *special-purpose*

[5] From AIEE Standards 1, General Principles upon Which Temperature Limits Are Based in the Rating of Electrical Machinery and Apparatus, June, 1947.

motor is specifically designated and listed for a particular application where the load requirements and duty cycle are definitely known. The permissible rise of temperature is 10°C lower for a general-purpose motor than for a special-purpose motor largely to allow a greater factor of safety where service conditions are unknown. Partially compensating the lower rise, however, is the fact that general-purpose motors are allowed a service factor of 1.15 when operated at rated voltage; *service factor* is a multiplier which, applied to the rated output, indicates a permissible loading which may be carried continuously under the conditions specified for that service factor. In general, a slight difference in performance from that at rated load may be expected at the permissible loading indicated by the service factor.

Table 4-1 also shows that a temperature increase of 20°C is allowed when Class B instead of Class A insulation is used. In spite of the thermal stability of fiberglass, mica, etc., the allowance is limited to this value because decomposition of Class B insulation is largely determined by the organic bonding material and varnishes. An important step toward the more complete utilization of the desirable properties of these inorganic materials is the development of the *silicones*, a group of organo-silicon compounds derived from silica and having molecular structures based upon chains of alternate silicon and oxygen atoms linked to various organic groups. They are semiinorganic compounds having a high order of thermal stability and resistance to moisture. Because of their mechanical softness and low film strength, their chief use as insulating materials is not that of being applied alone, but rather to provide the resinous dielectric necessary to bond inorganic materials together and to the iron and copper, and to exclude moisture. Extensive tests and studies have been conducted since 1942 on the use of silicone insulation in electric machinery, and thorough engineering and economic evaluation has yet to be achieved. An indication of the potential value of silicone resins used in conjunction with fiberglass and mica is given by comparison of the recommended hot-spot temperatures quoted earlier. The value of 180° C for Class H insulation is tentatively approved by the AIEE for a period of trial use. Further indication is given by Table 4-2, which lists proposed allowable rises for d-c machines based on a motor-exchange test program conducted jointly by a group of manufacturers.[6] The principal applications of Class H insulation may be expected to be in apparatus where size and weight are at a premium and can be reduced through increased operating temperature without undue sacrifice in performance

[6] For details of these tests and proposals, see AIEE Subcommittee on D-C Machines of the AIEE Rotating Machinery Committee, Temperature Rise Values for Direct-current Machines, *Trans. AIEE*, vol. 68, pp. 206–212, 1949. The suggested values for the short-time-rated and special-purpose machines only are quoted in Table 4-2.

TABLE 4-1*
LIMITING OBSERVABLE MOTOR TEMPERATURE RISES IN DEGREES CENTIGRADE

Temperature Measurement by Thermometer unless Otherwise Noted
(Cooling-air temperature not in excess of 40°C; altitude below 3,300 ft)

Machine part	General-purpose motors	Totally enclosed, totally enclosed fan-cooled, explosion-proof, waterproof, dust-tight, and submersible motors (d-c and induction motors)		Other d-c and induction motors	
	Class A insulation	Class A insulation	Class B insulation	Class A insulation	Class B insulation
Windings other than squirrel-cage and field windings	40	55	75	50	70
Insulated field windings†	50‡	60	80	60	80
Cores and mechanical parts in contact with or adjacent to insulation	40	55	75	50	70
Collector rings and commutators	55	65	85	65	85

Squirrel-cage windings and miscellaneous parts (brush holders, brushes, pole tips, etc.) may attain such temperatures as will not injure the machine in any respect.

* Compiled from data appearing in ASA Standards, *Rotating Electrical Machinery*, C50-1943, American Standards Association, New York, 1943. This table should be used only to obtain a general idea of temperature limitations. The latest edition of the Standards should be consulted for authoritative and more comprehensive specifications.

† Temperature rise by resistance measurement for other than series-field windings. Where field-winding temperature rises by thermometer are also specified, they are 10°C below those by resistance measurements.

‡ Except 0.8-power-factor synchronous motors, where 60°C rise by resistance is allowed for Class A insulation.

features, where operation at high ambient temperatures must be tolerated, as in powerhouse auxiliary-drive motors, and in other special-purpose machines.[7]

[7] For accounts of the development and potential applications of the silicones to electric machinery, see T. A. Kauppi and G. L. Moses, Organo-silicon Compounds for Insulating Electric Machines, *Trans. AIEE*, vol. 64, pp. 90–93, 1945; J. DeKiep, L. R. Hill, and G. L. Moses, The Application of Silicone Resins to Insulation for Electric Machinery, *Trans. AIEE*, vol. 64, pp. 94–98, 1945.

Application of the silicones is but one of many examples of the influence of improved properties of materials on machines and on the ratings which can be obtained from a given amount of iron and copper. A more notable example is offered by the improvements in the magnetic characteristics of iron which have taken place through the years. Such examples serve as reminders that there is much more involved in the development of commercially successful machinery, and in engineering in general, than is indicated by a series of equations based on mathematical physics.

TABLE 4-2*
PROPOSED LIMITING OBSERVABLE TEMPERATURE RISES IN DEGREES CENTIGRADE FOR D-C MACHINES

Machine part	Method of temperature measurement	Short-time-rated machines						Special-purpose machines with continuous rating†		
		30-min to 2-hr ratings			Ratings of 15 min or less					
		Class A	Class B	Class H	Class A	Class B	Class H	Class A	Class B	Class H
Armature windings	Thermometer	55	75	100	55	75	100	50	70	90
	Resistance	80	110	140	90	120	160	60	85	110
Shunt-field windings	Thermometer	55	75	100	55	75	100	50	70	90
	Resistance	70	90	120	70	100	130	70	90	120
Single-layer field windings with exposed copper	Thermometer	65	85	110	65	85	110	60	80	100
	Resistance	80	110	140	90	120	160	60	85	110
Cores and mechanical parts	Thermometer	55	75	100	55	75	100	50	70	90
Commutators and collector rings	Thermometer	65	85	110	65	85	110	65	85	110

* Adapted from, and partially reproducing, Table 1 of the reference cited in footnote 6.

† Generators having a 2-hr 25 per cent overload rating will have temperature limits 10°C lower than as given in the last three columns for the continuous load; they will have the same values at the end of the 2-hr overload as given for 2-hr-rated machines.

The most common machine rating is the *continuous rating* defining the output (in kilowatts for d-c generators, kilovolt-amperes at a specified power factor for a-c generators, and horsepower for motors) which can be carried indefinitely without exceeding established limitations. For intermittent, periodic, or varying duty a machine may be given a *short-time rating* defining the load which can be carried for a specified time. Standard periods for short-time ratings are 5, 15, 30, and 60 min. Speeds, voltages, and frequencies are also specified in machine ratings, and provision is made for possible variations in voltage and frequency. Motors, for example, must operate successfully at voltages 10 per cent above and below rated voltage and, for a-c motors, at frequencies 5 per cent above and below rated frequency; the combined variation of voltage and frequency may not exceed 10 per cent. Other performance conditions are so established that reasonable short-time overloads may be carried. Thus, the user of a motor may expect to be able to apply for a short time an overload of, say, 25 per cent at 90 per cent of normal voltage with an ample margin of safety.

The converse problem to the rating of machinery, that of choosing the size of machine for a particular application, is a relatively simple one when the load requirements remain substantially constant. For many motor applications, however, the load requirements vary more or less cyclically and over a wide range. The duty cycle of a typical crane or hoist motor may readily be visualized as an example. From the thermal viewpoint, the average heating of the motor must be found by detailed study of the motor losses during the various parts of the cycle. Account must be taken of changes in ventilation with motor speed for open and semienclosed motors. Judicious selection is based on a large amount of experimental data and considerable experience with the motors involved. For estimating the required size of motors operating at substantially constant speeds, it is sometimes assumed that the heating of the insulation varies as the square of the horsepower load, an assumption which obviously overemphasizes the role of armature I^2R loss at the expense of the core loss. The rms ordinate of the horsepower-time curve representing the duty cycle is obtained by the same technique used to find the rms value of periodically varying currents, and a motor rating is chosen on the basis of the result; *i.e.*,

$$\text{rms hp} = \sqrt{\frac{\Sigma\,(\text{hp})^2 \times (\text{time})}{\text{running time} + (\text{standstill time}/k)}} \tag{4-87}$$

where the constant k accounts for the poorer ventilation at standstill and equals approximately 4 for an open motor. The time for a complete cycle must be short compared with the time for the motor to reach a steady temperature.

Although crude, the rms-horsepower method is used fairly often. The necessity for rounding off the result to a commercially available motor size obviates the need for precise computations; if the rms horsepower were 87, for example, a 100-hp motor would be chosen. Special consideration must be given to motors that are frequently started or reversed, for such operations are thermally equivalent to heavy overloads. Consideration must also be given to duty cycles having such high torque peaks that motors with continuous ratings chosen on purely thermal bases would be unable to furnish the torques required. It is to such duty cycles that special-purpose motors with short-time ratings are often applied. Short-time-rated motors in general have better torque-producing ability than motors rated to produce the same power output continuously, although, of course, they have a lower thermal capacity. Both of these properties follow from the fact that a short-time-rated motor is designed for high flux densities in the iron and high current densities in the copper. In general, the ratio of torque capacity to thermal capacity increases as the period of the short-time rating decreases. As indicated in the fourth column of Table 4-1, higher temperature rises are allowed than for general-purpose motors. A motor with a 150-hp 1-hr, 50°C rating, for example, may have the torque ability of a 200-hp continuously rated motor; it will be able to carry only about 0.8 of its rated output, or 120 hp, continuously, however. In many cases it will be the economical solution for a drive requiring a continuous thermal capacity of 120 hp but having torque peaks which require the ability of a 200-hp continuously rated motor.

4-13. Résumé. The Analysis of Machines. The synchronous machine is a special case of the induction machine in which zero-frequency or direct current is supplied to the rotor and which therefore must operate at zero slip or synchronous speed; the d-c machine is a special case of the synchronous machine in which a mechanical switching device, the commutator, is associated with the armature winding: these two statements typify many restricted and specific expressions of the basic unity underlying the various machine types. This unity forms the principal theme of Chap. 3, where the properties of machines and, to a considerable extent, the machines themselves are developed qualitatively from simple concepts relating torque, voltage, and change of flux linkages.

In Chap. 3 the preliminary analysis of the practicability of these machines for energy conversion is based on sinusoidal flux-density and mmf waves. In this chapter the influence of departures from these assumptions is investigated, and modifications are made whenever reasonable accuracy and the direct or indirect influence of these departures necessitate them. Since the waveforms are largely functions of the winding arrangements and general machine geometry, which in turn are dictated by optimum suitability to the intended service, the analytical details for a-c and d-c machines begin to follow diverging branches on the basic trunk. Similar divergence between the analytical details of induction- and synchronous-machine theory will be found in subsequent chapters.

In a-c machines the principal effects of the harmonics which represent the departures from sine waves are to cause distortion of the generated-voltage waveform, to introduce serious possibilities of noise and vibration, and, of particular importance in induction motors, to produce at standstill or at low speeds parasitic torques which impair the starting performance. Consequently it is essential that definite steps be taken to minimize the harmonics. These steps include distributing the winding in several slots per pole per phase, chording the winding, the use of a fractional-slot winding, skewing the rotor structure, and careful choice of rotor and stator slot combinations. When the appropriate steps have been taken to avoid the obnoxious effects of harmonics, all the effects under normal steady-state running conditions may be ignored except the contribution of harmonic fluxes to leakage reactance. Analysis of a-c machines may therefore be based directly on the principles discussed in Chap. 3. Important equations which form the basis of detailed analyses in subsequent chapters are 4-14 for the generated voltage and 4-5 and 4-13 for the breadth and pitch factors; 4-23 for the amplitude of the rotating mmf wave, in conjunction with the same breadth and pitch factors; and 4-46 and 4-47 for electromagnetic torque in terms of machine current and voltage.

For d-c machines, a careful examination of the commutated armature winding shows it to be more faithfully represented by a current sheet with uniform angular current density under each pole (but, of course, with reversal of current direction in going from under a north pole to under a south pole), and hence by a triangular rather than a sinusoidal mmf wave. This discovery necessitates reexamination of the torque expression. Reexamination shows that, for the normal d-c machine with brushes on the neutral, both the torque and the average voltage depend only on the flux per pole and not on the flux distribution. The resulting equations are 4-56 and 4-61 for torque and 4-38 for generated voltage. Again correlation of the torque equation with energy-conservation concepts suggests a potentially fruitful approach.

Idealization of the machine is a necessary preliminary to the foregoing investigations, the principal assumptions being that the air gap is smooth and of uniform width, that the reluctance of the iron is negligible, and that hysteresis and eddy currents are absent. Idealization before analysis is a very common engineering procedure, and it is indeed a rare problem which does not require simplifying assumptions to make it amenable to mathematical treatment. Such assumptions must, of course, not be too unrealistic, or the resulting analysis becomes worthless. They are usually made on the basis of previous experience with similar problems and are always carefully checked by experiment. Not infrequently some of the idealizations which appear desirable at the very outset of a new investigation turn out later to be unnecessary or to be replaceable by less drastic assumptions. Contrast between the handling of current-sheet, flux-density, and mmf waveforms in Chap. 3 and in the present chapter illustrates this point. In Chap. 3 these waveforms are all assumed to be sinusoidal. In this chapter the assumptions are found to be not at all drastic for steady-state operation of normal a-c machines; for d-c machines the current-sheet and mmf assumptions are replaced by more representative ones, and the flux-density assumption is found to be entirely unnecessary in the normal case.

Analysis of the idealized machine must be followed by another step very common in engineering: adapting the analysis to the actual machine. This step involves studies of the departures from the ideal and the devising of artifices and stratagems to include any appreciable effects of the departures. Use of the magnetization curve to take account of the magnetic-potential drop in the iron is but one of a number of examples. Such artifices generally emerge from a thorough physical understanding of the happenings and, in their final form, may be the result of years of experiment and study. In fact, the history of machine theory shows the path to present-day methods frequently to have been from a physical picture, to a more or less crude formulation of the picture, and finally to thoroughgoing mathematical investigation confirming or partially correcting the semiintuitive approach. Mistakes, and sometimes serious mistakes, have been made during this process. For example, the principal early use of armature leakage reactance of a synchronous machine was in conjunction with the open-circuit characteristic to calculate the voltage of an alternator under load. Later and more detailed study showed that the method of computing leakage reactance from design data gave values which were too high by some 25 to 100 per cent and that the discrepancy had been approximately offset by an inadequate allowance for the effects of field leakage on the mutual flux. Continuing advances in engineering and mathematical analysis and in experimental techniques make the occurrence of such errors progressively less likely and greatly accelerate the attainment of comprehensive and satisfactory solutions.

Later on in the text, additional or alternative simplifying assumptions unique to certain problems will be introduced. The need for assumptions is thus a continuing one, and one for which the basis may shift from problem to problem as dictated by the need for simpler methods, for greater accuracy, or because new problems arising in practice demand that a hitherto neglected factor be taken into account. One illustration which we have already encountered is offered by the drastic assumptions behind the rough-and-ready rms-horsepower method of determining required motor sizes. The making of admissible assumptions in the approach to a new engineering problem and the interpretation of results in the light of these assumptions are the two most difficult steps in engineering analysis; the intermediate operations are usually those of routine mathematics. From this viewpoint, thoroughgoing analysis of any one device adds appreciably to ability to analyze all devices.

It is sometimes thought that the full power of the Maxwell-equation electromagnetic-theory approach to the basic problems of machinery is overlooked. A comprehensive frontal attack utilizing this power cannot be made, however. The complex geometry of the machine and the need for incorporating the appropriate ferromagnetic characteristics render the solutions of even the simplest problems mathematically burdensome and of other problems impossible by present techniques. The field-theory approach is frequently used on detailed aspects—flux mapping, mentioned in Art. 4-10, is an example—and to provide valuable guides and checking points in the development of the conventional theory.[8] The most fruitful general attack, however, is that on the simpler magnetic-circuit basis.

The aptness of a method of analysis can also be judged in terms of the uses ultimately to be made of the method. As already indicated, the torque-speed characteristics of motors and the voltage-load characteristics of generators, together with knowledge of the limits between which these characteristics can be varied and ideas of how such variations may be obtained, are factors of outstanding importance in machine applications. In many problems primary interest is focused not so much on happenings inside the machine as on the interactions between the machine and the electrical or mechanical system to which it is connected—in other words, on the behavior of the machine as a system element. The ordinary electric power system, for example, consists of hundreds of electrically coupled machines whose performances are, to widely varying degrees, mutually dependent. On a smaller physical scale, it is not infrequently necessary to employ a group of several machines interconnected with each other and with other elements in order to achieve the desired versatility of performance and control.

In so far as the electrical-system aspects alone are concerned, it is desirable to represent the machines at their electrical terminals by simple equivalent circuits. These circuits are preferably composed of linear circuit elements in association with constant voltages. They usually consist of rather simple two-terminal networks of impedances or of two-terminal networks behind which constant or easily determinable voltages exist, and the terminals are usually connected to sources or consumers of bulk electrical power. Such equivalent circuits are developed in the following six chapters for the various machines in the steady state. Simplicity of the resulting equivalents is an obvious necessity when a large group of machines is involved, and this fact has a direct bearing on the

[8] See, for instance, B. Hague, "Electromagnetic Problems in Electrical Engineering," Oxford University Press, New York, 1929, which is devoted almost entirely to the application of electromagnetic-field theory to rotating machines. Note that most of the analyses are based on infinitely permeable iron and uniform air gaps.

theoretical approach to the individual machine. At the same time the limitations of the simple equivalents must be carefully studied and taken into account. In this manner the complex phenomena of electromagnetic energy conversion are fitted to the mathematical niceness of linear circuit theory.

When the major concern is with the dynamic behavior of the over-all system including the nonelectrical as well as the electrical components, the machine equivalent must usually be a more comprehensive one representing mechanical as well as purely electromagnetic features. The input terminals of the equivalent may be connected to a bulk source of electrical power, but more commonly they are the terminals on which is impressed a command signal demanding a certain response at the output—a change in field current of a d-c motor demanding a change in the speed of its shaft, for example. The quantity emerging at the output terminals may be electrical power, but frequently it will be the electromechanical equivalent of a change in shaft position, speed, or acceleration. These types of equivalent circuits are usually two-terminal-pair networks (as are the equivalent circuits of a two-winding transformer for instance) in which the machine is the transfer medium or coupling element between the two input terminals and the two output terminals. They are frequently characterized by transfer constants or transfer parameters, just as are the corresponding networks in electric-circuit theory. Because of their comprehensiveness, they demand even greater simplicity in representing the electromagnetic phenomena in a machine than do the equivalent circuits representing purely electrical aspects; the accompanying sacrifice in accuracy may also be very much greater. Their study is accordingly postponed until Chap. 13 in order that a more complete background of machine behavior may be available. Existence of these problems, however, provides another conditioning influence on the theoretical approach to the individual machine.

Although the electric machine in its essence is an energy-conversion device, it is extremely helpful in leading up to the foregoing dynamic problems to view the machine also as an amplifier—a dynamoelectric power amplifier having much in common with electronic amplifiers. A separately excited d-c generator, for example, may for some purposes be regarded as analogous to a single-stage electronic amplifier. The function of the d-c generator may be regarded as that of controlling a comparatively large amount of electrical power flow from the armature by a small amount of power in the field circuit. The field circuit thus serves the same purpose as the grid circuit of the electronic amplifier, and the armature circuit with its load is analogous to the plate circuit. The mechanical power at the generator shaft becomes the equivalent of the plate-supply power. To be sure, the speed of response of the electronic case cannot be reached, but the great power-handling ability of the machine is a distinct advantage. Alternatively, the process may be regarded as one of modulation, in which the power output from the armature is uniquely conditioned by a voltage signal at the field terminals; if a series field is added to convert the machine to a compound generator, in which the output exerts a certain amount of direct control over machine performance, the situation is like that in a feedback amplifier; if the machine is converted to a self-excited generator, the process may be regarded as similar to that in a feedback oscillator. The general amplifier viewpoint may also be applied to motors when the output is taken as a nonelectrical quantity such as mechanical power or the position, speed, or acceleration of a shaft. When power amplification is needed at certain electrical power levels, one problem may be to choose from amplification by high-vacuum tubes, by grid- or igniter-controlled gas-filled tubes, by electrodynamic methods using machines, or by a combination of the possibilities in cascade.

These amplifier analogies serve a number of useful purposes. Recognition of the existence of similarities is an obvious help in the study of the devices. Of greater benefit is discernment of similarities in the methodology—for example, the use of equivalent circuits in order that advantage may be taken of the huge catalogue of circuit properties and techniques, and the use of graphical methods where nonlinearities are significant. Most important, however, is the fact that interborrowing of special techniques becomes more feasible. Thus the frequency-response methods and stability criteria developed for electronic circuits become applicable in substance to the dynamic analysis of systems involving machines. The machine in other words, becomes functionally a circuit element in the broader sense of the word *circuit*, and as such it supplements or competes with other similar circuit elements such as electronic amplifiers or hydraulic, pneumatic, and mechanical elements.

PROBLEMS

4-1. A 3-phase 8-pole winding of the double-layer type described in Art. 4-1 is to be placed on a stator with 96 slots. The coil pitch is to be 5/6.

a. Draw a sketch similar to Fig. 4-6 showing in developed cross-sectional form the arrangement of 2 poles of this winding.

b. Draw a vector diagram showing the fundamental voltages induced in the coil sides of 1 phase.

c. From the vector relations of *b*, compute the fundamental winding factor k_w.

d. Compute the fundamental pitch and breadth factors.

e. If each coil has 2 turns and all the coils in each phase are connected in series, find the number of series turns per phase.

f. If the phases are Y-connected, find the fundamental flux per pole in webers for a line-to-line voltage of 440 volts at 60 cps.

g. Compute the peak value of the fundamental component of the mmf wave, in ampere-turns per pole, for balanced 3-phase line currents of 100 amp.

4-2. A 3-phase Y-connected 25-cps 12-pole alternator is rated to deliver 7,500 kva at a line-to-line terminal voltage of 12,000 volts. The stator has 180 slots with four inductors per slot arranged to form a two-layer series winding. The coil pitch is 12 slots.

a. What is the no-load line-to-line terminal voltage when the air-gap flux of 52.0 megalines per pole is sinusoidally distributed?

b. When the alternator is operating at full-load stator current, what is the amplitude of the fundamental component of the stator-mmf wave?

4-3. A 3-phase Y-connected 60-cps 2-pole synchronous machine with a cylindrical rotor has 12 slots. Each stator slot contains 2 coil sides. Each coil contains 100 turns. The coil pitch is 5⁄6. A developed diagram of the winding is given in Fig. 4-6. For sinusoidal balanced currents of 1.0 amp per phase with an *abc* phase sequence, determine the analytical expression for the mmf wave, taking the origin for θ to be at the center of slot 2 in Fig. 4-6. Consider only the fundamental component, and neglect effect of slots. For current direction, assume $+i_a$ is current into terminal *a*, and that slot 2 then has current out of the paper.

4-4. For the machine of Prob. 4-3, calculate the induced emf in phase *a* (line to neutral) caused by the flux-density wave corresponding to the mmf wave determined above. Consider the positive sign for induced emf to mean terminal *a* positive with respect to neutral. Assume an effective air gap of 0.002 m, a rotor diameter of 0.198 m, and a rotor length of 0.20 m. Neglect the effect of slots, and consider iron infinitely permeable.

4-5. The voltage generated in the armature winding of a d-c machine is given by Eq. 4-38.

a. In view of the fact that an appreciable fraction of the total number of conductors are short-circuited by the brushes, should Z be the total number of conductors or the number of active conductors? Assume that the brushes are located at the neutral position.

b. Comment on the validity of this expression when the brushes are shifted away from the neutral position.

4-6. A 3-phase Y-connected 6-pole 25-kva synchronous generator has 12 slots per pole in its stator (armature) winding. The breadth factor of the stator winding is 0.958, and the coil pitch is 10 slots, for which the pitch factor is 0.966. Each slot contains 2 coil sides, and each coil has 4 turns. The field winding provides a sinusoidally distributed flux wave with a magnitude of 0.0212 weber per pole. The generator is driven at a constant speed of 1,200 rpm.

a. Find the line-to-line voltage at the generator terminals at no load.

b. The generator is connected to a 3-phase load that draws a line current of 25 amp. The power factor is such that the current in the stator winding lags by 30° the voltage induced by the field flux. Find the torque in newton-meters that must be supplied by the prime mover. Neglect all losses.

4-7. A 230-volt 25-hp 6-pole wave-wound d-c shunt motor has 56 slots on its armature. Each slot contains 2 coil sides, and each coil consists of 8 turns. The resistance of each coil is 0.0143 ohm. The brushes are in the neutral position.

a. What external resistance must be added in series with the armature circuit to limit the starting current supplied to the armature to 200 amp when 230 volts is applied?

b. Under running conditions, the motor drives a load that requires a torque of 95 newton-m independent of speed. The current supplied to the armature terminals then is 50 amp with rated armature terminal voltage and no external resistance. Assume that the electromagnetic torque developed is the same as the output torque. Find the speed at which the motor operates.

4-8. The flux density in an idealized d-c machine has a rectangular waveform of height B_{peak}. The armature-mmf waveform is an isosceles triangle of height F_{peak}. The space-phase displacement between the two axes is 90°.

a. Write torque and voltage equations in terms of B_{peak} and F_{peak} and other necessary quantities (1) for the actual waveforms shown and (2) by considering the fundamental components of these waves only. Compare the results.

b. Discuss why in the analysis of synchronous and induction machines the harmonics are treated separately, whereas the actual waves are considered in deriving the fundamental equations for d-c machines.

4-9. D-c machines are almost invariably equipped with short-pitch windings. The torque and voltage equations, however, are derived without paying any attention to this fact. Do you think something should be done about it? If so, what modifications should be made in these equations? If not, support your answer with full explanation.

4-10. A 3-phase Y-connected 60-cps 20-pole synchronous generator has 300 stator slots. The armature winding consists of coils having a pitch of $4/5$.

a. Determine the fundamental, third-harmonic, and fifth-harmonic breadth and pitch factors.

b. The air-gap flux-density wave has third- and fifth-harmonic components whose amplitudes are, respectively, 30 per cent and 20 per cent of the fundamental components. Determine the per cent third- and fifth-harmonic components which will be present in the generated voltage per phase.

c. For the conditions of *b*, determine the rms value of the line-to-line voltage of the machine when it is unloaded, in terms of the rms value of the fundamental component of the phase voltage.

4-11. A 2-pole 3-phase 60-cps Y-connected alternator has 36 stator slots. Each slot holds 2 coil sides, and each coil has 1 turn. The fundamental flux per pole is 2.0 webers. The coil pitch is $2/3$. The fundamental component of the line-to-neutral voltage has an rms value of 5,300 volts, and the fifth-harmonic component is 218 volts.

a. What is the value of the maximum fifth-harmonic flux density relative to the maximum fundamental flux density?

b. What is the fifth-harmonic flux per fifth-harmonic pole?

4-12. A Y-connected 3-phase alternator whose field has a rectangular space distribution is observed to have zero third- and fifth-harmonic components in its line-to-line voltages. By what factor could the fundamental component be increased by using full-pitch windings? Assume that the maximum fundamental, consistent with the harmonics specified and a pitch less than 1.00, is being developed.

4-13. A 3-phase Y-connected 60-cps 16-pole synchronous generator has 192 stator slots. The armature winding consists of coils having a pitch of $5/6$. The phase spread is $1/3$ of a pole pitch. All the coils of each phase are connected in series.

An oscillogram of the voltage generated in one of the coils when the armature is open-circuited, the field is excited with direct current, and the rotor is driven at synchronous speed shows that the coil voltage contains fundamental, third-, and fifth-harmonic components whose rms values are 100, 25, and 5 volts, respectively.

a. Find the relative amplitudes of the third- and fifth-harmonic components in the air-gap flux-density wave as compared with the fundamental.

b. Find the rms value of the line-to-line voltage.

4-14. The armature of a 3-phase 4-pole alternator has 30 slots. Design a double-layer 0.8-pitch winding for the armature, showing:

a. The slot vector diagram.

b. The complete winding layout. Indicate the starting and finishing points of each phase in the winding diagram.

c. Compute the winding factor.

4-15. A 3-phase stator winding has 15 slots per pole and a coil pitch of $\frac{4}{5}$. When this winding is excited by balanced sinusoidal 3-phase currents whose rms value is 10 amp, the amplitude of the fundamental rotating mmf wave is 490 amp-turns per pole.

What is the magnitude of the lowest-order-harmonic mmf wave present in the air gap?

4-16. A wound-rotor induction motor is used on a 60-cps 3-phase line. At full load its speed is 1,720 rpm. An examination of the winding on the stator shows that there are 3 slots per phase per pole and 2 coil sides in each slot. The corresponding coil sides are 80 mechanical degrees apart.

a. Calculate the ratio of the amplitude of each harmonic component to the amplitude of the fundamental component of the resultant mmf wave, up to and including the fifth harmonic.

b. What are the practical reasons for attempting to minimize the harmonics in the mmf wave?

4-17. Solve Prob. 4-3 considering the third and fifth harmonics of the mmf wave as well as the fundamental.

4-18. Solve Prob. 4-4 considering the third and fifth harmonics in the flux-density wave as well as the fundamental.

4-19. Quantitative analysis of polyphase synchronous and induction machines is based directly on the torque equation, 3-22, developed in Chap. 3. Briefly present in your own words a justification of the apparent neglect of harmonics in this procedure.

4-20. The magnetization curve of a d-c generator contains the following points, all taken at a speed of 1,000 rpm:

Field current, amp	1.5	1.25	1.00	0.50
Induced voltage, volts	250	230	200	100

a. If the field current is adjusted to 1.25 amp, how fast must the generator be driven to generate 250 volts at no load?

b. What must be the field current to generate 200 volts at 800 rpm, no load?

c. If the machine is connected as a motor to a 230-volt line and the field current is adjusted to 1.0 amp, how fast will it run at no load? Neglect rotational losses.

4-21. The following data pertain to the wave-wound armature of a 250-volt 1,750-rpm 4-pole d-c machine:

Number of armature inductors = 444
Armature-winding resistance = 0.14 ohm
Brush drop under load = 2.0 volts

The rotational losses for a speed of 1,750 rpm and an armature generated voltage of 250 volts are 700 watts. Stray load losses may be neglected.

a. The machine is operating at rated speed with an armature current of 40 amp and an armature generated voltage of 250 volts. Find the electromagnetic torque.

b. Determine the mechanical shaft power input and the armature electric power output when the machine in *a* is operating as a generator.

c. Determine the armature electric power input and the mechanical shaft power output when the machine in *a* in operating as a motor.

d. Consider that the motor in *c* is driving a mechanical load of such a nature that the electromagnetic torque required of the motor remains constant regardless of the speed at which the motor operates. (To a fair approximation this statement is the same as saying that the mechanical torque required by the load is independent of speed, for the change in rotational losses of the motor constitutes the only difference.) To what value does the motor speed change when the armature terminal voltage is halved with the resultant flux per pole remaining the same as before?

e. Consider that the motor of *c* is driving a mechanical load of such a nature that the electromagnetic power required of the motor remains constant regardless of speed. The armature terminal voltage remains as in *c*, but the resultant flux is reduced to 0.80 of its former value by weakening the field excitation. To what value does the motor speed change?

4-22. In a machine shop using five boring mills, it is desired to compare the total annual charges of group drive with those of individual drive for the mills. Group drive requires one 20-hp motor, while individual drive requires five 5-hp motors.

The following data are estimated:

	20-hp motor	5-hp motor
Input with load on	16,200 watts	3,650 watts
Input with load off	2,000 watts	700 watts
Cost installed	$708	$315
Expected life	10 years	10 years
Yearly maintenance cost	$ 30	$ 15

Input under load to the 20-hp motor is estimated for four of the five mills in operation.

The line-shaft hangers and pulleys cost $500 installed and have an assumed life of 10 years and an annual maintenance charge of $30. Electric power costs may be taken as 1.5 cents per kilowatthour.

Assume that the plant runs 8 hr each day, 300 days a year, and that each mill runs four-fifths of the time. When individual drives are used, it is the practice to shut down the motor when not actually boring. Assume straight-line depreciation and that other fixed charges amount to 7.5 per cent.

Compute the annual cost for each method of operation.

4-23. Electric power is purchased for an electrochemical plant at 13,200 volts, 3-phase, 60 cps, at an incremental cost of 0.48 cent per kilowatthour. It is desired to generate 4,000 kw at 600 volts d-c for one of the plant processes. To do so, a 4,000-kw 600-volt d-c generator is to be driven by a 6,000-hp 2,300-volt 3-phase synchronous motor. The synchronous motor is to be supplied with power from a 3-phase transformer stepping down the 13,200 to 2,300 volts. The load on the motor-generator may be considered constant at 4,000 kw for 24 hr a day, 7 days a week.

The following data are available for full load on the generator:

D-C Generator Losses at Full Load:

Core loss, friction, and windage = 120 kw
Stray load loss = 40.0 kw
Shunt-field loss (including rheostat) = 20.0 kw
Armature-circuit copper loss (including series field) = 64.4 kw
Brush-contact loss = 13.3 kw

Synchronous Motor:

Efficiency of motor at full load on generator (including exciter losses) = 96.2 per cent

Transformer:

Efficiency at full load on generator = 99.1 per cent

Installed cost of the motor-generator, transformer, and the necessary control and protective equipment is $92,000. Repairs and attendance will average $500 a year. Fixed charges are 15 per cent per year.

Compute the cost of a d-c kilowatthour.

4-24. General-purpose 3-phase 60-cps induction motors are available in 2-, 4-, 6-, and 8-pole designs and in the following horsepower ratings: 2, 3, 5, 7.5, 10, 15, 20, etc. These motors develop rated output at a slip of about 5 per cent and develop a maximum torque of 200 per cent of rated torque at a slip of about 15 per cent.

Select the appropriate motor for an application requiring a torque of 50 lb-ft at a speed of about 1,500 rpm for a period of 30 sec, followed by 4 min running at no load, followed by repetitions of the same load cycle. Specify the horsepower and synchronous-speed ratings.

4-25. A d-c compound motor is to be selected for the operation of a lift. The motor is to drive continuously a steel cable which runs over pulleys at the bottom and the top of the lift. When the load is descending, the motor becomes a generator and pumps power back into the line, the resulting torque supplying a braking action.

The operating cycle is as follows and is repeated continuously throughout the day:

Load going up (1 min) = 75 hp
Loading period at top (2 min) = 5 hp
Load going down (1 min) = −60 hp
Loading period at bottom (3 min) = 5 hp

On the basis of heating, select the smallest motor suitable for this application. Motors are available in the following sizes: 25, 30, 40, 50, 60, 75, and 100 hp.

What other factors, besides heating, should be considered?

4-26. In the design of a grab-bucket hoist for unloading coal from a barge into a bunker, a study is made of the mechanical requirements to determine the motor duty cycle. The results are given in the following table for an average cycle:

Part of cycle	Elapsed time, sec	Required output, hp
Close bucket	6	40
Hoist	10	80
Open bucket	3	30
Lower bucket	10	45
Rest	16	0

Because of the conditions of service, a dustproof enclosed motor without forced ventilation is to be used, and the constant k associated with the standstill time may be taken as unity.

a. Using the rms method, specify the continuous horsepower rating of the motor. Choose a commercially available motor size.

b. Proposals to furnish this motor are submitted by two manufacturers. These proposals contain the following efficiency guarantees and prices:

Motor	Efficiencies, per cent					
	¼ load	½ load	¾ load	1.0 load	1¼ load	1½ load
A	83.4	90.5	90.3	88.0	86.8	85.0
B	81.3	88.6	90.3	90.6	90.3	89.6

Motor A, net price $2,145; motor B, net price $2,415. (Both prices fob factory, freight allowed.)

The average net cost of energy at this plant is 1.5 cents per kilowatthour. Interest charges are 5 per cent. It is the practice to use straight-line depreciation and to write off all equipment in 5 years. The hoist will be in operation an average of 2,000 hr per year.

Which of these two motors would you recommend?

CHAPTER 5

D-C MACHINES: ANALYSIS OF PERFORMANCE

In the study of all types of electric machinery, our ultimate object is to obtain a reasonably complete physical and analytical picture of the energy-conversion process, of the performance characteristics of the machine, of the factors tending to limit the conditions under which the machine may operate successfully, and of practical means for combating these factors and extending these limits. Such study usually divides itself naturally into two parts. The first part, presented in Chaps. 1 to 4, is the derivation from fundamental physical laws of expressions for the generated voltage and electromagnetic torque for the machine concerned, together with examination of the physical processes involved. The second part, presented in the next six chapters, is study of the specific techniques leading to the most facile application of these expressions to the obtaining of numerical performance specifications, together with a summarizing of the principal operating features as revealed by these performance studies.

From the analytic viewpoint, the principal objects of this chapter are to develop methods by which the characteristics of the machines and their effects on the external circuits may be determined. Among the most important characteristics are the variation of speed with load for a motor and the variation of terminal voltage with load for a generator. In addition, qualitative consideration must be given to certain potential operating difficulties and to means for overcoming them. Thus, our previous discussions have ignored the act of switching which must take place at the commutator every time a segment passes under a brush, yet the performance of this continued switching without sparking or arcing is essential to successful machine operation. Again, our previous discussions have dealt with the role of armature mmf in the production of electromagnetic torque but have not considered its effect in distorting the resultant air-gap flux and so affecting both the commutation problem and the machine characteristics.

5-1. Flux and MMF Distributions. Armature mmf or armature reaction has definite effects on both the space distribution of the air-gap flux and the magnitude of the net flux per pole. The effect on flux distribution is important because the limits of successful commutation are directly influenced; the effect on flux magnitude is important because both the generated voltage and torque per unit of armature current are influenced thereby. These effects and the problems arising from them are described in this and the next article.

a. Brushes in the Neutral Position. It is shown in Art. 4-4 and by Figs. 4-11 to 4-13 that the armature-mmf wave may be closely approximated by a triangle, corresponding to the wave produced by a finely distributed armature winding or current sheet. For a machine with brushes in the neutral position, the idealized mmf wave is again shown by the dotted triangle in Fig. 5-1, in which a positive mmf ordinate

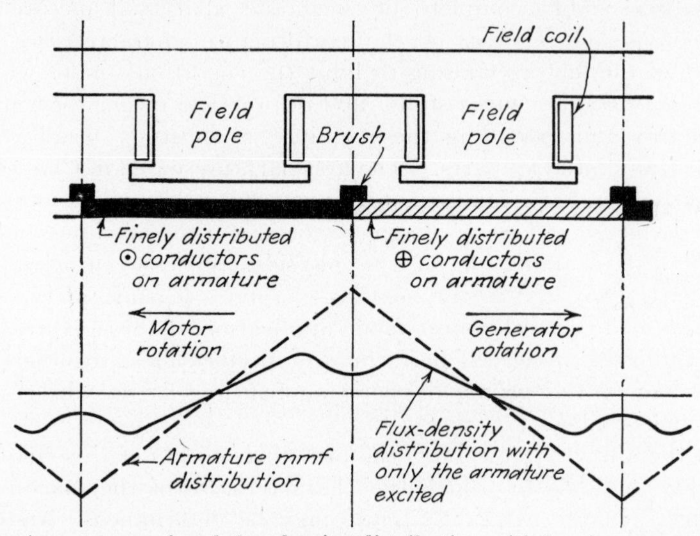

FIG. 5-1. Armature-mmf and flux-density distribution with brushes on neutral and only the armature excited.

denotes flux lines leaving the armature surface. Current directions in all windings other than the main field are indicated by black and cross-hatched bands. Because of the salient-pole field structure found on almost all d-c machines, the associated space distribution of flux will not be triangular. The distribution of air-gap flux density with only the armature excited is given by the solid curve of Fig. 5-1. As may readily be seen, it is appreciably decreased by the long air path in the interpolar space.

An approximate version of the corresponding flux map is given in Fig. 5-2, where the presence of slots in the armature iron is ignored. For purposes of comparison, a similar approximate map of the main-field flux is given in Fig. 5-3 for a machine with only the field winding excited. The flux scale on these two figures is not the same, however; *i.e.*, one flux line in Fig. 5-3 represents more actual flux in the normal machine than does one line in Fig. 5-2. The effect of the armature mmf is seen to be that of creating flux sweeping across the pole faces; thus, its path in the pole shoes crosses the path of the main-field flux. For this reason, armature reaction of this type is called *cross-magnetizing armature reaction.* It evidently causes a decrease in the resultant air-gap flux under one half of the pole and an increase under the other half.

When the armature and field windings are both excited, the resultant air-gap flux-density distribution is of the form given by the solid curve of Fig. 5-4. Superimposed on this figure are the flux distributions with

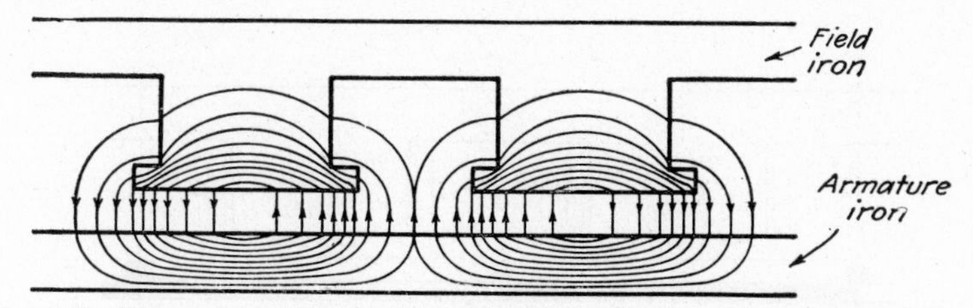

FIG. 5-2. Flux map with only the armature excited and brushes on neutral.

only the armature excited (dashed curve) and only the field excited (dotted curve). The effect of cross-magnetizing armature reaction in decreasing the flux under one pole tip and increasing it under the other may be seen by comparing the solid and dotted curves. In general, the solid curve is not the algebraic sum of the dotted and dashed curves because of the nonlinearity of the iron magnetic circuit. Because of saturation of the iron, the flux density is decreased by a greater amount under one pole tip than it is increased under the other. Accordingly, the resultant flux per pole is lower than would be produced by the field

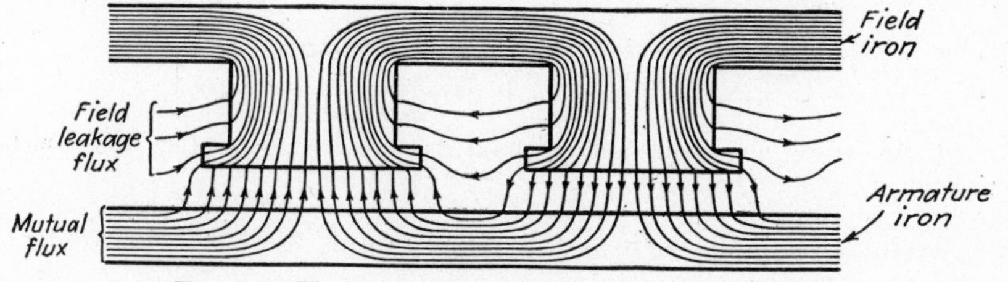

FIG. 5-3. Flux map with only the main field excited.

winding alone, a consequence known as the *demagnetizing effect of cross-magnetizing armature reaction.* Since it is caused by saturation, its magnitude is a nonlinear function of both the field current and the armature current. For normal machine operation at the flux densities used commercially, the effect is usually significant, especially at heavy loads, and must often be taken into account in analyses of performance and in the design of the machine.

The distortion of the flux distribution caused by cross-magnetizing armature reaction may be a detrimental influence on ability to commutate the current, especially if the distortion becomes excessive. In fact, this distortion, and the possibility of instability discussed in Art. 5-7, usually are the factors limiting the short-time overload of a d-c machine. Tendency toward distortion of flux distribution is most pronounced in a machine, such as a shunt motor, where the field excitation remains substantially constant while the armature mmf may reach very significant proportions at heavy loads. The tendency is least pronounced in a

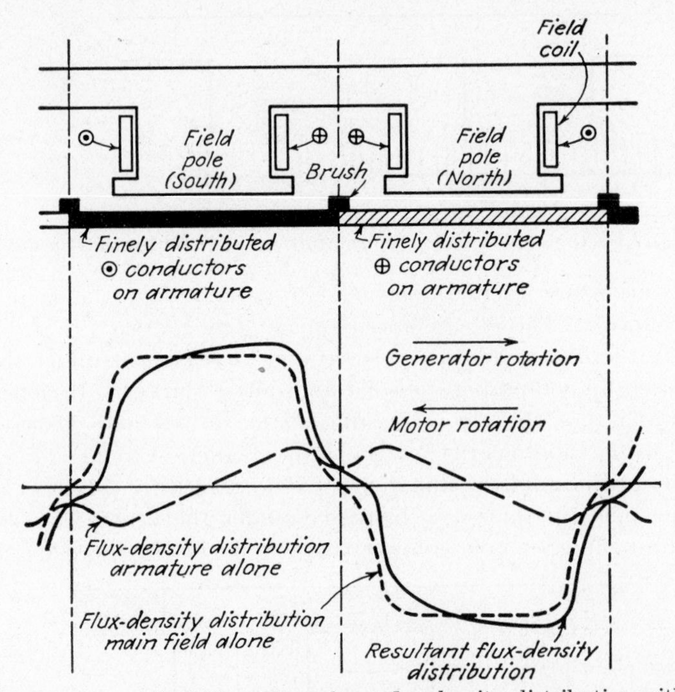

FIG. 5-4. Armature, main-field, and resultant flux-density distribution with brushes on neutral.

series-excited machine, such as the series motor, for both the field and armature mmfs increase with load.

The effect of cross-magnetizing armature reaction may be limited in the design and construction of the machine. The mmf of the main field should exert predominating control on the air-gap flux, so that the condition of weak field mmf and strong armature mmf may be avoided. The reluctance of the cross-flux path—essentially, the armature teeth, pole shoes, and the air gap, especially at the pole tips—may be increased by increasing the degree of saturation in the teeth and pole faces, by avoiding too small an air gap, and by using a chamfered or eccentric pole face (Fig. 5-5), which increases the air gap at the pole tips. These expedients affect the path of the main flux as well, but the influence on the cross flux is much greater. The best but also the most expensive curative measure is to compensate the armature mmf by means of a winding embedded in the pole faces, a measure which is discussed in Art. 5-2.

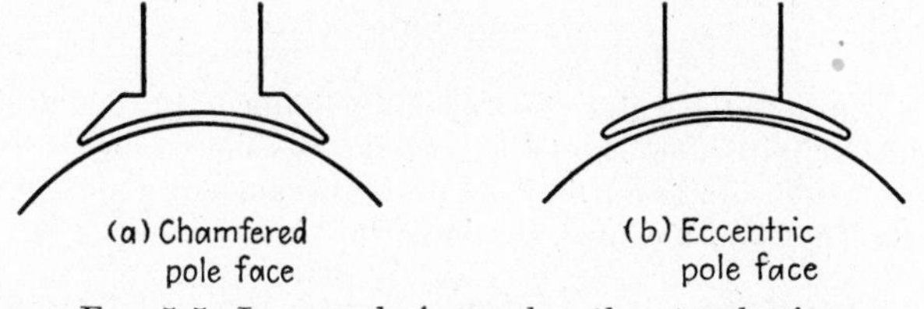

FIG. 5-5. Increased air-gap lengths at pole tips.

Example 5-1. The wave-wound armature of a 250-volt 1,750-rpm 4-pole d-c machine has 37 slots with six coil sides per slot and 2 turns per coil. The ratio ψ of pole arc to pole pitch is ⅔. Normal field excitation of the machine corresponds to a main-field mmf of 1,400 amp-turns per pole, of which 85 per cent are required to overcome the reluctance of the air gap and armature teeth. The brushes are in the neutral position.

As the armature current increases, the distorting effect of cross-magnetizing armature reaction likewise increases. Consider that the allowable limit of such distortion is fixed at the point for which the flux density at the weakened pole tip becomes zero.

a. Compute the armature current corresponding to this limit at normal field excitation.

b. Suppose that the armature current remains constant at 40 amp while the field excitation is weakened in order to increase the speed when the machine is operating as a motor. Find the value of field excitation corresponding to this limit.

Solution. *a.* The armature mmf acting at the pole tip and tending to create an armature component flux density at that point is equal to the ordinate of the triangular armature-mmf wave at that point. This ordinate is the fraction ψ of the triangular amplitude F_A, or, in accordance with Eq. 4-43,

$$\psi F_A = \psi \frac{Z}{2p}\frac{I_a}{a} = \frac{2}{3} \times \frac{444}{2 \times 4}\frac{I_a}{2} = 18.5 I_a \qquad \text{amp-turns}$$

As indicated in Fig. 5-2, the path of the cross-magnetizing armature component flux is through the armature teeth, across the air gap, through the pole face, back across the gap, and through the armature teeth and core to close the path. So far as magnetic reluctance is concerned, the significant portions of the path are the air gap and armature teeth, for the reluctance of the remaining portions is comparatively small. It is therefore essentially correct to regard the mmf ψF_A as acting across the air gap and teeth at each pole tip.

At the weakened pole tip, this mmf is opposed by the portion of the main-field mmf required by the gap and teeth. When these opposing mmfs are equal, the flux density at the weakened tip is zero. Hence,

$$18.5 I_a = 0.85 \times 1{,}400$$

or

$$I_a = 64.3 \text{ amp}$$

A greater armature current will cause reversal of the resultant flux at this tip.

b. At an armature current of 40 amp,

$$\psi F_A = 18.5 \times 40 = 740 \text{ amp-turns per pole tip}$$

The minimum field excitation, corresponding to zero flux density at the weakened pole tip, is then

$$\frac{740}{0.85} = 871 \text{ amp-turns per pole}$$

These general considerations give rise to definite limits on the operation of a particular d-c machine, notably on short-time overloads (short-time so that armature heating does not establish a lower limit) and on the range of motor speed control by field weakening. They are, of course, also important in the design of the machine.

b. Brushes Shifted from the Neutral. When the brushes are not in the neutral position, armature mmf produces not only cross magnetization

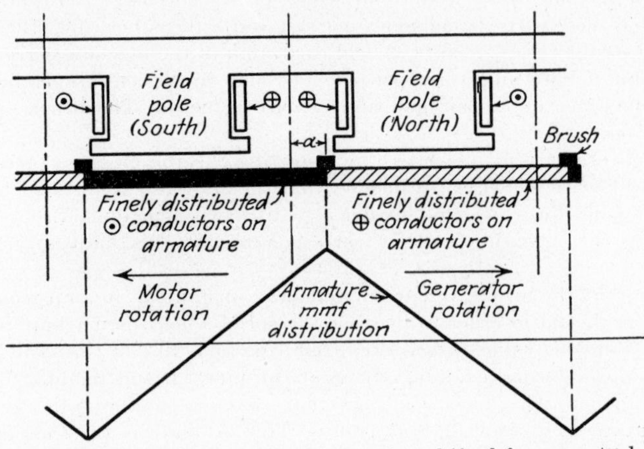

FIG. 5-6. Armature mmf with brushes shifted from neutral.

but also a *direct demagnetizing or magnetizing effect*, depending on the direction of brush shift. In a modern d-c machine, shifting of the brushes from the neutral is usually inadvertent. In early machines, however, shifting of the brushes was a common method of securing satisfactory commutation, the direction of the shift being such that demagnetizing action was produced. Strictly speaking, a shift of the brushes from the neutral violates the conditions of Arts. 4-3 and 4-5 upon which the fundamental voltage and torque equations are based. For such shifts as may normally be encountered, though, analyses based on these equations may be used without significant error.

The effects of a brush shift may be examined by recalling from Art. 3-9 that the axis of the armature-mmf distribution in space is determined by the brush position. When the brushes in Fig. 5-1 are shifted through the electrical angle α from the neutral position, the triangular mmf wave is shifted an equal amount in the same direction. For a shift in the direction of rotation for a generator or against rotation for a motor, the idealized armature-mmf wave becomes that in Fig. 5-6. Neither the mmf wave nor the bands of armature conductors producing it are now symmetrical with respect to either the pole axes or the interpolar axes. Under these circumstances, the effect of the shift is most readily seen by dividing the bands into the two component groups shown in Fig. 5-7. The first is composed of armature conductors centered about the polar axis and covering the angle $90° - \alpha$ either side of it. The second is composed of armature conductors centered about the interpolar axis and covering the angle α either side of it.

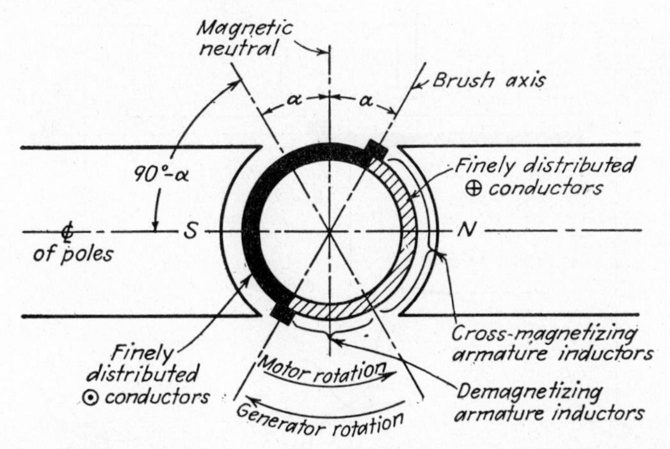

FIG. 5-7. Schematic sketch of armature with brushes shifted from neutral.

The flux produced by the first component alone will be entirely cross flux and will follow the pattern given in the flux map of Fig. 5-2. This component of the armature mmf is accordingly referred to as the *cross-magnetizing component of armature reaction*. All of the comments made previously with regard to distortion and demagnetizing effect apply to it. In the previous discussion, it is the only component present.

The component armature mmf produced by the second group acts on the main magnetic circuit just as do the main-field coils, for it is coaxial with the main-field coils. With the direction of brush shift in Figs. 5-6 and 5-7, this component opposes the main-field mmf. It is therefore referred to as the *direct demagnetizing component of armature reaction*. If the brushes were shifted in the opposite direction, this component mmf would aid the main-field mmf and hence would be a *magnetizing component*.

The combined effect of the two components on the flux distribution is shown in Fig. 5-8. In general, the resultant flux-density waveform is very like that of Fig. 5-4 with the brushes in the neutral. For the same armature and field currents, the ordinates are all somewhat smaller because of the direct demagnetization.

The direct demagnetizing or magnetizing mmf in ampere-turns per pole is the fraction $2\alpha/\pi$ of the total armature ampere-turns per pole. It is very easy to include in analyses since it either subtracts from or adds to the main-field mmf. The demagnetizing effect of cross-magnetizing armature reaction is still present, to be taken into account through the medium of experimental or empirical data. When desired, then, the

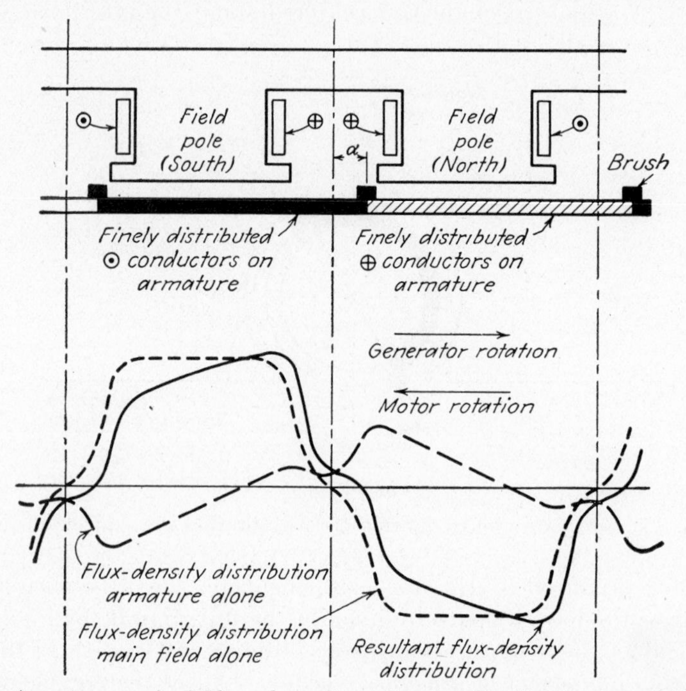

FIG. 5-8. Armature, main-field, and resultant flux-density distribution with brushes shifted from neutral.

direct demagnetizing effect may be included with the same data. Cross-magnetizing armature reaction is the more important, however, because of the relatively infrequent occurrence of appreciable brush shift in modern machines.

5-2. Commutation. Commutating and Compensating Windings. One of the most important limiting factors on satisfactory operation of a d-c machine is the ability to transfer the necessary armature current through the brush contact at the commutator without sparking and without excessive local losses and heating of the brushes and commutator. Sparking causes destructive blackening, pitting, and wear of both commutator and brushes, conditions which rapidly become worse and lead to burning away of the copper and carbon. It may be caused by faulty mechanical conditions, such as chattering of the brushes or a rough, unevenly worn commutator, or, as in any switching problem, by electrical conditions. Attention here will be concentrated on the electrical conditions.

As indicated in Art. 3-9, a coil undergoing commutation is in transition between two groups of armature coils: at the end of the commutation period, the coil current must be equal but opposite to that at the beginning. Thus, while the armature is rotating between the two positions shown in Figs. 3-37 and 3-38, the current in the coils composed of inductors 6, 7, 8, 9, 14, 15, 16, and 1 must reverse. Figure 5-9 shows the armature in an intermediate position during which the coils formed by inductors 7, 8, 15, and 16 are being commutated. The commutated coils are short-circuited by the brushes. During this period, however, the brushes must continue to conduct the armature current I_a from the armature winding to the external circuit. This fact is emphasized in Fig. 5-10, which shows the coil composed of inductors 8 and 15 in the middle of the commutation period and on which is superposed the resultant flux-density wave obtained in Fig. 5-4. The true complexity of the events begins to exhibit itself in Fig. 5-10. The short-circuited coil constitutes an inductive circuit with time-varying resistances at the brush contact, with, in general, rotational voltages induced in the coil, and with both conductive and inductive coupling to the rest of the armature winding.

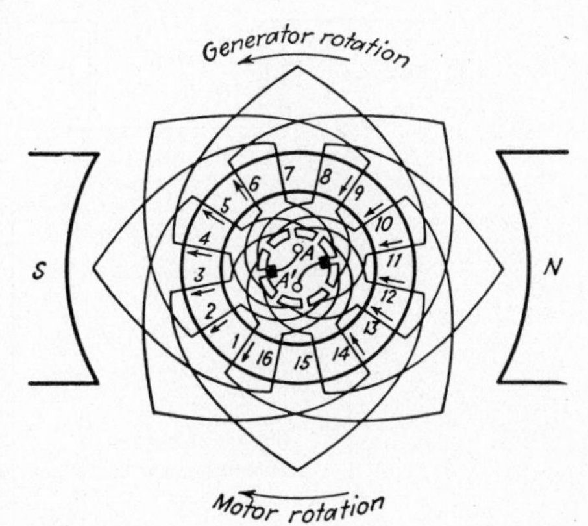

FIG. 5-9. Armature winding with coils formed by inductors 7, 8, 15, and 16 undergoing commutation.

Actually, the attainment of good commutation is more an empirical art than a quantitative science. Accordingly, this article will be restricted to a discussion of the factors involved rather than presenting a quantitative analysis.[1] The principal obstacle to quantitative analysis lies in the electrical behavior of the carbon-copper contact film. Its resistance is nonlinear and is a function of current density, current direction, temperature, brush material, moisture, and atmospheric pressure. Its

[1] For analytical treatments, see A. S. Langsdorf, "Principles of Direct-current Machines," 4th ed., Chap. VIII, McGraw-Hill Book Company, Inc., New York, 1931; and A. Gray, "Electrical Machine Design," 2d ed., Chaps. VIII and IX, McGraw-Hill Book Company, Inc., New York, 1926.

behavior in some respects is like that of an ionized gas. From the pragmatic viewpoint, the most significant fact is that an unduly high current density in a portion of the brush surface (and hence an unduly high energy density in that part of the contact film) results in sparking and a breakdown of the film at that point. The boundary film also plays an important part in the mechanical behavior of the rubbing surfaces.

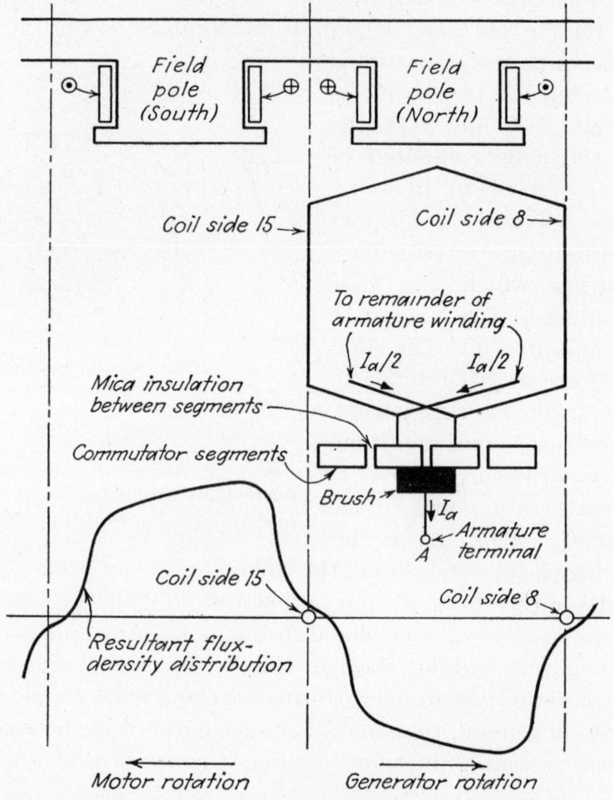

FIG. 5-10. Armature coil undergoing commutation.

At high altitudes, definite steps must be taken to preserve it, or extremely rapid brush wear takes place.

The empirical basis of securing sparkless commutation, then, is to avoid excessive current densities at any point in the copper-carbon contact. This basis, combined with the principle of utilizing all material to the fullest extent, indicates that optimum conditions are obtained when the current density is uniform over the brush surface during the entire commutation period. The circumstances of more than the allowable density in one portion but less in another are thereby avoided, and the limiting total current has its highest value. It is therefore appropriate to examine the implications of uniform current density. Although it will be assumed that the brush width equals the commutator-segment width, with negligible thickness of mica between segments, nevertheless, substantially the same conclusions apply to the more general practical cases.

Figure 5-11 shows schematically the position of the pertinent coil at five equally spaced instants during the commutating period. In Fig. 5-11*a*, the brush bears entirely on one segment, and the coil carries the current $0.50I_a$ toward the right. Somewhat later (Fig. 5-11*b*), one-quarter of the brush area is on the left segment and three-quarters on

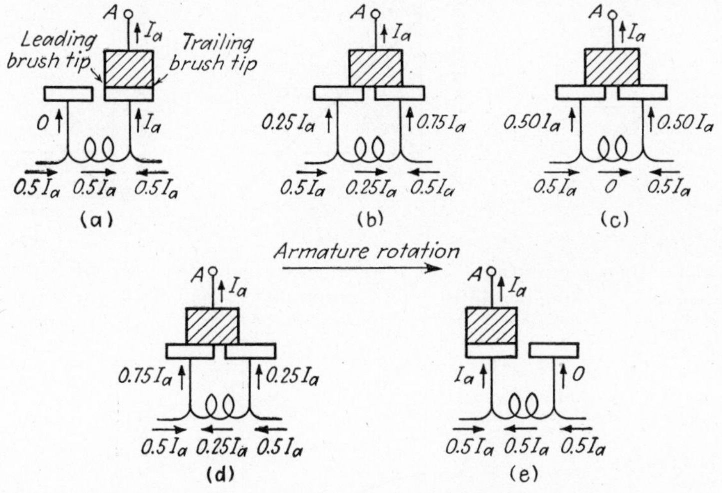

FIG. 5-11. Five stages of the commutation process.

the right segment. Since the total current leaving the armature must still be I_a, uniformity of current density demands that $0.75I_a$ leave via the right segment and $0.25I_a$ via the left; Kirchhoff's current law then requires the coil current to be $0.25I_a$ toward the right. Similar reasoning applied to Fig. 5-11*c*, *d*, and *e* shows that the coil current must be zero, $0.25I_a$ to the left, and $0.50I_a$ to the left, respectively. Accordingly, as illustrated in Fig. 5-12, uniform current density is obtained if the coil current changes at a linear rate. This process is known as *linear commutation*. The currents in the trailing and leading brush tips (see Fig. 5-11*a*) also vary linearly with time, and the uniform current density is I_a/A_B, where A_B is the brush area.

The principal factors tending to produce linear commutation are changes in brush-contact resistance resulting from the linear decrease in area at the trailing brush edge and linear increase in area at the leading edge. Several electrical factors militate against linearity. Resistance in the commutated coil, for example, will cause a somewhat different distribution from those shown in Fig. 5-11*b* and *d*. Usually, however, the voltage drop at the brush contacts is sufficiently large (of the order of 1.0 volt) in comparison with the resistance drop in a single armature coil so that the latter may be ignored. Coil inductance is a much more serious factor. Both the voltage of self-induction in the commutated coil and the voltage of mutual induction from other coils (particularly those in the same slot) undergoing commutation at the same time oppose

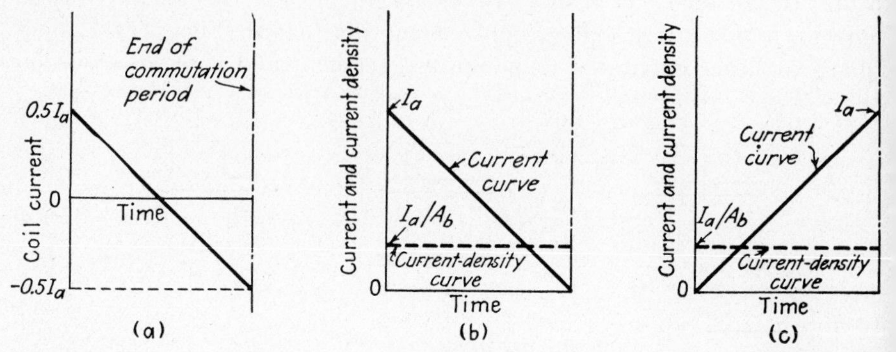

FIG. 5-12. Linear commutation. (*a*) Current in commutated coil. (*b*) Current and current density in trailing brush tip. (*c*) Current and current density in leading brush tip.

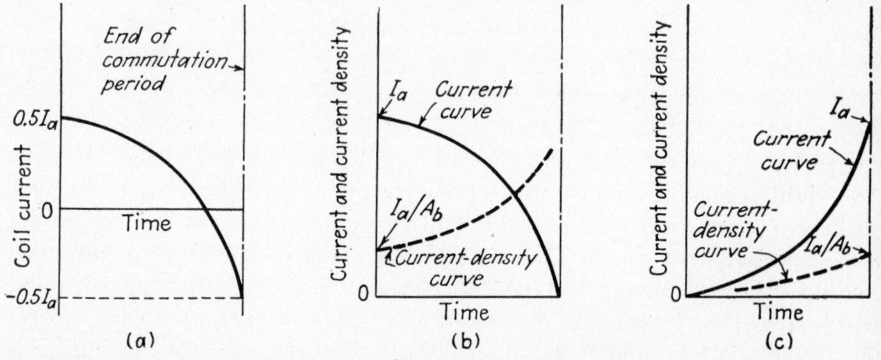

FIG. 5-13. Undercommutation. (*a*) Current in commutated coil. (*b*) Current and current density in trailing brush tip. (*c*) Current and current density in leading brush tip.

changes in current in the commutated coil. The sum of these two voltages is often referred to as the *reactance voltage*. Its result is that current values in the short-circuited coil lag in time the values dictated by linear change, and the current-time curve becomes that of Fig. 5-13*a*. This condition is known as *undercommutation* or *delayed commutation*. The associated currents in the trailing and leading brush edges are shown in Fig. 5-13*b* and *c*. Since the area at the trailing edge decreases faster than the current through it, the corresponding current density may increase to many times the average value I_a/A_B; on the other hand, the current density in the leading edge may be quite low during most of the commutation period. Armature inductance thus tends to produce high losses and sparking at the trailing brush tip.

For best commutation, inductance must be held to a minimum by using the fewest possible number of turns per armature coil and by using a multipolar design with a short armature. The effect of a given reactance voltage in delaying commutation is minimized when the resistive brush-contact voltage drop is significant compared with it. This fact is the main reason for the use of carbon brushes with their appreciable contact drop. When good commutation is secured by virtue of resistance drops, the process is referred to as *resistance commutation*. It is used today as the exclusive means only in fractional-horsepower machines.

Another important factor in the commutation process is the rotational voltage induced in the short-circuited coil. Depending on its sign, this voltage may hinder or aid commutation. In Figs. 5-4 and 5-10, for example, cross-magnetizing armature reaction creates a definite flux in the interpolar region. The direction of the rotational voltage in the commutated coil of both figures is such that commutation is delayed. Thus, consider that the machine of Fig. 5-10 is a generator. The short-circuited coil will then have a rotational voltage of the same sign as it had under the immediately preceding pole face. This voltage then encourages the continuance of current in the old direction and, like the reactance voltage, opposes its reversal. Similar reasoning leads to the same conclusion for motor action.

In Fig. 5-8, the brushes have been so shifted that the coil undergoing commutation is in a region of substantially zero flux density. A further shift in the same direction will place the coil in flux density opposite to that of Fig. 5-10, causing a rotational voltage opposing the reactance voltage and hence aiding commutation. By the appropriate brush shift, the reactance voltage can be substantially neutralized at a given load. If the brushes are shifted too far, the reactance voltage is more than neutralized, and *accelerated commutation* or *overcommutation* takes place. As shown in Fig. 5-14, the coil current reverses at faster than a linear rate and may even overshoot. The current density in the trailing brush tip becomes zero fairly rapidly and may ultimately reach excessive values in the opposite direction. Current in the leading brush tip builds up more rapidly than does brush area, so that high densities may occur at the leading tip. Once more, high losses and sparking appear.

Shifting of the brushes was at one time a common way of securing good commutation. The method is now obsolete, however. But the general principle behind brush shifting—that of producing in the coil undergoing commutation a rotational voltage which approximately compensates for the reactance voltage, a principle called *voltage commutation*—is used on almost all modern commutating machines. The brushes remain in the neutral position, and the appropriate flux density is introduced in the commutating zone by means of small, narrow poles located between the main poles. These auxiliary poles are called *interpoles* or

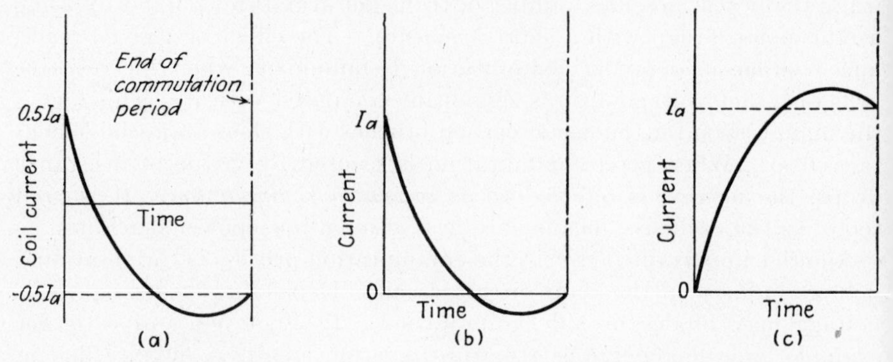

Fig. 5-14. Overcommutation. Current in (*a*) commutated coil, (*b*) trailing brush tip, and (*c*) leading brush tip.

commutating poles, and their windings are called *commutating* or *interpole windings*.

The general appearance of interpoles and an approximate map of the flux produced when they alone are excited may be seen in Fig. 5-15. The interpoles are the smaller poles between the larger main poles in Fig. 1-9. The form of the resultant flux-density wave with the machine under load is shown in Fig. 5-16. The polarity of the commutating pole must be that of the main pole just ahead of it (*i.e.*, in the direction of rotation) for a generator and just behind it for a motor. Inspection of

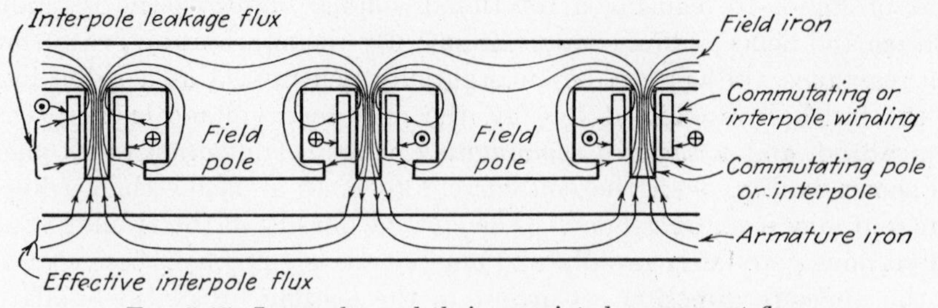

Fig. 5-15. Interpoles and their associated component flux.

Figs. 5-1 and 5-16 shows that the interpole mmf must be sufficient to neutralize the cross-magnetizing armature mmf in the interpolar region and enough more to furnish the flux density required for the rotational voltage in the short-circuited armature coil to cancel the reactance voltage. Since both the armature mmf and the reactance voltage are proportional to the armature current, the commutating winding must be connected in series with the armature. To preserve the desired linearity, the commutating pole should operate at low saturations. Final adjustment of the interpole flux for optimum commutation may be made by adjusting the interpole air gap by means of magnetic or nonmagnetic shims at the base of the pole. Shunting the interpole winding so that only a portion of the armature current passes through it is also a possibility, but has the disadvantage of poorer commutation under transient conditions.

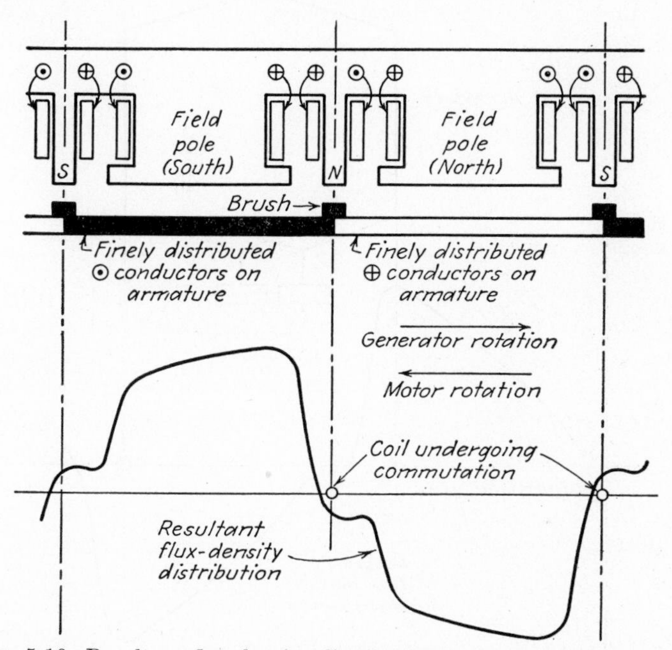

FIG. 5-16. Resultant flux-density distribution in an interpole machine.

The interpole provides a low-reluctance path for armature flux, increasing the armature inductance and therefore the reactance voltage. This effect is minimized by use of a comparatively long air gap at the interpoles. In interpole machines, it is important that the brushes be in the neutral position; otherwise the magnetizing and demagnetizing effects of a brush shift, discussed in Art. 5-1, are accentuated by the interpole flux. Since the interpole flux is a function of armature current, the interpole field may produce cumulative or differential compounding, depending on the direction of brush shift. The inadvertent appearance of these effects may be highly undesirable.

By the use of commutating fields, then, sparkless commutation is secured over a wide range in modern machines. In accordance with the performance standards of the NEMA, general-purpose d-c machines must be capable of carrying with successful commutation for 1 min loads of 150 per cent of the current corresponding to the continuous rating with the field rheostat set for rated-load excitation.

For machines subjected to heavy overloads, rapidly changing loads, or operation with a weak main field, the potentiality of trouble other than simply sparking at the brushes appears. Figure 5-17 shows a resultant flux distribution distorted by excessive cross-magnetizing arma-

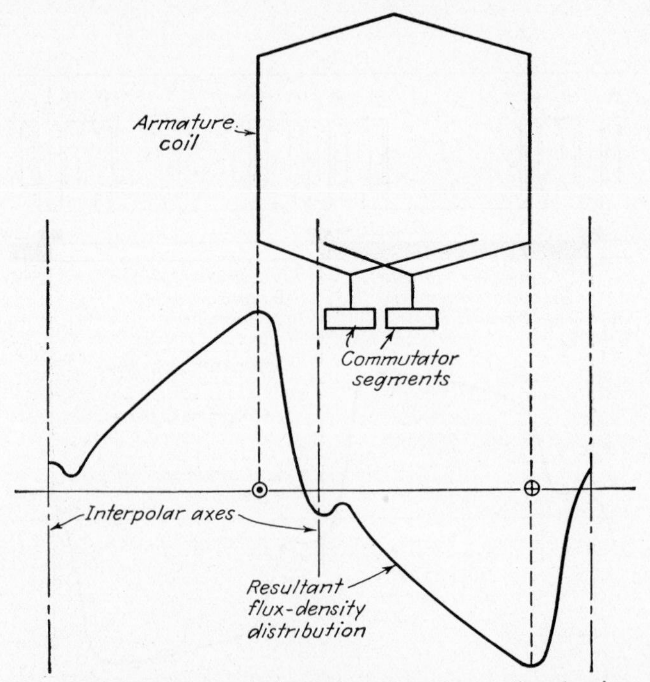

Fig. 5-17. Armature coil in region of maximum flux density.

ture reaction. At the instant that an armature coil is located at the peak of the wave, the coil voltage may be high enough to break down the air between the adjacent segments to which the coil is connected and result in *flashover*, or arcing, between segments. The breakdown voltage here is not high because the air near the commutator is in a condition favorable to breakdown. The maximum allowable voltage between segments is of the order of 30 to 40 volts, a fact which limits the average voltage between segments to lower values and thus determines the minimum number of segments which may be used in a proposed design. Under transient conditions, high voltages between segments may result from the induced voltages associated with growth and decay of armature flux. Inspection of Fig. 5-2, for instance, may enable one to visualize very appreciable voltages of this nature being induced in a coil under the pole centers by the growth or decay of the armature flux shown in the sketch. Consideration of the sign of this induced voltage will show that it adds to the normal rotational emf when load is dropped from a generator or added to a motor. Flashing between seg-

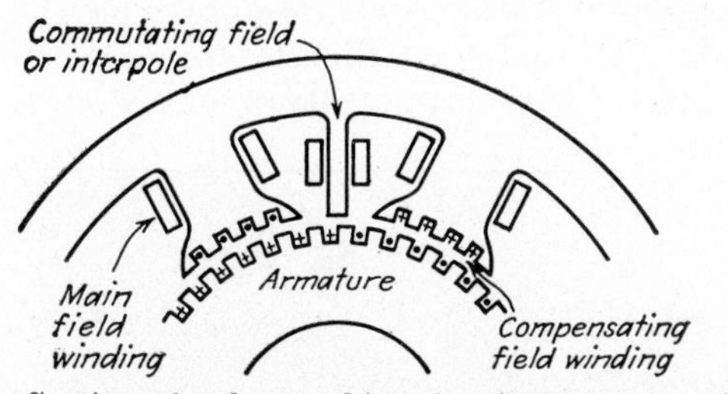

FIG. 5-18. Section of a d-c machine showing compensating field.

FIG. 5-19. Compensating winding and details of main-pole assembly of 3,000-kw 600-volt 360-rpm d-c generator for steel-mill service. (*Courtesy of Allis-Chalmers Manufacturing Company.*)

ments may quickly spread around the entire commutator and, in addition to its possibly destructive effects on the commutator, constitutes a direct short circuit on the line. Even with interpoles present, therefore, armature reaction under the poles definitely limits the conditions under which a machine may operate.

These limitations may be considerably extended by compensating or neutralizing the armature mmf under the pole faces. Such compensation can be achieved by means of a *compensating* or *pole-face winding* (Fig. 5-18), embedded in slots in the pole face and having a polarity opposite to that of the adjoining armature winding. The physical details of a typical pole-face winding are shown in Fig. 5-19. Such a winding may be seen in the completed stator of Fig. 5-20. Since the axis of the compensating winding is the same as that of the armature, it will almost completely neutralize the armature reaction of the armature inductors

FIG. 5-20. Frame and field structure of a 600-hp 600-volt 6-pole 575/1,150-rpm adjustable-speed d-c motor showing commutating poles and compensating windings in the faces of the main poles. (*Courtesy of General Electric Company.*)

under the pole faces when it is given the proper number of turns. It must be connected in series with the armature in order that it may carry a proportional current. The net effect of the main field, armature, commutating winding, and compensating winding on the air-gap flux is shown in Fig. 5-21. It will be observed that, except for the commutation zone, the resultant flux-density distribution is substantially the same as that produced by the main field alone, Fig. 5-4. The slots necessary to accommodate the compensating winding in the pole faces are ignored in this sketch.

The main disadvantage of pole-face windings is their expense. They are used in machines designed for heavy overloads or rapidly changing loads—steel-mill motors are a good example of machines subjected to severe duty cycles—or in motors intended to operate over wide speed ranges by shunt-field control. By way of a schematic summary, Fig.

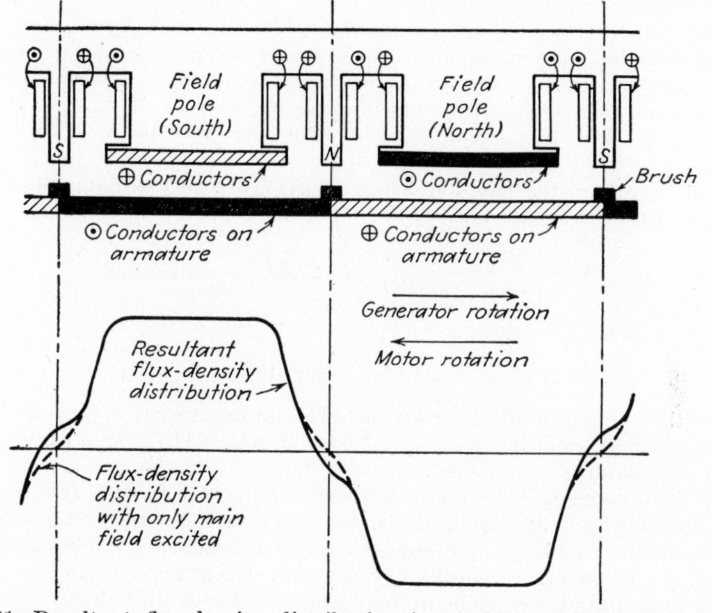

FIG. 5-21. Resultant flux-density distribution in machine with commutating and compensating fields.

5-22 shows the circuit diagram of a compound machine with a compensating winding. The relative position of the coils in this diagram indicates that the commutating and compensating fields act along the armature axis, and the shunt and series fields act along the axis of the main poles. Rather complete control of air-gap flux around the entire armature periphery is thus achieved.

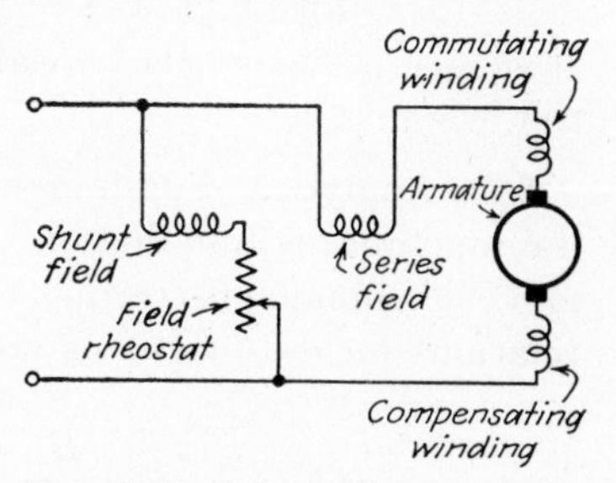

FIG. 5-22. Schematic connection diagram of d-c machine.

Example 5-2. This example is based on the machine for which data are given in Example 5-1.

a. Assume that the machine is to be equipped with four interpoles but no compensating winding. To furnish the appropriate commutating flux, the interpole mmf is to be approximately 25 per cent greater than the ampere-turns of cross-magnetizing armature reaction per interpole position. Determine the required number of turns on each interpole.

b. Occasionally a number of interpoles equal to half the number of main poles is used, as in the d-c machine of Fig. 1-9. The interpole excitation must then be increased to about 50 per cent greater than the ampere-turns of cross-magnetizing armature reaction per interpole position. Determine the required number of interpole turns under these circumstances.

c. If interpoles were not used, the allowable limit on the distortion caused by cross-magnetizing armature reaction would have to be set at a point appreciably lower than that suggested in Example 5-1 in order that the appropriate flux may exist in the interpolar space to provide good commutation. The mmf of armature reaction at the pole tips should then not exceed about 60 per cent of the field mmf for the air gap and teeth. Compute the allowable armature current at normal excitation under these conditions, and compare with the value in Example 5-1.

d. Compute the required number of inductors per pole face for a compensating winding.

Solution. *a.* The armature mmf acting at the center of each interpole is the full amplitude of the triangular mmf wave. For this machine, from Eq. 4-43,

$$F_A = \frac{Z}{2p}\frac{I_a}{a} = \frac{444}{2 \times 4}\frac{I_a}{2} = 27.8I_a \qquad \text{amp-turns}$$

The interpole mmf is then

$$1.25 \times 27.8I_a = 34.8I_a \qquad \text{amp-turns per interpole}$$

and since the interpole winding carries the full armature current, 35 turns are required.

b. The interpole mmf is increased to $1.50 \times 27.8I_a = 41.7I_a$ amp-turns per interpole, so that 42 turns are required.

c. The allowable armature current will now be only 60 per cent of that in Example 5-1, or $0.60 \times 64.3 = 38.6$ amp. This comparison indicates the principal economic reason for the invariable use of interpoles in integral-horsepower and integral-kilowatt d-c machines: a much larger output may be obtained from a specific amount of copper and iron comprising the machine without serious operating difficulties.

d. The compensating winding must neutralize the mmf of the armature inductors under the pole faces. It must therefore have a number of ampere-inductors per pole face equal to the fraction ψ of the armature ampere-inductors per pole, or since each armature inductor carries the current $I_a/2$,

$$\frac{2}{3} \times \frac{444}{4} \times \frac{I_a}{2} = 37I_a \qquad \text{amp-inductors}$$

Since each pole-face inductor carries the full armature current I_a, 37 inductors per pole face are required.

5-3. Analytical Fundamentals: Electric-circuit Aspects.

Analysis of d-c machines is founded on the basic equations for generated voltage E_a and electromagnetic torque T developed in the preceding chapter. These relations for d-c machines are given by Eqs. 4-38 and 4-56 as

$$E_a = p\Phi \frac{Z}{a}\frac{n}{60} = k_E\Phi n \tag{5-1}$$

and

$$T = \frac{p}{2\pi}\frac{Z}{a}\Phi I_a = k_T\Phi I_a \tag{5-2}$$

where p is the number of poles, Z the number of armature conductors, a the number of parallel paths through the armature, Φ the flux per pole,

I_a the armature current, and n the speed in rpm. The units of all quantities except speed n are in the mks system. The two quantities

$$k_E = \frac{p}{60} \frac{Z}{a} \tag{5-3}$$

and

$$k_T = \frac{p}{2\pi} \frac{Z}{a} \tag{5-4}$$

are determined by design and remain constant for a specific machine. The voltage and torque relations (Eqs. 5-1 and 5-2) yield, when combined

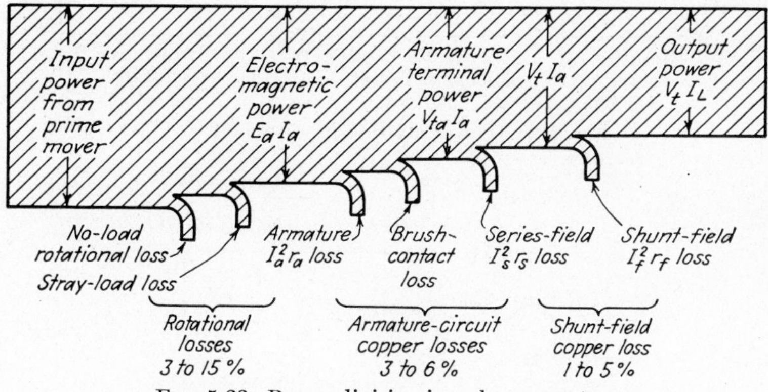

FIG. 5-23. Power division in a d-c generator.

algebraically, the relation

$$T = \frac{60}{2\pi n} E_a I_a = \frac{60}{2\pi n} P \tag{5-5}$$

where

$$P = E_a I_a \tag{5-6}$$

is the *electromagnetic power* associated with the torque T.

Figures 5-23 and 5-24 present in graphical form power balances for d-c generators and motors, respectively, with both shunt and series fields. The connection diagram is given in Fig. 5-25. When either the shunt or the series field is not present in the machine, the associated entry is omitted from Figs. 5-23 to 5-25. In these diagrams, V_t is the machine terminal voltage, V_{ta} the armature terminal voltage, I_L the line current, I_s the series-field current (equal to I_a for the connections shown in Fig. 5-25), I_f the shunt-field current, r_a the armature resistance, r_f the shunt-field resistance, and r_s the series-field resistance. Included in r_a is the resistance of any commutating and compensating winding. The armature-circuit copper losses, field-circuit copper losses, and rotational losses are those originally considered in Art. 4-11; typical full-load orders of magnitude of these losses, expressed in per cent of the machine input, are quoted in Figs. 5-23 and 5-24 for general-purpose generators and

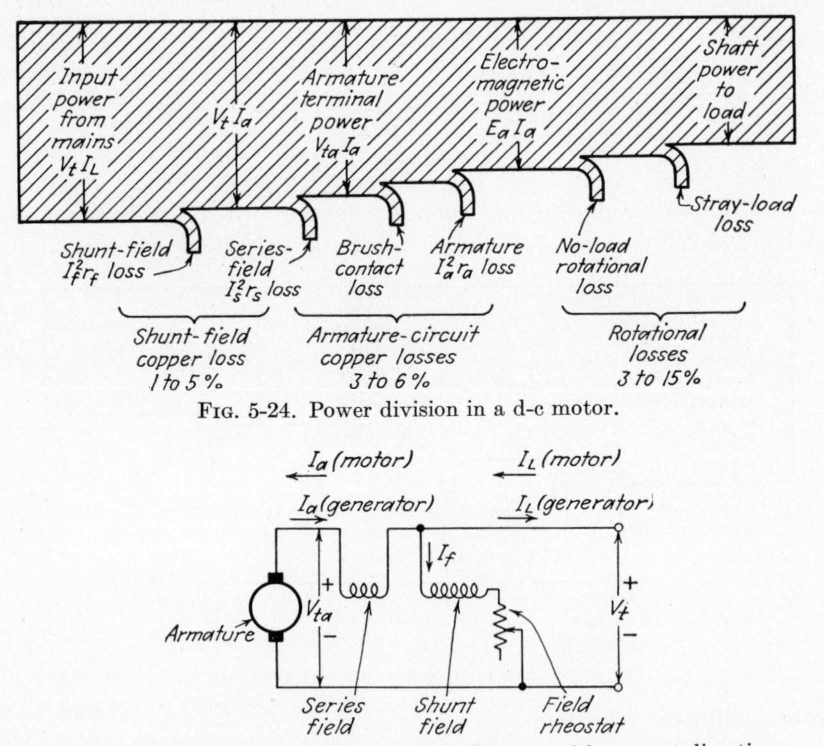

FIG. 5-24. Power division in a d-c motor.

FIG. 5-25. Motor or generator connection diagram with current directions.

motors in the 1- to 100-kw or 1- to 100-hp range, with the smaller percentages applying to the larger ratings.

The electromagnetic power differs from the mechanical power at the machine shaft by the rotational losses and differs from the electrical power at the machine terminals by the copper losses. The latter difference is accounted for in the equivalent circuit of Fig. 5-26. The only differences in the equivalent circuit for motors and generators are in the directions of power and current. The electromagnetic power is that measured at the points across which E_a exists; numerical addition of the rotational losses for generators and subtraction for motors yield the mechanical power at the shaft. These d-c-machine equivalent circuits

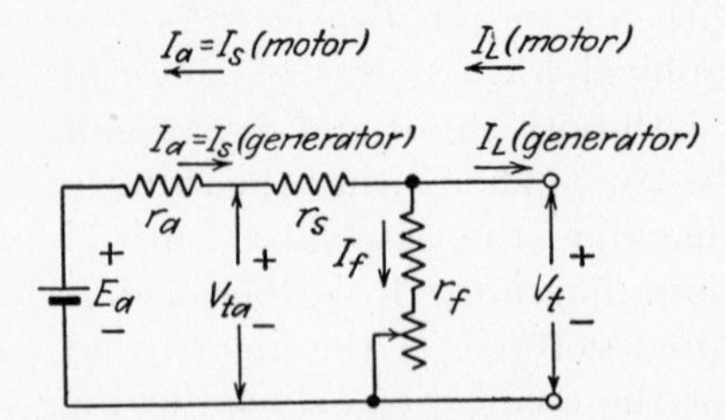

FIG. 5-26. Motor or generator equivalent circuit.

resemble and play the same general role as the equivalent circuits of many practical devices in electrical engineering. Through the medium of such equivalent circuits, all of the highly developed methods of circuit theory become available for the study of the performance of the device.

The interrelations between voltage and current are immediately evident from the equivalent circuit and connection diagram. Thus,

$$V_{ta} = E_a \pm I_a r_a \tag{5-7}$$
$$V_t = E_a \pm I_a(r_a + r_s) \tag{5-8}$$

and

$$I_L = I_a \pm I_f \tag{5-9}$$

where the plus sign is used for a motor and the minus sign for a generator. Some of the terms in Eqs. 5-7 to 5-9 may be omitted when the machine connections are simpler than those shown in Figs. 5-25 and 5-26. The resistance r_a is to be interpreted as that of the armature plus brushes unless specifically stated otherwise. Sometimes, r_a is taken as the resistance of the armature winding alone, and the brush-contact drop is accounted for as a separate item, usually assumed to be 2 volts.

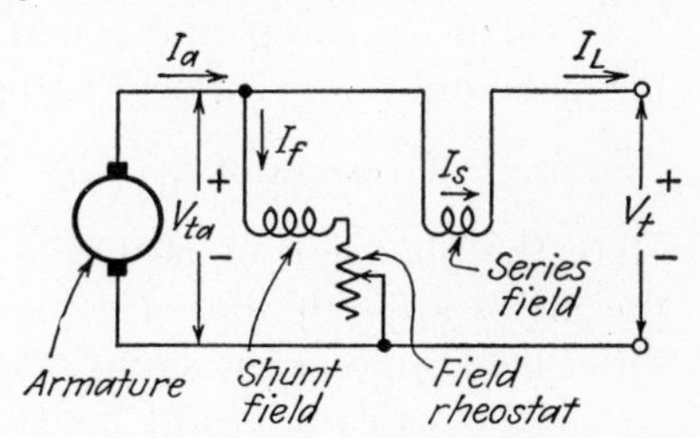

FIG. 5-27. Short-shunt compound generator.

For compound machines, another variation may occur. Figures 5-25 and 5-26 show a so-called *long-shunt connection* in that the shunt field is connected directly across the line terminals with the series field between it and the armature. An alternative possibility is the *short-shunt connection*, illustrated in Fig. 5-27 for a compound generator, with the shunt field directly across the armature and the series field between it and the line terminals. The series-field current is then I_L instead of I_a, and the voltage equations are modified accordingly. There is so little practical difference between these two connections that the distinction may usually be ignored; unless otherwise stated, compound machines will be treated as though they were long-shunt-connected.

Although the difference between terminal voltage V_t and armature generated voltage E_a is comparatively small for normal operation, it has a definite bearing on performance characteristics. In effect, this difference, acting in conjunction with the circuit resistances and energy-conversion requirements, affects the value of armature current I_a and hence the rotor field strength. Complete determination of machine behavior requires a similar investigation of factors influencing the stator field strength, or, more particularly, the net flux per pole Φ. Such an investigation is equivalent to an examination of magnetic-circuit conditions.

5-4. Analytical Fundamentals: Magnetic-circuit Aspects. The flux per pole is that resulting from the combined armature and field mmfs. The interdependence of armature generated voltage E_a and magnetic-circuit conditions in the machine is accordingly a function of the sum of all the mmfs on the polar- or direct-axis flux path. This sum is often referred to as the *net excitation* or *net mmf.* That part of the total which is purposely placed on the stator main poles in order to create the working flux is called the *gross excitation* or *gross mmf.* The difference between the gross and net excitation is caused by the armature-reaction mmf. In order to focus attention on the principal magnetic-circuit aspects, armature reaction will be ignored in this article. The modifications arising when its quantitative effect is included will be treated in the next article.

In the usual compound generator or motor having N_f shunt-field turns per pole and N_s series-field turns per pole,

$$\text{Gross mmf} = N_f I_f \pm N_s I_s \qquad \text{amp-turns per pole} \tag{5-10}$$

Here the plus sign is used when the two mmfs are aiding, or when the two fields are cumulatively connected; the minus sign is used when the series field opposes the shunt field, or for a differential connection. When either the series or shunt field is absent, the corresponding term in Eq. 5-10 naturally is omitted. Some d-c machines may have additional field windings on the main poles (and, unlike the compensating or pole-face windings of Art. 5-2, wound concentric with the normal field windings), usually to permit specialized control of machine performance. In any case, the gross excitation is the algebraic sum of the mmfs on the main or direct-axis poles.

Equation 5-10 thus sums up in ampere-turns per pole the gross mmf acting on the main magnetic circuit. The magnetization curve for a d-c machine is generally given in terms of current in only the main field winding, which is almost invariably the shunt-field winding when one is present. The mmf units of such a magnetization curve and of Eq. 5-10 may be made the same by one of two rather obvious steps: the field current on the magnetization curve may be multiplied by the turns per pole in that winding, giving a curve in terms of ampere-turns per pole; or both sides of Eq. 5-10 may be divided by N_f, converting the units to the equivalent current in the N_f coil alone which produces the same mmf. Thus

$$\text{Gross mmf} = I_f \pm \frac{N_s}{N_f} I_s \qquad \text{equivalent shunt-field amp} \tag{5-11}$$

The latter procedure is often the more convenient and the one more commonly adopted.

Use of the magnetization curve in machine analysis is based on the assumption that the curve represents the relation between air-gap flux under load and the resultant mmf on the magnetic circuit—between armature generated voltage E_a and total excitation, in other words. An example of a magnetization curve for a d-c machine is given in Fig. 5-28. The numerical scales on the left-hand and lower axes give representative values for a 100-kw 250-volt 1,200-rpm generator; the mmf scale is given in both shunt-field current and ampere-turns per pole, the latter being

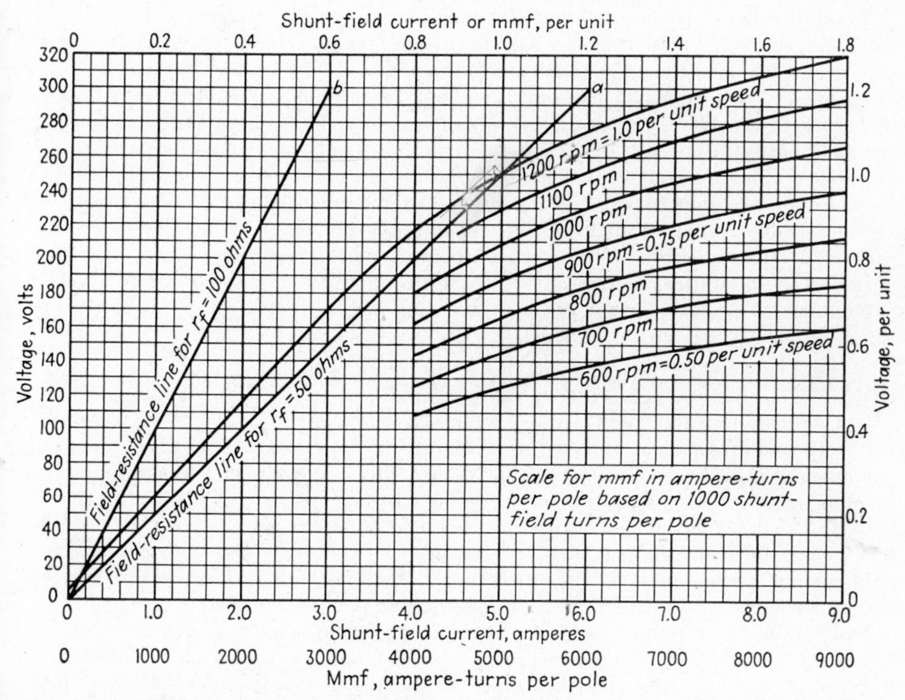

FIG. 5-28 Magnetization curve of a 250-volt 1,200-rpm d-c machine. Typical for a 100-kw generator or 100-hp motor.

derived from the former on the basis of a 1,000 turn per pole shunt field. The characteristic may also be presented in *normalized* or *per-unit form*, as shown by the upper mmf and right-hand voltage scale. On these scales, 1.0 *per-unit field current* or mmf is that required to produce rated voltage at rated speed when the machine is unloaded; similarly, 1.0 *per-unit voltage* equals rated voltage. When plotted in this nondimensional form, the characteristic may be regarded as typical of a wide variety of general-purpose motors and generators.

Use of the magnetization curve with generated voltage rather than flux plotted on the vertical axis may be somewhat complicated by the fact that the speed of a d-c machine need not remain constant, and speed enters into the relation between flux and generated voltage. Hence generated-voltage ordinates correspond to a unique machine speed. For this reason, magnetization curves at several different speeds are given in Fig. 5-28. Any one of these curves is readily obtainable from any other by recognizing from Eq. 5-1 that voltage is directly proportional to speed for a fixed flux or field current. Alternatively, only the magnetization curve for rated speed may be given and use made of it for other speeds by adjusting the voltage scale in the ratio of speeds.

Example 5-3. A 100-kw 250-volt 400-amp d-c generator has an armature resistance (including brushes) of 0.025 ohm and the magnetization curve of Fig. 5-28. It is driven at 1,200 rpm by a constant-speed prime mover.

For many applications, it is desirable to hold the terminal voltage constant regardless of the load on the generator. Such constancy may be maintained by readjusting the field current after each load change, an action usually performed by means of an automatic voltage regulator which measures the terminal voltage and adjusts the field-circuit resistance to restore the voltage to the correct value.

The terminal voltage V_t is to be held constant at 250 volts from no load to 125 per cent load. Plot a curve of the required field current I_f as a function of armature current I_a. Armature-reaction effects are to be ignored.

Solution. The field current for $I_a = 400$ amp will be found as a sample computation. From Eq. 5-8 with r_s omitted,

$$E_a = V_t + I_a r_a = 250 + 400 \times 0.025 = 260 \text{ volts}$$

The 1,200-rpm magnetization curve of Fig. 5-28 indicates that a generated voltage of 260 volts requires a field current of 5.32 amp. Computations for other armature currents result in the dotted curve of Fig. 5-29. This curve applies to operation of the machine as either a separately excited generator or a shunt generator. In the former case, the load current or line current I_L is equal to the armature current I_a. In the latter case, the load current is smaller than the armature current by the amount of the field current. Since the field current is such a small fraction of the armature current at any significant load, the distinction is of no practical importance.

Example 5-4. A 100-kw 250-volt 400-amp long-shunt compound generator has an armature resistance (including brushes) of 0.025 ohm, a series-field resistance of 0.005 ohm, and the magnetization curve of Fig. 5-28. There are 1,000 shunt-field turns per pole and 3 series-field turns per pole.

Compute the terminal voltage at rated current output when the shunt-field current is 4.7 amp and the speed is 1,150 rpm. Neglect armature reaction.

Solution. $I_s = I_a = I_L + I_f = 400 + 4.7 = 405$ amp. From Eq. 5-11, the total field mmf is

$$4.7 + \frac{3}{1{,}000} \times 405 = 5.9 \text{ equivalent shunt-field amp}$$

By entering Fig. 5-28 with this value and at a point midway between the 1,100- and 1,200-rpm curves, it is found that $E_a = 262$ volts. Alternatively, one may enter the 1,200-rpm curve, read 274 volts, and reduce this in the ratio of speeds to find

$$E_a = 274 \times \frac{1{,}150}{1{,}200} = 262 \text{ volts}$$

Then,

$$\begin{aligned} V_t &= E_a - I_a(r_a + r_s) \\ &= 262 - 405(0.025 + 0.005) = 250 \text{ volts} \end{aligned}$$

The gist of these magnetic-circuit considerations lies in the interpretation of the magnetization curve as the graphical relation between machine excitation and armature generated voltage. The machine excitation is determined in accordance with the usual magnetic-circuit principle of algebraically summing the mmfs on the main magnetic circuit. The analysis of d-c machines is a combination of the foregoing electric- and magnetic-circuit aspects.

5-5. Armature Demagnetizing MMF. Analytic inclusion of the effects of armature mmf is neither a simple nor a straightforward task. The gross or main-field mmf and the armature mmf act along two different axes in space and hence influence the flux along different paths in the magnetic circuit of the machine. One is forced to adopt a somewhat artificial approach based on empiricism and leaning upon tests of the specific machine or of similar machines for the determination of pertinent data.

The method normally used is to recognize that, even though the armature mmf may act at right angles to the main-field mmf, yet it does influence the magnitude of the resultant flux per pole whenever the iron of the armature or field poles is at all saturated. Even cross-magnetizing armature reaction produces a demagnetizing effect on the resultant flux like that of ampere-turns acting on the same axis as the gross mmf. A simple measure of this effect can be obtained by computing the excitation required to achieve specified load conditions with armature reaction ignored, and comparing it with the experimentally determined value for the same load conditions. The latter value will include armature-reaction effects, and the difference between the two values can be ascribed to armature reaction. Thus the dotted curve in Fig. 5-29 shows the field current required to maintain rated terminal voltage for a wide range of armature currents as computed in Example 5-3 with armature reaction ignored. The solid curve gives the corresponding excitations as they might have been determined experimentally. If there were no armature demagnetizing effect, the two curves would coincide. The actual difference between the solid curve and the dotted curve at a specified armature current therefore gives the corresponding armature-reaction effect as measured in equivalent shunt-field amperes. Alternatively, it may be measured in ampere-turns per pole. Since these values indicate the mmf which must be added to the main-field excitation to overcome armature reaction, they provide a logical manner of specifying its effect quantitatively. When measured in units of ampere-turns per pole, the symbol F_a will be used for *the demagnetizing effect of armature-reaction mmf.* The quantity F_a is not the same as the armature mmf F_A. The value of F_a depends on the magnitude of F_A, but it also depends on the geometry and degree of saturation of the magnetic circuit. No simple relation exists between F_a and F_A, nor is F_a a linear function of armature current I_a except as an occasional simplifying approximation. (Note, for instance, that the distance between the solid and dotted curves of Fig. 5-29 is not a linear function of I_a.) Accordingly, the armature-reaction mmf is usually determined by explicit tests on the machine or from experience with similar machines.

The solid curve of Fig. 5-29 is called an *armature characteristic* or *field-compounding curve.* Per-unit numerical scales are also added, *unit armature current* equaling rated current.

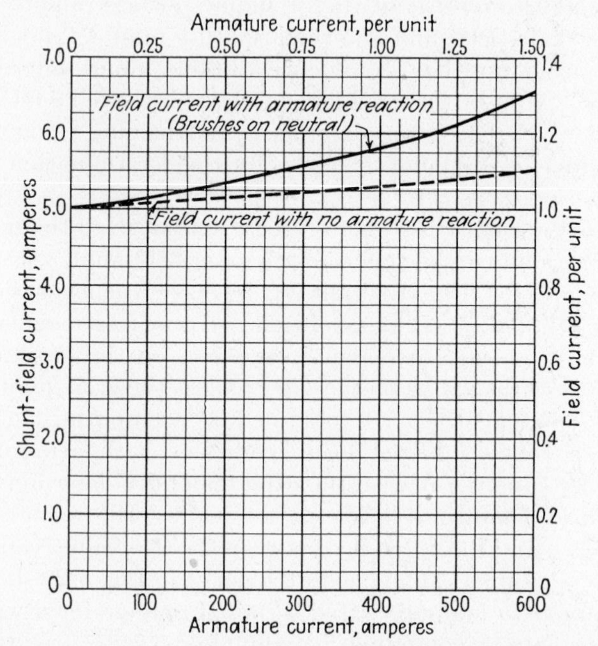

FIG. 5-29. Armature characteristic (solid curve) and plot of field current with no armature reaction (dotted curve). Armature terminal voltage constant at 250 volts, speed constant at 1,200 rpm, armature resistance 0.025 ohm.

The armature characteristic is the result of one common test method for quantitative determination of F_a for existing machines when convenient loading methods are at hand. It is normally taken with the machine operating as a generator at rated speed and constant terminal voltage, and for a range of armature currents. For compound-wound machines, the series field is usually disconnected during the test. When F_a is found from the armature characteristic, the curve should be taken for a terminal voltage close to the anticipated actual value, for the demagnetizing effect depends on the degree of pole-tip saturation and hence on the operating voltage of the machine. The amount of armature reaction present in Fig. 5-29 is chosen so that some of its disadvantageous effects will appear in a pronounced form in subsequent numerical examples illustrating generator and motor performance features. (At full load, the amount is roughly two or more times what one would expect to find in a well-designed machine operating at normal field current.)

In effect, the concept of armature-reaction mmf F_a is a hypothetical and artificial one which permits the replacement on paper of the demagnetizing effect of the actual armature mmf by an equivalent quantity acting on the same magnetic axis as the gross mmf. The criterion of equivalence is simply that the same magnitude of resultant flux per pole be produced. Physically, it is still the actual armature mmf F_A which is effective in the energy-conversion process.

When the brushes are shifted from the neutral position, the armature mmf has a component in line with the field axis as well as one in quadrature. This situation has already been discussed in Art. 5-1. Since it acts along the same axis as the gross mmf, the direct demagnetizing component may be added algebraically to the gross mmf if desired. The cross-magnetizing component, however, must still be handled in terms of an equivalent. As a result, it is customary to use a single equivalent armature-reaction mmf F_a to replace both the demagnetizing and cross-magnetizing components. In modern conventional machines, the cross-magnetizing component is of greater importance because brushes are usually in the neutral.

In summary, then, the *net excitation* or resultant excitation on the magnetic circuit of the machine is

$$\text{Net mmf} = \text{gross mmf} - \text{armature-reaction mmf} \qquad (5\text{-}12)$$

or, in terms of Eq. 5-10,

$$\text{Net mmf} = N_f I_f \pm N_s I_s - F_a \qquad \text{amp-turns per pole} \qquad (5\text{-}13)$$

Similarly, in terms of Eq. 5-11,

$$\text{Net mmf} = I_f \pm \frac{N_s}{N_f} I_s - \frac{F_a}{N_f} \qquad \text{equivalent shunt-field amp} \qquad (5\text{-}14)$$

The minus sign is used with F_a on the basis that it will usually be demagnetizing. If, as occasionally happens because of an inadvertent brush shift, the armature reaction is magnetizing, the sign before F_a in Eqs. 5-12 to 5-14 must be changed.

Example 5-5. Solve Example 5-4 under the assumption that the machine has the armature characteristic of Fig. 5-29. Consider that the dotted curve in this figure is not present, since such data are not ordinarily given.

Solution. The armature-reaction mmf F_a will be determined from Fig. 5-29 on the assumption that the degree of saturation corresponds closely enough to that for the specified operating conditions. At the 405-amp point on the armature characteristic,

$$E_a = 250 + 405 \times 0.025 = 260 \text{ volts}$$

From Fig. 5-28, this voltage requires a net mmf corresponding to 5.3 amp. Figure 5-29 shows that 5.8 amp is actually required. Hence, the armature reaction is

$$F_a = 5.8 - 5.3 = 0.5 \text{ equivalent shunt-field amp}$$

The net mmf under the specified operating conditions is therefore

$$4.7 + \frac{3}{1{,}000} \times 405 - 0.5 = 5.4 \text{ equivalent shunt-field amp}$$

Then, in the manner of Example 5-4,

$$E_a = 262 \frac{1{,}150}{1{,}200} = 251 \text{ volts}$$

and

$$V_t = 251 - 405(0.025 + 0.005) = 239 \text{ volts}$$

The armature-reaction mmf F_a is occasionally assumed to be a linear function of armature current I_a, either as a simplifying approximation or because of a lack of more complete data. Under such an assumption,

$$F_a = k_a I_a \qquad \text{amp-turns per pole} \tag{5-15}$$

Such an assumption has the advantage that only one test point for a convenient load condition is required. This approximation may be expected to give reasonable results at other values of armature current and also for other values of generated voltage. Best results are obtained when the test point most nearly corresponds to the degree of saturation and armature current associated with the load condition to be investigated.

5-6. Analysis of Generator Performance. Although identically the same principles apply to analysis of a d-c machine acting as a generator as to one acting as a motor, the general nature of the problems ordinarily encountered is somewhat different for the two methods of operation. For a generator, the speed is usually fixed by the prime mover, and problems often met are to determine the terminal voltage corresponding to a specified load and excitation or to find the excitation required for a specified load and terminal voltage. For a motor, on the other hand, problems frequently encountered are to determine the speed corresponding to a specified load and excitation or to find the excitation required for specified load and speed conditions; terminal voltage is often fixed at the value of the available supply mains. The routine techniques of applying the common basic principles therefore differ to the extent that the problems differ. This article is concerned with generator operation.

a. Separately Excited Generators. Since the main-field current is independent of the generator voltage, separately excited generators are the simplest to analyze. For a given load, the net excitation is given by Eq. 5-14, and the associated armature generated voltage E_a is determined by the magnetization curve. This voltage, together with Eq. 5-7 or 5-8, fixes the terminal voltage. As shown by curve 1, Fig. 5-30, the voltage of a separately excited generator with no series field drops off somewhat with load because of increasing armature reaction and armature resistance drop. Such a curve is known as the *external characteristic* of a d-c generator.

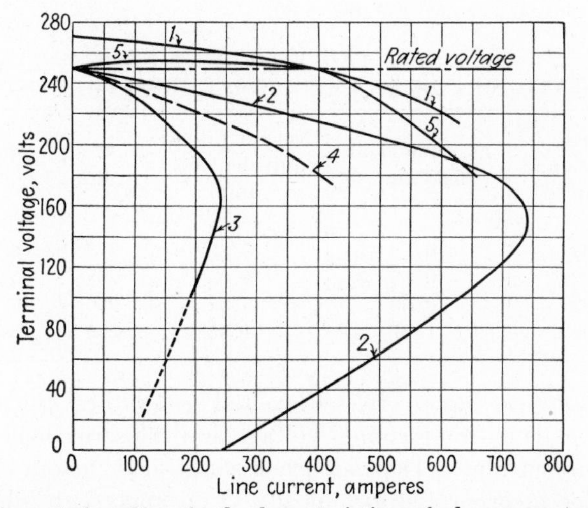

FIG. 5-30. Computed voltage-load characteristics of d-c generators. Curve 1: separately excited, rated voltage at full load. Curve 2: shunt-excited, rated voltage at no load, armature reaction ignored. Curve 3: same as curve 2, but armature reaction included. Curve 4: estimate of curve 3 if armature reaction were adjusted with decreasing voltage. Curve 5: flat-compound generator.

Example 5-6. A 100-kw 250-volt 400-amp 1,200-rpm d-c generator has the magnetization curve of Fig. 5-28 and armature characteristic of Fig. 5-29. For simplicity, the armature reaction determined for a particular armature current from this characteristic may be assumed to hold for generated voltages other than those in Fig. 5-29; otherwise, a family of armature characteristics at different voltages would be required. As in Fig. 5-29, the machine has an armature-circuit resistance (including brushes) of 0.025 ohm.

This generator is driven at constant speed by a 1,200-rpm synchronous motor, and its field is separately excited from a constant-voltage d-c source. Compute and plot a curve of terminal voltage as a function of current output with the excitation adjusted to give rated voltage at rated load.

Solution. First, the field current must be found from the specified full-load conditions. At $I_a = 400$ amp,

$$E_a = V_t + I_a r_a = 250 + 400 \times 0.025 = 260 \text{ volts}$$

From the magnetization curve, Fig. 5-28, the corresponding net excitation is 5.32 amp. At $I_a = 400$ amp, the armature-reaction mmf $F_a = 0.50$ equivalent field ampere (equal to the difference in ordinates of the solid and dotted curves of Fig. 5-29 at 400 amp). Hence the gross excitation required is $5.32 + 0.50 = 5.82$ amp. The field current is therefore constant at 5.82 amp throughout the example.

Computations for other points on the curve are summarized in Table 5-1. At $I_a = 300$ amp, for instance, $F_a = 0.34$ equivalent field ampere, and the net excitation is $5.82 - 0.34 = 5.48$ equivalent field amperes. The corresponding armature generated voltage $E_a = 264$ volts (Fig. 5-28), and the terminal voltage is

$$V_t = 264 - 300 \times 0.025 = 257 \text{ volts}$$

The results are plotted as curve 1 of Fig. 5-30.

TABLE 5-1
COMPUTATIONS FOR EXAMPLE 5-6, CURVE 1 OF FIG. 5-30

I_a, amp	Gross excitation, amp	F_a, equivalent field amp	Net excitation, equivalent field amp	E_a, volts	$I_a r_a$ volts	V_t, volts
0	5.82	0	5.82	272	0	272
200	5.82	0.19	5.63	268	5.0	263
400	5.82	0.50	5.32	260	10.0	250
600	5.82	1.27	4.55	235	15.0	220

b. Self-excited Generators. In self-excited generators, the shunt-field excitation depends on the terminal voltage and the series-field excitation on the armature current. Dependence of shunt-field current on terminal voltage may be incorporated graphically in an analysis by drawing the *field-resistance line,* the line *Oa* in Fig. 5-28, on the magnetization curve. (Consider that the speed is 1,200 rpm, so that only the 1,200-rpm curve is of interest here.) The field-resistance line *Oa* is simply a graphical representation of Ohm's law for the shunt field. It is the locus of the terminal-voltage vs. shunt-field-current operating point. Thus, the line *Oa* is drawn for $r_f = 50$ ohms and hence passes through the origin and the point (1.0 amp, 50 volts).

One instance of the interdependence of magnetic- and electric-circuit conditions may be seen by examining the *build-up of voltage* for an unloaded shunt generator. When the field circuit is closed, the small voltage from residual magnetism (the 6-volt intercept of the magnetization curve, Fig. 5-28) causes a small field current. If the flux produced by the resulting ampere-turns adds to the residual flux, progressively greater voltages and field currents are obtained. If the field ampere-turns oppose the residual magnetism, the shunt-field terminals must be reversed to obtain build-up. Build-up continues until the volt-ampere relations represented by the magnetization curve and the field-resistance line are simultaneously satisfied (*i.e.,* at their intersections, 250 volts for line *Oa* in Fig. 5-28). This statement ignores the extremely small voltage drop caused by the shunt-field current in the armature-circuit resistance. Notice that if the field resistance is too high, as shown by line Ob for $r_f = 100$ ohms, the intersection is at very low voltage and build-up is not obtained. Notice also that if the field-resistance line is essentially tangent to the lower part of the magnetization curve, corresponding to 57 ohms in Fig. 5-28, the intersection may be anywhere from about 60 to 170 volts, resulting in very unstable conditions. The corresponding resistance is the *critical field resistance,* beyond which build-up will not be obtained. The same build-up process and the same conclusions apply to compound generators; in a long-shunt compound generator, the series-field mmf created by the shunt-field current is entirely negligible.

This build-up of voltage is evidently a transient process in which, at any particular point, the vertical difference between the field-resistance line and the magnetization curve is the voltage serving to increase the current through the shunt-field inductance. The transient process is studied quantitatively in Chap. 12.

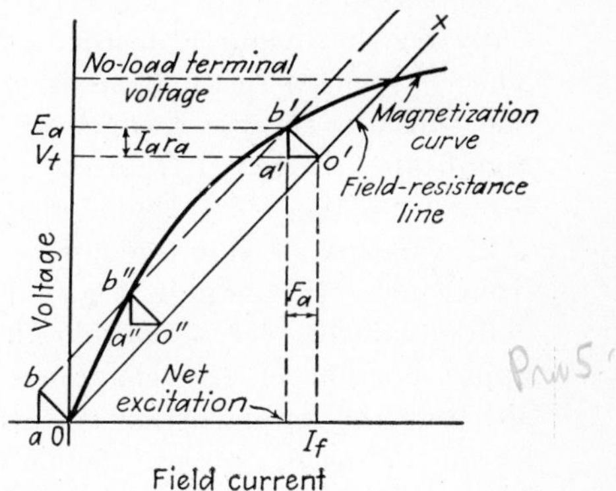

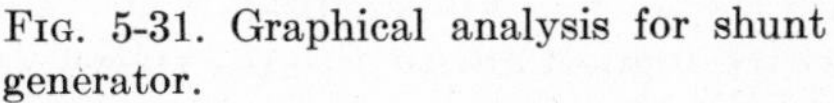
FIG. 5-31. Graphical analysis for shunt generator.

c. Shunt Generators. In the study of shunt-generator operation, use may be made of the fact that at each load there is a point O' (Fig. 5-31) on the field-resistance line determined by the terminal voltage V_t and shunt-field current I_f, and an associated point b' on the magnetization curve determined by the generated emf E_a and the net excitation. The horizontal displacement $O'a'$ between the associated points must equal the armature-reaction mmf F_a; the vertical displacement $a'b'$ must equal the armature resistance drop $I_a r_a$. Determination of the terminal voltage V_t for a given armature current I_a is then simply a matter of constructing a right triangle $O'a'b'$ with $O'a' = F_a$ and $a'b' = I_a r_a$, and placing this triangle as in Fig. 5-31 so that O' is on the field-resistance line and b' on the magnetization curve. The ordinate of point O' is then the desired terminal voltage. Triangle $O'a'b'$ may be appropriately placed by successive trials, or the following geometric construction may be used: Draw triangle Oab at the origin with $Oa = F_a$ and $ab = I_a r_a$; through point b draw $bb''b'$ parallel to the field-resistance line Ox; the intersection b' with the magnetization curve establishes the vertex b' of triangle $O'a'b'$. In general, there is a second intersection b'' with the magnetization curve, so that a second triangle $O''a''b''$ may be fitted in at a lower voltage. Under these circumstances, two possible operating voltages exist, and the external characteristic is double-valued in this region. When line $bb''b'$ is tangent to the magnetization curve, the armature current I_a has its maximum value.

Great precision is evidently not obtained from the foregoing computational process, since much depends upon the size of the small quantities F_a and $I_a r_a$. The uncertainties caused by magnetic hysteresis in d-c machines make high precision unattainable in any event. In general, the magnetization curve on which the machine operates on any given occasion may range from the rising to the falling part of the rather fat hysteresis loop for the magnetic circuit of the machine, depending essentially on the magnetic history of the iron just prior to that occasion. The curve used for analysis is usually the mean magnetization curve, and thus the results obtained are substantially correct on the average. Significant departures from the average may be encountered in the performance of any d-c machine at a particular time, however.

The nature of shunt-generator external characteristics may be seen from curves 2, 3, and 4, Fig. 5-30, in which it is evident that they are double-valued over a considerable range of armature currents. The upper portion of the characteristic is the normal operating region, although the lower portion is stable and may be reached experimentally by continuing to decrease the load resistance after the maximum current is reached. The voltage of a shunt generator naturally decreases faster with load than for a separately excited generator, because the field excitation also decreases as the terminal voltage drops.

Example 5-7. Consider that the generator of Example 5-6 is to be shunt-excited. Compute and plot curves of terminal voltage as a function of current output under the following conditions:

a. Excitation adjusted to give rated voltage at no load; armature reaction neglected.

b. Excitation adjusted to give rated voltage at no load; armature reaction in accordance with Fig. 5-29 as described in Example 5-6.

Solution. *a.* The field-resistance line Oa (Fig. 5-28) passes through the 250-volt 5.0-amp point of the magnetization curve. Computations are summarized in Table 5-2. Thus at $I_a = 400$ amp,

$$I_a r_a = 400 \times 0.025 = 10 \text{ volts}$$

A vertical distance of 10 volts exists between the magnetization curve and the field-resistance line at a field current of 4.28 amp, corresponding to $V_t = 214$ volts. The associated line current is

$$I_L = I_a - I_f = 400 - 4.26 = 396 \text{ amp}$$

But a vertical distance of 10 volts also exist at a field current of 0.80 amp, corresponding to $V_t = 80$ volts. The external characteristic is accordingly double-valued in this region. Final results are plotted as curve 2 of Fig. 5-30.

TABLE 5-2
COMPUTATIONS FOR EXAMPLE 5-7*a*, CURVE 2 OF FIG. 5-30

I_a, amp	$I_a r_a$, volts	V_t, volts	I_f, amp	I_L, amp
5	....	250	5.0	0
200	5.0	235	4.7	195
400	10.0	214	4.3	396
600	15.0	193	3.9	596
740	18.5	156	3.1	737
600	15.0	92	1.8	598
400	10.0	40	0.8	399

b. The field-resistance line Oa (Fig. 5-28) still holds, but corresponding points on it and the magnetization curve are now displaced by the F_a, $I_a r_a$ triangle. For example, at $I_a = 200$ amp, $F_a = 0.19$ equivalent field ampere, and $I_a r_a = 5$ volts. When the corresponding triangle is fitted in as in Fig. 5-31, the associated terminal voltage and field current are found to be $V_t = 196$ volts, and $I_f = 3.9$ amp. The output current is

$$I_L = I_a - I_f = 200 - 3.9 = 196 \text{ amp}$$

Again, the external characteristic is double-valued in this region, for the triangle can also be fitted in at a lower point. Computations for other points are summarized in Table 5-3. The end results are plotted as curve 3 of Fig. 5-30.

Comparison of curves 2 and 3 shows that the magnitude of armature reaction considered here has a pronounced effect on the external characteristic. Actually, the assumption that F_a has the same magnitude at reduced voltages as in the neighborhood of rated voltage is unduly pessimistic. At the lower voltages, saturation and hence the demagnetizing effect of cross-magnetizing armature reaction are appreciably reduced. If this reduction were taken into account, the external characteristic would follow a course about like that of curve 4, between curves 2 and 3.

TABLE 5-3
COMPUTATIONS FOR EXAMPLE 5-7*b*, CURVE 3 OF FIG. 5-30

I_a, amp	$I_a r_a$, volts	F_a, equivalent field amp	V_t, volts	I_f, amp	I_L, amp
5	...	....	250	5.0	0
100	2.5	0.07	232	4.6	95
200	5.0	0.19	196	3.9	196
240	6.0	0.25	165	3.3	237
200	5.0	0.19	109	2.2	198

Inspection of the results of this example shows the desirability of minimizing armature reaction in a machine which is to act as a shunt generator. Also evident is the need for a voltage regulator when a substantially constant output voltage is desired.

d. Series Generators. Build-up of a *series generator* conforms to the same general pattern as for a shunt generator. In fact, when the load consists of a resistance with no counter emf, the same build-up argument may be used provided that the shunt-field-resistance line of Fig. 5-28 be replaced by a similar line determined by the combined resistance of the load, series field, and armature. As indicated in Fig. 3-48, the external characteristic of a series generator resembles the magnetization curve; points on the external characteristic are shifted downward and to the right, however, by the effects of machine resistance and demagnetizing armature reaction. Because industrial power systems are almost exclusively constant-voltage systems, series generators are seldom used. Occasional use of low-voltage generators (called *series boosters*) in series with long, heavily loaded, d-c feeders to compensate for resistance drop is one application found in this country. Performance analysis may be carried out readily by simple adaptation of the methods discussed for other d-c machines.

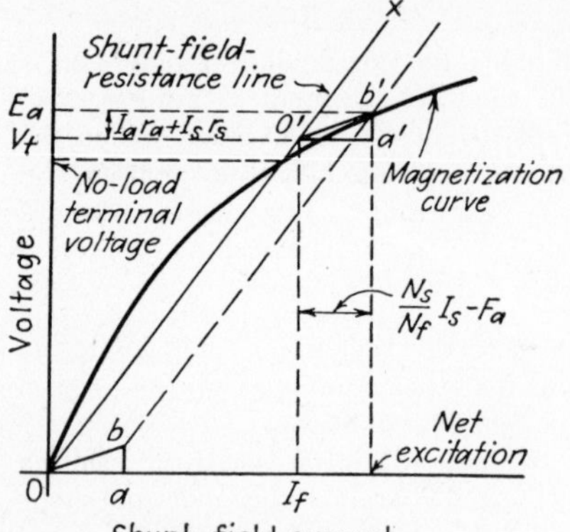

FIG. 5-32. Graphical analysis for compound generator.

e. Compound Generators. In the study of *cumulative-compound-generator* operation, use may again be made of the mmf-voltage triangle as in the shunt generator. The corresponding points O' (Fig. 5-32) on the field-resistance line and b' on the magnetization curve are now displaced vertically by the drop $I_a r_a + I_s r_s$ in the armature and series field, and horizontally by combined mmf $(N_s I_s / N_f) - F_a$ of the series field and armature reaction. This combined mmf is usually magnetizing, so that the net excitation, unlike that in the shunt generator, is usually greater than the shunt-field mmf alone. Consequently, the mmf leg Oa of the mmf-voltage triangle Oab is drawn in the positive or magnetizing direction in Fig. 5-32. The straight line bb' drawn parallel to the shunt-field-resistance line Ox determines the point b' on the magnetization curve and enables the triangle $O'a'b'$ to be drawn in its proper position. The ordinate of point O' is the terminal voltage corresponding to the armature current for which the mmf-voltage triangle is drawn. Of course, the triangle $O'a'b'$ may be placed by trial if one wishes to avoid the foregoing geometrical construction.

The terminal voltage of an *overcompounded generator* increases with load in the earlier part of the curve, and the full-load voltage is greater than the no-load voltage. The external characteristic of an *undercompounded generator* may rise at first, but the full-load voltage is smaller than the no-load voltage. Intermediate between these two is the voltage-load curve of a *flat-compounded generator* in which the no-load and full-load voltages are equal; a sample characteristic is given by curve 5 of Fig. 5-30. The degree of compounding of a particular machine may be adjusted conveniently by use of a low-resistance shunt around the series field (sometimes called a *series-field diverter*) to by-pass a fraction of the total current.

Example 5-8. The generator of Example 5-6 has added to it a series field of 4 turns per pole having a resistance of 0.005 ohm; there are 1,000 turns per pole in the shunt field. It is to be operated as a self-excited flat-compounded long-shunt generator by adjusting a diverter across the series field so that the full-load voltage is 250 volts when the shunt-field rheostat is adjusted to give a no-load voltage of 250 volts. Armature reaction is to be included in accordance with Fig. 5-29 as described in Example 5-6.

Compute and plot a curve of terminal voltage as a function of current output.

Solution. For the no-load voltage to be 250 volts, the shunt-field resistance must be 50 ohms, and the field-resistance line is Oa (Fig. 5-28). The degree of current diversion from the series field must first be determined from the specified full-load conditions.

At full load, $I_f = 5.0$ amp because $V_t = 250$ volts. Then,

$$I_a = 400 + 5.0 = 405 \text{ amp}$$

and

$$E_a = 250 + 405(0.025 + 0.005) = 262 \text{ volts}$$

In the last equation, the effect of the diverter in reducing the series-field-circuit resistance is ignored, a neglect which is permissible in view of the degree of precision warranted. From the magnetization curve (Fig. 5-28) an E_a of 262 volts requires a net excitation of 5.4 equivalent shunt-field amperes. Since $F_a = 0.5$, the series-field mmf is given by

$$5.4 = 5.0 + \frac{N_s}{N_f} I_s - 0.5$$

or

$$\frac{N_s}{N_f} I_s = \frac{4}{1{,}000} I_s = 0.9$$

and

$$I_s = 225 \text{ amp}$$

Hence, only 225 of the total 405 amp of armature current must pass through the series field, a process requiring that the series field be shunted by a resistor of

$$\frac{225 \times 0.005}{405 - 225} = 0.0063 \text{ ohm}$$

The combined resistance r_s of the series field and its diverter is then just under 0.003 ohm.

The point on the external characteristic at which $I_a = 300$ amp will be found as a sample computation. For this point,

$$I_s = 0.56 \times 300 = 168 \text{ amp}$$

$$\frac{N_s}{N_f} I_s = \frac{4}{1{,}000} \times 168 = 0.67 \text{ equivalent shunt-field amp}$$

and

$$I_a(r_a + r_s) = 300(0.025 + 0.003) = 8.4 \text{ volts}$$

Since, from Fig. 5-29, $F_a = 0.34$, the combined effect of the series field and armature reaction is a magnetizing action to the extent of

$$0.67 - 0.34 = 0.33 \text{ equivalent shunt-field amp}$$

The corresponding triangle may be fitted in as shown in Fig. 5-32. The result is that

$$V_t = 252 \text{ volts} \qquad \text{and} \qquad I_f = 5.04 \text{ amp}$$

The corresponding line current is

$$I_L = 300 - 5.04 = 295$$

Computations for other points may be summarized in tabular form. The resulting external characteristic is plotted as curve 5 of Fig. 5-30.

The voltage-load curve of a *differentially compounded generator* drops off faster than that of a shunt generator since the action of the series field is to add to the demagnetizing armature reaction. Analysis of its performance follows the routine for shunt generators except that the mmf leg of the mmf-voltage triangle represents the demagnetizing armature reaction F_a plus the demagnetizing series-field mmf N_sI_s/N_f. The maximum current output of a differentially compounded generator is, of course, even more severely limited than that of a shunt generator. Differential compounding is accordingly used only where a definite limit on the output current is desired, as in welding generators.

5-7. Analysis of Motor Performance. Since the terminal voltage of motors is usually substantially constant at a specified value, there is no dependence of shunt-field excitation on a varying voltage as in shunt and compound generators. Hence, motor analysis most nearly resembles that for separately excited generators, although speed is now an important variable and often the one whose value is to be found. Analytical essentials include Eqs. 5-7 and 5-8 relating terminal voltage and generated or counter emf, Eq. 5-14 for net excitation, the magnetization curve as the graphical relation between counter emf and net excitation, Eq. 5-2 showing the dependence of electromagnetic torque on flux and armature current, and Eq. 5-1 relating counter emf with flux and speed. The last two relations are particularly significant in motor analysis. The former is pertinent because the interdependence of torque and the stator and rotor field strengths must often be examined. The latter is the usual medium for determining motor speed from other specified operating conditions.

Motor speed corresponding to a given armature current I_a may be found by first computing the actual generated voltage E_a from Eq. 5-7 or 5-8. Next obtain the net excitation from Eq. 5-14. Since the magnetization curve will be plotted for a constant speed n_{mc} which in general will be different from the actual motor speed n, the generated voltage $E_{a(mc)}$ read from the magnetization curve at the foregoing net excitation will correspond to the correct flux conditions but to the speed n_{mc}. But, from Eq. 5-1, it follows that

$$n = \frac{E_a}{E_{a(mc)}} n_{mc} \tag{5-16}$$

Accordingly, when the voltage $E_{a(mc)}$ is found from the magnetization curve at the correct net mmf, the actual motor speed may be determined by substitution in Eq. 5-16.

It will be noted that knowledge of the armature current is postulated at the start of this process. When, as is frequently the case, the speed at a stated shaft power or torque output is to be found, successive trials based on assumed values of I_a usually form the simplest procedure. Plotting of the successive trials permits speedy determination of the correct armature current and speed at the desired output.

a. Series Motors. For the series motor, the typical speed-load characteristic (computed in Example 5-9 on the basis of the magnetization curve in Fig. 5-33), showing a very rapid decrease of speed as load is increased, is plotted in Fig. 5-34 with coordinates in per-unit form. Unity values of power, torque, and speed are the output values at rated load. Evident from these curves is the outstanding feature of a series motor—that it is a varying-speed motor capable of cushioning the effect of a large torque overload by a decided drop in speed. Series motors must always be operated under load unless definite provisions are made in the control circuit to circumvent the destructively high light-load and no-load speeds.

Example 5-9. Following are the name-plate data of a d-c series motor driving a skip hoist: 230 volts, 20 hp, 75.0 amp, 50°C, 1-hr rating. The magnetization curve at 900 rpm is plotted in Fig. 5-33. The armature resistance r_a = 0.09 ohm, and the series-field resistance r_s = 0.06 ohm. Armature reaction may be neglected in this example.

a. Compute and plot curves of motor speed as a function of the shaft power and torque outputs. Use per-unit coordinates with unity speed, power, and torque equal to the output values at rated load. The sum of the rotational and stray-load losses is 1,500 watts and may be considered to remain constant. Because of the widely varying speed and flux conditions in a series motor, this assumption is often an appreciably more drastic one than it is for a shunt machine. It is not a completely unrealistic assumption, however, for the increase of iron losses and the decrease of friction and windage losses at least partially compensate each other.

b. Compute the starting torque for an allowable starting current of 100 amp.

Solution. a. The point at which I_a = 100 amp is chosen for a sample computation.

$$\begin{aligned} E_a &= V_t - I_a(r_a + r_s) \\ &= 230 - 100(0.09 + 0.06) = 215 \text{ volts} \end{aligned}$$

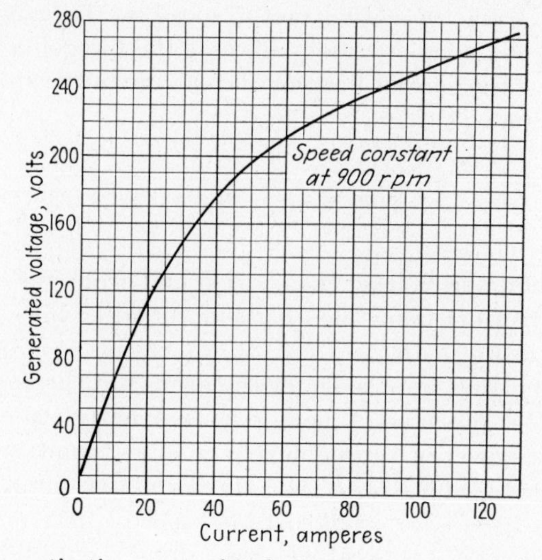

FIG. 5-33. Magnetization curve of 20-hp 230-volt series motor, Example 5-9.

From the 100-amp point on the 900-rpm magnetization curve,

$$E_{a(mc)} = 251 \text{ volts}$$

so that, from Eq. 5-16,

$$n = {}^{215}\!/_{251} \times 900 = 771 \text{ rpm}$$

The associated shaft power output may be found by computing the electromagnetic power E_aI_a and deducting $P_r + P_{SL}$; that is,

$$P_o = 215 \times 100 - 1{,}500 = 20{,}000 \text{ watts}$$

TABLE 5-4
COMPUTATION FOR EXAMPLE 5-9*a*, FIG. 5-34

I_a, amp	25	50	75	100	125
$I_a(r_a + r_s)$, volts	3.8	7.5	11.3	15.0	18.8
E_a, volts	226	223	219	215	211
$E_{a(mc)}$, volts	132	196	228	251	271
n, rpm	1,540	1,020	865	771	701
E_aI_a, kw	5.7	11.2	16.4	21.5	26.4
P_o, kw	4.2	9.7	14.9	20.0	24.9
n, per unit	1.78	1.18	1.00	0.89	0.81
P_o, per unit	0.28	0.65	1.00	1.34	1.67
T_o, per unit	0.16	0.55	1.00	1.55	2.06

Similar computations for other points are summarized in Table 5-4. The last three rows of this table are obtained by dividing the corresponding quantities in their absolute units by the values in the same units at $I_a = 75.0$ amp, the rated operating point. The final results are plotted in Fig. 5-34.

b. First the electromagnetic torque at full load will be computed from the data in *a*. Since electromagnetic torque in mks units and power are related by Eq. 5-5, full-load electromagnetic torque is

$$T = \frac{60}{2\pi \times 865} \times 219 \times 75 = 181.5 \text{ newton-m}$$

Now by virtue of the torque relation (Eq. 5-2) this value must also be the starting electromagnetic torque for an allowable starting current of 75 amp, for both the flux and the armature current are then the same at starting as under full-load running conditions, and torque depends on only these two quantities. The starting torque

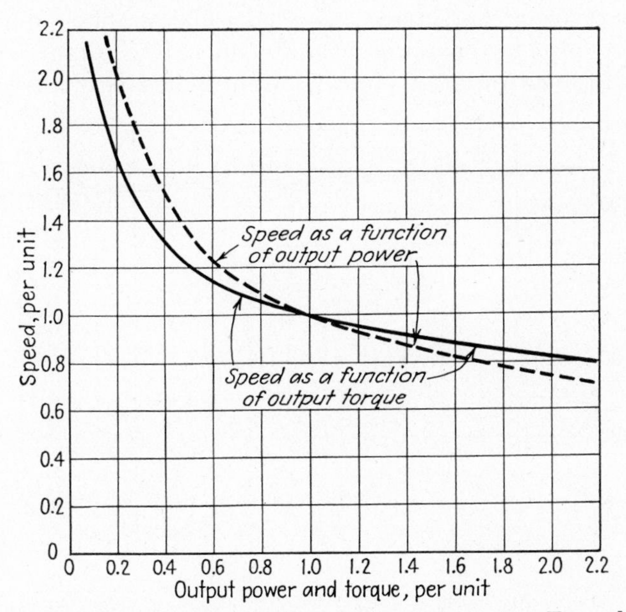

FIG. 5-34. Computed speed-load curves for series motor, Example 5-9.

for any other current may be obtained by multiplying this torque by the following two ratios:

$$\frac{\text{Starting current}}{\text{Full-load current}} \quad \text{and} \quad \frac{\text{Flux for starting current}}{\text{Flux for full-load current}}$$

From Eq. 5-16, the flux ratio will be the same as the ratio of the two emfs, $E_{a(mc)}$, read from the magnetization curve at the associated currents. Thus, at a starting current of 100 amp, the starting torque is

$$181.5 \times \frac{100}{75.0} \times \frac{251}{228} = 266 \text{ newton-m}$$

or $266/181.5 = 1.47$ times full-load electromagnetic torque.

b. Shunt Motors. For the shunt motor, typical numerical examples of speed-load characteristics are shown in Fig. 5-35 as computed for a 100-hp motor in Examples 5-10 and 5-11. The normal characteristic shows a slight decrease in speed with added load, in about the manner of curve 1, Fig. 5-35. This decrease is the result of increased armature resistance drop as load is added. The effect of an appreciable amount of demagnetizing armature reaction, however, is to lessen the speed decrease, and it may even cause the characteristic to be almost flat or to show a small rise in speed as load is added. Thus, the amount of armature reaction included in curve 2, Fig. 5-35, results in the speed rising at overload points.

For reasons considered below in discussing differentially compounded motors, this type of characteristic is usually undesirable. When a shunt motor is intended for operation at approximately constant field current or with fairly small variation of field current by means of a field rheostat,

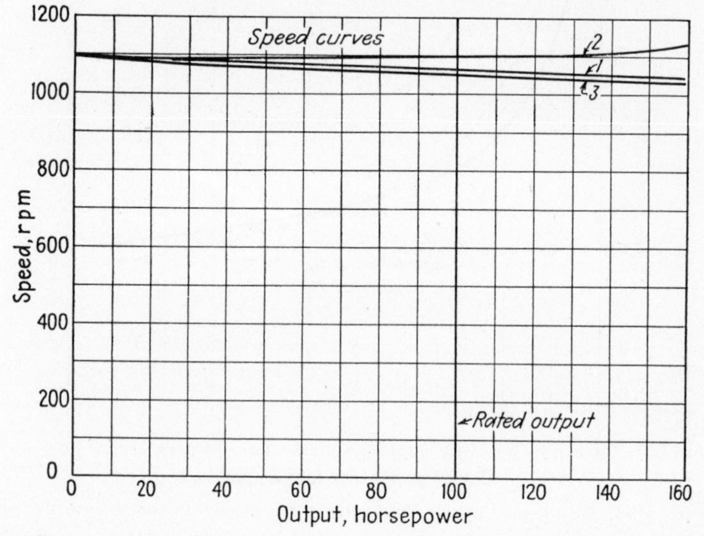

FIG. 5-35. Computed speed-load characteristics for shunt motor with (1) armature reaction neglected, (2) armature reaction included, and (3) series stabilizing winding added.

such a characteristic is avoided in the design of the motor by making the number of field ampere-turns large compared with the armature ampere-turns. With adjustable-speed motors intended for operation over a wide speed range by shunt-field control, however, a *stabilizing winding* consisting of a few turns of cumulative series field is frequently installed. Such a stabilizing winding ensures attainment of a drooping speed-load characteristic even at weak shunt-field currents and heavy loads. The effect of a stabilizing winding is computed in Example 5-11 and shown as curve 3 of Fig. 5-35.

Example 5-10. A 100-hp 250-volt d-c shunt motor has the magnetization curve of Fig. 5-28 and armature characteristic of Fig. 5-29. The armature circuit resistance (including brushes) is 0.025 ohm. Rotational losses may be considered constant at 2,000 watts, and stray-load losses equal 1.0 per cent of the output.

The field rheostat is adjusted for a no-load speed of 1,100 rpm. Compute and plot curves of motor speed as a function of horsepower output with

a. Armature reaction neglected

b. Armature reaction included in accordance with Fig. 5-29

Solution. *a.* A magnetization curve is unnecessary with constant field current and negligible armature reaction. Since the no-load speed is 1,100 rpm, the armature generated voltage corresponding to a speed of 1,100 rpm is constant at 250 volts.

At the point for which $I_a = 400$ amp,

$$E_a = 250 - 400 \times 0.025 = 240 \text{ volts}$$

The corresponding speed is then

$$n = {}^{240}\!/_{250} \times 1{,}100 = 1{,}057 \text{ rpm}$$

and the electromagnetic power is

$$E_a I_a = 240 \times 400 = 96{,}000 \text{ watts}$$

Deduction of the rotational losses leaves 94,000 watts. With stray-load losses accounted for, the power output P_o is given by

$$94{,}000 - 0.01P_o = P_o$$

or

$$P_o = 93.1 \text{ kw} = 124.7 \text{ hp}$$

Similar computations may be made for other assumed values of I_a. The results are plotted as curve 1 of Fig. 5-35.

b. It will be considered that only one magnetization curve, that at 1,200 rpm in Fig. 5-28, is given. At no load, $E_a = 250$ volts, and the corresponding point on the 1,200-rpm curve is at

$$E_{a(mc)} = 250 \times \frac{1{,}200}{1{,}100} = 273 \text{ volts}$$

for which $I_f = 5.90$ amp. The field current remains constant at this value, and the armature-reaction mmf may be read from Fig. 5-29.

At $I_a = 400$ amp, $F_a = 0.50$ equivalent field ampere,

$$E_a = 250 - 400 \times 0.025 = 240 \text{ volts}$$

and

Net mmf $= 5.90 - 0.50 = 5.40$ equivalent field amperes

From Fig. 5-28,

$$E_{a(mc)} = 262 \text{ volts}$$

so that

$$n = {}^{240}\!/_{262} \times 1{,}200 = 1{,}100 \text{ rpm}$$

As in part *a*, the associated electromagnetic power is 96.0 kw, and deduction of rotational and stray-load losses gives a shaft output of 124.7 hp.

Computations for other points may be carried out similarly, preferably in tabular form to systematize the work. The resulting speed-load characteristic is plotted as curve 2 of Fig. 5-35.

c. Compound Motors. Cumulatively compounded motors have speed-load characteristics which are intermediate between those of series and shunt motors and whose shapes depend on the relative strengths of the series and shunt fields. The most heavily compounded motor is essentially a series motor to which a light shunt field has been added to limit the no-load speed to a mechanically allowable value; its characteristics are therefore those of a series motor, but without the excessive no-load speed. A lightly compounded motor, on the other hand, has essentially shunt-motor characteristics but with a somewhat greater droop to the speed-load curve.

Analysis of the running performance of a compound motor is illustrated in Example 5-11 by computing the effects of adding a stabilizing winding to the shunt motor of Example 5-10.

Example 5-11. Because the speed-load characteristic (curve 2 of Fig. 5-35) of the shunt motor in Example 5-10 is undesirable, a stabilizing winding consisting of 1½ cumulative series turns per pole is to be added. The resistance of this winding is negligible. There are 1,000 turns per pole in the shunt field.

Compute and plot the new speed-load curve.

Solution. As in Example 5-10, the shunt-field current is constant at 5.90 amp. At $I_a = 400$ amp, $F_a = 0.50$,

$$\frac{N_s}{N_f} I_s = \frac{1.5}{1{,}000} \times 400 = 0.60$$

and

$$\text{Net mmf} = 5.90 + 0.60 - 0.50 = 6.00$$

all in equivalent shunt-field amperes. The armature generated voltage is

$$E_a = 250 - 400 \times 0.025 = 240 \text{ volts}$$

and, from Fig. 5-28 at the above net mmf,

$$E_{a(mc)} = 276 \text{ volts}$$

Hence

$$n = {}^{240}\!/_{276} \times 1{,}200 = 1{,}043 \text{ rpm}$$

Computations for other armature currents may be carried out in tabular form. The results are plotted as curve 3 of Fig. 5-35.

Differentially compounded motors in general have rising speed-load characteristics, the increase in speed with load being caused by the combined demagnetization of armature reaction and the differential series field. Performance calculations follow the same routine as that for cumulatively compounded motors except for the change in sign of the series-field mmf.

Because rising speed-load curves inherently produce instability with many types of loads, differentially compounded motors are not used industrially. To see the causes of instability, imagine that the motor characteristic is given by the rising curve of Fig. 5-36*a*, and that, as shown by the dotted curve, the load requires constant torque regardless of speed. The operating point is at the intersection of these two curves. Now assume a small disturbance causing the motor speed to increase slightly. As a result, the motor output torque increases, while the torque required by the load remains constant. The torque differential then further accelerates the motor. This process continues until the motor breakers or fuses are tripped by excess current. A similar argument shows that a small disturbance causing a speed decrease also becomes cumulative. When, on the other hand, the same reasoning is applied to the drooping motor characteristic of Fig. 5-36*b*, it is found that the torque differentials set up by an assumed disturbance are in such a direction as to restore the initial operating conditions. The general conclusion is that the torque speed characteristic of the motor must have an algebraically smaller slope dT/dn than that of the load for stability to result. Motors such as the differentially compounded motor or the shunt motor with excessive armature reaction are therefore undesirable practically. It may also be shown that they may perform erratically at starting or under heavy transient loads.

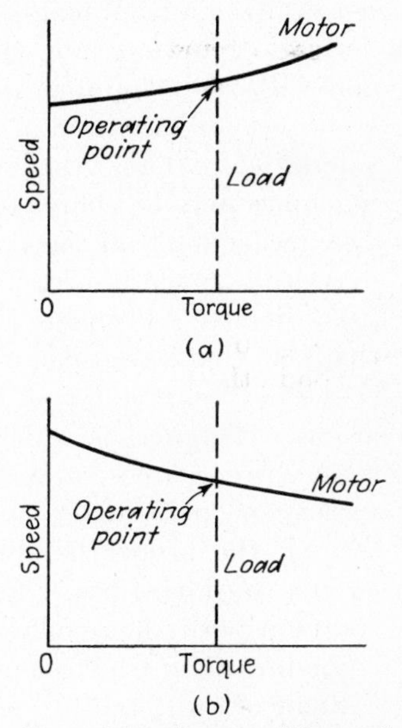

FIG. 5-36. Superposition of motor and load characteristics with (*a*) rising and (*b*) drooping motor speed-torque curve.

5-8. Résumé. In the analysis of d-c machine performance, we are concerned primarily with the variations of rotor mmf and of the resultant air-gap flux. For a particular machine, rotor-mmf variation becomes synonymous with armature-current variation and therefore is influenced by simple Kirchhoff-law considerations in the armature circuit (Eqs. 5-7 to 5-9). Determination of the resultant air-gap flux is largely a magnetic-circuit problem in which appropriate account is taken of armature- and main-field-mmf sources in finding the net excitation (Eq. 5-14). The magnetization curve, because of its interpretation as a relation between net excitation and armature generated voltage, forms the connecting link between the electric- and magnetic-circuit aspects. The most common problems for generators are the computation of voltages corresponding to specified loads, or, conversely, the specification of machine conditions necessary for maintenance of a stated voltage level. These determinations involve only straightforward application of the electric- and magnetic-circuit aspects for separately excited generators. Because the excitation of shunt and compound generators necessarily depends on the terminal voltage, and also because of the nonlinearity of the magnetization curve, graphical aids to the analysis of self-excited generators are of value (Figs. 5-31 and 5-32). The most common problems for motors resolve into the computation of speeds corresponding to specified loads, or, conversely, the specification of machine conditions necessary to the attainment of a stated speed-load characteristic. A special case of motor problems is that involving zero speed or starting conditions. The connecting link between speed and electromagnetic aspects is once more the magnetization curve; many speed problems are solved by computing the armature emf from electrical conditions and the net excitation from magnetic-circuit conditions, and then using the magnetization curve to find what the speed must be to produce the computed emf with the computed net excitation. Of course, rotational and stray-load losses as discussed in Art. 4-11 enter into machine input-output considerations. Thus, the performance characteristics of the various d-c machines may be completely investigated.

A resurvey of all the factors involved in the analysis of d-c machines may lead to the impression that such analysis is somewhat plagued by fussy details. Probably this impression is correct—and this in spite of the facts that variations of torque angle do not enter and that resistance is the only parameter affecting steady-state equivalent-circuit considerations. The details which must be discussed for a full treatment arise from three sources: first, the d-c machine offers flexibility and a great variety of performance characteristics to the designer and operator; second, the proper handling of saturation requires detailed magnetic-circuit considerations, a respect in which the d-c machine has much in common with the synchronous machine; and third, the need for good commutation introduces unique and important problems.

Some of the details, to be sure, are relatively unimportant. They need to be discussed briefly, however, to show that they are unimportant and to ensure against the appearance of a sloppy thought process. The distinction between a long-shunt and short-shunt compound machine is an obvious example. The voltage drop caused by the field current in the armature of a shunt generator is another example of a minor effect which can be taken into account without much trouble, but which nevertheless constitutes a distraction from the main line of attack. The main factor to bear in mind in passing judgment on such small effects is the degree of uncertainty introduced by magnetic hysteresis. The magnetization curve is taken as the average operating condition within the hysteresis loop, but the behavior of the machine on any one occasion depends on the previous history of the magnetic circuit.

Others of the details, on the other hand, are of the utmost importance. Armature reaction and commutation phenomena definitely limit the conditions under which a d-c machine may operate. They are of determining importance in establishing the maximum allowable short-time overload of both motors and generators, and they directly affect the upper limit of motor speed which can be attained by field weakening. For shunt motors, especially under weak-field conditions, the indirect demagnetization caused by armature reaction may result in rising speed-load characteristics with their attendant unstable or widely fluctuating operation. This entire situation is in direct contrast to that in induction and synchronous machines, where torque-angle considerations and the existence of definite breakdown or pull-out torques furnish the comparable limiting factors.

With shunt or separate excitation, the magnitude of the flux per pole may be adjusted externally by means of rheostats in the field windings; with series excitation, the flux per pole tends to increase naturally with load on the machine because of the increasing series-field mmf. As a result of these control possibilities, we find the d-c machine to be a versatile energy-conversion device. Typical performance characteristics may be reviewed by inspecting the curves of Figs. 5-30, 5-34, and 5-35. A summary in words of the outstanding features is postponed to Art. 6-5, where it is given as part of a discussion of d-c machine applications.

PROBLEMS

5-1. A cumulatively compounded generator with interpoles and with its brushes on neutral is to be used as a compound motor.

If no changes are made in the internal connections, will the motor be cumulatively or differentially compounded? Will the polarity of the interpoles be correct? Will the direction of rotation be the same as or opposite to the direction in which it was driven as a generator?

5-2. A self-excited d-c machine with interpoles is adjusted for proper operation as an overcompounded generator. The machine is shut down, the connections to the shunt field are reversed, and the machine is then started with the direction of rotation reversed. The machine builds up normal terminal voltage. Answer the following questions, and give a brief explanation.

Is the terminal-voltage polarity the same as before? Is the machine still cumulatively compounded? Do the interpoles have the proper polarity for good commutation?

5-3. It is desired to reverse the terminal-voltage polarity of a generator which has been operating properly as a short-shunt cumulatively compounded generator with interpoles. To produce the reversal, the machine was stopped, and the residual magnetism was reversed by temporarily disconnecting the shunt field and separately exciting it with reversed current. The connections were then restored exactly as they were before. The generator is then driven in the same direction of rotation as before, and the terminal voltage builds up with reversed polarity.

Will it be necessary to reverse the interpole connections to get good commutation? Will the compounding be cumulative or differential?

5-4. A 5-kw 250-volt 1,150-rpm compound generator is flat-compounded when operated at its rated voltage and speed. State what kind of compounding (over. under, or flat) it will have for the following cases of operation under other than rated conditions, and explain briefly:

a. Speed 1,350 rpm, shunt-field rheostat adjusted for rated voltage at no load.

b. Rated speed, shunt-field rheostat adjusted for 230 volts at no load.

5-5. The generator of Example 5-3 is to have a series field added so that the terminal voltage at a remote load may be 250 volts at both no load and full load (400 amp). The resistance of the feeder interconnecting generator and load is 0.025 ohm. Armature reaction and the added resistance of the series field are to be neglected.

a. Determine the series turns per pole when the generator is driven by a constant-speed 1,200-rpm prime mover.

b. Determine the series turns per pole when the prime-mover speed drops from 1,200 rpm at no load to 1,150 rpm at full load.

5-6. A 100-kw 250-volt d-c shunt generator has an armature resistance of 0.020 ohm and the magnetization curve of Fig. 5-28. The armature reaction is 0.50 amp-turn per pole per ampere of armature current. The generator is driven at a constant speed of 1,200 rpm with the shunt-field rheostat adjusted to produce rated terminal voltage at no load.

What is the maximum steady-state current which may be drawn from the machine?

5-7. The generator of Prob. 5-6 is connected for short-shunt cumulative compounding with a series field having 5 turns per pole and a total resistance of 0.010 ohm. There are 1,000 turns per pole on the shunt field.

What resistance must be connected in parallel with the series field to bring about flat compounding at a terminal voltage of 250 volts?

5-8. A 250-volt 25-kw 1,200-rpm short-shunt overcompounded generator has 2,000 shunt-field turns per pole. The resistance of the armature (including brushes) is 0.10 ohm, and the resistance of the series field is 0.05 ohm. With the shunt-field rheostat set to give a terminal voltage of 230 volts at no load, the terminal voltage at full load is 250 volts.

The following two tests were made on the machine:

Test 1. Speed constant at 1,200 rpm, generator on open circuit:

Terminal volts	230	240	250	260	270
Shunt-field amp	2.20	2.35	2.52	2.71	2.92

Test 2. Run as separately excited generator (series field disconnected), speed constant at 1,200 rpm, and terminal voltage constant at 230 volts:

Armature amp	20	40	60	80	100	120
Shunt-field amp	2.26	2.32	2.40	2.48	2.58	2.68

On the assumption that armature reaction is independent of flux, determine the full-load demagnetizing armature reaction in equivalent shunt-field amperes and the number of series-field turns per pole.

5-9. A cumulatively compounded d-c machine has 2,000 shunt-field turns per pole, 12 series-field turns per pole, 0.12 ohm armature resistance (including brushes), 0.04 ohm series-field resistance, and 210 ohms shunt-field circuit resistance. Its magnetization curve at 1,800 rpm is:

E_a, volts	200	210	220	230	240	250
I_f, amp	1.10	1.17	1.25	1.34	1.44	1.56

As a long-shunt generator, this machine delivers 75 amp load current at 218 volts when driven at 1,800 rpm. Assume that the armature reaction is independent of the flux. At what speed must it be driven if it is to deliver 75 amp load current at 240 volts?

5-10. A 10-kw 230-volt 1,150-rpm shunt generator is driven by a prime mover whose speed is 1,195 rpm when the generator delivers no load. The speed falls to 1,150 rpm when the generator delivers 10 kw and may be assumed to decrease in proportion to the generator output. The generator is to be changed into a short-shunt compound generator by equipping it with a series field which will cause its voltage to rise from 230 volts at no load to 250 volts for a load of 43.5 amp. It is estimated that the series field will have a resistance of 0.09 ohm. The armature resistance (including brushes) is 0.26 ohm. The shunt-field winding has 1,800 turns per pole.

In order to determine the necessary series-field turns, the machine is run as a separately excited generator and the following load data obtained: armature terminal voltage, 254 volts; armature current, 44.7 amp; field current, 1.95 amp; speed, 1,145 rpm.

The magnetization curve at 1,195 rpm is as follows:

E_a, volts	230	240	250	260	270
I_f, amp	1.05	1.13	1.26	1.46	1.67

a. Determine the necessary number of series-field turns per pole.

b. Determine the armature reaction in ampere-turns per pole for $I_a = 44.7$ amp.

5-11. A small lightweight d-c shunt generator for use in aircraft has a rating of 9 kw, 30 volts, 300 amp. It is driven by one of the main engines of the airplane through an auxiliary power shaft. The generator speed is proportional to the main-engine speed and may have any value from 4,500 rpm to 8,000 rpm. The terminal voltage of the generator is held constant at 30 volts for all speeds and loads by means of a voltage regulator which automatically adjusts a carbon-pile field rheostat whose minimum resistance is 0.75 ohm. The resistances of the shunt-field, commutating, and armature (including brushes) windings are, respectively, 2.50, 0.0040, and 0.0120 ohms.

Data for the magnetization curve at 4,550 rpm are:

I_f, amp	0	2.0	4.0	5.0	6.0	8.0	11.7
E_a, volts	1.0	18.0	30.5	33.6	35.5	38.0	40.5

In a load test at 4,550 rpm, the field current required to maintain rated terminal voltage at rated load is 7.00 amp.

Determine the following characteristics of this generator:

a. Maximum resistance required in the field rheostat

b. Maximum power dissipated in the field rheostat

c. Demagnetizing effect of armature reaction at rated load and 4,550 rpm, expressed in terms of equivalent shunt-field current

5-12. Assume that the demagnetizing effect of armature reaction in the aircraft generator of Prob. 5-11 is proportional to the armature current.

a. Plot the curve of terminal voltage as a function of line current for minimum field-rheostat resistance and 4,550 rpm.

b. When the airplane is on the ground and the engines are idling, the generator speed may be below 4,500 rpm. Plot a curve of terminal voltage as a function of speed with minimum field-rheostat resistance and a constant line current of 300 amp covering the subnormal speed range from 4,550 to 3,500 rpm. Estimate the minimum speed at which the generator is capable of delivering 300 amp.

5-13. The data in Table 5-5 are taken on a 500-kw 500-volt d-c shunt generator. All data are taken at constant speed of 1,000 rpm, separately excited. The armature resistance (including brushes) is 0.023 ohm.

TABLE 5-5

Terminal voltage, volts	Armature current, amp	Field current, amp
450	0	16.8
475	0	18.3
500	0	20.0
525	0	22.5
544	0	25.0
550	0	26.3
500	0	20.0
500	200	21.1
500	400	22.2
500	600	23.1
500	800	24.0
500	1,000	25.0
500	1,200	25.1

a. Plot the terminal volt-ampere characteristics for separate excitation at a field current of 25 amp.

b. Plot the terminal volt-ampere characteristics for operation as a shunt generator with shunt-field resistance constant at the value giving rated voltage at no load.

c. Plot the terminal volt-ampere characteristic for long-shunt cumulative-compound connection when the number of series-field turns equals 0.005 times the number of shunt-field turns and the shunt-field resistance is 25 ohms.

d. For part *c*, what percentage change in the number of series turns is needed for the machine to be flat-compounded?

5-14. A d-c series motor operates at 750 rpm with a line current of 80 amp from the 230-volt mains. Its armature circuit resistance is 0.14 ohm, and its field resistance is 0.11 ohm.

Assuming that the flux corresponding to a current of 20 amp is 40 per cent of that corresponding to a current of 80 amp, find the motor speed at a line current of 20 amp at 230 volts.

5-15. A certain series motor is so designed that flux densities in the iron part of the magnetic circuit are low enough to result in a linear relationship between field flux and field current throughout the normal range of operation. The rating of this motor is 50 hp, 190 amp, 220 volts, 600 rpm. Losses at full load in percentage of motor input are:

Armature copper loss (including brush loss) = 3.7 per cent
Field copper loss = 3.2 per cent
Rotational loss = 2.8 per cent

Rotational loss may be assumed constant; armature reaction and stray-load loss may be neglected.

When this motor is operating from a 220-volt supply with a current of half the rated value, what will be:

a. The speed in rpm
b. The shaft power output in horsepower

5-16. A 150-hp 600-volt 600-rpm d-c series-wound railway motor has a combined field and armature resistance (including brushes) of 0.155 ohm. The full-load current at rated voltage and speed is 206 amp. The magnetization curve at 400 rpm is as follows:

Induced volts	375	400	425	450	475
Field amp	188	216	250	290	333

Determine the internal starting torque when the starting current is limited to 350 amp. Assume armature reaction to vary as the square of the current.

5-17. Following are the nameplate data of a certain d-c motor: 230 volts, 75.7 amp, 20 hp, 900 rpm full-load, 50°C 1-hr rating, series-wound. The field winding has 33 turns per pole and a hot resistance of 0.06 ohm; the hot armature circuit resistance is 0.09 ohm (including brushes). Points on the magnetization curve at 900 rpm are as follows:

Amp-turns per pole	500	1,000	1,500	2,000	2,500	3,000
Generated voltage	95	150	188	212	229	243

To determine the fitness of this motor for driving a skip hoist, points on the motor speed-load curve are to be computed.

a. For currents equal to ⅓, ⅔, 1, and 4⁄3 of the nameplate value, compute the speed of the motor. Neglect armature reaction.

b. For the same currents, compute the shaft horsepower outputs. For this purpose, consider rotational losses to remain constant at the value determined by nameplate conditions.

c. Compute the pulley torques in pound-feet corresponding to the values in *b*. Arrange the results of parts *a*, *b*, and *c* in tabular form for convenience in checking.

d. The maximum safe speed for the motor is 250 per cent of full-load speed. What is the motor power input at this point?

e. What value of resistance connected in series with the motor will enable the production of full-load electromagnetic torque at a speed of 500 rpm?

5-18. *a.* A d-c series motor is connected to a constant-torque load which, for purposes of this problem, may be considered to require a constant electromagnetic torque regardless of the motor speed. The armature and series-field resistances are negligible, as are the effects of saturation.

By what per cent is the motor speed changed when the line voltage is decreased from 230 to 200 volts?

b. Consider that the motor in *a* is replaced by a d-c shunt motor with negligible armature circuit resistance and negligible saturation. What is the corresponding percentage speed change?

c. State briefly what effect saturation might have on the answers to *a* and *b*.

5-19. A 15-hp 230-volt 1,150-rpm shunt motor has 4 poles, an armature winding with $Z = 540$ inductors and two parallel paths, and an armature circuit resistance of 0.26 ohm. At rated speed and output, the armature and field currents are 55 and 1.5 amp, respectively. Calculate

a. The electromagnetic torque
b. The flux per pole
c. The rotational losses
d. The efficiency
e. The shaft torque

5-20. A 10-hp 230-volt shunt motor has an armature circuit resistance of 0.30 ohm and a field resistance of 170 ohms. At no load and rated voltage, the speed is 1,200 rpm, and the armature current is 2.7 amp. At full load and rated voltage, the line current is 38.4 amp, and, because of armature reaction, the flux is 4 per cent less than its no-load value.

What is the full-load speed?

5-21. A 100-hp 250-volt shunt motor has an armature circuit resistance of 0.025 ohm. Its magnetization curve is given in Fig. 5-28. When loaded until its armature current is 350 amp, its speed is 1,050 rpm. Armature reaction is negligible, and the field-rheostat setting is unchanged.

a. Calculate the speed when the armature current is 200 amp.

b. Consider that the output is 100 hp when the armature current is 325 amp. Compute the shaft torque and the electromagnetic torque.

c. Calculate the rotational losses under the conditions of *b.*

5-22. A 36-in. axial-flow disk pressure fan is rated to deliver 27,120 ft³ of air per minute against a static pressure of ½ in. of water when rotating at a speed of 1,165 rpm. This fan has the following speed-load characteristics:

Speed, rpm.	700	800	900	1,000	1,100	1,200
Input, hp.	2.9	3.9	5.2	6.7	8.6	11.1

It is proposed to drive the fan by a 10-hp 230-volt 37.5 amp 4-pole d-c shunt motor. The motor has an armature winding with two parallel paths and $Z = 666$ active inductors. Armature circuit resistance is 0.267 ohm. The armature flux per pole is $\Phi = 10^6$ lines; armature reaction is negligible. No-load rotational losses (considered constant) are estimated at 600 watts, a typical value for such a motor.

Determine the shaft horsepower output and the operating speed of the motor when it is connected to the fan load.

5-23. The machine for which data are given in Prob. 5-13 is to be used as a shunt motor.

a. Determine the field current required to make this machine run as a motor at 1,000 rpm when connected to a 550-volt d-c line and drawing an armature current of 1,000 amp.

b. What is the armature reaction in equivalent shunt-field amperes?

c. Determine the electromagnetic torque developed under the conditions in *a.*

d. Determine the speed at which this motor will operate when the load is removed if no other change is made.

5-24. A 100-hp 250-volt d-c shunt motor has the magnetization curve of Fig. 5-28 and an armature resistance (including brushes) of 0.025 ohm. There are 1,000 turns per pole on the shunt field.

When the shunt-field rheostat is set for a motor speed of 1,200 rpm at no load, the armature current is 8.0 amp. How many series-field turns per pole must be added if the speed is to be 950 rpm for a load requiring an armature current of 350 amp? Neglect armature reaction and the added resistance of the series field.

5-25. A shunt motor operating from a 230-volt line draws a full-load armature current of 38.5 amp and runs at a speed of 1,200 rpm at both no load and full load. The following data are available on this motor:

Armature circuit resistance (including brushes) = 0.21 ohm
Shunt-field turns per pole = 2,000 turns
Magnetization curve taken as a generator at no load and 1,200 rpm.

E_a, volts	180	200	220	240	250
I_f, amp	0.74	0.86	1.10	1.45	1.70

a. Determine the shunt-field current of this motor at no load and 1,200 rpm when connected to a 230-volt line. Assume negligible armature circuit resistance drop and armature reaction at no load.

b. Determine the effective armature reaction at full load in ampere-turns per pole.

c. How many series-field turns should be added to make this machine into a long-shunt cumulatively compounded motor whose speed will be 1,090 rpm when the armature current is 38.5 amp and the applied voltage is 230 volts? The series field will have a resistance of 0.052 ohm.

d. If a series-field winding having 25 turns per pole and a resistance of 0.052 ohm is installed, determine the speed when the armature current is 38.5 amp and the applied voltage is 230 volts.

5-26. A 10-hp 230-volt shunt motor has 2,000 shunt-field turns per pole, an armature resistance (including brushes) of 0.20 ohm, and a commutating-field resistance of 0.041 ohm. The shunt-field resistance (exclusive of rheostat) is 235 ohms. When operated at no load with rated terminal voltage and varying field resistance, the following data are taken:

Speed, rpm	1,110	1,130	1,160	1,200	1,240
I_f, amp	0.932	0.880	0.830	0.770	0.725

The no-load armature current is negligible. When operated at full load and rated terminal voltage, the armature current is 37.5 amp, the field current is 0.770 amp, and the speed is 1,180 rpm.

a. Calculate the full-load armature reaction in ampere-turns per pole.

b. Calculate the full-load electromagnetic torque.

c. What starting torque will the motor exert with maximum field current if the starting armature current is limited to 75 amp? The armature reaction under these conditions is 160 amp-turns per pole.

d. Design a series field to give a full-load speed of 1,100 rpm when the no-load speed is 1,200 rpm.

5-27. If the machine described in Prob. 5-9 with shunt-field circuit resistance of 210 ohms is used as a long-shunt cumulatively compounded motor supplied with power from a 230-volt line, what will be the difference in speed between no load and that load at which it draws 77.1 amp line current? Neglect the effects of armature current at no load.

5-28. When operated at rated voltage, a 230-volt shunt motor runs at 1,600 rpm at full load and also at no load. The full-load armature current is 50.0 amp. The shunt-field winding has 1,000 turns per pole. The resistance of the armature circuit (including brushes and interpoles) is 0.20 ohm. The magnetization curve at 1,600 rpm is:

E_a, volts	200	210	220	230	240	250
I_f, amp	0.80	0.88	0.97	1.10	1.22	1.43

a. Compute the demagnetizing effect of armature reaction at full load, in ampere-turns per pole.

b. A long-shunt cumulative series-field winding having 5 turns per pole and a resistance of 0.05 ohm is added to the machine. Compute the speed at full-load current and rated voltage, with the same shunt-field circuit resistance as in *a*.

c. With the series-field winding of *b* installed, compute the internal starting torque in newton-meters if the starting armature current is limited to 100 amp and the shunt-field current has its normal value. Assume that the corresponding demagnetizing effect of armature reaction is 260 amp-turns per pole.

5-29. A weak shunt-field winding is to be added to a 50-hp 230-volt 600-rpm series hoist motor for the purpose of preventing excessive speeds at very light loads. Its resistance will be 230 ohms. The combined resistance of the interpole and armature winding (including brushes) is 0.055 ohm. The series-field winding has 24 turns per pole with a total resistance of 0.021 ohm.

In order to determine its design, the following test data were obtained before the shunt field was installed:

Load Test as a Series Motor (output not measured):

$$V_t = 230 \text{ volts} \qquad I_a = 184 \text{ amp} \qquad n = 600 \text{ rpm}$$

No-load Test with Series Field Separately Excited:

Voltage applied to armature, volts	Speed, rpm	Armature current, amp	Series-field current, amp
230	1500	10.0	60
230	1200	9.2	74
230	900	8.0	103
215	700	7.7	135
215	600	7.5	175
215	550	7.2	201
215	525	7.1	225
215	500	7.0	264

a. Determine the number of shunt-field turns per pole if the no-load speed at rated voltage is to be 1,500 rpm. The armature, series-field, and interpole winding resistance drops are negligible at no load.

b. Determine the speed after installation of the shunt field when the motor is operated at rated voltage with a load which results in a line current of 185 amp. Armature reaction is unchanged by addition of the shunt field.

CHAPTER 6

D-C MACHINES: APPLICATION ASPECTS

WE NOW have available detailed methods for the analysis of the steady-state performance of d-c machines under a wide variety of possible operating conditions. Such theoretical studies naturally lead to and culminate in discussions of the fields of application of the machine and of the operating problems arising in their use. To present samples of such discussions is the primary object of this chapter. Motor speed control, motor starting, and the interconnected operation of d-c machines are three important operating problems which at the same time illustrate some of the thought processes associated with machine applications. Machine testing may also be included here because the nature of the service conditions plays a considerable part in dictating the types of tests to be conducted. One of the end results is the viewpoint that the machine plus its control equipment, rather than the machine alone, often dictates the final choice for a proposed application. And one of the strong points in favor of d-c machines is their adaptability to control.

6-1. Motor Speed Control. An abundance of evidence of the inherent versatility of d-c machines is offered by the variety of load-voltage and speed-load characteristics which may be obtained by simple combinations of shunt, series, and separate excitation. Further evidence—evidence which is of great practical importance in applications of d-c machines—is afforded by consideration of the speed-adjustment possibilities of d-c motors. In examining the various methods, chief interest is concentrated on the practical questions relating to technical and economic factors limiting the speed range, to the speed regulation or degree of constancy of speed at any given setting as the load changes, and to the limitations on motor output as speed changes.

As may have been gleaned from the preliminary broad survey of energy-conversion phenomena in Chap. 3, d-c machines are in general much more adaptable to adjustable-speed service than are the a-c machines associated with a constant-speed rotating field. Indeed, the ready susceptibility of d-c motors to adjustment of their operating speed over wide ranges and by a variety of methods is one of the important reasons for the strong competitive position of d-c machinery in modern industrial applications. From the analytical viewpoint, substitution of Eq. 5-1 in

5-7 shows the speed of a motor to be

$$n = \frac{V_{ta} - I_a r_a}{k_E \Phi} \tag{6-1}$$

Three basic methods of speed control are therefore adjustment of the flux Φ, usually by means of a shunt-field rheostat, adjustment of the resistance associated with the armature circuit, and adjustment of the armature terminal voltage V_{ta}.

Shunt-field-rheostat control is the most commonly used of the three methods and forms one of the outstanding advantages of shunt motors. The method is, of course, also applicable to compound motors. Adjustment of field current and hence of flux and speed by adjustment of the shunt-field circuit resistance is accomplished simply, inexpensively, and without much change in motor losses. The degree of speed change with load at the various rheostat settings is of the same order of magnitude as that discussed for shunt and compound motors in Art. 5-7.

The lowest speed obtainable is that corresponding to full field or zero resistance in the field rheostat; the highest speed is limited electrically by the effects of armature reaction under weak-field conditions in causing motor instability or poor commutation. Addition of a stabilizing winding (Art. 5-7 and Example 5-11) increases the speed range appreciably, and the alternative addition of a compensating winding (Art. 5-2) still further increases the range. With a compensating winding, the over-all range may be as high as 8 to 1 for a small integral-horsepower motor. Economic factors limit the feasible range for very large motors to about 2 to 1, however, with 4 to 1 often regarded as the limit for the average-sized motor.

To examine approximately the limitations on the allowable continuous motor output as the speed is changed, neglect the influence of changing ventilation and changing rotational losses on the allowable output. The maximum armature current I_a is then fixed at the nameplate value in order that the motor shall not overheat, and the counter emf E_a remains constant because the effect of a speed change is compensated by the change of flux causing it. The $E_a I_a$ product and hence the allowable motor output then remain substantially constant over the speed range. The d-c motor with shunt-field-rheostat speed control is accordingly referred to as a *constant-horsepower drive.* Torque, on the other hand (from Eq. 5-2, $T = k_T \Phi I_a$), varies directly with flux and therefore has its highest allowable value at the lowest speed. Field-rheostat control is thus best suited to drives requiring increased torque at low speeds. When a motor so controlled is used with a load requiring constant torque over the speed range, the rating and size of the machine are determined by the product of the torque and the highest speed. Such a drive is inherently oversize at the lower speeds, which is the principal economic factor limiting the practical speed range of large motors.

Armature-circuit-resistance control consists in obtaining reduced speeds by the insertion of external series resistance in the armature circuit. It may be used with series, shunt, and compound motors; for the last two types, the series resistor must be connected between the shunt field and the armature, as in Fig. 6-1, not between the line and the motor. It is the common method of speed control for series motors and is generally analogous in action to wound-rotor-induction-motor control by series rotor resistance.

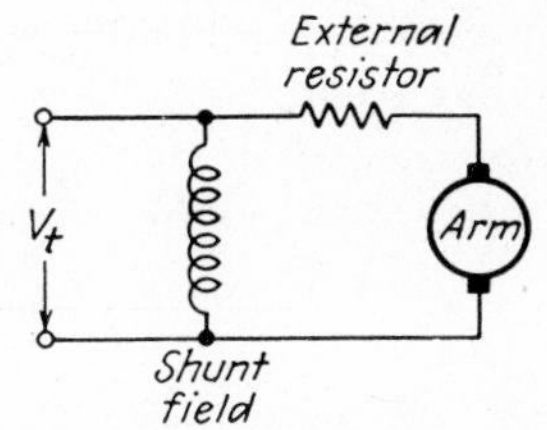

FIG. 6-1. Shunt motor with series armature resistance.

For a fixed value of series armature resistance, the speed will vary widely with load, since the speed depends on the voltage drop in this resistance and hence on the armature current demanded by the load. For example, a 1,200-rpm shunt motor whose speed under load is reduced to 750 rpm by series armature resistance will return to almost 1,200-rpm operation when the load is thrown off because the effect of the no-load current in the series resistance is insignificant. The disadvantage of poor speed regulation may not be important in a series motor, which is used only where varying speed service is required or satisfactory anyway.

Also, the power loss in the external resistor is large, especially when the speed is greatly reduced. In fact, for a constant-torque load, the power input to the motor plus resistor remains constant, while the power output to the load decreases in proportion to the speed. Operating costs are therefore comparatively high for long-time running at reduced speeds. Because of its low initial cost, however, the series-resistance method (or the variation of it discussed in the next paragraph) will often be attractive economically for short-time or intermittent slowdowns such as for accurately positioning a machine tool at the start of a cut or for matching colors in some printing machinery, to mention two examples of shunt-motor application. Unlike shunt-field control armature-resistance control offers a *constant-torque drive* because both flux and, to a first approximation, allowable armature current remain constant as speed changes.

A variation of this control scheme is given by the *shunted-armature method*,[1] which may be applied to a series motor as in Fig. 6-2*a* or a shunt motor as in Fig. 6-2*b*. In effect, resistors R_1 and R_2 act as a voltage divider applying a reduced voltage to the armature. Greater flexibility is possible because two resistors may now be adjusted to provide the desired performance. For series motors, the no-load speed may be

[1] See G. F. Leland and L. T. Rader, Industrial Control—Shunted-armature Connection for a D-c Shunt Motor, *Trans. AIEE*, vol. 63, pp. 617–619, September, 1944.

adjusted to a finite, reasonable value, and the scheme is therefore applicable to the production of slow speeds at light loads. For shunt motors, the speed regulation in the low-speed range is appreciably improved because the no-load speed is definitely lower than the value with no controlling resistors.

Armature-terminal-voltage control, also called the *Ward Leonard system*, utilizes the fact that a change in the armature terminal voltage of a shunt

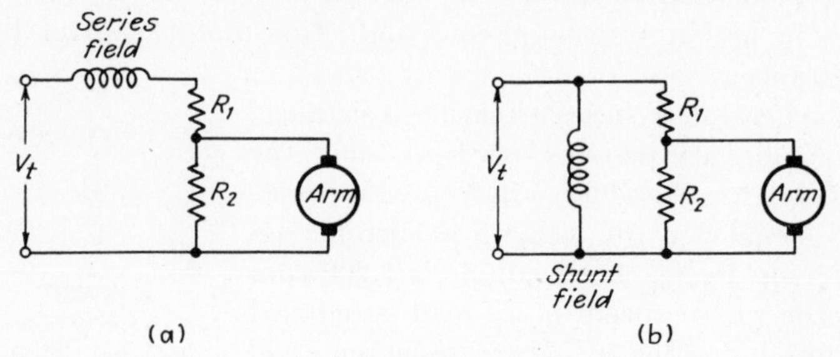

FIG. 6-2. Shunted-armature method of speed control applied to (*a*) series motor and (*b*) shunt motor.

motor is accompanied in the steady state by a substantially equal change in the counter emf and, with constant motor flux, a consequent proportional change in motor speed. The conventional scheme, shown schematically in Fig. 6-3, requires an individual motor-generator set to supply power to the armature of the motor whose speed is to be controlled. Control of the armature voltage of the main motor M is obtained by field-rheostat adjustment in the separately excited generator G, per-

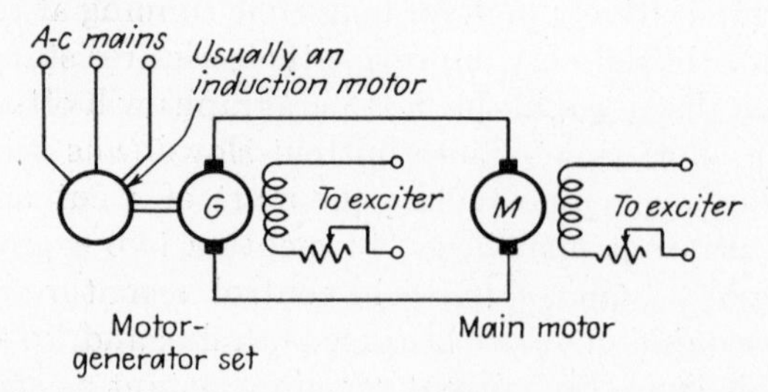

FIG. 6-3. Adjustable-armature-voltage or Ward Leonard method of speed control.

mitting close control of speed over a wide range. Usually the fields of the d-c motor and generator are supplied from a small flat-compounded exciter also mounted on the shaft of the motor-generator set, so that only an a-c power source is required. An obvious disadvantage is the initial investment in three full-size machines in contrast to that in a single motor. The speed-control equipment is located in low-power field circuits, however, rather than in the main power circuits. The smoothness and versatility of control are such that the method or one of its variants is often applied, the driving of passenger elevators being a common example.

Frequently the control of generator voltage is combined with motor-field control, as indicated by the rheostat in the field of motor M in Fig. 6-3, in order to achieve the widest possible speed range. With such dual control, *base speed* may be defined as the normal-armature-voltage full-field speed of the motor. Speeds above base speed are obtained by motor-field control; speeds below base speed are obtained by armature-voltage control. As discussed in connection with shunt-field-rheostat control, the range above base speed is that of a constant-horsepower drive. The range below base speed is that of a constant-torque drive because,

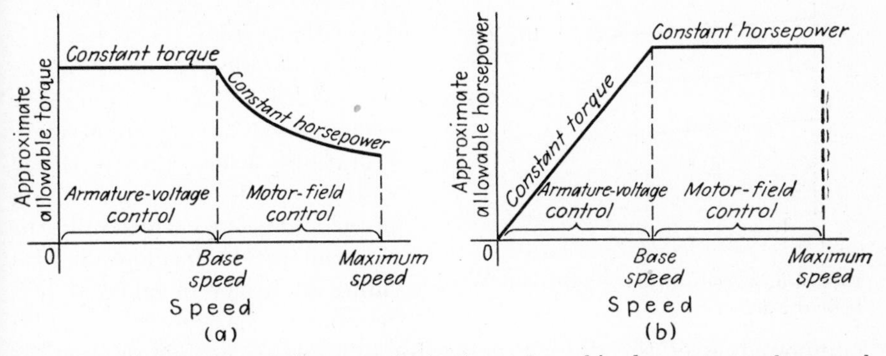

FIG. 6-4. (*a*) Torque and (*b*) power limitations of combined armature-voltage and field-rheostat methods of speed control.

as in armature-resistance control, the flux and the allowable armature current remain approximately constant. The over-all output limitations are therefore as shown in Fig. 6-4*a* for approximate allowable torque and Fig. 6-4*b* for approximate allowable horsepower. The constant-torque characteristic is well suited to many applications in the machine-tool industry, where many loads consist largely of overcoming the friction of moving parts and hence have essentially constant-torque requirements.

The speed regulation and the limitations on the speed range above base speed are those already presented with reference to shunt-field-rheostat control; the maximum speed thus does not ordinarily exceed four times base speed, and preferably not twice base speed. In the region of armature-voltage control, the principal limitation in the basic system is residual magnetism in the generator, although considerations of speed regulation may also be determining. For conventional machines, the lower limit for reliable and stable operation is about 0.1 of base speed, corresponding to a total maximum-to-minimum range not exceeding 40 to 1. With armature reaction ignored, the decrease in speed from no-load to full-load torque is caused entirely by the full-load armature resistance drop in the d-c generator and motor. This full-load armature resistance drop is constant over the voltage-control range, since full-load torque and hence full-load current are usually regarded as constant in that range. When measured in rpm, therefore, the speed decrease from no-load to full-load torque is a constant, independent of the no-load speed. The torque-speed curves (Fig. 6-5) accordingly are closely approximated by a series of parallel straight lines for the various generator-field adjustments. Now a speed decrease of, say, 40 rpm from a no-load speed of 1,200 rpm is often of little importance; a decrease of 40 rpm from a no-load speed of 120 rpm, however, may at times be of critical importance and require corrective steps in the layout of the system.

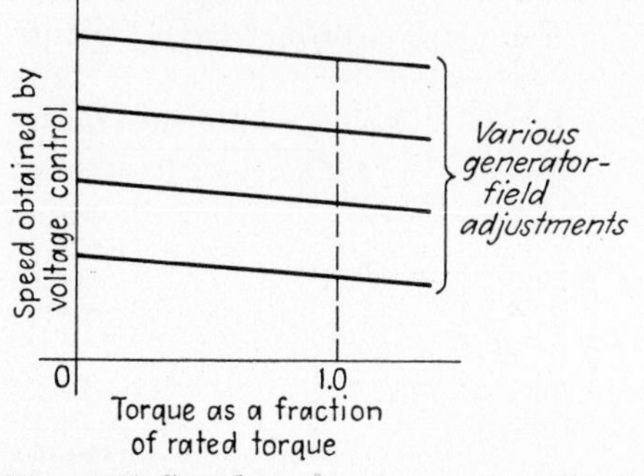

FIG. 6-5. Speed-torque curves for Ward Leonard drive.

Many detailed variations of the basic Ward Leonard system have been devised to overcome these limitations when precise speed control over a wide range is required and also to utilize fully the versatility of d-c machines in providing a variety of inherent performance characteristics. Flat compounding of the d-c generator, for example, is one simple method of improving the natural speed regulation. Control-type generators such as the Amplidyne and Rototrol, discussed in Chap. 11, may be used either as the main generator G (Fig. 6-3) in low-power systems or to supply and control the excitation for this generator in heavy-power systems. Greater flexibility is thereby provided, the residual-magnetism limitation may be alleviated, and excellent speed regulation over a range as high as 120 to 1 may be obtained.[2] For precise speed control over a wide range and under rapidly varying conditions, the control scheme must be arranged so that the actual motor speed or a quantity proportional to it is measured and compared with a standard representing the desired speed. Such a scheme becomes a *closed-cycle system,* discussed in detail in Chap. 13, where it will be found that both armature-voltage and motor-field control may play prominent parts in the electrodynamic systems. In fact, by these means it is readily possible to control not only the speed of the output member but also its instantaneous position.

When a motor armature is supplied from its own individual d-c generator, the shape of the speed-torque curve of the system may also be controlled by incorporating special features in the generator. An example is

[2] See, for instance, G. A. Caldwell and W. H. Formhals, Electrical Drives for Wide Speed Ranges, *Trans. AIEE,* vol. 61, pp. 54–56, February, 1942.

the use of a *three-field generator* to supply the armature of a shunt motor. This special-purpose generator has a separately excited winding, a shunt-connected winding, and a differentially connected series winding, a combination which permits the placing of an adjustable limit on the torque output of the system and in particular on the torque and current when the motor is stalled.[3] In other systems, the torque and current while accelerating may be limited by the appropriate controls. In effect, the degrees of freedom are such that, within rather wide limits, a tailor-made drive may be devised.

Another variation is used for speed control of d-c motors supplied from a-c sources through electronic rectifiers. Separate rectifiers are used for the armature and field circuits, and the voltage output of the armature-supply rectifier is controlled electronically, thereby controlling the motor speed. For wide speed ranges, the field-supply rectifier is controlled at the higher speeds. Thus, the equivalent of an a-c motor with wide speed control is obtained.

6-2. Motor Starting. Under starting conditions, the initial current inrush to a d-c motor is limited essentially by the armature circuit resistance only, since the counter emf does not appear until the armature is rotating. Thus, for the 100-hp motor of Example 5-10, the inrush current with full-voltage starting would be 10,000 amp (the effect of the usually small self-inductance of the armature being ignored) compared with a full-load current of 325 amp. For this reason, all except very small d-c motors are started with external resistance in series with their armatures. This resistance is cut out either manually or automatically as the motor comes up to speed.

The allowable starting current is limited by the value which the motor can commutate successfully (and at times is also limited by the capacity of the branch or feeder supplying the motor). Since torque is determined by the product of flux and armature current (Eq. 5-2), the starting torque is limited accordingly. Because in a series motor the main-field mmf increases with armature current, both the allowable value of armature current and the torque increment for a given armature current increment are relatively high. In a comparable shunt motor, on the other hand, the more pronounced armature-reaction effects at high armature currents limit the allowable current to lower values; the torque increment per unit increase in armature current is also lower because the flux does not increase with armature current but generally decreases somewhat because of armature reaction. Series motors are therefore adapted to appreciably heavier starting duties. A compound motor will, of course, be intermediate between shunt and series motors in this respect.

[3] See T. R. Rhea, The Three-field Direct-current Generator, *Gen. Elec. Rev.*, November, 1934.

To illustrate typical motor-starting procedures, circuits and equipment used in the manual and automatic starting of shunt and compound motors are presented in Figs. 6-6 to 6-13. The circuits of two *starting boxes* for manual starting are shown in Figs. 6-6 and 6-7. In both figures, the starting resistor is cut out in steps as the arm of the box is rotated to the right against the action of a spring, and the arm is held in the final running position by the hold-up magnet. In the *three-point box* (so called

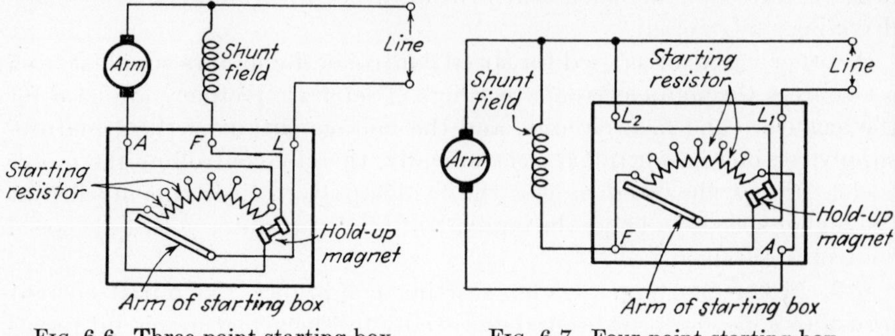

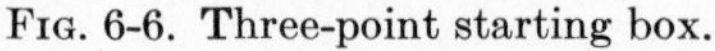

FIG. 6-6. Three-point starting box.

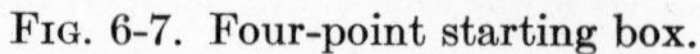

FIG. 6-7. Four-point starting box.

because it has three terminals) of Fig. 6-6, the hold-up magnet is excited by the motor field current and acts as a no-field release by allowing the arm to drop back to the *off* position if the field circuit should be opened. In the *four-point box* of Fig. 6-7, the hold-up magnet is excited by the line voltage and acts as a no-voltage release. The latter box is the one commonly used.

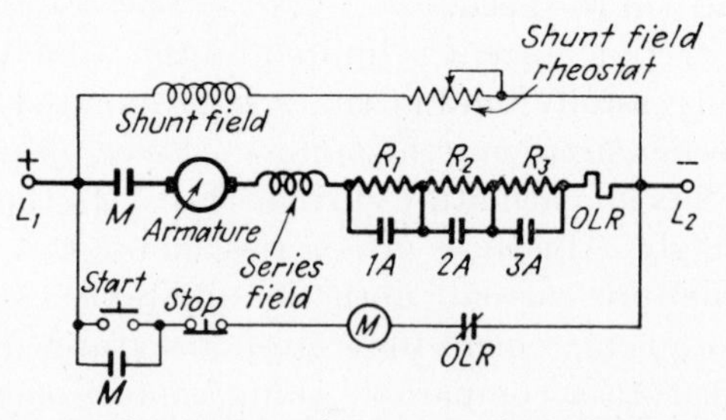

FIG. 6-8. Elements of a nonreversing magnetic controller for a d-c motor.

Figure 6-8 shows a basic circuit in which removal of the starting resistance is accomplished automatically in several steps by magnetic contactors as the motor attains speed and builds up a counter emf. Diagrammatic symbols for the contactors are summarized in Fig. 6-9 for ease of reference. The symbol of Fig. 6-9*a* denotes a normally open contact (*i.e.*, open when the operating coil of the contactor is not energized), that of Fig. 6-9*b* a normally closed contact, and that of Fig. 6-9*c* the operating coil of a contactor. The operating coils of contactors 1*A*, 2*A*, and 3*A* are not shown in Fig. 6-8.

When the *start* button is pressed, main contactor *M* closes, applying power to the motor armature through resistors R_1, R_2, and R_3 and also supplying a holding circuit for the operating coil of *M* so that only momentary push-button contact is necessary. After a lapse of time or when the inrush current has dropped to a sufficiently low value, accelerating contactors 1*A*, then 2*A*, and still later 3*A* are closed, connecting the armature directly to the line. Actually, the number of steps required in this process is a function of the desired smoothness of start and of the torque and current limits. If the motor is overloaded for too long a time, *thermal overload relay* OLR (usually consisting of a bimetallic strip heated by the armature current) opens its normally closed contacts in the main-contactor-operating-coil circuit and takes the motor off the line. Pressing the *stop* button disconnects the motor in the same manner. Either the *start* or *stop* button or both may be replaced by a float-operated switch, pressure-operated switch, limit switch, or the like.

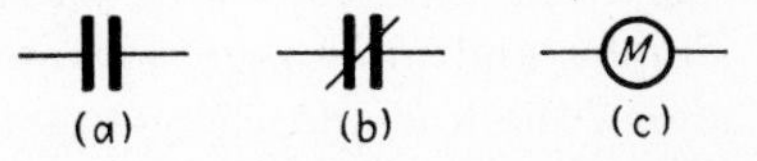

FIG. 6-9. Symbols used in controller diagrams. (*a*) Normally open contact. (*b*) Normally closed contact. (*c*) Operating coil of a contactor. Operating coil and contact it operates bear the same letter.

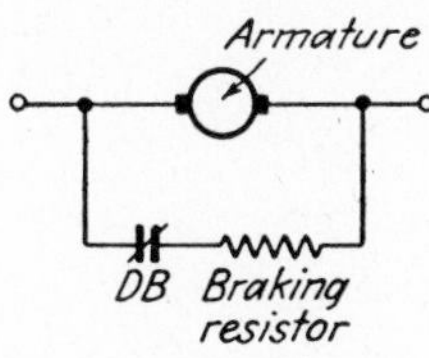

FIG. 6-10. Connection of dynamic-braking resistor and contactor.

When a quick stop is required, a resistor is connected across the armature terminals at the same time that they are disconnected from the line. *Dynamic braking* is then obtained by virtue of the machine acting as a generator dissipating the stored energy of rotation as heat in the braking resistor. The dynamic-braking contacts *DB* (Fig. 6-10) are open whenever the armature is connected to the line; otherwise, the braking resistor is always connected to the armature.

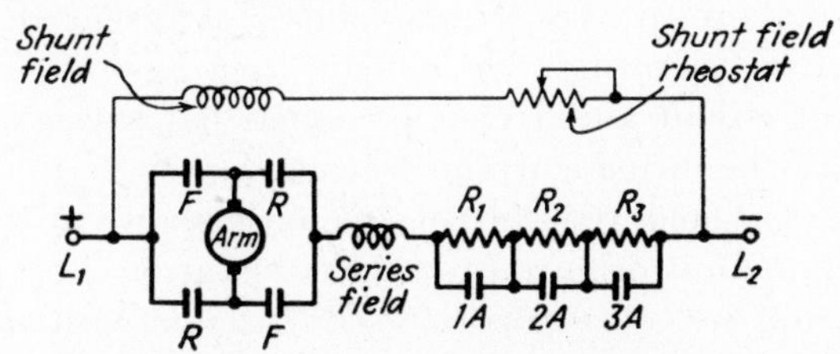

FIG. 6-11. Elements of a reversing magnetic controller for a d-c motor.

In a reversing controller, the two main contactors *F* for forward and *R* for reverse are connected as in Fig. 6-11 to change the polarity of the armature. The controls must be electrically or mechanically interlocked so that the F and R contactors cannot be closed at the same time and so that the motor cannot be prematurely energized at full-line voltage in the reverse direction.

Operation of accelerating contactors 1A, 2A, and 3A may be based on *time-limit acceleration* or *current-limit acceleration*. The former is the simpler and more common method, the operating coils being connected across the line and the contactors closing in a definitely timed sequence. Timing is obtained mechanically by means of dashpots, escapement mechanisms, or motor-driven cams, or electrically by utilizing the time

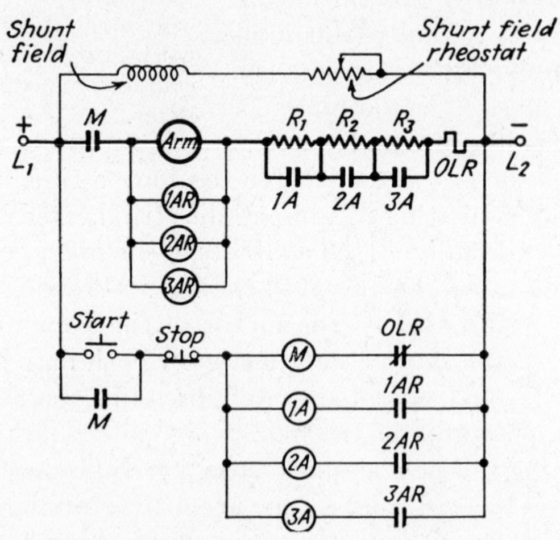

FIG. 6-12. Nonreversing magnetic controller with counter-emf acceleration.

constants of RL or RC circuits. A method of current-limit acceleration known as the counter-emf method is illustrated in Fig. 6-12. Accelerating relays 1AR, 2AR, and 3AR are voltage-sensitive relays with their operating coils connected across the motor armature; they close their contacts and cause the associated contactors to operate when the armature voltage has built up to prescribed values. Alternative schemes use current-sensitive accelerating relays with their operating coils in the armature current circuit and are so arranged that successive contactors do not close until the inrush current drops to a predetermined value. A typical push-button-operated starting panel is shown in Fig. 6-13. In some cases of time-limit or current-limit acceleration, it is advantageous for the 1A, 2A, and 3A contactors to be constructed with normally closed contacts and an extra operating coil to open them immediately after the *start* button is pressed. The contactors then reclose in sequence during motor acceleration and remain closed for normal running. One of the advantages of this scheme is that a failure in the contactor-operating-coil circuit during normal running of the motor does not interfere with continuation of that normal running.[4]

Protection against operation of the motor with no shunt-field excitation may be gained from a relay with its operating coil in series with the field and its normally open contacts in series with coil M (Fig. 6-8 or 6-12). The motor is thereby disconnected from the line unless the field is excited. An additional relay may be used to short-circuit the shunt-field rheostat during starting and dynamic braking so that the fullest starting and braking torque is obtained. Protection against undervoltage is inherently present in Figs. 6-8 and 6-12 because contactor M will drop out when the line voltage is unduly low.

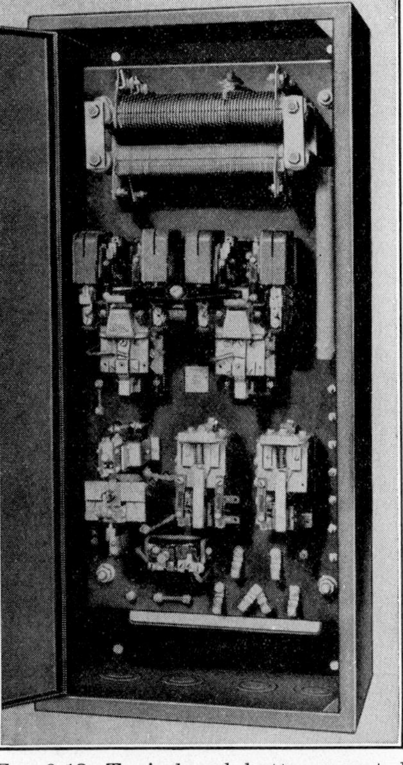

FIG. 6-13. Typical push-button-operated magnetic controller for d-c motor in lower integral-horsepower range. (*Courtesy of Westinghouse Electric Corporation.*)

Example 6-1. Attempts to generalize some of the performance characteristics of d-c machines are best carried out by expressing pertinent quantities such as voltage, current, and resistance in a nondimensional or per-unit form as a fraction of specified base values instead of in the conventional volts, amperes, and ohms. Base values are usually the rated values of the quantities concerned. To apply this method to drawing certain conclusions about shunt-motor starting, consider that base voltage equals rated line voltage, base armature current equals full-load armature current, and base resistance equals the ratio of base voltage to base current. Magnitudes expressed as fractions of these base values may then be substituted in all the usual circuit relations.

It is desired that the motor be started automatically by means of the three-step resistor $R_1R_2R_3$ of Fig. 6-8. The effects of armature reaction are to be ignored (*e.g.*, the motor is equipped with a compensating winding), and the motor is to be started with normal field flux. During starting, the armature current and hence the electromagnetic torque are not to exceed twice the rated values, and a step of the starting

[4] Thorough treatments of automatic starting methods will be found in P. B. Harwood, "Control of Electric Motors," 2d ed., John Wiley & Sons, Inc., New York, 1944, and G. W. Heumann, "Magnetic Control of Industrial Motors," John Wiley & Sons, Inc., New York, 1947.

resistor is to be cut out by an accelerating contactor whenever the armature current drops to its rated value. Armature inductance is to be considered negligibly small.

a. What is the minimum per-unit value of armature resistance which will permit these conditions to be met by a three-step starting resistor?

b. Above what per-unit value of armature resistance will a two-step resistor suffice?

c. For the armature resistance of *a*, what are the per-unit resistance values R_1, R_2, and R_3 of the starting resistor?

d. For a motor with the armature resistance of *a*, being started by the counter-emf method of Fig. 6-12, at which fractions of rated line voltage should the accelerating relays $1AR$, $2AR$, and $3AR$ pick up and close their contacts?

e. For a motor with the armature resistance of *a*, sketch approximate curves of armature current, electromagnetic torque, and speed during the starting process, and label the ordinates with the appropriate per-unit values at significant instants of time.

f. For a 10-hp 230-volt 500-rpm d-c shunt motor having a full-load armature current of 37 amp and fulfilling the conditions of *a*, list numerical values in their usual units for armature resistance, the results of *c* and *d*, and the ordinate labelings of *e*.

Solution. a. In order that the armature current not exceed 2.00 per unit at the instant main contactor M closes,

$$R_1 + R_2 + R_3 + r_a = \frac{V_t}{I_a} = \frac{1.00}{2.00} = 0.50$$

When the current has dropped to 1.00 per unit,

$$E_{a1} = V_t - I_a(R_1 + R_2 + R_3 + r_a) = 1.00 - 1.00 \times 0.50 = 0.50$$

At the instant that accelerating contactor 1A closes, short-circuiting R_1, the counter emf has attained this numerical value. Then, in order that the allowable armature current shall not be exceeded,

$$R_2 + R_3 + r_a = \frac{V_t - E_{a1}}{I_a} = \frac{1.00 - 0.50}{2.00} = 0.25$$

When the current has again dropped to 1.00 per unit,

$$E_{a2} = V_t - I_a(R_2 + R_3 + r_a) = 1.00 - 1.00 \times 0.25 = 0.75$$

Repetition of this procedure for the closing of accelerating contactors $2A$ and $3A$ yields the following results:

$$R_3 + r_a = 0.125$$
$$E_{a3} = 0.875$$
$$r_a = 0.0625$$

and

$$\text{Final } E_a \text{ at full load} = 0.938$$

The desired minimum per-unit value of r_a is therefore 0.0625, for a lower value will allow the armature current to exceed twice the rated value when contactor $3A$ is closed.

b. If a two-step resistor is to suffice, R_3 must be zero. Since, from *a*,

$$R_3 + r_a = 0.125$$

it follows that a three-step resistor is not required when r_a is equal to or greater than 0.125.

Under the specified starting conditions, a three-step resistor is appropriate for motors whose armature circuit resistances are between 0.0625 and 0.125 per unit. For general-purpose continuously rated shunt motors, these values correspond to the lower integral-horsepower sizes. On the average, motor sizes up to about 10 hp will conform to these requirements, although the size limit will be lower for high-speed motors and higher for slow-speed motors. For larger motors, either additional steps must be provided or the limit on current and torque peaks must be relaxed. The results of this analysis are conservative because the armature resistance under transient conditions is higher than the static value.

c. From the relations in part *a*, the per-unit starting resistances are

$$R_3 = 0.125 - 0.0625 = 0.0625$$
$$R_2 = 0.25 - 0.0625 - 0.0625 = 0.125$$

and

$$R_1 = 0.50 - 0.0625 - 0.0625 - 0.125 = 0.25$$

d. Just before contactor 1*A* closes,

$$V_{ta1} = E_{a1} + I_a r_a = 0.50 + 1.00 \times 0.0625 = 0.563$$

In like manner,

$$V_{ta2} = 0.75 + 1.00 \times 0.0625 = 0.813$$

and

$$V_{ta3} = 0.875 + 1.00 \times 0.0625 = 0.938$$

Accelerating relays 1*AR*, 2*AR*, and 3*AR*, respectively, should pick up at these fractions of rated line voltage.

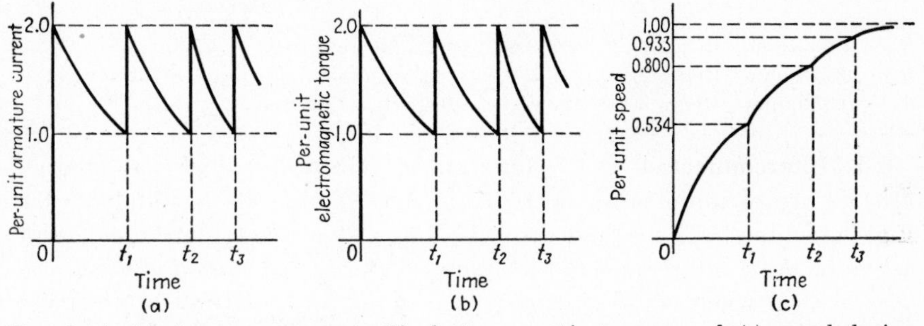

FIG. 6-14. (*a*) Armature current, (*b*) electromagnetic torque, and (*c*) speed during starting of a d-c motor, Example 6-1.

e. Consider that main contactor *M* closes at $t = 0$ and that accelerating contactors 1*A*, 2*A*, and 3*A* close respectively at times t_1, t_2, and t_3. These values of time are not known (when armature and load inertias and torque-speed curve of the load are given, values of time can be computed by the methods of Chap. 13), so that only the general shapes of the current, electromagnetic torque, and speed curves can be given. They are indicated in Fig. 6-14.

The labeling of the speed curve follows from the fact that a counter emf $E_a = 0.938$ corresponds to rated speed at rated load and hence to unity speed. Other speeds are in proportion to E_a; thus, at t_1, t_2, and t_3 respectively,

$$n_1 = \frac{0.50}{0.938} \times 1.00 = 0.534$$

$$n_2 = \frac{0.75}{0.938} \times 1.00 = 0.800$$

and

$$n_3 = \frac{0.875}{0.938} \times 1.00 = 0.933$$

f. Base quantities for this motor are as follows:
Base voltage = 230 volts
Base armature current = 37 amp
Base armature circuit resistance = $^{230}/_{37}$ = 6.22 ohms
Base speed = 500 rpm

$$\text{Base electromagnetic torque} = \frac{60}{2\pi n} E_a I_a$$
$$= \frac{60}{2\pi \times 500} (230 - 37 \times 0.0625 \times 6.22) \times 37$$
$$= 152 \text{ newton-m.}$$

Note that rated electromagnetic torque will be greater than rated shaft torque because of rotational and stray load lossses.

The motor armature resistance is

$$r_a = 0.0625 \times 6.22 = 0.389 \text{ ohm}$$

Values for the other quantities desired are listed in Table 6-1.

TABLE 6-1
ABSOLUTE VALUES FOR EXAMPLE 6-1*f*

Part *c*	Part *d*	Part *e*, scales of Fig. 6-14
R_1 = 1.56 ohms	Relay 1*AR*: 129 volts	1.0 armature current = 37 amp
R_2 = 0.778 ohm	Relay 2*AR*: 187 volts	1.0 electromagnetic torque = 152 newton-m
R_3 = 0.389 ohm	Relay 3*AR*: 216 volts	1.0 speed = 500 rpm

6-3. Interconnected D-C Generators. Generator external characteristics are of importance not only in determining the suitability of a single machine for its intended service but also in studying the behavior of two or more interconnected machines. *Parallel operation of d-c generators* is used when considerations of economy and continuity of service in spite of machine outages militate against relatively large single power sources, and when, at the same time, there are no determining advantages in control of system performance by allocating portions of the load to individual generators without interconnecting them electrically. Parallel operation is not nearly so common for d-c generators as for alternators because, as already pointed out, most bulk conversion from mechanical to electrical energy is performed by alternators, and much of bulk conversion from alternating to direct current is handled by rectifiers or by the obsolescent synchronous converter. One interesting example of the paralleling of d-c generators is found in the electrical system of large multiengine aircraft using d-c supply.[5]

[5] See, for instance, W. K. Boice and L. G. Levoy, Basic Considerations in Selection of Electrical Systems for Large Aircraft, *Trans. AIEE*, vol. 63, pp. 279–287, June, 1944.

The two principal problems in interconnecting d-c generators relate to the division of load between the machines and to the stability of this load division. Consider, for example, the two paralleled shunt generators of Fig. 6-15. Evidently,

$$I_{a1} = \frac{E_{a1} - V_t}{r_{a1}} \tag{6-2}$$

and

$$I_{a2} = \frac{E_{a2} - V_t}{r_{a2}} \tag{6-3}$$

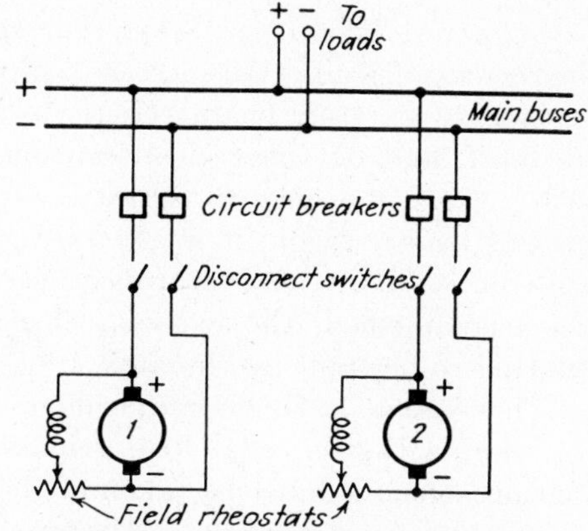

FIG. 6-15. Paralleled shunt generators.

the terminal voltage V_t being the same for each machine. If the system operator wishes to shift load from generator 2 to generator 1, he need only increase E_{a1} and decrease E_{a2} accordingly by means of the two field rheostats. The shift may be accompanied by prime-mover speed changes, but that is immaterial so long as the proper values of E_{a1} and E_{a2} are obtained. If he so desires, the operator can remove all the load from one machine in this manner and can even cause

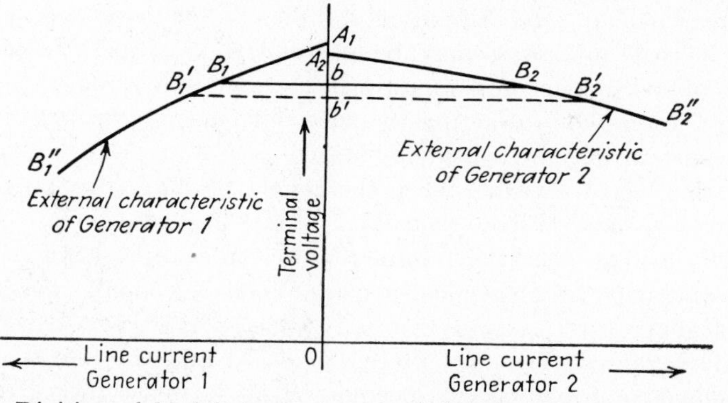

FIG. 6-16. Division of load between two paralleled d-c generators with drooping external characteristics.

it to act as a motor producing a torque in conjunction with the prime-mover torque.

For constant field-rheostat position and constant speed, the division of load is determined by the external characteristics of the machines. The external characteristics of two shunt or separately excited (without series fields) generators are given in Fig. 6-16. When the two are in parallel and supplying a total load current equal to B_1B_2 amp, the terminal voltage is Ob, generator 1 supplies bB_1 amp, and generator 2 supplies bB_2 amp. If the load current increases to $B'_1B'_2$, the terminal voltage becomes Ob' and the generators furnish $b'B'_1$ and $b'B'_2$ amp, respectively. In so far as inherent load division is concerned, then, the machine with the greatest droop in its external characteristic takes on the smallest increment of load. An increase in speed or a decrease in field resistance causes the external characteristic to be shifted upward, roughly parallel to itself, and by these means an operator controls the load division at will. Since the operator is often not in constant attendance to assure proper load division, it is generally desirable that paralleled generators inherently divide load in proportion to their ratings. For this action to be accomplished, the external characteristics must be identical when plotted to per-unit coordinates.

The second problem requiring examination is the stability of load division with the total load remaining constant. In such an examination, account must be taken of the spontaneous reaction of the prime movers to load changes. All prime movers in practical use show a decrease in speed with increasing load, even though this decrease be only temporary and be ultimately compensated by the action of a governor or other regulating mechanism. This statement holds true even for a synchronous motor, for the instantaneous speed must decrease temporarily to allow the torque angle to assume the larger value required by the increased load. In examining stability of load division, a small or virtual increase of speed may be postulated as a disturbance; if the increase of speed is accompanied by an increase in load on the associated generator, forces counteracting the speed increase are brought into play, and the system may be considered stable.

That this test is satisfied when the generators have drooping external characteristics may be seen from Fig. 6-17. The solid lines A_1B_1, A_2B_2, and B_1B_2 are the external characteristics and total load current for normal operation at a specified constant load. A small increase in the speed of generator 1, arising from any cause whatever, will result in its external characteristic being altered to $A'_1B'_1$, and the line representing the specified total load current becomes $B'_1B'_2$. Since $b'B'_1$ is greater than bB_1, the load on generator 1 is increased, creating a compensating tendency to decrease its prime-mover speed and restore the initial equilibrium conditions. The system may then be considered stable.

On the other hand, the test is not satisfied when the external characteristics are rising curves, as with overcompounded generators. In Fig. 6-18, A_1B_1, A_2B_2, and B_1B_2 are again the external characteristics and specified constant load current for parallel operation. When a small increase in the speed of generator 1 shifts its external characteristic to $A'_1B'_1$, the generator load drops from bB_1 to $b'B'_1$. The reaction of the prime mover to this load decrease is to increase the speed further, causing a still greater load decrease. The process becomes cumulative and is made all the worse by the decrease in speed of generator 2 because of its increased load. The result is that generator 2 not only takes all the load

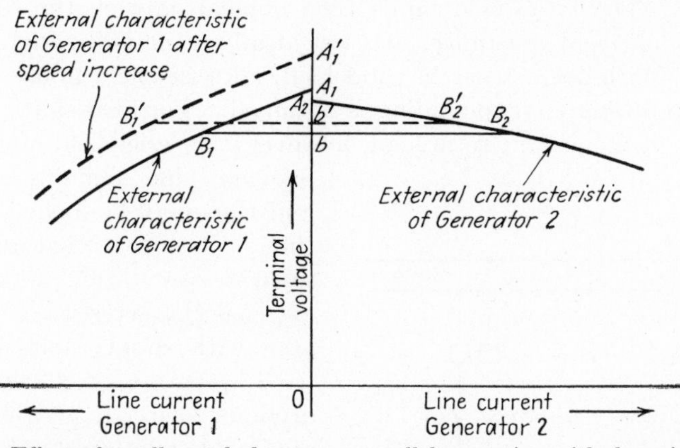

FIG. 6-17. Effect of small speed change on parallel operation with drooping external characteristics.

but also drives generator 1 as a motor; practically, of course, the machines are taken off the line by the associated circuit breakers. The system is therefore unstable.

Nevertheless, it is often highly desirable that paralleled d-c generators be overcompounded in order to compensate for increased feeder drop with

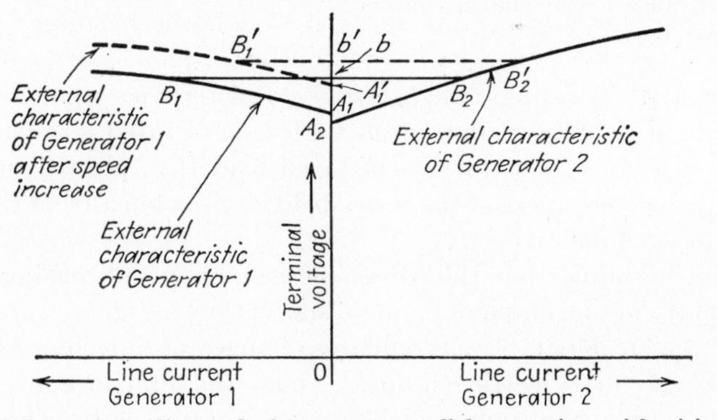

FIG. 6-18. Effect of small speed change on parallel operation with rising external characteristics.

increased load. The problem then is for the machines as a group to have a rising voltage characteristic for increases in total system load but drooping individual characteristics for shifts in load from one machine to another at a constant system load. This action may be obtained by the use of an *equalizer bus* (Fig. 6-19) which places the series fields in parallel; note that in this diagram one end of each series field is connected to the negative main bus, and the other end is connected to the equalizer bus. Physically, the equalizer bus is simply a low-resistance conductor. The series-field mmfs then depend only on the total load and individual field resistances and not at all on the individual machine loadings. With an increase in total load, all series-field mmfs increase, and the appropriate compounding is obtained. For load shifts between generators at a constant total load, however, the series-field mmf of any one machine remains constant and thus may be looked upon as though it were a fixed amount of separate excitation. Now, the external characteristic of a generator with shunt excitation plus fixed separate excitation is a drooping one. Repetition of the argument relating to Fig. 6-17 therefore shows that paralleled overcompounded generators are stable when an equalizer is used. Load can be shifted by an operator from one generator to another in Fig. 6-19 in the same manner as for the shunt generators of Fig. 6-15. If the machines are inherently to share load increments in proportion to their ratings, the external characteristics must be identical when terminal voltage is plotted as a fraction of rated terminal voltage and load is plotted as a fraction of rated load (*i.e.*, plotted in per-unit form); and the resistances of the series-field circuits must be in the inverse ratio of the machine ratings.

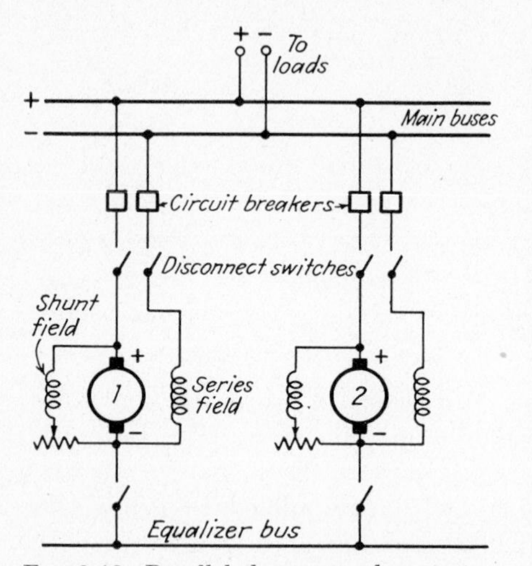

FIG. 6-19. Paralleled compound generators with equalizer bus.

It should be noted that the foregoing arguments concerning stability and instability are incomplete in one respect: they all ignore the electrical transients which inevitably accompany changes of current or load in a machine or in any electric circuit. Thus, the influence of armature inductance under conditions of changing armature current is ignored. While armature inductance is normally small, nevertheless a complete and rigorous stability argument should take all pertinent factors into account. Such a complete discussion, involving, as it does, machine transients, is beyond the scope of the text at this point. The conclusions regarding stability and instability which we have reached are definitely substantiated both by more complete examinations and by experiment.

When a system of parallel generators becomes unstable, however, the generator or generators which assume all of the electrical load are determined not only by the slope of the prime-mover characteristics but also by the relative values of armature circuit inductance.

Similar problems may arise when paralleled shunt or compound generators are equipped with automatic voltage regulators. In such cases, special attention must be given to the voltage regulators to ensure stability and proper load division among the machines. An interesting example, already mentioned at the beginning of this article, is offered by the paralleled d-c generators supplying the electrical system of some types of aircraft.[6]

A method of interconnected operation which is of value in machine testing arises when one of the two paralleled power sources is formed by the d-c power mains. The load on the generator connected to the mains, and hence on its prime mover, may be readily adjusted by means of the generator field rheostat. A convenient and economical method is thus available for loading and testing either the generator or its prime mover. When the prime mover is a d-c motor also connected to the mains, the method is referred to by the terms *loading back, pump-back,* or *electrical supply of losses;* the mains need only supply the losses in the two machines, and the efficiencies may be readily determined when the losses are properly allocated.[7]

Example 6-2. Two compound generators of equal rating are to be connected as in Fig. 6-19 for parallel operation, and it is desired that they share load equally over a wide load range. It is found, however, that one generator takes an unduly large portion of load increments. When the machines are tested separately, it is found that their series-field resistances are each 0.01 ohm, that generator 1 is flat-compounded, and that generator 2 is decidedly overcompounded. The latter generator can be flat-compounded by diverting half of its armature current from its series field; its external characteristic is then practically identical with that of the other machine.

Can equal load division be achieved by shunting the series field of the overcompounded generator by a 0.01-ohm resistor? If not, what steps should be taken to ensure successful parallel operation?

Solution. One must recognize that, because of the equalizer bus, the 0.01-ohm resistor will shunt both series fields, as shown by Fig. 6-20*a*. If the line current is 200 amp, for example, each of the three branches carries 67 amp. But for the two machines to share this load equally, the series field of generator 1 should carry 100 amp, and that of generator 2 should carry 50 amp. Hence, the inherent load division will still not be correct.

As indicated in Fig. 6-20*b*, proper load division can be obtained by using a 0.02-ohm

[6] See A. Siegal and D. G. DeCourcey, Paralleling and Regulation of 24-28-volt D-c Generators in Multiengine Aircraft, *Trans. AIEE*, vol. 63, pp. 854–857, November, 1944.

[7] Detailed testing techniques using these methods may be found in C. W. Ricker and C. E. Tucker, "Electrical Engineering Laboratory Experiments," 4th ed., McGraw-Hill Book Company, Inc., New York, 1940.

shunt and connecting a 0.01-ohm resistor in the series field of generator 2. The desired current division between the two fields is then obtained.

6-4. Testing of D-C Machines. Both the development of the theoretical principles of d-c-machine analysis in previous chapters and their use in considering important application problems in this chapter are based on the availability of certain machine constants and characteristics. These constants and characteristics in turn are usually the results of tests made on either the machine concerned or on a generally similar machine. Even when they are computed from design data and dimensions, a great deal of machine testing and experience lies in the background to form complete substantiation of the computational approach. In addition to

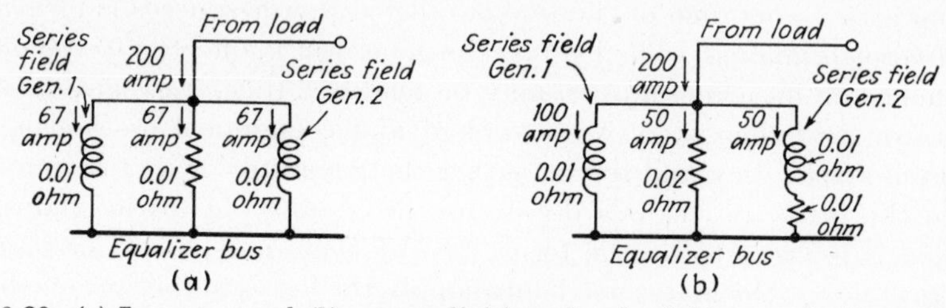

FIG. 6-20. (*a*) Improper and (*b*) proper division of series-field currents, Example 6-2.

tests leading to these constants and characteristics, the machine-applications engineer and the machine operator are interested in tests indicating that a certain minimum standard of quality has been observed in the design and construction of the machine.

Like those for the majority of electrical devices, the tests commonly made on d-c machines may be divided into three broad classes:

1. Tests whose primary purpose is to ensure the quality of the materials and construction details
2. Tests whose primary purpose is the determination of efficiency and losses
3. Tests whose primary purpose is the determination of performance under specified operating conditions or the determination of data from which the performance may be computed

Some overlapping among these categories is, of course, inevitable. The common tests of d-c machines will be outlined briefly under these three headings. Emphasis is placed on stating the nature of the tests rather than on giving detailed test procedures.[8] Where tests and procedures have been standardized, the statements made conform to the

[8] Detailed test procedures are given in the test manuals of the several manufacturers, such as General Electric Company and Westinghouse Electric Corporation, and in various laboratory textbooks. See, for instance, footnote 7.

standards, but no attempt is made to present complete statements of the standard requirements.[9]

Tests to ensure quality include items such as measurement of insulation resistance, high-potential tests, checking for proper brush setting, judging the quality of commutation, and determining that the field coils are wound and connected for the correct relative polarity and with all field coils containing the same number of turns of the same size wire with no turns short-circuited. An unduly low value of insulation resistance may indicate defects in the insulation or the need for cleaning and drying the windings. High-potential or dielectric tests determine the ability of the insulation to withstand high voltages between each pair of electric circuits in the machine and between these circuits and grounded metal parts of the machine. The standard test voltage is an alternating voltage whose rms value is 1,000 volts plus twice the rated voltage of the machine. In addition to the other tests listed, studies may be made to determine whether or not the machine is sufficiently quiet in operation.[10]

Tests relating to efficiency and losses may take the form of actual load runs on the machine, with both the input and output carefully measured; or they may take the form of measuring the separate losses. Load runs have the advantage of reproducing or closely approximating actual service conditions; they have the disadvantage that an error in measurement of input or output shows up as the same order of magnitude of error in the efficiency. Load runs on very large machines may also be very difficult and expensive to perform. (The pump-back method, mentioned in Art. 6-3, or one of its variants, often offers an expedient procedure.) Direct measurement of the individual losses (listed in Art. 4-11 and included in the diagrams of Fig. 5-23 and 5-24) avoids both of these disadvantages.

The I^2R losses of the various windings are computed from d-c measurements of the winding resistances, either by the drop-in-potential method or by bridge methods. The armature resistance should be that of the winding only, since separate allowance of 2.0 volts is made for the brush and brush-contact drop (see Art. 4-11). The temperature of the windings at the time of measurement must be noted and the measured resistances converted to the corresponding values at the standard temperature of 75°C. Values of current to be used in computing the respective I^2R

[9] The following three references present the standards and test procedures applicable to d-c machines: ASA Standards, Rotating Electrical Machinery, C50-1943, American Standards Association, New York, 1943; Test Code for Direct-current Machines, AIEE No. 501, American Institute of Electrical Engineers, New York, July, 1941; NEMA Standards for Motors and Generators, *Pub.* MG1, National Electrical Manufacturers Association, New York, 1949.

[10] Details of noise tests may be found in Test Code for Apparatus Noise Measurement, AIEE No. 520, American Institute of Electrical Engineers, New York, March, 1939.

losses should be those existing in the respective windings under the operating conditions for which the efficiency is to be determined.

Except for stray load loss, the remaining losses are determined by measuring the input required to drive the machine when it is operating without load but under specified conditions otherwise. The input may be determined by measuring the electrical input to the armature with the machine operating as an unloaded motor or the mechanical input to the shaft with the machine operating as an unloaded, separately excited generator. The no-load rotational losses are given by the input with the machine operating at normal speed and excited to produce a voltage at its terminals corresponding to the calculated internal voltage E_a under the pertinent load condition; the proper internal voltage is computed by correcting the rated terminal voltage for brush-contact drop and the armature-circuit resistance drop (including the drop in any commutating-, compensating-, and series-field windings) at the appropriate armature current. The friction and windage loss, including brush-friction loss, is the input at normal speed with the machine unexcited. The core loss is the difference between these two inputs.

As indicated in Art. 4-11, stray load loss is a difficult one to determine accurately. It is therefore normally not measured for d-c machines but, instead, assumed by convention to be 1.0 per cent of the output power. When measurements are made, the usual approach is to conduct a careful input-output test to determine total losses. Copper losses are computed from resistance measurements, and no-load rotational losses found as described above. The difference between the total losses and the sum of the copper losses, brush-contact loss, and no-load rotational losses is taken as the stray load loss. Any such approach, based on taking differences between two almost equal quantities, is inherently an inaccurate one. The results of one series of tests based on this method, however, indicates that the 1.0 per cent conventional allowance for stray load loss may be too low.[11] Based on tests conducted on motors ranging from ½ to 50 hp, these results indicate an over-all average of 3 per cent, with an average of 2 per cent obtaining at full-load output.

Tests to determine performance under specified operating conditions may be of two types: tests in which the operating conditions are directly reproduced, and tests yielding basic data for performance computations. The input-output method of measuring efficiency may again be classed in the first type of these tests. At the same time that the machine is loaded, data may be taken for the external characteristic if the machine is a generator or the speed-load curve if it is a motor. Another common

[11] For details on these tests, see AIEE Subcommittee on D-c Machines of the AIEE Rotating Machinery Committee, Stray Load Losses Measured in D-c Motors, *Trans. AIEE*, vol. 68, pp. 219–223, 1949.

test involving loading of the machine is a heat run. The object is to determine whether temperature-rise specifications, such as those outlined in Art. 4-12, are fulfilled. The method is to load the machine to the prescribed conditions and to measure the final temperature rises of the various windings and machine parts by thermometer, thermocouple, or resistance measurements. For a short-time-rated machine, the heat run is taken over the period prescribed in the rating; for a machine with a continuous rating, the heat run is continued until no further temperature rise is discernible. The pump-back loading methods previously mentioned are frequently used for load tests on d-c machines.

The general nature of tests yielding basic data for performance computations follows from the previous theoretical considerations, especially those of Chap. 5. Resistance measurements of the various windings must be classified again in this category. Data on losses must also be at hand for realistic analyses. Magnetic-saturation data are given by the magnetization curve, usually taken with the machine separately driven and with the field current supplied from a separate source. Only the shunt-field winding of a compound machine is excited. The standard procedure is to take simultaneous readings of field current and armature voltage with rising field current up to a maximum voltage which is usually 125 per cent of the rated value. The field current is never carried beyond the desired point and then decreased lest small hysteresis loops distort the curve. Three of the readings are taken as near as possible to 90 per cent, 100 per cent, and 110 per cent of normal voltage. After the maximum voltage is reached, another set of readings are taken with falling field current. When a separate drive is not available for the machine, the magnetization curve may be taken with it operating as an unloaded motor. The standard procedure requires connection to a power source whose voltage can be varied from 25 to 125 per cent of the rated voltage of the machine. Simultaneous readings are then taken of field current and impressed armature voltage with the machine operating at rated speed at each point.

Resistance data, loss data, and magnetic-saturation data are all the experimental results required for performance studies when armature-reaction mmf is ignored. When it is to be taken into account, excitation data for at least one load point must be determined. Only one point is required when the linearity assumption of Eq. 5-15 is adopted. Although it is naturally desirable that this point provide data which are as representative as possible, nevertheless expediency of testing can control selection of the point to a certain extent. More comprehensive inclusion of armature-reaction mmf requires the equivalent of the armature characteristic of Fig. 5-29 at normal voltage or a family of these curves for different voltages.

The general nature of the test data required for performance computations on d-c machines has much in common with that for other electrical devices. For simplicity and economy of testing, it is obviously desirable that as many basic data as possible be determined without actually loading the machine. Resistance measurements, loss measurements, and saturation measurements all conform to this desire. Machine theory and analysis then fills the gap between the measurements under no load and the actual performance under load. When some effects, such as armature-reaction mmf, require the presence of load for their measurement, the theory of the machine should be so formulated, if possible, that the simplest and most expedient load tests give the required data. Thus, the nature of the tests which can be conducted readily, economically, and accurately has a definite influence on the formulation of machine theory: a theory developed in terms of readily measurable constants and characteristics is of much greater value than one in terms of quantities difficult to measure. Moreover, the final proof of any theory usually lies in comparison of computed and experimental results. Although it expresses a needlessly restricted viewpoint, it can be said that one very important object of machine theory is to permit the results of a few, relatively simple, standardized tests to be used in predicting performance under a wide variety of possible operating conditions. Even when a large number of data from load tests are necessary, as in the extreme case of furnishing a family of armature characteristics for different operating voltages, the tester is at least relieved from reproducing every conceivable operating condition which the analyst or applications engineer may devise.

6-5. Résumé. D-C-machine Applications. Discussion of d-c-machine applications involves recapitulation of the high lights of the machine's performance features, together with economic and technical evaluation of the machine's position with respect to competing energy-conversion devices. For d-c machines in general, the outstanding advantage lies in their flexibility and versatility—controllability is another way of saying it. The principal disadvantage is apt to lie in the initial investment concerned. The Ward Leonard system and its variants, for example, obviously provide both a versatile and an expensive drive. A d-c-motor installation must usually be penalized by at least the incremental cost of a-c to d-c conversion. Yet the advantages of d-c motors are such that their yearly horsepower sales in the integral-horsepower sizes are roughly of the same order of magnitude as for competing a-c motors.

Direct-current generators are the obvious answer to the problem of converting mechanical energy to electrical energy in d-c form. When the consumer of electrical energy is geographically removed from the site of energy conversion by any appreciable distance, however, the advantages of a-c generation, voltage transformation, and transmission are such that energy conversion and transmission in a-c form are almost always adopted with a-c to d-c transformation taking place at or near the consumer. Direct-current electric railways and electrochemical plants are good examples of d-c consumers following this general pattern. For a-c to d-c transformation, the d-c generator as part of an a-c to d-c motor-generator set must compete with mercury-arc rectifiers and ignitrons. When large-power rectification from a-c to constant-voltage d-c form is involved, the electronic methods usually possess determining economic advantages. Thus, both modern d-c electric railway systems and modern electrochemical plants use electronic rectification at points very near the ultimate energy-consuming device. The principal applications of d-c generators, therefore, are to cases where ability freely to control the output voltage in a prescribed manner is necessary or where the primary energy conversion occurs very near the point of consumption. The generators of the Ward Leonard system and those used for the excitation of alternators are examples of the former cases. Applications to gas-electric busses, diesel-electric locomotives, and d-c electric ship propulsion are examples of the latter type; and in these three examples it is the unique adaptability of the d-c motor which dictates the form of energy conversion. Aircraft electric power systems present a special set of problems all their own in the choice of energy-conversion methods.[12]

Among d-c generators themselves, separately excited and cumulatively compounded, self-excited machines are the most common. Separately excited generators (often with small shunt or flat-compounded generators as exciters) have the advantage of permitting a wide range of output voltages, whereas self-excited machines may produce unstable voltages in the lower ranges where the field-resistance line becomes essentially tangent to the magnetization curve. Cumulatively compounded generators may produce a substantially flat voltage characteristic or one which rises with load, whereas shunt or separately excited generators (assuming no series field in the latter, which, of course, is not at all a practical restriction) produce a drooping voltage characteristic unless external regulating means are added. So far as the control potentialities of d-c generators are concerned, the control-type generators (Amplidynes, Rototrols, and similar machines) discussed in Chap. 11 represent the results of a fuller exploration of the inherent possibilities.

Among d-c motors, the outstanding characteristics of each type are as follows: The series motor operates with a decidedly drooping speed as load is added, the no-load speed usually being prohibitively high; the torque is proportional to almost the square of the current at low saturations and to some power between 1 and 2 as saturation increases. The shunt motor at constant field current operates at a slightly drooping but

[12] See footnote 5.

almost constant speed as load is added, the torque being almost proportional to armature current; equally important, however, is the fact that its speed may be controlled over wide ranges by shunt-field control or armature-voltage control or a combination of both. Depending on the relative strengths of shunt and series field, the cumulatively compounded motor is intermediate between the other two and may be given essentially the advantages of one or the other.

By virtue of its ability to handle heavy torque overloads while at the same time cushioning the associated power overload with a speed drop, and by virtue of its ability to withstand severe starting duties, the series motor is best adapted to hoist, crane, and traction-type loads. Its ability is almost unrivaled in this respect. Speed changes are usually achieved by armature-resistance control. In some instances, the wound-rotor induction motor with rotor-resistance control competes with the series motor, but the principal argument concerns the availability and economics of a d-c power supply rather than one of inherent motor characteristics. The a-c series motor, with almost the same characteristics but with a much more severe commutation problem, also competes in some traction applications; again the argument is one of power-supply economics.

Compound motors with a heavy series field have performance features approaching those of series motors except that the shunt field limits the no-load speed to safe values; the general remarks for series motors therefore apply. Compound motors with lighter series windings not infrequently find competition from squirrel-cage induction motors with high-resistance rotors—so-called *high-slip* motors (referred to in Chap. 9 as Class D induction motors). Both motors provide a definitely drooping speed-load characteristic such as is desirable, for example, when flywheels are used as load equalizers to smooth out intermittent load peaks. The compound motor provides the drop in speed with load by virtue of the associated increase in excitation and without any significant increase in losses. The high-slip induction motor, on the other hand, provides the speed drop at the expense of a significant increase in resistance losses. Complete economic comparison of the two competing types must reflect both the usually higher initial cost of a compound-motor installation and the usually higher cost of losses in the high-slip induction motor. Evidently a comparison of this nature can be made only for a definitely specified duty cycle, and other service conditions must be included in the final decision.

Because of the comparative simplicity, cheapness, and ruggedness of the squirrel-cage induction motor, the shunt motor is not in a favorable competitive position for constant-speed service except at low speeds, where it becomes difficult and expensive to build high-performance induction motors with the requisite number of poles. The comparison at these low speeds is often apt to be between synchronous and d-c motors. The outstanding feature of the shunt motor is its adaptability to adjustable-speed service by means of armature-resistance control for speeds below the full-field speed, field-rheostat control for speeds above the full-field speed, and armature-voltage or Ward Leonard control for speeds below (and, at times, somewhat above) the normal-voltage full-field speed. Armature-resistance control achieves low speeds at the expense of greatly increased losses and with the concomitant poor speed regulation under changing loads. Such a method finds economic justification especially for duty cycles involving occasional short-time slowdowns. Shunt-field control, involving no significant increase in losses and no heavy-power control equipment, is the least elaborate and most elegant of all motor speed-control methods. The combination of armature-voltage control and shunt-field control, together with the possibility of additional field windings in either the motor or the associated generator to provide desirable inherent characteristics, gives the d-c drives an enviable degree of flexibility. For heavy-power applications, the rotor-voltage-control methods for wound-rotor induction motors, discussed in Chap. 9, compete with d-c drives.[13] The control-type d-c generators of Chap. 11 definitely reinforce the competitive position of d-c machines where complete control of operation is important.

It should be emphasized that the choice of equipment for a significant engineering application to adjustable-speed drives is rarely a cut-and-dried matter or one to be decided from a mere verbal list of advantages and disadvantages. In general, specific, quantitative, economic, and technical comparison of all possibilities should be undertaken. Consideration must often be given to the transient-response aspects of Chap. 12 and the dynamic-response details of Chap. 13. Local conditions and the characteristics of the driven equipment (*e.g.*, constant-horsepower, constant-torque, and variable-horsepower variable-torque requirements) invariably play an important role. One may, for example, compare all possible methods for a particular large-horsepower adjustable-speed drive, even including the nonelectrical possibility of an adjustable-speed steam turbine. And the final answer may be a synchronous motor! The determining advantage in such an instance may be the power-factor-correcting ability of the synchronous motor in a plant with a rather poor power factor otherwise. The synchronous motor becomes a candidate for an adjustable-speed drive when an adjustable-speed coupling (an eddy-

[13] An interesting account of a variety of motor applications, many of which involve d-c machines, may be found in D. R. Shoults, C. J. Rife, and T. C. Johnson "Electric Motors in Industry," Chaps. IX, X, and XI, John Wiley & Sons, Inc., New York, 1942.

current slip coupling, for example) is interposed between its shaft and the load.

One should also be reminded that comparative studies of motor cost and characteristics are based on the combination of motor and control equipment, for the latter plays an important part in determining motor performance under specific conditions and represents a by no means negligible portion of the total initial cost. We say, for example, that the d-c series motor is very well adapted to crane service. We say also that the no-load speed of a series motor is prohibitively high. But when a crane is lowering, the motor load may be practically zero or actually overhauling—*i.e.*, negative. Reconciliation of these statements is effected by the control equipment, which reconnects the motor so that it lowers as a shunt motor or under dynamic-braking conditions or provides a motor torque in the opposite direction so that gravity lowers the load at a controllable rate. Control equipment coupled with susceptibility to control make d-c machines the versatile energy-conversion devices that they are.

PROBLEMS

6-1. *a.* A 230-volt d-c shunt-wound motor is used as an adjustable-speed drive over the range from zero to 1,000 rpm. Speeds from zero to 500 rpm are obtained by adjusting the armature terminal voltage from zero to 230 volts with the field current kept constant. Speeds from 500 to 1,000 rpm are obtained by decreasing the field current with the armature terminal voltage maintained at 230 volts. Over the entire speed range, the torque required by the load remains constant.

Show the general form of the curve of armature current vs. speed over the entire range. Ignore machine losses and armature-reaction effects.

b. Suppose that, instead of keeping the load torque constant, the armature current is not to exceed a specified value. Show the general form of the curve of allowable load torque vs. speed. Conditions otherwise are as in *a*.

6-2. *a.* Two adjustable-speed d-c shunt motors have maximum speeds of 1,650 rpm and minimum speeds of 450 rpm. Speed adjustment is obtained by field-rheostat control. Motor A drives a load requiring constant horsepower over the speed range; motor B drives one requiring constant torque. All losses and armature reaction may be neglected.

1. If the horsepower outputs are equal at 1,650 rpm and the armature currents are each 100 amp, what will be the armature currents at 450 rpm?

2. If the horsepower outputs are equal at 450 rpm and the armature currents are each 100 amp, what will be the armature currents at 1,650 rpm?

b. Answer part *a* for speed adjustment by armature-voltage control with conditions otherwise the same.

6-3. The following table has been made up for the comparison of shunt-field speed control and Ward Leonard speed control of a 250-volt 10-hp 35-amp adjustable-speed d-c shunt motor for a constant-horsepower and a constant-torque load. Maximum speed is to be 2,000 rpm and minimum speed 400 rpm. For the purposes of comparison, neglect armature resistance, armature reaction, and losses. Assume a linear saturation curve. Fill in the blanks in the table.

Motor speed, rpm	Shunt-field control, voltage supply constant				Ward Leonard control, field current constant			
	Constant hp		Constant T		Constant hp		Constant T	
	I_a	I_f	I_a	I_f	I_a	V	I_a	V
2,000 400	30	0.5	30	0.5	30	250	30	250
400 2,000	30	2.5	30	2.5	30	50	30	50

6-4. A 230-volt d-c shunt motor has an armature circuit resistance of 0.1 ohm. This motor operates on the 230-volt mains and takes an armature current of 100 amp. An external resistance of 1.0 ohm is now inserted in series with the armature, and the electromagnetic torque and field-rheostat setting are unchanged.

a. Give the percentage change in the total current taken by the motor from the mains.

b. Give the percentage change in the speed of the motor, and state whether this will be an increase or a decrease.

6-5. Consider a d-c shunt motor having an armature circuit resistance (including brushes) of 0.10 ohm, connected to a constant-voltage 230-volt d-c source, and driving a load requiring a constant electromagnetic torque. Armature reaction is negligible. The operating speed is initially 1,000 rpm, and the armature current is 100 amp.

a. The resultant air-gap flux is increased by 10.0 per cent. What is the speed?

b. With the resultant air-gap flux restored to its initial value, a 1.4-ohm resistor is connected in series with the armature. What is the speed?

c. With the resistor of *b* still in the circuit, the resultant air-gap flux is again increased by 10.0 per cent. What is the speed?

d. In parts *a* and *c*, note first whether the speeds have increased or decreased as a result of the increase in flux. Then explain why the speeds change as they do in response to the flux change.

6-6. A punch press is found to operate satisfactorily when driven by a 10-hp 230-volt compound motor having a no-load speed of 1,800 rpm and a full-load speed of 1,200 rpm when the torque is 43.8 lb-ft. The motor is temporarily out of service, and the only available replacement is a compound motor with the following characteristics:

Rating = 230 volts, 12.5 hp
No-load current = 4 amp
No-load speed = 1,820 rpm
Full-load speed = 1,600 rpm
Full-load current = 57.0 amp
Full-load torque = 43.8 lb-ft
Armature circuit resistance = 0.2 ohm
Shunt-field current = 1.6 amp

It is desired to use this motor as an emergency drive for the press without making any change in its field windings.

a. How can it be made to have the desired speed regulation?

b. Draw the pertinent circuit diagram, and give complete specifications of the necessary apparatus.

6-7. Consider a d-c shunt motor connected to constant-voltage mains and driving a load requiring constant electromagnetic torque. Show that if $E_a > 0.5V_t$ (the normal situation), increasing the resultant air-gap flux decreases the speed, whereas if $E_a < 0.5V_t$ (as might be brought about by inserting a relatively high resistance in series with the armature), increasing the resultant air-gap flux increases the speed.

6-8. Two identical 5-hp 230-volt 17-amp d-c shunt machines are to be used as the generator and motor, respectively, in a Ward Leonard system. The generator is driven by a synchronous motor whose speed is constant at 1,200 rpm. The armature circuit resistance of each machine is 0.47 ohm (including brushes). Armature reaction is negligible. Data for the magnetization curve of each machine at 1,200 rpm are as follows:

I_f, amp	0.2	0.4	0.6	0.8	1.0	1.2
E_a, volts	108	183	230	254	267	276

a. Compute the maximum and minimum values of generator field current needed to give the motor a speed range from 300 to 1,500 rpm at full-load armature current (17.0 amp), with the motor field current held constant at 0.50 amp.

b. Compute the speed regulation of the motor for the conditions of maximum speed and minimum speed found in part *a*.

c. Compute the maximum motor speed obtainable at full-load armature current if the motor field current is reduced to 0.20 amp and the generator field current is not allowed to exceed 1.10 amp.

6-9. Two identical machines for which basic data are given in Prob. 5-13 are to be used as the generator and motor, respectively, in a Ward Leonard system. The generator is driven at a constant speed of 1,000 rpm.

Consider that the maximum allowable continuous armature current is 1,000 amp and that the motor field is constant at the value producing 1,000 rpm at no load with the motor armature voltage at 500 volts. Compute and plot curves of (1) the maximum allowable continuous electromagnetic motor torque, (2) the associated armature terminal voltage, (3) the associated generator field current, and (4) the associated electromagnetic motor power, all as functions of speed.

6-10. One of the commonest industrial applications of d-c series motors is for crane and hoist drives. This problem relates to the computation of selected motor performance characteristics for such a drive. The specific motor concerned is a series-wound 230-volt totally enclosed motor having a ½-hr crane rating of 65 hp with a 75°C temperature rise. The performance characteristics of the motor alone on 230 volts as taken from the manufacturer's catalogue are listed in Table 6-2.

The resistance of the armature (including brushes) plus commutating field is 0.090 ohm, and that of the series-field winding is 0.040 ohm. Armature reaction should be ignored. The handling of rotational and stray load losses is to be discussed in part *i* of the problem.

The motor is to be connected as in Fig. 6-21 for hoisting and Fig. 6-22 for lowering. The former connection is simply one for series-resistance control. The latter connection is one for lowering by dynamic braking with the field reconnected in shunt and having an adjustable resistance in series with it.

A few samples of the torque-speed curves determining the suitability of the motor and control for its particular application are to be plotted. Plot all these curves on the same sheet with torque horizontally and speed vertically, covering about the torque-magnitude range embraced in Table 6-2. Provide for both positive and negative values of speed, corresponding, respectively, to hoisting and lowering; provide also for both positive and negative values of torque, corresponding, respectively, to torque in the direction of raising the load and torque in the direction of lowering the load; thus, use all four quadrants of the conventional rectangular coordinate system.

TABLE 6-2

Line current, amp	Shaft torque, lb-ft	Speed, rpm
50	80	940
100	210	630
150	380	530
200	545	475
250	730	438
300	910	407
350	1,105	385
400	1,365	370

a. For the hoisting connection, plot torque-speed curves for the control resistor R_c set at 0, 0.65 ohm, and 1.30 ohms. If any of these curves extend into the fourth quadrant within the range of torques covered, plot them in that region and interpret physically what operation there means.

b. Discuss the suitability of these characteristics for the hoisting operation.

c. For the lowering connection, plot a torque-speed curve for $R_1 = 0.65$ ohm and R_2 set at 0.65 ohm. The most important portion of this curve is in the fourth quadrant, but if it extends into the third quadrant, that region should also be plotted and interpreted physically.

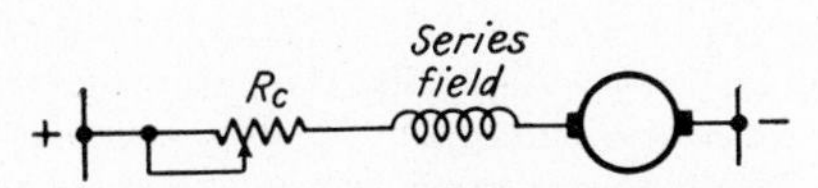

FIG. 6-21. Series motor with series-resistance control, Prob. 6-10.

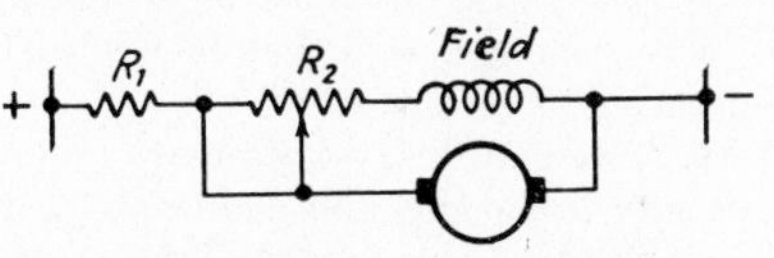

FIG. 6-22. Series motor with field reconnected in parallel with armature and control resistors added, Prob. 6-10.

d. In *c*, what is the lowering speed corresponding to rated torque?

e. How is the speed in *d* affected by decreasing R_2? Why?

f. How is the speed in *d* affected by decreasing R_1? Why?

g. How would the speed of *d* be affected by adding resistance in series with the motor armature? Why?

h. Discuss the suitability of these characteristics for the lowering operation.

i. What assumptions, if any, concerning rotational and stray load losses have you found it necessary to make because of having limited data on the motor? Discuss this point.

6-11. An automatic starter is to be designed for a 15-hp 230-volt shunt motor. The resistance of the armature circuit is 0.162 ohm. When operated at rated voltage and loaded until its armature current is 32 amp, the motor runs at a speed of 1,100 rpm with a field circuit resistance of 115 ohms. When delivering rated output, the armature current is 56 amp.

The motor is to be started with a load which requires a torque proportional to speed and which under running conditions requires 15 hp. The field winding is connected across the 230-volt mains, and the resistance in series with the armature is to be adjusted automatically so that during the starting period the armature current does not exceed 200 per cent of rated value or fall below rated value. That is, the machine is to start with 200 per cent of rated armature current, and as soon as the current falls to rated value, sufficient series resistance is to be cut out to restore current to 200 per cent. This process is repeated until all of the series resistance has been cut out.

a. What should be the total resistance of the starter?

b. How much resistance should be cut out at each step in the starting operation?

6-12. A 220-volt 850-rpm shunt motor is to be started by the three-step counter-emf controller of Fig. 6-12. The armature resistance is 0.15 ohm. Full-load armature current is 100 amp. The starting armature current is not to exceed twice the full-load value, and additional resistance is to be shorted out when the current drops to rated value.

Compute the armature current for the instant just after closure of contactor 3*A*.

6-13. Two d-c shunt machines whose shafts are coupled together are connected electrically in parallel to d-c mains. The field current of machine 1 is adjusted so that the voltage generated in its armature exactly equals the line voltage, the speed being 1,200 rpm.

It is now desired to make machine 1 become a generator by adjusting its field rheostat.

a. Should the field current of machine 1 be increased or decreased if the field current of machine 2 is unchanged?

b. Will the speed increase or decrease?

c. How can the speed then be readjusted to 1,200 rpm, the field current in machine 1 remaining as in part *a*?

6-14. Two identical d-c shunt-wound machines are mechanically coupled and operate electrically in parallel and connected to the 230-volt d-c mains. No other equipment is connected to the shaft of these machines. The following are points on the 1,000-rpm magnetization curve for each machine.

Field current, amp	1.3	1.4
Generated emf, volts	186.7	195.9

Machine A has a field current of 1.4 amp, and machine B has a field current of 1.3 amp The armature resistance of each machine (including brushes) is 0.1 ohm. The speed is 1,200 rpm.

a. Which machine is motoring and which generating? Explain.

b. What is the combined rotational loss of the two machines?

c. Can the roles of the two machines be interchanged (with the speed still kept at 1,200 rpm) by adjustment of the field rheostats? Explain.

d. Can both machines be made simultaneously to take power from the mains with the speed still kept at 1,200 rpm? Explain.

e. Can both machines be made simultaneously to supply power to the mains with the speed still kept at 1,200 rpm? Explain.

6-15. Two over-compounded, short-shunt generators when tested separately give the following data:

MACHINE A		MACHINE B	
Rating: 250 volts, 25 kw		Rating: 250 volts, 50 kw	
Terminal voltage	*Load current*	*Terminal voltage*	*Load current*
230	0	230	0
236	20	237	40
241	40	243	80
246	60	249	120
249	80	253	160
250	100	255	200
252	120	258	240
$r_a = 0.14$ ohm		$r_a = 0.070$ ohm	
$r_s = 0.10$ ohm		$r_s = 0.025$ ohm	
$r_f = 92.5$ ohms		$r_f = 62.5$ ohms	

It is desired to operate these machines in parallel.

a. Specify the rating of any auxiliary equipment necessary to make them divide load properly.

b. Show a complete circuit diagram for the parallel operation of these machines.

c. Calculate the armature current of each machine at full load when in parallel after the equipment computed in *a* has been installed.

d. Calculate the shunt-field current of each machine for the conditions of *c*.

6-16. A salesman is called upon to submit a bid on a d-c motor to be coupled to a centrifugal pump operating at 850 rpm and delivering 820 gal of water per minute against a total head of 85 ft. The efficiency of the pump is 70 per cent.

a. Determine the size of motor to be recommended for this job (1 gal of water weighs 8.32 lb).

After quoting on a motor of suitable capacity at a price of $600 and guaranteed full-load efficiency of 90 per cent, the salesman learns that his competitor has offered a motor of corresponding rating at a price of $500 and having a full-load efficiency of only 88 per cent. He also learns that the pump is to be operated 6 days per week, 14 hr per day, and that the cost of power is 3 cents per kilowatthour.

b. Indicate definitely how the salesman should attempt to justify the purchase of his motor in preference to the less expensive unit. (Note that all the data required for a detailed and complete economic comparison are not at hand so that a certain degree of judgment must be used.)

6-17. A single-stage 1,700-rpm centrifugal pump, driven by a 30-hp shunt motor, discharges 195 ft^3 of water a minute against a head of 48 ft. Under these conditions, the following data are taken:

Motor terminal voltage = 228 volts
Motor field current = 3.25 amp
Motor armature current = 89.5 amp
Motor speed = 1,700 rpm

When the pump is disconnected from the motor, the following data are taken:

Motor terminal voltage = 219 volts
Motor armature current = 5.75 amp
Motor field current = 3.12 amp
Motor speed = 1,700 rpm

Motor-armature circuit resistance at operating temperature exclusive of brushes is 0.105 ohm. Voltage drop at the brushes should be taken as 2 volts. Stray load loss in this problem may be taken as 1 per cent of the armature power input.

What is the efficiency of the centrifugal pump?

6-18. A 500-hp shunt motor is sold with a guaranteed efficiency. It is rated as follows: 500 hp, 575 volts, 710 amp, 1,150 rpm at full load.

Data taken with the motor at 75°C are as follows:

Machine Stationary:

Voltage drop across armature, exclusive of brushes = 14.2 volts
Current through armature = 508 amp
Voltage across field = 575 volts
Current through field = 9.13 amp

Machine Operating at No Load:

Voltage across armature, including brushes = 555 volts
Armature current = 22.5 amp
Field current = 8.57 amp
Speed = 1,150 rpm

Calculate the conventional efficiency for rated conditions.

NOTE: American Standards for Rotating Electrical Machinery C50-1943 prescribe that:

1. Copper losses shall be determined for 75°C.
2. Brush and brush-contact drop shall be taken as 2 volts for carbon and graphite brushes with shunts attached.
3. Core loss shall be determined by operating the machine (motor) at rated voltage less the resistance drop in the armature exclusive of the brushes.
4. Stray load losses shall be taken as 1 per cent of the output.
5. Field-rheostat loss is not to be charged against the machine.

6-19. A 4,000-kw compound generator is sold for steel-mill service with a guaranteed efficiency. It is rated as follows: 4,000 kw, 600 volts, 6,665 amp, 180 rpm at full load.

Data taken with the machine at 75°C are as follows:

Machine Stationary:

Voltage drop across armature, exclusive of brushes = 3.91 volts
Current through armature = 5,000 amp
Voltage drop across commutating and compensating windings in series = 1.94 volts
Current through commutating and compensating windings = 5,000 amp
Voltage drop across series field = 1.39 volts
Current through series field = 5,000 amp

Machine Operating at No Load as a Motor:

Voltage across armature, including brushes, volts	605	610	615
Armature current, amp	196	197	198
Field current, amp	34.6	34.9	35.2
Voltage drop across field, exclusive of rheostat, volts	570	574	578
Speed, rpm	180	180	180

Calculate the conventional efficiency for rated full-load conditions.

NOTE: See note to Prob. 6-18, but change item 3 to read as follows:

Core loss and friction and windage shall be determined by operating the machine (generator) at rated voltage plus the resistance drop in the armature (exclusive of the brushes), the commutating winding, the compensating winding, and the series field.

CHAPTER 7

SYNCHRONOUS MACHINES: ANALYSIS OF PERFORMANCE

A SYNCHRONOUS machine is an a-c machine whose speed under steady-state conditions is proportional to the frequency of the current in its armature. Polyphase d-c-excited synchronous machines comprise a polyphase armature winding of the type described in Art. 4-1 and a d-c field winding. At synchronous speed, the rotating magnetic field created by the armature currents travels at the same speed as the field created by the field current, and a steady torque results. An elementary physical picture of how a synchronous machine works has already been given in Art. 3-8, with emphasis on torque production in terms of the interactions among its magnetic fields.

The purpose of this chapter is to develop a quantitative theory from which both the electrical and mechanical characteristics of synchronous motors and generators can be determined. The synchronous machine is idealized to the extent that the effects of salient poles and magnetic saturation are not included, except in a qualitative way. These effects are discussed in some detail in Chap. 8.

7-1. Structural Features. Synchronous machines can be classified as *cylindrical-rotor* or *salient-pole* machines. The cylindrical-rotor construction is used in high-speed steam-turbine-driven generators. The armature windings consist of laminated conductors placed in the stator slots as in Fig. 1-4. They are usually 3-phase Y-connected windings, and voltages of about 13,800 volts, line to line, are common in sizes above several thousand kilowatts. The rotor carries the d-c field winding. A photograph of a rotor is shown in Fig. 1-15 and a cutaway view of an assembled machine in Fig. 7-1. Most of the turbine generators being built at present for 60-cps service are 2-pole 3,600-rpm machines. Because of the economies of high-speed high-temperature (1,050°F) high-pressure (1,500 psi) steam turbines, much study and some real pioneering work have been devoted to improvements in materials and design of both generators and turbines, and the maximum ratings for which 3,600-rpm machines have been built have approximately doubled during the decade from 1938 to 1948. Machines as large as 100,000 kw have been built for this speed. At a temperature of 1,050°F, the turbine parts exposed to the live steam glow a dull red. When one realizes that the investment in a set of this size, including boilers, condensers, and other auxiliaries, is in the vicinity of 10 million dollars, it is obvious that the engineering must be right the first time.

The advantages of large units are: somewhat increased efficiency, somewhat lower capital cost per kilowatt, and lower plant operating cost because of the greater ease of operating a generating station consisting of a relatively few large units as compared with one consisting of many

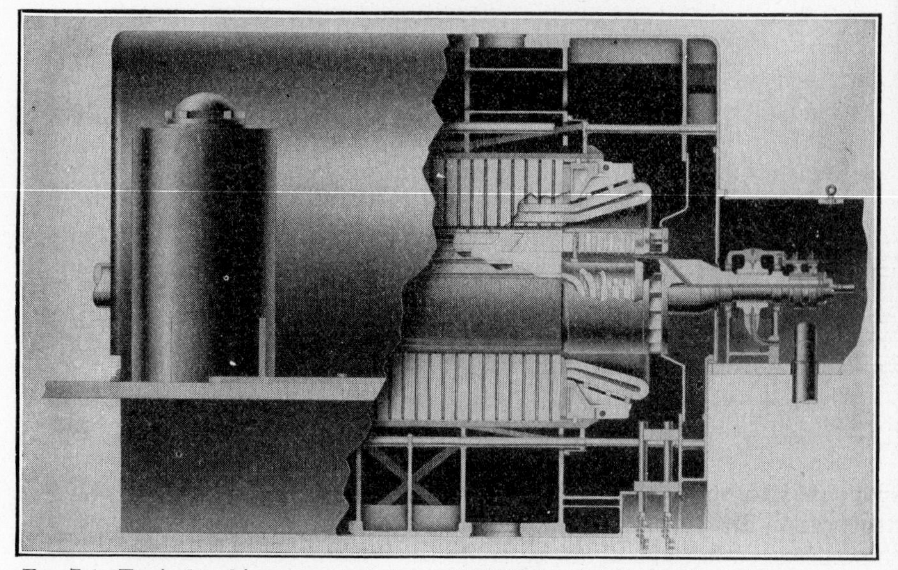

FIG. 7-1. Typical turbine generator of about 10,000 kw rating, showing totally enclosed construction. The vertical cylinder at the left is one of four water-cooled heat exchangers for removing heat from the cooling medium (air or hydrogen) after it has been blown through the ventilating ducts in the machine. (*Courtesy of General Electric Company.*)

smaller units. Two outstandingly large 4-pole 1,800-rpm machines are rated 200,000 kva, 0.8 power factor, and 183,333 kva, 0.9 power factor. There are at present, however, relatively few places where the concentration of such a large part of the generating capacity of a system in a single unit is advisable. Large machines are often built as *double-winding generators; i.e.*, they have two independent armature windings connected through independent circuit breakers to separate sections of the busbars in the generating station. By this arrangement the short-circuit currents are reduced.

The field windings are embedded in axial slots cut in the rotor and are held in place by metal wedges. They usually consist of concentric coils of insulated copper strap laid flat in the slots. The rotor coil ends and end connections are firmly held in place by retaining rings shrunk on over the ends of the coils. The leads are connected to slip rings which make contact with carbon brushes through which the field current is introduced.

The mmf wave created by such a winding is shown by the step wave in Fig. 7-2*a*. The height of each step in the wave is proportional to the total current in the slot below it. The space-fundamental component of the step wave is shown dotted in Fig. 7-2*a*. Its peak value F_{peak} can be determined by a line of reasoning similar to that of Art. 4-2. Consider

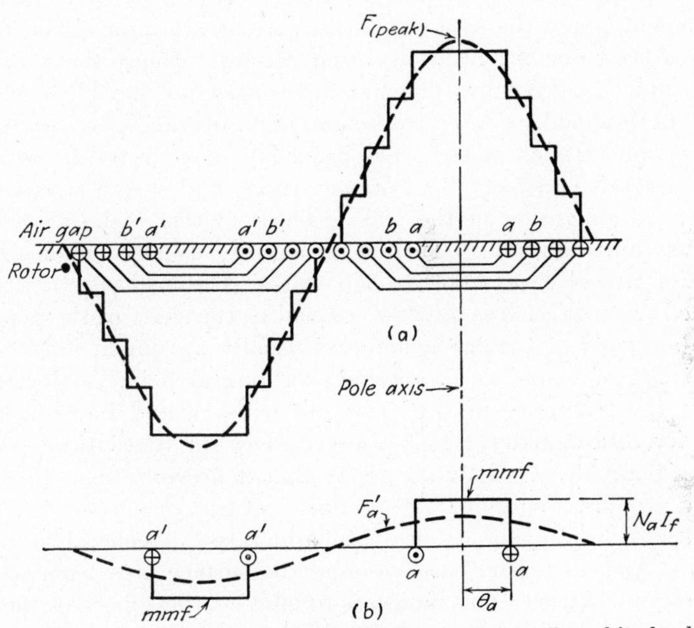

FIG. 7-2. (*a*) Rotor-mmf wave. (*b*) Mmf of the inner pair of coils and its fundamental component.

the rectangular mmf wave produced by the inside coil groups *aa* and *a'a'* in Fig. 7-2*b*. Its amplitude is $N_a I_f$ amp-turns per pole, where N_a is the number of turns in one of these coils and I_f is the current in the coil. On resolving this rectangular wave into a Fourier series, the peak value $F'_{a(\text{peak})}$ of the fundamental component is found to be

$$F'_{a(\text{peak})} = \frac{4}{\pi} N_a I_f \sin \theta_a \tag{7-1}$$

where θ_a is the angle from the pole axis to the coil side. The mmf waves of the other pairs of coils can be treated similarly, and since the fundamental components of all the individual coils are in line with the pole axis, the resultant space-fundamental mmf is the numerical sum of the components. Therefore the peak value F_{peak} of the resultant fundamental component is

$$F_{peak} = \frac{4}{\pi} I_f(N_a \sin \theta_a + N_b \sin \theta_b + \cdot \cdot \cdot) \quad \text{amp-turns per pole} \tag{7-2}$$

By suitable distribution of the winding, the step wave can be made to approach a sinusoid quite closely.

Because of the high rotational stresses, the rotors of turbine generators must be designed for as small a diameter as is consistent with other requirements. At the same time, limitations are imposed on the axial length of the rotor by vibration considerations. Hence the design of the rotor is indeed a difficult problem, and the design of the whole machine is largely determined by it. Stresses are high, operating temperatures are high, and space is cramped. The insulation is subjected to severe rotational stresses, relatively high temperatures, and severe stresses caused by thermal expansion of the coils. These factors make a low-voltage rotor winding desirable. Turbine generators usually are designed for excitation at voltages of 125 to 375 volts. The field current usually is obtained from an exciter directly coupled to the shaft of the generator.

The air gaps of turbine generators usually are much longer than in other types of machines—sometimes as long as 3 in. A long air gap reduces the reactance of the armature winding and improves voltage regulation and stability. It is also necessary for ventilation. An obvious disadvantage of a long air gap is that it necessitates a greater field mmf to produce a specified air-gap flux.

The cooling problem in electrical apparatus in general increases in difficulty with increasing size, because the surface area from which the heat must be carried away increases roughly as the square of the dimensions, while the heat developed by the losses is roughly proportional to the volume and therefore increases approximately as the cube of the dimensions. Because of their compactness, this problem is a serious one with large turbine generators. Rather elaborate systems of cooling ducts must be provided through which the cooling air is blown, either by a fan on the rotor or by a separately driven blower. A closed ventilating system is commonly used in machines rated above a few thousand kva, as shown in Fig. 7-1. After passing through the machine, the hot air is blown through a water-cooled heat exchanger and recirculated in a closed system.

The use of a totally enclosed ventilating system brings up the possibility of using hydrogen as the cooling medium. Hydrogen has the following properties which make it well suited to the purpose:[1]

[1] A classic paper on the subject of hydrogen cooling is E. Knowlton, C. W. Rice, and E. H. Freiburghouse, Hydrogen as a Cooling Medium for Electrical Machinery,

1. Its density is only about 0.07 that of air at the same temperature and pressure, and therefore windage and ventilating losses are much less.

2. Its specific heat on an equal weight basis is about 14.5 times that of air. This means that for the same temperature and pressure, hydrogen and air are about equally effective in their heat-storing capacity per unit volume. But the heat transfer by forced convection between the hot parts of the machine and the cooling gas is considerably greater with hydrogen than with air.

3. The life of the insulation is increased and maintenance expenses are decreased, because of the absence of dirt, moisture, and oxygen.

4. The fire hazard is eliminated. A hydrogen-air mixture will not explode if the hydrogen content is above about 70 per cent. As a matter of fact, hydrogen-cooled machines are easily constructed so that they would be undamaged by an explosion.

The result of the first two properties is that for the same operating conditions the heat which must be dissipated is reduced, while at the same time the ease with which it can be carried off is improved.

The machine and its water-cooled heat exchanger must be sealed in a gastight envelope. The crux of the problem is in sealing the bearings. The system is maintained at a slight pressure (at least 0.5 psi) above atmospheric so that gas leakage is outward and an explosive mixture cannot accumulate within the machine. At this pressure, the rating of the machine can be increased by about 30 per cent above its air-cooled rating and the full-load efficiency increased by about 0.5 per cent. The trend is toward the use of higher pressures (15 to 30 psi). Increasing the hydrogen pressure from 0.5 to 30 psi increases the output for the same temperature rise by about 25 per cent.

The salient-pole construction is best suited to multipolar medium- or low-speed machines. It is therefore commonly used for waterwheel- and engine-driven alternators and for synchronous motors. Alternators driven by medium- or low-head hydraulic turbines usually are vertical-shaft machines, the weight of the rotor and turbine runner and the axial thrust of the turbine being supported by a massive thrust bearing. A cross-sectional drawing of a machine of this type is shown in Fig. 1-23. Outstandingly large machines are the generators for the Grand Coulee

---

Trans. AIEE, vol. 44, pp. 922–932, 1925. For discussions of the turbine-generator problem, see D. S. Snell, The Hydrogen-cooled Turbine Generator, *Trans. AIEE*, vol. 59, pp. 35–45, January, 1940; M. D. Ross and C. C. Sterett, Hydrogen-cooled Turbine Generators, *Trans. AIEE*, vol. 59, pp. 11–15, January, 1940; R. B. Roberts, Hydrogen Cooling for Turbine Generators, *Westinghouse Eng.*, vol. 7, No. 5, pp. 138–142, September, 1947. Cooling systems using liquids and various combinations of liquids and gases are being studied intensively. See C. J. Fechheimer, Liquid Cooling of A-c Turbine Generators, *Trans. AIEE*, vol. 69, pp. 165–171, 1950.

power and irrigation development on the Columbia River; they are rated 108,000 kva, 1.0 power factor, 13,800 volts, 120 rpm, 60 cps. The stator of one of these machines is shown in Fig. 7-3.

As explained in Art. 3-8, a synchronous motor per se has no starting torque. To make the motor self-starting, a squirrel-cage amortisseur or damper winding is inserted in slots in the faces of the field poles, as shown in Figs. 1-40 and 3-27. The motor starts by induction-motor action of the damper winding. During this process the field winding is either open-

FIG. 7-3. Stator of a 108,000-kva 1.0-power-factor 120-rpm hydrogenerator assembled at the factory. It will be shipped in four pieces. (*Courtesy of Westinghouse Electric Corporation.*)

circuited or short-circuited through a suitable field-discharge resistor. If it is open-circuited, high voltages may be induced in it which must be provided for in the field insulation. The motor comes up to almost synchronous speed by induction-motor action. The field winding is then energized, and if the shaft load and inertia are not too great, the motor pulls into synchronism. The ability of a motor to synchronize depends on the inertia of its rotor and load, the speed-torque characteristic of its damper winding, the retarding torque of friction, windage, and shaft load, its field excitation, and the instantaneous angular position of its rotor with respect to the rotating magnetic field at the moment excitation is applied.[2]

[2] D. R. Shoults, S. B. Crary, and A. H. Lauder, Pull-in Characteristics of Synchronous Motors, *Trans. AIEE*, vol. 54, No. 12, pp. 1385–1395, December, 1935.

Many synchronous-motor controllers apply excitation at random after the motor has come up to the proper speed. Controllers are available, however, which apply excitation at more favorable angles and result in synchronization with higher pull-in torque. *Pull-in torque* is defined as the maximum constant load torque under which the motor will pull its connected inertia load into synchronism. It is the most difficult torque for which to obtain large values in synchronous-motor design. Table 7-1 shows the performance standards required of general-purpose synchronous motors according to the NEMA.[3] The torques are expressed in per cent of rated torque at rated voltage and frequency. The pull-in torque is based on normal field current and normal inertia loads defined

TABLE 7-1
TORQUE REQUIREMENTS OF GENERAL-PURPOSE SYNCHRONOUS MOTORS
(514 to 1,200 rpm, 60 cps)

	1.0 power factor 20–200 hp	0.8-power-factor lead 20–150 hp
Starting torque..........	110	125
Pull-in torque............	110	125
Pull-out torque..........	175	250

in the reference cited in footnote 3. The pull-out torque is the maximum steady torque, slowly applied, which the motor can deliver without loss of synchronism and is based on normal field current. Starting current will average from six to seven times full-load current if full-voltage starting is used. With reduced-voltage starting, the current is proportional to the voltage, and the starting and pull-in torques are approximately proportional to the square of the voltage.

The fact that damper windings must be inserted for starting should not be considered a disadvantage of synchronous motors. At times it may be a decided advantage, for the motor starts on one set of windings and runs on another. Special design of the damper windings for high starting torque therefore need not penalize operating conditions, particularly the efficiency. Under normal, balanced, steady-state operating conditions the damper winding has no effect, because no voltage is induced in it. Damper windings are also effective in reducing hunting. They are sometimes used in generators to improve transient stability and to prevent overvoltages during double-line-to-neutral faults.

[3] NEMA Standards, Motor and Generator Standards, National Electrical Manufacturers' Association, New York, *Integral-horsepower and Synchronous Motors*, Part 8, p. 29, 1950.

7-2. Flux and MMF Waves in Cylindrical-rotor Machines. Consider a 3-phase synchronous machine connected to a balanced 3-phase system which can either absorb electrical power from or supply electrical power to the synchronous machine. The effects of magnetic saturation will be neglected temporarily, so that the resultant air-gap flux can be considered as the sum of component fluxes produced by the field mmf and by the armature mmf.

A developed sketch of two poles of the armature and field windings of a cylindrical-rotor machine is shown in Fig. 7-4*a*, in which slot openings

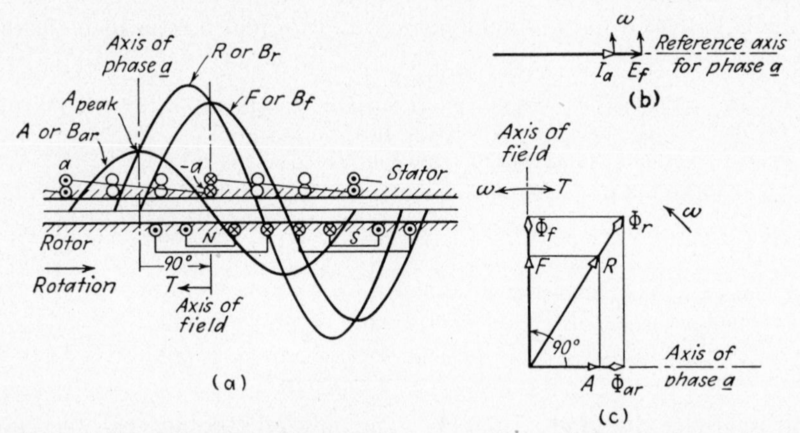

FIG. 7-4. (*a*) Spatial mmf and flux-density waves in a cylindrical-rotor synchronous generator. Armature current in phase with excitation voltage. (*b*) Time vector diagram. (*c*) Space vector diagram.

are omitted and the stator (armature) winding is represented by concentrated full-pitch coils whose coil sides are located at the centers of the phase belts. The actual armature winding would, of course, be distributed in several slots per phase belt. The field current establishes an mmf and a flux-density wave rotating with the rotor and generating 3-phase voltages in the armature windings. The internal emf generated by the component flux produced by the field current is known as the *excitation emf* or *excitation voltage.* It differs from the terminal voltage by the voltage drops caused by the armature currents. We shall concern ourselves with only time-fundamental components of the voltages and currents and only space-fundamental mmf and flux-density waves.

The space-fundamental component of the mmf wave produced by the field current is shown by the sine wave F in Fig. 7-4*a*. This sine wave may also be regarded as representing the component flux-density wave produced by the field current, as indicated by the alternative designation B_f. A positive ordinate means flux crossing the air gap from the rotor toward the stator. The cross sections of the phase-a armature coils are shown by the dark circles. The b- and c-phase coils are shown by light circles. For balanced operating conditions the events in only one armature phase need be considered since, except for the phase angle of 120°, exactly similar events are taking place in the other phases.

Figure 7-4a may be regarded as one frame from a motion-picture film showing the rotating air-gap fields. It is drawn for an instant of time when the axis of a north field pole has revolved 90 electrical degrees beyond the axis of phase a. At this instant the flux linkage with phase a produced by the field flux is zero, but the time rate of change of flux linkage is a maximum and the excitation emf generated in phase a has its maximum value. The instantaneous direction of the emf can be determined by Lenz' law and is shown by the dots and crosses representing the heads and tails of arrows on the phase-a coil sides. In Fig. 7-4b the excitation emf is represented by a rotating time vector E_f whose projection on the reference axis for phase a is proportional to the instantaneous emf in the arrow direction of Fig. 7-4a. At the moment under consideration, the vector E_f lies along the reference axis because the emf then has its maximum instantaneous value.

Because sinusoids can conveniently be added by vector methods, it is helpful to represent the sinusoidal space waves of mmf and flux by vectors whose angular positions mark the locations of the positive peaks of the waves. The field mmf and flux waves accordingly can be represented by vectors F and Φ_f drawn along the axis of a north field pole and rotating with the rotor. The magnitude of the vector F equals the peak value of the space-fundamental component of the field mmf. (In order to simplify the notation, the subscript *peak* previously used to designate the peak value of an mmf wave will be omitted in the rest of this chapter.) The magnitude of the vector Φ_f equals the fundamental flux per pole produced by the field current. The vectors F and Φ_f are shown in Fig. 7-4c.

Now consider the magnetic field created by the armature currents. As shown in Arts. 3-6 and 4-2, balanced polyphase currents in a symmetrical polyphase winding create an mmf wave consisting of a constant-amplitude space-fundamental component rotating at synchronous speed and a family of comparatively small harmonic components. The synchronously rotating space-fundamental component is usually called the *armature-reaction mmf*. Its peak value is given by Eq. 4-25. As in a d-c machine, it is an mmf wave which is stationary with respect to the field poles, and the resultant air-gap flux is produced by the combined effects of field mmf and armature reaction. In d-c machines the space-phase relation between the field- and armature-reaction-mmf waves is determined by the position of the brushes; with synchronous machines, however, this space-phase relation is determined by the power factor at which the machine is operating.

For example, suppose the machine is acting as a generator under conditions which result in the phase-a current being in time phase with the excitation emf, as shown by the vector I_a in Fig. 7-4b. The phase-a current then has its maximum instantaneous value and is in the same direction as the excitation emf at the moment depicted in Fig. 7-4. Now recall from Art. 3-6 that the rotating field created by the armature currents is directly opposite phase a at the instant when the phase-a current has its maximum value, as shown by the sine wave A in Fig. 7-4a; the

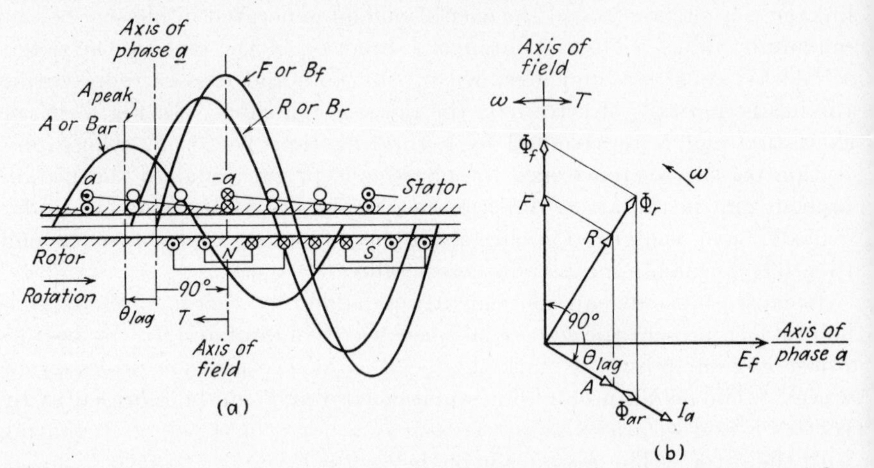

FIG. 7-5. (a) Magnetic fields in a synchronous generator. Armature current lags excitation voltage. (b) Combined space and time vector diagram.

corresponding space vector A, whose magnitude equals the peak value of the armature-reaction-mmf wave and whose angular position marks the location of a positive peak of the wave, lies along the axis of phase a at this moment, as shown in Fig. 7-4c. If magnetic saturation is neglected, the sine wave A may also be regarded as representing the component flux-density wave produced by the armature reaction, as indicated by the alternative designation B_{ar} in Fig. 7-4a. The corresponding vector representing the armature-reaction flux per pole is Φ_{ar} in Fig. 7-4c. The resultant magnetic field is the sum of the components produced by the field current and armature reaction, respectively. The components can be added vectorially, as in Fig. 7-4c, wherein the vector R represents the resultant mmf and the vector Φ_r represents the resultant fundamental air-gap flux per pole. The corresponding space waves of resultant mmf and of resultant air-gap flux density are shown by the sine wave labeled R or B_r in Fig. 7-4a.

Now suppose that, instead of being in phase with the excitation emf, the armature current lags the excitation emf by the time-phase angle θ_{lag}, as shown by the time vectors I_a and E_f in Fig. 7-5*b*. (Note that θ_{lag} is *not* the power-factor angle with respect to the terminal voltage but is the power-factor angle with respect to the *excitation voltage*.) The machine is still considered to be acting as a generator. Figure 7-5*b* is drawn for an instant of time when the excitation voltage has its maximum instantaneous value and a north field pole has revolved 90 electrical degrees beyond the axis of phase *a*. Just as in Fig. 7-4*c*, the space vectors F and Φ_f representing the field mmf and flux are 90° ahead of the phase-*a* reference axis, as shown in Fig. 7-5*b*, wherein space vectors representing

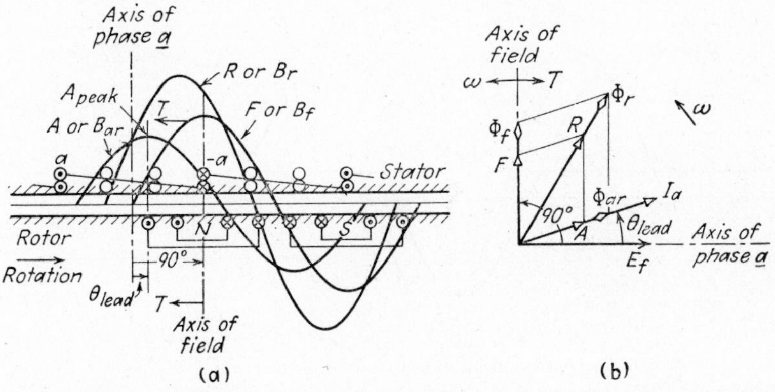

FIG. 7-6. (*a*) Magnetic fields in a synchronous generator. Armature current leads excitation voltage. (*b*) Vector diagram.

the magnetic fields are combined in the same vector diagram with time vectors representing current and voltage. The phase-*a* current will not reach its maximum instantaneous value and the armature-reaction wave will not be opposite phase *a* until a time angle θ_{lag} later than that shown in Fig. 7-5. In other words, at the moment shown in Fig. 7-5 the armature-reaction wave lags the axis of phase *a* by an electrical space angle equal to the time lag angle θ_{lag}, as shown by the sine wave labeled A or B_{ar} in Fig. 7-5*a*, and by the space vectors A and Φ_{ar} in Fig. 7-5*b*. The armature reaction is in phase with the armature current.

For comparison, the space waves and vector diagram for a machine operating as a generator under conditions which result in the armature current leading the excitation emf by a time-phase angle θ_{lead} are shown in Fig. 7-6.

Now consider motor action under operating conditions which result in unity power factor with respect to the excitation voltage. At the moment when the excitation emf has its maximum instantaneous value in the arrow direction of Fig. 7-7*a*, the armature current also has its maximum value but is in the *opposite* direction; *i.e.*, the armature current and excitation emf are in phase opposition when the positive directions for both are defined as in the arrow direction. The armature-reaction wave A or B_{ar} in Fig. 7-7*a* then has the opposite polarity to that shown in Fig. 7-4*a*; the corresponding vector diagram is shown in Fig. 7-7*b*.

For comparison, Fig. 7-8 shows motor action at a leading power factor with respect to the excitation voltage (that is, $-I_a$ leads E_f), and Fig. 7-9 shows motor action at a lagging power factor.

The way in which the space-phase position of the armature-reaction-mmf wave with respect to the field poles depends on the time-phase angle between the armature current and the excitation voltage can now

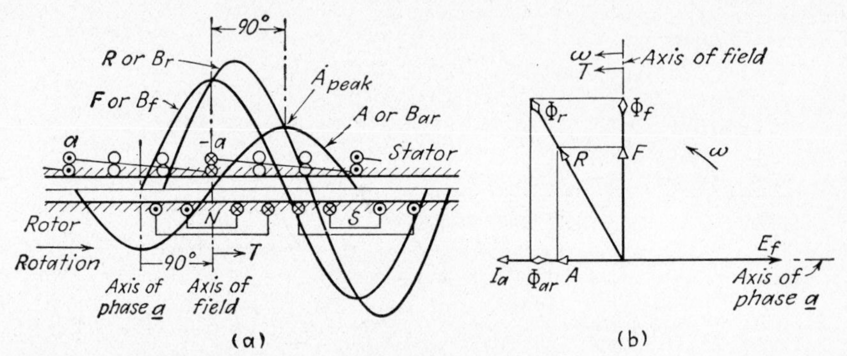

FIG. 7-7. (*a*) Magnetic fields in a synchronous motor. Unity power factor with respect to excitation voltage. (*b*) Vector diagram.

be summarized by examining Figs. 7-4 to 7-9 as a group. At unity power factor with respect to the excitation voltage (Figs. 7-4 and 7-7) the peak of the armature-reaction wave lies midway between the centers of the field poles, and the field and armature-reaction waves are in space quadrature. For generator action at a lagging power factor (Fig. 7-5) or motor action at a leading power factor (Fig. 7-8), the space-phase angle between the field and armature-reaction waves is greater than 90 electrical degrees; except at power factors near unity the armature reaction then exerts a demagnetizing effect (*i.e.*, the resultant mmf R is smaller than the field mmf F). For generator action at a leading power factor (Fig. 7-6) or motor action at a lagging power factor (Fig. 7-9), this space-phase angle is less than 90 electrical degrees, and the armature reaction exerts a magnetizing effect.

Two assumptions are implicit in our method of combining the effects of field and armature-reaction mmf in Figs. 7-4 to 7-9. It has been assumed that (1) the armature-reaction-mmf wave results in the same space-fundamental air-gap flux as a field-mmf wave of the same fundamental amplitude, and (2) the flux produced by an mmf wave is independent of the spatial alignment of the wave with respect to the field poles. The former assumption is equivalent to the usual one made in handling magnetic-circuit problems involving iron paths in series with an air gap, *viz.*, that for equal mmfs the same air-gap flux is produced by either of two coils acting on such a magnetic circuit, even though the coils may be located at different places on the core. The latter assumption merely states that in a cylindrical-rotor machine the air-gap reluctance is considered to be independent of the spatial alignment of the mmf wave with respect to the field poles, because the air-gap length is the same at all points around the periphery. The resultant flux wave then merely assumes the position dictated to it by the resultant of the field- and armature-reaction-mmf waves. In other words, there is no pre-

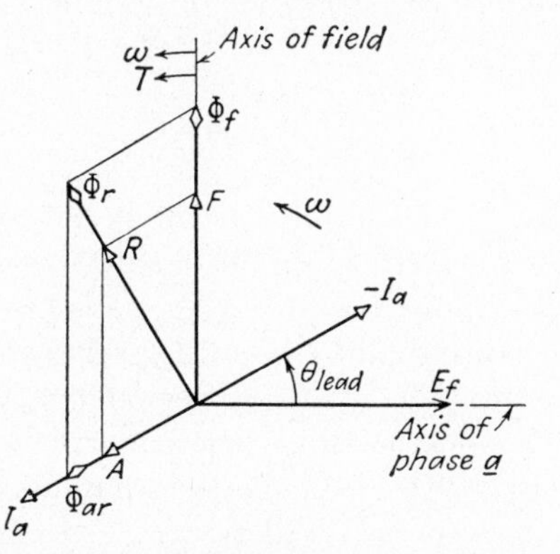

FIG. 7-8. Vector diagram of a synchronous motor. Leading power factor with respect to excitation voltage.

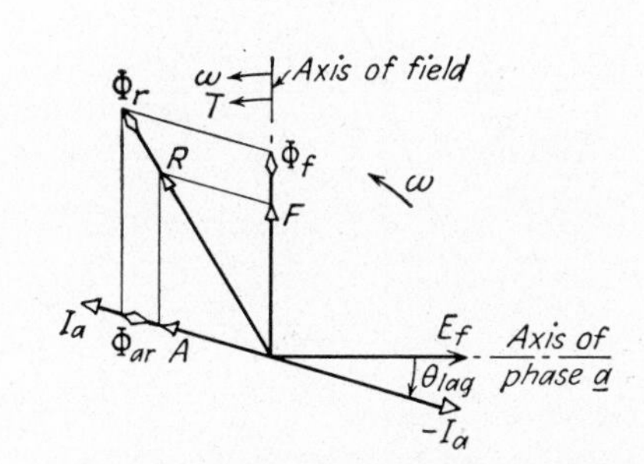

FIG. 7-9. Vector diagram of a synchronous motor. Lagging power factor with respect to excitation voltage.

ferred direction of magnetization as there would be with salient poles. This fact, and the related one that reluctance torques need not be considered, greatly simplifies the theory of uniform-air-gap machines. The treatment of armature reaction must be reexamined, as in Art. 8-4, when the effects of salient poles are considered.

7-3. Basic Concepts of Synchronous-machine Performance. Examination of Figs. 7-4 to 7-9 in some detail may be helpful in correlating the simple, physical picture of synchronous-machine torque-angle characteristics described in Art. 3-8 with the way in which the armature current adjusts itself to the operating conditions imposed by the torque impressed on the shaft and the voltages applied to the windings.

The electromagnetic torque on the rotor acts in a direction to urge the field poles into alignment with the resultant air-gap flux and armature-reaction flux waves, as shown by the arrows labeled T attached to the field axes in Figs. 7-4 to 7-9. If the field poles lead the resultant air-gap flux wave, as in Figs. 7-4, 7-5, and 7-6, the electromagnetic torque on the rotor acts in opposition to the rotation—in other words, the machine must be acting as a generator. On the other hand, if the field poles lag the resultant air-gap flux wave, as in Figs. 7-7, 7-8, and 7-9, the electromagnetic torque acts in the direction of rotation—*i.e.*, the machine must be acting as a motor. An alternative statement is that for generator action the field poles must be driven ahead of the resultant air-gap flux wave by the forward torque of a prime mover, while for motor action the field poles must be dragged behind the resultant air-gap flux wave by the retarding torque of a shaft load.

The magnitude of the torque can be expressed in terms of the resultant fundamental air-gap flux per pole Φ_r and the peak value F of the space-fundamental field-mmf wave. From Eq. 3-22,

$$T = \frac{\pi}{2}\left(\frac{p}{2}\right)^2 \Phi_r F \sin \delta_{RF} \qquad (7\text{-}3)$$

where δ_{RF} is the space-phase angle in electrical degrees between the resultant-flux and field-mmf waves.

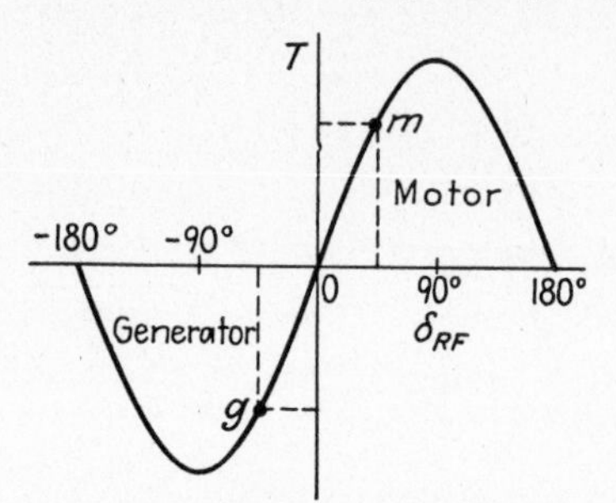

FIG. 7-10. Torque-angle characteristic.

To gain insight into the adjustment processes within the machine, consider again a synchronous machine operating in synchronism with a balanced polyphase system which can either absorb or deliver electrical power. Assume that the voltage and frequency of the system are constant. Such a system is commonly called an *infinite bus.* Also neglect armature resistance and leakage reactance in the machine. The voltage E_r generated by the resultant air-gap flux, known as the *air-gap voltage,* must equal the armature terminal voltage per phase. The resultant air-gap flux wave Φ_r is thus fixed in amplitude and phase by the voltage of the infinite bus. This statement is equivalent to the statement for a static transformer that the resultant core flux is fixed in amplitude and phase if the primary terminal voltage and frequency are constant and the primary resistance and leakage reactance are negligible. The field and armature-reaction mmfs must always adjust themselves so that their vector sum equals the mmf required to create the resultant air-gap flux.

For a fixed setting of the field rheostat, the field mmf F is constant in magnitude. In Eq. 7-3, therefore, F and Φ_r are constant. The torque-angle characteristic is then that of Fig. 7-10, and the machine accommodates itself to variations in the torque imposed on its shaft by adjusting its torque angle δ_{RF}. The resulting change in phase of the field mmf F with respect to the resultant flux must be compensated by a change in the armature-reaction mmf, and consequently in the armature current, in such a way that the resultant mmf is constant in magnitude and phase.

Suppose that the machine is operating as a motor at no load with negligible rotational losses. The torque and δ_{RF} are zero. Suppose also that the field current is adjusted so that its mmf is exactly the value required to create the flux specified by the voltage of the infinite bus. The armature current then is zero, and the machine merely "floats" on the system. The vector diagram is shown in Fig. 7-11*a*.

If shaft load is now added, causing the machine to become a motor, the rotor momentarily slows down a little under the influence of the

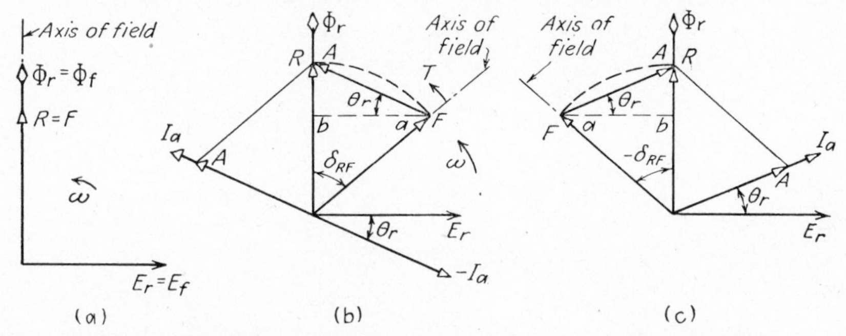

FIG. 7-11. Vector diagrams showing the effects of shaft torque. (*a*) No load. (*b*) Motor action. (*c*) Generator action.

retarding torque, and the field poles slide back in space phase with respect to the resultant air-gap flux wave; that is, δ_{RF} increases, and the machine develops motor torque. After a transient period, steady-state operation at synchronous speed is resumed when δ_{RF} has assumed the value required to supply the load torque, as shown by point m in Fig. 7-10. The vector diagram is now as shown in Fig. 7-11*b*. The field mmf is no longer in phase with the resultant flux wave, and the discrepancy in mmf must be made up by the armature reaction, thus giving rise to the armature current needed to supply the electrical power input corresponding to the mechanical power output. Note that

$$F \sin \delta_{RF} = A \cos \theta_r \tag{7-4}$$

as indicated by the dotted line ab, where θ_r is the power-factor angle of the armature current with respect to the air-gap voltage E_r. But $A \cos \theta_r$ is proportional to the active-power component $I_a \cos \theta_r$ of the armature current, and from Eq. 7-3, $F \sin \delta_{RF}$ is proportional to the torque. That is, the electrical active-power input is proportional to the mechanical torque output as, of course, it must be.

If, instead of being loaded as a motor, the shaft is driven forward by the torque of a prime mover, the field poles advance in phase ahead of the resultant flux wave to an angle $-\delta_{RF}$ where the counter torque $-T$ developed by the machine equals the driving torque of the prime mover, as shown by point g in Fig. 7-10. The effects on the armature reaction and armature current are shown vectorially in Fig. 7-11c. The machine has now become a generator.

In Fig. 7-11b and c, note that for the components of F and A in phase with R,

$$F \cos \delta_{RF} + A \sin \theta_r = R \tag{7-5}$$

That is, not only must the active-power component $I_a \cos \theta_r$ of the armature current adjust itself to supply the torque, as implied in Eq. 7-4, but also the reactive component $I_a \sin \theta_r$ must adjust itself so that the corresponding component $A \sin \theta_r$ of the armature-reaction mmf combines with the component $F \cos \delta_{RF}$ of the field mmf to produce the required resultant mmf R. The reactive kva can therefore be controlled by adjusting the field excitation.

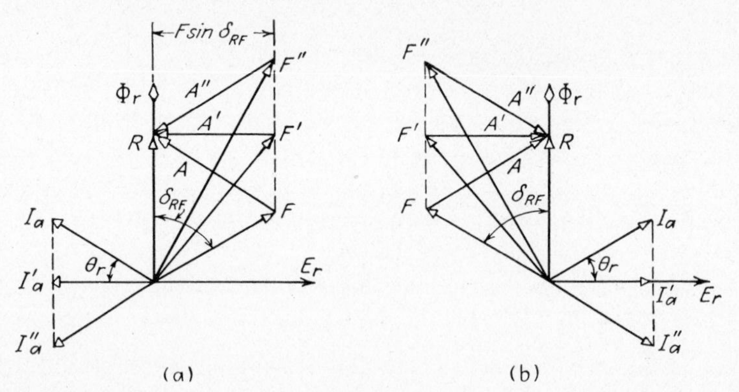

FIG. 7-12. Vector diagrams showing the effects of changes in excitation. (a) Motor. (b) Generator.

For example, suppose the machine is running as a motor with field mmf F, Fig. 7-12a. The corresponding armature-reaction and armature current vectors are A and I_a, respectively. Now suppose the field mmf is increased, the shaft load being unchanged. If Φ_r is constant (as we are assuming it to be for the present), then at constant torque $F \sin \delta_{RF}$ must be constant; *i.e.*, the machine adjusts itself to an increase in F by decreasing its torque angle δ_{RF}. The locus of the vector F as field current is changed therefore is as shown by the vertical dotted line through the tips of the F vectors in Fig. 7-12a. The corresponding locus of the armature current vector I_a is also shown. The active-power component $I_a \cos \theta_r$ is constant, but the reactive component varies. For comparison, the corresponding loci for a generator with constant Φ_r and constant prime-mover torque are shown in Fig. 7-12*b*. In these figures, if the field current is adjusted to the value F', the machine operates at unity power factor with respect to the air-gap voltage E_r. If the field current is insufficient to create the required resultant mmf without the help of the armature mmf, as shown by the vectors F in these two figures, the machine is said to be *underexcited*. For both motor and generator action, the reactive component of the armature current I_a then leads E_r by 90°. Recall that I_a represents current in the direction of the emf generated in the machine and therefore represents electrical output. Thus an underexcited synchronous machine generates leading reactive kva. Alternatively, it can be regarded as absorbing lagging reactive kva from the system. On the other hand, if the field current is more than sufficient to create the required resultant mmf, as shown by the vectors F'' in Fig. 7-12*a* and *b*, the machine is said to be *overexcited*. For both motor and generator action, the reactive component of I_a then lags E_r by 90°. An overexcited synchronous motor therefore can be regarded as generating lagging reactive kva or as absorbing leading reactive kva. The magnitude and direction of the reactive-kva flow are determined by the field excitation and are thus under the control of the operator.

7-4. Power Factor in A-C Machines. The power factor at which a-c machines operate is an economically important feature because of the cost of reactive kva. Low power factor adversely affects system operation in three principal ways. In the first place, generators, transformers, and transmission equipment are rated in terms of kva rather than kilowatts, because their losses and heating are very nearly determined by voltage and current regardless of power factor. The physical size and cost of a-c apparatus is roughly proportional to its kva rating. The investment in generators, transformers, and transmission equipment for supplying a given useful amount of active power therefore is roughly inversely proportional to the power factor. In the second place, low power factor means more current and greater copper losses in the generating and transmitting equipment. A further disadvantage is poor voltage regulation.

Factors influencing reactive-kva requirements in motors can be visualized readily in terms of the relationship of these requirements to the establishment of magnetic flux. As in any electromagnetic device, the resultant flux necessary for motor operation must be established by a magnetizing component of current. It makes no difference either in the magnetic circuit or in the fundamental energy-conversion process whether this magnetizing current be carried by the rotor or stator winding, just as it makes no basic difference in a transformer which winding carries the exciting current. In some cases, part of it is supplied from each winding. If all or part of the magnetizing current is supplied to an a-c winding, the input to that winding must include lagging reactive kva, because magnetizing current lags voltage drop by 90°. In effect, the lagging reactive kva sets up flux in the motor.

The only possible source of excitation in an induction motor is the stator input. The induction motor therefore must operate at a lagging power factor. This power factor is very low at no load and increases to about 85 or 90 per cent at full load, the improvement being caused by the increased active-power requirements with increasing load.

With a synchronous motor, there are two possible sources of excitation: alternating current in the armature, or direct current in the field winding. If the field current is just sufficient to supply the necessary mmf, no magnetizing-current component or reactive kva is needed in the armature and the motor operates at unity power factor. If the field current is less (*i.e.*, the motor is underexcited), the deficit in mmf must be made up by the armature, and the motor operates at a lagging power factor. If the field current is greater (*i.e.*, the motor is overexcited), the excess mmf must be counterbalanced in the armature, and a leading component of current is present; the motor then operates at a leading power factor.

Because magnetizing current must be supplied to inductive loads, such as transformers and induction motors, the ability of overexcited synchronous motors to absorb leading current is a highly desirable feature which may have considerable economic importance. In effect, overexcited synchronous motors act as generators of lagging reactive kva and thereby relieve the power company of the necessity for supplying this component. Sometimes unloaded synchronous machines are installed on power systems solely for power-factor correction or for control of reactive-kva flow. Such machines, called *synchronous condensers*, may be more economical in the larger sizes than static capacitors.

Many power companies include a power-factor clause in their rate schedules for industrial consumers. These rate schedules usually involve an extra charge if the power factor is below a specified value, usually about 0.85 lagging; sometimes the energy rate is reduced if the power factor is above 0.90. Usually, however, the rate is stated so that it does not pay to try to improve the power factor much above 0.90 or 0.95 lagging, because of the incremental cost of power-factor-correction equipment. If a plant contains one or more moderate or large machines for which constant-speed drive is satisfactory, synchronous motors should be applied to them. Synchronous motors are seldom economical, however, in sizes below about 50 hp, and usually not below 100 hp.

The kva rating for a specified horsepower output is very nearly inversely proportional to the rated full-load power factor. The size, and therefore the cost, is approximately inversely proportional to the rated power factor. Because of its larger frame size and higher field current, a motor rated for 0.80 power factor has higher starting, pull-in, and pull-out torques than a 1.0-power-factor motor, as shown in Table 7-1.

7-5. The Synchronous Machine as an Impedance. A very useful and refreshingly simple equivalent circuit representing the steady-state behavior of a cylindrical-rotor synchronous machine under balanced, polyphase conditions is obtained if the effect of the armature-reaction flux is represented by an inductive reactance. For the purpose of this preliminary discussion, consider an unsaturated cylindrical-rotor machine. Although neglect of magnetic saturation may appear to be a rather drastic simplification, it will be shown that the results which we are about to obtain can be modified so as to take saturation into account.

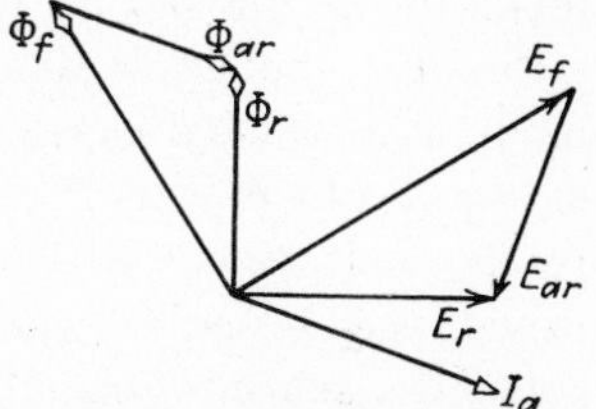

FIG. 7-13. Vector diagram of component fluxes and corresponding voltages.

The resultant air-gap flux can be considered as the vector sum of the component fluxes created by the field and armature-reaction mmfs, respectively, as shown by vectors Φ_f, Φ_{ar}, and Φ_r in Fig. 7-13. From the viewpoint of the armature windings, these fluxes manifest themselves as generated emfs. The resultant air-gap voltage E_r can then be considered as the vector sum of the excitation voltage E_f generated by the field flux and the voltage E_{ar} generated by the armature-reaction flux. The component emfs E_f and E_{ar} are proportional to the field and armature currents, respectively, and according to the conventions for positive directions established in Art. 7-2 (Fig. 7-4) each of these component emfs lags the flux which generates it by 90°, as shown vectorially in Fig. 7-13. But the armature-reaction flux Φ_{ar} is in phase with the

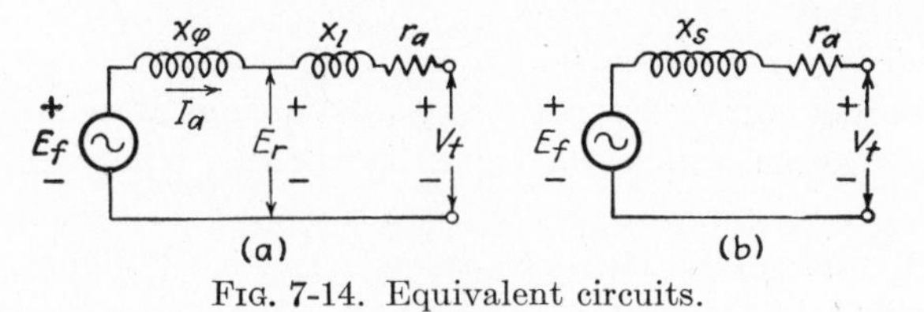

FIG. 7-14. Equivalent circuits.

armature current I_a, and consequently the armature-reaction emf E_{ar} lags the armature current by 90°. Thus,

$$E_f - jI_a x_\varphi = E_r \tag{7-6}$$

where x_φ is the constant of proportionality relating the rms values of E_{ar} and I_a. Note that Eq. 7-6 also applies to that portion of the circuit of Fig. 7-14a to the left of E_r. The effect of armature reaction therefore is simply that of an inductive reactance x_φ accounting for the component voltage generated by the space-fundamental flux created by armature reaction. This reactance is commonly called the *magnetizing reactance* or *reactance of armature reaction.*

The air-gap voltage E_r differs from the terminal voltage by the armature resistance and leakage-reactance voltage drops, as shown to the right of E_r in Fig. 7-14*a* wherein r_a is the armature resistance, x_l is the armature leakage reactance, and V_t is the terminal voltage. All quantities are per phase (line to neutral in a Y-connected machine). The armature leakage reactance accounts for the voltages induced by the component fluxes which are not included in the air-gap voltage E_r. These fluxes are slot and coil-end leakage and the space-harmonic rotating fields produced in the air gap by the armature currents, as described in Art. 4-9.

Finally, the equivalent circuit for an unsaturated cylindrical-rotor machine under balanced polyphase conditions reduces to the form shown in Fig. 7-14*b* in which the machine is represented on a per-phase basis by its excitation voltage E_f in series with a simple impedance. This impedance is called the *synchronous impedance.* Its reactance x_s is called the *synchronous reactance.* In terms of the magnetizing and leakage reactances,

$$x_s = x_\varphi + x_l \tag{7-7}$$

The synchronous reactance x_s takes into account all the flux produced by balanced polyphase armature currents, while the excitation voltage takes into account the flux produced by the field current. In an unsaturated cylindrical-rotor machine at constant frequency, the synchronous reactance is a constant. Furthermore, the excitation voltage is proportional to the field current and equals the voltage which would appear at the terminals if the armature were open-circuited, the speed and field current being held constant.

It is helpful to have a rough idea as to the order of magnitude of the impedance components. For machines with ratings above a few hundred kva, the armature-resistance voltage drop at rated current usually is less than 0.01 of rated voltage; *i.e.*, the armature resistance usually is less than 0.01 per unit on the machine rating as a base. (The per-unit system is described in Appendix A, Art. A-10.) The armature leakage reactance usually is in the range from 0.1 to 0.2 per unit, and the synchronous reactance is in the vicinity of 1.0 per unit. In general, the per-unit armature resistance increases and the per-unit synchronous reactance decreases with decreasing size of the machine. In small machines, such as those in educational laboratories, the armature resistance may be in the vicinity of 0.05 per unit and the synchronous reactance in the vicinity of 0.5 per unit. In all but small machines, the armature resistance usually is neglected except in so far as its effect on losses and heating is concerned.

7-6. Open-circuit and Short-circuit Characteristics. The synchronous reactance can be determined from the results of open-circuit and short-circuit tests. At the same time information can be obtained from these tests regarding the power losses.

a. Open-circuit Characteristic and No-load Rotational Losses. Like the magnetization curve for a d-c machine, the open-circuit characteristic of a synchronous machine is a curve of the armature terminal voltage on open circuit as a function of the field excitation when the machine is running at synchronous speed, as shown by the curve labeled *occ* in Fig. 7-15*a*. If the machine is an existing one, the open-circuit characteristic

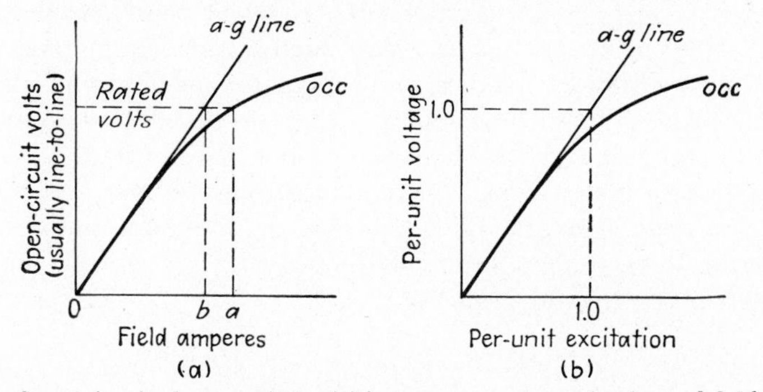

FIG. 7-15. Open-circuit characteristic, (*a*) in terms armature of volts and field amperes, (*b*) in per unit.

is usually determined experimentally by driving it mechanically at synchronous speed with its armature terminals on open circuit and reading the terminal voltage corresponding to a series of values of field current.[4] The open-circuit characteristic often is plotted in per-unit terms, as in Fig. 7-15*b*. In the per-unit system the *unit of voltage* is the rated voltage of the machine, and the *unit of excitation* usually is defined as the excitation corresponding to rated voltage on the air-gap line, as in Fig. 7-15*b*. That is, the excitation *Ob* amp in Fig. 7-15*a* equals 1.00-per-unit excitation in Fig. 7-15*b*.

If the mechanical power required to drive the synchronous machine during the open-circuit test is measured, the no-load rotational losses can be obtained. These losses comprise friction, windage, and core loss corresponding to the flux in the machine at no load. The friction and windage losses at synchronous speed are constant, while the open-circuit core loss is a function of the flux, which in turn is proportional to the open-circuit voltage.

[4] Other test methods can be used on synchronous motors and in cases when the mechanical driving method is inconvenient. For useful information concerning practical test methods, see AIEE Test Code for Synchronous Machines, No. 503, American Institute of Electrical Engineers, New York, 1945.

The mechanical power required to drive the machine at synchronous speed and unexcited is its friction and windage loss. When its field is excited, the mechanical power equals the sum of its friction, windage, and open-circuit core loss. The open-circuit core loss therefore can be found from the difference between these two values of mechanical power. A curve of open-circuit core loss as a function of open-circuit voltage is shown in Fig. 7-16.

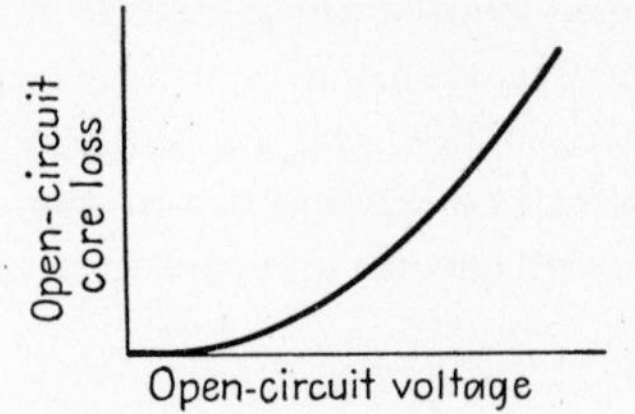

Fig. 7-16. Open-circuit core-loss curve.

b. Short-circuit Characteristic and Short-circuit Load Loss. If the armature terminals of a synchronous machine which is being driven as a generator at synchronous speed are short-circuited through suitable ammeters, as shown in Fig. 7-17*a*, and the field current is gradually increased until the armature current has reached a maximum safe value (perhaps twice rated current), data can be obtained from which the short-circuit armature current can be plotted against the field current. This relation is known as the *short-circuit characteristic.* An open-circuit characteristic *occ* and a short-circuit characteristic *scc* are shown in Fig. 7-17*b*.

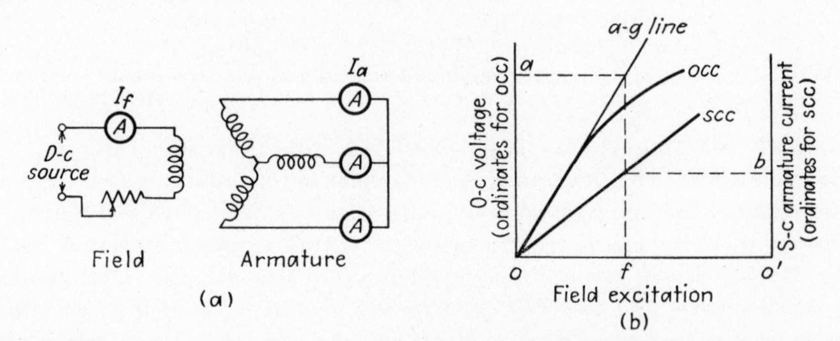

FIG. 7-17. (*a*) Connections for short-circuit test. (*b*) Open-circuit and short-circuit characteristics.

The vector relation between the excitation voltage E_f and the steady-state armature current I_a under polyphase short-circuit conditions is

$$E_f = I_a(r_a + jx_s) \tag{7-8}$$

The vector diagram is shown in Fig. 7-18. Because the resistance is much smaller than the synchronous reactance, the armature current lags the excitation voltage by very nearly 90°. Consequently the armature-reaction-mmf wave is very nearly in line with the axis of the field poles and in opposition to the field mmf, as shown by the vectors A and F representing the space waves of armature-reaction and field mmf, respectively. An mmf wave centered on the axis of the field poles is called a *direct-axis mmf*. In accordance with this terminology the short-circuit characteristic is often called the *direct-axis synchronous impedance characteristic*, a name which has particular significance in salient-pole machines.

The resultant mmf creates the resultant air-gap flux wave which generates the air-gap voltage E_r equal to the voltage consumed in armature resistance r_a and leakage reactance x_l; as an equation,

$$E_r = I_a(r_a + jx_l) \tag{7-9}$$

In most synchronous machines the armature resistance is negligible, and the leakage reactance is between 0.10 and 0.20 per unit—a representative value is about 0.15 per unit. That is, at rated armature current the leakage-reactance voltage drop is about 0.15 per unit. From Eq. 7-9, therefore, the air-gap voltage at rated armature current on short circuit is about 0.15 per unit; that is to say, the resultant air-gap flux is only about 0.15 of its normal-voltage value. Consequently the machine is operating in an unsaturated condition. The short-circuit armature current therefore is directly proportional to the field current over the range from zero to well above rated armature current.

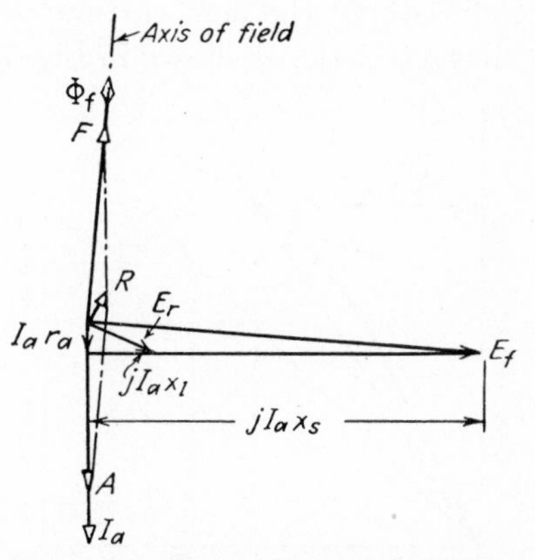

FIG. 7-18. Vector diagram for short-circuit conditions.

The unsaturated synchronous reactance can be found from the open-circuit and short-circuit data. At any convenient field excitation, such as Of in Fig. 7-17*b*, the armature current on short circuit is $O'b$, and the excitation voltage for the same field current corresponds to Oa read from the air-gap line. Note that the voltage on the air-gap line should be used, because the machine is operating on short circuit in an unsaturated condition. If the voltage per phase corresponding to Oa is $E_{f(ag)}$ and the armature current per phase corresponding to $O'b$ is $I_{a(sc)}$, then from Eq. 7-8, with armature resistance neglected, the unsaturated value $x_{s(ag)}$ of the synchronous reactance is

$$x_{s(ag)} = \frac{E_{f(ag)}}{I_{a(sc)}} \tag{7-10}$$

where the subscripts (ag) indicate air-gap-line conditions. If $E_{f(ag)}$ and $I_{a(sc)}$ are expressed in per unit, the synchronous reactance will be in per unit. If $E_{f(ag)}$ and $I_{a(sc)}$ are expressed in volts per phase and amperes per phase, respectively, the synchronous reactance will be in ohms per phase.

For operation at or near rated terminal voltage, it is sometimes assumed that the machine is equivalent to an unsaturated one whose magnetization curve is a straight line through the origin and the rated-voltage point on the open-circuit characteristic, as shown by the dotted line Op in Fig. 7-19. According to this approximation, the saturated value of the synchronous reactance at rated voltage V_t is

$$x_s = \frac{V_t}{I'_{a(sc)}} \tag{7-11}$$

where $I'_{a(sc)}$ is the armature current $O'c$ read from the short-circuit characteristic at the field current Of' corresponding to V_t on the open-circuit characteristic, as shown in Fig. 7-19. This method of handling the effects of saturation usually gives satisfactory results when great accuracy is not required. A more accurate method is described in Art. 8-3.

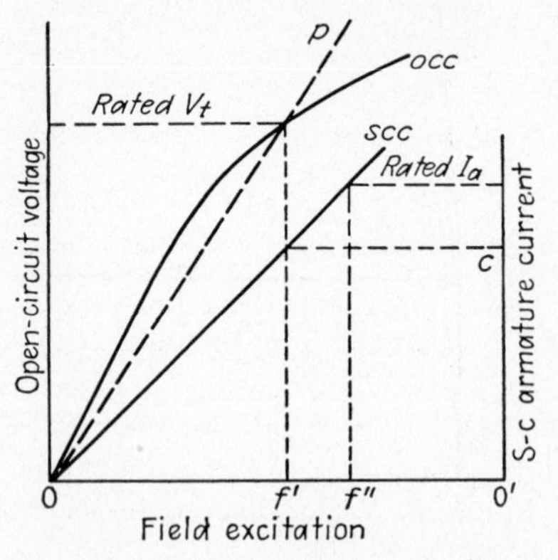

FIG. 7-19. Open-circuit and short-circuit characteristics.

The *short-circuit ratio* is defined as the ratio of the field current required for rated voltage on open circuit to the field current required for rated armature current on short circuit. That is, in Fig. 7-19 the short-circuit ratio SCR is

$$\text{SCR} = \frac{Of'}{Of''} \tag{7-12}$$

It can be shown that the short-circuit ratio is the reciprocal of the per-unit value of the saturated synchronous reactance given by Eq. 7-11.

Example 7-1. The following data are taken from the open-circuit and short-circuit characteristics of a 45-kva 3-phase Y-connected 220-volt (line-to-line) 6-pole 60-cps synchronous machine:

From open-circuit characteristic:

Line-to-line voltage = 220 volts
Field current = 2.84 amp

From short-circuit characteristic:

Armature current, amp	118	152
Field current, amp	2.20	2.84

From air-gap line:

Field current = 2.20 amp
Line-to-line voltage = 202 volts

Compute the unsaturated value of the synchronous reactance, its saturated value at rated voltage in accordance with Eq. 7-11, and the short-circuit ratio. Express the synchronous reactance in ohms per phase and also in per unit on the machine rating as a base.

Solution. At a field current of 2.20 amp, the voltage to neutral on the air-gap line is

$$E_{f(ag)} = \frac{202}{\sqrt{3}} = 116.7 \text{ volts}$$

and for the same field current, the armature current on short circuit is

$$I_{a(sc)} = 118 \text{ amp}$$

From Eq. 7-10,

$$x_{s(ag)} = \frac{116.7}{118} = 0.987 \text{ ohm per phase.}$$

Note that rated armature current is $45{,}000/\sqrt{3}\,(220) = 118$ amp. Therefore $I_{a(sc)} = 1.00$ per unit. The corresponding air-gap-line voltage is

$$E_{f(ag)} = {}^{202}\!/_{220} = 0.92 \text{ per unit}$$

From Eq. 7-10 in per unit,

$$x_{s(ag)} = \frac{0.92}{1.00} = 0.92 \text{ per unit}$$

From the open-circuit and short-circuit characteristics and Eq. 7-11,

$$x_s = \frac{220}{\sqrt{3}\,(152)} = 0.836 \text{ ohm per phase}$$

In per unit, $I'_{a(sc)} = {}^{152}\!/_{118} = 1.29$, and from Eq. 7-11

$$x_s = \frac{1.00}{1.29} = 0.775 \text{ per unit}$$

From the open-circuit and short-circuit characteristics and Eq. 7-12,

$$\text{SCR} = \frac{2.84}{2.20} = 1.29$$

If the mechanical power required to drive the machine is measured while the short-circuit test is being made, information can be obtained regarding the losses caused by the armature current. The mechanical power required to drive the synchronous machine during the short-circuit test equals the sum of friction and windage plus losses caused by the armature current. The losses caused by the armature current can then be found by subtracting friction and windage from the driving power. The losses caused by the short-circuit armature current are known collectively as the *short-circuit load loss*. A curve of short-circuit load loss plotted against armature current is shown in Fig. 7-20. It is approximately parabolic.

The short-circuit load loss comprises copper loss in the armature winding, local core losses caused by the armature leakage flux, and a very small core loss caused by the resultant flux. The d-c resistance loss can be computed if the d-c resistance is measured and corrected, when necessary, for the temperature of the windings during the short-circuit test. For copper conductors

$$\frac{r_T}{r_t} = \frac{234.5 + T}{234.5 + t} \tag{7-13}$$

where r_T and r_t are the resistances at centigrade temperatures T and t, respectively. If this d-c resistance loss is subtracted from the short-circuit load loss, the difference will be the loss due to skin effect and eddy currents in the armature conductors plus the local core losses caused by the armature leakage flux. (The core loss caused by the resultant flux on short circuit is customarily neglected.) This difference between the short-circuit load loss and the d-c resistance loss is the additional loss caused by the alternating current in the armature. It is the stray load loss described in Art. 4-11 and is commonly considered to have the same value under normal load conditions as on short circuit. It is a function of the armature current, as shown by the curve in Fig. 7-20.

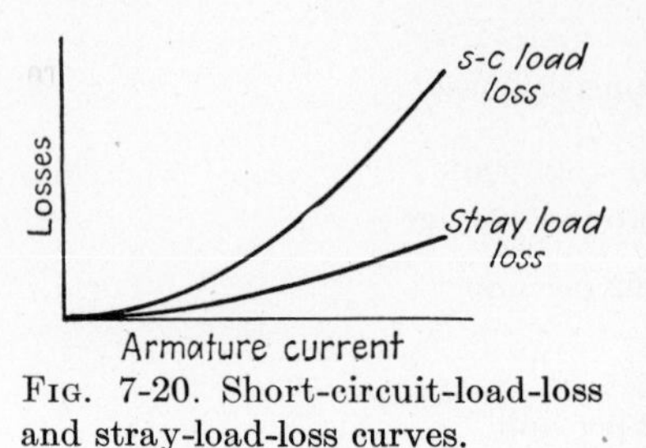

FIG. 7-20. Short-circuit-load-loss and stray-load-loss curves.

As with any a-c device, the effective resistance of the armature is the power loss attributable to the armature current divided by the square of the current. On the assumption that the stray load loss is a function of only the armature current, the effective resistance $r_{a(\text{eff})}$ of the armature can be determined from the short-circuit load loss; thus

$$r_{a(\text{eff})} = \frac{\text{s-c load loss}}{(\text{s-c armature current})^2} \tag{7-14}$$

If the short-circuit load loss and armature current are in per unit, the effective resistance will be in per unit. If they are in watts per phase and amperes per phase, respectively, the effective resistance will be in ohms per phase. Usually it is sufficiently accurate to find the value of $r_{a(\text{eff})}$ at rated current and then to assume it to be constant.

Example 7-2. For the 45-kva 3-phase Y-connected synchronous machine of Example 7-1, at rated armature current (118 amp) the short-circuit load loss (total for 3 phases) is 1.80 kw at a temperature of 25°C. (See Fig. 7-25.) The d-c resistance of the armature at this temperature is 0.0335 ohm per phase.

Compute the armature effective resistance, in per unit and in ohms per phase at 25°C.

Solution. In per unit, the short-circuit load loss is

$$\frac{1.80}{45} = 0.040$$

at $I_a = 1.00$ per unit. Therefore

$$r_{a(\text{eff})} = \frac{0.040}{(1.00)^2} = 0.040 \text{ per unit}$$

On a per-phase basis the short-circuit load loss is

$$\frac{1{,}800}{3} \text{ watts per phase}$$

and consequently the effective resistance is

$$r_{a(\text{eff})} = \frac{1{,}800}{3(118)^2} = 0.043 \text{ ohm per phase}$$

The ratio of a-c to d-c resistance is

$$\frac{r_{a(\text{eff})}}{r_{a(dc)}} = \frac{0.043}{0.0335} = 1.28$$

Because this is a small machine, its per-unit resistance is relatively high. The armature resistance of machines with ratings above a few hundred kva usually is less than 0.01 per unit.

7-7. Steady-state Operating Characteristics. The principal steady-state operating characteristics are the interrelations among terminal voltage, field current, armature current, and power factor, and the efficiency. In many applicational studies these characteristics can be computed with sufficient accuracy on the basis of simple cylindrical-rotor theory. The effects of saturation in the normal-voltage range can be accounted for approximately by assuming constant synchronous reactance adjusted for saturation as in Eq. 7-11 and an equivalent straight-line magnetization curve such as *Op* in Fig. 7-19. The analysis of the steady-state performance of a synchronous machine then reduces to the simple problem of power flow through an impedance which consists almost wholly of inductive reactance, as in Fig. 7-14. For greater accuracy a more complete treatment of the effects of saturation is required, and the effects of salient poles must sometimes be accounted for. These matters are treated in Chap. 8.

Consider a synchronous generator delivering power at constant frequency to a load whose power factor is constant. The curve showing the field current required to maintain rated terminal voltage as the constant-power-factor load is varied is known as a *compounding curve*. It is similar to the armature characteristic of a d-c machine (Fig. 5-29). Three compounding curves at various constant power factors are shown in Fig. 7-21.

If the field current is held constant while the load varies, the terminal voltage will vary. Characteristic curves of terminal voltage plotted against armature current for three constant power factors are shown in Fig. 7-22. Each curve is drawn for a constant field current, but the field current has a different value for each curve. In each case, the field current equals the value required to give rated terminal voltage at rated armature current and corresponds to the rated-armature-current value read from the compounding curves (Fig. 7-21).

Synchronous generators are usually rated in terms of the maximum kva load at a specified voltage and power factor (often 0.8 lagging) which they can carry continuously without overheating. Field heating at the excitation required with lagging-power-factor loads may be the most stringent restriction, especially in turbine generators. For normal loads, the field current usually is regulated so that rated terminal voltage is maintained as the load changes, and the machine then operates along a compounding curve. At overloads, the field current often is held con-

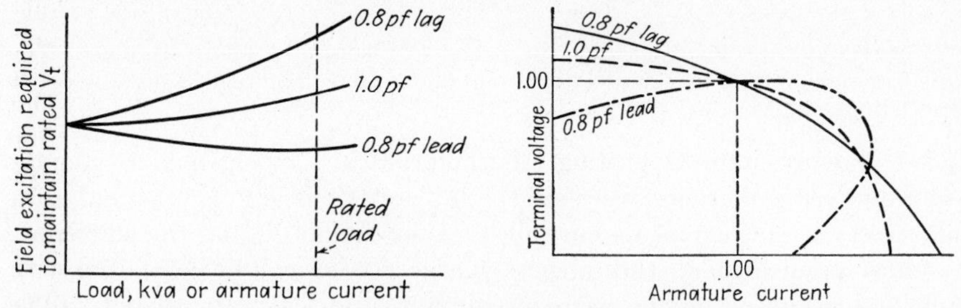

FIG. 7-21. Generator compounding curves.

FIG. 7-22. Generator constant-field-current volt-ampere characteristics.

stant at the maximum permissible value set by field-heating limitations, and the machine then operates along a constant-field-current volt-ampere characteristic. Thus during an emergency overload, service is maintained, but at a reduced voltage. The resulting composite characteristics at constant power factor are shown in Fig. 7-23.

In Art. 7-3 it has already been shown that the power factor at which a synchronous motor operates, and hence its armature current, can be controlled by adjusting its field excitation. The curve showing the relation between armature current and field current at a constant terminal voltage and with a constant shaft load is known as a *V curve,* because of its characteristic shape. A family of V curves is shown in Fig. 7-24. For constant power output, armature current is, of course, a minimum at unity power factor and increases as power factor decreases. The dotted lines are loci of constant power factor. They are the synchronous-motor compounding curves showing how the field current must be varied as load is changed in order to maintain constant power factor. Points to the right of the unity-power-factor compounding curve correspond to overexcitation and leading current input; points to the left correspond to underexcitation and lagging current input. The synchronous-motor compounding curves are very similar to the generator compounding curves of Fig. 7-21. (Note the interchange of armature-current and field-current axes when comparing Figs. 7-21 and 7-24.) In fact, if it were not for the small effects of armature resistance, the motor and generator compounding curves would be identical except that the lagging- and leading-power-factor curves would be interchanged.

Like all electromagnetic machines, the losses in synchronous machines comprise I^2R losses in the windings, core losses, and mechanical losses.

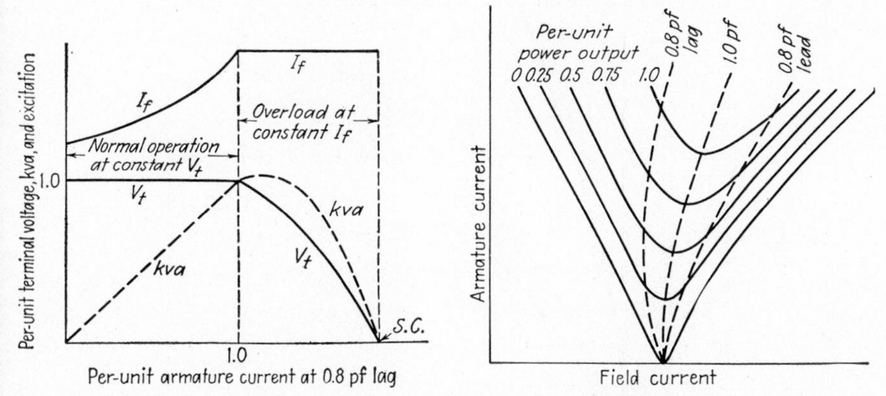

FIG. 7-23. Generator characteristics at 0.8 power factor lagging.

FIG. 7-24. Synchronous-motor V curves.

The conventional efficiency is computed in accordance with a set of rules agreed upon by the ASA.[5] The general principles upon which these rules are based are described in Art. 4-11. The purpose of the following example is to show how these rules are applied specifically to synchronous machines.

Example 7-3. Data are given in Fig. 7-25 with respect to the losses of the 45-kva synchronous machine of Examples 7-1 and 7-2. Compute its efficiency when running as a synchronous motor at a terminal voltage of 230 volts and with a power input to its armature of 45 kw at 0.80 power factor, leading current. The field current measured in a load test taken under these conditions is I_f (test) = 5.50 amp.

Solution. For the specified operating conditions the armature current is

$$I_a = \frac{45{,}000}{\sqrt{3}\,(230)(0.80)} = 141 \text{ amp}$$

The copper losses are to be computed on the basis of the d-c resistances of the windings at 75°C. Correcting the winding resistances by means of Eq. 7-13 gives

Field-winding resistance r_f at 75°C = 35.5 ohms
Armature d-c resistance r_a at 75°C = 0.0399 ohm per phase

[5] ASA Standards, Rotating Electrical Machinery, *Bull.* C50-1943, p. 31, American Standards Association, New York, 1943.

The field copper loss is

$$I_f^2 r_f = (5.50)^2(35.5) = 1,070 \text{ watts, or } 1.07 \text{ kw}$$

According to the ASA Standards, field-rheostat and exciter losses are not charged against the machine. The armature copper loss is

$$3I_a^2 r_a = 3(141)^2(0.0399) = 2,380 \text{ watts, or } 2.38 \text{ kw}$$

and from Fig. 7-25, at $I_a = 141$ amp, stray load loss $= 0.56$ kw. According to the ASA Standards, no temperature correction is to be applied to the stray load loss.

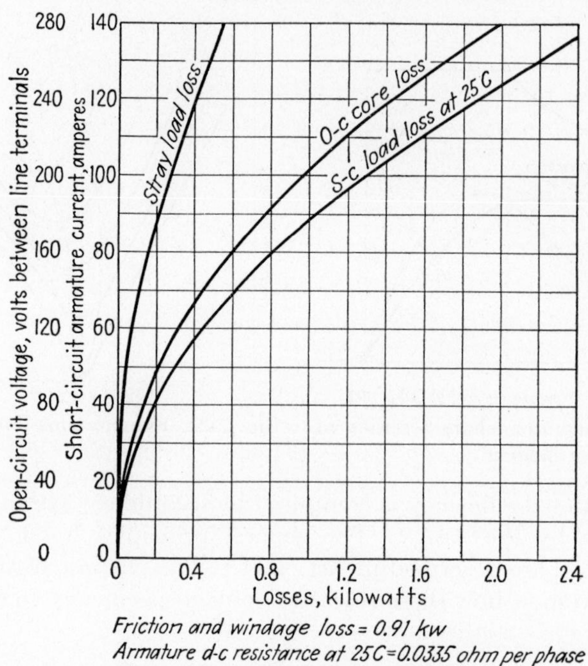

FIG. 7-25. Losses in a 45-kva 3-phase Y-connected 220-volt 60-cps 6-pole synchronous machine.

The core loss is read from the open-circuit core-loss curve at a voltage equal to the internal voltage "behind" the resistance of the machine. The stray load loss is considered to account for the losses caused by the armature leakage flux. For motor action this internal voltage is, vectorially,

$$\begin{aligned} V_t - I_a r_a &= \frac{230}{\sqrt{3}} - 141(0.80 + j0.60)(0.0399) \\ &= 128.4 - j3.4 \end{aligned}$$

The magnitude is 128.4 volts per phase or 222 volts between line terminals. From Fig. 7-25, open-circuit core loss $= 1.20$ kw. Also friction and windage loss $= 0.91$ kw. All losses have now been found.

$$\text{Total losses} = 1.07 + 2.38 + 0.56 + 1.20 + 0.91 = 6.12 \text{ kw}$$

The power input is the sum of the a-c input to the armature and the d-c input to the field, or

$$\text{Input} = 46.07 \text{ kw}$$

Therefore

$$\text{Efficiency} = 1 - \frac{\text{losses}}{\text{input}} = 1 - \frac{6.12}{46.1} = 0.867$$

7-8. Steady-state Power-angle Characteristics. The maximum short-time overload which a synchronous machine can deliver is determined by the maximum torque which can be applied without loss of synchronism. The purpose of this article is to derive expressions for the steady-state power limits of simple systems on the basis of cylindrical-rotor theory and gradually applied loads, including the heretofore neglected effects of external impedances. The study of synchronous-machine power limits is merely a special case of the more general problem of the limitations on power flow through an inductive impedance.

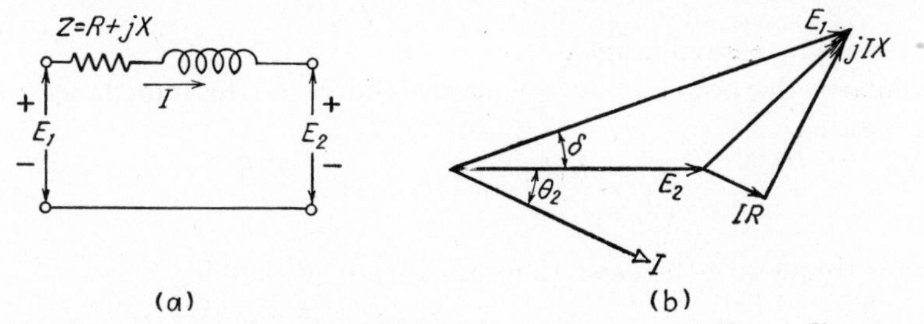

FIG. 7-26. (a) Impedance in series with two voltages. (b) Vector diagram.

Consider the simple circuit of Fig. 7-26*a* comprising two a-c voltages E_1 and E_2 connected by an impedance Z through which the current is I. The vector diagram is shown in Fig. 7-26*b*. The power P_2 delivered through the impedance to the load end E_2 is

$$P_2 = E_2 I \cos \theta_2 \tag{7-15}$$

where θ_2 is the phase angle of I with respect to E_2. The current is, vectorially,

$$I = \frac{E_1 - E_2}{Z} \tag{7-16}$$

If the vector voltages and the impedance are expressed in polar form,

$$I = \frac{E_1\underline{/\delta} - E_2\underline{/0^\circ}}{Z\underline{/\theta_Z}} = \frac{E_1}{Z}\underline{/\delta - \theta_Z} - \frac{E_2}{Z}\underline{/-\theta_Z} \tag{7-17}$$

wherein E_1 and E_2 are the magnitudes of the voltages, δ is the phase angle by which E_1 leads E_2, Z is the magnitude of the impedance, and θ_Z is its angle in polar form. The real part of the vector equation, 7-17, is the component of I in phase with E_2, whence

$$I \cos \theta_2 = \frac{E_1}{Z} \cos (\delta - \theta_Z) - \frac{E_2}{Z} \cos (-\theta_Z) \tag{7-18}$$

Substitution of Eq. 7-18 in Eq. 7-15, noting that $\cos (-\theta_Z) = \cos \theta_Z = R/Z$, gives

$$P_2 = \frac{E_1 E_2}{Z} \cos (\delta - \theta_Z) - \frac{E_2^2 R}{Z^2} \tag{7-19}$$

$$= \frac{E_1 E_2}{Z} \sin (\delta + \alpha_Z) - \frac{E_2^2 R}{Z^2} \tag{7-20}$$

where

$$\alpha_Z = 90° - \theta_Z = \tan^{-1} \frac{R}{X} \tag{7-21}$$

and usually is a small angle.

Similarly the power P_1 at the source end E_1 of the impedance can be expressed as

$$P_1 = \frac{E_1 E_2}{Z} \sin (\delta - \alpha_Z) + \frac{E_1^2 R}{Z^2} \tag{7-22}$$

If, as is frequently the case, the resistance is negligible,

$$P_1 = P_2 = \frac{E_1 E_2}{X} \sin \delta \tag{7-23}$$

If the resistance is negligible and the voltages are constant, the maximum power is

$$P_{1\,\max} = P_{2\,\max} = \frac{E_1 E_2}{X} \tag{7-24}$$

and occurs when $\delta = 90°$.

Equation 7-23 may be compared with the basic torque equation, 3-22 or 7-3, in terms of the interacting flux and mmf waves. In Eq. 7-3, the resultant air-gap flux Φ_r generates the air-gap voltage E_r, and the field mmf F generates the excitation voltage E_f. If saturation is neglected, the excitation voltage E_f is linearly proportional to the field mmf F. The time-phase angle between the voltages E_r and E_f equals the space-phase angle δ_{RF} between the corresponding flux waves. If the constants of proportionality relating mmf to flux and flux to emf are evaluated, Eq. 7-3 can be expressed as

$$T = \frac{q}{\omega_s} \frac{E_r E_f}{x_\varphi} \sin \delta_{RF} \tag{7-25}$$

where q is the number of phases, ω_s is the synchronous speed in mechanical radians per second, and x_φ is the magnetizing reactance. Hence the internal electromechanical power per phase is

$$P = \frac{E_r E_f}{x_\varphi} \sin \delta_{RF} \tag{7-26}$$

Equation 7-26 therefore agrees with Eq. 7-23 for the power flow through a reactance x_φ with voltages E_r and E_f at its two ends.

Note that Eq. 7-26 is a general relation among the five quantities involved. However, it is a sine curve with a maximum value at $\delta_{RF} = 90°$ only when E_r, E_f, and x_φ are constants. In an actual machine the air-gap voltage is not constant with changes in load, because of the changing voltage drops in the armature leakage impedance and in the external circuits. The analysis of the problem in circuit terms, however, allows us easily to account for the effects of these impedances as well as the internal interactions of the magnetic fields.

Example 7-4. A 2,000-hp 1.0-power-factor 3-phase Y-connected 2,300-volt 30-pole 60-cps synchronous motor has a synchronous reactance of 1.95 ohms per phase. For the purposes of this problem all losses may be neglected.

a. Compute the maximum torque in pound-feet which this motor can deliver if it is supplied with power from an infinite bus of rated voltage and frequency and if its field excitation is constant at the value which would result in 1.00 power factor at rated load.

b. Instead of the infinite bus of part *a*, suppose that the motor were supplied with power from a 3-phase Y-connected 2,300-volt 1,750-kva 2-pole 3,600-rpm turbine generator whose synchronous reactance is 2.65 ohms per phase. The generator is driven at rated speed, and the field excitations of generator and motor are adjusted so that the motor runs at 1.00 power factor and rated terminal voltage at full load. The field excitations of both machines are then held constant, and the mechanical load on the synchronous motor is gradually increased. Compute the maximum motor torque under these conditions. Also compute the terminal voltage when the motor is delivering its maximum torque.

Solution. Although this machine is undoubtedly of the salient-pole type, we shall solve the problem by simple cylindrical-rotor theory. The solution accordingly neglects reluctance torque. The machine actually would develop a maximum torque somewhat greater than our computed value.

a. The equivalent circuit is shown in Fig. 7-27*a*, and the vector diagram at full load in Fig. 7-27*b*, wherein E_{fm} is the excitation voltage of the motor and x_{sm} is its synchronous reactance. From the motor rating with losses neglected,

$$\text{Rated kva} = 2{,}000 \times 0.746 = 1{,}492 \text{ kva, 3-phase} = 497 \text{ kva per phase}$$

$$\text{Rated voltage} = \frac{2{,}300}{\sqrt{3}} = 1{,}330 \text{ volts to neutral}$$

$$\text{Rated current} = \frac{497{,}000}{1{,}330} = 374 \text{ amp per phase Y}$$

$$I_a x_{sm} = 374 \times 1.95 = 730 \text{ volts per phase}$$

From the vector diagram at full load

$$E_{fm} = \sqrt{V_t^2 + (I_a x_{sm})^2} = 1{,}515 \text{ volts}$$

When the power source is an infinite bus and the field excitation is constant, V_t and E_{fm} are constant. Substitution of V_t for E_1, E_{fm} for E_2, and x_{sm} for X in Eq. 7-24 then gives

$$P_{\max} = \frac{V_t E_{fm}}{x_{sm}} \tag{7-27}$$
$$= \frac{1{,}330 \times 1{,}515}{1.95} = 1{,}030 \times 10^3 \text{ watts per phase}$$
$$= 3{,}090 \text{ kw for 3 phases}$$

(In per unit, $P_{\max} = 3{,}090/1{,}492 = 2.07$.) With 30 poles at 60 cps, synchronous speed = 4 rev/sec.

$$T_{\max} = \frac{P_{\max}}{\omega_s} = \frac{3{,}090 \times 10^3}{2\pi \times 4} = 123 \times 10^3 \text{ newton-m}$$
$$= 0.738(123 \times 10^3) = 90{,}600 \text{ lb-ft}$$

b. When the power source is the turbine generator, the equivalent circuit becomes that shown in Fig. 7-27*c*, wherein E_{fg} is the excitation voltage of the generator and

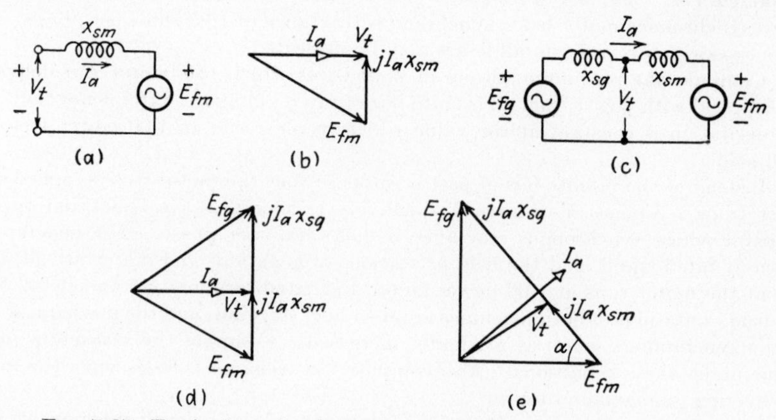

FIG. 7-27. Equivalent circuits and vector diagrams for Example 7-4.

x_{sg} is its synchronous reactance. The vector diagram at full motor load, 1.00 power factor, is shown in Fig. 7-27*d*. As before,

$$V_t = 1{,}330 \text{ volts at full load}$$
$$E_{fm} = 1{,}515 \text{ volts}$$

The synchronous-reactance drop in the generator is

$$I_a x_{sg} = 374 \times 2.65 = 991 \text{ volts}$$

and from the vector diagram

$$E_{fg} = \sqrt{V_t^2 + (I_a x_{sg})^2} = 1{,}655 \text{ volts}$$

Since the field excitations and speeds of both machines are constant, E_{fg} and E_{fm} are constant. Substitution of E_{fg} for E_1, E_{fm} for E_2, and $x_{sg} + x_{sm}$ for X in Eq. 7-24 then gives

$$P_{\max} = \frac{E_{fg}E_{fm}}{x_{sg} + x_{sm}} \tag{7-28}$$

$$= \frac{1{,}655 \times 1{,}515}{4.60} = 545 \times 10^3 \text{ watts per phase}$$

$$= 1{,}635 \text{ kw for 3 phases}$$

(In per unit, $P_{\max} = 1{,}635/1{,}492 = 1.095$.)

$$T_{\max} = \frac{P_{\max}}{\omega_s} = \frac{1{,}635 \times 10^3}{2\pi \times 4} = 65 \times 10^3 \text{ newton-m}$$

$$= 48{,}000 \text{ lb-ft}$$

Synchronism would be lost if a load torque greater than this value were applied to the motor shaft. The motor would stall, the generator would tend to overspeed, and the circuit would be opened by circuit-breaker action.

With fixed excitations, maximum power occurs when E_{fg} leads E_{fm} by 90°, as shown in Fig. 7-27*e*. From this vector diagram

$$I_a(x_{sg} + x_{sm}) = \sqrt{E_{fg}^2 + E_{fm}^2} = 2{,}240 \text{ volts}$$

$$I_a = \frac{2{,}240}{4.60} = 488 \text{ amp}$$

$$I_a x_{sm} = 488 \times 1.95 = 951 \text{ volts}$$

$$\cos\alpha = \frac{E_{fm}}{I_a(x_{sg} + x_{sm})} = \frac{1{,}515}{2{,}240} = 0.676$$

$$\sin\alpha = \frac{E_{fg}}{I_a(x_{sg} + x_{sm})} = \frac{1{,}655}{2{,}240} = 0.739$$

The vector equation for the terminal voltage is

$$V_t = E_{fm} + jI_a x_{sm} = E_{fm} - I_a x_{sm}\cos\alpha + jI_a x_{sm}\sin\alpha$$

$$= 1{,}515 - 643 + j703 = 872 + j703$$

The magnitude of V_t is

$$V_t = 1{,}120 \text{ volts to neutral}$$

$$= 1{,}940 \text{ volts, line to line}$$

When the source is the turbine generator, as in part *b*, the effect of its impedance causes the terminal voltage to decrease with increasing load, thereby reducing the maximum power from 3,090 kw in part *a* to 1,635 kw in part *b*.

7-9. Interconnected Synchronous Generators. Synchronous generators can readily be operated in parallel, and, in fact, the electricity supply systems of highly industrialized countries may have scores or even hundreds of alternators operating in parallel, interconnected by hundreds of miles of transmission lines, and supplying electrical energy to loads scattered over areas of hundreds of thousands of square miles. These huge systems have grown in spite of the necessity for designing the system so that synchronism will be maintained following disturbances, and the problems, both technical and administrative, which must be solved to coordinate the operation of such a complex system of machines and personnel.

The principal reasons for these interconnected systems are continuity of service and economies in plant investment and operating costs. The economy aspects involve a number of considerations such as the fuel economies resulting from combining hydro and steam generating stations on the same system so that the water power can be utilized fully during periods of high water, while the steam power is available for low-water periods. Each generating station on the system usually consists of several alternators operating in parallel.[6]

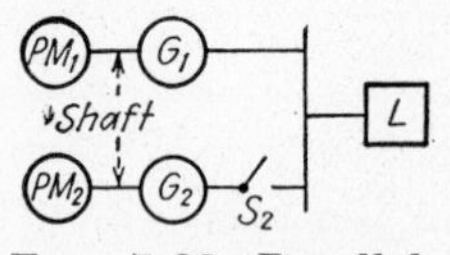

FIG. 7-28. Parallel operation of two synchronous generators.

To illustrate the basic features of parallel operation on a simple scale, consider an elementary system comprising two identical 3-phase generators G_1 and G_2 with their prime movers PM_1 and PM_2 supplying power to a load L, as shown in the single-line diagram of Fig. 7-28. Suppose generator G_1 is supplying the load at rated voltage and frequency, with generator G_2 disconnected. Generator G_2 can be paralleled with G_1 by driving it at synchronous speed and adjusting its field rheostat so that its voltage equals that of the bus. If the frequency of the incoming machine is not exactly equal to that of the bus, the phase relation between its voltage and that of the bus will vary at a frequency equal to the difference between the frequencies of the two voltages—perhaps a fraction of a cycle per second. The switch S_2 should be closed when the two voltages are momentarily in phase and the voltage across the switch is zero. A device for indicating the appropriate moment is known as a *synchroscope*. After G_2 has been synchronized in this manner, each machine can be made to take its share of the active- and reactive-power load by appropriate adjustments of the prime-mover throttles and field rheostats.

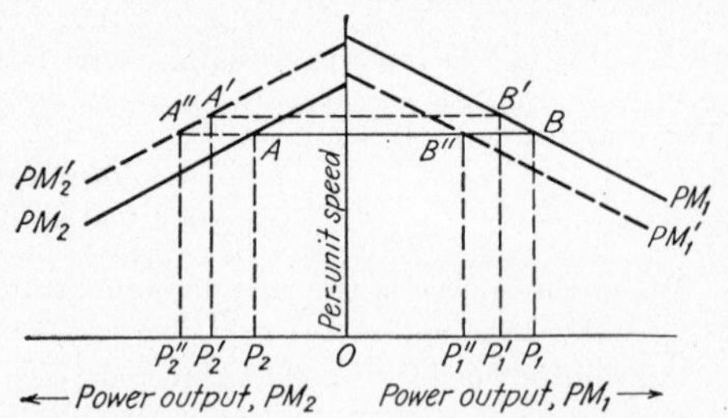

FIG. 7-29. Prime-mover speed-power characteristics.

In contrast with d-c generators, paralleled synchronous generators must run at exactly the same steady-state speed (for the same number of poles). Consequently the way in which the active power divides between them depends almost wholly on the speed-power characteristics of their prime movers. In Fig. 7-29 the sloping solid lines PM_1 and PM_2 represent the speed-power characteristics of the two prime movers for constant throttle openings. All practical prime movers have drooping speed-power char-

[6] For a discussion of the economic and social implications as well as some of the technical aspects of modern electric power systems, see Philip Sporn, "The Integrated Power System," McGraw-Hill Book Company, Inc., New York, 1950.

acteristics. The total load P_L is shown by the solid horizontal line AB, and the generator power outputs are P_1 and P_2 (losses being neglected). Now suppose the throttle opening of PM_2 is increased, translating its speed-power curve upward to the dotted line PM'_2. The dotted line $A'B'$ now represents the load power. Note that the power output of generator 2 has now increased from P_2 to P'_2 while that of generator 1 has decreased from P_1 to P'_1. At the same time, the system frequency has increased. The frequency can be restored to normal with a further load shift from generator 1 to generator 2 by closing the throttle on generator 1, lowering its speed-power curve to the dotted line PM'_1. The load power is now represented by $A''B''$, and the power outputs of the generators are P''_1 and P''_2. Thus the system frequency and the division of active power between the generators can be controlled by means of the prime-mover throttles.

A comparison of the foregoing reasoning with that of Art. 6-3 shows that there are important differences between the parallel operation of synchronous and of d-c generators. With d-c generators the armature current is determined entirely by the difference between the generated emf E_a and the terminal voltage V_t, as in Eqs. 6-2 and 6-3. The division of load between them is determined entirely by their volt-ampere characteristics, as in Figs. 6-16 and 6-17. Load may be shifted from one generator to the other by adjustment of the field rheostats. It makes no difference if changes in load are accompanied by unequal changes in speed. With synchronous generators, however, the power output is not determined by the excitation and terminal voltages, because these voltages can adjust their phase angle δ, in accordance with the power-angle relation (Eq. 7-23). Rather, the electric power output is determined by the mechanical power input from the prime mover, as in Fig. 7-29. Changes in generator excitation are accompanied by changes in the angle δ, but the division of active power is practically unaffected.

Changes in excitation do, however, affect the terminal voltage and reactive-kva distribution. For example, let the two identical generators of Fig. 7-28 be adjusted to share the active and reactive loads equally. The vector diagram is shown by the solid lines in Fig. 7-30, wherein V_t is the terminal voltage, I_L is the load current, I_a is the armature current in each generator, and E_f is the excitation voltage. The synchronous-reactance drop in each generator is $jI_a x_s$, and the resistance drops are neglected. Now suppose the excitation of generator 1 is increased. The bus voltage V_t will increase. It can then be restored to normal by decreasing the excitation of generator 2. The final condition is shown by the dotted vectors in Fig. 7-30. The terminal voltage, load current, and load power factor have been unchanged. Since the prime-mover throttles have not been touched, the power output and in-phase components of the generator armature currents have not been changed. The excitation voltages E_{f1} and E_{f2} have shifted in phase so that $E_f \sin \delta$ remains constant in accordance with the requirement for constant power in Eq. 7-23. The generator with the increased excitation has now taken on more of the lagging reactive-kva load. For the condition shown by the dotted vectors in Fig. 7-30, generator 1 is supplying all the reactive kva, and generator 2 is operating at unity power factor. Thus the terminal voltage and reactive-kva distribution between the generators can be controlled by means of the field rheostats.

Usually the prime-mover throttles are controlled by governors and automatic frequency regulators so that system frequency is maintained very nearly constant and power is divided properly among the generators. Voltage and reactive-kva flow often are automatically regulated by voltage regulators acting on the field circuits of the generators and by transformers with automatic tap-changing devices.

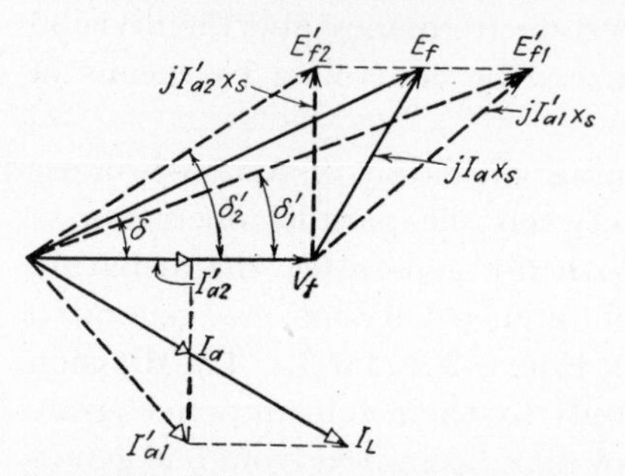

Fig. 7-30. Effects of changing excitations in two paralleled synchronous generators.

7-10. Résumé. Stripped down to its essentials, the workings of a symmetrical polyphase synchronous machine are rather simple. The d-c-excited field winding creates a magnetic field rotating with the rotor. Balanced, polyphase armature currents also create a component magnetic field which rotates around the air gap, traveling through a mechanical angle equal to the angle subtended by two adjacent poles in a time corresponding to one cycle. If the rotor is turning at this speed, the component stator and rotor fields are stationary with respect to each other and a steady torque is produced by their interaction. The resultant air-gap flux is produced by the combined effect of the field and armature currents.

A synchronous machine has two outstanding characteristics: (1) the constancy of its speed when operated at constant frequency, and (2) its ability to accommodate itself to operation over a wide range of power factor.

The first characteristic is a result of the relation between the speed of the rotating magnetic field produced by its armature currents and the frequency of these currents. Only at this speed are the conditions for the production of steady, useful torque fulfilled. Although the speed may differ momentarily from synchronous speed, as during the transient period of adjustment from one steady-state operating condition to another, the average steady-state speed must be constant. The machine accommodates itself to changes in shaft torque by adjusting its torque angle, as in Eq. 7-3. The electromagnetic torque on the rotor acts in a direction to urge the field poles into alignment with the resultant air-gap flux wave. For generator action, the field poles must be driven ahead of the resultant air-gap flux wave by the forward torque of a prime mover, while for motor action the field poles must be dragged behind the resultant air-gap flux wave by the retarding torque of a shaft load. It is as if the field poles were attached to the rotating resultant air-gap flux wave by elastic bands.

The second outstanding characteristic (the adjustability of power factor) is a consequence of the fact that the resultant mmf creating the air-gap flux is the combined effect of a-c magnetizing current in the armature and d-c excitation in the field winding. Adjustment of the field current therefore results in compensating changes in the magnetizing reactive kva in the armature. Thus an overexcited synchronous motor operates at a leading power factor. Alternatively, it may be said that an overexcited synchronous motor is a generator of lagging reactive kva. Because of the economic importance of power factor, the ability of a synchronous motor to operate at a leading power factor is a valuable asset. The adjustability of power factor usually is the chief reason for choosing a synchronous motor instead of an induction motor.

The equivalence of synchronous generators and motors as sources of reactive kva gives rise to a method of thinking which is of value to the power-system engineer, who is faced with the problem of supplying prescribed amounts of lagging reactive kva to his system loads. He recognizes that, within certain limits, economic rather than technical factors can control the location of the excitation needed to furnish the lagging reactive kva. It may be introduced in the generator fields, in the fields of synchronous motors or condensers, or by way of static capacitors connected at strategic points.

With a physical picture of the internal workings in terms of rotating magnetic fields as a background, the next step in our development of synchronous-machine theory is to show that from the viewpoint of its armature circuits a synchronous machine operating under balanced polyphase conditions can be represented on a per-phase basis by a very simple equivalent circuit comprising an internal emf in series with its armature resistance and an inductive reactance. The internal emf is the excitation voltage. The reactance is the synchronous reactance. It accounts for the voltages induced in the reference phase by balanced polyphase armature currents. In Art. 7-5 the synchronous reactance is derived by replacing the effect of the rotating armature-reaction flux wave by a reactance x_φ, called the *magnetizing reactance*. Flux linkages with the reference phase caused by component fluxes which are not included in the armature reaction, such as slot and coil-end leakage and space-harmonic rotating fields, are accounted for by the armature leakage reactance x_l. The synchronous reactance is the sum of the magnetizing and leakage reactances.

The unsaturated synchronous reactance can be found from the results of an open-circuit and a short-circuit test, as in Eq. 7-10. These test methods are a variation of a testing technique applicable not only to synchronous machines but also to anything whose behavior can be approximated by a linear equivalent circuit to which Thévenin's theorem applies. From the Thévenin-theorem viewpoint, an open-circuit test gives the internal emf, and a short-circuit test gives information regarding the internal impedance. From the more specific viewpoint of electromagnetic machinery, an open-circuit test gives information regarding excitation requirements, core losses, and (for rotating machines) friction and windage losses; a short-circuit test gives information regarding the magnetic reactions of the load current, leakage impedances, and losses associated with the load current such as copper and stray load losses. The only real complication arises from the effects of magnetic nonlinearity, effects which can be taken into account approximately by considering the machine to be equivalent to an unsaturated one whose magnetization curve is the straight line *Op* of Fig. 7-19 and whose synchronous reactance is empirically adjusted for saturation as in Eq. 7-11. More accurate methods of handling saturation are discussed in Art. 8-3.

In terms of the equivalent circuit, the prediction of the steady-state synchronous-machine characteristics becomes merely a study of power flow through a simple impedance with constant or easily determinable voltages at its ends. Study of the maximum-power limits for short-time overloads is merely a special case of the limitations on power flow through an inductive impedance. The power flow through such an impedance can be expressed conveniently in terms of the voltages at its sending and receiving ends and the phase angle between these voltages, as in Eq. 7-23 when the resistance is neglected. On the basis of this equation, the internal phenomena in synchronous machines are those of power flow through the magnetizing reactance x_φ with the air-gap voltage E_r at one end and the excitation voltage E_f at the other, the time-phase angle between these voltages being the internal torque angle between the interacting magnetic fields within the machine. The result so obtained is completely in agreement with the basic torque equation, 3-22 or 7-3, on which our theory of torque production in rotating machines is based. Equations 7-20, 7-22, and 7-23, however, allow us to take into account not only the internal electromechanical energy-conversion phenomena within the machine but also the purely electrical phenomena associated with the flow of power through the external circuits. In these equations the angle δ is a sort of generalized torque angle equal to the sum of the internal torque angle of the machine plus the time-phase angle between its air-gap voltage and the external system voltage.

When synchronous generators are operated in parallel, they must be running in synchronism. Consequently the system frequency and the division of active power among them depend on their prime-mover throttle settings and speed-power characteristics, as discussed in Art. 7-9. Generator field control affects system voltage and the division of reactive kva among paralleled alternators. Unlike paralleled d-c generators, however, field control has essentially no effect on the division of the active-power load.

Although we have simplified the synchronous machine considerably in this chapter, nevertheless the results which we have obtained here enable us to predict the normal steady-state characteristics with sufficient accuracy for many purposes. When more accurate results are required, the effects of magnetic saturation and of salient poles must be properly accounted for. These effects are the subject of Chap. 8.

PROBLEMS

7-1. A synchronous generator is supplying power to a large system with its field current adjusted so that the armature current lags the terminal voltage. For the purposes of this problem armature resistance and leakage reactance may be neglected.

The field current is now increased 10 per cent without changing the driving torque of the primer mover. Qualitatively, what changes occur in power output, in magnitude and phase of the armature current, and in magnitude of the torque angle δ_{RF}? Explain by means of vector diagrams representing the flux and mmf waves.

If, instead of changing the field current, the driving torque of the prime mover is increased 10 per cent, what changes will occur?

7-2. A synchronous motor is operating at half load. An increase in its field excitation causes a decrease in armature current. Does the armature current lead or lag the terminal voltage?

7-3. The full-load torque angle δ_{RF} of a synchronous motor at rated voltage and frequency is 30 electrical degrees. Neglect the effects of armature resistance and leakage reactance. If the field current is constant, how would the torque angle be affected by the following changes in operating conditions?

a. Frequency reduced 10 per cent, load torque constant

b. Frequency reduced 10 per cent, load power constant

c. Both frequency and applied voltage reduced 10 per cent, load torque constant

d. Both frequency and applied voltage reduced 10 per cent, load power constant

7-4. A 100-hp 80 per cent power-factor synchronous motor costs 12 per cent more than a 100 per cent power-factor motor of the same rating. The latter motor costs $1,050 installed and has full-load losses totaling 8.5 kw; the 80 per cent power-factor motor has full-load losses of 9.5 kw.

The proposed application calls for operation at full load for 3,000 hr per year, the motor being shut down the remainder of the time. The incremental power cost is 1.0 cent per kilowatthour, and the total investment charges are 15 per cent per year.

What is the cost per kvar of the power-factor correction provided by the 80 per cent power-factor motor?

7-5. In an industrial plant, need arises for the installation of a 50-hp 3-phase 460-volt 60-cps motor to drive an air compressor. At the same time, a survey of power conditions in the plant shows the average load (prior to this installation) to be 365 kw at 70 per cent power factor lagging. This survey, in conjunction with the particular rate structure in force, shows definite economic advantages in favor of raising the plant power factor to 90 per cent.

The following data regarding motors suitable for driving the air compressor are obtained from an electrical manufacturer:

Cost of induction motor = \$496
Cost of 100 per cent power-factor synchronous motor, including exciter = \$748
Cost of 80 per cent power-factor synchronous motor, including exciter = \$796
Full-load efficiency, all motors = 89 per cent
Full-load power factor of induction motor = 89.5 per cent
Cost of 460-volt capacitors = \$9 per kva

All prices are fob factory, freight allowed. Installation costs are 9 per cent of delivered price for the induction motor, 12 per cent for both synchronous motors, and 45 cents per kva for the capacitors. Capacitors should be assumed to be available in blocks of 5 kva.

In view of these conditions, which of the three motors would you recommend buying? In substantiating your recommendation, assume that all equipment has the same useful life.

7-6. A d-c shunt motor is mechanically coupled to a 3-phase synchronous generator. The d-c motor is connected to a 230-volt constant-potential d-c supply, and the a-c generator is connected to a 230-volt (line-to-line) constant-potential constant-frequency 3-phase supply. The 4-pole Y-connected synchronous machine is rated 25 kva, 230 volts, and has a saturated synchronous reactance of 1.60 ohms per phase which will be considered constant in this problem. The 4-pole d-c machine is rated 25 kw, 230 volts. All losses are to be neglected in this problem.

a. If the two machines act as a motor-generator set receiving power from the d-c mains and delivering power to the a-c mains, what is the excitation voltage of the a-c machine in volts per phase (line to neutral) when it delivers rated kva at 1.00 power factor?

b. Leaving the field current of the a-c machine as in part *a*, what adjustment can be made to reduce the power transfer (between a-c and d-c) to zero? Under this condition of zero power transfer what is the armature current of the d-c machine? What is the armature current of the a-c machine?

c. Leaving the field current of the a-c machine as in parts *a* and *b*, what adjustment can be made to cause 25 kw to be taken from the a-c mains and delivered to the d-c mains? Under these conditions, what is the armature current of the d-c machine? What are the magnitude and phase of the current of the a-c machine?

7-7. The following readings are taken from the results of an open-circuit and a short-circuit test on a 9,375-kva 3-phase Y-connected 13,800-volt (line-to-line) 2-pole 60-cps turbine generator driven at synchronous speed:

Field current	169	192
Armature current, short-circuit test	392	446
Line voltage, open-circuit characteristic	13,000	13,800
Line voltage, air-gap line	15,400	17,500

The armature resistance is 0.064 ohm per phase. The armature leakage reactance is 0.10 per unit on the generator rating as a base.

a. Find the unsaturated value of the synchronous reactance in ohms per phase and also in per unit.

b. Find the short-circuit ratio.

c. Find the value of the synchronous reactance adjusted for saturation at rated voltage. Express in ohms per phase and also in per unit.

d. If a short-circuit test is taken at half speed, find the armature current for a field excitation of 169 amp.

7-8. *a*. Compute the field current required in the generator of Prob. 7-7 at rated voltage, rated kva load, 0.80 power factor lagging. Account for saturation under load by the method described in the paragraph relating to Eq. 7-11.

b. In addition to the data given in Prob. 7-7, more points on the open-circuit characteristic are given below:

Field current..........	200	250	300	350
Line voltage..........	14,100	15,200	16,000	16,600

Find the voltage regulation for the load of part *a*. *Voltage regulation* is defined as the rise in voltage when load is removed, the speed and field excitation being held constant. It is usually expressed as a percentage of the voltage under load.

7-9. For the generator of Probs. 7-7 and 7-8, draw characteristic curves similar to those of Fig. 7-23 for a load power factor of 0.80 lagging. Compute a sufficient number of points so that the curves can be sketched fairly accurately.

7-10. Loss data for the generator of Prob. 7-7 are as follows:

Open-circuit core loss at 13,800 volts = 68 kw
Short-circuit load loss at 392 amp, 75°C = 50 kw
Friction and windage = 87 kw
Field-winding resistance at 75°C = 0.285 ohm

Compute the efficiency at rated load, 0.80 power factor lagging.

7-11. A 3-phase synchronous generator is rated 12,000 kva, 13,800 volts, 0.80 power factor, 60 cps. What should be its kva and voltage rating at 0.80 power factor and 50 cps if the field and armature copper losses are to be the same as at 60 cps? If its voltage regulation at rated load and 60 cps is 18 per cent, what will be the value of the voltage regulation at its rated load for 50-cps operation? The effect of armature-resistance voltage drop on regulation may be neglected.

7-12. A 150-hp 0.8-power-factor 2,300-volt 38.0-amp 60-cps 3-phase synchronous motor has a direct-connected exciter to supply its field current. For the purposes of this problem, the efficiency of the exciter may be assumed constant at a value of 80 per cent. The synchronous motor is run at no load from a 2,300-volt 60-cps circuit, with its field current supplied by its exciter, and the following readings taken:

Armature voltage between terminals = 2,300 volts
Armature current = 38.0 amp per terminal
Three-phase power input = 13.7 kw
Field current = 20.0 amp
Voltage applied to field from armature terminals of the exciter = 300 volts

When the synchronous motor is loaded so that its input is 38.0 amp at 0.800 power factor and 2,300 volts between terminals, its field current is found to be 17.3 amp. Under these conditions, what is the efficiency of the synchronous motor exclusive of the losses in its exciter? What is the useful mechanical power output in horsepower?

7-13. From the vector diagram of a synchronous machine with constant synchronous reactance x_s operating at constant terminal voltage V_t and constant excitation voltage E_f, show that the locus of the tip of the armature-current vector is a circle.

On a vector diagram with terminal voltage chosen as the reference vector indicate the position of the center of this circle and its radius. Express the coordinates of the center and the radius of the circle in terms of V_t, E_f, and x_s.

On rectangular-coordinate graph paper draw a chart showing a family of these circular loci for the generator of Prob. 7-7 operating at rated terminal voltage and with excitation voltage as a parameter. Express the chart in per unit, and show circles for values of $E_f = 0.75$, 1.00, 1.25, 1.50, 1.75, and 2.00 per unit. On the chart also draw a family of straight lines showing the loci of operating points for constant values of the angle δ, where δ is the angle by which E_f leads V_t. Draw these constant-angle lines for values of $\delta = -90°$, $-60°$, $-30°$, $0°$, $30°$, $60°$, and $90°$.

7-14. A synchronous motor is supplied by a constant-voltage source through power mains containing inductive reactance and negligible resistance. At no load the motor current is observed to be negligibly small at an excitation of 0.90 per unit. When the motor is loaded without changing the excitation, however, it falls out of step at 81 per cent of its rated power output. A short-circuit test on the machine shows that full load current is produced by an excitation of 0.75 per unit. Saturation and armature resistance may be neglected.

a. What is the per-unit synchronous reactance of the motor?

b. What is the per-unit inductive reactance of the power mains?

c. At what per-unit load will the motor fall out of step if its excitation is increased to 1.25 per unit?

d. What are the per-unit current, the per-unit voltage, and the power factor of the motor under the conditions of *c*?

7-15. Plot curves of per-unit pull-out torque against short-circuit ratio for (*a*) 1.00-power factor, (*b*) 0.80-power-factor synchronous motors. Consider that the excitations are adjusted for rated power factor at rated load and are then held constant. Assume rated terminal voltage from an infinite bus, and neglect all losses.

7-16. A synchronous generator supplies power to a large system through a transmission line. The receiving system is equivalent to an infinite bus whose voltage is 1.00 per unit. The synchronous reactance of the generator is 0.80 per unit, and the reactance of the transmission line is 0.20 per unit based on the generator rating. The resistances of the generator and transmission line are negligible.

The power output and excitation of the generator are adjusted so that the power delivered to the receiving system is 1.00 per unit at 1.00 power factor.

a. Draw the combined vector diagram of the transmission line and generator.

b. Compute the voltage and power factor at the generator terminals.

c. Compute the excitation voltage of the generator.

The power output and excitation of the generator are now readjusted so that it delivers its rated kva at rated terminal voltage.

d. Draw the combined vector diagram of the transmission line and generator for these conditions.

e. Compute the power factor at the generator terminals.

f. Compute the excitation voltage of the generator.

The excitation voltage of the generator is now readjusted to a value corresponding to $E_f = 1.50$ per unit and held constant. The prime-mover torque is then slowly increased.

g. Under these conditions, compute the maximum power which can be delivered to the receiving system without loss of synchronism.

7-17. A 1,000-hp synchronous motor is supplied with power from a synchronous generator driven by a constant-speed prime mover. The cables connecting the generator and motor have negligible impedance. The motor and generator are identical. The synchronous reactance of each is 0.577 per unit. For the purposes of this problem all losses may be neglected.

The excitations of the two synchronous machines are initially adjusted so that they operate at rated terminal voltage, rated armature current, and 1.00 power factor when the shaft load on the synchronous motor equals its rated value.

The excitations are then held constant, and the shaft load on the synchronous motor is slowly increased.

a. Compute the maximum power that the synchronous motor can deliver, in horsepower.

b. Draw a vector diagram for the maximum-power condition, showing the two excitation voltages, terminal voltage, and armature current.

c. Find the power factor at the maximum-power condition.

d. Compute the per-unit values of the terminal voltage and armature current at the maximum-power condition.

e. Compute the maximum power if, instead of remaining constant, the field excitations of the machines are slowly increased so as always to maintain rated terminal voltage and 1.00 power factor while the shaft load is increased.

7-18. A 2,500-hp 2,300-volt Y-connected 3-phase 60-cps 40-pole synchronous motor is supplied with power from a 2,000-kva 2,300-volt Y-connected 60-cps synchronous generator. The synchronous motor drives a load whose torque varies as the square of the speed. The synchronous reactances of the generator and motor are, respectively, 2.00 and 1.50 ohms per phase (saturated values at rated voltage and frequency). For the purposes of this problem all losses may be neglected. The excitations of generator and motor are both adjusted to the values which result in rated terminal voltage when the power delivered to the motor is 2,000 kw at 1.00 power factor. The frequency is then 60 cps. The field currents are then held constant.

If the load is now slowly increased by increasing the generator speed, what is the maximum torque in pound-feet that can be delivered by the motor without loss of synchronism?

7-19. Three 32,500-kva alternators operating in parallel are driven by hydraulic turbines whose prime movers are adjusted so that the speed falls four revolutions from no load to full load at unity power factor on the generators. Assume that no other generators are connected to the system. These generators are delivering a combined load of 75,000 kw at normal frequency (150 rpm). Two of the generators are each delivering 30,000 kw, the balance of the load being taken by the third generator.

a. If the third generator is disconnected from the line, what will be the per cent change in the frequency for a combined output of 75,000 kw?

b. If the combined output is increased to 90,000 kw, how will it be divided among the three generators?

c. If the combined output is reduced to 60,000 kw and the first generator is disconnected from the line, how will the second and third generators divide the load between them?

7-20. Two identical 3-phase alternators, connected in parallel, are driven by prime movers which have dissimilar speed-load characteristics. When the excitations of the alternators are equal, the first delivers 100 amp at 0.9 power factor lagging; and the second, 75 amp at 0.7 power factor lagging.

a. What per cent of the total kilowatt load does each alternator deliver?

b. What is the power factor of the load?

c. If the field excitations are adjusted so that both alternators operate at the same power factor, what current will each deliver? Assume that the load current and power factor are constant.

d. If the field excitations are adjusted so that the total armature copper loss is reduced to its least value, at what power factor will each alternator operate?

CHAPTER 8

SYNCHRONOUS MACHINES: EFFECTS OF SATURATION AND SALIENT POLES

THE basic theory of synchronous machines in Chap. 7 is sufficient for a general understanding of how the machine works and what its principal operating characteristics are. For many practical purposes this theory gives sufficiently accurate quantitative results. In order to concentrate on the essentials, however, the effects of magnetic saturation are given only brief mention in Chap. 7, and the effects of salient poles are omitted entirely. The purpose of this chapter is to discuss the refinements which must be introduced to take into account these effects. The result will be a reasonably complete and accurate theory of the steady-state behavior of polyphase synchronous machines under balanced operating conditions. An important by-product should be a sense of perspective with respect to the quantitative accuracy of the simplified theory of Chap. 7.

8-1. Saturation under Load. The open-circuit characteristic represents essentially the relation between the space-fundamental component of the air-gap flux and the mmf on the magnetic circuit when the field winding constitutes the only mmf source. When the machine is loaded, magnetic conditions are determined by the combined influence of field and armature mmfs. The treatment of saturation is inherently a difficult problem requiring the use of judiciously chosen simplifying assumptions for its solution. The thought process has much in common with that respecting saturation effects in d-c machines and transformers.

Two assumptions usually are made, assumptions which concern principally the leakage fluxes:

1. The armature leakage reactance is assumed to be constant and independent of saturation. The leakage fluxes are in air for a considerable portion of their path lengths, so that they are relatively little affected by saturation. Tests seem to confirm the validity of this assumption.[1] The thought process here is essentially the same as that which leads to the conclusion that the leakage reactances of a transformer should be unaffected by saturation.

2. The saturation is assumed to be determined by the resultant air-gap

[1] T. A. Rogers, Test Values of Armature Leakage Reactance, *Trans. AIEE*, vol. 54, No. 7, pp. 700–705, July, 1935.

flux, and it is assumed that the resultant mmf corresponding to a specified value of air-gap flux is the same under load as on open circuit. The open-circuit characteristic can then be interpreted as the relation between the air-gap voltage E_r and the resultant mmf R of field excitation and armature reaction. This assumption neglects the effects of armature leakage flux on the saturation of the armature iron and of changes in field leakage flux on the saturation of the field iron. Omission of these effects usually is not serious, because the leakage fluxes usually are small and their paths coincide with the main flux for only a small part of the

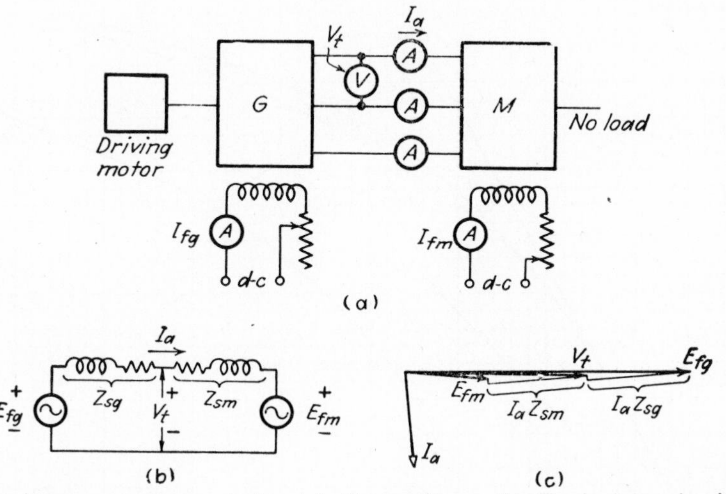

FIG. 8-1. Zero-power-factor test. (a) Connections. (b) Equivalent circuit. (c) Vector diagram.

main flux path. Here also the thought process is like that for transformers. Also neglected are the effect of the armature mmf on the waveform of the synchronously rotating air-gap flux wave and the effect on the flux in the body of the rotor caused by the shifting of the resultant flux wave from its no-load position with respect to the field poles. None of these effects is important in cylindrical-rotor machines, though some of them may be appreciable in salient-pole machines.

8-2. Zero-power-factor Characteristic and Potier Triangle. A special case of considerable theoretical importance is that of a synchronous machine operating at zero (or near-zero) power factor overexcited, because information needed for the handling of saturation effects at normal loads and power factors can be obtained from relatively simple tests at near-zero power factor.

Figure 8-1a shows a synchronous generator G supplying power to an unloaded synchronous motor M of about the same kva rating. The generator G is driven at synchronous speed. The equivalent circuit is shown in Fig. 8-1b, in which I_a is the armature current in the arrow direction, V_t is the terminal voltage, E_{fg} and E_{fm} are the excitation voltages, Z_{sg} and Z_{sm} are the synchronous impedances. Vectorially

$$I_a = \frac{E_{fg} - E_{fm}}{Z_{sg} + Z_{sm}} \tag{8-1}$$

If the difference between the two excitation voltages is made sufficiently great, the armature current can be adjusted to equal its rated full-load

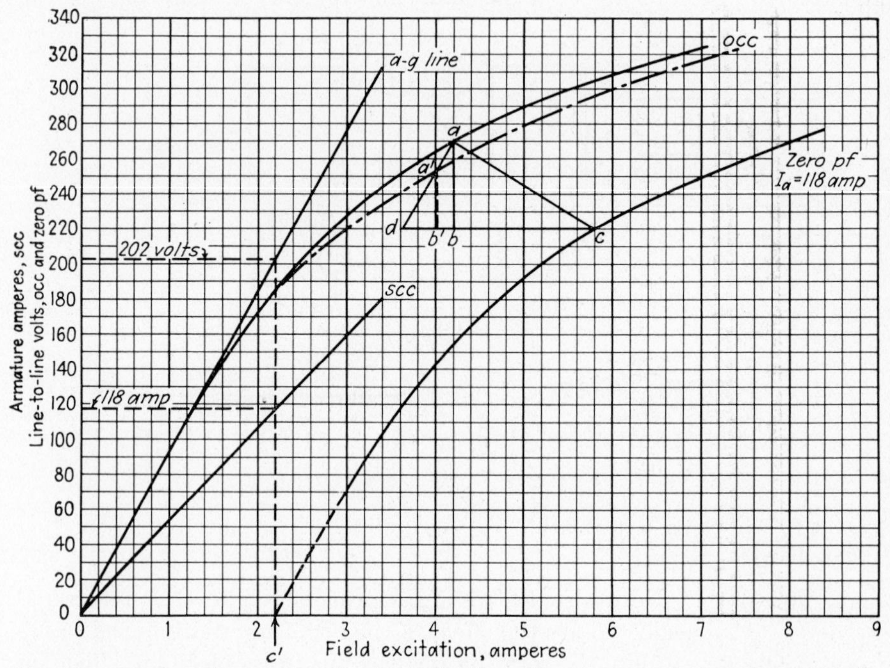

FIG. 8-2. Measured open-circuit, short-circuit, and zero-power-factor characteristics of a 3-phase Y-connected 45-kva 220-volt 118-amp 1,200-rpm 60-cps salient-pole synchronous machine.

value. But the power required by the synchronous motor is only the small amount consumed by its losses. The power factor therefore is very nearly zero. The vector diagram when the generator is overexcited is shown in Fig. 8-1c.

By varying the two field currents, data can be obtained for a curve of terminal voltage as a function of generator field current when the armature current is constant at its rated full-load value and the power factor is near zero. This curve is known as the *zero-power-factor characteristic* of the generator at rated armature current. If the generator is overexcited while the motor is underexcited, the power factor is lagging, as in

Fig. 8-1c. A typical overexcited zero-power-factor characteristic is shown in Fig. 8-2. Alternatively, the motor can be overexcited while the generator is underexcited, and data can be obtained for the overexcited zero-power-factor characteristic of the synchronous motor. Because the losses have very little effect, the characteristic obtained by testing a machine as an overexcited generator at near-zero power factor is very nearly the same as that obtained by testing it as an overexcited motor at no load.

Figure 8-2 shows that the zero-power-factor curve looks like the open-circuit characteristic shifted downward and to the right. This shape can

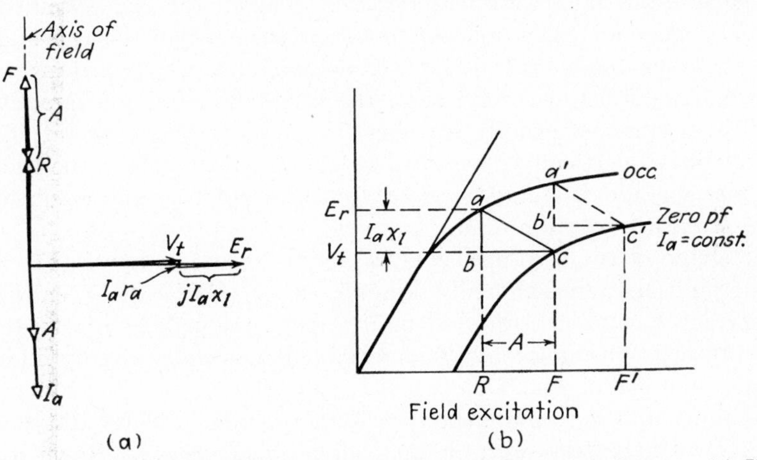

FIG. 8-3. Overexcited synchronous machine at near-zero power factor. (a) Vector diagram. (b) Open-circuit and zero-power-factor characteristics.

be explained in terms of the vector diagram and open-circuit characteristic shown in Fig. 8-3. The thought process is essentially the same as that which led to the graphical method of analysis of self-excited d-c generators in terms of the mmf-voltage triangle described in Art. 5-6c.

The vector diagram is shown in Fig. 8-3a, from which it can be seen that the terminal voltage V_t and the air-gap voltage E_r are very nearly in phase and related by the simple algebraic equation

$$V_t = E_r - I_a x_l \tag{8-2}$$

where x_l is the armature leakage reactance. Also, the resultant mmf R and the field mmf F are very nearly in phase and related by the simple algebraic equation

$$F = R + A \tag{8-3}$$

where A is the magnitude of the armature-reaction mmf.

In accordance with Art. 8-1, assume that the open-circuit characteristic *occ* in Fig. 8-3b is also the relation between the air-gap voltage E_r and the resultant mmf R under load. Corresponding to a point a on the open-circuit characteristic is an operating point c at zero power factor for which the terminal voltage V_t is given by Eq. 8-2 and the field excitation F is given by Eq. 8-3, as shown graphically by the triangle *abc* in Fig. 8-3*b* in which *ab* equals the leakage-reactance voltage drop $I_a x_l$ and *bc* equals the armature-reaction mmf A. If the field excitation is increased to F' and the armature current is held constant, the triangle *abc* remains constant in size, shifting parallel to itself to the position $a'b'c'$ with its corner a remaining on the open-circuit characteristic and its corner c tracing out the zero-power-factor characteristic. Thus if the open-circuit characteristic were an exact relation between the air-gap voltage and the resultant mmf under load, if the leakage reactance were constant, and if the armature resistance were zero, the zero-power-factor characteristic would be a curve of exactly the same shape as the open-circuit characteristic shifted vertically downward by an amount equal to the leakage-reactance voltage drop and horizontally to the right by an amount equal to the armature-reaction mmf.

The shape of the zero-power-factor characteristic suggests that if the open-circuit characteristic truly represented the relation between the air-gap voltage E_r and the resultant mmf R, then the leakage reactance and armature-reaction mmf could be determined experimentally by finding a triangle, like *abc* of Fig. 8-3*b*, which would fit everywhere between the open-circuit and zero-power-factor characteristics. These test curves, together with the test short-circuit characteristic *scc*, are shown in Fig. 8-2. The point c', which is the extension of the zero-power-factor characteristic to zero terminal voltage, can be determined by reading from the short-circuit characteristic the field current corresponding to the armature current at which the zero-power-factor test was taken.

The geometrical construction for finding the triangle *abc* is as follows: Select a point c on the zero-power-factor characteristic above the knee of the curve—say at rated voltage (Fig. 8-2). Draw the horizontal line *cd* equal in length to the field excitation $c'O$ on short circuit. Through point d draw the straight line *da* parallel to the air-gap line, intersecting the open-circuit characteristic at a. Draw the vertical line *ab*. The triangle *abc* is commonly called the *Potier triangle* after its inventor. The voltage represented by the length *ab* is known as the *Potier-reactance voltage drop*. The *Potier reactance* x_p is given by

$$x_p = \frac{\text{voltage drop } ab \text{ per phase}}{\text{zero-power-factor armature current } I_a \text{ per phase}} \tag{8-4}$$

Example 8-1. Find the value of the Potier reactance of the synchronous machine of Fig. 8-2 at rated voltage. Express the result in ohms per phase and also in per unit on the rating of the machine as a base.

Solution. From the Potier triangle *abc* (Fig. 8-2) the Potier-reactance voltage drop *ab* is 50 volts, line to line, at 118 amp per phase. Therefore

$$x_p = \frac{50}{\sqrt{3}\,(118)} = 0.245 \text{ ohm per phase}$$

The per-unit value of the Potier-reactance voltage drop is $50/220 = 0.227$ at $I_a = 1.00$ per unit. Hence

$$x_p = \frac{0.227}{1.00} = 0.227 \text{ per unit}$$

Comparison of the Potier triangle with the triangle *abc* of Fig. 8-3*b* shows that if the relation between the air-gap voltage E_r and the resultant mmf R were exactly the same as the open-circuit characteristic, and if the leakage reactance were constant, then the Potier reactance x_p would equal the leakage reactance x_l. Also, the horizontal side *bc* of the Potier triangle would equal the armature-reaction mmf A corresponding to the armature current at which the zero-power-factor test was taken. The same Potier triangle *abc* moved parallel to itself would fit between the open-circuit and zero-power-factor characteristics at any part of the curves.

The saturation curve relating the air-gap voltage E_r and the resultant mmf R under load is not, however, exactly the same as the open-circuit characteristic. The most important factor causing the discrepancy is the difference between the field-leakage flux under load and at no load. In cylindrical-rotor machines this discrepancy usually is small, and the Potier reactance usually nearly equals the armature leakage reactance.

The effects of field-leakage flux usually are more important in salient-pole machines particularly those having long, slim poles, and hence rather large field leakage. At zero power factor overexcited, the field current is larger for a given air-gap voltage than for the same voltage on open circuit. Consequently the field-leakage flux is larger, and the magnetic circuit is more saturated to an extent determined by the magnetization curve for the portion of the flux path common to the main air-gap flux and the field-leakage flux. This path includes the field poles and rotor core. The saturation curve relating the air-gap voltage and the resultant mmf at zero power factor then lies somewhat to the right of the open-circuit characteristic, as shown by the dash-dot curve in Fig. 8-2. This load saturation curve intersects the line *da* at a'. The armature leakage-reactance voltage drop equals the vertical distance $a'b'$, whereas the Potier-reactance voltage drop is *ab*. Thus if the effects of field leakage are appreciable, the Potier reactance is somewhat larger than the armature leakage reactance. The load saturation curve and the open-circuit characteristic usually become vertically nearer together as saturation is increased to high values. The value of the armature leakage reactance can usually be measured with fair accuracy by measuring the Potier triangle at very high values of saturation.[2]

Occasionally the effects on saturation of changes in field leakage under load are included by use of a family of load saturation curves computed with the appropriate values of field-leakage flux.[3] This refinement will not be adopted here, however. Instead, it will be assumed that the open-circuit characteristic is also the saturation curve under load. The use of the Potier reactance at normal voltage as if it were the armature leakage reactance then makes an empirical allowance for the errors introduced by using the open-circuit characteristic as if it were the saturation curve under load.

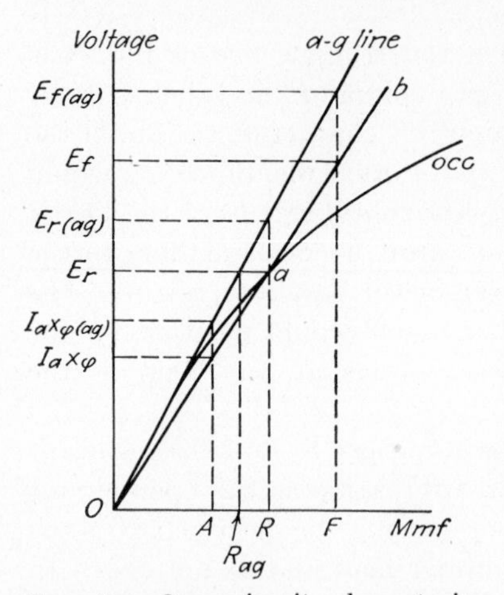

FIG. 8-4. Open-circuit characteristic, showing the effects of saturation on the component mmfs and voltages.

8-3. Saturated Synchronous Machine. The effects of saturation under load can be taken into account with good accuracy by use of a saturation factor determined from the open-circuit characteristic.[4] Although this method of handling saturation is based on simple cylindrical-rotor theory, it is also commonly applied as an approximation to salient-pole machines, with satisfactory results over the normal operating range.

According to the assumptions of Art. 8-1, conditions in the magnetic circuit are determined by the air-gap voltage E_r and the resultant mmf R read from the saturation curve, as shown by point a in Fig. 8-4. If it were not for the effects of saturation, however, the resultant mmf corresponding to E_r would be the value R_{ag} read from the air-gap line. The degree of saturation can be described in terms of a *saturation factor* k defined as

$$k = \frac{R}{R_{ag}} \tag{8-5}$$

It can be shown by simple proportion that k is also given by

$$k = \frac{E_{r(ag)}}{E_r} \tag{8-6}$$

[2] L. A. March and S. B. Crary, Armature Leakage Reactance of Synchronous Machines, *Trans. AIEE*, vol. 54, No. 4, pp. 378–381, April, 1935.

[3] B. L. Robertson, T. A. Rogers, and C. F. Dalziel, The Saturated Synchronous Machine, *Trans. AIEE*, vol. 56, No. 7, pp. 858–863, July, 1937.

[4] Charles Kingsley, Jr., Saturated Synchronous Reactance, *Trans. AIEE*, vol. 54, No. 3, pp. 300–305, March, 1935.

where $E_{r(ag)}$ is the voltage corresponding to the resultant mmf R as read from the air-gap line. The saturation factor k is a function of the air-gap voltage E_r, as shown by the curve k in Fig. 8-5.

If it were not for the effects of saturation, the excitation voltage would equal the voltage $E_{f(ag)}$ read from the air-gap line corresponding to the field mmf F, as shown in Fig. 8-4, and the voltage generated by the armature-reaction flux would be $I_a x_{\varphi(ag)}$ on the air-gap line corresponding to the armature-reaction mmf A, where $x_{\varphi(ag)}$ is the *unsaturated value* of the mag-

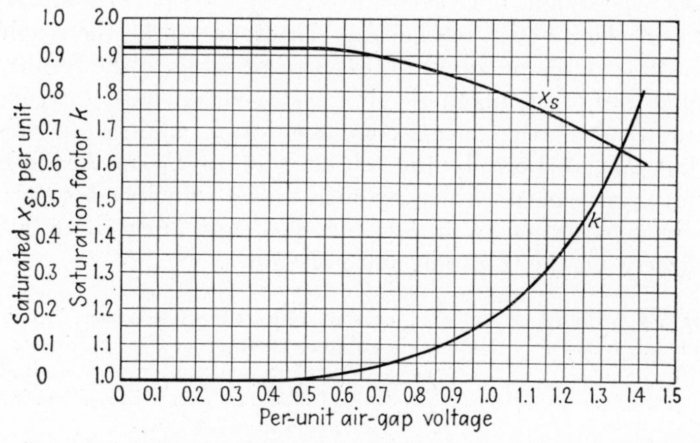

FIG. 8-5. Curves of saturation factor k and saturated synchronous reactance x_s as functions of air-gap voltage for machine of Fig. 8-2.

netizing reactance. In terms of the unsaturated value $x_{s(ag)}$ of the synchronous reactance

$$x_{\varphi(ag)} = x_{s(ag)} - x_l \tag{8-7}$$

where x_l is the leakage reactance.

Because of the effects of saturation, however, the reluctance of the magnetic circuit is k times its unsaturated value, and the component fluxes are reduced to $1/k$ times their unsaturated values. Under *saturated* conditions the excitation voltage E_f therefore is

$$E_f = \frac{E_{f(ag)}}{k} \tag{8-8}$$

and the *saturated value* x_φ of the magnetizing reactance is

$$x_\varphi = \frac{x_{\varphi(ag)}}{k} = \frac{x_{s(ag)} - x_l}{k} \tag{8-9}$$

The *saturated synchronous reactance* x_s then is

$$x_s = x_l + \frac{x_{s(ag)} - x_l}{k} \tag{8-10}$$

In accordance with the assumptions of Art. 8-2, the Potier reactance x_p may be used in place of the leakage reactance x_l when the open-circuit characteristic is used as the saturation curve under load. The saturated synchronous reactance is a function of the air-gap voltage, as shown by the curve x_s in Fig. 8-5.

Comparison of Eqs. 8-8 and 8-9 with Fig. 8-4 shows that the saturated values of the component voltages generated by the component fluxes produced by field excitation and armature reaction are given by readings taken from the straight line *Oab* drawn through the point *a* on the saturation curve at the air-gap voltage E_r. In other words, the machine has been linearized at the magnetic state corresponding to the resultant flux. If the reluctance of the magnetic circuit stayed constant, the component mmfs *F* and *A* would then create component fluxes and voltages along the straight line *Oab*, as shown by the voltage readings E_f and $I_a x_\varphi$ in Fig. 8-4. The thought process is an extension of the linear principle of superposition to a nonlinear situation by linearizing cause and effect along a straight line predicated on the resultant state of affairs.

Example 8-2. Compute the field current required for a power factor of 0.80, leading current, when the 45-kva synchronous machine of Fig. 8-2 is running as a synchronous motor at a terminal voltage of 230 volts and with a power input to its armature of 45 kw.

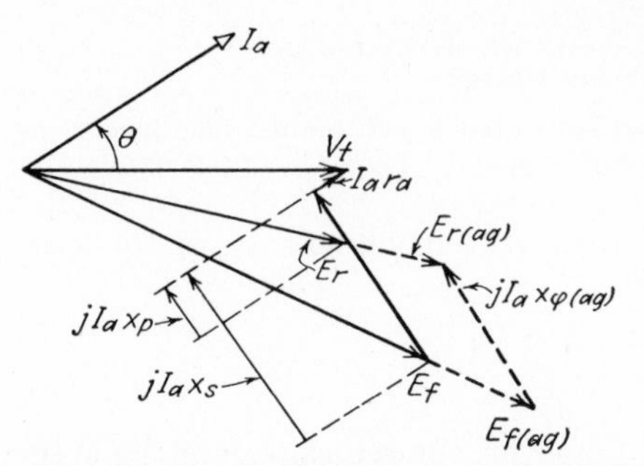

FIG. 8-6. Vector diagram of a saturated synchronous motor, Example 8-2.

Solution. The vector diagram is shown in Fig. 8-6, in which I_a represents motor input current. The per-unit system of units will be used. From Example 7-1, $x_{s(ag)} = 0.92$ per unit, and from Example 8-1, $x_p = 0.227$ per unit. Since this is a small machine, armature-resistance voltage drop is appreciable but refinements such as the effects of temperature on resistance may be neglected. From Example 7-2, $r_{a(\text{eff})} = 0.040$ per unit. (The d-c resistance may be used without introducing appreciable error.) The voltage V_t in per unit is $^{230}\!/_{220} = 1.045$, and the kva input is $1.00/0.80 = 1.25$ per unit. With V_t as the reference vector,

$$I_a = \frac{1.25}{1.045}(0.80 + j0.60) = 0.956 + j0.718 \text{ per unit}$$

The next step is to compute the air-gap voltage E_r, so that the saturation can be determined. From Fig. 8-6,

$$\begin{aligned} E_r &= V_t - I_a(r_a + jx_p) \qquad (8\text{-}11) \\ &= 1.045 - (0.956 + j0.718)(0.040 + j0.227) = 1.170 - j0.246 \end{aligned}$$

The magnitude of $E_r = 1.20$ per unit. We can then proceed in either of the two ways shown below:

1. From the curves of Fig. 8-5 at $E_r = 1.20$, $k = 1.375$, and $x_s = 0.730$. The saturated value E_f of the excitation voltage is given vectorially by

$$E_f = V_t - I_a(r_a + jx_s) \tag{8-12}$$
$$= 1.045 - (0.956 + j0.718)(0.040 + j0.730) = 1.531 - j0.727$$

The magnitude of $E_f = 1.70$. This can be translated to field current by computing the corresponding air-gap-line value; thus, from Eq. 8-8

$$E_{f(ag)} = kE_f = (1.375)(1.70) = 2.33$$

This is the per-unit value of the field excitation, when unit excitation is defined as the value corresponding to unit voltage on the air-gap line, as in Fig. 7-15*b*. For the machine of this problem, from Fig. 8-2, 1.00 per-unit excitation is 2.40 field amperes. Therefore the field current for the specified load is

$$I_f = (2.33)(2.40) = 5.60 \text{ amp}$$

2. If the curves of Fig. 8-5 have not been plotted, the saturation factor k can be determined directly from Fig. 8-4. Then from Eq. 8-6, the unsaturated value of the air-gap voltage is

$$E_{r(ag)} = kE_r \tag{8-13}$$

as shown by the dotted vector $E_{r(ag)}$ in Fig. 8-6. The unsaturated value of the excitation voltage is

$$E_{f(ag)} = E_{r(ag)} - jI_a x_{\varphi(ag)} \tag{8-14}$$

as shown by the dotted vectors in Fig. 8-6, where $x_{\varphi(ag)}$ is found from Eq. 8-7 with x_p used in place of x_l; the magnitude of $E_{f(ag)}$ is, of course, identical to the value found by the first method. As before, the corresponding field current is 5.60 amp. The value obtained by an actual load test is

$$I_f(\text{test}) = 5.50 \text{ amp}$$

Results calculated by these methods usually check tests with errors of only a few per cent for normally saturated machines of either cylindrical-rotor or salient-pole construction.

a. Approximations. The methods of handling saturation illustrated in Example 8-2 are well suited to problems in which the air-gap voltage is known or can readily be computed. It may be necessary to resort to a cut-and-try process when the data are given in such a way that the air-gap voltage cannot be computed directly. The difficulties encountered and two approximate methods of handling saturation are illustrated in the following example.

Example 8-3. A turboalternator supplies power to a large system through a transmission line, as shown in Fig. 8-7*a*. The receiving system may be considered an infinite bus whose voltage $E_e = 1.00$ per unit. The line has a reactance of 0.30 per unit on the generator rating as a base. The unsaturated value of the synchronous reactance of the generator is $x_{s(ag)} = 0.970$ per unit, and its Potier reactance at rated voltage is $x_p = 0.105$ per unit. Resistances can be neglected. The saturation factor of the generator is given in Fig. 8-8.

Let the generator excitation be adjusted so that the power factor is 1.00 at the receiving end of the line when the generator delivers rated current. The excitation is then held constant.

Compute the steady-state power limit of the system on the assumption that the saturation of the machine stays constant at the value corresponding to the stated initial operating conditions. Discuss the effects of this assumption.

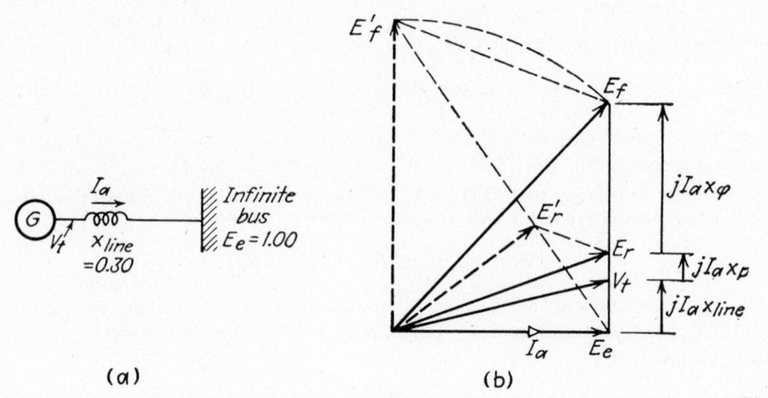

FIG. 8-7. Synchronous generator and transmission line for Example 8-3. (a) Single-line diagram. (b) Vector diagram.

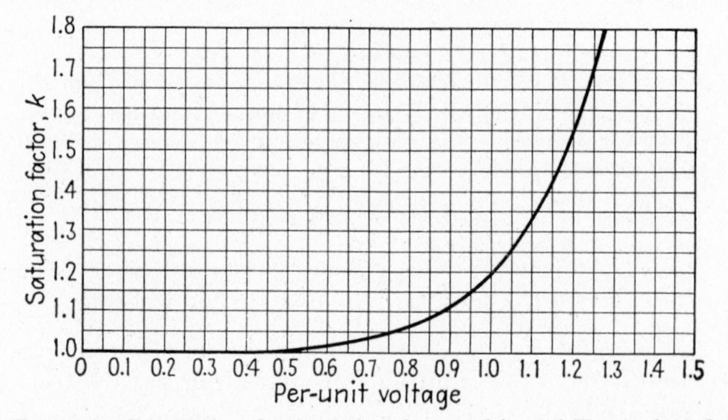

FIG. 8-8. Saturation factor k for the machine of Example 8-3.

Solution. The vector diagram for the stated initial conditions is shown by the solid lines in Fig. 8-7b, with the voltage E_e as the reference vector. The air-gap voltage E_r is

$$\begin{aligned} E_r &= E_e + jI_a(x_{\text{line}} + x_p) \qquad (8\text{-}15) \\ &= 1.00 + j(1.00)(0.405) = 1.00 + j0.405 \end{aligned}$$

The magnitude of E_r is 1.08, and from Fig. 8-8, $k = 1.30$. From Eq. 8-10, the saturated synchronous reactance is

$$x_s = 0.105 + \frac{0.970 - 0.105}{1.30} = 0.770$$

and the saturated value of the complete system reactance is

$$x_{\text{total}} = x_{\text{line}} + x_s = 1.07$$

The saturated value of the excitation voltage is

$$E_f = E_e + jI_a x_{\text{total}} = 1.00 + j1.07$$

and the magnitude of E_f is 1.46 per unit. The initial values have now been computed.

If it is assumed that the saturation stays constant when the driving torque of the prime mover is increased, the power limit would occur when the angle by which the excitation voltage leads the receiver-bus voltage becomes 90°, as shown by the dotted vector E'_f in Fig. 8-7*b*. The corresponding power limit for constant excitation is, by Eq. 7-24,

$$P_{\max} = \frac{E_f E_e}{x_{\text{total}}} = \frac{(1.46)(1.00)}{1.07} = 1.37 \text{ per unit}$$

However, the saturation actually does not stay constant. When the excitation voltage has swung to the position E'_f, the air-gap voltage has decreased as shown by the vector E'_r in Fig. 8-7*b*. The saturation therefore has decreased. The saturated values of E_f and x_φ are not constant, and strictly speaking, the power limit does not occur at exactly 90°. In general, the saturation decreases as the power limit is approached. The field current therefore is able to produce a larger component flux, and the maximum power actually is somewhat larger than the value computed here. A much longer calculation based on the method described in the reference cited in footnote 4 gives $P_{\max} = 1.45$.

Sometimes it is assumed that the saturation is determined by the *terminal voltage* (rather than by the air-gap voltage) and that the leakage reactance and magnetizing reactance both are reduced by the effects of saturation. With these assumptions, the saturated value of the synchronous reactance is

$$x_s = \frac{x_{s(ag)}}{k_t} \tag{8-16}$$

where k_t is the saturation factor at the terminal voltage. Note that this method of handling saturation is the same as the approximate method of Eq. 7-11 and Fig. 7-19. Although this method probably does not reflect the true state of affairs in the magnetic circuit as accurately as does Eq. 8-10, it has the advantage of simplicity.[5] Recomputation of the power limit of Example 8-3 on this basis gives a value of 1.36 per unit.

b. ASA Method. The method of handling saturation recommended by the American Standards Association[6] is primarily concerned with the calculation of field current for specified conditions of terminal voltage, armature current, and power factor. Essentially it consists in treating the machine as an unsaturated one, and then adding an additional component of excitation to account for saturation. This additional component is found from the saturation corresponding to the air-gap voltage. The same data are required as for the saturated-synchronous-reactance method of Example 8-2, the computations are similar, and the results are almost identical. The essentials of the method are described in the fol-

[5] For a study of turbine-generator power limits based on this method of handling saturation see C. G. Adams and J. B. McClure, Underexcited Operation of Turbogenerators, *Trans. AIEE*, vol. 67, pp. 521–526, 1948.

[6] ASA Standards, Rotating Electrical Machinery, *Bull.* C50-1943, p. 33, American Standards Association, New York, 1943.

lowing example. We shall, however, depart slightly from the ASA method in the working out of details.

Example 8-4. Solve Example 8-2 by the ASA method.

Solution. First the field current will be computed, neglecting saturation. The constants of the machine are given in Example 8-2. The vector diagram is shown in Fig. 8-9, wherein I_a represents motor input current. The per-unit values of V_t and I_a are the same as in Example 8-2. If the machine were unsaturated, the excitation voltage E_f (unsaturated) would be

$$E_f \text{ (unsaturated)} = V_t - I_a(r_a + jx_{s(ag)}) \tag{8-17}$$
$$= 1.045 - (0.956 + j0.718)(0.040 + j0.92) = 1.667 - j0.909$$

The magnitude of E_f (unsaturated) is 1.90 per unit. The corresponding field current on the air-gap line is

$$I_{f(ag)} = (1.90)(2.40) = 4.55 \text{ amp}$$

where 2.40 amp is the field current corresponding to 1.00 per-unit voltage (220 volts) on the air-gap line in Fig. 8-2.

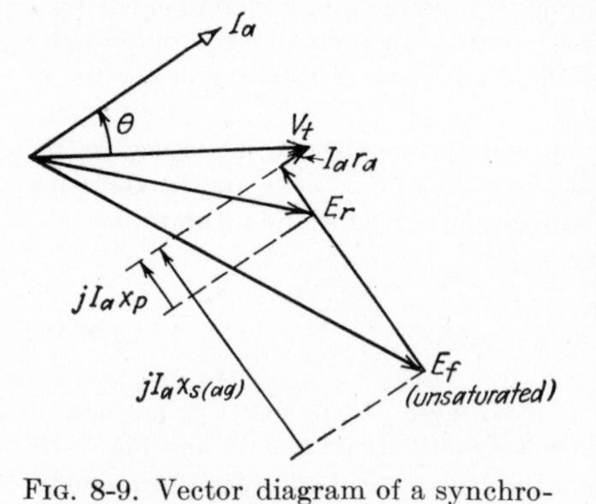

FIG. 8-9. Vector diagram of a synchronous motor with saturation neglected, Example 8-4.

The increment in field current caused by saturation is now found from the air-gap voltage and the open-circuit characteristic. The air-gap voltage E_r computed as in Eq. 8-11 is 1.20 per unit, or 264 volts line to line. From Fig. 8-2, the corresponding field current on the open-circuit characteristic is 3.95 amp and on the air-gap line is 2.87 amp. The increment ΔI_f caused by saturation is

$$\Delta I_f = 3.95 - 2.87 = 1.08 \text{ amp}$$

In the ASA method this increment is added directly to the field current computed without saturation. Accordingly the field current corrected for saturation is

$$I_f = I_{f(ag)} + \Delta I_f = 4.55 + 1.08 = 5.63 \text{ amp}$$

Compare with the value of 5.60 amp computed in Example 8-2 and the value, 5.50 amp, obtained by an actual load test.

8-4. Effects of Salient Poles. Introduction to Two-reactance Theory. In Art. 7-2 we have seen that the spatial position of the armature-reaction flux wave with respect to the field poles depends on the phase angle of the armature current with respect to the excitation voltage. In a uniform-air-gap machine the reluctance of the magnetic circuit is independent of the spatial position of the flux wave. Consequently in such a machine the inductive effect of balanced polyphase armature currents can be accounted for by a synchronous reactance which is independent of power factor.

In a salient-pole machine, however, quite a different state of affairs exists. The purpose of this article is to show what modifications must be made in the elementary concepts of Chap. 7 in order to account for the effects of the nonuniform air gap, and to give some indications of when the effects of saliency should be taken into account. We shall find that the armature currents can be resolved into time-quadrature components which produce two synchronously rotating components of armature reaction, one in line with and the other in space quadrature with the axes of the field poles. The effects of each of these components can then be treated separately. This method of analysis was first propounded by Blondel at the turn of the century and later developed by Doherty and Nickle[7] into the reasonably simple quantitative theory the fundamentals

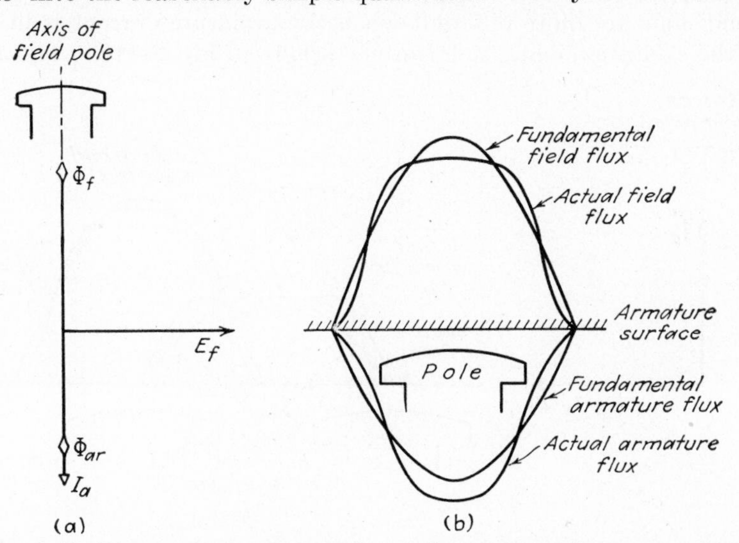

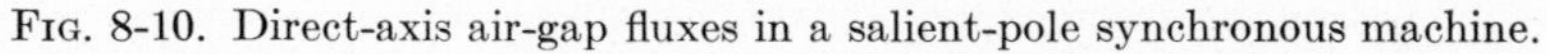

FIG. 8-10. Direct-axis air-gap fluxes in a salient-pole synchronous machine.

of which are discussed in this article. Only balanced steady-state conditions will be considered, and the effects of magnetic saturation will be neglected so that the resultant flux conditions can be considered as the sum of component fluxes.

In Art. 7-2 it has been shown that the armature-reaction flux wave lags the field flux wave by a space angle of $90° + \theta_{lag}$, where θ_{lag} is the time-phase angle by which the armature current in the direction of the excitation emf lags the excitation emf. If the armature current I_a lags the excitation emf E_f by 90°, the armature-reaction flux wave Φ_{ar} is directly opposite the field poles and in the opposite direction to the field flux Φ_f, as shown vectorially in Fig. 8-10*a*. The corresponding component flux-density waves at the armature surface produced by the field current and

[7] R. E. Doherty and C. A. Nickle, Synchronous Machines. Part I—An Extension of Blondel's Two-reaction Theory. Part II—Steady-state Power-angle Characteristics, *Trans. AIEE*, vol. 45, pp. 912–947, 1926. Other papers in this classic series deal with transient conditions.

by the synchronously rotating space-fundamental component of armature-reaction mmf are shown in Fig. 8-10*b*, in which the effects of slots are neglected. The waves consist of a space-fundamental and a family of odd-harmonic components rotating at synchronous speed. The harmonic fluxes generate harmonic emfs in the armature windings, but their effects usually are small because of the smoothing influence of distributed armature windings. Accordingly only the space-fundamental components will be considered. It is the fundamental components which are represented by the flux-per-pole vectors Φ_f and Φ_{ar} in Fig. 8-10*a*.

Conditions are quite different when the armature current is in phase with the excitation emf, as shown vectorially in Fig. 8-11*a*. The axis of

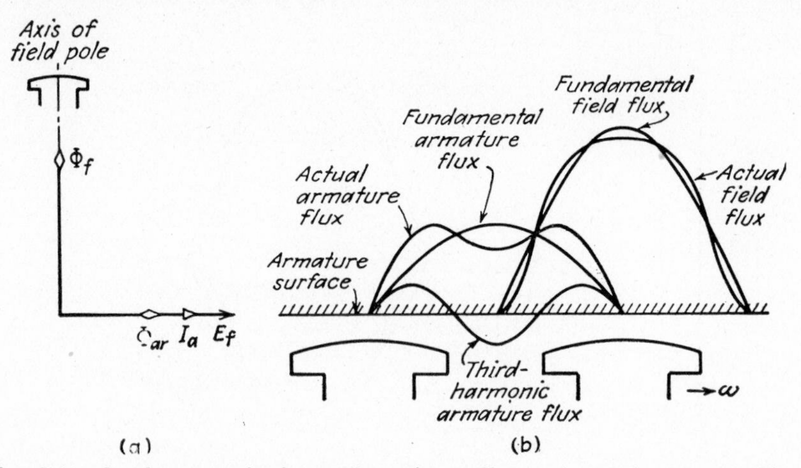

FIG. 8-11. Quadrature-axis air-gap fluxes in a salient-pole synchronous machine.

the armature-reaction wave then is opposite an interpolar space, as shown in Fig. 8-11*b*. The armature-reaction flux wave is badly distorted, comprising principally a fundamental and a prominent third space harmonic. The third-harmonic flux wave generates third-harmonic emfs in the armature phases, but these voltages do not appear between the line terminals (see Art. 4-6*c*).

Because of the high reluctance of the air gap between poles, the space-fundamental armature-reaction flux when the armature reaction is in quadrature with the field poles (Fig. 8-11*b*) is less than the space-fundamental armature-reaction flux which would be created by the same armature current if the armature flux wave were directly opposite the field poles (Fig. 8-10*b*). Hence the magnetizing reactance is less when the armature current is in time phase with the excitation emf (Fig. 8-11*a*) than when it is in time quadrature with respect to the excitation emf (Fig. 8-10*a*).

The effects of salient poles can be taken into account by resolving the armature current I_a into two components, one in time quadrature with and the other in time phase with the excitation voltage E_f, as shown vectorially in Fig. 8-12, which is drawn for a salient-pole generator operating at a lagging power factor. The component I_d of the armature current, in time quadrature with the excitation voltage, produces a component fundamental armature-reaction flux Φ_{ad} along the axes of the field poles, as in Fig. 8-10. The component I_q, in phase with the excitation voltage, produces a component fundamental armature-reaction flux Φ_{aq} in space quadrature with the field poles, as in Fig. 8-11. The subscripts d and q refer to the space phase of the armature-reaction fluxes, and not to the

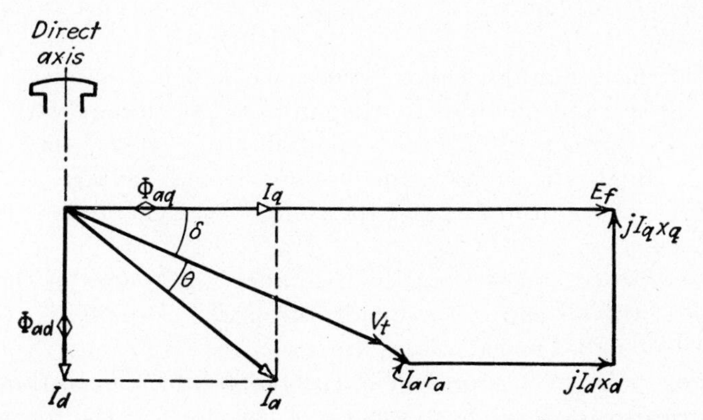

FIG. 8-12. Basic vector diagram of a salient-pole synchronous generator.

time phase of the component currents producing them. Thus a *direct-axis* quantity is one whose magnetic effect is centered on the axes of the field poles. Direct-axis mmfs act on the main magnetic circuit. A *quadrature-axis* quantity is one whose magnetic effect is centered on the interpolar space. With each of the component currents I_d and I_q there is associated a component synchronous-reactance voltage drop, jI_dx_d and jI_qx_q, respectively. The reactances x_d and x_q are, respectively, the direct- and quadrature-axis synchronous reactances. They are defined as follows:[8]

The *direct-axis synchronous reactance* is the ratio of the fundamental component of reactive armature voltage, due to the fundamental direct-axis component of armature current, to this component of current under steady-state conditions and at rated frequency.

The *quadrature-axis synchronous reactance* is the ratio of the fundamental component of reactive armature voltage, due to the fundamental quadrature-axis component of armature current, to this component of current under steady-state conditions and at rated frequency.

[8] AIEE Test Code for Synchronous Machines, No. 503, American Institute of Electrical Engineers, New York, June, 1945.

The synchronous reactances account for the inductive effects of all the fundamental-frequency-generating fluxes created by the armature currents, including both armature-leakage and armature-reaction fluxes. Thus the inductive effects of the direct- and quadrature-axis armature-reaction flux waves can be accounted for by *direct-* and *quadrature-axis magnetizing reactances* $x_{\varphi d}$ and $x_{\varphi q}$, respectively, similar to the magnetizing reactance x_φ of cylindrical-rotor theory. The direct- and quadrature-axis synchronous reactances then are

$$x_d = x_l + x_{\varphi d} \tag{8-18}$$
$$x_q = x_l + x_{\varphi q} \tag{8-19}$$

where x_l is the armature leakage reactance and is assumed to be the same for direct- and quadrature-axis currents. Compare with Eq. 7-7. As shown in the generator vector diagram (Fig. 8-12), the excitation voltage E_f equals the vector sum of the terminal voltage V_t plus the armature-resistance drop $I_a r_a$ and the component synchronous-reactance drops $jI_d x_d + jI_q x_q$.

The reactance x_q is less than the reactance x_d, because of the greater reluctance of the air gap in the quadrature axis. Usually x_q is between 0.6 and 0.7 of x_d. Typical values are given in Table 8-1. Note that a small salient-pole effect is present in turboalternators, even though they are cylindrical-rotor machines, because of the effect of the rotor slots on the quadrature-axis reluctance.

TABLE 8-1
TYPICAL PER-UNIT VALUES OF MACHINE REACTANCES
(Machine kva rating as base)

	Synchronous motors		Synchronous condensers	Water-wheel generators	Turbo-alternators
	High speed	Low speed			
x_d	0.65 (min) 0.80 (av) 0.90 (max)	0.80 1.10 1.50	1.60	0.60 1.00 1.25	1.15
x_q	0.50 (min) 0.65 (av) 0.70 (max)	0.60 0.80 1.10	1.00	0.40 0.65 0.80	1.00

In using the vector diagram of Fig. 8-12, the armature current must be resolved into its direct- and quadrature-axis components. This resolution assumes that the phase angle $\theta + \delta$ of the armature current with respect to the excitation voltage is known. Often, however, the power-factor angle θ at the machine terminals is explicitly known, rather than the internal power-factor angle $\theta + \delta$. The vector diagram of Fig. 8-12 is repeated by the solid-line vectors in Fig. 8-13. Study of this vector diagram shows that the dotted vector $o'a'$, perpendicular to I_a,

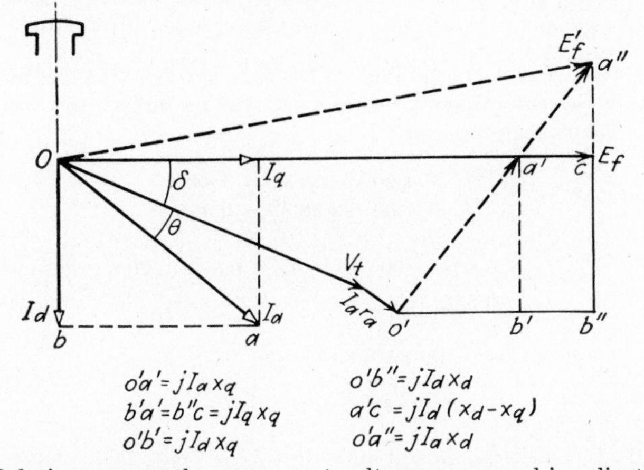

FIG. 8-13. Relations among the component voltages concerned in salient-pole theory.

equals jI_ax_q. This result follows geometrically from the fact that triangles $o'a'b'$ and oab are similar, because their corresponding sides are perpendicular. Thus

$$\frac{o'a'}{oa} = \frac{b'a'}{ba} \tag{8-20}$$

or

$$o'a' = \frac{b'a'}{ba} oa = \frac{jI_qx_q}{I_q} I_a = jI_ax_q \tag{8-21}$$

The vector sum $V_t + I_ar_a + jI_ax_q$ then locates the angular position of the excitation voltage E_f and therefore the direct and quadrature axes. Physically this must be so, because all the field excitation in a normal machine is in the direct axis. One use of these relations in determining the excitation requirements for specified operating conditions at the terminals of a salient-pole machine is illustrated in Example 8-5.

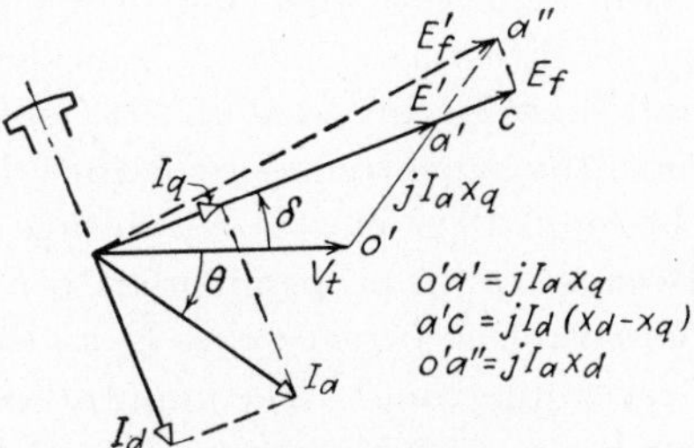

FIG. 8-14. Vector diagram of the salient-pole synchronous generator of Example 8-5.

Example 8-5. The reactances x_d and x_q of a salient-pole synchronous generator are 1.00 and 0.60 per unit, respectively. The armature resistance is negligible.

Compute the excitation voltage when the generator delivers rated kva at 0.80 power factor, lagging current, and rated terminal voltage.

Solution. First, the phase of E_f must be found so that I_a can be resolved into its direct- and quadrature-axis components. The vector diagram is shown in Fig. 8-14. Vectorially,

$$\begin{aligned} I_a &= 0.80 - j0.60 = 1.00\underline{/-36.9^\circ} \\ jI_a x_q &= j(0.80 - j0.60)(0.60) = 0.36 + j0.48 \\ V_t &= \text{reference vector} \qquad = 1.00 + j0 \\ \text{Vector sum} &= E' \qquad = 1.36 + j0.48 = 1.44\underline{/19.4^\circ} \end{aligned}$$

The angle $\delta = 19.4°$, and the phase angle between E_f and I_a is $36.9° + 19.4° = 56.3°$.

The armature current can now be resolved into its direct- and quadrature-axis components. Their magnitudes are

$$\begin{aligned} I_d &= 1.00 \sin 56.3^\circ = 0.832 \\ I_q &= 1.00 \cos 56.3^\circ = 0.555 \end{aligned}$$

Vectorially:

$$\begin{aligned} I_d &= 0.832\underline{/-90^\circ + 19.4^\circ} = 0.832\underline{/-70.6^\circ} \\ I_q &= 0.555\underline{/19.4^\circ} \end{aligned}$$

We could now find E_f from the vector relation

$$E_f = V_t + jI_d x_d + jI_q x_q \tag{8-22}$$

A shorter method, however, is to add numerically the length $a'c = I_d(x_d - x_q)$ to the magnitude of E'; thus, the magnitude of the excitation voltage is the algebraic sum

$$\begin{aligned} E_f &= E' + I_d(x_d - x_q) \\ &= 1.44 + (0.832)(0.40) = 1.77 \text{ per unit} \end{aligned} \tag{8-23}$$

Vectorially, $E_f = 1.77\underline{/19.4^\circ}$.

In the simplified theory of Chap. 7 a synchronous machine was assumed to be representable by a single reactance—the synchronous reactance of Art. 7-5. The question naturally arises as to how serious an approximation is involved if a salient-pole machine is treated in this simple fashion. Suppose the salient-pole machine of Figs. 8-13 and 8-14 were treated by cylindrical-rotor theory as if it had a single synchronous reactance equal to its direct-axis value x_d, as determined from the simple open-circuit and short-circuit tests of Art. 7-6. For the same conditions at its terminals, the synchronous-reactance drop $jI_a x_d$ would be the vector $o'a''$, and the equivalent excitation voltage would be E'_f as shown in these figures. Because ca'' is perpendicular to E_f, there is little difference in magnitude between the correct value E_f and the approximate value E'_f for a normally excited machine. Recomputation of the excitation voltage on this basis for Example 8-5 gives a value of $1.79\underline{/26.6^\circ}$.

In so far as the interrelations among terminal voltage, armature current, power, and excitation over the normal operating range are concerned, the effects of salient poles usually are of minor importance, and such characteristics of a salient-pole machine (for example, compounding curves, volt-ampere characteristics, and V curves) usually can be computed with satisfactory accuracy by the simple cylindrical-rotor theory of Chap. 7. Only at small excitations will the differences between cylindrical-rotor and salient-pole theory become important.

There is, however, considerable difference in the phase angles of E_f and E'_f in Figs. 8-13 and 8-14. This difference is caused by the reluctance torque in a salient-pole machine. Its effect is investigated in the following article.

8-5. Power-angle Characteristics of Salient-pole Machines. In Art. 7-8 we have seen that the power flow in a cylindrical-rotor synchronous machine is merely a special case of power flow through an inductive impedance. The power flow through such an impedance can be expressed in terms of its resistance and reactance, the magnitudes of the voltages at its two ends, and the phase angle between these voltages. The purpose

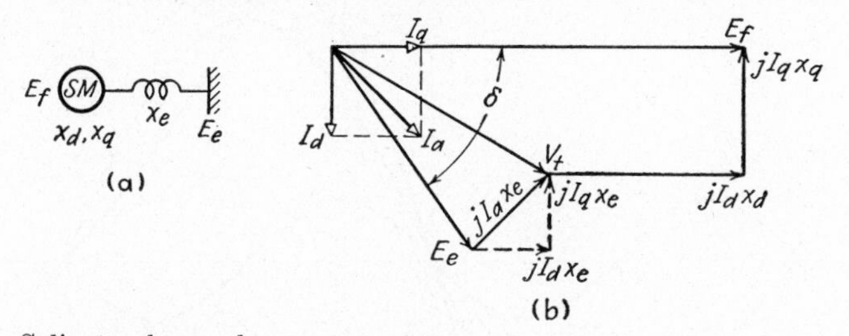

FIG. 8-15. Salient-pole synchronous machine and series impedance. (*a*) Single-line diagram. (*b*) Vector diagram.

of the following discussion is to derive similar expressions for salient-pole machines.

a. Basic Theory. We shall limit the discussion to the simple system shown in the schematic diagram of Fig. 8-15*a*, comprising a salient-pole synchronous machine *SM* connected to an infinite bus of voltage E_e through a series impedance of reactance x_e per phase. Resistance will be neglected because it usually is small. Consider that the synchronous machine is acting as a generator. The vector diagram is shown by the solid-line vectors in Fig. 8-15*b*. The dotted vectors show the external reactance drop resolved into components due to I_d and I_q. The effect of the external impedance is merely to add its reactance to the reactances of the machine; *i.e.*, the total values of reactance interposed between the excitation voltage E_f and the bus voltage E_e are

$$X_d = x_d + x_e \tag{8-24}$$

$$X_q = x_q + x_e \tag{8-25}$$

If the bus voltage E_e is resolved into components $E_e \sin \delta$ and $E_e \cos \delta$ in phase with I_d and I_q, respectively, the power P delivered to the bus per phase is

$$P = I_dE_e \sin \delta + I_qE_e \cos \delta \tag{8-26}$$

Also, from Fig. 8-15b,

$$I_d = \frac{E_f - E_e \cos \delta}{X_d} \tag{8-27}$$

$$I_q = \frac{E_e \sin \delta}{X_q} \tag{8-28}$$

Substitution of Eqs. 8-27 and 8-28 in Eq. 8-26 gives

$$P = \frac{E_f E_e}{X_d} \sin \delta + E_e^2 \frac{X_d - X_q}{2X_d X_q} \sin 2\delta \tag{8-29}$$

The power-angle characteristic (Eq. 8-29) is shown in Fig. 8-16. The first term is the same as the expression obtained for a cylindrical-rotor

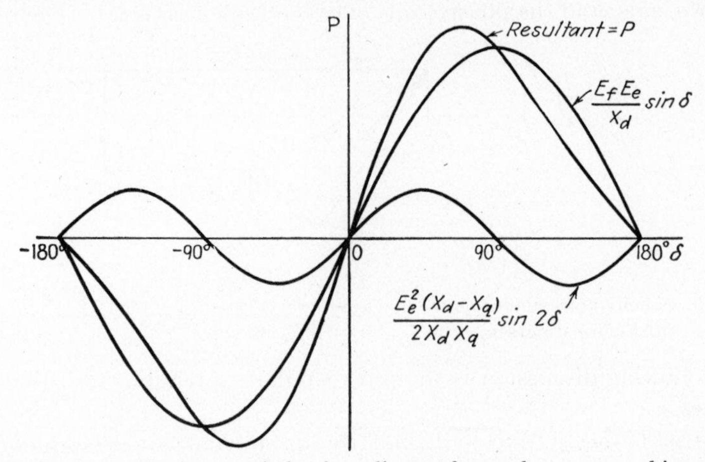

FIG. 8-16. Power-angle characteristic of a salient-pole synchronous machine, showing fundamental component due to field excitation and second-harmonic component due to reluctance torque.

machine. This term is merely an extension of the basic concepts of Chap. 3 to include the effects of series reactance. The second term introduces the effect of salient poles. It represents the fact that the air-gap flux wave creates torque tending to align the field poles in the position of minimum reluctance. This term is the power corresponding to the *reluctance torque* and is of the same general nature as the reluctance torque discussed in Art. 2-2. Note that the reluctance torque is independent of field excitation. Note, also, that if $X_d = X_q$, as in a uniform-air-gap machine, there is no preferential direction of magnetization, the reluctance torque is zero, and Eq. 8-29 reduces to the power-angle equation for a cylindrical-rotor machine whose synchronous reactance is X_d.

Figure 8-17 shows a family of power-angle characteristics at various values of excitation and constant terminal voltage. Only positive values of δ are shown. The curves for negative values of δ are the same except for a reversal in the sign of P. That is, the generator and motor regions are alike if the effects of resistance are negligible. For generator action E_f leads E_e; for motor action E_f lags E_e. Steady-state operation is stable over the range where the slope of the power-angle characteristic is positive. Because of the reluctance torque, a salient-pole machine is stiffer than one with a cylindrical rotor—*i.e.*, for equal voltages and equal

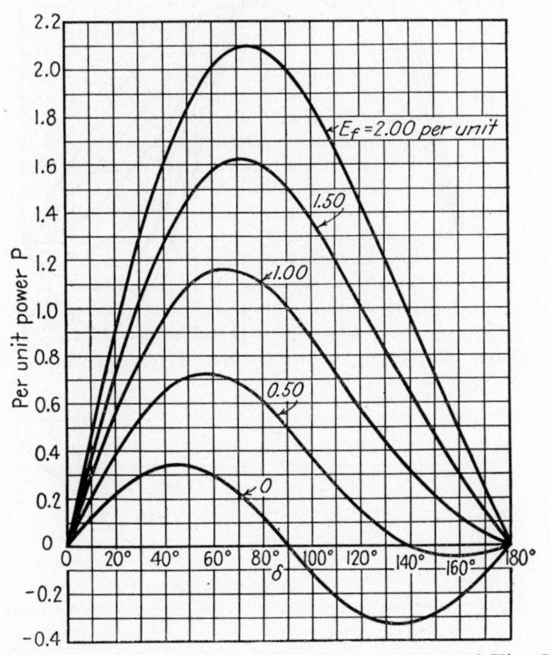

FIG. 8-17. Family of power-angle characteristics for system of Fig. 8-15*a* with E_e = 1.00, $R = 0$, $X_d = 1.00$, $X_q = 0.60$.

values of X_d, a salient-pole machine develops a given torque at a smaller value of δ, and the maximum torque which can be developed is somewhat greater.

b. Normalized Power-angle Characteristics. Equation 8-29 contains six quantities—the two variables P and δ, and the four parameters E_f, E_e, X_d, and X_q. To simplify the notation, let the maximum power due to the field excitation be designated by $P_{f\,\max}$ and the maximum power due to the reluctance torque be designated by $P_{r\,\max}$. Then Eq. 8-29 can be expressed as

$$P = P_{f\,\max} \sin \delta + P_{r\,\max} \sin 2\delta \tag{8-30}$$

A further reduction of the number of parameters can be obtained if

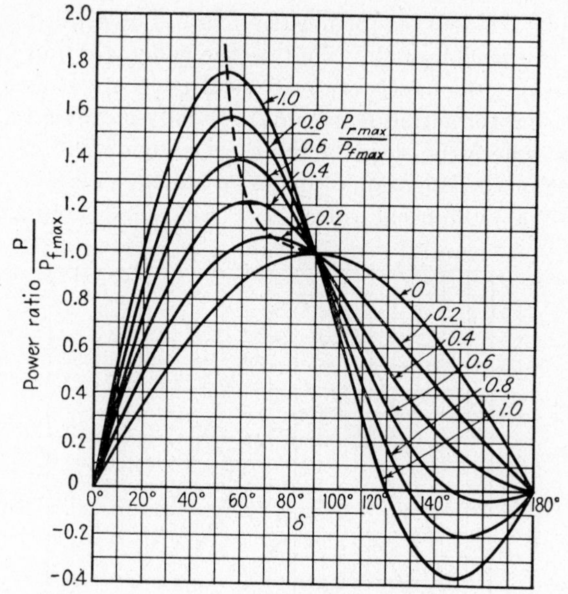

FIG. 8-18. Normalized power-angle characteristics for system of Fig. 8-15*a* with $R = 0$.

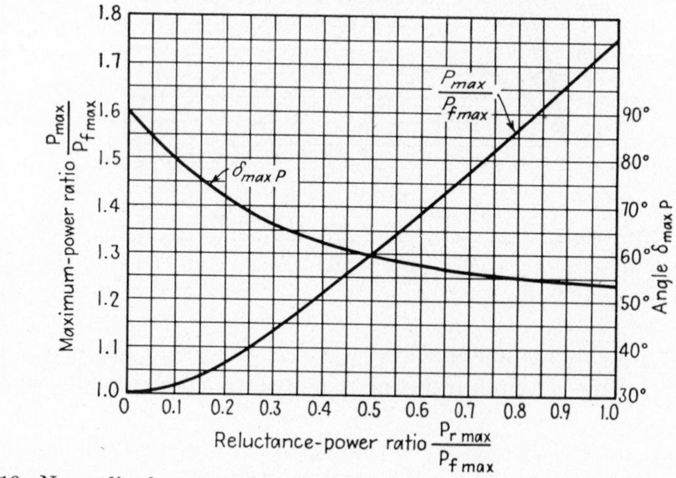

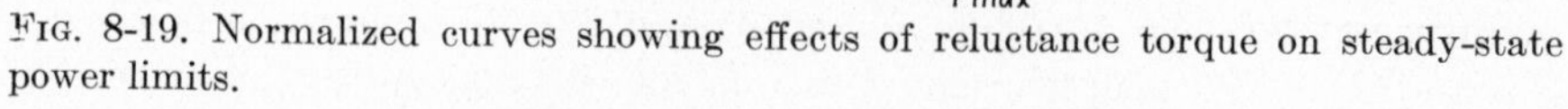
FIG. 8-19. Normalized curves showing effects of reluctance torque on steady-state power limits.

Eq. 8-30 is divided by $P_{f\,\max}$; thus

$$\frac{P}{P_{f\,\max}} = \sin \delta + \frac{P_{r\,\max}}{P_{f\,\max}} \sin 2\delta \tag{8-31}$$

Equation 8-31 is in normalized form. It applies to all possible combinations of a synchronous machine and an external system, as in Fig.

8-15a, so long as the resistance is negligible. A family of curves can be plotted from Eq. 8-31, as shown in Fig. 8-18. The maximum value $P_{max}/P_{f\,max}$ of the power ratio and the angle $\delta_{max\,P}$ at which maximum power occurs are shown as functions of the reluctance-power ratio $P_{r\,max}/P_{f\,max}$ in Fig. 8-19. These curves correspond to the dotted locus of the maximum points on the curves of Fig. 8-18. Use of these curves for computing steady-state power limits is illustrated in Example 8-6.

Example 8-6. The 2,000-hp 1.0-power-factor 3-phase Y-connected 2,300-volt synchronous motor of Example 7-4 has reactances of $x_d = 1.95$ and $x_q = 1.40$ ohms per phase. All losses may be neglected.

Compute the maximum mechanical power in kilowatts which this motor can deliver if it is supplied with electrical power from an infinite bus (Fig. 8-20a) at rated

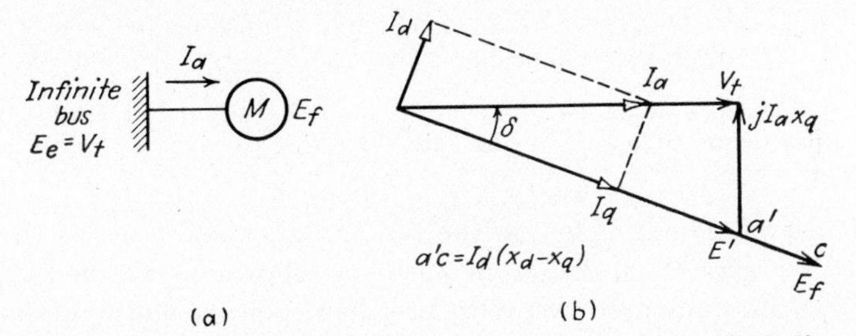

FIG. 8-20. Salient-pole synchronous motor of Example 8-6. (a) Single-line diagram. (b) Vector diagram.

voltage and frequency, and if its field excitation is constant at the value which would result in 1.00 power factor at rated load. The shaft load is assumed to be increased gradually so that transient swings are negligible and the steady-state power limit applies. Include the effects of salient poles.

Solution. The first step is to compute the synchronous-motor excitation at rated voltage, full load, 1.0 power factor. As in Example 7-4, the full-load terminal voltage and current are 1,330 volts to neutral and 374 amp per phase Y. The vector diagram for the specified full-load conditions is shown in Fig. 8-20b. The only essential difference between this vector diagram and the generator vector diagram of Fig. 8-14 is that I_a in Fig. 8-20 represents motor *input* current. The vector voltage equation corresponding to Eq. 8-22 then becomes

$$E_f = V_t - jI_d x_d - jI_q x_q \tag{8-32}$$

In Fig. 8-20b,

$$\begin{aligned} E' &= V_t - jI_a x_q \\ &= 1{,}330 + j0 - j(374)(1.40) = 1{,}429\underline{/-21.5^\circ} \end{aligned} \tag{8-33}$$

That is, the angle δ is 21.5°, with E_f lagging V_t. The magnitude of I_d is

$$I_d = I_a \sin \delta = (374)(0.367) = 137 \text{ amp}$$

The magnitude of E_f can now be found by adding numerically the length $a'c = I_d(x_d - x_q)$ to the magnitude of E'; thus

$$\begin{aligned} E_f &= E' + I_d(x_d - x_q) \\ &= 1{,}429 + (137)(0.55) = 1{,}504 \text{ volts to neutral} \end{aligned} \tag{8-34}$$

The maximum values of the field-excitation and reluctance-torque components of the power can now be computed. From Eqs. 8-30 and 8-31,

$$P_{f\,\max} = \frac{(1{,}504)(1{,}330)}{1.95} = 1{,}025 \times 10^3 \text{ watts per phase}$$

$$P_{r\,\max} = \frac{(1{,}330)^2(0.55)}{2(1.95)(1.40)} = 178 \times 10^3 \text{ watts per phase}$$

whence

$$\frac{P_{r\,\max}}{P_{f\,\max}} = 0.174$$

From Fig. 8-19, the corresponding value of the maximum-power ratio is

$$P_{\max}/P_{f\,\max} = 1.05,$$

whence the maximum power is

$$P_{\max} = 1.05P_{f\,\max} = (1.05)(1{,}025 \times 10^3) = 1{,}080 \text{ kw per phase}$$
$$= 3{,}240 \text{ kw for 3 phases}$$

Compare with $P_{\max} = 3{,}090$ kw found in Example 7-4, where the effects of salient poles were neglected. The error caused by neglecting saliency is slightly less than 5 per cent.

The effect of salient poles on the power limits increases as the reluctance-power ratio $P_{r\,\max}/P_{f\,\max}$ increases, as shown in Fig. 8-19. For a normally excited machine the effect of salient poles usually amounts to a few per cent at most. Only at small excitations does the reluctance torque become important. Except at small excitations or when exceptionally accurate results are required, a salient-pole machine usually can be treated by simple cylindrical-rotor theory.

8-6. Measurement of the Synchronous Reactances. The unsaturated value of the direct-axis synchronous reactance can be found from the results of an open-circuit and a short-circuit test as described in Art. 7-6*b*. The effects of saturation can be accounted for by the saturated-synchronous-reactance method of Eqs. 8-8 and 8-10, a procedure which treats the saturation as if it were entirely in the armature iron.[9]

Two methods of measuring the quadrature-axis synchronous reactance are described in the AIEE Test Code for Synchronous Machines (footnote 8). These methods are the slip test and the maximum-lagging-current test and are described below.[10]

In the *slip test* the machine is driven mechanically at a speed slightly different from synchronous speed, with its field winding open, and with

[9] For an alternative and theoretically more complete procedure, see S. B. Crary, L. A. March, and L. P. Shildneck, Equivalent Reactance of Synchronous Machines, *Trans. AIEE*, vol. 53, No. 1, pp. 124–132, January, 1934. Also see footnote 3.

[10] For further information concerning these and other test methods see R. V. Shepherd and C. E. Kilbourne, The Quadrature Synchronous Reactance of Salient-pole Synchronous Machines, *Trans. AIEE*, vol. 62, No. 11, pp. 684–689, November, 1943.

balanced polyphase voltages of the correct phase sequence applied to its armature terminals. Under these conditions the armature-mmf wave glides slowly past the field poles at slip speed. Oscillograms are taken of the armature current, voltage applied to the armature terminals, and voltage induced in the open field winding. Figure 8-21 shows the general appearance of the oscillograms, but for the sake of clarity a much larger value of slip is shown than would be used in practice. When the armature-mmf wave is in line with the axes of the field poles, the impedance of the machine equals its direct-axis value. One-quarter of a slip cycle

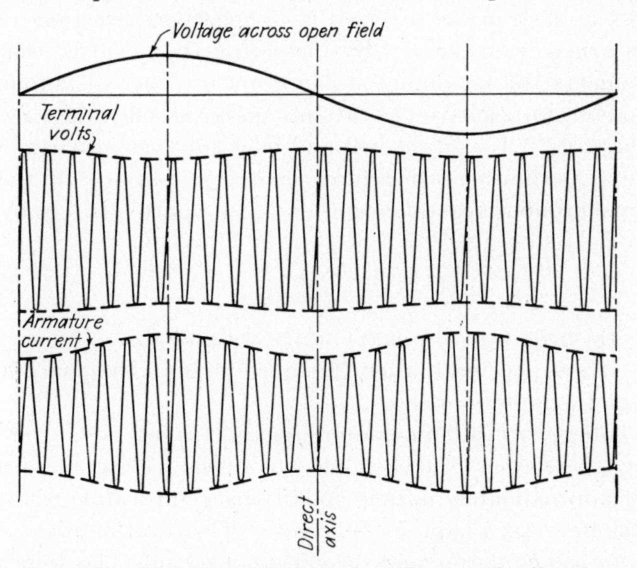

FIG. 8-21. General appearance of oscillograms in slip test.

later the armature-mmf wave is in line with the quadrature axis, and the impedance equals its quadrature-axis value. If the armature resistance is negligible, the direct-axis synchronous reactance x_d equals the maximum ratio of armature applied voltage per phase to armature current per phase and occurs when the instantaneous voltage induced in the field winding is zero. The quadrature-axis synchronous reactance x_q is the minimum value of this ratio and occurs when the instantaneous voltage induced in the field winding has its maximum value. Best results for x_q can be obtained by finding the ratio x_q/x_d from the slip test and using the value of x_d from the open-circuit and short-circuit tests.

The principal shortcoming of the slip test is that large errors may be produced by the effects of current induced in rotor circuits such as damper windings, unless the slip is made to be very small. It may be difficult to meet this condition because of the tendency of the machine to lock into step and run as a reluctance motor in synchronism with the armature-mmf wave. Usually, therefore, the test must be made at small values of armature voltage. The value obtained for x_q then is its unsaturated value. Since oscillograms usually must be taken, the accuracy of the results is limited by the accuracy with which the oscillograms can be read.

The *maximum-lagging current* test avoids both of these difficulties. For this test the machine is run as an unloaded synchronous motor with normal balanced polyphase voltages applied to its armature terminals. The field current is reduced to zero. The machine is then running as a reluctance motor. The polarity of the field current is then reversed and a small field current applied in the reversed (*i.e.*, negative) direction, causing an increase in armature current. By increasing the negative excitation in small increments the maximum stable armature current is found. Any further increase in negative excitation causes the machine to fall out of step momentarily. Usually it will pull back into synchronism after slipping a pole. As shown in the reference cited in footnote 10, the quadrature-axis synchronous reactance is then given approximately by

$$x_q = \frac{V_t}{I_{a(po)}} \tag{8-35}$$

where V_t is the armature terminal voltage per phase and $I_{a(po)}$ is the stable armature current per phase when the machine is on the point of, but has not yet begun, slipping a pole.

An advantage of the maximum-lagging-current test over the slip test is that the former can be made at normal voltage, and the value of x_q under approximately normal conditions of saturation can be found.

8-7. Résumé. In Chap. 7 the effects of saturation were dismissed with an empirical equation, and the effects of salient poles were neglected entirely. In Chap. 8 we dealt with both these effects. The most significant conclusion from Chap. 8, backed up by experimental evidence, is that the somewhat crude methods of Chap. 7 work surprisingly well in many practical situations.

The handling of saturation is an excellent example of the engineering approach to problems which are inherently so complex that an exact solution is hopeless. By the use of judiciously chosen simplifying assumptions based on a physical picture of what goes on, a reasonably simple quantitative theory can be formulated and checked against actual load tests. These assumptions are that the leakage reactance is constant and that the open-circuit characteristic can be used as if it were the saturation curve relating air-gap voltage and resultant mmf under load. The thought process has much in common with that applying to d-c machines and transformers. With these assumptions, the degree of saturation can be described quantitatively in terms of a saturation factor k which is a function of the air-gap voltage, as in Eq. 8-6. The synchronous reactance is assumed to consist of a constant part and a part which is affected by saturation. The constant part can be found by means of the Potier triangle (Fig. 8-2), which is based on the assumption that the overexcited zero-power-factor characteristic is identical to the open-circuit characteristic shifted vertically downward by a constant voltage drop and horizontally to the right by a constant mmf. The use of the Potier reactance in saturation problems as if it were the leakage reactance makes an empirical allowance for errors resulting from use of the open-circuit characteristic as if it were the saturation curve under load. Although this method of treating saturation is based on cylindrical-rotor theory, the results obtained by applying it to a salient-pole machine check well with actual tests.

The effects of salient poles can be taken into account by resolving the armature currents into direct- and quadrature-axis components which produce two synchronously rotating components of armature reaction, one in line with and the other in space quadrature with the axes of the field poles, as in Figs. 8-10 and 8-11. With each of these armature-current components there is associated an appropriate value of the synchronous reactance. The quadrature-axis synchronous reactance x_q is considerably smaller than the direct-axis synchronous reactance x_d, because of the greater reluctance of the quadrature-axis magnetic circuit. The vector diagram of a salient-pole machine can then be drawn as in Fig. 8-12. Analysis of this vector diagram shows that saliency has relatively little effect on the interrelations among field excitation, terminal voltage, armature current, and power; but that the power-angle characteristics are affected by the presence of a reluctance-torque component, as in Eq. 8-29 and Fig. 8-16. Because of the reluctance torque, a salient-pole machine is stiffer than one with a cylindrical rotor.

Examination of the power-angle equation, 8-29, suggests that it be put in a generalized form in terms of dimensionless ratios, as in Eq. 8-31 and Figs. 8-18 and 8-19. This form of expression is an example of normalization, applicable to a wide variety of problems in nature. The number of variables can always be reduced by expressing the behavior of a physical system in terms of appropriate dimensionless ratios, and a more penetrating physical insight into the basic phenomena is obtained.

A question may arise regarding why the effects of quadrature-axis flux are treated so differently in salient-pole synchronous machines and in d-c machines. After all, both are salient-pole machines, and both have cross-magnetizing components of armature reaction. One reason is that the effects of flux-density waveform are unimportant in d-c machines. More important, however, is the effect of the commutator. In d-c machines with brushes located at the neutral position, the cross flux generates no voltage between brushes. The brushes restrict the effective flux to the net flux over the armature surface occupied by active coils between brushes. A quadrature-axis component shifts the flux wave in space but has no direct effect observable between brushes—it merely alters the distribution of generated voltage among the various coils constituting the winding between brushes. In commutator machines, the only effect of cross-magnetizing armature reaction observable between brushes is the indirect effect which the resulting flux distortion has on the saturation of the direct-axis flux paths.

In synchronous machines the cross or quadrature-axis flux does generate a voltage which appears at the terminals of the armature winding. The quadrature-axis flux shifts the spatial position of the resultant air-gap flux wave with respect to the field poles, as in d-c machines, but unlike the d-c machine, the synchronous machine does not have brushes which pick up only the voltage generated by direct-axis flux. The shift in spatial position of the resultant air-gap flux wave merely results in a shift in time phase of the air-gap voltage with respect to the excitation voltage. Thus the quadrature-axis flux must be accounted for as a generated voltage (the quadrature-axis synchronous-reactance voltage drop).

PROBLEMS

8-1. The following data relate to a 16,000-kva 3-phase 11,000-volt 60-cps 40-pole hydroelectric generator.

Open-circuit Characteristic:

I_f, amp	100	150	205	250	300	350	400	450
V_t (line), kv	6.45	9.0	11.0	12.2	13.4	14.0	14.5	15.0

Short-circuit Test:

$$I_f = 186 \text{ amp} \qquad I_a = 840 \text{ amp}$$

Zero-power-factor Test:

$$I_f = 550 \text{ amp} \qquad I_a = 840 \text{ amp} \qquad V_t = 11{,}000 \text{ volts}$$

Plot the test data, and draw the Potier triangle. On the assumption that this triangle stays constant in size, draw the zero-power-factor characteristic.

For operation at rated voltage, rated load, 0.80 power factor lagging, compute:

a. The air-gap voltage
b. The saturation factor
c. The saturated synchronous reactance
d. The field current

8-2. A synchronous motor is supplied from an infinite bus. The open-circuit and short-circuit characteristics are available for the machine. It is possible to remove the shaft load of the motor, but the only source of terminal voltage is the infinite bus. Explain how you would determine the Potier reactance of this machine. Illustrate your explanation with suitable diagrams or sketches.

8-3. Assume that the size of the Potier triangle is proportional to the armature current. Construct a family of zero-power-factor characteristics for the synchronous machine of Fig. 8-2 at several values of armature current, both lagging and leading. From these curves collect data to plot a synchronous-motor no-load V curve for this machine at rated voltage.

8-4. Compute the field current of the 45-kva machine of Figs. 8-2 and 8-5 when it is running as a synchronous motor at rated voltage and frequency, with an input of 36 kw at 0.80 power factor leading. Use (*a*) the saturated-synchronous-reactance method of Example 8-2; (*b*) the ASA method of Example 8-4. For comparison, the field current measured in an actual load test under these load conditions is 4.80 amp.

8-5. What per cent of its rated output will a salient-pole synchronous motor deliver without loss of synchronism when the applied voltage is normal and the field excitation is zero, if $x_d = 0.80$ per unit and $x_q = 0.50$ per unit? Draw the vector diagram at the maximum-power condition. Compute the power factor and per-unit armature current at maximum power.

8-6. From the vector diagram of an overexcited synchronous motor, show that

$$\tan \delta = \frac{I_a x_q \cos \theta + I_a r_a \sin \theta}{V_t + I_a x_q \sin \theta - I_a r_a \cos \theta}$$

8-7. From the vector diagram of an overexcited synchronous motor, show that

$$x_q = \frac{V_t \sin \delta - I_a r_a \sin (\theta + \delta)}{I_a \cos (\theta + \delta)}$$

From this relation, the saturated value of x_q can be measured under actual load conditions, by measuring V_t, I_a, power, and δ. The torque angle δ can be measured with a stroboscope.

8-8. For the system of Fig. 8-15*a*, derive an expression for the reactive power Q delivered to the infinite bus, in terms of the excitation voltage E_f, the bus voltage E_e, the reactances X_d and X_q, and the angle δ. Neglect resistances, and consider that lagging reactive power delivered to the bus is positive.

8-9. A salient-pole synchronous motor has $x_d = 0.80$ and $x_q = 0.50$ per unit. It is running from an infinite bus of $V_t = 1.00$ per unit. Neglect all losses. What is the minimum per-unit excitation for which the machine will stay in synchronism with full-load torque?

8-10. Show that x_q can be found from the maximum-lagging-current test, as in Eq. 8-35. Neglect armature resistance, and assume that rotational losses are small.

8-11. The 45-kva 3-phase Y-connected 220-volt salient-pole machine of Fig. 8-2 was tested by the maximum-lagging-current method, and the following readings were obtained just before it slipped a pole and while it was still running stably:

Line-to-line voltage = 208 volts
Armature current = 216 amp
Field current = −1.7 amp
Three-phase power = 6.4 kw

Compute the value of x_q. Express the result in ohms per phase and also in per unit on the machine rating as a base.

CHAPTER 9

POLYPHASE INDUCTION MACHINES

IN THE induction motor, alternating current is supplied to the stator winding directly and to the rotor winding by induction from the stator. Balanced polyphase stator and rotor currents create stator- and rotor-component-mmf waves of constant amplitude rotating in the air gap at synchronous speed and therefore stationary with respect to each other regardless of the mechanical speed of the rotor. The resultant of these mmfs creates the resultant air-gap flux-density wave. Interaction of the flux wave and the rotor-mmf wave gives rise to torque. All of the conditions are fulfilled for the production of a steady value of torque at all speeds other than synchronous speed.

The objects of this chapter are to develop equivalent circuits for the polyphase induction motor from which both the effects of the motor on its supply circuit and the characteristics of the motor itself can be determined, and to study these effects and characteristics. The general form of equivalent circuit is suggested by the similarity of an induction machine to a transformer.

9-1. Coupled-circuit Aspects and Equivalent Circuits. Only induction machines with symmetrical polyphase windings excited by balanced polyphase voltages will be considered in this chapter. Attention can be focused on any one phase, since the only distinction between phases is the characteristic time-phase angle of a balanced polyphase system. All voltages, currents, and impedances, therefore, are values for one phase of the machine. For 3-phase machines, it may be helpful to think consistently in terms of a Y connection, so that currents are always line values, and voltages always line-to-neutral values. All currents and voltages are assumed to be sinusoidal in waveform, and the effects of space harmonics in the flux distribution are ignored except in so far as they enter into the stator and rotor leakage reactances, as indicated in Art. 4-9.

First consider conditions in the stator. The synchronously rotating air-gap flux wave generates balanced polyphase counter emfs in the phases of the stator. The stator terminal voltage differs from the counter emf by the voltage drop in the stator leakage impedance, the vector relation for the phase under consideration being

$$V_1 = E_1 + I_1 (r_1 + jx_1) \tag{9-1}$$

where V_1 is the stator terminal voltage, E_1 is the counter emf generated by the resultant air-gap flux, I_1 is the stator current, r_1 is the stator effective resistance, and x_1 is the stator leakage reactance. The positive directions are shown in the equivalent circuit of Fig. 9-1*a*.

The resultant air-gap flux is created by the combined mmfs of the stator and rotor currents. Just as in the transformer analogue, the stator current can be resolved into two components, a load component and an exciting component. The load component I_2 produces an mmf which exactly counteracts the mmf of the rotor current. The exciting component I_φ is the additional stator current required to create the resultant air-gap flux and is a function of the emf E_1. The exciting current can be resolved into a core-loss component I_c in phase with E_1 and a magnetizing

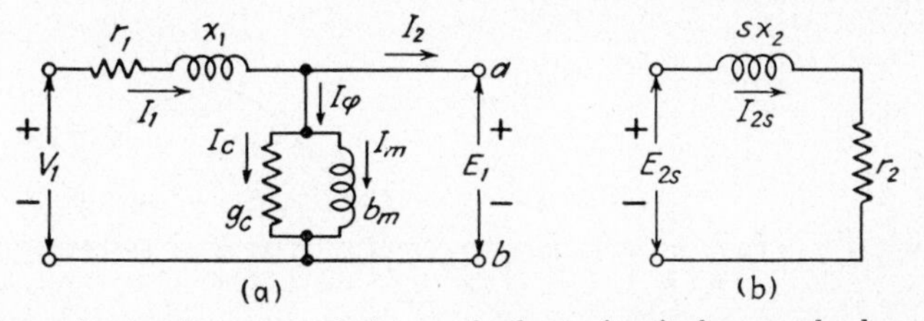

FIG. 9-1. Steps in development of the equivalent circuit for a polyphase induction motor.

component I_m lagging E_1 by 90°. In the equivalent circuit, the exciting current can be accounted for by means of a shunt branch, formed by core-loss conductance g_c and magnetizing susceptance b_m in parallel, connected across E_1, as in Fig. 9-1*a*. Both g_c and b_m are usually determined at rated stator frequency and for a value of E_1 close to the expected operating value; they are then assumed to remain constant for the small departures from that value associated with normal operation of the motor.

So far, the equivalent circuit representing stator phenomena is exactly like that for the primary of a transformer. To complete the circuit, the effects of the rotor must be incorporated. The rotor may be of either the squirrel-cage or the symmetrical polyphase coil-wound type; in either case, the basic phenomena are the same.

Consider conditions existing when the rotor is turning at a speed n corresponding to a per-unit slip s. The space-fundamental component of the resultant air-gap flux wave then travels past the rotor at slip speed and induces slip-frequency emfs in the rotor circuits. These emfs produce slip-frequency currents in the short-circuited rotor phases or bars. If the rotor is of the coil-wound type, it must be wound for the same number of poles as the stator, although it need not be wound for the same number of phases. In a coil-wound rotor, the slip-frequency rotor currents create an mmf wave whose space-fundamental component has the same number of poles as the inducing flux wave and which travels at slip speed with respect to the rotor. The space-phase angle between the inducing flux wave and the rotor-mmf wave is the torque angle. As shown in Art. 3-7*c* and Fig. 3-22, the torque angle δ is 90° greater than the rotor power-factor angle θ_2.

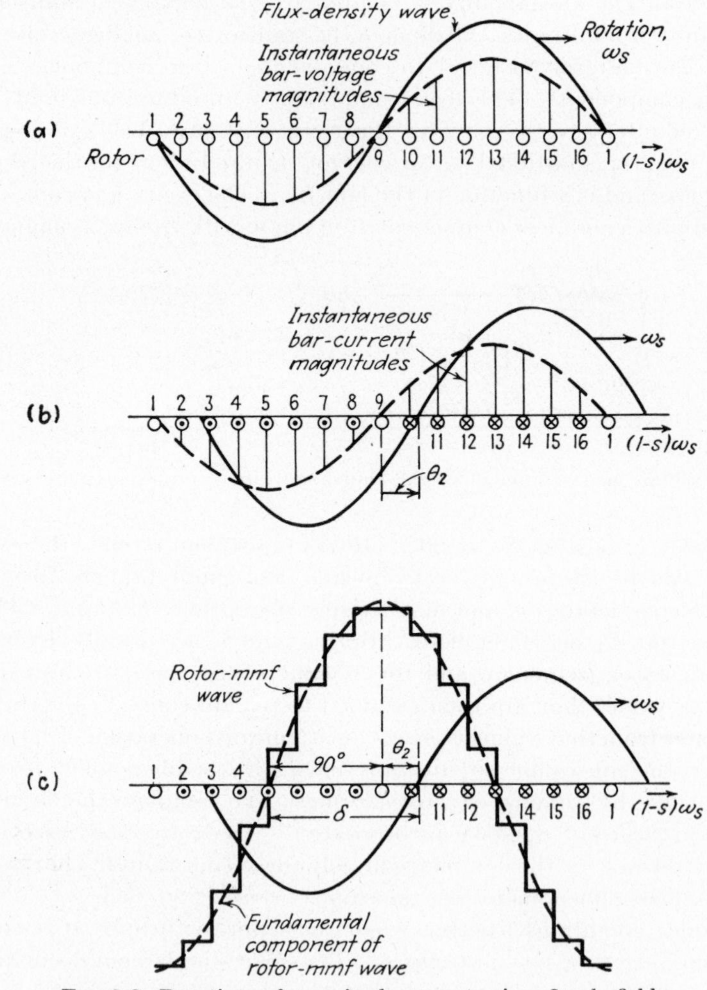

FIG. 9-2. Reactions of a squirrel-cage rotor in a 2-pole field.

It is also pointed out in Art. 3-7*c* that a cage rotor, acting under the influence of the air-gap flux, automatically becomes a polyphase winding having a number of poles equal to the number in the air-gap field. The general nature of the rotor happenings is shown pictorially in Fig. 9-2. In this figure, a 16-bar rotor, placed in a 2-pole field, is shown in developed form. For simplicity of drafting, only a relatively small number of rotor bars is chosen, and the number is an integral multiple of the number of poles, a choice normally avoided in order to prevent harmful harmonic effects. In Fig. 9-2*a*, the sinusoidal flux-density wave induces a voltage in each bar which, in accordance with the *Blv* concept, has an instantaneous value indicated by the solid vertical lines. At a somewhat later instant of time, the bar currents assume the instantaneous values indicated by the solid vertical lines in Fig. 9-2*b*, the time lag being the rotor power-factor angle θ_2. In this time interval, the flux-density wave has traveled in its direction of rotation with respect to the rotor through a space angle θ_2 and is then in the position shown in Fig. 9-2*b*. The corresponding rotor-mmf wave is shown by the step wave of Fig. 9-2*c*. The fundamental component is shown by the dotted sinusoid and the flux-density wave by the solid sinusoid. Study of these figures confirms the general principle that the number of rotor poles is determined by the inducing flux wave.

Thus, in so far as fundamental components are concerned, both squirrel-cage and wound rotors react by producing an mmf wave having the same number of poles as the inducing flux wave, traveling at the same speed as the flux wave, and with a torque angle 90° greater than the rotor power-factor angle. The reaction of the rotor-mmf wave on the stator calls for the compensating load component of stator current and thereby enables the stator to absorb from the line the power needed to sustain the torque created by the interaction of the flux and mmf waves. The only way in which the stator knows what is happening is through the medium of the air-gap flux and rotor-mmf waves. Consequently if the rotor were replaced by one having the same mmf and power factor at the same speed, the stator would be unable to detect the change.

As a simple example, consider a coil-wound rotor, wound for the same number of poles and phases as the stator. The number of effective turns per phase in the stator winding is a times the number in the rotor winding. The effective turns are defined as the actual turns corrected for the effects of fundamental pitch and breadth. Compare the magnetic effect of this rotor with that of a magnetically equivalent rotor having the same number of turns as the stator. For the same flux and speed, the relation between the voltage E_{rotor} induced in the actual rotor and the voltage E_{2s} induced in the equivalent rotor is

$$E_{2s} = aE_{\text{rotor}} \tag{9-2}$$

If the rotors are to be magnetically equivalent, their ampere-turns must be equal, whence the relation between the actual rotor current I_{rotor} and the current I_{2s} in the equivalent rotor must be

$$I_{2s} = \frac{I_{\text{rotor}}}{a} \tag{9-3}$$

Consequently the relation between the slip-frequency leakage impedance Z_{2s} of the equivalent rotor and the slip-frequency leakage impedance Z_{rotor} of the actual rotor must be

$$Z_{2s} = \frac{E_{2s}}{I_{2s}} = \frac{a^2 E_{\text{rotor}}}{I_{\text{rotor}}} = a^2 Z_{\text{rotor}} \tag{9-4}$$

The voltages, currents, and impedances in the equivalent rotor are defined as their values *referred to the stator*. The thought process is essentially like that involved in referring secondary quantities to the primary in static-transformer theory (see Art. A-3). The referring factors are ratios of effective turns and are the same in essence as in transformer theory.

The referring factors must, of course, be known when one is concerned specifically with what is happening in the actual rotor circuits. From the viewpoint of the stator, however, the reflected effects of the rotor show up in terms of the referred quantities, and the theory of both coil-wound and cage rotors can be formulated in terms of the referred rotor. In order to proceed with the basic theory, detailed consideration of the referring factors is postponed until Art. 9-7. In the rest of this article it may be assumed that the referred rotor constants are known.

Since the rotor is short-circuited, the vector relation between the slip-frequency emf E_{2s} generated in the reference phase of the referred rotor and the current I_{2s} in this phase is

$$\frac{E_{2s}}{I_{2s}} = Z_{2s} = r_2 + jsx_2 \tag{9-5}$$

where Z_{2s} is the slip-frequency rotor leakage impedance per phase referred to the stator, r_2 the referred effective resistance, and sx_2 the referred leakage reactance at slip frequency. The reactance is expressed in this way because it is proportional to rotor frequency and therefore to slip. Thus x_2 is defined as the value the referred rotor leakage reactance would have at stator frequency. The slip-frequency equivalent circuit for one phase of the referred rotor is shown in Fig. 9-1*b*.

The stator sees a flux wave and an mmf wave rotating at synchronous speed. The flux wave induces the slip-frequency rotor voltage E_{2s} and the stator counter emf E_1. If it were not for the effect of speed, the referred rotor voltage would equal the stator voltage, since the referred rotor winding is identical to the stator winding. Because the relative speed of the flux wave with respect to the rotor is s times its speed with respect to the stator, the relation between the effective values of stator and rotor emfs is

$$E_{2s} = sE_1 \tag{9-6}$$

The rotor-mmf wave is opposed by the mmf of the load component I_2 of stator current, and therefore, for effective values,

$$I_{2s} = I_2 \tag{9-7}$$

Division of Eq. 9-6 by Eq. 9-7 then gives, for effective values,

$$\frac{E_{2s}}{I_{2s}} = \frac{sE_1}{I_2} \tag{9-8}$$

Furthermore, the mmf wave created by the stator load current I_2 must be space-displaced from the resultant flux wave by the same space angle as that between the rotor-mmf wave and the resultant flux wave, *viz.*, the torque angle δ. The time-phase angle between the stator voltage E_1 and the stator load current I_2 therefore must equal the corresponding time angle for the rotor, *viz.*, the rotor power-factor angle θ_2. The fact that the rotor and stator mmfs are in opposition is accounted for, since the rotor current I_{2s} is created by the rotor emf E_{2s}, whereas the stator current I_2 is flowing against the stator counter emf E_1. Therefore Eq. 9-8 is true, not only for effective values, but also in a vector sense. Through substitution of Eq. 9-5 in the vector equivalent of Eq. 9-8

$$\frac{sE_1}{I_2} = \frac{E_{2s}}{I_{2s}} = r_2 + jsx_2 \tag{9-9}$$

Division by s then gives

$$\frac{E_1}{I_2} = \frac{r_2}{s} + jx_2 \tag{9-10}$$

That is, the stator sees magnetic conditions in the air gap which result in stator counter emf E_1 and stator load current I_2, and by Eq. 9-10 these conditions are identical with the result of connecting an impedance $(r_2/s) + jx_2$ across E_1. Consequently the effect of the rotor can be incorporated in the equivalent circuit of Fig. 9-1*a* by this impedance connected across the terminals *ab*. The final result is shown in Fig. 9-3. The combined effect of shaft load and rotor resistance appears as a reflected resistance r_2/s, a function of slip and therefore of the mechanical load. The current in the reflected rotor impedance equals the load component I_2 of stator current; the voltage across this impedance equals the stator emf E_1. It should be noted that when rotor currents and voltages are reflected into the stator, their frequency is also changed to stator frequency. All rotor electrical

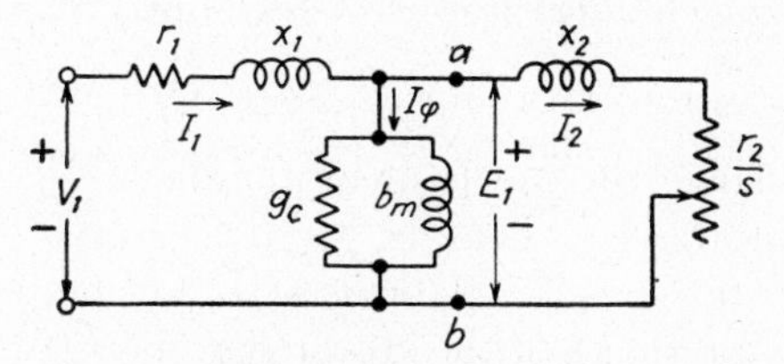

FIG. 9-3. Equivalent circuit for a polyphase induction motor.

phenomena, when viewed from the stator, become stator-frequency phenomena, because the stator winding simply sees mmf and flux waves traveling at synchronous speed.

9-2. Analysis of the Equivalent Circuit. By use of the equivalent circuit of Fig. 9-3 the current, power, and reactive power taken by the motor at any specified slip s can be computed. Moreover, mechanical output conditions can be determined by application of the torque relationships developed in Chaps. 3 and 4. From Eq. 4-47, the internal electromagnetic torque T, in newton-meters, is

$$T = \frac{p}{4\pi f} q_1 E_1 I_2 \cos \theta_2 = \frac{1}{\omega_s} q_1 E_1 I_2 \cos \theta_2 \tag{9-11}$$

where ω_s is the synchronous angular velocity in mechanical radians per second and q_1 is the number of stator phases. The quantity $q_1 E_1 I_2 \cos \theta_2$ is the power P_{g1} delivered to the air gap by the stator windings. Consequently

$$T = \frac{1}{\omega_s} P_{g1} \tag{9-12}$$

The equivalent circuit shows that P_{g1} equals the power absorbed by the reflected rotor resistance r_2/s for all phases, or

$$P_{g1} = q_1 I_2^2 \frac{r_2}{s} \tag{9-13}$$

Hence

$$T = \frac{1}{\omega_s} q_1 I_2^2 \frac{r_2}{s} \tag{9-14}$$

Mechanical power equals torque times angular velocity. The internal mechanical power P developed by the motor therefore is

$$P = (1 - s)\omega_s T = (1 - s)P_{g1} \tag{9-15}$$

since the mechanical angular velocity of the rotor at slip s is $(1 - s)\omega_s$ rad/sec. That is, the fraction $1 - s$ of the power absorbed from the stator is transformed to mechanical power. The remainder, or the fraction s of the stator power, is transferred by transformer action to the electric circuits of the rotor. The slip-frequency electric power P_{g2} generated in the rotor therefore is

$$P_{g2} = sP_{g1} \tag{9-16}$$

The induction machine is thus seen to be a generalized electromechanical transformer absorbing electrical power in its primary windings, converting the fraction $1 - s$ of this power to mechanical power, and transforming the fraction s to electrical power in its secondary windings with a corresponding change in frequency. In the induction motor with short-circuited rotor windings, the power P_{g2} is dissipated as rotor-circuit copper loss, whence the total rotor copper loss for all phases is

$$\text{Rotor copper loss} = sP_{g1} = s\omega_s T \tag{9-17}$$

a conclusion in agreement with the result of multiplying Eq. 9-13 by s. An induction motor running at a high slip is inherently an inefficient means for producing torque.

Substitution of Eq. 9-13 in Eq. 9-15 gives for the internal mechanical power

$$P = q_1 I_2^2 r_2 \frac{1 - s}{s} \tag{9-18}$$

When power aspects are to be emphasized, the equivalent circuit is frequently redrawn in the manner of Fig. 9-4. The internal mechanical

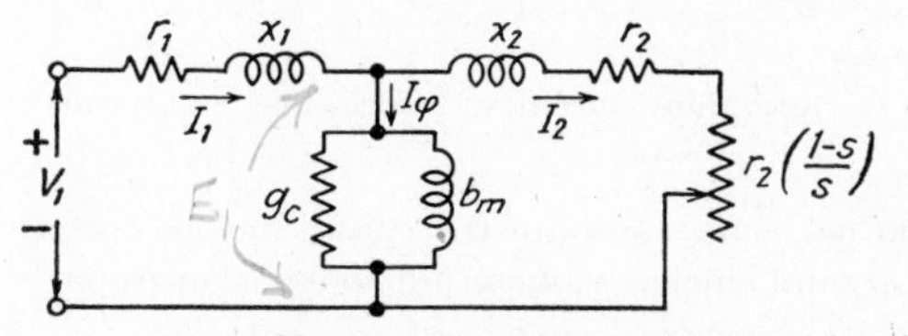

FIG. 9-4. Alternative form of the equivalent circuit.

power per stator phase is equal to the power absorbed by the resistance $r_2(1 - s)/s$.

The torque T and power P are not the output values available at the shaft, because friction, windage, and stray load losses remain to be accounted for. It is obviously correct to subtract friction and windage effects from T or P, and it is generally assumed that stray load effects may be subtracted in the same manner. The final remainder is available in mechanical form at the shaft for useful work.

In static-transformer theory, analysis of the equivalent circuit is often simplified by either neglecting the exciting branch entirely or adopting the approximation of moving it out directly to the primary terminals. Such approximations are not permissible for the induction motor under normal running conditions, because the presence of the air gap makes necessary a much higher exciting current—30 to 50 per cent of full-load current—and because the leakage reactances are also necessarily higher. Some simplification of the induction-motor equivalent circuit results if the shunt conductance g_c is omitted and the associated core-loss effect deducted from T or P at the same time that friction, windage, and stray load effects are subtracted. The equivalent circuit then becomes that of Fig. 9-5a or b, and the error introduced is negligible. Such a procedure also has an advantage during motor testing, for no-load core loss need not then be separated from friction and windage. These last circuits will be used in subsequent discussions.

Example 9-1. A 3-phase Y-connected 220-volt (line to line) 10-hp 60-cps 6-pole induction motor has the following constants in ohms per phase referred to the stator:

$$r_1 = 0.294 \qquad r_2 = 0.144$$
$$x_1 = 0.503 \qquad x_2 = 0.209 \qquad x_\varphi = 13.25$$

No-load rotational loss at rated voltage and frequency = 336 watts. Stray load loss = 67 watts. The rotational and stray load losses may be assumed to be constant, independent of load.

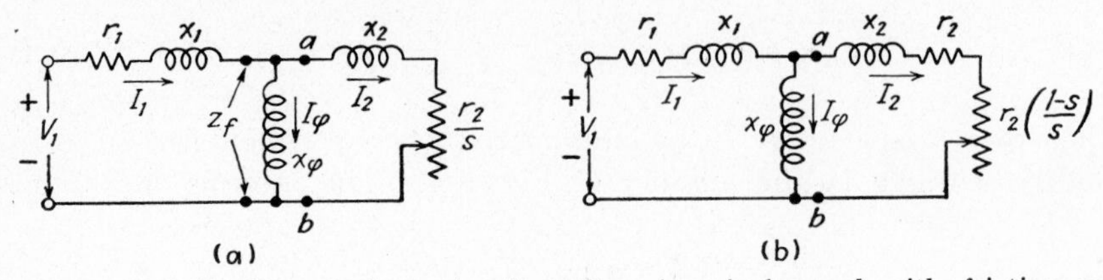

FIG. 9-5. Simplified equivalent circuits. Core loss is lumped with friction and windage.

For a slip of 2.00 per cent, compute the speed, output torque and power, stator current, power factor, and efficiency, when the motor is operated at rated voltage and frequency.

Solution. The impedance Z_f (Fig. 9-5a) represents physically the per-phase impedance presented to the stator by the air-gap field, both the reflected effect of the rotor and the effect of the exciting current being included therein. From Fig. 9-5a,

$$Z_f = R_f + jX_f = \frac{r_2}{s} + jx_2 \qquad \text{in parallel with } jx_\varphi \tag{9-19}$$

Substitution of numerical values in Eq. 9-19 gives, for $s = 0.0200$

$$\begin{aligned} R_f + jX_f &= 5.41 + j3.11 \\ r_1 + jx_1 &= 0.29 + j0.50 \\ \text{Sum} &= 5.70 + j3.61 = 6.75\underline{/32.4^\circ} \text{ ohms} \end{aligned}$$

$$\text{Applied voltage to neutral} = \frac{220}{\sqrt{3}} = 127 \text{ volts}$$

$$\text{Stator current } I_1 = \frac{127}{6.75} = 18.8 \text{ amp}$$

$$\text{Power factor} = \cos 32.4^\circ = 0.844$$

$$\text{Synchronous speed} = \frac{2f}{p} = \frac{120}{6} = 20 \text{ rev/sec, or } 1{,}200 \text{ rpm}$$

$$\omega_s = 2\pi(20) = 125.6 \text{ rad/sec}$$

$$\begin{aligned} \text{Rotor speed} &= (1 - s) \times (\text{synchronous speed}) \\ &= (0.98)(1{,}200) = 1{,}176 \text{ rpm} \end{aligned}$$

When the magnetizing branch is considered to be nonresistive, as in Fig. 9-5a,

$$\begin{aligned} P_{g1} &= q_1 I_2^2 \frac{r_2}{s} = q_1 I_1^2 R_f \qquad (9\text{-}20) \\ &= (3)(18.8)^2(5.41) = 5{,}740 \text{ watts} \end{aligned}$$

From Eq. 9-15, the internal mechanical power is

$$P = (0.98)(5{,}740) = 5{,}630 \text{ watts}$$

Deducting rotational and stray load losses of 403 watts gives

$$\text{Output power} = 5{,}630 - 403 = 5{,}230 \text{ watts, or } 7.00 \text{ hp}$$

$$\text{Output torque} = \frac{\text{output power}}{\omega_{\text{rotor}}} = \frac{5{,}230}{(0.98)(125.6)} = 42.5 \text{ newton-m, or } 31.4 \text{ lb-ft}$$

The efficiency is calculated from the losses.

Total stator copper loss = $3(18.8)^2(0.294)$	=	312 watts
Rotor copper loss (from Eq. 9-17) = $(0.0200)(5{,}740)$	=	115
Rotational plus stray load losses	=	403
Total losses	=	830 watts
Output	=	5,230
Input	=	6,060 watts

$$\frac{\text{Losses}}{\text{Input}} = \frac{830}{6{,}060} = 0.137 \qquad \text{Efficiency} = 1.000 - 0.137 = 0.863$$

The complete performance characteristics of the motor can be determined by repeating these calculations for other assumed values of slip.

9-3. Torque and Power by Use of Thévenin's Theorem.

When torque and power relations are to be emphasized, considerable simplification

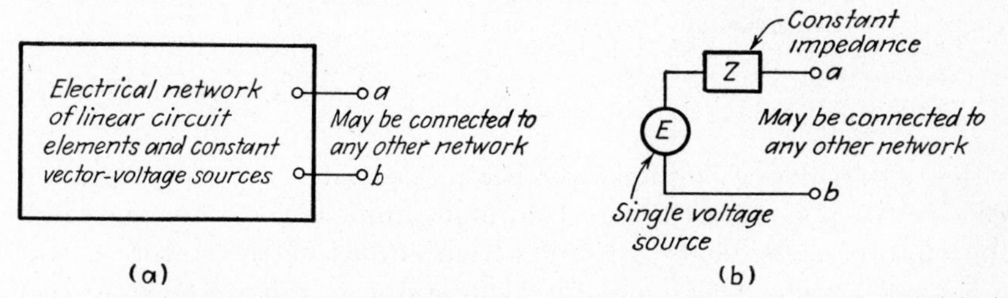

FIG. 9-6. Illustrating Thévenin's theorem. (*a*) General linear network, and (*b*) its equivalent at terminals *ab*.

results from application of Thévenin's network theorem to the induction-motor equivalent circuit.

In its general form, Thévenin's theorem permits the replacement of any network of linear circuit elements and constant vector-voltage sources, as viewed from two terminals *a* and *b* in Fig. 9-6*a*, by a single vector-voltage source E in series with a single impedance Z, (Fig. 9-6*b*).[1] The voltage E is that appearing across terminals *a* and *b* of the original network when these terminals are open-circuited; the impedance Z is

[1] Discussions of Thévenin's theorem may be found in most textbooks on circuit theory. See, for instance, EE Staff, MIT, "Electric Circuits," pp. 144–146, 469–470, John Wiley & Sons, Inc., New York, 1940; R. H. Frazier, "Elementary Electric-circuit Theory," pp. 113–116, 203, McGraw-Hill Book Company, Inc., New York, 1945.

that viewed from the same terminals when all voltage sources within the network are short-circuited. For application to the induction-motor equivalent circuit, points a and b are taken as those so designated in Figs. 9-5a and b. The equivalent circuit then assumes the forms given in Fig. 9-7. So far as phenomena to the right of points a and b are concerned, the circuits of Figs. 9-5 and 9-7 are identical when the voltage V_{1a} and the impedance $R_1 + jX_1$ have the proper values. According to Thévenin's theorem, the equivalent source voltage V_{1a} is the voltage that would appear across terminals a and b of Fig. 9-5 with the rotor

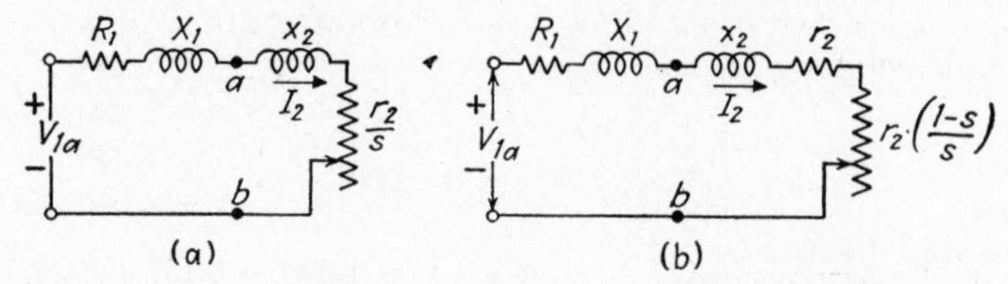

FIG. 9-7. Induction-motor equivalent circuits simplified by Thévenin's theorem.

circuits open and is

$$V_{1a} = V_1 - I_0(r_1 + jx_1) = V_1 \frac{jx_\varphi}{r_1 + jx_{11}} \tag{9-21}$$

where I_0 is the zero-load exciting current, and

$$x_{11} = x_1 + x_\varphi \tag{9-22}$$

is the self-reactance of the stator per phase and very nearly equals the reactive component of the zero-load motor impedance. For most induction motors, negligible error results from neglecting the stator resistance in Eq. 9-21. The Thévenin-equivalent stator impedance $R_1 + jX_1$ is the impedance between terminals a and b of Fig. 9-5, viewed toward the source with the source voltage short-circuited, and therefore is

$$R_1 + jX_1 = (r_1 + jx_1) \text{ in parallel with } jx_\varphi \tag{9-23}$$

So far as the load component I_2 of stator current is concerned, the T circuits of Fig. 9-5 have been reduced to the simple series circuits of Fig. 9-7. The voltage V_{1a} and all the circuit parameters, except r_2/s in Fig. 9-7a and $r_2(1 - s)/s$ in Fig. 9-7b, are constant, independent of load. Both circuits, then, reduce to a constant-voltage constant-impedance source supplying power to a variable-resistance load. The load component I_2 of the stator current can readily be determined from Fig. 9-7a, in terms of the applied stator voltage, motor constants, and slip. The internal torque and power are then given by Eqs. 9-14 and 9-18, respectively. For example,

$$T = \frac{1}{\omega_s} \frac{q_1 V_{1a}^2 (r_2/s)}{\left(R_1 + \frac{r_2}{s}\right)^2 + (X_1 + x_2)^2} \tag{9-24}$$

Curves of stator load-component current I_2, internal torque T, and internal power P as functions of slip s are shown in Fig. 9-8. Data for these curves are computed in Example 9-2. Starting conditions are those for $s = 1$. In order physically to obtain operation in the region of s greater than 1, the motor must be driven backward, against the direction

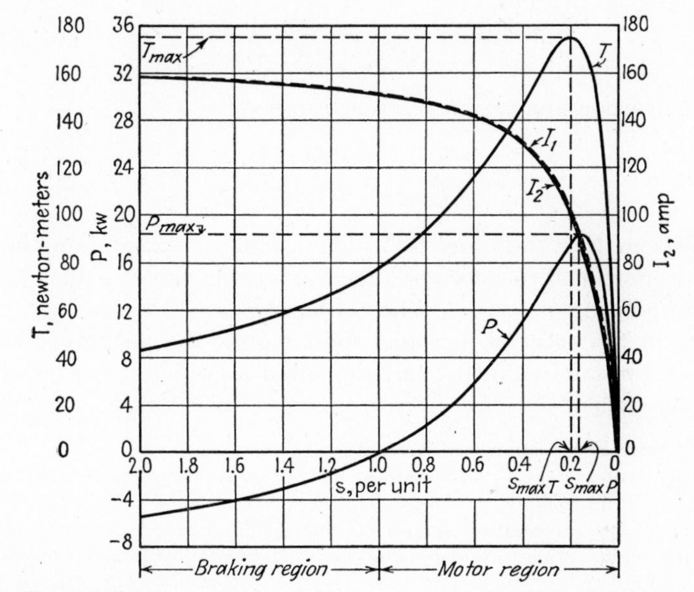

FIG. 9-8. Computed torque, power, and current curves for 10-hp induction motor of Examples 9-1 and 9-2.

of rotation of its magnetic field, by a source of mechanical power capable of counteracting the internal torque T. The chief practical usefulness of this region is in bringing motors to a quick stop by a method called *plugging*. By interchange of two stator leads in a 3-phase motor, the phase sequence, and hence the direction of rotation of the magnetic field, is reversed suddenly; the motor comes to a stop under the influence of the torque T and is disconnected from the line before it can start in the other direction. Accordingly, the region from $s = 1.0$ to $s = 2.0$ is labeled *Braking region* in Fig. 9-8.

The maximum internal or breakdown torque T_{max} and the maximum internal power P_{max}, indicated on Fig. 9-8, can be obtained readily from circuit considerations. Note that maximum torque and maximum power do not occur at the same speed. Internal torque is a maximum when the power delivered to r_2/s in Fig. 9-7a is a maximum. Now by the familiar impedance-matching principle in circuit theory, this power will be greatest when the impedance of r_2/s equals the magnitude of the impedance between it and the constant voltage V_{1a}, or at a value $s_{\max T}$ of slip for which

$$\frac{r_2}{s_{\max T}} = \sqrt{R_1^2 + (X_1 + x_2)^2} \tag{9-25}$$

The slip $s_{\max T}$ at maximum torque is therefore

$$s_{\max T} = \frac{r_2}{\sqrt{R_1^2 + (X_1 + x_2)^2}} \tag{9-26}$$

and the corresponding torque is, from Eq. 9-24,

$$T_{\max} = \frac{1}{\omega_s} \frac{0.5 q_1 V_{1a}^2}{R_1 + \sqrt{R_1^2 + (X_1 + x_2)^2}} \tag{9-27}$$

Notice from Eqs. 9-26 and 9-27 that the slip at maximum torque is directly proportional to rotor resistance r_2, but the value of the maximum torque is independent of r_2. When r_2 is increased by inserting external resistance in the rotor of a wound-rotor motor, the maximum internal torque is therefore unaffected but the speed at which it occurs may be directly controlled.

Example 9-2. For the motor of Example 9-1, determine:

a. The load component I_2 of the stator current, the internal torque T, and the internal power P for a slip $s = 0.03$

b. The maximum internal torque and the corresponding speed

c. The internal starting torque and the corresponding stator load current I_2

Solution. First reduce the circuit to its Thévenin-theorem form. From Eq. 9-21, $V_{1a} = 122.3$; and from Eq. 9-23, $R_1 + jX_1 = 0.273 + j0.490$.

a. At $s = 0.03$, $r_2/s = 4.80$. Then from Fig. 9-7a,

$$I_2 = \frac{122.3}{\sqrt{(5.07)^2 + (0.699)^2}} = 23.9 \text{ amp}$$

From Eq. 9-14,

$$T = \frac{1}{125.6}(3)(23.9)^2(4.80) = 65.5 \text{ newton-m}$$

From Eq. 9-18,

$$P = (3)(23.9)^2(4.80)(0.97) = 7{,}970 \text{ watts}$$

Data for the curves of Fig. 9-8 were computed by repeating these calculations for a number of assumed values of s.

b. At the maximum-torque point, from Eq. 9-26,

$$s_{\max T} = \frac{0.144}{\sqrt{(0.273)^2 + (0.699)^2}} = \frac{0.144}{0.750} = 0.192$$

$$\text{Speed at } T_{\max} = (1 - 0.192)(1{,}200) = 970 \text{ rpm}$$

From Eq. 9-27,

$$T_{\max} = \frac{1}{125.6}\,\frac{(0.5)(3)(122.3)^2}{0.273 + 0.750} = 175 \text{ newton-m}$$

c. At starting, $s = 1$, and r_2 will be assumed constant. Therefore,

$$\frac{r_2}{s} = r_2 = 0.144 \qquad R_1 + \frac{r_2}{s} = 0.417$$

$$I_{2\,\text{start}} = \frac{122.3}{\sqrt{(0.417)^2 + (0.699)^2}} = 150.5 \text{ amp}$$

From Eq. 9-14,

$$T_{\text{start}} = \frac{1}{125.6}(3)(150.5)^2(0.144) = 78.0 \text{ newton-m}$$

9-4. Normalized Torque-Slip Curves. A feature common to all branches of engineering is that equations expressing the performance of devices may present somewhat complicated arrays involving a multitude of different quantities. Equation 9-24, for example, contains nine quantities, including the dependent and independent variables T and s. It is frequently of value to simplify such equations by writing them in dimensionless form as relations between ratios rather than between absolute magnitudes. For the induction motor, such a result is obtained by expressing the torque-slip relation as one between the ratios $T/T_{\max}$ and $s/s_{\max T}$. From Eqs. 9-24 and 9-27,

$$\frac{T}{T_{\max}} = \frac{2\left[R_1 + \sqrt{R_1^2 + (X_1 + x_2)^2}\right]\dfrac{r_2}{s}}{\left(R_1 + \dfrac{r_2}{s}\right)^2 + (X_1 + x_2)^2} \tag{9-28}$$

Since the final result is to be a function of $s/s_{\max T}$ instead of simply s, r_2 in Eq. 9-28 must now be replaced by its value in terms of $s_{\max T}$ from Eq. 9-26. After algebraic reduction, this process yields

$$\frac{T}{T_{\max}} = \frac{1 + \sqrt{Q^2 + 1}}{1 + \frac{1}{2}\sqrt{Q^2 + 1}\left(\dfrac{s}{s_{\max T}} + \dfrac{s_{\max T}}{s}\right)} \tag{9-29}$$

where

$$Q = \frac{X_1 + x_2}{R_1} \tag{9-30}$$

The symbol Q is used because of the similarity of this ratio to the quality factor Q or reactance-to-resistance ratio in circuit theory.

In a similar manner, the ratio of stator load current I_2 to that at maximum torque $I_{2\,\max T}$ can be shown to be

$$\frac{I_2}{I_{2\,\max T}} = \sqrt{\frac{(1 + \sqrt{1 + Q^2})^2 + Q^2}{\left(1 + \frac{s_{\max T}}{s}\sqrt{1 + Q^2}\right)^2 + Q^2}} \tag{9-31}$$

Curves of $T/T_{\max}$ are plotted as functions of the appropriate slip ratio for several values of the Q ratio in Fig. 9-9, and curves of the current ratio $I_2/I_{2\,\max T}$ in Fig. 9-10. Most induction motors will fall in the region between $Q = 3$ and $Q = 7$, and the average will lie about midway between

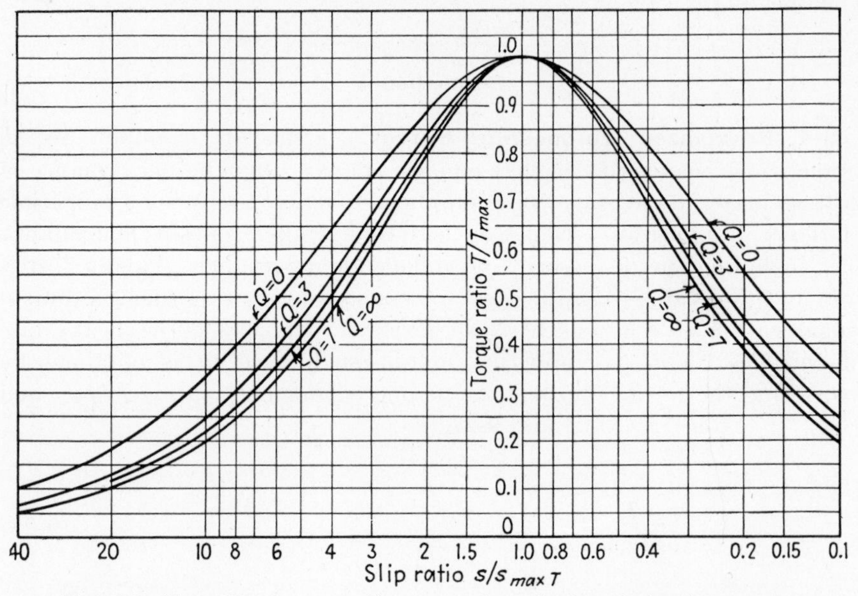

FIG. 9-9. Normalized torque-slip curves for polyphase induction motors.

the curves for these two values. Notice the rather small influence which variation of Q has on these curves; bear in mind, however, that the curves are plots of ratios, not of absolute magnitudes.

One characteristic feature of simple induction motors is shown by the very fact that the torque-slip curves can be normalized in the manner of Fig. 9-9: except for the relatively small effect of the Q ratio, if the maximum torque and the slip at which it occurs are specified, the speed-torque characteristic is approximately fixed throughout the entire speed range. This statement is, of course, subject to the limitation that the parameters of the motor are constant and therefore does not apply to motors with variable rotor resistance.

Example 9-3. An induction motor with constant rotor resistance develops a maximum torque of 2.5 times its full-load torque at a slip of 0.20. Estimate its slip at full load and its starting torque at rated voltage.

Solution. At full load, $T/T_{\max} = 0.40$. From Fig. 9-9, the corresponding value of $s/s_{\max T}$ lies between 0.17 and 0.19 for values of Q between 3 and 7, the range for normal motors. Consequently the full-load slip lies between $(0.17)(0.20) = 0.034$ and $(0.19)(0.20) = 0.038$.

At starting, $s/s_{\max T} = 1/0.20 = 5.0$. From Fig. 9-9 the corresponding value of $T/T_{\max}$ lies between 0.42 and 0.45 for values of Q between 7 and 3. The starting torque therefore lies between $(0.42)(2.5) = 1.05$ and $(0.45)(2.5) = 1.13$ times full-load torque.

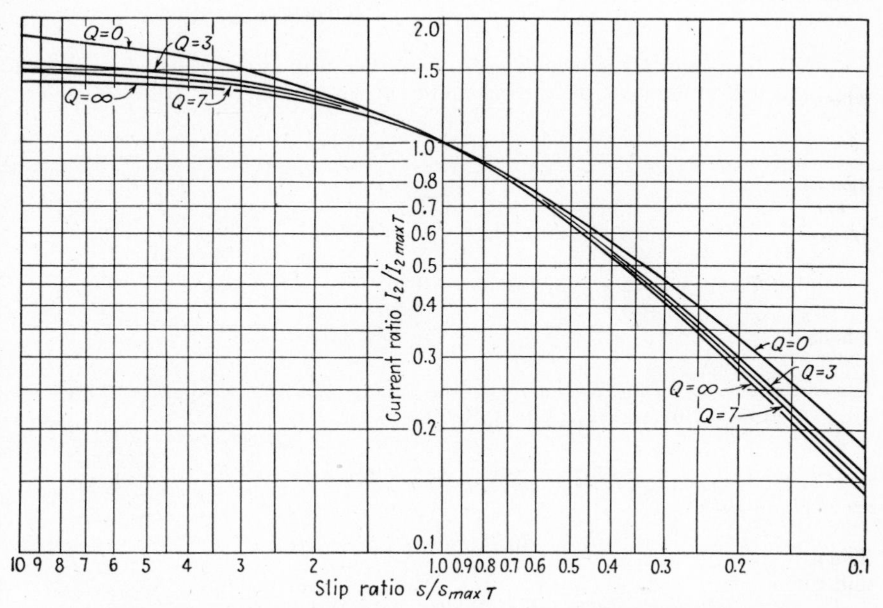

FIG. 9-10. Normalized current-slip curves for polyphase induction motors.

Example 9-4. When operated at rated voltage and frequency with its rotor windings short-circuited, a 500-hp wound-rotor induction motor develops its rated full-load output at a slip of 1.5 per cent. The maximum torque which this motor can develop is 200 per cent of full-load torque. The Q of its Thévenin equivalent circuit is 7.0. For the purposes of this example, rotational and stray load losses may be neglected. Determine:

a. The rotor I^2R loss at full load, in kilowatts
b. The slip at maximum torque
c. The rotor current at maximum torque
d. The torque at a slip of 20 per cent
e. The rotor current at a slip of 20 per cent

Express the torque and rotor currents in per unit based on their full-load values.

Solution. *a. Rotor I^2R at Full Load.* The power P_{g1} absorbed from the stator divides between mechanical power P and rotor I^2R in the ratio $(1 - s)/s$, as in Eqs. 9-15 and 9-17. Consequently, at full load (neglecting rotational and stray load losses)

$$P_{g1} = \frac{P}{1 - s} = \frac{(500)(0.746)}{0.985} = 379 \text{ kw}$$

$$\text{Rotor } I^2R = sP_{g1} = (0.015)(379) = 5.69 \text{ kw}$$

Parts *b* to *e* can readily be solved by means of the normalized curves, Figs. 9-9 and 9-10.

b. Slip at Maximum Torque. From the data, $T_{fl}/T_{\max} = 0.50$, where the subscripts fl indicate full load. From Fig. 9-9 at $Q = 7.0$ and $T/T_{\max} = 0.50$,

$$\frac{s}{s_{\max T}} = \frac{s_{fl}}{s_{\max T}} = 0.25$$

whence

$$s_{\max T} = \frac{s_{fl}}{0.25} = \frac{0.015}{0.25} = 0.060$$

c. Rotor Current at Maximum Torque. From Fig. 9-10 at $Q = 7.0$ and a slip ratio $s/s_{\max T} = 0.25$ at full load, the corresponding current ratio is

$$\frac{I_2}{I_{2\max T}} = \frac{I_{2fl}}{I_{2\max T}} = 0.355$$

whence

$$I_{2\max T} = \frac{I_{2fl}}{0.355} = 2.82 I_{2fl}$$

d and *e. Torque and Rotor Current at* $s = 0.20$. The slip ratio is

$$\frac{s}{s_{\max T}} = \frac{0.20}{0.060} = 3.33$$

The corresponding torque and current ratios can be read from the curves of Figs. 9-9 and 9-10 at $Q = 7.0$ and $s/s_{\max T} = 3.33$. From Fig. 9-9

$$\frac{T}{T_{\max}} = 0.60 \quad \text{or} \quad T = 0.60 T_{\max} = 1.20 T_{fl}$$

From Fig. 9-10

$$\frac{I_2}{I_{2\max T}} = 1.40 \quad \text{or} \quad I_2 = 1.40 I_{2\max T}$$

and from *c*

$$I_2 = (1.40)(2.82 I_{2fl}) = 3.95 I_{2fl}$$

9-5. Effects of Rotor Resistance; Double-squirrel-cage Rotors; Applicational Considerations. A basic limitation of induction motors with constant rotor resistance is that the rotor design has to be a compromise. High efficiency under normal running conditions requires a low rotor resistance; but a low rotor resistance results in a low starting torque and high starting current at a low starting power factor.

a. Wound-rotor Motors. The use of a wound rotor is one effective way of avoiding the necessity for compromise. The terminals of the rotor winding are connected to slip rings in contact with brushes, as described in Art. 3-7*c*. For starting, resistors may be connected in series with the rotor windings, the result being increased starting torque and reduced starting current at an improved power factor. The general nature of the effects on the torque-speed characteristics caused by varying rotor resistance is shown in Fig. 3-23. By use of the appropriate value of rotor resistance, the maximum torque can be made to occur at standstill if high starting torque is needed. As the rotor speeds up, the external resistances can be decreased, making maximum torque available throughout the accelerating range. Since most of the rotor I^2R loss is dissipated in the external resistors, the rotor temperature rise during starting is lower than it would be if the resistance were incorporated in the rotor winding. For normal running, the rotor winding can be short-circuited directly at the brushes. The rotor winding is designed to have low resistance so that running efficiency is high and full-load slip is low. Besides their use when starting requirements are severe, wound-rotor induction motors may be used for adjustable-speed drives. The chief disadvantage of wound-rotor motors is their greater cost as compared with squirrel-cage motors.

The principal effects of varying rotor resistance on the starting and running characteristics of induction motors can be shown quantitatively by means of the following example:

Example 9-5. The rotor winding of the motor of Example 9-4 is 3-phase, Y-connected, and has a resistance of r_{rotor}.

If the rotor-circuit resistance is increased to $5r_{\text{rotor}}$ by connecting noninductive resistances in series with each rotor slip ring, determine:

a. The slip at which the motor will develop the same full-load torque as in Example 9-4

b. The total rotor-circuit I^2R loss at full-load torque

c. The horsepower output at full-load torque

d. The slip at maximum torque

e. The rotor current at maximum torque

f. The starting torque

g. The rotor current at starting

Express the torques and rotor currents in per unit based on the full-load-torque values.

Solution. The solution involves recognition of the fact that the only way in which the stator is cognizant of the happenings in the rotor is through the effect of the resistance r_2/s. Examination of the equivalent circuit (Fig. 9-5*a* or 9-7*a*) shows that for specified applied voltage and frequency everything concerning the stator performance is fixed by the value of r_2/s, the other impedance elements being constant. For example, if r_2 is doubled and s is simultaneously doubled, the stator is unaware that any change has been made. The stator current and power factor, the power delivered to the air gap, and the torque are constant so long as the ratio r_2/s is the same.

Added physical significance can be given to the argument by examining the effects of simultaneously doubling r_2 and s from the view point of the rotor. An observer on the rotor then sees the resultant air-gap flux wave traveling past him at twice the original slip speed, generating twice the original rotor voltage at twice the original slip frequency. The rotor reactance therefore is doubled, and since the original premise is that the rotor resistance also is doubled, the rotor impedance is doubled but the rotor power factor is unchanged. Since rotor voltage and impedance are both doubled, the effective value of the rotor current remains the same; only its frequency is changed. The air gap still has the same synchronously rotating flux and mmf waves with the same torque angle. The observer on the rotor therefore agrees with his counterpart on the stator that the torque is unchanged when both rotor resistance and slip are changed proportionally.

The observer on the rotor, however, is aware of two changes not apparent in the stator: (1) the rotor I^2R loss has doubled, and (2) the rotor is turning more slowly and therefore developing less mechanical power with the same torque. In other words, more of the power absorbed from the stator goes into I^2R heat in the rotor, and less is available for mechanical power.

The preceding thought processes now can readily be applied to the solution of Example 9-5.

a. Slip at Full-load Torque. If the rotor resistance is increased 5 times, the slip must increase 5 times for the same value of r_2/s and therefore for the same torque. But the original slip at full load, as given in Example 9-4, is 0.015. The new slip at full-load torque therefore is (5) (0.015) = 0.075.

b. Rotor I^2R at Full-load Torque. The effective value of the rotor current is the same as its full-load value in Example 9-4, and therefore the rotor I^2R loss is 5 times the full-load value of 5.69 kw found in part *a* of Example 9-4; or

$$\text{Rotor } I^2R = (5)(5.69) = 28.45 \text{ kw}$$

The same result can, of course, be arrived at from the equivalent circuit and the equations of Art. 9-2.

c. Power Output at Full-load Torque. The increased slip has caused the per-unit speed at full-load torque to drop from $1 - s = 0.985$ in Example 9-4 down to $1 - s = 0.925$ with added rotor resistance. The torque is the same. The power output therefore has dropped proportionally, or

$$P = \frac{0.925}{0.985}(500) = 469.5 \text{ hp}$$

The decrease in output equals the increase in rotor I^2R loss.

d. Slip at Maximum Torque. If rotor resistance is increased 5 times, the slip at maximum torque simply increases 5 times. But the original slip at maximum torque is 0.060, as found in part *b* of Example 9-4. The new slip at maximum torque with the added rotor resistance therefore is

$$s_{\max T} = (5)(0.060) = 0.30$$

e. Rotor Current at Maximum Torque. The effective value of the rotor current at maximum torque is independent of rotor resistance; only its frequency is changed when rotor resistance is varied. Therefore, from part *c* of Example 9-4,

$$I_{2\max T} = 2.82 I_{2fl}$$

f. Starting Torque. With the rotor resistance increased 5 times, the starting torque will be the same as the original running torque at a slip of 0.20 and therefore equals the running torque in part *d* of Example 9-4, *viz.*,

$$T_{\text{start}} = 1.20 T_{fl}$$

g. Rotor Current at Starting. The rotor current at starting with the added rotor resistances will be the same as the rotor current when running at a slip of 0.20 with the slip rings short-circuited as in part *e* of Example 9-4, viz.,

$$I_{2\text{ start}} = 3.95 I_{2fl}$$

b. Deep-bar and Double-squirrel-cage Rotors. An ingenious and simple way for obtaining a rotor resistance which will automatically vary with speed makes use of the fact that at standstill, the rotor frequency equals the stator frequency; as the motor accelerates, the rotor frequency decreases to a very low value—perhaps 2 or 3 cps at full load in a 60-cps motor. By use of suitable shapes and arrangements of rotor bars, squirrel-cage rotors can be designed so that their effective resistance at 60 cps is several times their resistance at 2 or 3 cps. The various schemes all make use of the inductive effect of the slot-leakage flux on the current distribution in the rotor bars. The phenomena are basically the same as the skin and proximity effect in any system of conductors with alternating current in them.

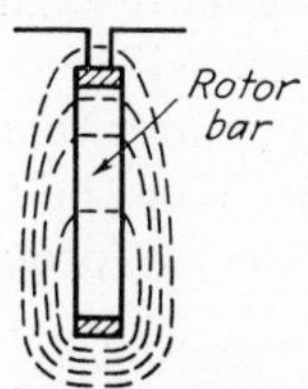

Fig. 9-11. Deep rotor bar and slot-leakage flux.

Consider first a squirrel-cage rotor having deep, narrow bars like those shown in cross section in Fig. 9-11. The general character of the slot-leakage field produced by the current in the bar within this slot is shown in the figure. If the rotor iron had infinite permeability, all of the leakage-flux lines would close in paths below the slot, as shown. Now imagine the bar to consist of an infinite number of layers of differential depth; one at the bottom and one at the top are indicated crosshatched in Fig. 9-11. The leakage inductance of the bottom layer is greater than that of the top layer, because the bottom layer is linked by more leakage flux. But all the layers are electrically in parallel. Consequently, with alternating current, the current in the low-reactance upper layers will be greater than that in the high-reactance lower layers; the current will be forced toward the top of the slot, and the current in the upper layers will lead the current in the lower ones. The nonuniform current distribution results in an increase in the effective resistance and a smaller decrease in the effective leakage inductance of the bar. Since the distortion in current distribution depends on an inductive effect, the effective resistance is a function of the frequency. It is also a function of the depth of the bar and of the permeability and resistivity of the bar material.[2] Figure 9-12 shows a curve of the ratio of a-c effective resistance to d-c resistance as a function of frequency computed for a copper bar 1.00 in. deep. A squirrel-cage rotor with deep bars can readily be designed to have an effective resistance at stator frequency (standstill) several times greater than its d-c resistance. As the motor

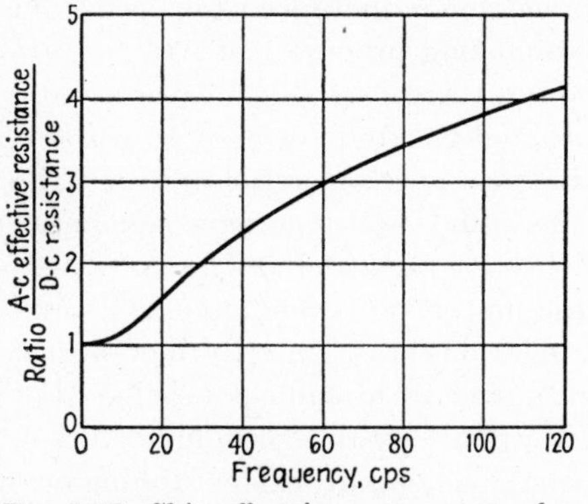

Fig. 9-12. Skin effect in a copper rotor bar 1.00 in. deep.

[2] For a detailed analysis, see W. V. Lyon, Heat Losses in the Conductors of Alternating-current Machines, *Trans. AIEE*, vol. 40, pp. 1361–1395, 1921.

accelerates, the rotor frequency decreases and therefore the rotor effective resistance decreases, approaching its d-c value at small slips.

An alternative way of attaining similar results is the double-cage arrangement shown in Fig. 9-13. The squirrel-cage winding consists of two layers of bars short-circuited by end rings. The upper bars are of smaller cross-sectional area than the lower bars and consequently have higher resistance. The general nature of the slot-leakage field is shown in Fig. 9-13, from which it can be seen that the inductance of the lower bars is greater than that of the upper ones, because of the flux crossing the slot between the two layers. The difference in inductance can be made quite large by properly proportioning the constriction in the slot between the two bars. At standstill, when rotor frequency equals stator frequency, there is relatively little current in the lower bars because of their high reactance; the effective resistance of the rotor at standstill then approximates that of the high-resistance upper layer. At the low rotor frequencies corresponding to small slips, however, reactance becomes unimportant, and the rotor resistance then approaches that of the two layers in parallel.

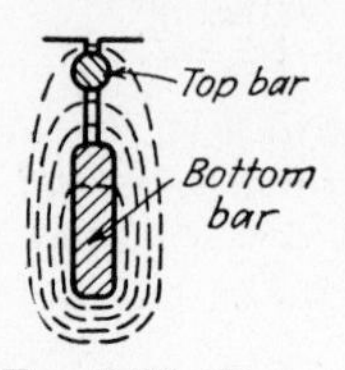

FIG. 9-13. Double-squirrel-cage rotor bars and slot-leakage flux.

Note that, since the effective resistance and leakage inductance of double-cage and deep-bar rotors vary with frequency, the parameters r_2 and x_2 representing the referred effects of rotor resistance and leakage inductance as viewed from the stator are not constant. The normalizing processes of Art. 9-4 are therefore no longer strictly applicable, and their use in such cases is more or less of an approximation. A more complicated form of equivalent circuit is required if the reactions of the rotor are to be represented by the effects of slip together with constant resistance and reactance elements.[3]

The simple equivalent circuits which have been derived in Arts. 9-1, 9-2, and 9-3 still correctly represent the motor, however, but now r_2 and x_2 are functions of slip. All the basic relations still apply to the motor if the values of r_2 and x_2 are properly adjusted with changes in slip. For example, in computing the starting performance, r_2 and x_2 should be taken as their effective values at stator frequency; in computing the running performance at small slips, however, r_2 should be taken as its effective value at a low frequency, and x_2 should be taken as the stator-frequency-value of the reactance corresponding to a low-frequency effective value of the rotor leakage inductance. Over the normal running range of slips, the rotor resistance and leakage inductance usually can be considered constant at substantially their d-c values.

[3] For example, see S. S. L. Chang, General Theory of Multiple-cage Induction Motors, *Trans. AIEE*, vol. 68, Part 2, pp. 1139–1143, Part 2, 1949.

c. Applicational Considerations. By use of double-cage and deep-bar rotors, squirrel-cage motors can be designed to have the good starting characteristics resulting from high rotor resistance and at the same time the good running characteristics resulting from low rotor resistance. The design is necessarily somewhat of a compromise, however, and the motor lacks the flexibility of the wound-rotor machine with external rotor resistance. The wound-rotor motor should be used when starting requirements are very severe.

To meet the usual needs of industry, integral-horsepower 2- and 3-phase squirrel-cage motors are available from manufacturers' stock in a range of standard ratings up to 200 hp at various standard frequencies, voltages, and speeds.[4] According to the terminology established by the NEMA, several standard designs are available to meet various starting and running requirements. Representative torque-speed characteristics of the four commonest designs are shown in Fig. 9-14. These curves are fairly typical of 1,800-rpm (synchronous speed) motors in ratings from 7.5 to 200 hp, although it should be understood that individual motors may differ appreciably from these average curves. Briefly, the characteristic features of these designs[5] are as follows:

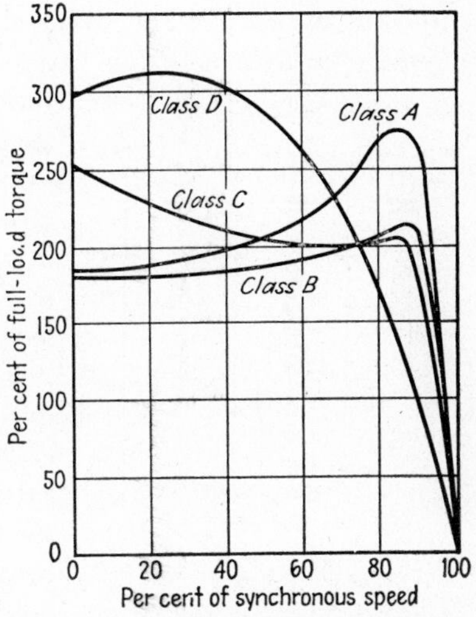

FIG. 9-14. Typical torque-speed curves for 1,800-rpm general-purpose induction motors.

DESIGN CLASS A: *Normal starting torque, normal starting current, low slip.* This design usually has a low-resistance single-cage rotor. It emphasizes good running performance at the expense of starting. The full-load slip is low and the full-load efficiency high. The maximum torque usually is well over 200 per cent of full-load torque and occurs at a small slip (less than 20 per cent). The starting torque at full voltage varies from about 200 per cent of full-load torque in small motors to about 100 per cent in large motors. The high starting current (500 to 800 per cent of full-load

[4] See ASA Standards, Rotating Electrical Machinery, C50-1943, American Standards Association, New York, 1943; NEMA Standards, Motor and Generator Standards, 45-102, National Electrical Manufacturers' Association, New York, 1945.

[5] For a more complete discussion of applicational considerations, see D. R. Shoults, C. J. Rife, and T. C. Johnson, "Electric Motors in Industry," Chaps. IV and V, John Wiley & Sons, Inc., New York, 1942.

current when started at rated voltage) is the principal disadvantage of this design. In sizes below about 7.5 hp, these starting currents usually are within the limits on inrush current which the distribution system supplying the motor can withstand, and across-the-line starting at full voltage then can be used; otherwise, reduced-voltage starting must be used. Reduced-voltage starting results in a decrease in starting torque, because the starting torque is proportional to the volt-ampere input to the motor, which in turn is proportional to the square of the voltage applied to the motor terminals. The reduced voltage for starting is usually obtained from an autotransformer, called a *starting compensator*, which may be manually operated, or automatically operated by relays which cause full voltage to be applied after the motor is up to speed. A circuit diagram of one type of compensator is shown in Fig. 9-15. If a smoother start is necessary, series resistance or reactance in the stator may be used.[6]

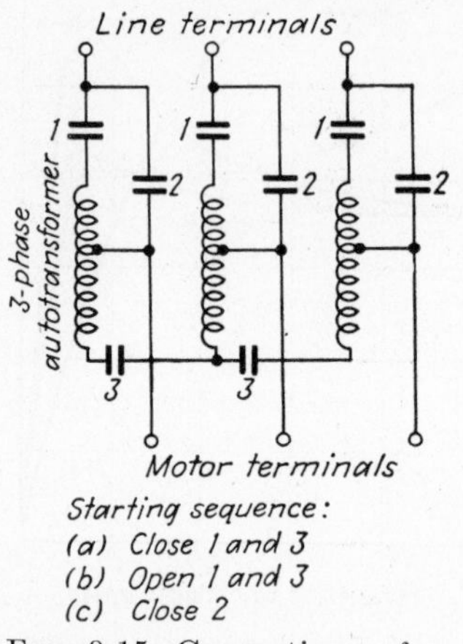

FIG. 9-15. Connections of a one-step starting autotransformer.

The Class A motor is the basic standard design in sizes below about 7.5 and above about 200 hp. It is also used in intermediate ratings wherein design considerations may make it difficult to meet the starting-current limitations of the Class B design. Its field of application is about the same as that of the Class B design described below.

DESIGN CLASS B: *Normal starting torque, low starting current, low slip.* This design has approximately the same starting torque as the Class A design with but 75 per cent of the starting current. Full-voltage starting therefore may be used with larger sizes than with Class A. The starting current is reduced by designing for relatively high leakage reactance, and the starting torque is maintained by use of a double-cage or deep-bar rotor. The full-load slip and efficiency are good—about the same as for the Class A design. However, the use of high reactance slightly decreases the power factor and decidedly lowers the maximum torque (usually only slightly over 200 per cent of full-load torque being obtainable).

This design is the commonest in the 7.5- to 200-hp range of sizes. It is used for substantially constant-speed drives where starting-torque requirements are not severe, such as in driving fans, blowers, pumps, and machine tools.

DESIGN CLASS C: *High starting torque, low starting current.* This design uses a double-cage rotor with higher rotor resistance than the Class B

[6] For a comparison of starting methods, see Chap. V of reference cited in footnote 5.

design. The result is higher starting torque with low starting current but somewhat lower running efficiency and higher slip than the Class A and Class B designs. Typical applications are in driving compressors and conveyers.

DESIGN CLASS D: *High starting torque, high slip.* This design usually has a single-cage high-resistance rotor (frequently brass bars). It produces very high starting torque at low starting current, high maximum torque at 50 to 100 per cent slip, but runs at a high slip at full load (7 to 11 per cent) and consequently has low running efficiency. Its principal uses are for driving intermittent loads involving high accelerating duty and for driving high-impact loads such as punch presses and shears. When driving high-impact loads, the motor is generally aided by a flywheel which helps supply the impact and reduces the pulsations in power drawn from the supply system. A motor whose speed falls appreciably with increase in torque is required in order that the flywheel may slow down and deliver some of its kinetic energy to the impact.

9-6. Performance Calculations from No-load and Blocked-rotor Tests. The data needed for computing the performance of a polyphase induction motor under load can be obtained from the results of a no-load test, a blocked-rotor test, and measurements of the d-c resistances of the stator windings. The stray load losses, which must be taken into account when accurate values of efficiency are to be calculated, can also be measured by tests which do not require loading the motor. The stray-load-loss tests will not be described here, however.[7]

Like the open-circuit test on a transformer, the no-load test on an induction motor gives information with respect to exciting current and no-load losses. The test is ordinarily taken at rated frequency and with balanced polyphase voltages applied to the stator terminals. Readings are taken at rated voltage, after the motor has been running long enough so that the bearings are properly lubricated. The total rotational loss at rated voltage and frequency under load usually is considered to be constant and equal to its no-load value.

At no load, the rotor current is only the very small value needed to produce sufficient torque to overcome friction and windage. The no-load rotor copper loss therefore is negligibly small. Unlike a transformer, whose no-load primary copper loss is negligible, the no-load stator copper loss of an induction motor may be appreciable, because of its larger exciting current. The rotational loss P_R for normal running conditions is

$$P_R = P_{nl} - q_1 I_{nl}^2 r_1 \tag{9-32}$$

[7] For information concerning test methods, see AIEE Test Code for Polyphase Induction Machines, No. 500, American Institute of Electrical Engineers, New York, 1937.

where P_{nl} and I_{nl} are, respectively, the total polyphase power input and the current per phase, q_1 is the number of stator phases, and r_1 is the stator resistance per phase.

Because the slip at no load is very small, the reflected rotor resistance r_2/s_{nl} is very large. The parallel combination of rotor and magnetizing branches then becomes jx_φ shunted by a very high resistance, and the reactance of this parallel combination therefore very nearly equals x_φ. Consequently the apparent reactance X_{nl} measured at the stator terminals at no load very nearly equals $x_1 + x_\varphi$ which is the self-reactance x_{11} of the stator; *i.e.*,

$$x_{11} = x_1 + x_\varphi = X_{nl} \tag{9-33}$$

The self-reactance of the stator therefore can be determined from the instrument readings at no load. For a 3-phase machine, considered to be Y-connected, the magnitude of the no-load impedance Z_{nl} per phase is

$$Z_{nl} = \frac{V_{nl}}{\sqrt{3}\, I_{nl}} \tag{9-34}$$

where V_{nl} is the line-to-line terminal voltage in the no-load test. The no-load resistance R_{nl} is

$$R_{nl} = \frac{P_{nl}}{3I_{nl}^2} \tag{9-35}$$

where P_{nl} is the total 3-phase power input at no load; the no-load reactance X_{nl} then is

$$X_{nl} = \sqrt{Z_{nl}^2 - R_{nl}^2} \tag{9-36}$$

Usually the no-load power factor is about 0.1, so that the no-load reactance very nearly equals the no-load impedance.

Like the short-circuit test on a transformer, the blocked-rotor test on an induction motor gives information with respect to the leakage impedances. The rotor is blocked so that it cannot rotate, and balanced polyphase voltages are applied to the stator terminals. Sometimes the blocked-rotor torque also is measured.

The equivalent circuit for blocked-rotor conditions is identical to that of a short-circuited transformer. An induction motor is more complicated than a transformer, however, because its leakage impedance may be affected by magnetic saturation of the leakage-flux paths and by rotor frequency. The blocked impedance may also be affected by rotor position, although this effect generally is small with cage rotors. The guiding principle is that the blocked-rotor test should be taken under conditions of current and rotor frequency approximately the same as those existing in the operating condition for which the performance is later to be calculated. For example, if one is interested in the characteristics at slips near unity, as in starting, the blocked-rotor test should be taken at normal frequency and with currents near the values encountered in starting. If, however, one is interested in the normal running characteristics, the blocked-rotor test should be taken at a reduced voltage which results in about rated current; the frequency also should be reduced, since the values of rotor effective resistance and leakage inductance at the low rotor frequencies corresponding to small slips may differ appreciably from their values at normal frequency, particularly with double-cage or deep-bar rotors. The AIEE Test Code (footnote 7) suggests a frequency of 15 cps for 60-cps motors, although a frequency of 25 cps may be used provided the results obtained at 25 cps do not differ materially from those obtained at 60 cps. The value of the blocked reactance at normal frequency can be computed from the test value at reduced frequency by considering the reactance to be proportional to frequency. The effects of frequency often are negligible for normal motors of less than 25-hp rating, and the blocked impedance may then be measured directly at normal frequency.

If exciting current is neglected, the blocked-rotor reactance X_{bl}, corrected to normal frequency, equals the sum of the normal-frequency stator and rotor leakage reactances, x_1 and x_2. The performance of the motor is relatively little affected by the way in which the total leakage reactance $x_1 + x_2$ is distributed between stator and rotor. The AIEE Test Code (footnote 7) recommends the empirical distribution shown in Table 9-1.

TABLE 9-1
EMPIRICAL DISTRIBUTION OF LEAKAGE REACTANCES IN INDUCTION MOTORS

Class of motor	Fraction of $x_1 + x_2$	
	x_1	x_2
Class A (normal starting torque, normal starting current)	0.5	0.5
Class B (normal starting torque, low starting current)	0.4	0.6
Class C (high starting torque, low starting current)	0.3	0.7
Class D (high starting torque, high slip)	0.5	0.5
Wound rotor	0.5	0.5

The magnetizing reactance x_φ now can be determined from the no-load test and the value of x_1; thus

$$x_\varphi = X_{nl} - x_1 \tag{9-37}$$

The stator resistance r_1 can be considered as its d-c value. The rotor resistance then can be determined as follows: From the blocked-rotor test, the blocked resistance R_{bl} can be computed by means of a relation similar to Eq. 9-35. The difference between the blocked resistance and the stator resistance then can be determined from the test data. Denoting this resistance by R, then

$$R = R_{bl} - r_1 \tag{9-38}$$

From the equivalent circuit (Fig. 9-5a), with $s = 1$, the resistance R is the resistance of the combination of $r_2 + jx_2$ in parallel with jx_φ. For this parallel combination,

$$R = r_2 \frac{x_\varphi^2}{r_2^2 + x_{22}^2} \approx r_2 \left(\frac{x_\varphi}{x_{22}}\right)^2 \tag{9-39}$$

where $x_{22} = x_2 + x_\varphi$ is the self-reactance of the rotor. If x_{22} is greater than $10r_2$, as is usually the case, less than 1 per cent error results from use of the approximate form of Eq. 9-39. Substitution of this approximate form in Eq. 9-38 and solution for r_2 then gives

$$r_2 = R\left(\frac{x_{22}}{x_\varphi}\right)^2 = (R_{bl} - r_1)\left(\frac{x_{22}}{x_\varphi}\right)^2 \tag{9-40}$$

All the equivalent-circuit constants have now been determined, and the motor performance under load can then be computed by the methods of Arts. 9-2 and 9-3.

Example 9-6. The following test data apply to a 7.5-hp 3-phase 220-volt 19-amp 60-cps 4-pole induction motor with a double-squirrel-cage rotor of the high-starting-torque low-starting-current type (design class C):

Test 1. *No-load Test at* 60 *cps:*

Applied voltage $V = 219$ volts, line to line
Average line current $I_{nl} = 5.70$ amp
Power (two wattmeters): $W_1 = 680$; $W_2 = -300$ watts

Test 2. *Blocked-rotor Test at* 15 *cps:*

$V = 26.5$ volts $\quad I = 18.57$ amp
$W_1 = 215$ watts $\quad W_2 = 460$ watts

Test 3. *Average D-C Resistance per Stator Phase* (measured immediately after Test 2):

$r_1 = 0.262$ ohm per phase (Y connection assumed)

Test 4. *Blocked-rotor Test at* 60 *cps:*

$V = 212$ volts $\quad I = 83.3$ amp
$W_1 = 3{,}300$ watts $\quad W_2 = 16{,}800$ watts
Measured starting torque $T_{start} = 54.6$ lb-ft

a. Compute the no-load rotational loss and the equivalent-circuit constants applying to the normal running conditions. Assume the same temperature as in Test 3.

b. Compute the internal starting torque from the input measurements of Test 4. Assume the same temperature as in Test 3.

Solution. *a.* From Test 1, $P_{nl} = 380$ watts, and by Eq. 9-32,

$$P_R = 380 - 3(5.70)^2(0.262) = 354 \text{ watts}$$

From Test 1 and Eqs. 9-34, 9-35, and 9-36,

$$Z_{nl} = \frac{219}{\sqrt{3}\,(5.70)} = 22.2 \text{ ohms per phase Y}$$

$$R_{nl} = \frac{380}{3(5.70)^2} = 3.9 \text{ ohms} \qquad X_{nl} = 21.8 \text{ ohms}$$

The blocked-rotor test at reduced frequency and rated current reproduces approximately normal running conditions in the rotor. From Test 2,

$$Z'_{bl} = \frac{26.5}{\sqrt{3}\,(18.57)} = 0.825 \text{ ohm per phase at 15 cps}$$

$$R_{bl} = \frac{675}{3(18.57)^2} = 0.654 \text{ ohm} \qquad X'_{bl} = 0.503 \text{ ohm at 15 cps}$$

where the primes indicate 15-cps values. The blocked reactance referred to normal frequency then is

$$X_{bl} = {}^{60}\!/_{15} \times (0.503) = 2.01 \text{ ohms per phase at 60 cps}$$

According to Table 9-1,

$$x_1 = 0.3(2.01) = 0.603 \qquad x_2 = 0.7(2.01) = 1.407 \text{ ohms per phase}$$

and by Eq. 9-37,

$$x_\varphi = 21.8 - 0.6 = 21.2 \text{ ohms per phase}$$

From Test 3 and Eqs. 9-38 and 9-40,

$$R = 0.654 - 0.262 = 0.392 \qquad r_2 = 0.392\left(\frac{22.6}{21.2}\right)^2 = 0.445 \text{ ohm per phase}$$

The constants of the equivalent circuit for small values of slip have now been calculated.

b. The internal starting torque can be computed from the input measurements in Test 4. From the power input and stator copper losses, the air-gap power P_{g1} is

$$P_{g1} = 20{,}100 - 3(83.3)^2(0.262) = 14{,}650 \text{ watts}$$

Synchronous speed $\omega_s = 188.5$ rad/sec, and by Eq. 9-12,

$$T_{\text{start}} = \frac{14{,}650}{188.5} = 77.6 \text{ newton-m., or } 57.3 \text{ lb-ft}$$

The test value, $T_{\text{start}} = 54.6$ lb-ft, is a few per cent less than the calculated value, because the calculations do not account for the power absorbed in stator core loss and in stray load losses.

9-7. Ratio of Transformation. The relations between the referred rotor quantities and the corresponding quantities in the actual rotor are required if one is concerned with what is happening in the actual rotor circuits or bars, as, for example, in computing the equivalent-circuit constants from design dimensions. The purpose of this article is to derive these referring factors.

a. Wound Rotors. The polyphase stator and rotor must, of course, be wound for the same number of poles p. They need not, however, be wound for the same number of phases. For greatest generality, the stator is considered to have q_1 phases, N_{ph1} turns in series per phase, and a combined fundamental pitch and breadth factor of k_{w1}; the corresponding quantities for the rotor winding are q_2, N_{ph2}, and k_{w2}.

The referred rotor is one which is considered to have the same number of phases, turns, and arrangement as the stator, and therefore, in so far as voltages induced by space-fundamental flux are concerned, the ratio of effective turns per phase in the referred rotor to effective turns per phase in the actual rotor is $N_{ph1}k_{w1}/N_{ph2}k_{w2}$. Consequently, for the same flux and speed, the relation between the actual slip-frequency rotor voltage per phase E_{rotor} and the corresponding slip-frequency rotor voltage E_{2s} referred to the stator is

$$E_{2s} = \frac{N_{ph1}k_{w1}}{N_{ph2}k_{w2}} E_{\text{rotor}} \tag{9-41}$$

Since the rotors are magnetically equivalent, their space-fundamental mmf waves must be equal, and therefore from Eq. 4-25 the relation between the actual rotor current per phase I_{rotor} and the rotor current I_{2s} referred to the stator is

$$I_{2s} = \frac{q_2 N_{ph2}k_{w2}}{q_1 N_{ph1}k_{w1}} I_{\text{rotor}} \tag{9-42}$$

The vector relation between the referred value Z_{2s} and the actual value Z_{rotor} of rotor impedance is

$$Z_{2s} = \frac{E_{2s}}{I_{2s}} = \frac{q_1}{q_2}\left(\frac{N_{ph1}k_{w1}}{N_{ph2}k_{w2}}\right)^2 \frac{E_{\text{rotor}}}{I_{\text{rotor}}} \tag{9-43}$$

or

$$r_2 + jsx_2 = \frac{q_1}{q_2}\left(\frac{N_{ph1}k_{w1}}{N_{ph2}k_{w2}}\right)^2 (r_{\text{rotor}} + jsx_{\text{rotor}}) \tag{9-44}$$

where r_2 and sx_2 are the referred values and r_{rotor} and sx_{rotor} are the actual values of rotor resistance and leakage reactance at slip frequency.

b. Cage Rotors. The quantities which will be referred to the stator are the induced bar voltage E_b, the bar current I_b, and the equivalent bar resistance r_{be} and leakage reactance x_{be}. Equivalent bar resistance and leakage reactance means the value for one bar plus an allowance for the effect of the segment of the end rings joining adjacent bars. The cage rotor can be considered as a symmetrical polyphase winding in which the time-phase angle between the voltages or currents in adjacent bars equals the electrical space angle between the bars. Consider specifically a squirrel cage with an integral number of slots per pole or with such a large number of slots that pairs of bars can be found which are very close to one pole pitch apart.[8] Equivalent single-turn full-pitch rotor coils may then be formed from pairs of rotor bars one pole pitch apart, with the associated end rings. In Fig. 9-2, bars 1 and 9, 2 and 10, 3 and 11, for example, form such coils. The winding factor k_w for these coils is 1. The slip-frequency voltage induced in such a coil is, by Eq. 4-1,

$$2E_b = 4.44sf\Phi \tag{9-45}$$

where E_b is the rms voltage induced in one bar and Φ is the fundamental flux per pole.

The amplitude of the rotor-mmf wave can be derived by the methods of Art. 4-2*a*. In accordance with Eq. 4-18 and Fig. 4-7, the amplitude of the space-fundamental component of the mmf wave produced by one of the equivalent full-pitch rotor coils—say bars 1 and 9 in Fig. 9-2—is

$$\frac{4}{\pi}\frac{1}{2}(\sqrt{2}\,I_b) = \frac{2\sqrt{2}}{\pi}\,I_b \tag{9-46}$$

where I_b is the rms value of the bar current. For a machine with more than two poles, there will be one similarly placed coil for every pair of poles. Equation 9-46 gives the amplitude of the mmf wave produced by all these coils. But there are S_2/p such groups of coils in a p-pole machine with S_2 rotor bars. Just as the factor $q/2$ brings in the contribution of the other phases in Eq. 4-23, the mmf given by Eq. 9-46 must be multiplied by $S_2/2p$ to account for the other rotor bars. Consequently the amplitude of the complete rotor-mmf wave is

$$F_2 = \frac{2\sqrt{2}}{\pi}\frac{S_2}{2p}\,I_b = 0.90\,\frac{S_2}{2p}\,I_b \tag{9-47}$$

It can be seen that this result agrees with Eq. 4-23 since $S_2/2p$ is the total number of turns per pole in the cage winding and equals the factor qN_{ph}/p in Eq. 4-23.

The referred rotor is one which is considered to have the same number of phases, turns, and arrangement as the stator, and therefore its slip-frequency induced voltage per phase is, by Eq. 4-1,

$$E_{2s} = 4.44N_{ph1}k_{w1}sf\Phi \tag{9-48}$$

Comparison of Eqs. 9-45 and 9-48 shows that the relation between the

[8] For a more general examination of rotor mmf not based on this restriction and including harmonic as well as fundamental effects, see E. E. Dreese, Synchronous Motor Effects in Induction Machines, *Trans. AIEE*, vol. 49, No. 3, pp. 1033–1042, July, 1930. The conclusions reached in our more restricted study are the same as those applying to the fundamental component in the general study.

referred rotor voltage E_{2s} and the actual bar voltage E_b is

$$E_{2s} = 2N_{ph1}k_{w1}E_b \tag{9-49}$$

The relation between the referred rotor current I_{2s} and the actual bar current I_b is established from the equivalence of their mmfs. The mmf of the referred rotor is, by Eq. 4-25,

$$F_2 = 0.90 \frac{q_1 N_{ph1} k_{w1}}{p} I_{2s} \tag{9-50}$$

Comparison with Eq. 9-47 then gives

$$I_{2s} = \frac{S_2}{2q_1 N_{ph1} k_{w1}} I_b \tag{9-51}$$

The referring factors for impedance can now be obtained from the quotient of Eq. 9-49 divided by Eq. 9-51; thus

$$r_2 + jsx_2 = \frac{4q_1(N_{ph1}k_{w1})^2}{S_2}(r_{be} + jsx_{be}) \tag{9-52}$$

Inspection of Eqs. 9-49 to 9-52 shows that the referred rotor quantities depend on the details of both the stator winding and the rotor cage.

9-8. Speed Control of Induction Motors. The simple induction motor fulfills admirably the requirements of substantially constant-speed drives. Many motor applications, however, require several speeds, or even a continuously variable range of speeds. From the earliest days of a-c power systems engineers have been interested in the development of variable-speed a-c motors. The purpose of this article is to investigate the general principles upon which speed-control methods for induction motors are based. To maintain perspective, the competitive position of d-c motors combined with a-c to d-c conversion equipment should be borne in mind throughout this discussion (see Art. 6-1).

The synchronous speed of an induction motor can be changed by (*a*) changing the number of poles p or (*b*) varying the line frequency f. The slip can be changed by (*c*) varying the line voltage, (*d*) varying the rotor resistance, or (*e*) inserting voltages of the appropriate frequency in the rotor circuits. The salient features of speed-control methods based on these five possibilities are discussed in the following five sections of this article.

a. Pole-changing Motors. The stator winding can be designed so that by simple changes in coil connections the number of poles can be changed in the ratio 2 to 1. Either of two synchronous speeds can be selected. The rotor is almost always of the squirrel-cage type. A cage winding always reacts by producing a rotor field having the same number of poles as the inducing stator field. If a wound rotor is used, additional complications are introduced because the rotor winding also must be arranged for pole changing. With two independent sets of stator windings, each arranged for pole changing, as many as four synchronous speeds can be obtained in a squirrel-cage motor—for example, 600, 900, 1,200, and 1,800 rpm.

The basic principles of the pole-changing winding are shown in Fig. 9-16 in which *aa* and *a'a'* are two coils comprising part of the phase-*a* stator winding. An actual winding would, of course, consist of several coils in each group. The windings for the other stator phases (not shown in the figure) would be similarly arranged. In Fig. 9-16*a* the coils are connected to produce a 4-pole field; in Fig. 9-16*b* the current in the *a'a'* coil

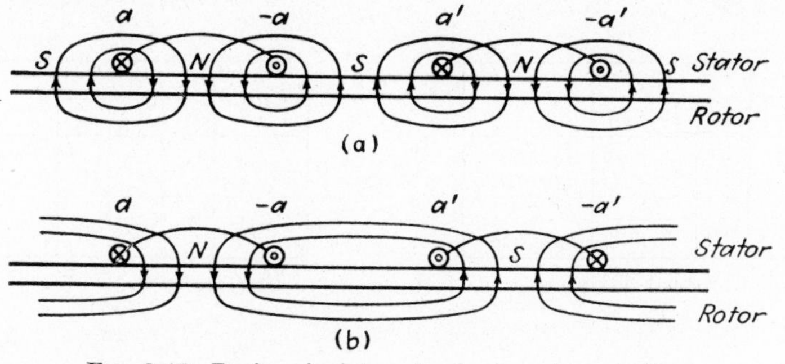

FIG. 9-16. Basic principles of pole-changing winding.

has been reversed by means of a controller, the result being a 2-pole field. At the same time that the controller reverses the *a'a'* coils, the connections of the two groups of coils may be changed from series to parallel and the connections among the phases from Y to Δ, or vice versa. By these means the air-gap flux density can be adjusted to produce the desired torque-speed characteristics on the two connections. Figure 9-17 shows three possibilities and their corresponding torque-speed characteristics for three motors having identical characteristics on the high-speed connection. Figure 9-17*a* results in approximately the same maximum torque on both speeds and is applicable to drives requiring approximately the same torque on both speeds (loads in which friction predominates, for example). Figure 9-17*b* results in approximately twice the maximum torque on the low speed and is applicable to drives requiring approximately constant power (such as machine tools and winches). Figure 9-17*c* results in considerably less maximum torque on the low speed and is applicable to drives requiring less torque on the low speed (fans and centrifugal pumps, for example). The constant-horsepower type is the most expensive because it is physically the largest.

b. Line-frequency Control. The synchronous speed of an induction motor can be controlled by varying the line frequency. In order to maintain approximately constant flux density, the line voltage should also be varied directly with the frequency. The maximum torque then remains very nearly constant. An induction motor used in this way has characteristics similar to those of a separately excited d-c motor with

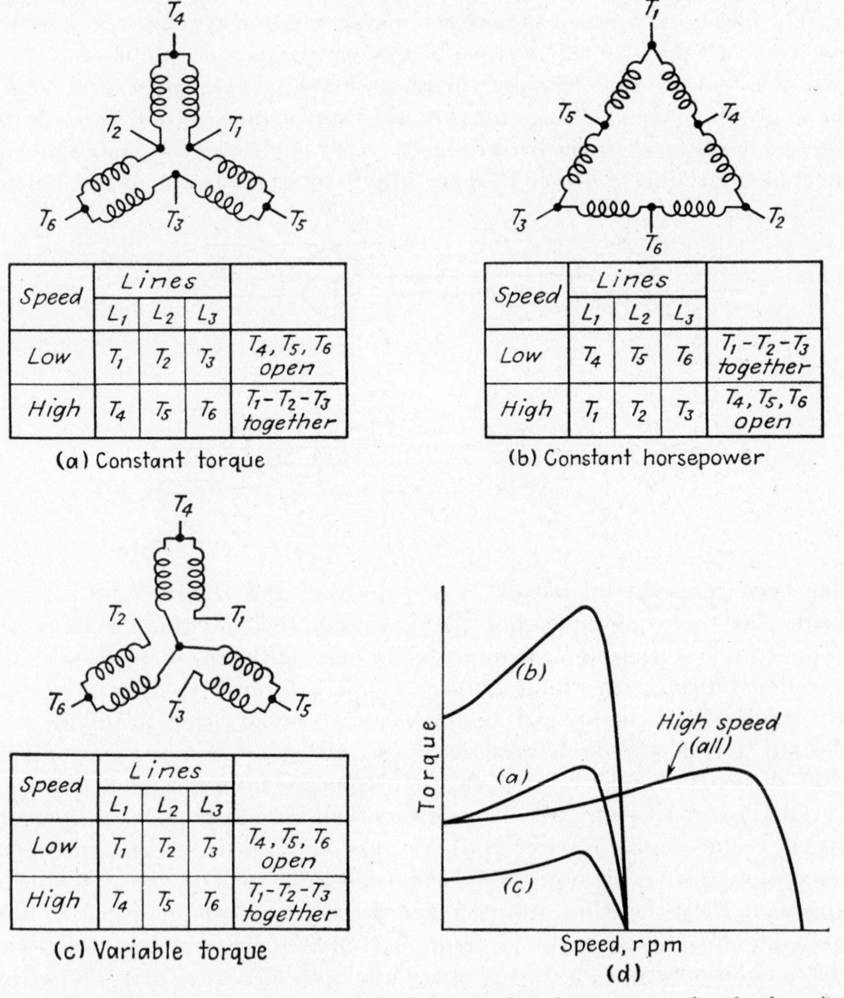

(a) Constant torque

Speed	Lines			
	L_1	L_2	L_3	
Low	T_1	T_2	T_3	T_4, T_5, T_6 open
High	T_4	T_5	T_6	T_1-T_2-T_3 together

(b) Constant horsepower

Speed	Lines			
	L_1	L_2	L_3	
Low	T_4	T_5	T_6	T_1-T_2-T_3 together
High	T_1	T_2	T_3	T_4, T_5, T_6 open

(c) Variable torque

Speed	Lines			
	L_1	L_2	L_3	
Low	T_1	T_2	T_3	T_4, T_5, T_6 open
High	T_4	T_5	T_6	T_1-T_2-T_3 together

FIG. 9-17. Connections and torque-speed curves for three types of pole-changing induction motors.

constant flux and variable armature voltage, as in the Ward Leonard system (Art. 6-1).

The major difficulty is how to get the variable frequency. One way is by means of a wound-rotor induction machine as a frequency changer, as described in Example 3-2. This arrangement requires a variable-speed drive for the frequency changer. In spite of the fact that this scheme is complicated, there are occasions when the compactness and simplicity of the squirrel-cage induction motor make the variable-frequency system highly desirable. A good example is the testing of scale-model airplanes in a wind tunnel.[9] The motors driving the propellers on powered models must be extremely compact and capable of high speeds. The requirements can be met with a water-cooled squirrel-cage motor supplied with the appropriate frequency.

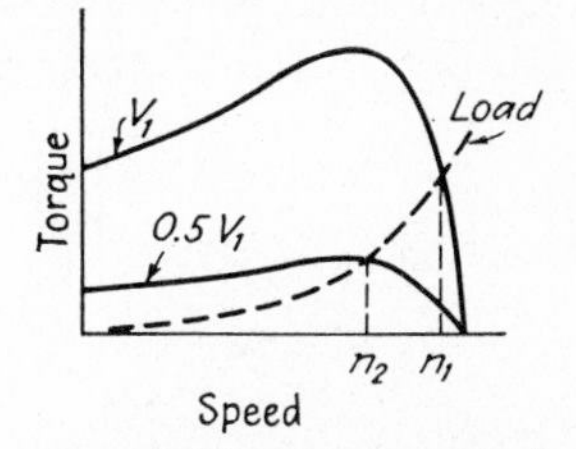

FIG. 9-18. Speed control by means of line voltage.

c. Line-voltage Control. The internal torque developed by an induction motor is proportional to the square of the voltage applied to its primary terminals, as shown by the two torque-speed characteristics in Fig. 9-18. If the load has the torque-speed characteristic shown by the dotted line, the speed will be reduced from n_1 to n_2. This method of speed control is commonly used with small squirrel-cage motors driving fans.

d. Rotor-resistance Control. The possibility of speed control of a wound-rotor motor by changing its rotor-circuit resistance has already been pointed out in Art. 9-5*a*. The torque-speed characteristics for three different values of rotor resistance are shown in Fig. 9-19. If the load has the torque-speed characteristic shown by the dotted line, the speeds corresponding to each of the values of rotor resistance are n_1, n_2, and n_3. This method of speed control has characteristics similar to those of d-c shunt-motor speed control by means of resistance in series with the armature.

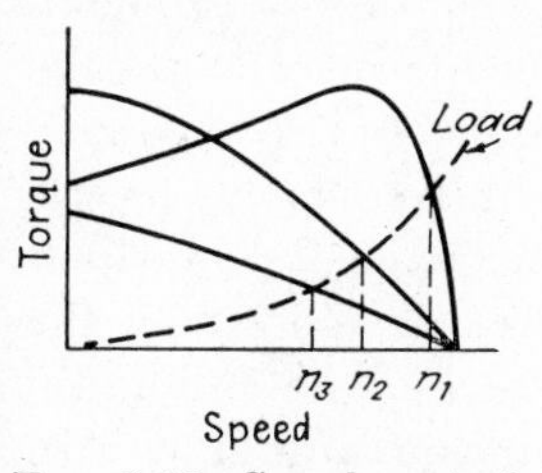

FIG. 9-19. Speed control by means of rotor resistance.

The principal disadvantages of both line-voltage and rotor-resistance control are low efficiency at reduced speeds and poor speed regulation with respect to change in load.

e. Control of Slip by Auxiliary Machines. In considering schemes for speed control by varying the slip, the fundamental laws relating the flow of power in induction machines should be borne in mind. As shown in Eq. 9-16, the fraction s of the power absorbed from the stator is transformed by electromagnetic induction to electric power in the rotor circuits.

[9] C. C. Clymer and M. A. de Ferranti, Electric Equipment for Cornell Variable Density Wind Tunnel, *Trans. AIEE*, vol. 65, No. 8, pp. 555–563, August, 1946; J. A. White, 150,000 Horsepower Applied to Aeronautical Research, *Trans. AIEE*, vol. 65, No. 12, pp. 833–839, December, 1946; G. W. Heumann, Adjustable Frequency Control of High-speed Induction Motors, *Trans. AIEE*, vol. 66, pp. 719–725, 1947.

If the rotor circuits are short-circuited, this power is wasted as rotor copper loss and operation at reduced speeds is inherently inefficient.

Numerous schemes have been invented for recovering this slip-frequency electric power. Although some of them are rather complicated in their details, they all comprise a means for introducing adjustable voltages of slip frequency into the rotor circuits of a wound-rotor induction motor. Broadly, they can be classified in two types, as shown in Fig. 9-20,

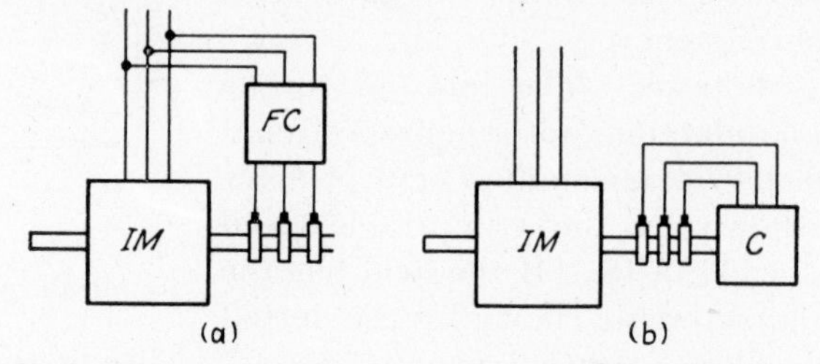

FIG. 9-20. Two basic schemes for induction-motor speed control by auxiliary machines.

where IM represents a 3-phase wound-rotor induction motor whose speed is to be regulated. In Fig. 9-20a the rotor circuits of IM are connected to auxiliary frequency-changing apparatus, represented by the box FC, in which the slip-frequency electric power generated in the rotor of the main motor is converted to electric power at line frequency and returned to the line. In Fig. 9-20b the rotor circuits of IM are connected to auxiliary apparatus, represented by the box C, in which the slip-frequency electric power is converted to mechanical power and added to the shaft power developed by the main motor. The boxes FC and C contain commutator-type machines of some kind. In both these schemes the speed and power factor of the main motor can be adjusted by controlling the magnitude and phase of the slip-frequency emfs of the auxiliary machines. The auxiliary apparatus may be a fairly complicated system of rotating machines and adjustable-ratio transformers. However, it can usually be relatively small compared with the main motor, because it has to handle only the fraction s of the stator power in the main motor. Three specific examples—the Leblanc system, the Schrage-type motor, and the modified Kramer system—are described briefly below.

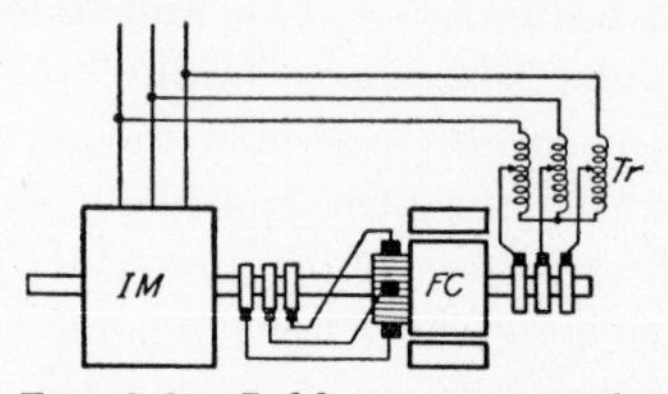

FIG. 9-21. Leblanc system of speed control.

One of the simplest arrangements is the *Leblanc system* shown in Fig. 9-21. The frequency changer FC comprises an armature winding like that of a d-c machine having the same number of poles as the main induction motor IM. This winding is connected to a commutator and also to three slip rings. Three sets of brushes spaced 120 electrical degrees apart bear on the commutator. The rotor is mechanically driven by the main induction motor and therefore runs at a per-unit speed of $1 - s$. The stator has no windings at all—it merely provides a low-reluctance path for the magnetic flux. Line-frequency voltages are applied to the slip rings and create a magnetic field rotating at synchronous speed with respect to the rotor and in the opposite direction. As viewed from the stator, therefore, this field rotates at slip speed, and 3-phase voltages of slip frequency are generated between pairs of brushes on the commutator (Art. 3-9*d*). These voltages are connected in series with the rotor circuits of the main

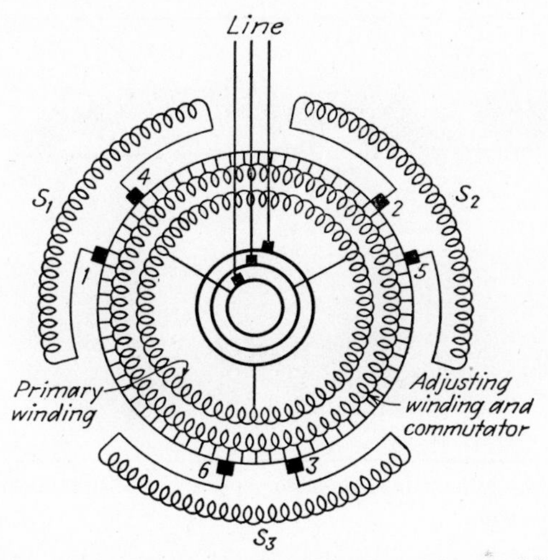

FIG. 9-22. Schematic diagram of adjustable-speed brush-shifting motor.

motor. The speed and power factor of the main motor can be controlled by adjusting the magnitude and phase of these voltages by means of the adjustable-ratio autotransformer *Tr* and by shifting the brushes. The slip-frequency electric power output of the main motor is converted to line-frequency power in the frequency changer and returned to the line.

The *Schrage-type brush-shifting motor* combines the frequency changer and the main motor in one frame. It is basically an inside-out induction motor with its secondary winding on the stator and its primary winding on the rotor connected to the supply line through slip rings, as shown in Fig. 9-22. Embedded in the same rotor slots is an adjusting winding connected to a commutator. A cutaway view is shown in Fig. 9-23. Line-frequency voltages are induced in the adjusting winding by transformer action from the primary, and slip-frequency voltages appear between brushes on the commutator, just as in the frequency changer of the Leblanc system.

Six sets of brushes are arranged on the commutator, and each phase S_1,

S_2, S_3 of the secondary winding is connected to a pair of them, as shown in Fig. 9-22. Brushes 1, 2, and 3 are mounted 120 electrical degrees apart on a yoke and can be shifted as a group. Brushes 4, 5, and 6 are similarly mounted on another movable yoke. The two sets of brushes can be adjusted as to angular position and relative spacing between them by means of a handwheel. The magnitude of the slip-frequency voltages inserted in series with the secondary windings depends on the spacing between the two sets of brushes, and the phase depends on their angular position. Thus both the speed and power factor can be controlled by means of the handwheel.[10]

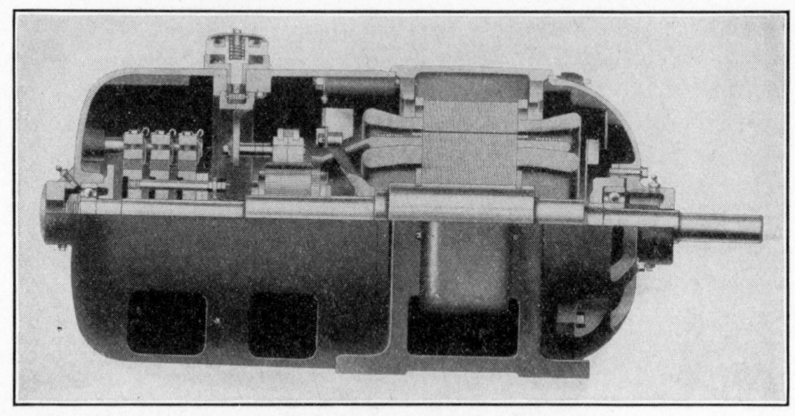

FIG. 9-23. Cutaway view of an adjustable-speed brush-shifting motor. (*Courtesy of General Electric Company.*)

Machines of this type are mainly used in sizes up to about 50 hp and for speed ranges of 6 to 1 or below.

The *modified Kramer system* is a type of adjustable-speed drive which can be built in very large sizes. It has been applied to large wind-tunnel drives in sizes up to 40,000 hp.[11] As shown in Fig. 9-24, it comprises a wound-rotor induction motor IM whose slip-frequency rotor power is delivered to a synchronous motor SM_1 which drives a d-c generator DC_1 at a speed proportional to the slip of the main motor IM. The electrical

[10] For analyses of this motor, see A. G. Conrad, F. Zweig, and J. G. Clarke, Theory of the Brush-shifting A-C Motor, Parts I and II, *Trans. AIEE*, vol. 60, No. 8, pp. 829–836, August, 1941, Parts III and IV, *Trans. AIEE*, vol. 61, No. 7, pp. 502–512, July, 1942; F. Baumann, Impedance Relationships of the Adjustable-speed A-C Brush-shifting Motor, *Trans. AIEE*, vol. 66, pp. 1460–1462, 1947; P. W. Franklin, A Study of the 3-phase Commutator Armature with Six Adjustable Brushes, *Trans. AIEE*, vol. 67, pp. 197–204, 1948.

[11] A. D. Dickey, C. M. Laffoon, and L. A. Kilgore, Variable-speed Drive for Wind Tunnel at Wright Field, *Trans. AIEE*, vol. 61, No. 3, pp. 126–130, March, 1942; S. L. Lindbeck and L. A. Kilgore, Big Winds for Model Planes, *Westinghouse Eng.*, vol. 8, No. 2, pp. 57–62, March, 1948.

output of DC_1 is delivered to a constant-speed d-c motor DC_2 which drives a synchronous generator SM_2 whose electrical output is returned to the line, as in Fig. 9-20*a*. The field circuits of the four auxiliary machines are supplied from a d-c bus, and the speed of the main motor IM is adjusted by controlling the speed of the auxiliary set SM_1DC_1 through field control of the two d-c machines, as in the Ward Leonard system. The variable-speed synchronous machine SM_1 must have about the same rating as the main induction motor, but the two d-c machines and the constant-speed synchronous machine SM_2 are smaller. For example, in a wind-tunnel drive the rating of SM_2 need be only about 20 per cent of the rating of IM.

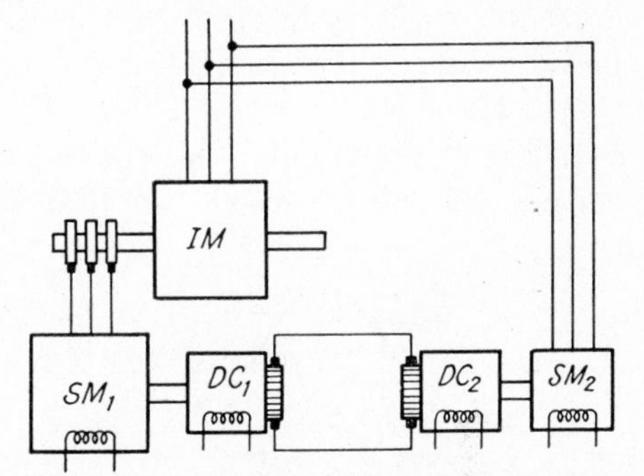

FIG. 9-24. Schematic diagram of modified Kramer system for speed control of large induction motors.

An advantage of this system is that it uses conventional synchronous and d-c machines which can be built in large sizes and for less cost than some of the more elaborate regulating machines required by other systems. A further advantage is that a very large induction motor can be started with no more disturbance to the supply line than that incident to starting the relatively small synchronous machine SM_2.

9-9. Self-synchronous Systems. There are numerous occasions when it is desired to maintain synchronism between two or more shafts, located some distance apart, without using clumsy mechanical connections between them. Such a link can be set up electrically by means of an arrangement known under various trade names such as *Selsyn*, *Autosyn*, or *Synchrotie systems*. In integral-horsepower sizes, these systems consist of 3-phase wound-rotor induction machines with their primary windings excited from the same 3-phase source and their secondary windings connected together, as shown in Fig. 9-25. If one of these machines is driven mechanically, the other will follow in synchronism with it, much as if the two shafts were connected mechanically. Such systems have been applied to maintain synchronism between the hoist motors raising the two ends of large lift bridges such as the Triborough Bridge in New York City, to maintain synchronism between parts of printing presses, and for many similar

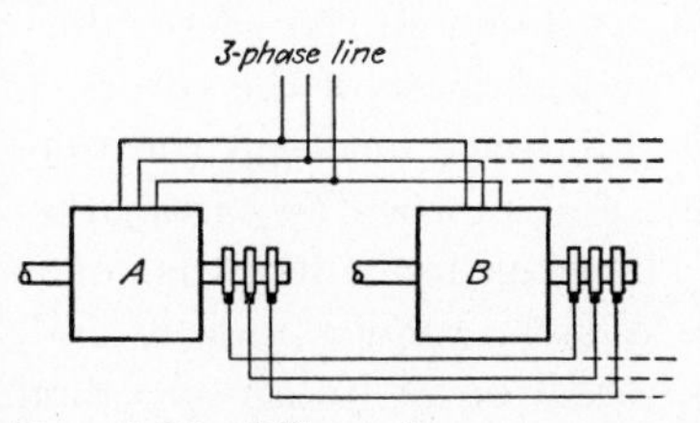

FIG. 9-25. Self-synchronous system comprising two induction motors with interconnected rotor circuits.

applications requiring speed coordination between parts of complex apparatus. In fractional-horsepower sizes, similar single-phase self-synchronous systems are used for a variety of purposes such as indicating the angular position of a remote shaft or the relative angular positions of two shafts. Here the problems are those of instrumentation, and the desirable characteristics are accuracy at a low torque level, rather than muscular strength. This article is primarily directed toward the 3-phase power types. The single-phase instrument types are discussed in Chap. **11**.

In Fig. 9-25, suppose that the two machines are standing still with their stators excited. Voltages are induced in the rotor windings whose time

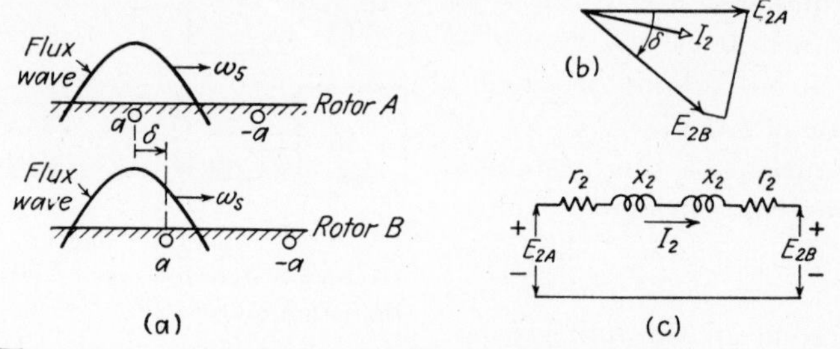

FIG. 9-26. Flux waves, vector diagram, and equivalent circuit for the self-synchronous system of Fig. 9-25 at zero speed.

phases depend on the angular positions of the two rotors. Corresponding phases are shown schematically by the coil sides *aa* in Fig. 9-26*a*, the angle between the two rotors being δ measured from A to B in the direction of rotation of the magnetic field. The rotor voltage in machine B then lags that in machine A by the time-phase angle δ, as shown in the vector diagram of Fig. 9-26*b*. The equivalent circuit for one phase of the rotors is shown in Fig. 9-26*c*. Because of the phase difference between the two voltages there is current in the rotor circuits, and power flows from the rotor of machine A to that of machine B. The situation is like that of a synchronous generator supplying power to a synchronous motor, and torque is created in each machine by the interaction of its air-gap flux and rotor-mmf waves. These torques act in directions to tend to reduce the angle δ—that is, to advance the rotor of A and retard that of B until the two rotors are in line. The induced voltages then balance each other, and the current is reduced to zero. Typical torque-angle characteristics at standstill are shown in Fig. 9-27.

Now suppose one of the machines is driven mechanically at a speed corresponding to a slip s. The other will run in synchronism with it, the displacement angle between the two rotors being a function of the mechanical load on the follower unit. The only difference between this situation and that at standstill is that an observer on the rotor now sees the air-gap flux wave traveling past him at slip speed. The induced voltages and rotor leakage reactances become s times their stator-frequency values.

The system can readily be analyzed by principles which have already been developed. Typical curves of maximum torque as a function of slip are shown in Fig. 9-28. Because of rotor resistance, the maximum torque falls off rapidly if the slip is decreased below about 0.3. Machines which are required to run in only one direction usually are connected to rotate in the opposite direction to their magnetic fields.[12]

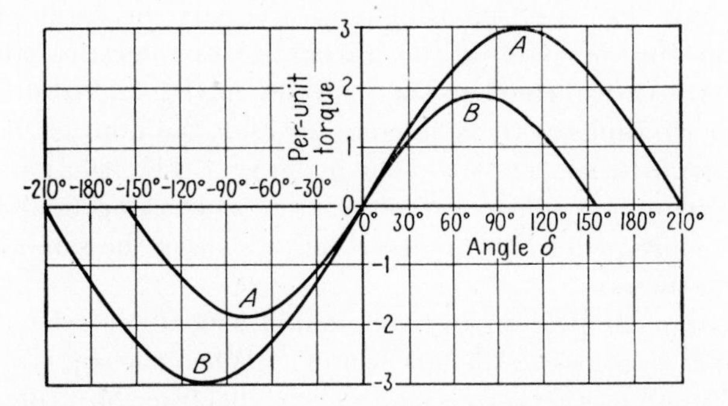

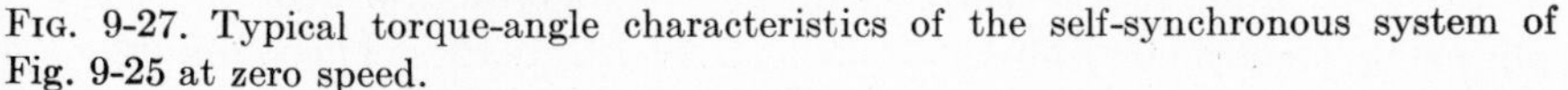

FIG. 9-27. Typical torque-angle characteristics of the self-synchronous system of Fig. 9-25 at zero speed.

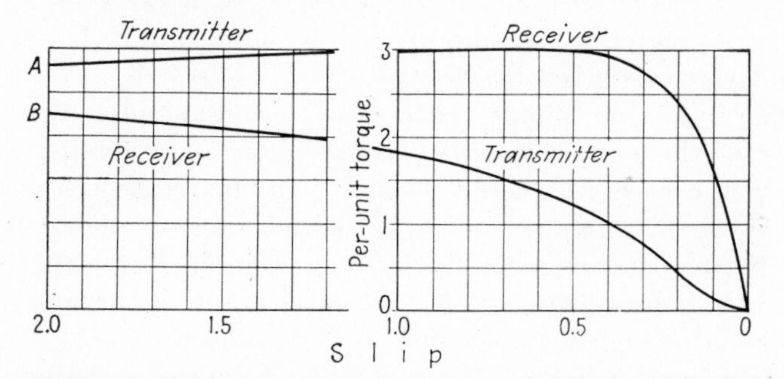

FIG. 9-28. Typical maximum-torque curves under running conditions for the self-synchronous system of Fig. 9-25.

9-10. Résumé. Electrically, a polyphase induction machine is a generalized transformer. Mechanically, it is a device depending on slip. These two basic properties determine its performance characteristics.

The polyphase induction machine depends on the rotating magnetic field created by balanced polyphase currents in a symmetrical polyphase stator winding. This field rotates at synchronous speed and induces emfs

[12] For further information on power applications of self-synchronous systems, see L. M. Nowacki, Induction Motors as Selsyn Drives, *Trans. AIEE*, vol. 53, pp. 1721–1726, 1934; L. A. Finzi and H. M. McConnell, The Torques of the Synchronous Tie—A Steady-state Analysis, *Trans. AIEE*, vol. 68, Part 2, pp. 1147–1152, 1949.

of stator frequency in the stator windings and of slip frequency in the rotor windings for all speeds of the rotor other than synchronous speed. Thus the induction machine transforms voltages and at the same time changes frequency, a property used to advantage in the induction-type frequency changer. The slip-frequency rotor currents create an mmf wave traveling at slip speed with respect to the rotor. The stator sees this rotor-mmf wave rotating at synchronous speed. Torque is created by the interaction of the resultant-flux-density and rotor-mmf waves in accordance with Eq. 3-22, in which sin δ equals the rotor power factor cos θ_2. From the viewpoint of the stator, all rotor electrical and magnetic phenomena are transformed to stator frequency. The rotor mmf reacts on the stator windings in the same manner that the mmf of the secondary current in a transformer reacts on the primary. The behavior in so far as stator phenomena are concerned is the same as in the primary of a transformer, and consequently the analysis follows along the same lines as that of the transformer.

The electromechanical-energy-conversion aspects stand out when one examines what happens to the power flow. When the slip is s, the electric power generated in the rotor windings is the fraction s of the electric power P_{g1} absorbed from the stator, as in Eq. 9-16. The remainder, or $(1 - s)P_{g1}$, is converted to mechanical power, as in Eq. 9-15. The internal torque T created by the interaction of the resultant-flux-density and rotor-mmf waves is given by Eq. 9-12.

For the induction motor with short-circuited rotor windings, the fraction s of the power absorbed from the stator is dissipated as heat in the resistances of the rotor circuits. In this respect, the induction machine is like a slipping mechanical clutch or any other power-transmission device operating with slip between its input and output members. An induction motor with short-circuited rotor is inherently inefficient when running at high values of slip.

As viewed from the stator, the equivalent circuit of an induction motor with short-circuited rotor is the same as that of a short-circuited transformer with secondary resistance r_2/s, as in Figs. 9-3, 9-4, and 9-5. The electrical and mechanical performance can be computed from these equivalent circuits, as in Eqs. 9-12 through 9-18. When torque and power relations are to be emphasized, the equivalent circuits can be transformed by Thévenin's theorem to the form shown in Fig. 9-7. Maximum torque occurs at the slip for which r_2/s "matches" the impedance in series with it in Fig. 9-7*a*. The maximum torque is independent of rotor resistance.

The slip at which maximum torque occurs can be controlled by adjusting the rotor resistance. A high rotor resistance gives optimum starting conditions but poor running performance. The design of a squirrel-cage motor therefore is a compromise. Marked improvement in the starting performance with relatively little sacrifice in running performance can be built into a squirrel-cage motor by using a deep-bar or double-cage rotor whose effective resistance increases with slip. A wound-rotor motor can be used for very severe starting conditions or when speed control by rotor resistance is required. A wound-rotor motor is more expensive than a squirrel-cage motor.

For applications requiring a substantially constant speed without excessively severe starting conditions, the squirrel-cage motor usually is unrivaled, because of its ruggedness, simplicity, and low cost. Its only disadvantage is its relatively low power factor (about 0.85 to 0.90 at full load for 4-pole 60-cps motors—considerably lower at light loads and for lower speed motors). The low power factor is a consequence of the fact that all the excitation must be supplied by lagging reactive kva taken from the a-c mains. When power costs include a power-factor penalty, the economic comparison usually is between a synchronous motor and an induction motor with static capacitors for power-factor correction. At speeds below about 500 rpm and ratings above about 50 hp or at medium speeds (500 to 900 rpm) and ratings above about 500 hp a synchronous motor will probably cost less than an induction motor.

The induction motor is at a disadvantage for adjustable-speed drives. A machine dependent on a constant-speed rotating magnetic field prefers to be a constant-speed machine. Pole changing, described in Art. 9-8*a*, is a good solution when only two, or perhaps four, speeds are required. Speed control by varying the slip is inherently inefficient unless one of the more or less elaborate schemes described in Art. 9-8*e* is used for recovering the slip energy. These schemes all involve an auxiliary commutator machine of some kind. A commutator-type machine is not subject to the constant-speed limitation, because the commutator takes out the effect of rotation. A d-c machine is readily adaptable to adjustable-speed service, as described in Art. 6-1. As pointed out in Art. 6-5, the economic comparison for adjustable-speed drives usually is between the cost of a d-c motor plus a-c to d-c conversion equipment and controls on the one hand, and the relatively elaborate schemes of induction-motor speed control described in Art. 9-8 on the other, without overlooking the possibilities of a variable-speed mechanical transmission interposed between a constant-speed motor and the driven load. In very large sizes, or at high speeds, or when space is at a premium (as in the wind-tunnel applications mentioned in Art. 9-8*b* and *e*, for example) the simplicity and compactness of the induction motor is a big advantage.

PROBLEMS

9-1. Redraw Fig. 9-2 for the same rotor placed in a sinusoidal 4-pole field.

9-2. In computations on induction motors, the impedance $Z_f = R_f + jX_f$ of the parallel combination of $(r_2/s) + jx_2$ and jx_φ must often be computed. Derive the following formulas:

$$R_f = \frac{x_\varphi^2}{x_{22}} \frac{1}{sQ_2 + (1/sQ_2)} \tag{9-53}$$

$$X_f = \frac{x_2 x_\varphi}{x_{22}} + \frac{R_f}{sQ_2} \tag{9-54}$$

where $x_{22} = x_2 + x_\varphi$ and $Q_2 = x_{22}/r_2$.

9-3. A 100-hp 3-phase Y-connected 440-volt 60-cps 8-pole squirrel-cage induction motor has the following equivalent-circuit constants in ohms per phase referred to the stator:

$$r_1 = 0.085 \qquad r_2 = 0.067$$
$$x_1 = 0.196 \qquad x_2 = 0.161 \qquad x_\varphi = 6.65$$

No-load rotational loss = 2.7 kw. Stray load loss = 0.5 kw. The rotational and stray load losses may be considered constant.

a. Compute the horsepower output, stator current, power factor, and efficiency at rated voltage and frequency for a slip of 3.00 per cent.

b. Compute the starting current and the internal starting torque in pound-feet at rated voltage and frequency.

9-4. A 10-hp 3-phase 60-cps 6-pole induction motor runs at a slip of 3.0 per cent at full load. Rotational and stray load losses at full load are 4.0 per cent of the output power. Compute:

a. The rotor copper loss at full load

b. The electromagnetic torque at full load, in newton-meters

c. The power delivered by the stator to the air gap at full load

9-5. A 3-phase Y-connected 4-pole 60-cps squirrel-cage motor has a stator resistance of 0.5 ohm per phase at operating temperature. When the line current to the motor is 10 amp and the total 3-phase power input is 3,000 watts, what is the internal torque in newton-meters? Neglect stator core loss.

9-6. An induction motor accelerates a flywheel from zero to very nearly synchronous speed. Derive an expression for the energy dissipated in rotor copper loss. Take the total moment of inertia, referred to the motor shaft, as J. How does the energy dissipated in rotor copper loss compare with the kinetic energy of the flywheel? Neglect rotational and stray load losses, and consider acceleration to be low enough so that steady-state theory may be applied.

9-7. A 10-hp 230-volt 3-phase Y-connected 60-cps 4-pole squirrel-cage induction motor develops full-load internal torque at a slip of 0.04 when operated at rated voltage and frequency. For the purposes of this problem rotational and core losses can be neglected. Impedance data on the motor are as follows:

Stator resistance $r_1 = 0.36$ ohm per phase
Leakage reactances $x_1 = x_2 = 0.47$ ohm per phase
Magnetizing reactance $x_\varphi = 15.5$ ohms per phase

Determine the maximum internal torque at rated voltage and frequency, the slip at maximum torque, and the internal starting torque at rated voltage and frequency. Express the torques in newton-meters.

9-8. Suppose the induction motor of Prob. 9-7 is supplied from a 240-volt constant-voltage 60-cps source through a feeder whose impedance is $0.50 + j0.30$ ohm per phase. Determine the maximum internal torque that the motor can deliver and the corresponding values of stator current and terminal voltage.

9-9. A 3-phase induction motor, at rated voltage and frequency, has a starting torque of 160 per cent and a maximum torque of 200 per cent of full-load torque. Neglect stator resistance and rotational losses, and assume constant rotor resistance. Determine:

a. The slip at full load

b. The slip at maximum torque

c. The rotor current at starting, in per unit of full-load rotor current

9-10. When operated at rated voltage and frequency, a 3-phase squirrel-cage induction motor (of the design classification known as a high-slip motor) delivers full load at a slip of 8.5 per cent and develops a maximum torque of 250 per cent of full-load torque at a slip of 50 per cent. Neglect core and rotational losses, and assume that the resistances and inductances of the motor are constant.

Determine the torque and rotor current at starting with rated voltage and frequency. Express the torque and rotor current in per unit based on their full-load values.

9-11. For a 25-hp 230-volt 3-phase 60-cps squirrel-cage motor operated at rated voltage and frequency, the rotor copper loss at maximum torque is 9.0 times that at full-load torque, and the slip at full-load torque is 0.030. Stator resistance and rotational losses may be neglected and the reactances and rotor resistance assumed to remain constant. Find:

a. The slip at maximum torque

b. The maximum torque

c. The starting torque

Express the torques in per unit of full-load torque.

9-12. A squirrel-cage induction motor runs at a slip of 5.0 per cent at full load. The rotor current at starting is 5.0 times the rotor current at full load. The rotor resistance is independent of rotor frequency, and rotational losses, stray load losses, and stator resistance may be neglected.

a. Compute the starting torque.

b. Compute the maximum torque and the slip at which maximum torque occurs. Express the torques in per unit of full-load torque.

9-13. From comparison of Eqs. 9-14 and 9-18 and the two equivalent circuits of Fig. 9-7, write down by inspection expressions similar to Eqs. 9-24, 9-26, and 9-27 for the internal mechanical power P, the slip $s_{\max P}$ at maximum power, and the maximum power $P_{\max}$. Then show that the normalized curves of Fig. 9-9 also give the relations between the power ratio $P/P_{\max}$ and the slip ratio $s(1 - s_{\max P})/s_{\max P}(1 - s)$ with the parameter $Q = (X_1 + x_2)/(R_1 + r_2)$.

9-14. A 50-hp 440-volt 3-phase 4-pole 60-cps wound-rotor induction motor develops a maximum internal torque of 250 per cent at a slip of 16 per cent when operating at rated voltage and frequency with its rotor short-circuited directly at the slip rings. Stator resistance and rotational losses may be neglected, and the rotor resistance may be assumed to be constant independent of rotor frequency. Determine:

a. The slip at full load, in per cent

b. The rotor copper loss at full load, in watts

c. The starting torque at rated voltage and frequency, in newton-meters

If the rotor resistance is now doubled (by inserting external series resistances) determine:

d. The torque in newton-meters when the stator current has its full-load value

e. The corresponding slip

9-15. A 50-hp 3-phase 480-volt 60-cps 4-pole squirrel-cage induction motor develops a maximum torque of 300 per cent and a starting torque of 150 per cent of full-load torque when operated at rated voltage and frequency. Neglect rotational losses and stator resistance, and assume that the rotor resistance is constant, independent of rotor frequency. For operation at rated voltage and frequency, find:

a. The slip at maximum torque

b. The rotor copper loss at full load, in watts

c. The full-load torque, in newton-meters

With a 50-cps applied voltage of 400 volts, find:

d. The horsepower output when the stator current has the value corresponding to the 60-cps full-load rating

e. The speed in rpm for maximum torque on 50 cps

f. The maximum torque on 50 cps, in newton-meters

g. The starting torque on 50 cps, in newton-meters

9-16. A 220-volt 3-phase 4-pole 60-cps 50-hp squirrel-cage induction motor takes a blocked-rotor current of 200 per cent and develops an internal starting torque of 16 per cent for an applied voltage of 30 per cent. A starting compensator is to be purchased for this motor. The starting compensator may be regarded as an ideal 3-phase step-down transformer connected between the supply line and the motor. Determine the per cent starting torque if the starting compensator limits the starting current in the supply line to 150 per cent of the motor full-load current. The supply-line voltage is 220 volts.

9-17. A 220-volt 3-phase 4-pole 60-cps wound-rotor induction motor develops an internal torque of 150 per cent with a line current of 155 per cent at a slip of 5.0 per cent when running at rated voltage and frequency with its rotor terminals short-circuited. (Torque and current are expressed as percentages of their full-load values.) The rotor resistance is 0.100 ohm between each pair of rotor terminals and may be assumed to be constant. What should be the resistance of each of three balanced Y-connected resistors inserted in series with each rotor terminal if the starting current at rated voltage and frequency is to be limited to 155 per cent? What internal starting torque will be developed?

9-18. A 220-volt 3-phase 4-pole 60-cps squirrel-cage induction motor develops a maximum internal torque of 250 per cent at a slip of 16 per cent when operating at rated voltage and frequency. If the effect of stator resistance is neglected, determine the maximum internal torque that this motor would develop if it were operated at 200 volts and 50 cps. Under these conditions, at what speed in rpm would maximum torque be developed?

9-19. At full load, the slip of a 500-hp 3-phase 8-pole 60-cps wound-rotor induction motor is 1.80 per cent when its rotor is short-circuited at the slip rings. The rotor winding is 3-phase, Y-connected, and has a resistance of 0.25 ohm per phase. Determine the slip, the torque, and the horsepower output when the current has its full-load value if resistances of 1.00 ohm are inserted in series with each phase of the rotor winding. Neglect rotational losses. Also determine the I^2R loss in each of these additional resistance units.

9-20. The following test data apply to a 50-hp 2,300-volt 60-cps 3-phase squirrel-cage induction motor:

No-load Test at Rated Voltage and Frequency:

Line current = 4.1 amp
3-phase power = 1,550 watts

Blocked-rotor Test at 15 *cps:*

Line voltage = 268 volts
Line current = 25.0 amp
3-phase power = 9,600 watts

Stator resistance between line terminals = 5.80 ohms
Stray load loss = 420 watts
Compute the stator current and power factor, horsepower output, and efficiency when this motor is operating at rated voltage and frequency with a slip of 3.00 per cent.

9-21. Two 50-hp 440-volt 59.8 amp 3-phase 6-pole 60-cps squirrel-cage induction motors have identical stators. The d-c resistance measured between any pair of stator line terminals is 0.212 ohm. The blocked-rotor tests at 60 cps are as follows:

Motor 1	*Motor* 2
V = 61.3 volts, line to line	V = 96.0 volts, line to line
I = 60.0 amp	I = 60.0 amp
P = 3.16 kw, 3-phase	P = 8.95 kw, 3-phase

Determine the ratio of the internal starting torque developed by motor 2 to that developed by motor 1, (*a*) for the same current, (*b*) for the same applied voltage.

9-22. The results of a blocked-rotor test on a 25-hp 3-phase 220-volt 60-cps 6-pole squirrel-cage induction motor are given below:

Line-to-line voltage = 110 volts
Line current = 220 amp
3-phase power = 21.0 kw
Torque = 65 lb-ft

Determine the starting torque at a line-to-line voltage of 220 volts and 50 cps.

9-23. What would be the effects on the characteristics of a wound-rotor induction motor caused by rewinding the rotor with twice as many turns of conductors having half the cross-sectional area of copper, the arrangements of the new and old windings being the same, and the space occupied by insulation being assumed to be the same?

9-24. A squirrel-cage rotor when used in a certain 2-pole 3-phase Y-connected stator results in a referred rotor resistance of $r_{2(2\text{-pole})}$. The same rotor when used in a 4-pole 3-phase Y-connected stator wound on the same stator core results in a referred rotor resistance of $r_{2(4\text{-pole})}$, the two stator windings being designed so that the amplitude of the space-fundamental air-gap flux-density wave is the same at the same voltage and frequency. Determine the approximate relationship between the 2-pole and 4-pole referred rotor resistances. Neglect the change in the effect of the end rings.

9-25. A frequency-changer set is to be designed for supplying variable-frequency power to induction motors driving the propellors on scale-model airplanes for wind-tunnel testing, as described in Art. 9-8*b*. The frequency changer is a wound-rotor induction machine driven by a d-c motor whose speed can be controlled. The 3-phase stator winding of the induction machine is excited from a 60-cps source, and variable-frequency 3-phase power is taken from its rotor winding. The set must meet the following specifications:

Output frequency range = 120 to 450 cps
Maximum speed not to exceed 3,000 rpm
Maximum power output = 80 kw at 0.80 power factor and 450 cps

The power required by the induction-motor load drops off rapidly with decreasing frequency, so that the maximum-speed condition determines the sizes of the machines.

On the basis of negligible exciting current, losses, and voltage drops in the induction machine, find:

a. The minimum number of poles for the induction machine
b. The corresponding maximum and minimum speeds
c. The kva rating of the stator winding of the induction machine
d. The horsepower rating of the d-c machine

9-26. The resistance measured between each pair of slip rings of a 3-phase 60-cps 300-hp 16-pole induction motor is 0.035 ohm. With the slip rings short-circuited, the full-load slip is 0.025, and it may be assumed that the slip-torque curve is a straight line from no load to full load. This motor drives a fan which requires 300 hp at the full-load speed of the motor. The torque required to drive the fan varies as the square of the speed. What resistances should be connected in series with each slip ring so that the fan will run at 300 rpm?

9-27. An adjustable-speed drive is to be furnished for a large fan in an industrial plant. The fan is to be driven by two wound-rotor induction motors coupled mechanically to the fan shaft and arranged so that lower speeds will be carried on the smaller motor and higher speeds on the larger motor. The speed control is to be arranged in steps so that the control will be uninterrupted from minimum to maximum speed and so that there will not be a sudden change in speed during the transfer from one motor to the other.

The larger motor is to be a 2,300-volt 3-phase 500-hp 60-cps 6-pole motor; the smaller motor is to be a 200-hp 60-cps 8-pole motor. The following motor data are furnished by the manufacturer:

Constants	200-hp motor	500-hp motor
Stator resistance	0.57 ohm	0.14 ohm
Rotor resistance	0.93	0.24
Stator plus rotor leakage reactance	2.6	0.98

These values are per-phase values (Y connection) referred to the stator. Motor rotational losses and exciting requirements may be ignored.

The minimum operating speed of the fan is to be 450 rpm; the maximum speed is to be approximately 1,170 rpm. The fan requires 450 hp at 1,170 rpm, and the power required at other speeds varies nearly as the cube of the speed.

The proposed control scheme is based on the stators of both motors being connected to the line at all times when the drive is in operation. In the lower speed range, the rotor of the 500-hp motor is open-circuited. This lower range is obtained by adjustment of external resistance in the rotor of the 200-hp motor. Above this lower speed range, the rotor of the 200-hp motor is open-circuited; speed adjustment in the upper range is obtained by adjustment of external resistance in the rotor of the 500-hp motor.

The transition between motors from the lower to the upper speed range is to be handled as follows:

1. All external rotor resistance is cut out of the 200-hp motor.

2. By means of a close-before-open type of contactor, the rotor circuit of the 500-hp motor is closed, and then the rotor circuit of the 200-hp motor is opened. The external rotor resistance in the 500-hp motor for this step has such a value that the speed will be the same as in the first step.

3. Higher speeds are obtained by cutting out rotor resistance in the 500-hp motor.

This procedure is essentially reversed in going from the higher to the lower speed range.

As plant engineer, you are asked to give consideration to some features of this proposal. In particular, you are asked to:

a. Determine the range of external rotor resistance (referred to the stator) which must be available for insertion in the 200-hp motor.

b. Determine the range of external rotor resistance which must be available for insertion in the 500-hp motor.

c. Discuss any features of the scheme which you may not like, and suggest alternatives.

d. Discuss from both the economic and technical viewpoints the use of two motors here rather than a single 500-hp motor. If you should decide that the question is entirely one of economics, outline how you would justify the expense of the 200-hp motor to a skeptical vice-president.

9-28. A 40,000-hp 60-cps 22-pole wound-rotor induction motor is used to drive a wind-tunnel fan. The power required to drive the fan varies as the cube of its speed and is 40,000 hp at 297 rpm.

The speed must be adjustable over a range from 297 to 37.5 rpm. If rotor-resistance speed control is used, plot curves of the following variables as functions of the speed in rpm:

a. Fan power, in kilowatts

b. Power input to the motor, in kilowatts. Neglect stator copper, rotational, and stray load losses

c. Total rotor-circuit copper loss, in kilowatts.

9-29. The modified Kramer system shown in Fig. 9-24 is to be used for the wind-tunnel drive described in Prob. 9-28. The synchronous motor SM_1 of the variable-speed motor-generator set in Fig. 9-24 has 14 poles, and the synchronous generator SM_2 of the constant-speed set has 12 poles. Speed is controlled by field control of the two d-c machines. For a fan speed of 75 per cent of its synchronous speed, both d-c machines are operated with maximum field current. For fan speeds below 75 per cent, the d-c machines operate at constant voltage, and speed control is obtained by weakening the field of DC_1. For fan speeds above 75 per cent, DC_1 operates at full field, and speed control is obtained by lowering the d-c voltage by means of field control of DC_2. (Because of the difficulty of building very large d-c machines, DC_1 and DC_2 in Fig. 9-24 are each actually two machines in series, but for analysis of the system each pair can be considered as an equivalent single machine, as in Fig. 9-24.)

If all losses in the system are neglected, plot curves of the following variables as functions of the fan speed in rpm:

a. Fan power, in kilowatts

b. Power flow through the auxiliary machines, in kilowatts

c. Direct-current voltage in per cent of its value at a fan speed of 75 per cent of synchronous

d. Current in the d-c machines in per cent of its value at maximum fan speed (297 rpm)

CHAPTER 10

FRACTIONAL-HORSEPOWER A-C MOTORS

THE importance of fractional-horsepower electric motors in modern civilization is so evident as to require very little comment. The reader may find it amusing to count the number of small motors he and his family use in their daily life—vacuum cleaners, electric refrigerators, washing machines, oil burners, fans, food mixers, to mention a few of them. In business and industry, fractional-horsepower motors also are very widely used—for example, in driving portable and small machine tools, office appliances, and air-conditioning equipment. Small motors find interesting applications in automatic-control devices of various kinds, and satisfactory solution of problems arising from such uses frequently requires a considerable amount of engineering skill on the parts of both motor designers and application engineers.

It is not surprising, then, that the small-motor business is one of the large branches of the electrical manufacturing industry. The electrical engineer who is not a specialist in the power field is probably more likely to come in contact with fractional-horsepower motors than with any other kind of electrical rotating machinery.

Although 3-phase induction motors are procurable in stock sizes down to $\frac{1}{6}$ hp, by far the commonest of the fractional-horsepower motors are the single-phase a-c types, for the obvious reason that such is usually the only power available where fractional-horsepower motors are used. The purpose of this chapter is first to give qualitative explanations of the behavior of the common types of small single-phase motors,[1] then to give a quantitative treatment of the induction motor with a single-phase winding in terms of the revolving-field theory, and finally to develop a generalized revolving-field theory of induction motors with 2-phase windings, from which both the starting and running characteristics of a variety of induction-motor types can be determined.

10-1. Single-phase Induction Motors—Qualitative Examination. Structurally, the commonest types of single-phase induction motors resemble polyphase squirrel-cage motors except for the arrangement of the stator windings. An induction motor with a cage rotor and a single-

[1] For practical information and qualitative treatments of a wide variety of fractional-horsepower motors, see C. G. Veinott, "Fractional Horsepower Electric Motors," 2d ed., McGraw-Hill Book Company, Inc., New York, 1948.

phase stator winding is represented schematically in Fig. 10-1, with the understanding that, instead of being a concentrated coil, the actual stator winding is distributed in slots so as to produce an approximately sinusoidal space distribution of mmf. Such a motor inherently has no starting torque, but if started by auxiliary means it will continue to run. Before considering auxiliary starting methods, the basic properties of the elementary motor of Fig. 10-1 will be described.

Consideration of conditions with the rotor at rest readily shows that no starting torque is produced. From Fig. 10-1, it is evident that the axis of the stator field remains fixed in position along the coil axis. With alternating current in the stator coil, the stator-mmf wave is stationary in space but pulsates in magnitude, the stator field strength alternating in polarity and varying sinusoidally with time. Currents are induced in the rotor by transformer action, these currents being in such a direction as to produce an mmf opposing the stator mmf. The axis of the rotor-mmf wave coincides with that of the stator field, the torque angle therefore is zero, and no starting torque is produced. The motor is merely a single-phase static transformer with a short-circuited secondary.

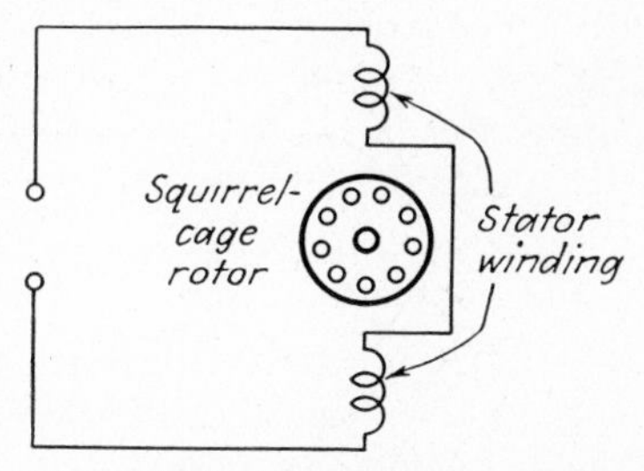

FIG. 10-1. Elementary single-phase induction motor.

Conditions are not so simple, however, when the rotor is made to revolve. Two different viewpoints may then be adopted in explaining the operation of the motor: the first is to derive the conditions from those already established for polyphase motors; the second is to start afresh and show that, under certain circumstances, the necessary conditions for the production of motor torque are satisfied. Both viewpoints, of course, lead to the same results, and both can be presented in quantitative terms. The resulting analytical methods are known as the *revolving-field theory* and the *cross-field theory*, respectively. Both viewpoints have their advantages, but on the whole there is little choice between them for computational purposes.

According to the cross-field theory, when the rotor is made to revolve, there is, in addition to the transformer voltage, a voltage generated in the rotor by virtue of its rotation in the stationary stator field. In Fig. 10-1, for example, the rotational voltages in the rotor conductors are all in one direction in the upper half of the rotor, and all in the other direction in the lower half. The rotational voltage produces a component rotor current and a component rotor-mmf wave whose axis is displaced 90 electrical degrees from the stator axis. The torque angle for this component of the rotor mmf is 90 degrees, and a torque is obtained. Further detailed analysis will show that this torque is in the direction of rotation and that the necessary conditions for the continued production of torque are satisfied.[2]

The argument in the revolving-field theory is that if a rotating magnetic field is produced, then an induction-motor torque results by the processes described in Art. 3-7. Moreover, this torque will be quantitatively similar to that of the polyphase motor treated in Chap. 9, and approximately the same type of performance can be expected. The treatment of single-phase induction motors in the rest of this chapter will be from the revolving-field point of view.

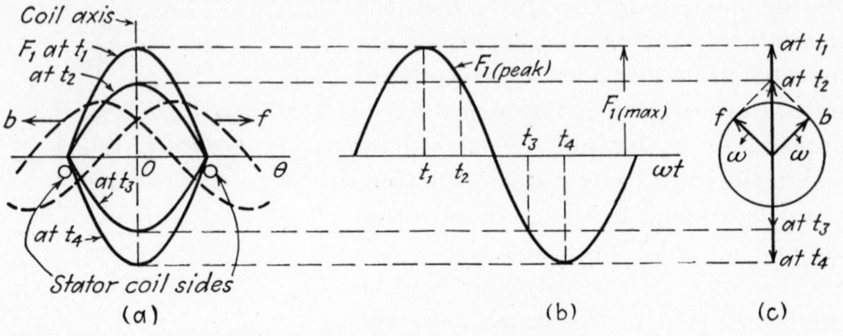

FIG. 10-2. Mmf waves in a single-phase induction motor. (a) Space waves. (b) Time variations. (c) Representation by space vectors.

Consider the elementary motor of Fig. 10-1, whose developed stator winding for one pole is represented schematically by the concentrated coil sides in Fig. 10-2a. Remember, however, that the stator winding actually is distributed in a number of slots so as to produce approximately a sinusoidal space distribution of mmf centered on the coil axis. If space harmonics are neglected, the space wave of stator mmf F_1 can then be expressed as

$$F_1 = F_{1(\text{peak})} \cos \theta \tag{10-1}$$

where θ is the electrical space angle measured from the stator coil axis, and $F_{1(\text{peak})}$ is the instantaneous value of the mmf wave at the coil axis and is proportional to the instantaneous stator current. If the stator current varies sinusoidally, then $F_{1(\text{peak})}$ varies sinusoidally with time, as shown in Fig. 10-2b. The space distributions of stator mmf F_1 corresponding to several instants of time are shown in Fig. 10-2a. The stator-mmf wave is stationary, and its amplitude varies sinusoidally with time.

[2] The cross-field theory is developed in a number of textbooks on a-c machinery. See, for example, A. F. Puchstein and T. C. Lloyd, "Alternating-current Machines," 2d ed., pp. 343–375, 384–392, John Wiley & Sons, Inc., New York, 1942; R. R. Lawrence, "Principles of Alternating-current Machinery," 3d ed., pp. 583–597, McGraw-Hill Book Company, Inc., New York, 1940. There is also an extensive literature in the technical press.

For analytical purposes, this pulsating, stationary wave can be resolved into two constant-amplitude traveling waves. Consider that the pulsating stator mmf may be represented by a space vector of varying length, pointing up half the time, down the other half, and having a magnitude and direction determined by the instantaneous magnitude and direction of the stator current. This space vector is shown by the vertical arrows in Fig. 10-2*c* for the same instants of time indicated in Fig. 10-2*a* and *b*. But it can be seen from Fig. 10-2*c* that such a vector may be considered as the sum of two equal vectors rotating in opposite directions, each component vector having a constant length equal to half the maximum length of the original pulsating vector. Consequently the pulsating stator-mmf wave can be divided into two rotating waves of equal magnitudes. These component waves rotate in opposite directions at synchronous speed. The forward- and backward-rotating mmf waves f and b are shown dotted in Fig. 10-2*a* for the instant of time t_2, and the corresponding rotating vectors representing them are f and b in Fig. 10-2*c*.

The same conclusions can be reached by analytical methods. The analysis is essentially the same as the rotating-field theory of Art. 3-6 except that we are now concerned with only one stator phase, whereas in Art. 3-6 the mmfs of three stator phases were involved. Thus, if the stator current is a cosine function of time, the instantaneous value of the spatial peak of the pulsating mmf wave is

$$F_{1(\text{peak})} = F_{1(\text{max})} \cos \omega t \tag{10-2}$$

where $F_{1(\text{max})}$ is the peak value corresponding to maximum instantaneous current. Consequently, by substitution of Eq. 10-2 in Eq. 10-1, the mmf wave as a function of both time and space is

$$F_1 = F_{1(\text{max})} \cos \omega t \cos \theta \tag{10-3}$$

and, from the relation for the product of two cosines,

$$F_1 = \tfrac{1}{2}F_{1(\text{max})} \cos (\theta - \omega t) + \tfrac{1}{2}F_{1(\text{max})} \cos (\theta + \omega t) \tag{10-4}$$

Each of the cosine terms in Eq. 10-4 describes a sinusoidal function of the space angle θ. Each has a peak value of half the maximum amplitude of the pulsating wave, and a space-phase angle ωt. Both waves are centered on the axis of the stator winding at the instant when the stator mmf has its maximum value. The angle ωt provides rotation of each wave around the air gap at the constant angular velocity ω electrical radians per second, the waves traveling in opposite directions. The first wave, whose argument is $\theta - \omega t$, travels in the forward direction of θ; the second wave, whose argument is $\theta + \omega t$, travels in the backward direction of θ. With a balanced polyphase winding the backward-rotating components cancel leaving only the forward components, as in Eq. 3-47 for a

3-phase winding. For a single-phase winding, however, both forward and backward components are present. Thus Eq. 10-4 leads to the same conclusion as that reached by means of the vector diagram of Fig. 10-2c.

Each of these component-mmf waves produces induction-motor action, but the corresponding torques are in opposite directions. With the rotor at rest, the forward and backward air-gap flux waves created by the combined mmfs of stator and rotor currents are equal, the component torques are equal, and no starting torque is produced. If the forward and backward air-gap flux waves remained equal when the rotor is revolving, each of the component fields would produce a torque-speed characteristic simi-

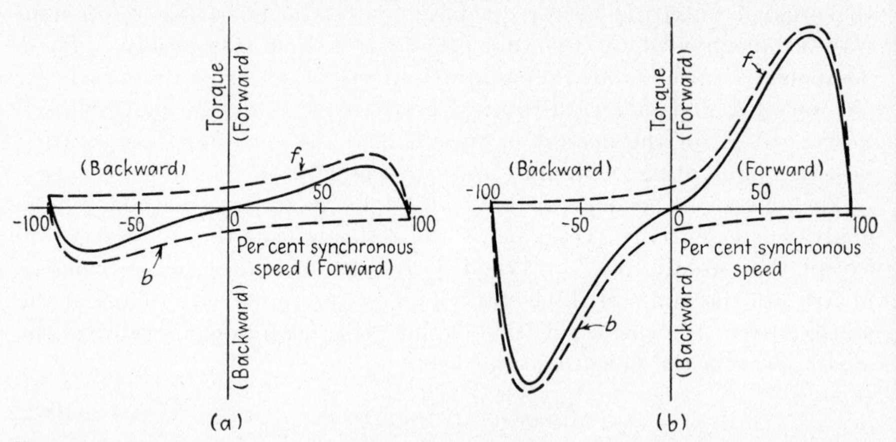

FIG. 10-3. Torque-speed characteristic of a single-phase induction motor, (a) on the basis of constant forward and backward flux waves; (b) taking into account changes in the flux waves.

lar to that of a polyphase motor with negligible stator leakage impedance, as illustrated by the dotted curves f and b in Fig. 10-3a. The resultant torque-speed characteristic, which is the algebraic sum of the two component curves, shows that if the motor were started by auxiliary means it would produce torque in whatever direction it was started.

The assumption that the air-gap flux waves remain equal when the rotor is in motion is a rather drastic simplification of the actual state of affairs. In the first place, the effects of stator leakage impedance are ignored. Furthermore the effects of induced rotor currents are not properly accounted for. Both of these effects will ultimately be included in the detailed quantitative theory of Art. 10-6a. The following qualitative explanation shows that the performance of a single-phase induction motor is considerably better than would be predicted on the basis of equal forward and backward flux waves.

When the rotor is in motion, the component rotor currents induced by the backward field are greater than at standstill and their power factor is lower. Their mmf, which opposes that of the stator current, results in a reduction of the backward flux wave. Conversely, the magnetic effect of the component currents induced by the forward field is less than at standstill, because the rotor currents are less and their power factor is higher. As speed increases, therefore, the forward flux wave increases while the backward flux wave decreases, their sum remaining roughly constant since it must induce the stator counter emf, which is approximately constant if the stator leakage-impedance voltage drop is small. Hence with the rotor in motion, the torque of the forward field is greater and that of the backward field is less than in Fig. 10-3*a*, the true situation being about as shown in Fig. 10-3*b*. In the normal running region at a few per cent slip, the forward field is several times greater than the backward field, and the flux wave does not differ greatly from the constant-amplitude revolving field in the air gap of a balanced polyphase motor. In the normal running region, therefore, the torque-speed characteristic of a single-phase motor is not too greatly inferior to that of a polyphase motor having the same rotor and operating with the same maximum air-gap flux density.

In addition to the torques shown in Fig. 10-3, double-stator-frequency torque pulsations are produced by the interactions of the oppositely rotating flux and mmf waves which glide past each other at twice synchronous speed. These interactions produce no average torque, but they tend to make the motor noisier than a polyphase motor. Such torque pulsations are unavoidable in a single-phase motor because of the pulsations in instantaneous power input inherent in a single-phase circuit. The effects of the pulsating torque can be minimized by using an elastic mounting for the motor. The torque referred to on the torque-speed curves is the time average of the instantaneous torque.

10-2. Starting and Running Performance of Single-phase Induction Motors. Single-phase induction motors are classified in accordance with the methods of starting and are usually referred to by names descriptive of these methods. As with integral-horsepower motors, selection of the appropriate type is made from the starting and running characteristics and comparative economies. Starting methods and resulting torque-speed characteristics will be considered qualitatively in this article. A starting method based on the repulsion-motor principle is described in Art. 10-5.

a. Split-phase. Split-phase motors have two stator windings, a main winding m and an auxiliary winding a, with their axes displaced 90 electrical degrees in space. They are connected as shown in Fig. 10-4*a*. The auxiliary winding has a higher resistance-to-reactance ratio than the main winding, so that the two currents are out of phase, as indicated in the vector diagram of Fig. 10-4*b*, which is representative of conditions at starting. Since the auxiliary-winding current I_a leads the main-winding current I_m, the stator field first reaches a maximum along the axis of the auxiliary winding and then somewhat later in time reaches a maximum along the axis of the main winding. The winding currents are equivalent to unbalanced 2-phase currents, and the motor is equivalent to an unbalanced 2-phase motor. The result is a rotating stator field which causes the motor to start. After the motor starts, the auxiliary winding is disconnected, usually by means of a centrifugal switch that operates at about 75 per cent of synchronous speed. The simple way to obtain the high resistance-to-reactance ratio for the auxiliary winding is to wind it

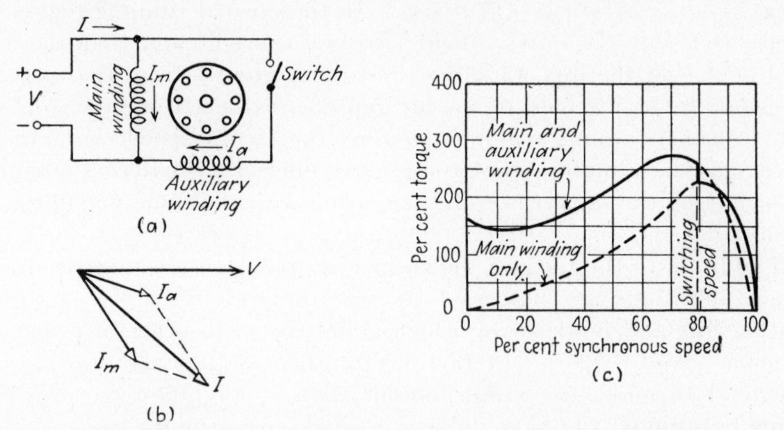

FIG. 10-4. Split-phase motor. (*a*) Connections. (*b*) Vector diagram at starting. (*c*) Typical torque-speed characteristic.

with smaller wire than the main winding, a permissible procedure because this winding is in circuit only during starting. Its reactance can be reduced somewhat by placing it in the tops of the slots. A typical torque-speed characteristic is shown in Fig. 10-4*c*.

b. Capacitor-start Induction-run. This is also a split-phase motor, but the time-phase displacement between the two currents is obtained by means of a capacitor in series with the auxiliary winding, as shown in Fig. 10-5*a*. Again the auxiliary winding is disconnected after the motor has started, and consequently the auxiliary winding and capacitor can be designed cheaply for intermittent service. Dry-type a-c electrolytic capacitors are commonly used, since they are compact and inexpensive. Such capacitors inherently have intermittent ratings and are sensitive to overvoltage, and care must be taken to apply them properly. For 110-volt motor-starting duty they are usually guaranteed for 25 per cent overvoltage and for not more than 20 periods of operation per hour, each period not to exceed 3 sec in duration. By use of a starting capacitor of appropriate value, the auxiliary-winding current I_a at standstill could be made to lead the main-winding current I_m by 90 electrical degrees, as it would in a balanced 2-phase motor (see Fig. 10-5b). Actually, the best compromise among the factors of starting torque, starting current, and costs results with a phase angle somewhat less than 90°. A typical

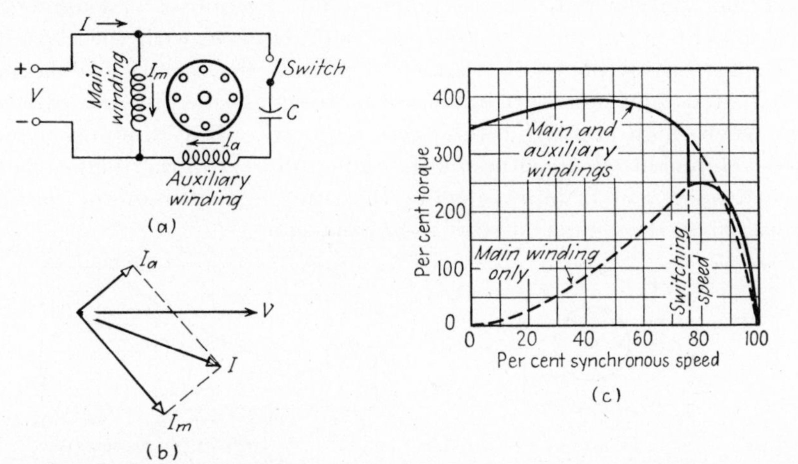

FIG. 10-5. Capacitor-start motor. (a) Connections. (b) Vector diagram at starting (c) Typical torque-speed characteristic.

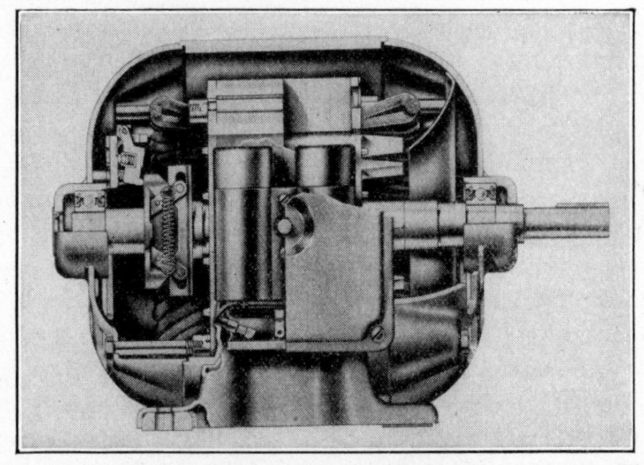

FIG. 10-6. Cutaway view of a capacitor-start induction motor. The centrifugal starting switch is at the left of the rotor. The starting capacitors are the two cylinders in the box on the side of the motor. (*Courtesy of Westinghouse Electric Corporation.*)

torque-speed characteristic is shown in Fig. 10-5c, high starting torque being an outstanding feature. A cutaway view of a capacitor-start motor is shown in Fig. 10-6.

The history of the development of capacitor motors is an interesting example of how developments in one engineering field affect progress in others. The fact that the starting torque of a split-phase motor could be increased if the phase angle between the auxiliary and main winding currents could be increased so as to approach 90° was recognized at an early stage in the development of split-phase motors. It was also recognized that a large value of capacitance would be required, and commercial development of capacitor motors was impracticable with the capacitors which were available at that time. Up until the late 1920's the more complicated repulsion-start induction motors described in Art. 10-5 were used where high starting torque was required. The stimulus given to the development of capacitors by the radio industry in the 1920's resulted in such spectacular improvements that the capacitor motor has now almost made the repulsion-start motor obsolete.

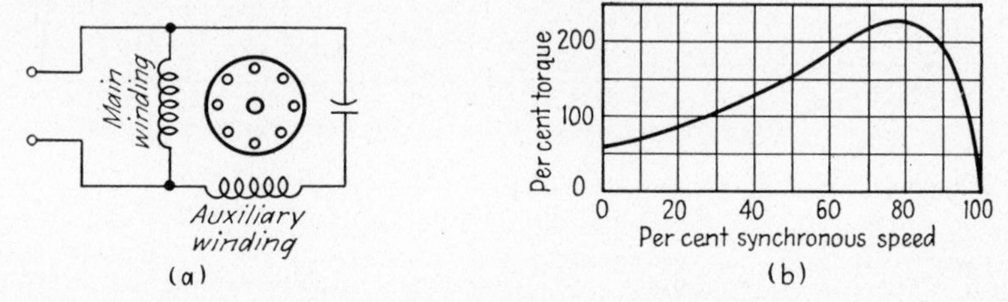

FIG. 10-7. Permanent-split-capacitor motor and typical torque-speed characteristic.

c. Permanent-split-capacitor. If the capacitor and auxiliary winding of the preceding motor are not cut out after starting, the construction can be simplified by omission of the switch, and the power factor, efficiency, and torque pulsations improved. For example, the capacitor and auxiliary winding could be designed for perfect 2-phase operation at any one desired load.[3] The backward field would then be eliminated, with resulting improvement in efficiency. The double-stator-frequency torque pulsations also would be eliminated, the capacitor serving as an energy-storage reservoir for smoothing out the pulsations in power input from the single-phase line. The result is a quiet motor. Since electrolytic capacitors are not suitable for continuous service, a more expensive oil-impregnated-paper type of capacitor must be used. Also starting torque must be sacrificed because the capacitance is necessarily a compromise between the best starting and running values. The resulting torque-speed characteristic, together with a schematic diagram, are given in Fig. 10-7.

d. Two-value-capacitor. If two capacitors are used, one for starting and one for running, theoretically optimum starting and running performance can both be obtained. One way of accomplishing this result is shown in Fig. 10-8*a*. The small value of capacitance required for opti-

[3] P. H. Trickey, Design of Capacitor Motors for Balanced Operation, *Trans. AIEE*, vol. 51, No. 3, pp. 780–785, September, 1932.

mum running conditions is an impregnated-paper capacitor permanently connected in series with the auxiliary winding, and the much larger value required for starting is obtained by an a-c electrolytic capacitor connected in parallel with the running capacitor. The starting capacitor is disconnected after the motor starts.

The design is somewhat of a compromise. A top limit on the number of turns in the auxiliary winding is imposed by the necessity for avoiding overvoltage on the electrolytic capacitor during starting. With this limitation on auxiliary-winding design, the running capacitor can seldom be made large enough, for economic reasons, for optimum full-load running conditions.

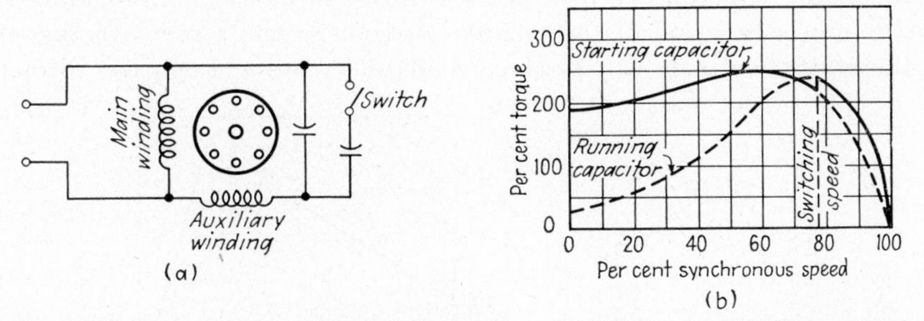

FIG. 10-8. Two-value-capacitor motor and typical torque-speed characteristic.

e. Shaded-pole. As illustrated schematically in Fig. 10-9*a*, the shaded-pole motor usually has salient poles with one portion of each pole surrounded by a short-circuited turn of copper called a *shading coil.* Induced currents in the shading coil cause the flux in the shaded portion of the pole to lag the flux in the other portion. The result is like a rotating field moving in the direction from the unshaded to the shaded portion of the pole, and a low starting torque is produced. A typical torque-speed characteristic is shown in Fig. 10-9*b*. The efficiency is low. This principle is used only in very small motors, such as small fans, and

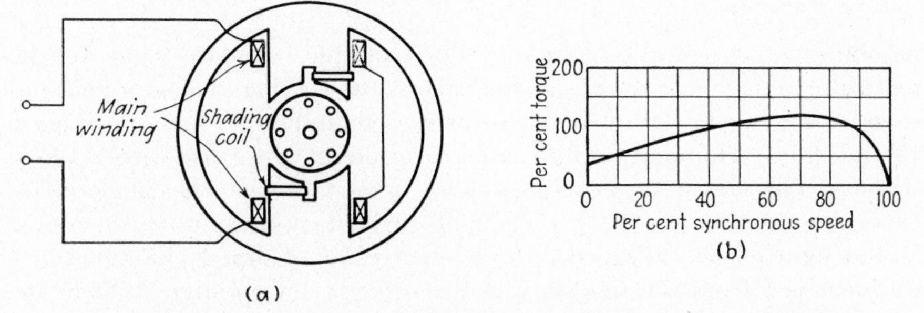

FIG. 10-9. Shaded-pole motor and typical torque-speed characteristic.

as a starting method for electric-clock motors. Its chief advantages are simplicity and low cost.[4]

10-3. Single-phase Synchronous Motors. Fractional-horsepower synchronous motors are usually of either the *reluctance type* described in Art. 2-2 or the hysteresis type described in part *b* of this article.

a. Self-starting Reluctance Motors. Any one of the induction-motor types described in Art. 10-2 can be made into a self-starting synchronous motor of the reluctance type. Anything which makes the reluctance of the air gap a function of the angular position of the rotor with respect to the stator coil axis will produce reluctance torque when the rotor is

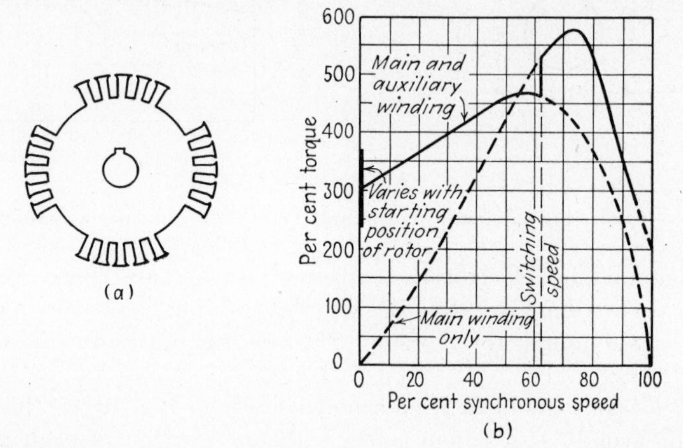

FIG. 10-10. Rotor punching for 4-pole reluctance-type synchronous motor and typical starting characteristics.

revolving at synchronous speed. For example, suppose some of the teeth are removed from a squirrel-cage rotor leaving the bars and end rings intact as in an ordinary squirrel-cage induction motor. Figure 10-10*a* shows a lamination for such a rotor designed for use with a 4-pole stator. The stator may be polyphase or any one of the single-phase types described in Art. 10-2. The motor will start as an induction motor and at light loads will speed up to a small value of slip. The reluctance torque arises from the tendency of the rotor to try to align itself in the minimum-reluctance position with respect to the synchronously revolving forward air-gap flux wave, in accordance with the principles explained in Chap. 2. At a small slip, this torque alternates slowly in direction; the rotor is accelerated during a positive half cycle of the torque variation and decelerated during the succeeding negative half cycle. If, however, the moment of inertia of the rotor and its mechanical load is sufficiently small, the rotor will be accelerated from slip speed up to synchronous

[4] For a quantitative theory, see S. S. L. Chang, Equivalent Circuits and their Application in Designing Shaded-pole Motors, *Trans. AIEE*, vol. 70, pp. 690–698, 1951.

speed during an accelerating half cycle of the reluctance torque. The rotor will then pull into step and continue to run at synchronous speed with characteristics similar to those described in Art. 2-2. A factor omitted in Art. 2-2 is the torque caused by induction-motor action of the backward-revolving field in a single-phase motor. This torque affects the synchronous-motor performance in the same way as an additional shaft load.

A typical torque-speed characteristic for a split-phase-start synchronous motor of the single-phase reluctance type is shown in Fig. 10-10*b*. Notice the high values of induction-motor torque. The reason for this is that in order to obtain satisfactory synchronous-motor characteristics it has been found necessary to build reluctance-type synchronous motors on frames which would be suitable for induction motors of two or three times the synchronous-motor rating.[5] Also notice that the principal effect of the salient-pole rotor on the induction-motor characteristic is at standstill, where considerable "cogging" is evident; *i.e.*, the torque varies considerably with rotor position.

b. Hysteresis Motors. The phenomenon of hysteresis can be used to produce mechanical torque.[6] In its simplest form, the rotor of a hysteresis motor is a smooth cylinder of magnetically hard steel, without windings or teeth. It is placed within a slotted stator carrying distributed windings designed to produce as nearly as possible a sinusoidal space distribution of flux, since undulations in the flux wave greatly increase the losses. In single-phase motors, the stator windings usually are the permanent-split-capacitor type, as in Fig. 10-7. The capacitor is chosen so as to result in approximately balanced 2-phase conditions within the motor windings. The stator then produces a rotating field, approximately constant in space waveform and revolving at synchronous speed.

Instantaneous magnetic conditions in the air gap and rotor are indicated in Fig. 10-11*a* for a 2-pole stator. The axis SS' of the stator-mmf wave revolves at synchronous speed. Because of hysteresis, the magnetization of the rotor lags behind the inducing mmf wave, and therefore the axis RR' of the rotor flux wave lags behind the axis of the stator-mmf wave by the hysteretic lag angle δ (Fig. 10-11*a*). If the rotor is stationary, starting torque is produced proportional to the product of the fundamental components of the stator mmf and rotor flux and the sine of the torque angle δ. The rotor then accelerates if the counter torque

[5] P. H. Trickey, Small Synchronous Motors without Exciters, *Elec. J.*, vol. 30, No. 4, pp. 160–162, April, 1933; P. H. Trickey, Performance Calculations on Polyphase Reluctance Motors, *Trans. AIEE*, vol. 65, No. 4, pp. 190–193, April, 1946.

[6] For detailed studies of hysteresis torque see H. C. Roters, The Hysteresis Motor—Advances which Permit Economical Fractional Horsepower Ratings, *Trans. AIEE*, vol. 66, pp. 1419–1430, 1947; B. R. Teare, Jr., Theory of Hysteresis-motor Torque, *Trans. AIEE*, vol. 59, pp. 907–912, 1940.

of the load is less than the developed torque of the motor. So long as the rotor is turning at less than synchronous speed, each particle of the rotor is subjected to a repetitive hysteresis cycle at slip frequency. While the rotor accelerates, the lag angle δ remains constant if the flux is constant, since the angle δ depends merely on the hysteresis loop of the rotor and is independent of the rate at which the loop is traversed. The motor therefore develops constant torque right up to synchronous speed, as shown in the idealized torque-speed characteristic of Fig. 10-11*b*. This feature is one of the advantages of the hysteresis motor. In contrast with a reluctance motor, which must "snap" its load into synchronism

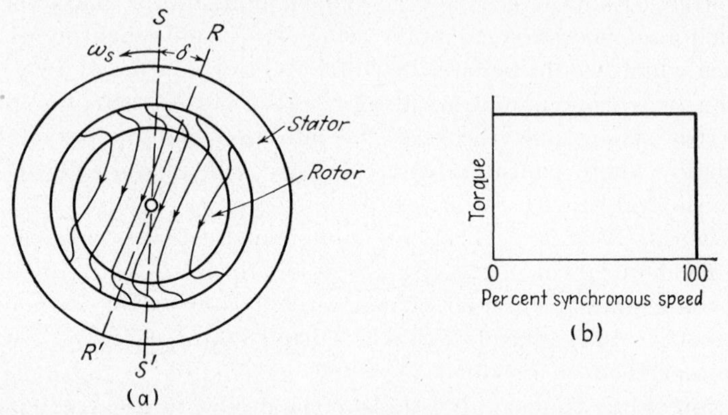

FIG. 10-11. (*a*) General nature of the magnetic field in the air gap and rotor of a hysteresis motor. (*b*) Idealized torque-speed characteristic.

from an induction-motor torque-speed characteristic, a hysteresis motor can synchronize any load which it can accelerate, no matter how great the inertia.

After reaching synchronism, the motor continues to run at synchronous speed and adjusts its torque angle so as to develop the torque required by the load. The mechanism by which the motor adjusts itself to load is described by Teare (footnote 6).

Until recently, the commonest application of hysteresis motors has been in electric clocks and other timing devices with outputs of a few milliwatts, inputs of 2 or 3 watts, and efficiencies of a few tenths of a per cent. They have also been used as record-player motors, where their quietness and ability to synchronize heavy inertia loads are advantageous. Recent changes in the art have resulted in practical designs as large as 1/7 hp, comparable in size and efficiency with ordinary induction motors.

10-4. A-C Series Motors. Universal Motors. It has already been pointed out (see Art. 3-4) that a series motor has the convenient ability to run on either alternating or direct current and with similar characteristics, provided both stator and rotor cores are laminated. Such a single-phase series motor therefore is commonly called a *universal motor*. The torque angle is fixed by the brush position and is normally at its optimum value of 90°. If alternating current is supplied to a series motor, the stator and rotor field strengths will vary in exact time phase. Both will reverse at the same instant, and consequently the torque will always be in the same direction, though pulsating in magnitude at twice line frequency. Average torque will be produced, and the performance of the motor will be generally similar to that with direct current. Commutation difficulties will be more severe than with direct current, however, limiting heavy-power usage to low frequencies such as 25 cps. In the larger sizes, a-c series motors are used principally for traction purposes. In the fractional-horsepower and small integral-horsepower sizes, the commutation difficulties at 60 cps can be overcome. Small universal motors are used where light weight is important, as in vacuum cleaners and portable tools, and usually operate at high speeds (1,500 to 15,000 rpm). Typical characteristics are shown in Fig. 10-12. They can be made to have constant-speed characteristics by means of mechanical governing devices. In food mixers and similar applications, the speed held by the governor can be adjusted by the user.

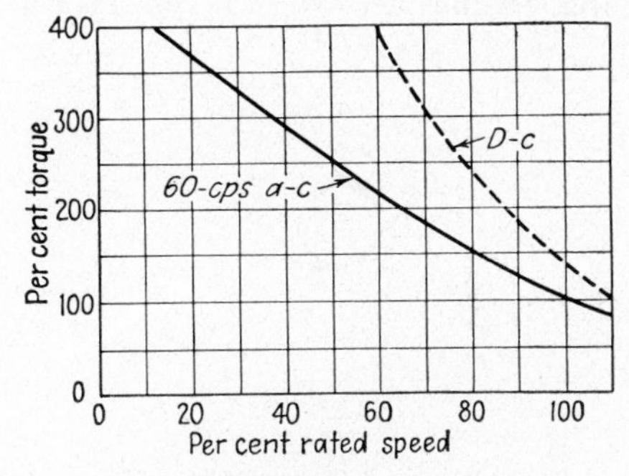

Fig. 10-12. Typical torque-speed characteristics of a universal series motor.

The a-c and d-c characteristics differ somewhat for two reasons: (1) with alternating current, reactance-voltage drops in the field and armature absorb part of the applied voltage, and therefore for a specified current and torque the rotational counter emf generated in the armature is less than with direct current and the speed tends to be lower; (2) with alternating current, the magnetic circuit may be appreciably saturated at the peaks of the current wave, and the rms value of the flux may thus be appreciably less with alternating current than with the same rms value of direct current; the torque therefore tends to be less and the speed higher with alternating than with direct current. When it is important to have similar a-c and d-c characteristics, the differences can be minimized by the use of compensating windings.

10-5. Repulsion Motors and Variations. In a-c series motors, the rotor and stator windings are conductively coupled—*i.e.*, the rotor current is obtained by conduction from the stator. Repulsion motors are similar to series motors except that the rotor and stator windings are inductively coupled—*i.e.*, the rotor current is obtained by transformer action from the stator. The stator usually carries a distributed winding like the main winding of an ordinary single-phase induction motor. The rotor carries a drum winding connected to a commutator, like the d-c armature windings described in Art. 3-9. The brushes are short-circuited. Such a motor is shown schematically in Fig. 10-13*a*. The magnetic axis of the rotor is determined by the brush position. If the rotor axis were in line with the stator-field axis, the current induced in the rotor by transformer action would produce an mmf opposing the stator mmf. No torque would be produced, however, because the torque angle would be zero. If the rotor axis were in quadrature with the stator-

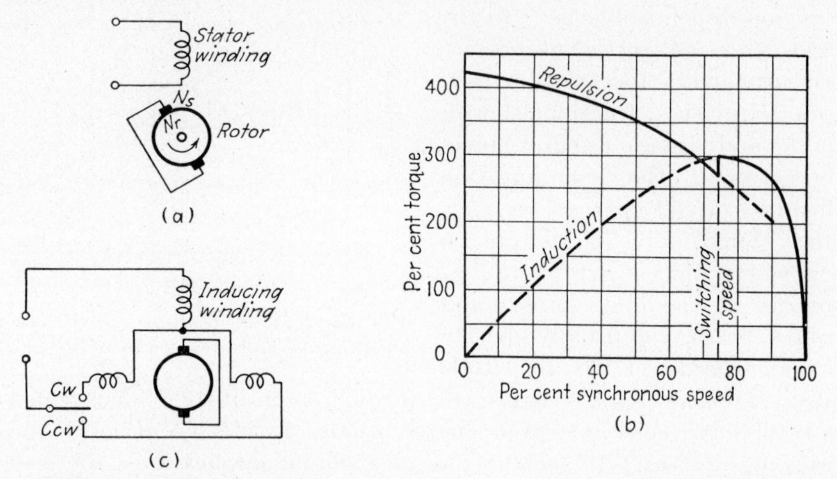

FIG. 10-13. (*a*) Schematic diagram of a repulsion motor. (*b*) Typical torque-speed characteristic of a repulsion-start induction motor. (*c*) Stator windings for reversing a repulsion motor.

field axis, the torque angle would be at its optimum value of 90° but no rotor current would be induced, because the net inductive coupling would be zero. Actually, the brushes are in an intermediate position, as shown in Fig. 10-13*a*. Since the rotor mmf opposes the stator mmf, a rotor pole of the same polarity as the nearest stator pole is produced by the induced rotor current, as indicated by the letters N_s and N_r designating instantaneous stator and rotor polarity, respectively, in Fig. 10-13*a*. Repulsion between these like poles produces torque on the rotor in the direction that the brushes are shifted from the maximum-current position.

The pure repulsion motor has the high-starting-torque varying-speed characteristic typical of series motors and permits speed adjustment by brush shifting. *Repulsion-induction motors* have both a commutated winding and a squirrel-cage rotor winding, the latter being buried in the slots below the commutated winding; hence they combine both repulsion and induction torques. In *repulsion-start induction-run motors,* a centrifugally operated device short-circuits all the commutator segments and usually also lifts the brushes when the motor reaches about 75 per cent of synchronous speed, after which the rotor winding is like a short-circuited squirrel cage and the motor operates as a single-phase induction motor. Typical characteristics of a repulsion-start induction-run motor are given in Fig. 10-13*b*. Prior to about 1930, these motors were widely used for applications requiring high starting torque. Since then, however, the simpler capacitor-start motors (see Art. 10-2*b* and Fig. 10-5) have generally taken over this field.

The motor of Fig. 10-13*a* is not electrically reversible. It must be reversed by shifting its brushes to the opposite side of the stator-field axis. One way of accomplishing electrical reversibility is to shift the stator axis without moving the brushes. In Fig. 10-13*c* the stator winding consists of an inducing winding and two field windings of opposite polarity placed on the stator in electrical quadrature with the inducing winding. Rotation in either direction can be obtained by energizing the inducing winding in series with one or the other of the quadrature field windings, as shown in Fig. 10-13*c*.

10-6. Revolving-field Theory of Single-phase Induction Motors. In Art. 10-1, the stator-mmf wave of a single-phase induction motor is shown to be equivalent to two constant-amplitude mmf waves revolving in opposite directions at synchronous speed. Each of these component stator-mmf waves induces its own component rotor currents and produces induction-motor action just as in a balanced polyphase motor. This double-revolving-field concept not only is useful for qualitative visualization but also can be developed into a quantitative theory applicable to a wide variety of induction-motor types. A simple and important case is that of the single-phase induction motor running on only its main winding.

a. Single-phase Induction Motors—Quantitative Analysis. First consider conditions with the rotor stationary and only the main stator winding m excited. The motor then is equivalent to a transformer with its secondary short-circuited. The equivalent circuit is shown in Fig. 10-14*a*, where r_{1m} and x_{1m} are, respectively, the resistance and leakage reactance of the main winding, x_φ is the magnetizing reactance, and r_2 and x_2 are the standstill values of the rotor resistance and leakage reactance referred to the main stator winding by use of the appropriate turns ratio. Core loss, which is omitted here, will be accounted for later as if it were a rotational loss. The applied voltage is V, and the main-winding current is I_m. The voltage E_m is the counter emf generated in the main winding by the stationary pulsating air-gap flux wave produced by the combined action of the stator and rotor currents.

In accordance with the double-revolving-field concept of Art. 10-1, the stator mmf can be resolved into half-amplitude forward- and backward-rotating fields. At standstill the amplitudes of the forward and backward resultant air-gap flux waves both equal half the amplitude of the pulsating field. In Fig. 10-14*b* the portion of the equivalent circuit representing the effects of the air-gap flux is split into two equal portions representing the effects of the forward and backward fields, respectively.

Now consider conditions after the motor has been brought up to speed by some auxiliary means and is running on only its main winding in the direction of the forward field at a per-unit slip s. The rotor currents

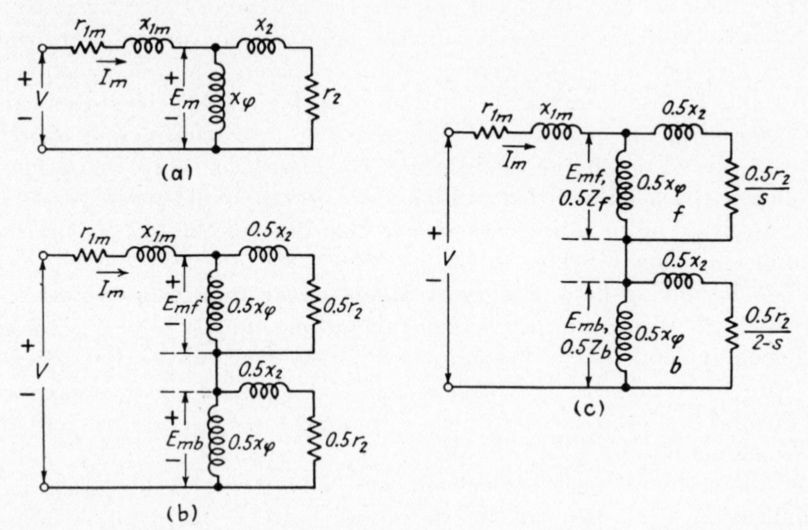

FIG. 10-14. Equivalent circuits for a single-phase induction motor. (*a*) Rotor blocked. (*b*) Rotor blocked, showing effects of forward and backward fields. (*c*) Running conditions.

induced by the forward field are of slip frequency sf, where f is the stator frequency. Just as in any polyphase motor with a symmetrical polyphase or cage rotor, these rotor currents produce an mmf wave traveling forward at slip speed with respect to the rotor and therefore at synchronous speed with respect to the stator. The resultant of the forward waves of stator and rotor mmf creates a resultant forward wave of air-gap flux which generates a counter emf E_{mf} in the main winding m of the stator. The reflected effect of the rotor as viewed from the stator is like that in a polyphase motor and can be represented by an impedance $\dfrac{0.5r_2}{s} + j0.5x_2$ in parallel with $j0.5x_\varphi$, as in the portion of the equivalent circuit (Fig. 10-14*c*) labeled f. The factors of 0.5 come from the resolution of the pulsating stator mmf into forward and backward components.

Now consider conditions with respect to the backward field. The rotor is still turning at a slip s with respect to the forward field, and its per-unit speed n in the direction of the forward field is

$$n = 1 - s \tag{10-5}$$

The relative speed of the rotor with respect to the backward field is $1 + n$, or its slip with respect to the backward field is

$$1 + n = 2 - s \tag{10-6}$$

The backward field then induces rotor currents whose frequency is $(2 - s)f$. For small slips, these rotor currents are of almost twice stator frequency. At a small slip, an oscillogram of rotor current therefore will show a high-frequency component from the backward field superposed on a low-frequency component from the forward field. As viewed from the stator, the rotor-mmf wave of the backward-field rotor currents travels at synchronous speed, but in the backward direction. The equivalent circuit representing these internal reactions from the viewpoint of the stator is like that of a polyphase motor whose slip is $2 - s$ and is shown in the portion of the equivalent circuit (Fig. 10-14*c*) labeled *b*. As with the forward field, the factors of 0.5 come from the resolution of the pulsating stator mmf into forward and backward components. The voltage E_{mb} across the parallel combination representing the backward field is the counter emf generated in the main winding m of the stator by the resultant backward field.

By use of the equivalent circuit of Fig. 10-14*c*, the stator current, power input, and power factor can be computed for any assumed value of slip when the applied voltage and the motor impedances are known. To simplify the notation, let

$$Z_f \equiv R_f + jX_f \equiv \left(\frac{r_2}{s} + jx_2\right) \text{ in parallel with } jx_\varphi \tag{10-7}$$

$$Z_b \equiv R_b + jX_b \equiv \left(\frac{r_2}{2 - s} + jx_2\right) \text{ in parallel with } jx_\varphi \tag{10-8}$$

The impedances representing the reactions of the forward and backward fields from the viewpoint of the single-phase stator winding m are $0.5Z_f$ and $0.5Z_b$, respectively, in Fig. 10-14*c*. (In much of the technical literature pertaining to single-phase motors, Z_f and Z_b are defined as half the values given by Eqs. 10-7 and 10-8, a notation somewhat simpler for the special case of operation on one phase, but not so well adapted to the generalized symmetrical-component theory which will be developed later in this chapter. With the definitions of Z_f and Z_b given in Eqs. 10-7 and 10-8, the factor of 0.5 accounting for the resolution of the stator mmf into half-amplitude forward- and backward-rotating fields must be included as an explicit factor.)

Examination of the equivalent circuit (Fig. 10-14c) confirms the conclusion, reached by qualitative reasoning in Art. 10-1 (Fig. 10-3b) that the forward air-gap flux wave increases and the backward wave decreases when the rotor is set in motion. When the motor is running at a small slip, the reflected effect of the rotor resistance in the forward field, $0.5r_2/s$, is much larger than its standstill value, while the corresponding effect in the backward field, $0.5r_2/(2 - s)$, is smaller. The forward-field impedance therefore is larger than its standstill value, while that of the backward field is smaller. The forward-field counter emf E_{mf} therefore is larger than its standstill value, while the backward-field counter emf E_{mb} is smaller; *i.e.*, the forward air-gap flux wave increases, while the backward flux wave decreases.

Moreover, mechanical output conditions can be computed by application of the torque and power relations developed for polyphase motors in Art. 9-2. Recall the argument in Arts. 4-5a and 9-2, where it is shown that the torque produced by the interaction of a flux wave and an mmf wave revolving at the same speed can be expressed in terms of the electrical power corresponding to the voltage induced by the flux wave and the current responsible for the mmf wave. The torques produced by the forward and backward fields can each be treated in this manner. The interactions of the oppositely rotating flux and mmf waves cause torque pulsations at twice stator frequency but produce no average torque.

As in Eq. 9-12, the internal torque T_f of the forward field in newton-meters equals $1/\omega_s$ times the power P_{gf} in watts delivered by the stator winding to the forward field, where ω_s is the synchronous angular velocity in mechanical radians per second; thus

$$T_f = \frac{1}{\omega_s} P_{gf} \tag{10-9}$$

When the magnetizing impedance is treated as purely inductive, P_{gf} is the power absorbed by the impedance $0.5Z_f$; that is,

$$P_{gf} = I_m^2 0.5R_f \tag{10-10}$$

where R_f is the resistive component of the forward-field impedance defined in Eq. 10-7. Similarly the internal torque T_b of the backward field is

$$T_b = \frac{1}{\omega_s} P_{gb} \tag{10-11}$$

where P_{gb} is the power delivered by the stator winding to the backward field, or

$$P_{gb} = I_m^2 0.5R_b \tag{10-12}$$

where R_b is the resistive component of the backward-field impedance Z_b defined in Eq. 10-8. The torque of the backward field is in the opposite direction to that of the forward field, and therefore the net internal torque T is

$$T = T_f - T_b = \frac{1}{\omega_s}(P_{gf} - P_{gb}) \tag{10-13}$$

Since the rotor currents produced by the two component air-gap fields are of different frequencies, the total rotor I^2R loss is the numerical sum of the losses caused by each field. In general, as shown in Eq. 9-17, the rotor copper loss caused by a rotating field equals the slip of the field times the power absorbed from the stator, whence

$$\text{Forward-field rotor } I^2R = sP_{gf} \tag{10-14}$$

$$\text{Backward-field rotor } I^2R = (2 - s)P_{gb} \tag{10-15}$$

$$\text{Total rotor } I^2R = sP_{gf} + (2 - s)P_{gb} \tag{10-16}$$

Since power is torque times angular velocity and the angular velocity of the rotor is $(1 - s)\omega_s$, the internal power P converted to mechanical form, in watts, is

$$P = (1 - s)\omega_s T = (1 - s)(P_{gf} - P_{gb}) \tag{10-17}$$

As in the polyphase motor, the internal torque T and internal power P are not the output values, because rotational losses remain to be accounted for. It is obviously correct to subtract friction and windage effects from T or P, and it is usually assumed that core losses may be treated in the same manner. For the small changes in speed encountered in normal operation, the rotational losses are often assumed to be constant.

Example 10-1. A ¼-hp 110-volt 60-cps 4-pole capacitor-start motor has the following constants and losses:

$$r_{1m} = 2.02 \text{ ohms} \qquad x_{1m} = 2.79 \text{ ohms}$$
$$r_2 = 4.12 \qquad x_2 = 2.12$$
$$x_\varphi = 66.8$$

Core loss = 24 watts   Friction and windage = 13 watts

For a slip of 0.05, determine the stator current, power factor, power output, speed, torque, and efficiency when this motor is running as a single-phase motor at rated voltage and frequency with its starting winding open.

Solution. The first step is to determine the values of the forward- and backward-field impedances at the assigned value of slip. The following relations, derived from Eq. 10-7, simplify the computations:

$$R_f = \frac{x_\varphi^2}{x_{22}} \frac{1}{sQ_2 + (1/sQ_2)} \tag{10-18}$$

$$X_f = \frac{x_2 x_\varphi}{x_{22}} + \frac{R_f}{sQ_2} \tag{10-19}$$

where

$$x_{22} = x_2 + x_\varphi \tag{10-20}$$

and

$$Q_2 = \frac{x_{22}}{r_2} \tag{10-21}$$

Substitution of numerical values gives, for $s = 0.05$,

$$R_f + jX_f = 31.9 + j40.3 \text{ ohms}$$

Corresponding relations for the backward-field impedance Z_b are obtained by substituting $2 - s$ for s in Eqs. 10-18 and 10-19. When $(2 - s)Q_2$ is greater than 10, as is usually the case, less than 1 per cent error results from use of the following approximate forms:

$$R_b = \frac{r_2}{2 - s}\left(\frac{x_\varphi}{x_{22}}\right)^2 \tag{10-22}$$

$$X_b = \frac{x_2 x_\varphi}{x_{22}} + \frac{R_b}{(2 - s)Q_2} \tag{10-23}$$

Substitution of numerical values gives, for $s = 0.05$,

$$R_b + jX_b = 1.98 + j2.12 \text{ ohms}$$

Addition of the series elements in the equivalent circuit of Fig. 10-14c gives

$$\begin{aligned} r_{1m} + jx_{1m} &= 2.02 + j2.79 \\ 0.5(R_f + jX_f) &= 15.95 + j20.15 \\ 0.5(R_b + jX_b) &= \underline{0.99 + j1.06} \\ \text{Input } Z = \text{sum} &= 18.96 + j24.00 = 30.6\underline{/51.7^\circ} \end{aligned}$$

$$\text{Stator current } I_m = \frac{110}{30.6} = 3.59 \text{ amp}$$

Power factor $= \cos 51.7^\circ = 0.620$

Power input $= (110)(3.59)(0.620) = 244$ watts

Power absorbed by forward field (Eq. 10-10)

$P_{gf} = (3.59)^2(15.95) = 206$ watts

Power absorbed by backward field (Eq. 10-12)

$P_{gb} = (3.59)^2(0.99) = 12.8$ watts

Internal mechanical power (Eq. 10-17)

$P = (0.95)(206 - 13) = 184$

Rotational loss $= 24 + 13 = \underline{37}$

Power output $=$ difference $= 147$ watts, or 0.197 hp

Synchronous speed $= 1{,}800$ rpm, or 30 rev/sec

$\omega_s = 2\pi(30) = 188.5$ rad/sec

Rotor speed $= (1 - s) \times$ (synchronous speed)

$= (0.95)(1{,}800) = 1{,}710$ rpm

$= (0.95)(188.5) = 179$ rad/sec

Torque $=$ power $\div$ angular velocity

$= 147/179 = 0.821$ newton-m, or 0.605 lb-ft

$$\text{Efficiency} = \frac{\text{output}}{\text{input}} = \frac{147}{244} = 0.602$$

As a check on the power bookkeeping, compute the losses:

Stator $I_m^2 r_{1m} = (3.59)^2(2.02)$	$= 26.0$
Forward-field rotor I^2R, Eq. 10-14 $= (0.05)(206)$	$= 10.3$
Backward-field rotor I^2R, Eq. 10-15 $= (1.95)(12.8)$	$= 25.0$
Rotational losses	$= 37.0$
Sum	$= 98.3$
From input $-$ output, total losses	$= 97$

(Checks within accuracy of computations.)

Examination of the order of magnitude of the numerical values in Example 10-1 suggests approximations which usually can be made. These approximations pertain particularly to the backward-field impedance. Note that the impedance $0.5(R_b + jX_b)$ is only about 5 per cent of the total motor impedance for a slip near full load. Consequently an approximation as large as 20 per cent of this impedance would cause only about 1 per cent error in the motor current. Although, strictly speaking, the backward-field impedance is a function of slip, very little error usually results from computing its value at any convenient slip in the normal running region—say 5 per cent—and then assuming R_b and X_b to be constants. With a slightly greater approximation, the shunting effect of jx_φ on the backward-field impedance can often be neglected, whence

$$Z_b \approx \frac{r_2}{2 - s} + jx_2 \tag{10-24}$$

This equation gives values of the backward-field resistance that are a few per cent high, as can be seen by comparison with Eq. 10-22. Neglecting s in Eq. 10-24 would tend to give values of the backward-field resistance that would be too low, and therefore such an approximation would tend to counteract the error in Eq. 10-24. Consequently, for small slips

$$Z_b \approx \frac{r_2}{2} + jx_2 \tag{10-25}$$

In the polyphase motor (Art. 9-3) maximum internal torque and the slip at which it occurs can easily be expressed in terms of the motor constants; the maximum internal torque is independent of rotor resistance. No such simple relations exist for the single-phase motor. The single-phase problem is much more involved because of the presence of the backward field, the effect of which is twofold: first, it absorbs some of the applied voltage, thus reducing the voltage available for the forward field and decreasing the forward torque developed; and second, the backward field then absorbs some of the forward-field torque. Both these effects depend on rotor resistance as well as leakage reactance. Consequently, unlike the polyphase motor, the maximum internal torque of a single-phase motor is influenced by rotor resistance; increasing the rotor resistance decreases the maximum torque and increases the slip at which maximum torque occurs.[7]

Principally because of the effects of the backward field, a single-phase induction motor is somewhat inferior to a polyphase motor using the same rotor and the same stator core. The single-phase motor has a lower maxi-

[7] For an analysis of the problem in terms of the cross-field theory, see A. F. Puchstein and T. C. Lloyd, Single-phase Induction-motor Performance, *Elec. Eng.*, vol. 56, No. 10, pp. 1277–1284, October, 1937.

mum torque which occurs at a lower slip. For the same torque, the single-phase motor has a higher slip and greater losses, principally because of the backward-field rotor copper loss. The volt-ampere input to the single-phase motor is greater, principally because of the power and reactive volt-amperes consumed by the backward field. The stator copper loss also is somewhat higher in the single-phase motor, because one phase, rather than several, must carry all the current. Because of the greater losses, the efficiency is lower, and the temperature rise for the same torque is higher. A larger frame size must be used for a single-phase motor than for a polyphase motor of the same power and speed rating. Because of the larger frame size, the maximum torque can be made comparable with that of a physically smaller but equally rated polyphase motor. In spite of the larger frame size and the necessity for auxiliary starting arrangements, general-purpose single-phase motors in the standard fractional-horsepower ratings cost less than correspondingly rated polyphase motors, because of the much greater volume of production of the former.

b. Blocked-rotor and No-load Tests. The constants of a single-phase induction motor can be determined from the results of a blocked-rotor test, a no-load test, and measurements of the stator resistance. The procedure is similar to that used with polyphase motors (see Art. 9-6), but the interpretation of the results is somewhat more involved, because of the effects of the backward field.[8]

The d-c resistance of the stator windings at room temperature should be measured first and the temperature noted. The main-winding resistance r_{1m} can then be considered to equal the d-c value corrected, when necessary, to the appropriate operating temperature in the usual way for copper conductors (see Eq. 7-13).

As with polyphase motors, the blocked-rotor test gives information regarding the reflected rotor resistance and the combined stator and rotor leakage reactances. For this test, the auxiliary winding of a split-phase or capacitor-start motor which runs single-phase may be open, in which case very little starting torque is produced—theoretically none, although cogging effects may give the motor enough of a "kick" to start it if bearing friction is small. In a repulsion-start induction-run motor, the commutator bars should all be short-circuited together, as they are when running as a single-phase induction motor. In single-phase motors, the effects of rotor frequency on rotor resistance usually are small, and the blocked-rotor test may be taken at rated frequency. The rotor effective resistance and leakage inductance usually can be considered as constants,

[8] For a practical discussion of fractional-horsepower-motor testing, see Chap. XIX of the reference cited in footnote 1. For an analysis of the theoretical aspects, see C. G. Veinott, Segregation of Losses in Single Phase Induction Motors, *Trans. AIEE*, vol. 54, No. 12, pp. 1302–1306, December, 1935.

independent of rotor frequency. The test may be taken at approximately rated voltage or at a reduced voltage. Experience seems to indicate that the rated-voltage test gives better results, but the motor then will heat rapidly. Simultaneous readings of the instruments should be taken within a few seconds, and the d-c resistance of the main stator winding should be measured again as quickly as possible after taking the blocked-rotor readings. The purpose of repeating the resistance measurement is to enable corrections for changes in resistance with temperature rise to be applied, as will be shown in the next paragraph.

With the rotor stationary, the equivalent circuit reduces to that of a short-circuited transformer, as shown in Fig. 10-14*a*. Let the impedance determined from the blocked-rotor readings, after applying instrument corrections, be

$$Z'_{bl} = R'_{bl} + jX_{bl} \tag{10-26}$$

and let the d-c resistance of the main stator winding measured immediately after the blocked-rotor test be r'_{1m}. If the temperature of the rotor is assumed to be the same as that of the stator, the blocked resistance can be corrected to any desired temperature by proportionality; thus if r_{1m} is the stator resistance at normal operating temperature, then the blocked resistance R_{bl} at normal operating temperature is

$$R_{bl} = R'_{bl} \frac{r_{1m}}{r'_{1m}} \tag{10-27}$$

The rest of this discussion assumes that the appropriate temperature corrections have been applied.

As with polyphase motors, the resistance R of the parallel combination of rotor and magnetizing branches can be obtained in terms of the test data; thus

$$R = R_{bl} - r_{1m} \tag{10-28}$$

The resistance R can also be expressed in terms of the constants of the rotor and magnetizing branches. From Eq. 9-39,

$$R = r_2 \frac{x_\varphi^2}{r_2^2 + x_{22}^2} \approx r_2 \left(\frac{x_\varphi}{x_{22}}\right)^2 \tag{10-29}$$

Further information, obtainable from the no-load test, is now needed to complete the determination of the motor constants.

As with polyphase motors, the no-load test gives information with respect to core and rotational losses, and exciting current. The no-load current and power taken by the motor are measured at rated voltage and frequency. Sometimes the voltage is varied, and data are obtained for curves of current and power plotted against voltage.

In a polyphase motor, the no-load rotor copper loss is very small indeed. In a single-phase motor, however, the backward field induces considerable rotor current and produces a backward torque, even at no load. The no-load slip must adjust itself so that the forward field induces enough rotor current to produce sufficient torque to overcome not only the rotational losses but also the retarding torque of the backward field. The no-load slip of a single-phase motor therefore is somewhat larger than that of a polyphase motor.

Even so, the forward-field rotor current usually is sufficiently small so that the rotor copper loss caused by it is negligible, as in a polyphase motor. The backward-field rotor copper loss is an appreciable part of the no-load power input, however. In accordance with the general principle that rotor copper loss is slip times power absorbed from the stator (see Eq. 10-15), the backward-field rotor copper loss is

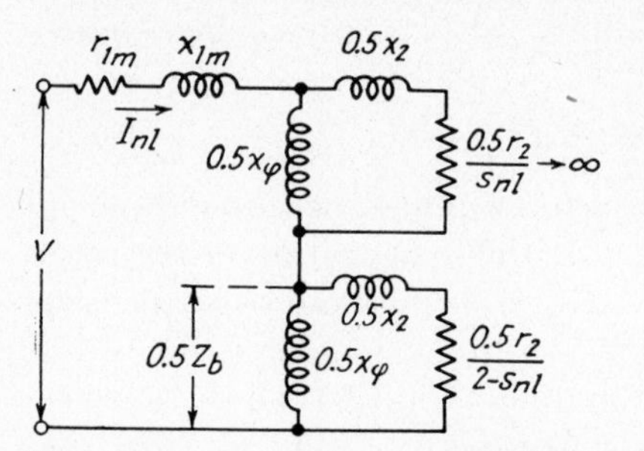

FIG. 10-15. Equivalent circuit for a single-phase induction motor at no load.

$$(2 - s_{nl})P_{gb} = (2 - s_{nl})I_{nl}^2 0.5R_b \qquad (10\text{-}30)$$

where s_{nl} is the no-load slip, P_{gb} is the power absorbed from the stator by the backward field, I_{nl} is the no-load stator current, and $0.5R_b$ is the resistance of the backward-field impedance $0.5Z_b$ in the no-load equivalent circuit of Fig. 10-15. But from Eqs. 10-22 and 10-29,

$$R_b = \frac{r_2}{2 - s_{nl}} \left(\frac{x_\varphi}{x_{22}}\right)^2 = \frac{R}{2 - s_{nl}} \qquad (10\text{-}31)$$

whence, by substitution in Eq. 10-30,

$$\text{Backward-field rotor } I^2R = I_{nl}^2 0.5R \qquad (10\text{-}32)$$

where R is the resistance of the parallel combination of rotor and magnetizing branches obtained from the blocked-rotor test and stator resistance, as in Eq. 10-28. The rotational loss P_R for normal running conditions (including both mechanical and core-loss components) can now be obtained by subtracting the stator and rotor copper losses from the measured no-load power input P_{nl}; thus

$$P_R = P_{nl} - I_{nl}^2 r_{1m} - I_{nl}^2 0.5R \qquad (10\text{-}33)$$

Note that, since the no-load slip is small, the backward-field rotor copper loss (Eq. 10-30) is almost twice the power P_{gb} absorbed from the stator by the backward field. That is, only a little more than half of the backward-field rotor copper loss is supplied to the rotor directly by the magnetic reaction of the backward field on the stator. The remainder of the rotor copper loss is supplied by the mechanical power absorbed in driving the rotor forward against the opposing torque created by the backward field. This portion then comes from the torque of the forward field and is absorbed from the stator by way of the forward field.

As with a polyphase motor, the self-reactance of the stator winding of a single-phase motor can be found from the no-load test, although the interpretation of the test results is somewhat more complicated. The situation with respect to the forward field is the same as in a polyphase motor; *i.e.*, the forward-field rotor current is sufficiently small so that its effect on the reactance is negligible. In other words, the reactance $0.5X_f$ representing the forward field in Fig. 10-15 very nearly equals the reactance of the magnetizing branch, $0.5x_\varphi$. The reactance $0.5X_b$ of the parallel combination representing the backward field in Fig. 10-15 is somewhat less than half the reactance of the parallel combination of $r_2 + jx_2$ and jx_φ at standstill, because the effect of the reflected rotor resistance on the reactance of the parallel combination is smaller when the rotor is running against the backward field than it is at standstill. Usually, however, negligible error results from assuming that

$$0.5X_b = 0.5(X_{bl} - x_{1m}) \tag{10-34}$$

where X_{bl} is the blocked reactance measured at the main-winding terminals. Consequently the no-load reactance X_{nl} at the main-winding terminals is

$$X_{nl} = x_{1m} + 0.5x_\varphi + 0.5(X_{bl} - x_{1m}) \tag{10-35}$$

$$= 0.5(x_{1m} + x_\varphi + X_{bl}) = 0.5(x_{11} + X_{bl}) \tag{10-36}$$

where

$$x_{11} \equiv x_{1m} + x_\varphi \tag{10-37}$$

is the self-reactance of the main winding. This important constant therefore can be determined from the test values of no-load and blocked reactance; thus

$$x_{11} = 2X_{nl} - X_{bl} \tag{10-38}$$

Approximate values of the equivalent-circuit constants can now be determined in a manner similar to that described for a polyphase motor in Art. 9-6. Thus, if the effect of the exciting current on the blocked reactance is neglected, and if the stator and rotor leakage reactances are assumed to be equal,

$$x_{1m} = x_2 = 0.5X_{bl} \tag{10-39}$$

The magnetizing reactance x_φ then is

$$x_\varphi = x_{11} - x_{1m} \tag{10-40}$$

where x_{11} can be determined from test data by Eq. 10-38. Just as with the polyphase motor (Eq. 9-40) the rotor resistance r_2 then is, very nearly,

$$r_2 = (R_{bl} - r_{1m}) \left(\frac{x_{22}}{x_\varphi}\right)^2 \tag{10-41}$$

where x_{22} is the self-reactance of the rotor and equals x_{11} according to the assumption that the stator and rotor leakage reactances are equal. All the equivalent-circuit constants are now known, and the motor performance under load can then be computed by the methods of Example 10-1.

Example 10-2. The following data were obtained in testing a ⅙-hp 110-volt 60-cps 6-pole split-phase induction motor (from the AIEE paper of footnote 8):

D-c resistance of main winding at 25°C = 2.48 ohms

Blocked-rotor test at 60 cps, with starting winding disconnected,

Applied voltage = 110 volts
Current = 11.65 amp
Power = 851 watts

D-c resistance of main winding measured immediately after the blocked-rotor test = 2.54 ohms

No-load test at 60 cps

Applied voltage = 110 volts
Current = 2.72 amp
Power = 63.8 watts

D-c resistance of main winding measured immediately after the no-load test = 2.65 ohms

The data given above are the values after the readings have been corrected for the current and power taken by the instruments.

Determine the no-load rotational loss and approximate values of the equivalent-circuit constants corrected to an assumed operating temperature of 65°C.

Solution. Correcting the main-winding resistance to 65°C in accordance with Eq. 7-13 gives

$$r_{1m} = \frac{234.5 + 65}{234.5 + 25} \times 2.48 = 2.86 \text{ ohms at } 65°\text{C}$$

From the blocked-rotor test

$$Z'_{bl} = \frac{V}{I} = \frac{110}{11.65} = 9.44 \text{ ohms}$$

$$R'_{bl} = \frac{P}{I^2} = \frac{851}{(11.65)^2} = 6.27 \text{ ohms}$$

$$X_{bl} = \sqrt{(9.44)^2 - (6.27)^2} = 7.06 \text{ ohms}$$

According to the assumption of Eq. 10-39,

$$x_{1m} = x_2 = \frac{7.06}{2} = 3.53 \text{ ohms}$$

Correcting the blocked resistance to 65°C in accordance with Eq. 10-27 gives

$$R_{bl} = 6.27\,\frac{2.86}{2.54} = 7.06 \text{ ohms at } 65°\text{C}$$

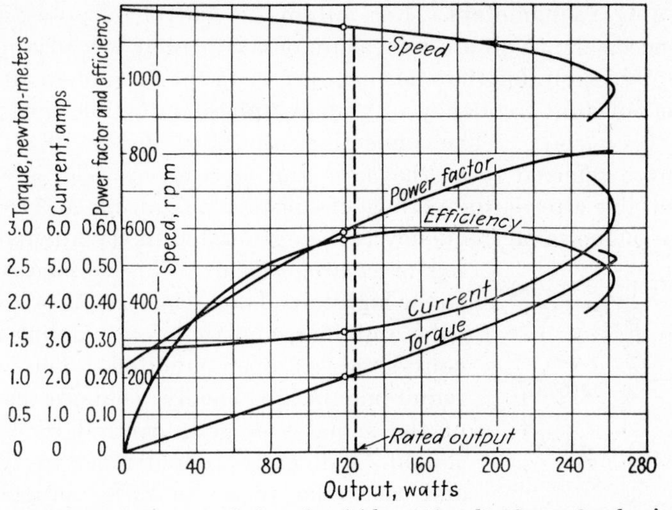

FIG. 10-16. Computed characteristics of a ⅙-hp 110-volt 60-cps 6-pole single-phase induction motor.

From the no-load test

$$Z_{nl} = \frac{110}{2.72} = 40.4 \text{ ohms}$$

$$R_{nl} = \frac{63.8}{(2.72)^2} = 8.62 \text{ ohms}$$

$$X_{nl} = \sqrt{(40.4)^2 - (8.62)^2} = 39.5 \text{ ohms}$$

From Eq. 10-38

$$x_{11} = 79.0 - 7.06 = 71.9 \text{ ohms}$$

and from Eq. 10-40

$$x_\varphi = 71.9 - 3.53 = 68.4 \text{ ohms}$$

From Eq. 10-41, at 65°C,

$$r_2 = (7.06 - 2.86)\left(\frac{71.9}{68.4}\right)^2 = 4.64 \text{ ohms}$$

Correcting the blocked resistance to the temperature of the no-load test gives

$$R_{bl} = 6.27\,\frac{2.65}{2.54} = 6.54$$

At this temperature, from Eq. 10-28,

$$R = 6.54 - 2.65 = 3.89$$

From Eq. 10-33, the no-load rotational loss is

$$P_R = 63.8 - (2.72)^2(2.65 + 1.95) = 29.8 \text{ watts}$$

From the equivalent-circuit constants and rotational loss found above, the complete performance characteristics of the motor can be computed as in Example 10-1 by assuming a series of values of slip. The results are shown in Fig. 10-16.

10-7. A-C Tachometers. For automatic-control purposes, it is frequently necessary to obtain a measure of the angular velocity of a shaft, and it is often desirable that this measure be in the form of an alternating voltage of constant frequency. A small 2-phase induction motor may be used for this purpose. The connections are shown in Fig. 10-17. Winding m, often referred to as the *fixed field* or *reference field*, is energized from a suitable alternating voltage of constant magnitude and frequency. A voltage of the same frequency is then generated in the auxiliary winding or *control field a*. This voltage is applied to the high-impedance grid circuits of a vacuum-tube amplifier, and therefore winding a can be considered as open-circuited. The electrical requirements are, ideally, that the magnitude of the signal voltage generated in winding a should be linearly proportional to the speed and that the phase of this voltage should be fixed with respect to the applied voltage V_m.

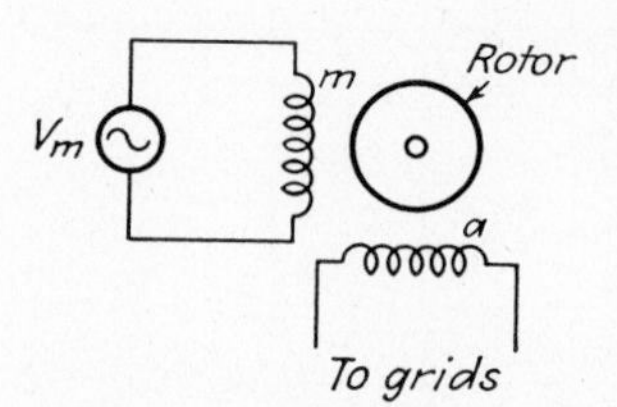

FIG. 10-17. Schematic diagram of a 2-phase tachometer.

The operation of the a-c tachometer may be visualized in terms of the double-revolving-field theory of Art. 10-6.[9] As viewed from the reference winding m, the tachometer is equivalent to a small single-phase induction motor, and the equivalent circuit of Fig. 10-14c therefore applies to conditions as viewed from this winding. The voltages across the impedances $0.5Z_f$ and $0.5Z_b$ in Fig. 10-14c are the voltages generated in winding m by the forward and backward flux waves, respectively. These flux waves also generate voltages in the auxiliary winding a. If the ratio of effective turns in winding a to effective turns in winding m is a, then the voltages generated in winding a are a times the corresponding voltages generated in winding m. By effective turns is meant the number of turns corrected for the effects of winding distribution in so far as fundamental space distributions of flux and mmf are concerned. If the direction of rotation is such that the forward field revolves past winding a a quarter cycle in time before it passes winding m, then the voltage E_{af} generated by the forward field in winding a leads the corresponding voltage E_{mf} generated in winding m by 90°, or vectorially

$$E_{af} = jaE_{mf} = jaI_m 0.5Z_f \tag{10-42}$$

where I_m is the vector current in winding m and is determined by the equivalent circuit of Fig. 10-14c. The backward field revolves in the opposite direction, and therefore the voltage E_{ab} generated by it in winding a lags the corresponding voltage E_{mb} generated in winding m by 90°,

[9] For a quantitative analysis, see R. H. Frazier, Analysis of the Drag-cup A-C Tachometer, *Trans. AIEE*, vol. 70, 1951.

or vectorially

$$E_{ab} = -jaE_{mb} = -jaI_m 0.5Z_b \tag{10-43}$$

The total voltage E_a generated in winding a is the sum of the components generated by each field, or

$$E_a = jaI_m 0.5(Z_f - Z_b) \tag{10-44}$$

At standstill, the forward and backward fields are equal, and no voltage is generated in winding a. When the rotor is revolving, however, the impedance of the forward field increases while that of the backward field decreases, the difference between them being a function of the speed. The voltage generated in winding a is therefore a function of speed. Reversal of the direction of rotation reverses the phase of the auxiliary-winding voltage.

The shapes of the curves of voltage magnitude and phase angle as functions of speed depend on the speed range and tachometer constants—primarily on the rotor self-reactance-to-resistance ratio Q_2. It can be shown that either a low-Q_2 rotor (x_{22}/r_2 less than about 0.1) or a high-Q_2 rotor (x_{22}/r_2 greater than about 10) will provide nearly a constant phase angle and nearly a linear relation between the auxiliary-winding voltage and speed. The sensitivity in volts per rpm is sacrificed if a low-Q_2 rotor is used, but the linear speed range is wide. On the other hand, if a high-Q_2 rotor is used, the speed range around zero speed is limited to a fairly small fraction of synchronous speed when the requirements for linearity of voltage and constancy of phase angle are strict. These restrictions on rotor Q_2 should not be taken too literally, however, since satisfactory performance may be obtained with intermediate values of Q_2 if the requirements for linearity of voltage and constancy of phase angle are not too severe.

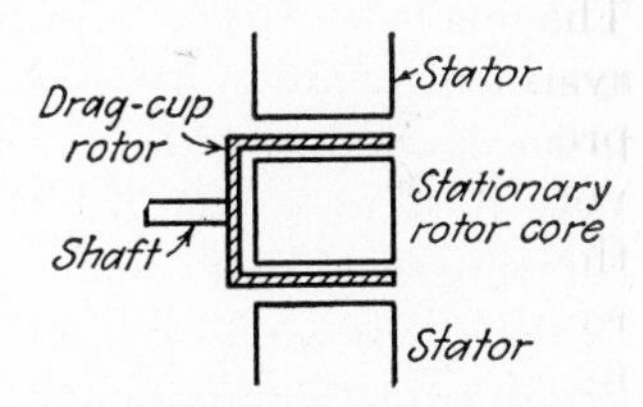

FIG. 10-18. Cross section of drag-cup rotor.

In common with other measuring instruments, the a-c tachometer should have as little effect as possible on the system into which it is inserted. In other words, its torque should be small compared with other torques acting in the system, and its inertia should be small when rapid speed variations are encountered, as in automatic-control systems. To minimize the inertia, a-c tachometers are often built with a thin metallic cup as the rotor, like a can with one end removed, as shown in the simplified sketch of Fig. 10-18. A stationary iron core, like a plug inside the cup, completes the magnetic circuit. This type of construction is known as a *drag-cup rotor*. Because of the relatively long air gap, this construction inherently gives a fairly low Q_2, which can be made still lower, if desired, by making the drag cup of high-resistivity material.

Alternating-current tachometers require precise workmanship and care in design and assembly, in order to maintain concentricity and to eliminate direct coupling through the leakage fluxes between the excited winding and the output winding. Such coupling would result in signal voltage at zero speed. Sometimes soft-iron shields are provided to minimize pick-up from stray fields. Frequently a-c tachometers are used in 400-cps systems.

10-8. Unbalanced Operation of Symmetrical Two-phase Machines—the Symmetrical-component Concept. In Art. 10-6*a* we have seen that the internal reactions in a single-phase induction machine with a uniform air gap and a symmetrical polyphase or cage rotor can be expressed in rather simple fashion in terms of the equivalent circuits of Fig. 10–14 when the stator-mmf wave is resolved into forward and backward traveling-wave components. One might expect, therefore, that the double-revolving-field concept should yield useful results when applied to a much wider variety of problems, and indeed this "hunch" proves to be correct. As a matter of fact, the thought process with respect to the double-revolving-field theory of induction machines is what led C. L. Fortescue to invent the method of symmetrical components for analysis of unbalanced polyphase systems.[10] Fortescue showed that an unbalanced polyphase system can be resolved into a number of component symmetrical systems. The internal behavior of rotating machines for each of these component systems can readily be expressed in terms of the simple fields which they produce. Out of this invention has grown an extensive theory with a voluminous literature.[11] It is probably no exaggeration to say, however, that if it were not for the ease with which many problems involving rotating machines can be treated in terms of constant-amplitude revolving fields, there would have been no impelling incentive for the invention of symmetrical components, since unbalanced static circuits can be treated about as easily by straightforward network theory.

The purpose of this article is to develop the symmetrical-component theory of 2-phase induction motors from the double-revolving-field concept. In Arts. 10-9 and 10-10 it will be shown that this theory can be extended to apply to a variety of problems involving induction motors having two stator windings in space quadrature.

[10] C. L. Fortescue, Method of Symmetrical Co-ordinates Applied to the Solution of Polyphase Networks, *Trans. AIEE*, vol. 37, Part 2, pp. 1027–1115, 1918.

[11] See, for example, Edith Clarke, "Circuit Analysis of A-C Power Systems," vol. I, Symmetrical and Related Components, John Wiley & Sons, Inc., New York, 1943; W. V. Lyon, "Applications of the Method of Symmetrical Components," McGraw-Hill Book Company, Inc., New York, 1933.

First consider in review what happens when balanced 2-phase voltages are applied to the stator terminals of a 2-phase machine having a uniform air gap, a symmetrical polyphase or cage rotor, and two identical stator windings a and m in space quadrature. The stator currents are equal in magnitude and in time quadrature. When the current in winding a has its instantaneous maximum, the current in winding m is zero, and the stator-mmf wave is centered on the axis of winding a. Similarly, the stator-mmf wave is centered on the axis of winding m at the instant when the current in winding m has its instantaneous maximum. The stator-mmf wave therefore travels 90 electrical degrees in space in an interval of

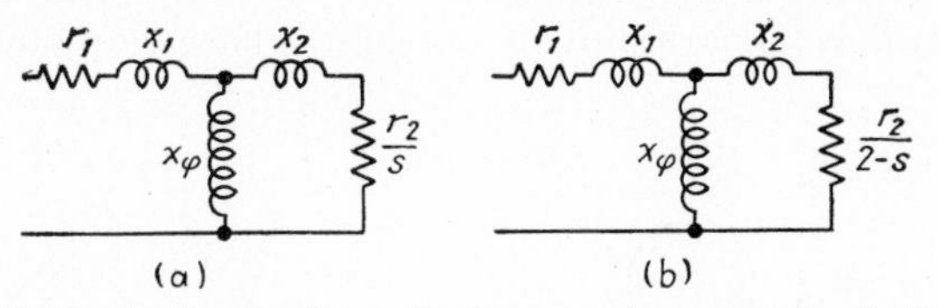

FIG. 10-19. Equivalent circuits for a 2-phase motor under unbalanced conditions. (*a*) Forward field. (*b*) Backward field.

90° in time, the direction of its travel depending on the phase sequence of the currents. A more complete analysis in the manner of Art. 3-6 or Fig. 10-2 proves that the traveling wave has constant amplitude and constant angular velocity. This fact is, of course, the basis of the whole theory of balanced operation of induction machines.

The behavior of the motor for balanced 2-phase applied voltages of either phase sequence can readily be determined. Thus if the rotor is turning at a per-unit speed n in the direction from winding a toward winding m, the terminal impedance per phase is given by the equivalent circuit of Fig. 10-19a when the applied voltage v_a leads the applied voltage v_m by 90°. Throughout the rest of this treatment, this phase sequence will be called *positive sequence* and will be designated by subscript f, since positive-sequence currents result in a forward field. With the rotor still forced to run at the same speed and in the same direction, the terminal impedance per phase is given by the equivalent circuit of Fig. 10-19b when v_a lags v_m by 90°. This phase sequence will be called *negative sequence* and will be designated by subscript b, since negative-sequence currents produce a backward field.

Suppose now that *two* balanced 2-phase voltage sources *of opposite phase sequence* are connected in series and applied simultaneously to the motor, as indicated in Fig. 10-20a, where vector voltages V_{mf} and jV_{mf} applied, respectively, to windings m and a form a balanced system of positive sequence, and vector voltages V_{mb} and $-jV_{mb}$ form another balanced system but of negative sequence. The resultant voltage V_m applied to winding m is, vectorially,

$$V_m = V_{mf} + V_{mb} \tag{10-45}$$

and that applied to winding a is

$$V_a = jV_{mf} - jV_{mb} \tag{10-46}$$

If, for example, the forward, or positive-sequence, system is given by the vectors V_{mf} and jV_{mf} in Fig. 10-20*b* and the backward, or negative-sequence, system is given by the vectors V_{mb} and $-jV_{mb}$, then the resultant voltages are given by the vectors V_m and V_a. An unbalanced 2-phase system of applied voltages V_m and V_a has thus been synthesized by combining two symmetrical systems of opposite phase sequence.

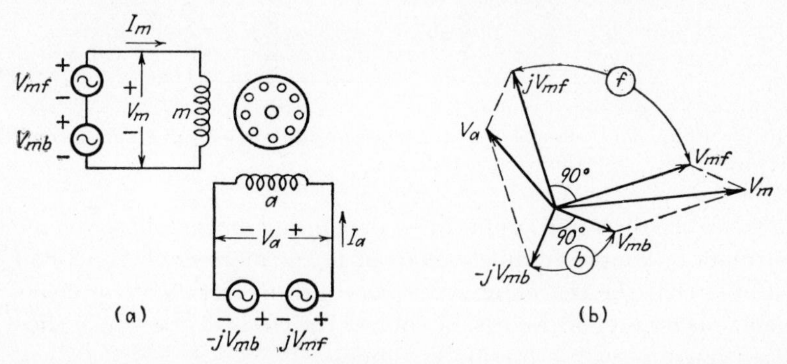

FIG. 10-20. Synthesis of an unbalanced 2-phase system from the sum of two balanced systems of opposite phase sequence.

The symmetrical component systems are, however, much easier to work with than is their unbalanced resultant system. Thus it is easy to compute the component currents produced by each symmetrical component system of applied voltages, because the induction motor operates as a balanced 2-phase motor for each component system. By superposition, the actual current in a winding then is the sum of its components. Thus if I_{mf} and I_{mb} are, respectively, the positive- and negative-sequence component vector currents in winding m, then the corresponding positive- and negative-sequence component vector currents in winding a are, respectively, jI_{mf} and $-jI_{mb}$ and the actual winding currents I_m and I_a are, vectorially,

$$I_m = I_{mf} + I_{mb} \tag{10-47}$$

$$I_a = jI_{mf} - jI_{mb} \tag{10-48}$$

The inverse operation of finding the symmetrical components of specified voltages or currents must often be performed. Solution of Eqs. 10-45 and 10-46 for the vector components V_{mf} and V_{mb} in terms of known vector voltages V_m and V_a gives

$$V_{mf} = \tfrac{1}{2}(V_m - jV_a) \quad (10\text{-}49)$$
$$V_{mb} = \tfrac{1}{2}(V_m + jV_a) \quad (10\text{-}50)$$

These operations are illustrated in the vector diagram of Fig. 10-21. Obviously, similar relations give the vector symmetrical components I_{mf} and I_{mb} of the current in winding m in terms of specified vector currents I_m and I_a in the two phases; thus

$$I_{mf} = \tfrac{1}{2}(I_m - jI_a) \quad (10\text{-}51)$$
$$I_{mb} = \tfrac{1}{2}(I_m + jI_a) \quad (10\text{-}52)$$

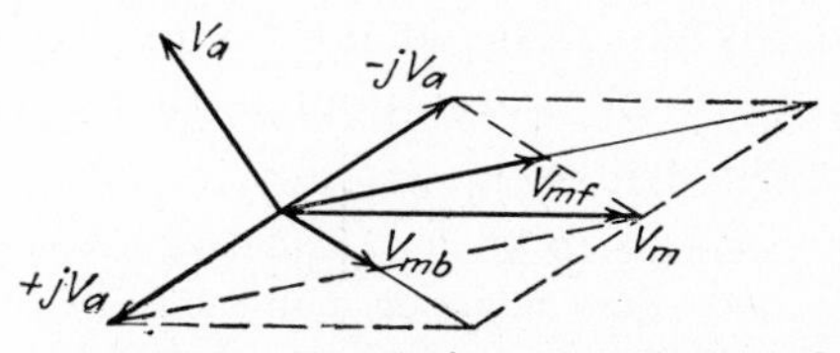

FIG. 10-21. Resolution of unbalanced 2-phase voltages into symmetrical components.

Resolution of the stator-mmf wave into its forward and backward components, as in Fig. 10-2c, may help to complete a physical picture of what is happening in the machine when one applies the symmetrical-component transformations of Eqs. 10-51 and 10-52. In Fig. 10-22a, I_m and I_a are rotating time vectors whose projections on the real axis are proportional to the instantaneous currents in the windings. Figure 10-22b is a space vector diagram in which the dash-dot lines m and a represent the winding axes and the vectors F_m and F_a represent the instantaneous values of the pulsating mmf waves produced by each winding. For simplicity, the

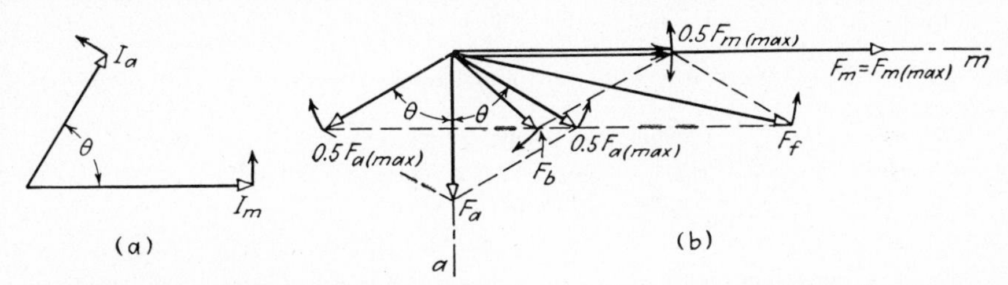

FIG. 10-22. (a) Unbalanced 2-phase currents, and (b) vector resolution of mmf waves into forward and backward components.

vectors are shown in their positions at the moment when i_m, and therefore F_m, has its instantaneous maximum $F_{m(\max)}$. Consequently when F_m is resolved into its forward and backward half-amplitude revolving components (in the manner of Fig. 10-2c and Eq. 10-4), the components at this instant are in line with the axis m, as shown by the two oppositely revolving components $0.5F_{m(\max)}$. At this same instant, however, i_a has passed beyond its maximum value by the time angle θ (Fig. 10-22a), and therefore the forward- and backward-revolving components $0.5F_{a(\max)}$ are in the two positions shown in Fig. 10-22b. The space vectors representing the resultant forward and backward fields F_f and F_b are the vector sums of the components, as in Fig. 10-22b. Because of the space angle between the two windings, the angle between the two revolving-field components $0.5F_{m(\max)}$ and $0.5F_{a(\max)}$ for the forward field is 90° less than the time-phase angle θ between the currents, and for the backward field is 90° greater. Consequently the vector summations by which the mmfs F_f and F_b are obtained in Fig. 10-22b are exactly similar to those of Eqs. 10-51 and 10-52 for obtaining the symmetrical-component currents. Thus when the currents are resolved into symmetrical components, as in Eqs. 10-51 and 10-52, the stator mmf is thereby resolved into forward and backward components.

Example 10-3. The equivalent-circuit constants of a 5-hp 220-volt 60-cps 2-phase squirrel-cage induction motor are given below, in ohms per phase:

$$r_1 = 0.534 \qquad x_1 = 2.45 \qquad x_\varphi = 70.1$$
$$r_2 = 0.956 \qquad x_2 = 2.96$$

This motor is operated from an unbalanced 2-phase source whose phase voltages are, respectively, 230 volts and 210 volts, the smaller voltage leading the larger by 80°. For a slip of 0.05, find:

a. The positive- and negative-sequence components of the applied voltages
b. The positive- and negative-sequence components of the stator phase currents
c. The effective values of the phase currents
d. The internal mechanical power

Solution. *a.* Let V_m and V_a denote the voltages applied to the two phases, respectively. Then

$$V_m = 230\underline{/0^\circ} = 230 + j0 \text{ volts}$$
$$V_a = 210\underline{/80^\circ} = 36.4 + j207 \text{ volts}$$

From Eqs. 10-49 and 10-50, the forward and backward components of voltages are, respectively,

$$V_{mf} = \tfrac{1}{2}(230 + j0 + 207 - j36.4)$$
$$= 218.5 - j18.2 = 219.5\underline{/-4.8^\circ} \text{ vector volts}$$
$$V_{mb} = \tfrac{1}{2}(230 + j0 - 207 + j36.4)$$
$$= 11.5 + j18.2 = 21.5\underline{/57.7^\circ} \text{ vector volts}$$

b. From Eqs. 10-18 and 10-19, the forward-field impedance is, for a slip of 0.05,

$$Z_f = 16.46 + j7.15 \text{ ohms}$$
$$r_1 + jx_1 = \underline{0.53 + j2.45} \text{ ohms}$$
$$16.99 + j9.60 = 19.50\underline{/29.4^\circ} \text{ ohms}$$

Hence the forward component of stator current is

$$I_{mf} = \frac{219.5\underline{/-4.8^\circ}}{19.50\underline{/29.4^\circ}} = 11.26\underline{/-34.2^\circ} \text{ amp}$$

For the same slip, from Eqs. 10-22 and 10-23 the backward-field impedance is

$$Z_b = 0.451 + j2.84 \text{ ohms}$$
$$r_1 + x_1 = \underline{0.534 + j2.45} \text{ ohms}$$
$$0.985 + j5.29 = 5.38\underline{/79.5^\circ} \text{ ohms}$$

Hence the backward component of stator current is

$$I_{mb} = \frac{21.5/\underline{57.7°}}{5.38/\underline{79.5°}} = 4.00/\underline{-21.8°} \text{ amp}$$

c. By Eqs. 10-47 and 10-48, the currents in the two phases are, respectively,

$$I_m = 13.06 - j7.79 = 15.2/\underline{-31°} \text{ amp}$$
$$I_a = 4.81 + j5.64 = 7.40/\underline{49.2°} \text{ amp}$$

Note that the currents are much more unbalanced than the applied voltages. Even though the motor is not overloaded in so far as shaft load is concerned, the losses are appreciably increased by the current unbalance, and the stator winding with the greatest current may overheat.

d. The power delivered to the forward field by the two stator phases is

$$P_{gf} = 2I_{mf}^2R_f = 2 \times 126.8 \times 16.46 = 4{,}175 \text{ watts}$$

and the power delivered to the backward field is

$$P_{gb} = 2I_{mb}^2R_b = 2 \times 16.0 \times 0.451 = 15 \text{ watts}$$

Thus, according to Eq. 10-17, the internal mechanical power developed is

$$P = 0.95(4{,}175 - 15) = 3{,}950 \text{ watts}$$

If the core losses, friction and windage, and stray load losses are known, the shaft output can be found by subtracting them from the internal power. The friction and windage losses depend solely on the speed and are the same as they would be for balanced operation at the same speed. The core and stray load losses, however, are somewhat greater than they would be for balanced operation with the same positive-sequence voltage and current. The increase is caused principally by the $(2 - s)$-frequency core and stray losses in the rotor caused by the backward field.

10-9. Two-phase Servomotors—Steady-state Characteristics. An important and interesting field of application of electric motors is in automatic-control systems, where the speed or angular position of a shaft must be controlled in some desired fashion. In the present discussion, attention will be focused on small-power positional systems, where the maximum power outputs are in the range from a fraction of a watt up to a few hundred watts. Two-phase induction motors are often used in such systems in a manner to be described later in this article. When appropriate assumptions are made, the symmetrical-component methods of Art. 10-8 provide a simple and effective means for analyzing their steady-state characteristics, as we shall soon see.

To acquire perspective, let us first consider briefly the general nature of the problems encountered in small-power positional control systems, particularly the aspects concerning the motor. Many applications of such systems arise in instrumentation and industrial process control. For example, suppose a continuous record is needed of what is going on in some process—perhaps a record of the level of liquid in a tank. Such a record may be obtained by means of a recording instrument consisting of a pen which traces a graph of the variable on a uniformly moving chart. The variable can be measured by some means which produces an electrical signal proportional to it. One of many possibilities is a resistance, inductance, or capacitance which is affected by the variable and which forms one arm of a bridge circuit. The position of the recording pen can be varied by driving it through reduction gearing from a small electric motor which also is arranged mechanically to vary another arm of the bridge circuit in accordance with the position of the pen, as shown schematically in Fig. 10-23. Because its function is to detect the error

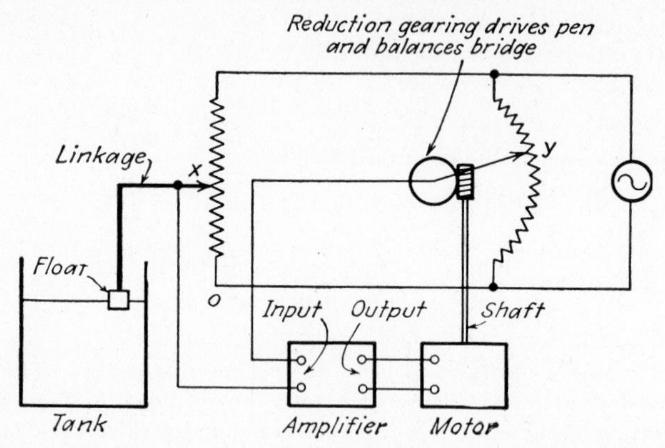

FIG. 10-23. Schematic diagram of a servomechanism for recording level of liquid in a tank.

between the position x set by the variable and the position y corresponding to the recording pen, the bridge circuit is known as an *error detector*. Thus, when the bridge is out of balance, a signal proportional to the error is applied to the input of an amplifier whose output drives the motor in such a direction as to bring the bridge into balance. Such a system is one example of a very ramified class of automatic-control systems known as *servomechanisms* (often abbreviated to *servos*), about which more will be said in Arts. 13-5 and 13-6.

The question may be raised as to why this complex system is needed. Why, for example, cannot the voltage V_{ox} in Fig. 10-23 be applied to a voltmeter movement deflecting the pen? If necessary, an amplifier can be interposed between V_{ox} and the voltmeter. Such an arrangement, however, would require that the characteristics of all components between the measuring circuit and the recording pen should remain absolutely constant. The effects of disturbances such as temperature changes, varying friction, changing tube characteristics, and fluctuating supply voltage might cause significant errors. There is no certainty that the position of the recording pen is really following the input signal.

In the servo system, however, so long as the pen fails to be in the correct position the bridge is unbalanced and the motor runs so as to drive the bridge into balance, even though the characteristics of the elements between the bridge and the pen may change. Inaccuracies caused by varying friction can be reduced by designing the servo system so that its output torque is large compared with friction torques present in the system. The accuracy therefore is very little affected by extraneous influences. One of the distinguishing features of a servomechanism is this feedback link by which the output is compared with the input and restoring forces are brought into play by the error between output and input. These general features may be recognized as having much in common with feedback amplifiers.

The requirements of a motor for positional-servo service are evidently rather different from those of a motor to drive a load at a more or less steady speed. The servo motor must obviously run in either direction, and usually its speed should be subject to continuous control. It seldom runs at a steady speed—in fact, it rarely reaches full speed. Most of the time it is running near zero speed, first forward for a few revolutions, and then perhaps backward. This type of duty cycle increases the difficulties of cooling the motor, since the fan effect of the rotor cannot be counted on to aid the circulation of cooling air. The motor must be capable of rapid acceleration and reversal, since sluggish response leads to inaccuracy in following the input signals and to other dynamic difficulties. Its stalled torque therefore should be high and its moment of inertia low. To reduce steady-state errors, the motor torque should be high compared with the friction torques of the system. Most of the motor power output is absorbed in accelerating its own inertia and that of its load. For reasons concerned with stability, the torque-speed characteristic should have a negative slope.

Although the squirrel-cage induction motor prefers to run at a small slip and therefore is most readily adaptable to constant-speed drives, nevertheless this type of motor has other features which are sufficiently attractive so that it is used extensively in low-power servo systems. The ruggedness and simplicity of the cage rotor is a great advantage for both economic and technical reasons. There are no brushes riding on sliding contacts, and requiring at least occasional inspection and maintenance in other types of motors. Because the rotor windings do not require insulation, the rotor temperature is limited only by mechanical considerations and indirectly by its effect on the stator-winding temperature. If suitable means are provided for cooling the stator windings, higher rotor losses can be tolerated than in other types of motors. Because there is relatively little inactive material, the inertia of a squirrel-cage motor can be made less than that of a correspondingly rated d-c motor. The drag-cup type of rotor (Fig. 10-18) can be used when the maximum power output is below a few watts. This type of rotor has a very low inertia.

The essentials of a servo system using a 2-phase induction motor are shown in Fig. 10-24, which is merely an adaptation of Fig. 10-23 for use with a 2-phase motor. The fixed, or reference, phase m of the motor is supplied from a constant-voltage constant-frequency source. The error detector, in this case a bridge circuit like that in Fig. 10-23, is supplied from the same source. As in Fig. 10-23, the position of the sliding contact x is set by the variable which is to be measured, and the contact y is driven by the motor in a direction to balance the bridge. The voltage V_{xy}, proportional to the error, is applied to the input of an amplifier whose output energizes the control phase a of the motor. The voltages

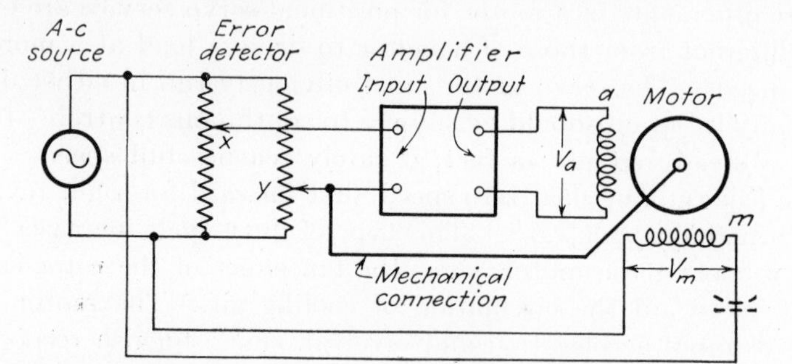

FIG. 10-24. Schematic diagram of a servomechanism using a 2-phase servomotor.

applied to the motor are made to be approximately in time quadrature, either by introducing a 90° phase shift in the amplifier or by connecting a suitable capacitor in series with the reference phase m, as shown in Fig. 10-24. The motor is thus supplied with unbalanced 2-phase voltages, the control-phase voltage V_a being proportional to the error. When the bridge is out of balance, the motor develops torque in a direction to restore balance, the torque being a function of the speed and the control-phase voltage V_a. A change in direction of the error results in a 180° phase shift of the amplifier voltage, and consequently a reversal in phase sequence of the voltages applied to the motor. The direction of the torque developed by the motor is thereby reversed. The simplicity of the system is a highly desirable feature.

The requirements of a positional servo system very nearly specify the shape of the torque-speed characteristic of a 2-phase induction motor suitable for such use. As with any motor for such service, the torque should be high at speeds near zero, and the slope of the torque-speed characteristic should be negative in the normal operating range around zero speed, as pointed out earlier in this article. Both of these requirements can be met by use of a high-resistance rotor designed so that maximum torque is developed at a reverse speed of approximately one-half of synchronous speed, as shown by the torque-speed characteristic labeled $V_a = 1.0$ in Fig. 10-25. Normal operation near zero speed is then in the stable region to the right of the maximum-torque points. A further requirement is that the motor must not tend to run as a single-phase motor when the error signal is zero. It can be shown that this requirement also is met by use of a high-resistance rotor.

Although the complete analysis of a servo system evidently is a dynamic problem, nevertheless some idea as to the performance of a motor in servo service can be formed from a study of its steady-state

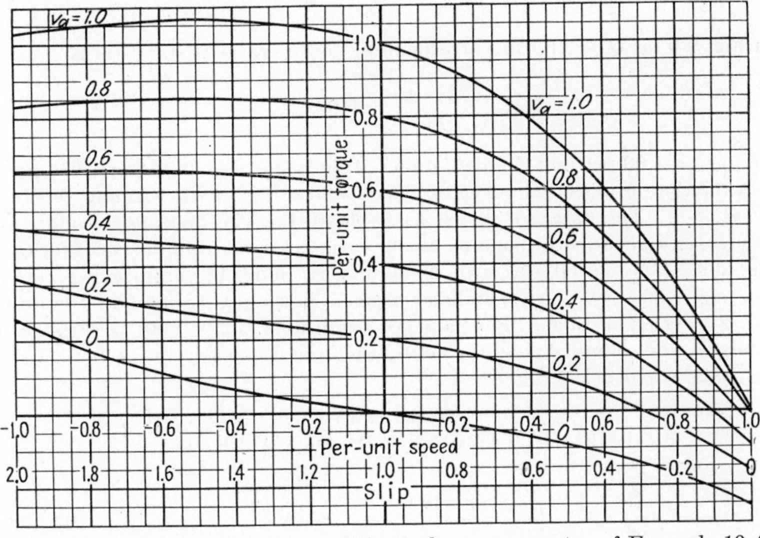

FIG. 10-25. Torque-speed curves of the 2-phase servomotor of Example 10-4.

characteristics. The analysis is greatly simplified if the currents and voltages are considered to be sinusoidal, if the effects of the source impedances are neglected, and if the motor is assumed to have identical 2-phase stator windings. The motor then is simply a symmetrical 2-phase motor operating from an unbalanced 2-phase source, and its characteristics can be computed by the methods of Art. 10-8. The more elaborate theory of Art. 10-10 is required to account for the effects of unbalanced impedances.

Example 10-4. A symmetrical 2-phase induction motor develops a maximum internal torque at a reverse speed of 0.50 per unit when balanced 2-phase voltages are applied to its stator terminals. The Q of its Thévenin equivalent circuit (see Art. 9-4) is 3.0. This motor is to be used as a 2-phase servomotor with constant voltage of 1.00 per unit applied to its reference phase and variable voltage applied to its control phase, these voltages being considered to be in time quadrature.

Plot a family of internal-torque–speed characteristics for per-unit values of the control-phase voltage of 1.00, 0.80, 0.60, 0.40, 0.20, and 0, covering a speed range from -1 to $+1$ per unit. Express the torque in per unit, considering the unit of torque to be the internal torque developed at standstill when balanced 2-phase voltages of 1.00 per unit are applied to the two stator phases.

Solution. The speed for maximum torque, the Q, and the stalled torque for balanced 2-phase voltages fix the curve for $V_a = 1.00$. This curve can readily be determined from the normalized torque-slip curves of Fig. 9-9. The rest of the family then can be computed from this curve by resolving the applied voltages into 2-phase symmetrical components.

Since the speed for maximum torque is given as -0.50 per unit, the slip for maximum torque $s_{\max T} = 1.50$. At standstill, then,

$$\frac{s}{s_{\max T}} = \frac{1.00}{1.50} = 0.667$$

From Fig. 9-9 for $Q = 3.0$, the corresponding torque ratio at standstill is

$$\frac{T_{\text{stalled}}}{T_{\max}} = 0.938$$

But $T_{\text{stalled}} \equiv 1.00$ per unit, by definition. Hence $T_{\max}$ is 1/0.938, or 1.066 per unit.

Data for the torque-speed curve for $V_a = 1.00$ in Fig. 10-25 can now be obtained from Fig. 9-9. The data are shown in Table 10-1. The first and second columns are slip ratios, and the corresponding torque ratios are read from the curve for $Q = 3.0$ in Fig. 9-9. The actual slip s in column 3 is found by multiplying column 1 by $s_{\max T}. = 1.50$. The corresponding torque T_f' in column 4 is found by multiplying column 2 by $T_{\max} = 1.066$. For balanced conditions ($V_a = 1.00$) there is no backward torque, and column 4 gives the net torque from which the curve labeled $V_a = 1.0$ in Fig. 10-25 is plotted.

TABLE 10-1
COMPUTATIONS FOR EXAMPLE 10-4

$\frac{s}{s_{\max T}}$	$\frac{T}{T_{\max}}$	s	T_f'	$2 - s$	T_b'
0	0	0	0	2.0	1.03
0.133	0.32	0.2	0.34	1.8	1.055
0.267	0.565	0.4	0.60	1.6	1.06
0.40	0.745	0.6	0.795	1.4	1.06
0.533	0.86	0.8	0.92	1.2	1.045
0.667	0.94	1.0	1.00	1.0	1.00
0.80	0.98	1.2	1.045	0.8	0.92
0.933	0.995	1.4	1.06	0.6	0.795
1.067	0.995	1.6	1.06	0.4	0.60
1.20	0.99	1.8	1.055	0.2	0.34
1.33	0.965	2.0	1.03	0	0

When the voltages are unbalanced, they can be resolved into symmetrical components. Let the per-unit magnitude of the control-phase voltage be V_a, and assume that this voltage leads the reference voltage V_m by 90°. The vector expression for the control-phase voltage then is jV_a, and Eqs. 10-49 and 10-50 reduce to

$$V_{mf} = \tfrac{1}{2}[1 - j(jV_a)] = \tfrac{1}{2}(1 + V_a) \tag{10-53}$$
$$V_{mb} = \tfrac{1}{2}[1 + j(jV_a)] = \tfrac{1}{2}(1 - V_a) \tag{10-54}$$

Both forward and backward fields are now present. The slip for the backward field is $2 - s$, as in column 5 of Table 10-1. Column 6 gives the values of backward torque T_b' that would be developed with negative-sequence voltages of 1.00 per unit and is obtained from column 4. (For example, the value of T_b' at a backward-field slip $2 - s = 1.8$ is the same as the value of T_f' at a forward-field slip $s = 1.8$.)

Now recall that the internal torque developed by a polyphase induction motor varies as the square of the voltage. The forward and backward torques therefore are

$$T_f = V_{mf}^2 T_f' \tag{10-55}$$
$$T_b = V_{mb}^2 T_b' \tag{10-56}$$

where V_{mf}, V_{mb} are the per-unit values of the positive- and negative-sequence components of the unbalanced applied voltages (Eqs. 10-53 and 10-54) and T_f', T_b' are the forward and backward torque corresponding to positive- and negative-sequence applied voltages, respectively, of 1.00 per unit, as given in columns 4 and 6. The net internal torque T is

$$T = T_f - T_b \tag{10-57}$$

The torque developed at any chosen values of V_a and slip can now be determined. For example, from Eqs. 10-53, 10-54, 10-55, and 10-56,
At $V_a = 0.60$:

$$V_{mf} = 0.80 \qquad T_f = 0.64T_f'$$
$$V_{mb} = 0.20 \qquad T_b = 0.04T_b'$$

Values of T_f' and T_b' can be read from Table 10-1. For example,
At $s = 0.20$:

$$T_f' = 0.34 \qquad T_f = (0.64)(0.34) = 0.218$$
$$T_b' = 1.055 \qquad T_b = (0.04)(1.055) = 0.042$$
$$T = T_f - T_b = 0.176$$

Data for the family of curves in Fig. 10-25 can be computed by repeating these simple calculations for other assumed values of V_a and slip. The calculations can be arranged systematically in tabular form.

The nondimensional curves of Fig. 10-25 are approximately applicable to all 2-phase servomotors since nearly all of them are designed to develop maximum torque at about the same per-unit speed and to have about the same Q. The slip $s_{\max T}$ at maximum torque and the Q fix the shape of the characteristics, so long as the rotor resistance is constant and the effects of saturation are negligible. Fairly wide variations in the parameters $s_{\max T}$ and Q have relatively little effect on the characteristics over the normal operating range.

The principal disadvantage of the 2-phase servomotor is the inherent inefficiency of a squirrel-cage induction motor running at a large slip. As pointed out in Art. 9-2, the efficiency of a polyphase induction motor with short-circuited rotor windings is like that of a slipping mechanical clutch; the slip is a direct measure of the rotor losses. The inherent limit on efficiency will be even lower in a speed-control scheme which involves unbalancing the applied voltages, because of the decrease in output and increase in rotor losses caused by the backward field. Speed-regulating schemes involving slip control of a squirrel-cage motor are not practicable for large motors, because the difficulties associated with cooling and with power supply increase with size, as does the economic importance of the losses.

10-10. Revolving-field Theory of Unsymmetrical Two-phase Induction Machines. We have seen that the double-revolving-field concept leads to a useful method of analyzing 2-phase machines with identical quadrature stator windings. The question naturally arises: Can the same thought processes be applied to machines having unsymmetrical stator circuits? Specifically, the problem we should like to solve is indicated in Fig. 10-26, which shows a 2-phase induction motor connected to two voltage sources V_m and V_a through unbalanced circuits of impedance Z_{em} and Z_{ea}. The motor has a uniform air gap and a symmetrical polyphase or cage rotor. The stator windings are in electrical space quadrature but may have unequal turns and unequal leakage impedances.[12] If an attack along these lines should be successful, the results would be applicable to a wide variety of induction-machine types. For example, split-phase and capacitor motors would be the special case in which V_m equals V_a. Single-phase operation would be the special case in which I_a is zero. In fact, the preceding investigations of Arts. 10-6 and 10-8 may be considered simply as exploratory ones, finally leading up to the generalized point of view to be investigated next.

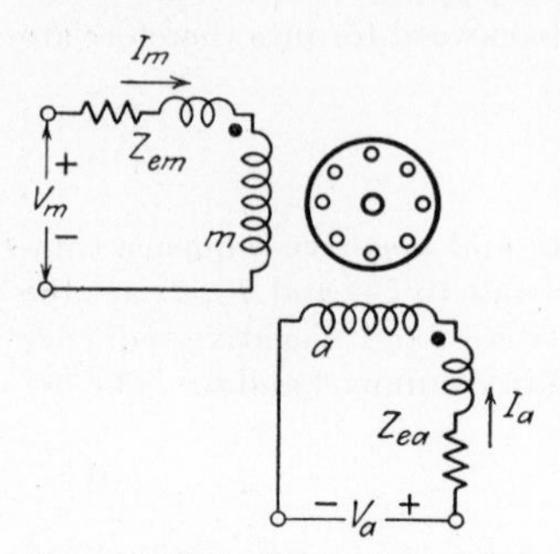

FIG. 10-26. Two-phase induction motor with unbalanced stator circuits.

a. Generalized Theory. The stator-circuit vector voltage equations for the generalized 2-phase motor of Fig. 10-26 can immediately be written as

$$V_m = I_m Z_{1m} + E_m \tag{10-58}$$
$$V_a = I_a Z_{1a} + E_a \tag{10-59}$$

where V_m, V_a are the vector source voltages; I_m, I_a are the vector phase currents; Z_{1m}, Z_{1a} are each the vector sum of the external-circuit impedance and the leakage impedance of a stator phase; and E_m, E_a are the counter emfs generated in the stator windings by the resultant air-gap

[12] For a general treatment of machines in which the windings need not be in quadrature, see W. V. Lyon and Charles Kingsley, Jr., Analysis of Unsymmetrical Machines, *Trans. AIEE*, vol. 55, No. 5, pp. 471–476, May, 1936. For an analysis of the quadrature case, see F. W. Suhr, Symmetrical Components as Applied to the Single-phase Induction Motor, *Trans. AIEE*, vol. 64, No. 9, pp. 651–656, September, 1945.

flux. In order to proceed further, the internal reactions of the air-gap flux waves must now be studied. The previous experience of Art. 10-8 leads one to suspect that a way to proceed is to resolve the stator currents into two sets of components that would produce, respectively, forward and backward mmf waves. The counter emfs can then be expressed in terms of the internal impedances to the component revolving fields. Only fundamental space distributions of flux and mmf will be considered.

Let N_m and N_a be the effective turns in windings m and a, respectively. By effective turns is meant the number of turns corrected for the effects of winding distribution in so far as fundamental space distribution of mmf is concerned. Exactly as in a balanced 2-phase motor, a constant-amplitude revolving field would result if the currents in the two windings produced equal-amplitude mmfs in time quadrature. The direction of rotation of the field would depend on the phase sequence of the currents. A constant-amplitude forward field would result if a set of vector currents I_{mf} and I_{af} in the windings m and a, respectively, satisfied the vector relationship

$$N_a I_{af} = jN_m I_{mf} \qquad (10\text{-}60)$$

or

$$I_{af} = j\frac{I_{mf}}{a} \qquad (10\text{-}61)$$

where a is the effective turns ratio N_a/N_m. Similarly, a constant-amplitude backward field would result if another set of vector currents I_{mb} and I_{ab} satisfied the vector relationship

$$I_{ab} = -j\frac{I_{mb}}{a} \qquad (10\text{-}62)$$

If both sets of currents existed simultaneously, the actual winding currents I_m and I_a would be, vectorially,

$$I_m = I_{mf} + I_{mb} \qquad (10\text{-}63)$$

$$I_a = I_{af} + I_{ab} = j\frac{I_{mf}}{a} - j\frac{I_{mb}}{a} \qquad (10\text{-}64)$$

and both a forward and a backward field would be present. Solution of these equations for the component currents I_{mf} and I_{mb} in terms of the actual winding currents I_m and I_a gives

$$I_{mf} = \tfrac{1}{2}(I_m - jaI_a) \qquad (10\text{-}65)$$

$$I_{mb} = \tfrac{1}{2}(I_m + jaI_a) \qquad (10\text{-}66)$$

Compare with Eqs. 10-51 and 10-52. Note that aI_a is simply the current in winding a referred to winding m, as in static-transformer theory.

From the viewpoint of winding m, the internal reactions of the forward and backward fields are just like those in a balanced 2-phase motor.

Thus, if the rotor and magnetizing impedances are referred to winding m, the forward- and backward-field impedances Z_f and Z_b as viewed from winding m are given by the equivalent circuits in Fig. 10-27, and the component counter emfs E_{mf} and E_{mb} generated in winding m by the forward and backward fields, respectively, equal the voltages across these impedances. The total counter emf E_m generated in winding m is, vectorially,

$$E_m = E_{mf} + E_{mb} = I_{mf}Z_f + I_{mb}Z_b \tag{10-67}$$

Because of the stator turns ratio, the component counter emfs generated in winding a will be a times the corresponding component voltages generated in winding m. Because of the directions in which the fields rotate,

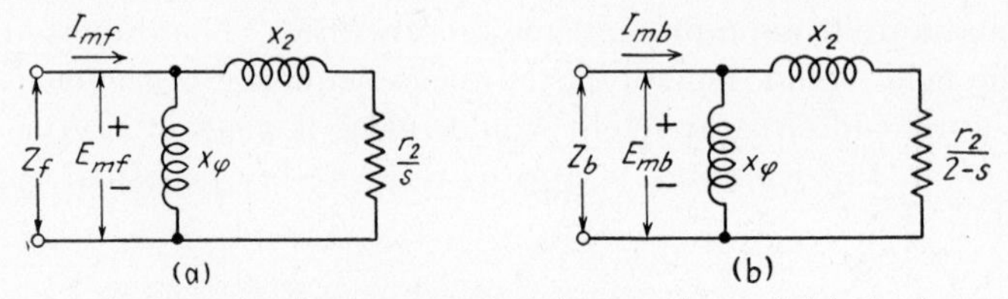

FIG. 10-27. Equivalent circuits representing the reactions of (a) the forward and (b) the backward fields as viewed from the main winding.

the forward-field component generated in winding a leads and the backward-field component lags the corresponding component generated in winding m. The total counter emf E_a generated in winding a by both fields therefore is, vectorially,

$$E_a = jaE_{mf} - jaE_{mb} = jaI_{mf}Z_f - jaI_{mb}Z_b \tag{10-68}$$

Note that aE_{mf} and aE_{mb} are merely the voltages of winding m referred to winding a.

Substitution of Eqs. 10-63, 10-64, 10-67, and 10-68 in Eqs. 10-58 and 10-59 then gives

$$V_m = (I_{mf} + I_{mb})Z_{1m} + I_{mf}Z_f + I_{mb}Z_b \tag{10-69}$$

$$V_a = \left(j\frac{I_{mf}}{a} - j\frac{I_{mb}}{a}\right)Z_{1a} + jaI_{mf}Z_f - jaI_{mb}Z_b \tag{10-70}$$

Rearrangement of terms in these equations and multiplication of Eq. 10-70 by $-j/a$ gives

$$V_m = I_{mf}(Z_{1m} + Z_f) + I_{mb}(Z_{1m} + Z_b) \tag{10-71}$$

$$-j\frac{V_a}{a} = I_{mf}\left(\frac{Z_{1a}}{a^2} + Z_f\right) - I_{mb}\left(\frac{Z_{1a}}{a^2} + Z_b\right) \tag{10-72}$$

Note that V_a/a and Z_{1a}/a^2 are, respectively, the phase-a voltage and stator-circuit impedance referred to winding m.

These equations can be solved for the currents in terms of the voltages and impedances, but experience with the symmetrical-component method, as in Art. 10-8, leads one to suspect that a rearrangement which introduces the symmetrical components of the applied voltages may lead to worth-while simplifications. Such a rearrangement is readily made; thus, addition of Eqs. 10-71 and 10-72 and division of the result by 2 gives

$$\frac{1}{2}\left(V_m - j\frac{V_a}{a}\right) = I_{mf}\left(\frac{\frac{Z_{1a}}{a^2} + Z_{1m}}{2} + Z_f\right) - I_{mb}\frac{\frac{Z_{1a}}{a^2} - Z_{1m}}{2} \tag{10-73}$$

Similarly, subtraction of Eq. 10-72 from Eq. 10-71 and division of the result by 2 gives

$$\frac{1}{2}\left(V_m + j\frac{V_a}{a}\right) = -I_{mf}\frac{\frac{Z_{1a}}{a^2} - Z_{1m}}{2} + I_{mb}\frac{\frac{Z_{1a}}{a^2} + Z_{1m}}{2} + Z_b \tag{10-74}$$

Now let

$$V_{mf} \equiv \frac{1}{2}\left(V_m - j\frac{V_a}{a}\right) \tag{10-75}$$

$$V_{mb} \equiv \frac{1}{2}\left(V_m + j\frac{V_a}{a}\right) \tag{10-76}$$

By comparison with Eqs. 10-49 and 10-50, these new voltages can be recognized as symmetrical components of the applied voltages referred to phase m. From Eqs. 10-75 and 10-76, the relations for the actual winding voltages in terms of the symmetrical components are

$$V_m = V_{mf} + V_{mb} \tag{10-77}$$

$$V_a = jaV_{mf} - jaV_{mb} \tag{10-78}$$

For further simplification of the notation, let

$$Z_o = \frac{1}{2}\left(\frac{Z_{1a}}{a^2} + Z_{1m}\right) \tag{10-79}$$

$$Z_d = \frac{1}{2}\left(\frac{Z_{1a}}{a^2} - Z_{1m}\right) \tag{10-80}$$

where Z_o is the average value of the impedances referred to the main winding and Z_d is half their difference (subscript d for difference). Substitution of the defining relations, Eqs. 10-75, 10-76, 10-79, and 10-80, in Eqs. 10-73 and 10-74 then gives

$$V_{mf} = I_{mf}(Z_o + Z_f) - I_{mb}Z_d \tag{10-81}$$

$$V_{mb} = -I_{mf}Z_d + I_{mb}(Z_o + Z_b) \tag{10-82}$$

Equations 10-81 and 10-82 are also the voltage equations for the coupled circuit shown in Fig. 10-28*a*, which is therefore an equivalent circuit for the motor. From Eqs. 10-79 and 10-80

$$Z_o - Z_d = Z_{1m} \tag{10-83}$$

Also recall that the impedances Z_f and Z_b are parallel combinations of the rotor and magnetizing branches (Fig. 10-27). The equivalent circuit therefore can be redrawn as in Fig. 10-28*b*.[13] The impedance Z_d is drawn as a capacitive impedance, because that is what it is in the important

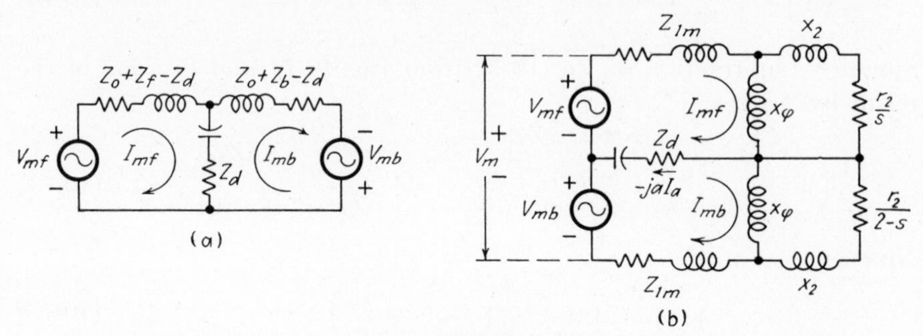

FIG. 10-28. Generalized equivalent circuits for 2-phase induction machines.

case of a capacitor motor. This impedance acts as a coupling, just like a mutual impedance, between the forward and backward fields and shows the manner in which these fields influence one another. The current in this impedance is

$$I_{mf} - I_{mb} = -jaI_a \tag{10-84}$$

Equations 10-81 and 10-82 and the equivalent circuit of Fig. 10-28*b* are applicable to a wide variety of induction-motor types. For example, if the stator-circuit impedances are equal when referred to the same winding, then $Z_d = 0$ and the forward and backward fields are independent of one another; this special case is exactly like that of the symmetrical motor of Art. 10-8 after all quantities have been referred to the same winding. If $Z_d = 0$ and if the referred voltages form a balanced 2-phase system of positive sequence, then Fig. 10-28*b* reduces to the equivalent circuit for balanced operation. If winding *a* is open, then Z_d is an open circuit; this is the special case of single-phase operation treated in Art. 10-6*a*. For

[13] For a derivation of a similar equivalent circuit by means of tensor analysis, see Gabriel Kron, Equivalent Circuit of the Capacitor Motor, *Gen. Elec. Rev.*, vol. 44, No. 9, pp. 511–513, September, 1941; also Gabriel Kron, Steady-state Equivalent Circuits of Synchronous and Induction Machines, *Trans. AIEE*, vol. 67, pp. 175–181, 1948. For a different form of equivalent circuit derived from the cross-field theory, see Sheldon S. L. Chang, The Equivalent Circuit of the Capacitor Motor, *Trans. AIEE*, vol. 66, pp. 631–640, 1947.

this special case $I_a = 0$, and Eqs. 10-65 and 10-66 become

$$I_{mf} = I_{mb} = \tfrac{1}{2}I_m \tag{10-85}$$

The equivalent circuit then reduces to V_m applied to the combination of $2Z_{1m}$ in series with the forward- and backward-field impedances. Division of the impedances by 2 gives the equivalent circuit of Fig. 10-14*c*.

Equations 10-81 and 10-82 can be solved for the currents, giving

$$I_{mf} = \frac{V_{mf}(Z_o + Z_b) + V_{mb}Z_d}{(Z_o + Z_f)(Z_o + Z_b) - Z_d^2} \tag{10-86}$$

$$I_{mb} = \frac{V_{mb}(Z_o + Z_f) + V_{mf}Z_d}{(Z_o + Z_f)(Z_o + Z_b) - Z_d^2} \tag{10-87}$$

If the motor constants and the applied voltages are known and a value of slip is assumed, the forward and backward components of the current in phase m can then be found. The power delivered to the forward field by phase m of the stator is $I_{mf}^2R_f$, and since the internal behavior of the motor for the forward-field components is the same as that of a balanced 2-phase motor, a like contribution is supplied by phase a. As in a balanced 2-phase motor, the total power P_{gf} delivered to the forward field by both phases of the stator therefore is

$$P_{gf} = 2I_{mf}^2R_f \tag{10-88}$$

Similarly, the total power P_{gb} delivered to the backward field is

$$P_{gb} = 2I_{mb}^2R_b \tag{10-89}$$

The internal torque, rotor I^2R losses, and internal mechanical power can then be determined from straightforward application of revolving-field theory, as in Eqs. 10-13, 10-16, and 10-17.

b. Starting Torque. The starting condition is an important and simple special case.[14] With the rotor stationary, the current in each winding can be determined from its own applied voltage and impedance (including any series impedances), there being no mutual effect between phases at standstill when the windings are in space quadrature. If the stator currents are now resolved into forward and backward components, the internal starting torque can then be determined from the basic torque relation (Eq. 10-13). Since the forward- and backward-field impedances are equal at standstill, the basic torque relation reduces to

$$T_{\text{start}} = \frac{2}{\omega_s}(I_{mf}^2 - I_{mb}^2)R \tag{10-90}$$

[14] For a thorough investigation of starting conditions in split-phase and capacitor motors, see C. G. Veinott, Starting Windings for Single-phase Induction Motors, *Trans. AIEE*, vol. 63, No. 6, pp. 288–294, June, 1944; T. C. Lloyd and J. H. Karr, Design of Starting Windings for Split-phase Motors, *Trans. AIEE*, vol. 63, No. 1, pp. 9–13, January, 1944.

where T_{start} is the internal starting torque in newton-meters and R is the resistance of the parallel combination of $r_2 + jx_2$ and jx_φ referred to winding m. The factor 2 is the number of stator phases.

A simple and convenient relation for the starting torque can now be obtained by expressing the difference between the squares of the effective values of the forward and backward currents in terms of the resultant stator currents and the phase angle between them. The resolution of the stator currents into forward and backward components in accordance with Eqs. 10-65 and 10-66 is shown in the vector diagram of Fig. 10-29.

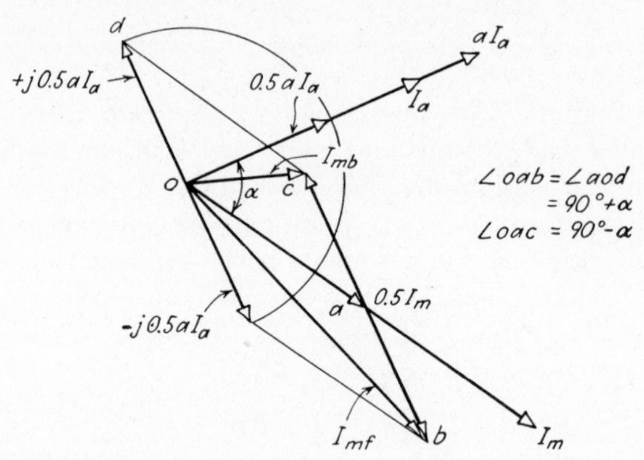

FIG. 10-29. Vector diagram of currents and their symmetrical components.

The phase angle between I_m and I_a is α. From the geometry of triangle oab,

$$(ob)^2 = (oa)^2 + (ab)^2 - 2(oa)(ab) \cos \angle oab \tag{10-91}$$

or, in terms of the effective values of the currents,

$$I_{mf}^2 = (0.5I_m)^2 + (0.5aI_a)^2 + 2(0.5I_m)(0.5aI_a) \sin \alpha \tag{10-92}$$

Similarly, for triangle oac

$$I_{mb}^2 = (0.5I_m)^2 + (0.5aI_a)^2 - 2(0.5I_m)(0.5aI_a) \sin \alpha \tag{10-93}$$

Substitution of the difference between Eqs. 10-92 and 10-93 in Eq. 10-90 then gives

$$T_{start} = \frac{2}{\omega_s} I_m a I_a R \sin \alpha \tag{10-94}$$

c. Capacitor and Split-phase Motors. Capacitor and split-phase motors are the special case in which

$$V_m = V_a = V \tag{10-95}$$

where V is the single-phase line voltage. Equations 10-75 and 10-76 then reduce to

$$V_{mf} = \frac{V}{2}\left(1 - \frac{j}{a}\right) \quad (10\text{-}96)$$

$$V_{mb} = \frac{V}{2}\left(1 + \frac{j}{a}\right) \quad (10\text{-}97)$$

In Eqs. 10-79 and 10-80, the impedance Z_{1m} is the leakage impedance of the main winding. The impedance Z_{1a} is the leakage impedance of the auxiliary winding plus (in the case of capacitor motors) the impedance of the capacitor. The single-phase line current is the vector sum of the winding currents. The application of the theory to the numerical calculation of performance characteristics can be illustrated by means of an example.

Example 10-5. A ¼-hp 110-volt 60-cps 4-pole two-value capacitor motor (capacitor-start, capacitor-run) has the following constants:

Rotor referred to m:	$r_2 = 4.12$ ohms	$x_2 = 2.12$ ohms
Magnetizing reactance referred to m:		$x_\varphi = 66.8$
Main winding:	$r_{1m} = 2.02$	$x_{1m} = 2.79$
Auxiliary winding:	$r_{1a} = 7.14$	$x_{1a} = 3.22$
Starting capacitor:	$r_c = 3.00$	$x_c = -14.5$
Running capacitor:	$r_c = 9.00$	$x_c = -172$

Effective turns ratio $N_a/N_m = a = 1.18$
No-load core loss = 24 watts
No-load friction and windage = 13 watts

a. For standstill conditions, compute the current in each winding, the line current and power factor, the voltage across the capacitor, and the internal torque.

b. With the starting capacitor still in the circuit, repeat *a* for a slip of 0.50.

Solution. From the constants of the rotor and magnetizing reactance referred to the main winding, the forward- and backward-field impedances Z_f and Z_b can be computed at the specified values of slip. The results are tabulated below:

$s = 1.0$	$s = 0.5$
$Z_f = Z_b = Z$	$Z_f = 7.62 + j2.97$
$= 3.87 + j2.29$	$Z_b = 2.58 + j2.16$

a. At standstill, the motor is a static circuit with no mutual effects between phases. The impedance at the line terminals of the main phase is

$$Z_m = Z_{1m} + Z = 2.02 + j2.79 + 3.87 + j2.29$$
$$= 6.89 + j5.08 = 7.78\underline{/40.8^\circ} \text{ ohms}$$

With the line voltage V as reference vector

$$I_m = \frac{V}{Z_m} = \frac{110}{7.78}\underline{/-40.8^\circ} = 14.14\underline{/-40.8^\circ} \text{ amp}$$
$$= 10.7 - j9.23$$

The rotor and magnetizing impedance referred to the auxiliary winding is

$$a^2Z = (1.18)^2(3.87 + j2.29) = 5.38 + j3.18$$

The impedance of the starting capacitor in series with the auxiliary-winding leakage impedance is

$$Z_{1a} = 3.00 - j14.5 + 7.14 + j3.22 = 10.14 - j11.28$$

The impedance at the line terminals of the auxiliary phase is

$$Z_a = Z_{1a} + a^2Z = 10.14 - j11.28 + 5.38 + j3.18 = 15.52 - j8.1$$
$$= 17.5\underline{/-27.5^\circ} \text{ ohms}$$

$$I_a = \frac{V}{Z_a} = \frac{110}{17.5}\underline{/+27.5^\circ} = 6.29\underline{/+27.5^\circ} \text{ amp}$$
$$= 5.57 + j2.91$$

Line current $I = I_m + I_a = 16.27 - j6.32 = 17.5\underline{/-21.3^\circ}$ amp

Power factor $= \cos 21.3^\circ = 0.932$

Impedance of starting capacitor $= \sqrt{r_c^2 + x_c^2} = 14.8$ ohms

Capacitor voltage at starting $= I_aZ_c = (6.29)(14.8) = 93$ volts

In Eq. 10-94

$$\omega_s = {}^{377}\!/_2 = 188.5 \qquad \alpha = 27.5^\circ + 40.8^\circ = 68.3^\circ$$
$$\sin \alpha = 0.929$$

$$T_{\text{start}} = \frac{2}{188.5}(14.14)(1.18)(6.29)(3.87)(0.929)$$
$$= 4.00 \text{ newton-m, or } 2.95 \text{ lb-ft}$$

b. With the rotor in motion the motor is no longer a simple static circuit, and the forward and backward currents must be computed by means of Eqs. 10-86 and 10-87. From Eqs. 10-96 and 10-97 with the line voltage as reference vector

$$V_{mf} = 55 - j\frac{55}{1.18} = 55 - j46.6 = 72.1\underline{/-40.3^\circ}$$
$$V_{mb} = 55 + j46.6 = 72.1\underline{/+40.3^\circ}$$

With the starting capacitor, from part *a*

$$\frac{Z_{1a}}{a^2} = \frac{1}{(1.18)^2}(10.14 - j11.28) = 7.30 - j8.10$$
$$Z_{1m} = 2.02 + j2.79$$

From Eqs. 10-79 and 10-80

$$Z_o = 4.66 - j2.66$$
$$Z_d = 2.64 - j5.45 \qquad -Z_d^2 = +22.7 + j28.9$$

At $s = 0.50$, from the table at the beginning of the solution,

$$Z_f = 7.62 + j2.97 \qquad Z_b = 2.58 + j2.16$$
$$Z_o = 4.66 - j2.66 \qquad Z_o = 4.66 - j2.66$$
$$Z_o + Z_f = 12.28 + j0.31 \qquad Z_o + Z_b = 7.24 - j0.50$$

Substitution of numerical values in Eqs. 10-86 and 10-87 then gives

$$I_{mf} = \frac{946\underline{/-35.0^\circ}}{114.0\underline{/11.6^\circ}} = 8.30\underline{/-46.6^\circ} = 5.69 - j6.03$$

$$I_{mb} = \frac{577\underline{/16.8^\circ}}{114.0\underline{/11.6^\circ}} = 5.05\underline{/5.2^\circ} = 5.03 + j0.46$$

Main-winding current $I_m = \text{sum} = 10.72 - j5.57 = 12.1$ amp

In Eq. 10-64,

$$j\frac{I_{mf}}{a} = 5.11 + j4.82$$

$$-j\frac{I_{mb}}{a} = \underline{0.39 - j4.27}$$

Auxiliary-winding current $I_a = 5.50 + j0.55 = 5.53$ amp
Line current $I = I_m + I_a = 16.22 - j5.02 = \underline{17.0/-17.2°}$
Power factor $= \cos 17.2° = 0.955$
Capacitor voltage $= (5.53)(14.8) = 81.8$ volts

In Eqs. 10-88 and 10-89,

$$P_{gf} = 2(8.30)^2(7.62) = 1{,}048 \text{ watts}$$
$$P_{gb} = 2(5.05)^2(2.58) = \underline{132}$$
$$\text{Difference} = 916$$

From Eq. 10-13,

$$T = \frac{916}{188.5} = 4.86 \text{ newton-m, or } 3.59 \text{ lb-ft}$$

Data for the curves of internal torque and capacitor voltage shown in Fig. 10-30 were computed by repeating similar calculations for other assumed values of slip. The general shape of the characteristics is typical of capacitor-start motors. Notice the rather rapid increase in the voltage across the capacitor for increasing speed above about 0.7. As the motor speed increases, its reactance increases and a condition analogous to resonance is approached. One of the problems confronting the designer is the proper choice of the correct combination of auxiliary-winding constants, turns ratio, and capacitor rating so that a suitable torque characteristic is obtained without causing excessive voltage across the capacitor.[15]

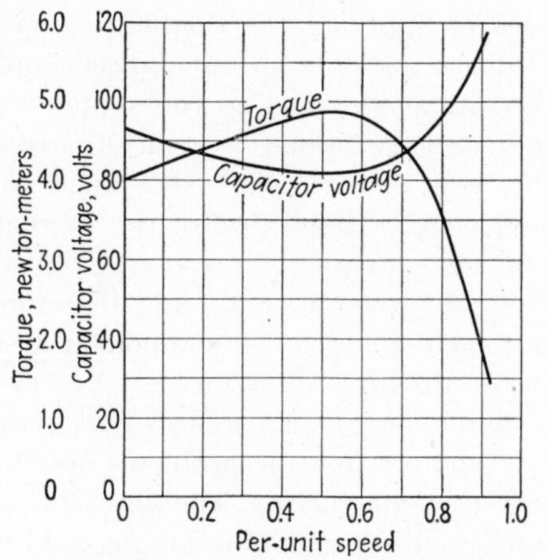

FIG. 10-30. Computed curves of torque and voltage across starting capacitor for ¼-hp 110-volt two-value capacitor motor of Example 10-5.

10-11. Résumé.

Although other topics are touched upon, the main theme of this chapter is a continuation of the induction-machine theory of Chap. 9. This theory is expanded in Chap. 10 by a step-by-step reasoning process from the simple revolving-field theory of the symmetrical polyphase induction motor. Reduced to essentials, the new concepts introduced in this chapter are few and simple. The basic concept is the resolution of the stator-mmf wave into two constant-amplitude travel-

[15] For design methods in terms of the cross-field theory, see T. C. Lloyd and Sheldon S. L. Chang, A Design Method for Capacitor Motors, *Trans. AIEE*, vol. 66, pp. 652–657, 1947; Sheldon S. L. Chang, A Design Method for Capacitor Start Motors, *Trans. AIEE*, vol. 66, pp. 1369–1374, 1947.

ing waves revolving around the air gap at synchronous speed in opposite directions. If the slip for the forward field is s, then that for the backward field is $2 - s$. Each of these component fields produces induction-motor action, just as in a symmetrical polyphase motor. From the viewpoint of the stator, the reflected effects of the rotor can be visualized and expressed quantitatively in terms of simple equivalent circuits. The ease with which the internal reactions can be accounted for in this manner is the essential reason for the usefulness of the double-revolving-field theory.

For a single-phase winding, the forward and backward component mmf waves are equal, and their amplitude is half the maximum value of the peak of the stationary pulsating mmf produced by the winding. The resolution of the stator mmf into its forward and backward components then leads to the physical concept of the single-phase motor described in Art. 10-1 and finally to the quantitative theory developed in Art. 10-6 and to the equivalent circuits of Fig. 10-14.

The next step in our expanding theory is investigation of the possibilities of applying the double-revolving-field resolution to a symmetrical 2-phase motor with unbalanced applied voltages, as in Art. 10-8. This investigation leads to the symmetrical-component concept whereby an unbalanced 2-phase system of currents or voltages can be resolved into the sum of two balanced 2-phase component systems of opposite phase sequence. Resolution of the currents into symmetrical-component systems is equivalent to resolving the stator-mmf wave into its forward and backward components, and therefore the internal reactions of the rotor for each symmetrical-component system are the same as those which we have already investigated. A very similar reasoning process, not considered here, leads to the well-known 3-phase symmetrical-component method for treating problems involving unbalanced operation of 3-phase rotating machines. The ease with which the rotating machine can be analyzed in terms of revolving-field theory is the chief reason for the usefulness of the symmetrical component method.

In so far as basic concepts are concerned, it is a simple matter to modify the symmetrical-component method of Art. 10-8 so that the effects of unequal turns in the stator windings of a 2-phase motor can be taken into account as in Art. 10-10. All that is necessary is that the currents and voltages be referred to the appropriate winding by use of the effective turns ratio, in the same manner as in static-transformer theory. The effects of unequal stator-circuit impedances also are included, but no new concepts are thereby introduced; only the algebra becomes somewhat longer. The effect of unbalanced stator impedances is to make the two symmetrical-component systems mutually interrelated, as shown in the equivalent circuit of Fig. 10-28*b*. This equivalent circuit applies to a wide variety of induction-motor types, of which capacitor and split-phase motors are important examples.

The symmetrical-component transformations of Arts. 10-8 and 10-10 may be regarded simply as a mathematical change of variable, an artifice whose purpose is to obtain new variables which can be dealt with rather easily and which have rather clear physical significance. Mathematical physics is full of transformations of this kind—for example, the resolution of a system of forces acting on a body into its X, Y, Z translational components acting through the center of gravity, together with couples acting to produce rotation about the center of gravity. Physical significance and mathematical simplicity generally seem to go hand in hand. If one has a clear physical concept of what goes on in simple situations, then more complex situations usually can be resolved into the net effect of simple elements. The symmetrical-component method is a good example.

PROBLEMS

10-1. What type of motor would you use in the following applications? Give reasons. Vacuum cleaner. Refrigerator. Washing machine. Domestic oil burner. Desk fan. Sewing machine. Emery wheel. Clock. Food mixer. Record player. Portable electric drill.

10-2. At standstill, the currents in the main and auxiliary windings of a capacitor-start induction motor are $I_m = 14.14$ amp and $I_a = 7.07$ amp. The auxiliary-winding current leads the main-winding current by 60°. The effective turns per pole—*i.e.*, the number of turns corrected for the effects of winding distribution—are $N_m = 80$ and $N_a = 100$. The windings are in space quadrature.

Determine the amplitudes of the forward and backward stator-mmf waves.

Suppose it were possible to adjust the magnitude and phase of the auxiliary-winding current. What should be its magnitude and phase to produce a pure forward mmf wave?

10-3. Find the mechanical power output of the ¼-hp 4-pole 110-volt 60-cps single-phase induction motor, whose constants are given below, at a slip of 0.05:

$$r_{1m} = 1.86 \text{ ohms} \qquad x_{1m} = 2.56 \text{ ohms} \qquad x_\varphi = 53.5 \text{ ohms}$$
$$r_2 = 3.56 \text{ ohms} \qquad x_2 = 2.56 \text{ ohms}$$

Core loss = 35 watts Friction and windage = 13.5 watts

10-4. The no-load rotational loss of a ⅙-hp 4-pole 110-volt 60-cps single-phase induction motor is 25.0 watts. At a slip $s = 0.06$ corresponding to rated load, the total rotor copper loss is 25 watts. The stator I^2R loss may be neglected for the purposes of this problem.

a. At a slip $s = 0.06$, what is the power input to the machine?

b. What is the rotor I^2R loss caused by the backward field?

10-5. The results of a load test on a ¼-hp 115-volt 60-cps 4-pole single-phase induction motor are as follows:

Applied voltage $V = 115$ volts at 60 cps
Main-winding current $I_m = 3.70$ amp
Power input = 270 watts

The starting winding was open-circuited during this test. Other data are as follows:

Main-winding stator resistance $r_{1m} = 2.00$ ohms
Resistive component of backward-field impedance, $R_b = 1.50$ ohms at the slip of the above test

Compute the net internal torque for the conditions of the load test. Express the torque in newton-meters. Neglect rotational and core losses.

10-6. For the single-phase induction motor of Example 10-1 running at a slip of 0.05, determine the ratio of the backward flux wave to the forward flux wave. Plot a half wave of the resultant flux distribution for instants of time corresponding to $\omega t = 0$, 45°, 90°, 135°, and 180°, zero time being chosen as the instant when the forward and backward flux waves are in space phase. If the forward and backward flux waves are represented by space vectors, like the mmf vectors f and b in Fig. 10-2c, draw a diagram showing the components and the resultant for the same five instants of time. Sketch the locus of the tip of the vector representing the resultant air-gap flux wave. What kind of curve do you think this locus is?

10-7. A ⅙-hp 110-volt 60-cps 4-pole single-phase induction motor is running at a slip $s = 0.03$ with rated voltage applied. It has a total rotor copper loss of 12.65 watts and develops a net internal torque of 0.324 newton-m. The locus of the tip of the vector representing the resultant air-gap flux wave is an ellipse having the ratio of the length of the major axis to the length of the minor axis equal to 1.136. For a slip $s = 0.03$ find the following:

a. The ratio of the backward flux wave to the forward flux wave
b. The power delivered by the stator winding to the backward field
c. The internal torque of the forward field
d. The ratio of the backward to the forward stator-mmf waves
e. The ratio of the rms value of the rotor current induced by the backward field to the rms value of the rotor current induced by the forward field

10-8. Derive an expression in terms of Q_2 for the nonzero speed of a single-phase induction motor at which the internal torque is zero (see Eq. 10-21).

10-9. The motor of Prob. 10-3 is driven mechanically at exactly synchronous speed.
a. Draw its equivalent circuit with numerical values of the parameters.
b. Compute the current taken from the line.
c. Compute the power delivered to the air gap from the line.
d. Compute the rotor copper losses caused by the forward and backward fields, respectively.
e. On the assumption that all the core loss is in the stator, compute the mechanical power required to drive the motor.
f. How are the rotor I^2R losses supplied to it?

10-10. From the following test data, find the equivalent-circuit parameters at 70°C and the no-load rotational loss. The data apply to a ¼-hp 110-volt 60-cps 4-pole single-phase induction motor.

No-load test	*Blocked-rotor test (main winding only)*
$V = 110$ volts	$V = 110$ volts
$I = 2.73$ amp	$I = 16.6$ amp
$P = 56$ watts	$P = 1{,}260$ watts

Resistance of main winding at 25°C = 1.463 ohms
Resistance of main winding after blocked-rotor test = 1.48 ohms

10-11. The results of a load test on a ⅙-hp 110-volt 60-cps 6-pole single-phase induction motor are as follows:

Applied voltage $V = 110$ volts at 60 cps
Main-winding current $I_m = 3.16$ amp (auxiliary winding open)
Power input $= 188$ watts

The mechanical power output was not measured. Other data with respect to this motor are as follows:

Main-winding resistance $r_{1m} = 2.86$ ohms
Rotor resistance $r_2 = 4.64$ ohms

Rotor $Q_2 = \dfrac{x_{22}}{r_2} = 15.5$

Reactance ratio $\dfrac{x_\varphi}{x_{22}} = 0.95$

Rotational loss (core loss plus friction and windage) $= 30$ watts

a. Compute the total motor losses for the conditions of the load test where the slip is known accurately as 0.043. Find the mechanical power output.

b. The slip can be determined quickly but inaccurately on test from a tachometer reading of speed. On the basis of a motor speed of 1,130 rpm as read on a tachometer for this load test, calculate the losses and the mechanical power output. Compare the results with those of part *a.*

10-12. A small 2-phase 2-pole induction motor has the following constants at 60 cps:

$$r_{1m} = 357 \text{ ohms} \qquad r_2 = 255 \text{ ohms}$$
$$x_{1m} = x_2 = 50 \text{ ohms} \qquad x_\varphi = 920 \text{ ohms}$$

The main and auxiliary windings have the same number of turns. This motor is used as a tachometer with a 60-cps reference voltage applied to its main winding, as in Fig. 10-17. Compute the speed voltage sensitivity in volts output per volt input per radian per second near zero speed. Also compute the phase angle of the output voltage relative to the input voltage.

10-13. *a.* Find the starting torque of the motor given in Example 10-3 for the conditions specified.

b. Compare the result of *a* with the torque which the motor would develop at starting when balanced 2-phase voltages of 220 volts are applied.

c. Show, in general, that if the stator voltages V_m and V_a of a 2-phase induction motor are in quadrature but unequal, the starting torque is the same as that developed when balanced 2-phase voltages of $\sqrt{V_m V_a}$ volts are applied.

10-14. The induction motor of Example 10-3 is supplied from an unbalanced 2-phase source by a 4-wire feeder having an impedance of $1.0 + j3.0$ ohms per phase. The source voltages can be expressed vectorially as

$$V_m = 240\underline{/0^\circ} \text{ volts} \qquad V_a = 200\underline{/75^\circ} \text{ volts}$$

For a slip of 0.05, show that the induction-motor performance is such that the motor's terminal voltages correspond more nearly to those of a balanced 2-phase system than those at the source.

10-15. The equivalent-circuit constants in ohms per phase referred to the stator for a 2-phase 1.5-hp 220-volt 4-pole 60-cps squirrel-cage induction motor are given below. The no-load rotational loss is 200 watts.

$$r_1 = 3.2 \qquad r_2 = 2.4$$
$$x_1 = x_2 = 3.2 \qquad x_\varphi = 100$$

a. The voltage applied to phase m is $220/\underline{0°}$ volts, and the voltage applied to phase a is $220/\underline{60°}$. At a slip $s = 0.04$, $Z_f = 41.9 + j27.2$ ohms, and $Z_b = 1.20 + j3.2$ ohms What is the net air-gap torque?

b. What is the starting torque with the applied voltages of *a*?

c. The applied voltages are readjusted so that $V_m = 220/\underline{0°}$ and $V_a = 220/\underline{90°}$. Full load on the machine occurs at $s = 0.04$. At what value of slip does maximum torque occur? What is the value of maximum air-gap torque in newton-meters?

d. While the motor is running as in *c*, phase a is open-circuited. What is the horsepower developed by the machine at slip $s = 0.04$?

e. What voltage appears across the open phase-a terminals under the conditions of *d* at $s = 0.04$?

10-16. The motor of Prob. 10-12 is used as a 2-phase servomotor. When the reference-field voltage is 100 volts and the control-field voltage is 70 volts and leads the reference voltage by 90° (both voltages at 60 cps), compute:

a. The ratio of the backward flux wave to the forward flux wave at standstill

b. The ratio of the backward flux wave to the forward flux wave at a slip $s = 0.80$

c. The internally developed mechanical power in watts at $s = 0.80$

10-17. For the 2-phase induction motor of Example 10-4, plot a family of curves of rotor power loss and internal power developed for per-unit values of control-phase voltage of 1.00, 0.50, and 0, covering a speed range from −1 to +1 per unit. The applied voltages are in quadrature. Express the power in per unit based on the power delivered to the air gap by the stator windings at standstill when balanced 2-phase voltages of 1.00 per unit are applied to the two stator phases.

10-18. A small 2-pole squirrel-cage induction motor for use in servo systems has symmetrical 2-phase stator windings. At standstill, the input impedance measured at the terminals of each stator winding at 60 cps is $305 + j51$ ohms. For the purposes of this problem rotational and core losses may be neglected. Three points on the torque-slip characteristic of this motor with balanced 2-phase voltages of 100 volts at 60 cps applied to its stator terminals are given below:

Torque, newton-m	0.064	0.082	0.088
Slip, per unit	0.50	1.00	1.50

If the reference-phase voltage is held constant at 100 volts, 60 cps, and the control-phase voltage is reduced to 50 volts (the two voltages being in time quadrature), compute:

a. The standstill torque, in newton-meters

b. The power input to the reference phase at standstill

c. The power input to the control phase at standstill

d. The total rotor I^2R loss at standstill

e. The torque at $s = 0.50$

10-19. For the 2-phase servomotor of Prob. 10-18 at standstill with 100 volts applied to the reference phase and variable voltage applied to the control phase, plot curves of the following variables as functions of the standstill torque:

a. Total rotor copper loss

b. Control-phase stator copper loss

c. Reference-phase stator copper loss

d. Power input to control phase

e. Power input to reference phase

10-20. A symmetrical 2-phase servomotor produces a torque of 1.25 lb-ft at standstill with balanced voltages of 100 volts applied.

If the motor is required to produce an acceleration at zero speed of 64.4 rad/sec² in a load having no friction but having an inertia of 0.5 lb-ft^2, what voltage must be supplied to the auxiliary winding when the main winding is supplied with 100 volts in time quadrature? (g = 32.2 ft/sec^2.)

10-21. At starting (rotor stationary) the currents in the main and auxiliary windings of a capacitor-start single-phase induction motor are, respectively,

$$I_m = 15 \text{ amp} \qquad I_a = 10 \text{ amp}$$

with I_a leading I_m by 60°. The auxiliary and main windings are in space quadrature, and the ratio of effective turns in the auxiliary winding to effective turns in the main winding is 1.50.

For starting conditions, compute:

a. The ratio of the amplitude of the forward stator-mmf wave to the amplitude of the backward stator-mmf wave

b. The ratio of the amplitude of the forward air-gap flux wave to the amplitude of the backward air-gap flux wave

c. The ratio of the forward torque to the backward torque

d. The ratio of the forward torque to the net starting torque

10-22. *a.* What value of starting capacitor is required to produce an auxiliary-winding current in time quadrature with the main-winding current at starting for the motor in Example 10-5? Assume the capacitor is lossless.

b. What starting torque does the motor produce with this starting capacitor?

c. Draw a vector diagram for starting conditions, using line voltage as the reference vector. Show the vector main-winding current, and the vector locus of the auxiliary-winding current when the capacitance of the starting capacitor is varied. All other parameters are constant. From an analysis based on study of this vector diagram, compute the maximum internal starting torque (in newton-meters) that this motor can be made to develop by varying the starting capacitor. Also compute the corresponding value of the capacitance in microfarads.

10-23. It is possible to design a capacitor motor and its capacitor so that the backward field is eliminated at one specified value of slip (see the reference cited in footnote 3). At this slip the motor runs as a balanced 2-phase motor. For the motor of Example 10-5, find the value of resistance and reactance of the capacitor which will result in balanced 2-phase operation at a slip s = 0.04.

10-24. While the capacitor motor of Example 10-5 is running at a slip s = 0.5, the auxiliary winding and starting capacitor in series accidentally are disconnected from the 110-volt supply and short-circuited. For s = 0.5, find the currents in the main and auxiliary windings and the net internal torque.

CHAPTER 11

CONTROL-TYPE GENERATORS AND SELF-SYNCHRONOUS MACHINES

THE specific objects of this chapter are to describe the construction and operation and to discuss the performance of two different classes of special-purpose machines: control-type d-c generators (Amplidyne, Rototrol, Regulex), and self-synchronous machines (Selsyn, Synchro, Autosyn). Machines in the first class have one or more separately excited fields in which the expenditure of a small amount of power permits almost complete control over the relatively large amount of power in the armature circuit. They differ from conventional separately excited d-c generators in that definite steps are taken to secure low expenditure of control power and better speed of response to a controlling signal. Their principal application is as a component of machine systems, such as the Ward Leonard system of Art. 6-1, in which precise control of the final output quantity is of paramount importance. The second class of machines are intended for applications such as keeping two or more shafts in exact or nearly exact synchronism. They may themselves directly furnish the torques required to maintain synchronism (as in the 3-phase power types of self-synchronous systems discussed in Chap. 9), or they may constitute a data-transmission system supplying in electrical form information regarding misalignment so that other equipment working at a relatively higher power level may act to correct the misalignment.

Conceptually, two related themes appear in the chapter. One is the flexibility of commutator machines; its development constitutes a further exploration of the degrees of freedom offered design and applications engineers striving to obtain the best economical match between actual machine or system performance and the desired ideal, especially when the ideal is exacting or highly complicated. The second theme, first enunciated in Art. 4-13, is that of the individual machine as a system element—as one part of an involved electromechanical energy-conversion or energy-transmission system, a part which must be appropriately matched at both its input and output to the remainder of the system.

We are concerned here primarily with the development of ideas, concepts, and methods which are of potential value in the attainment of specified performance features. Details such as the handling of saturation, the effects of air-gap nonuniformities, and, in general, factors which cause only departures of secondary importance from the established ideal are not investigated quantitatively. Thus, equations are used because of their property of expressing ideas and concepts concisely, and not with the thought of developing precise methods of numerical analysis. In many cases the nature of the modifications and refinements required to incorporate the neglected factors will be evident from the methods of the preceding six chapters.

11-1. D-C Machines with Armature Excitation. When the armature of a d-c machine carries current, an armature-mmf or armature-reaction wave, shown in Fig. 4-13 and discussed in more detail in Art. 5-1, is set up at the air gap, and a corresponding component of air-gap flux is established. This flux remains stationary in space; it is therefore cut by each of the revolving armature inductors, and it induces voltages in them. The net value of this voltage as measured between the normal brushes is zero, however, because the path from brush to brush through the winding includes opposing voltages of equal magnitude. But the possibility still remains that voltages of a definite magnitude may be obtained between additional brushes placed at other points on the commutator. This possibility is first investigated here for a machine with only the armature excited. Then the simultaneous use of both the armature and the field as exciting windings is considered. One of the practical results of this program is a separately excited generator with much lower field-power requirements than the conventional generator.

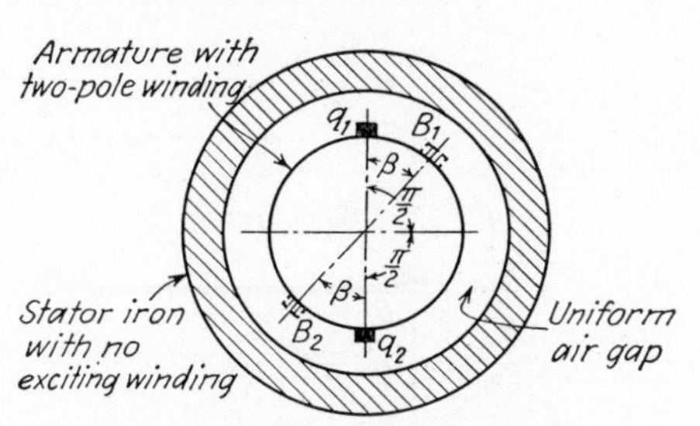

FIG. 11-1. Direct-current machine with armature excitation.

a. Armature Excitation Alone. To investigate the possibilities of armature excitation, consider the simple machine of Fig. 11-1. The armature has a conventional 2-pole drum winding of the type shown in Figs. 3-37 and 3-38 but with a sufficiently large number of armature inductors so that it may be considered a finely distributed winding. The resistances of the armature winding, brushes, and brush contacts are neglected. The stator structure contains no windings and accordingly simply completes the magnetic circuit of the machine. The air gap is entirely uniform, and the reluctance of the iron portions of the magnetic circuit is considered negligible. The two brushes q_1 and q_2, placed 180° apart on the commutator, are connected to a current source. Brushes in this and the following diagrammatic sketches of commutator machines are shown in the position of the armature inductors to which they are directly connected by the commutator. The designation q is used for these brushes because in a normal d-c machine they would be located electrically in the interpolar or quadrature axis.

When the steady direct current I_q traverses the armature circuit established by brushes q_1 and q_2, triangular mmf and flux-density waves are set up in the air gap. This fact is illustrated in Fig. 11-2, which shows a development of the machine patterned after Figs. 4-11 to 4-13. The equivalent current sheets created by the excited armature winding are indicated by black bands and bands with solid crosshatching. For

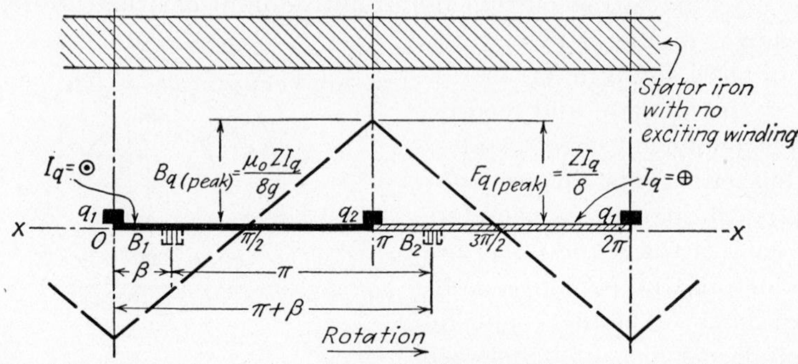

FIG. 11-2. Magnetomotive force and flux-density distribution in machine of Fig. 11-1. Brushes B_1 and B_2 not connected to external circuit.

simplicity, the same wave, indicated by the dashed line, is used to represent both the mmf and the corresponding flux density. A positive ordinate denotes flux leaving the rotor and directed radially across the air gap toward the stator.

From Eq. 4-43, written specifically for a 2-pole winding with two parallel paths, the amplitude of the mmf wave is

$$F_{q(\text{peak})} = \frac{ZI_q}{8} \tag{11-1}$$

where Z is the total number of armature inductors. The amplitude of the corresponding flux-density wave is

$$B_{q(\text{peak})} = \frac{\mu_0 Z I_q}{8g} \tag{11-2}$$

g being the gap length and μ_0 the permeability of the gap.

Now consider that the two additional brushes B_1 and B_2 (Figs. 11-1 and 11-2) are placed 180° apart on the commutator and displaced by the arbitrary angle β from brushes q_1 and q_2, respectively. Almost immediately the question of sparkless commutation at these brushes comes to mind; let us ignore this question for the moment, however, with the assurance that methods of providing satisfactory commutation will be presented later. Suppose first that brushes B_1 and B_2 are not connected to an external load or circuit. A voltage will appear across them which is a function of the flux established by I_q, the speed, and the angle β. As far as the armature circuits established by these brushes are concerned, a stationary flux-density wave, indicated by the dashed line of Fig. 11-2, exists in the air gap. It is immaterial whether the wave is created by the rotor or the stator: a voltage is induced in the armature inductors when they revolve through the wave, and the net induced voltage between brushes is the algebraic sum of the individual inductor voltages in an armature path between B_1 and B_2. For the specific brush position given by $\beta = \pi/2$, brushes B_1 and B_2 are in the normal position with respect to the air-gap flux-density wave for the brushes of a conventional d-c generator, and the most noticeable superficial difference is that the flux wave is triangular instead of the conventional flat-topped shape established by the normal field structure.

The magnitude of the open-circuit voltage between brushes B_1 and B_2 can be obtained by the process leading to Eq. 4-38. Thus from Eq. 4-35 with the limits of integration changed to represent the position of brushes B_1 and B_2, the induced voltage per turn is

$$E_{B(\text{turn})} = 4\frac{n}{60}\int_{\beta}^{\pi+\beta} B_\theta lr\, d\theta \tag{11-3}$$

The quantity n is the speed of the armature in rpm, and l and r are its axial length and radius, respectively. The symbol B_θ denotes the ordinate of the flux-density wave at the angle θ measured from the origin O of Fig. 11-2. For a 2-pole machine with its associated two parallel paths through the armature, there are $Z/4$ series turns between brushes. The resultant induced voltage E_B between brushes B_1 and B_2 is, accordingly,

$$E_B = \frac{nlrZ}{60}\int_{\beta}^{\pi+\beta} B_\theta\, d\theta \tag{11-4}$$

The voltage E_B is seen to be proportional to the net air-gap flux crossing the armature surface between these brushes.

The voltage E_B evidently has its largest value when $\beta = \pi/2$, and the machine is a more effective voltage-producing and power-transferring medium under these circumstances. Henceforth only this brush position will be considered, and the designation d will be used instead of B, indicating specifically the direct axis displaced 90 electrical degrees from the quadrature axis. The open-circuit voltage is then

$$E_d = \frac{nlrZ}{60}\int_{\pi/2}^{3\pi/2} B_\theta\, d\theta = \frac{nlrZ}{60}\frac{\pi}{2}B_{q(\text{peak})} \tag{11-5}$$

where the integral in Eq. 11-5 is evaluated by recognizing it as simply the area under one of the triangular halves of the flux-density wave. By use of Eq. 11-2, the voltage becomes

$$E_d = \frac{nlrZ}{60}\frac{\pi}{2}\frac{\mu_0 Z I_q}{8g} = \frac{\mu_0 \pi l r Z^2}{2 \times 8 \times 60g} I_q n \tag{11-6}$$

$$= K_{dq} I_q n \tag{11-7}$$

where

$$K_{dq} = \frac{\mu_0 \pi l r Z^2}{2 \times 8 \times 60g} \tag{11-8}$$

With no current drawn from brushes d_1 and d_2, no voltage need be impressed across brushes q_1 and q_2 to maintain the current I_q under the assumption of negligible armature resistance. For this reason it was initially specified that brushes q_1 and q_2 be connected to a current source rather than the more usual voltage source. Actually, of course, a sufficient voltage must be impressed to force the current I_q through the normally small armature resistance.

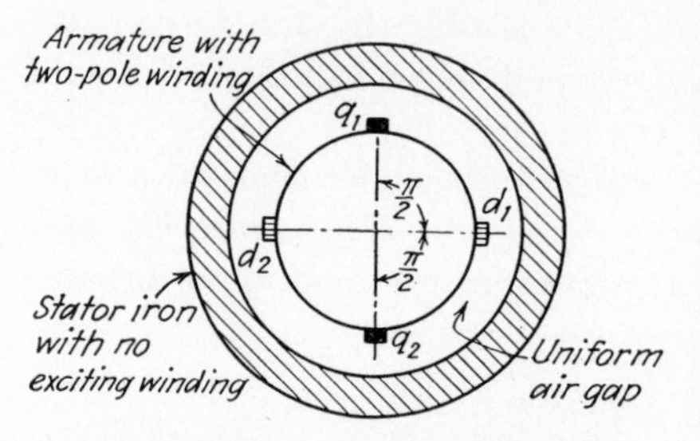

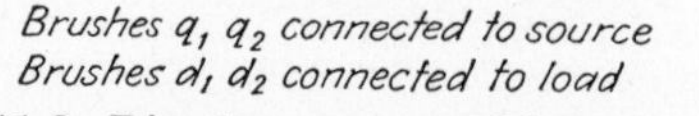

FIG. 11-3. Direct-current machine with armature excitation and brush axes displaced 90°.

When a load circuit is connected to brushes d_1 and d_2, conditions within the machine are changed because of the component armature mmf set up by the current I_d in these brushes. The machine is that shown schematically in Fig. 11-3 and by means of the developed diagram of Fig. 11-4. The two current components I_q and I_d now exist simultaneously in the armature. Since saturation is ignored, superposition of currents, mmfs, and fluxes may be used; *i.e.*, the effects of each current component may be considered separately and then combined to give the over-all effect. In Fig. 11-4, the directions of current I_q in the armature are indicated by the shaded and crosshatched areas above the horizontal line xx. These directions and areas are the same as in Fig. 11-2; the current directions change at each q brush. The directions of current I_d are similarly indicated by the areas below xx; these directions change at each d brush. In the quadrants of armature inductors between brushes d_1 and q_2 and between d_2 and q_1, the two current components add, so that these inductors are relatively heavily loaded. In the quadrants between q_1 and d_1 and between q_2 and d_2, the two current components oppose, so that these inductors are relatively lightly loaded.

As in Fig. 11-2, the current I_q sets up in the air gap the triangular mmf and flux-density wave indicated by the dashed line in Fig. 11-4. This wave induces between brushes d_1 and d_2 the voltage E_d given by Eq. 11-7. It induces no net voltage between brushes q_1 and q_2 because of the 90° displacement between the zero crossing of the wave and the position of these brushes. But the current I_d sets up the triangular mmf and flux-density wave indicated by the dotted line. By analogy with Eqs. 11-5 to 11-8, this dotted wave induces between brushes q_1 and q_2 the voltage

$$E_q = \frac{\mu_0 \pi l r Z^2}{2 \times 8 \times 60g} I_d n \tag{11-9}$$

$$= K_{dq} I_d n \tag{11-10}$$

where K_{dq} is still given by Eq. 11-8. Physically, the voltage is a counter voltage opposing the current I_q, and brushes q_1 and q_2 may now be con-

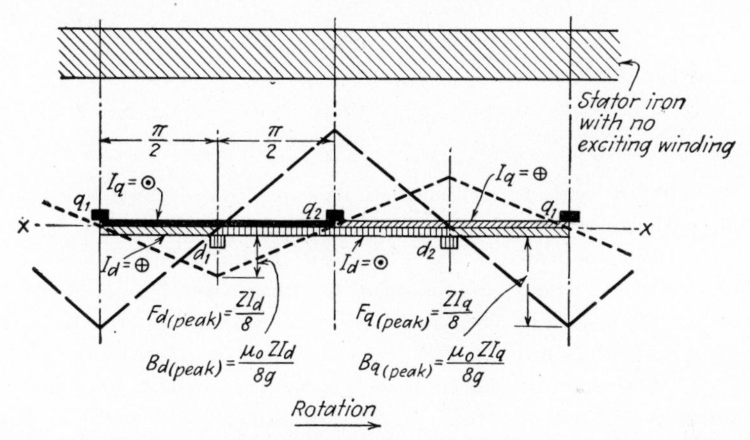

FIG. 11-4. Component mmf and flux-density distribution in machine of Fig. 11-3.

nected to a voltage source without fear of I_q being limited only by a negligibly small armature resistance. The dotted wave induces no net voltage between brushes d_1 and d_2 for the same reason that the dashed wave induces no net voltage between brushes q_1 and q_2.

The basic relations for the machine are therefore Eqs. 11-7 and 11-10. For complete determination of performance, these equations must be supplemented by relations between E_q and I_q dictated by the source and between E_d and I_d dictated by the load, and the speed must be given or determinable. From Eqs. 11-7 and 11-10, it follows that

$$\text{Electrical power output} = E_d I_d = K_{dq} I_q I_d n \tag{11-11}$$

and

$$\text{Electrical power input} = E_q I_q = K_{dq} I_q I_d n \tag{11-12}$$

so that

$$E_q I_q = E_d I_d \tag{11-13}$$

and no energy conversion takes place. The machine is thus a *d-c transformer* converting d-c energy at one voltage and current level to d-c energy at different voltage and current levels. From the energy-conversion viewpoint of Chap. 2, one might say that no electromagnetic torque is produced because the stored energy in the magnetic field is independent of rotor position, reluctance torques being ruled out by the assumption of a uniform air gap. Physically, the source connected to brushes q_1 and q_2 must supply the electrical input corresponding to the power output and the armature copper losses; the equipment revolving the rotor must supply only enough mechanical power to furnish the rotational losses.

As an example consider that the source voltage E_q and the speed n are constant. Then, from Eq. 11-10, the output current I_d is constant at the value

$$I_d = \frac{E_q}{K_{dq}n} \tag{11-14}$$

and, from Eq. 11-7,

$$I_q = \frac{E_d}{K_{dq}n} \tag{11-15}$$

with the output voltage determined by the characteristics of the load together with the constant current I_d. Constancy of I_d may be checked physically by inspection of Fig. 11-4, for if the speed and the voltage impressed across q_1 and q_2 are constant, the amplitude $F_{d(\text{peak})}$ of the dotted wave must also remain constant to create an equal counter voltage. Hence the current I_d must remain constant in order to provide constancy of $F_{d(\text{peak})}$. The machine under these circumstances is a *constant-voltage-to-constant-current transformer*. A possible application might be furnishing constant current to a d-c motor whose torque is to be controlled by adjusting its field excitation.

b. Armature and Field Excitation: The Rosenberg Generator. In order that energy conversion may be accomplished, a stator winding must be added to the machine of Fig. 11-3. One method of combining energy conversion with armature excitation is indicated in Fig. 11-5. Here the current I_q in the circuit formed by brushes q_1 and q_2 is introduced not from an external source but by virtue of the armature revolving in the magnetic field produced on the axis of the stator poles. Because brushes q_1 and q_2 are usually short-circuited, the resistance R_q is usually the low resistance of the armature, brushes, and brush contacts, so that a comparatively small excitation in the separately excited field winding may serve to maintain very significant values of I_q. The current I_q in turn serves as excitation for the d_1d_2 axis. When brushes d_1 and d_2 are connected to an external circuit, the current I_d sets up its own component field in the air gap, a component on the same axis as the stator field and which opposes that field. All three component fields are shown in the developed diagram of Fig. 11-6. In order to show the position of the stator poles simply and definitely, salient stator poles are drawn in Figs. 11-5 and 11-6; the air gap is still to be considered uniform, however, and the mmf and flux-density waves in Fig. 11-6 are drawn with such uniformity in mind.

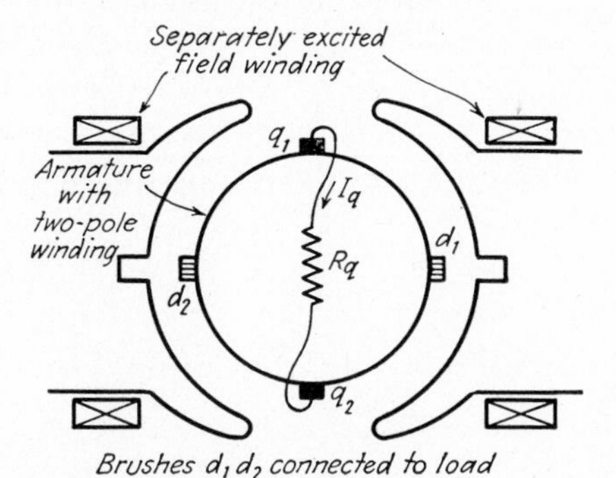

FIG. 11-5. Direct-current machine with armature and field excitation (Rosenberg generator).

Only the dashed triangular wave of Fig. 11-6 contributes to the voltage between brushes d_1 and d_2, a situation comparable with that already discussed in Art. 11-1*a*. Accordingly, from Eq. 11-7,

$$E_d = K_{dq}I_q n \qquad (11\text{-}16)$$

Both the solid wave created by the separately excited field winding and the dotted wave created by I_d contribute to the induced voltage between

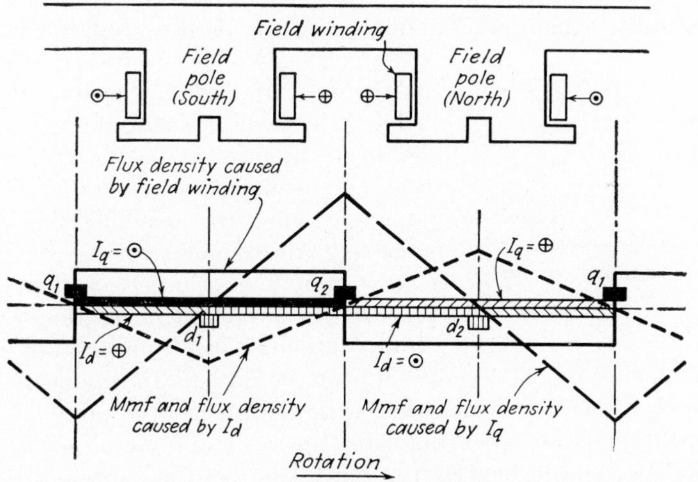

FIG. 11-6. Component mmf and flux-density distributions in machine of Fig. 11-5.

brushes q_1 and q_2. The net voltage E_q is therefore, from Eqs. 4-39 and 11-10,

$$E_q = k_E\Phi_f n - K_{dq}I_d n \qquad (11\text{-}17)$$

where Φ_f is the flux per pole created by the separately excited winding alone and $k_E = Z/60$ for a 2-pole machine. The first term on the right-hand side of Eq. 11-17 gives the voltage component induced by the solid wave of Fig. 11-6, and the second term gives the component induced by the dotted wave; the minus sign is used because the two waves oppose.

The current in brushes q_1 and q_2 is then

$$I_q = \frac{E_q}{R_q} = \frac{k_E \Phi_f n - K_{dq} I_d n}{R_q} \tag{11-18}$$

When this relation is substituted in Eq. 11-16, the output voltage becomes

$$E_d = \frac{n^2}{R_q} (k_E K_{dq} \Phi_f - K_{dq}^2 I_d) \tag{11-19}$$

or, alternatively, the output current is

$$I_d = \frac{k_E}{K_{dq}} \Phi_f - \frac{R_q}{K_{dq}^2 n^2} E_d \tag{11-20}$$

From both Eqs. 11-18 and 11-20, it follows that there is an upper limit to I_d,

$$I_{d(\max)} = \frac{k_E}{K_{dq}} \Phi_f \tag{11-21}$$

approached as the speed increases or as the load becomes more nearly a short circuit. This limit is independent of speed and of the nature of the output circuit but is directly dependent on the excitation of the separately excited field. Physically, at the limit (never quite reached) the flux per pole of the solid and that of the dotted waves (Fig. 11-6) are equal, making the machine fluxless and causing I_q to become zero.

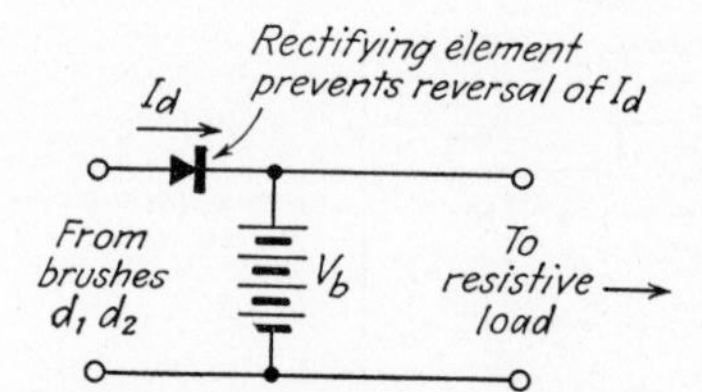

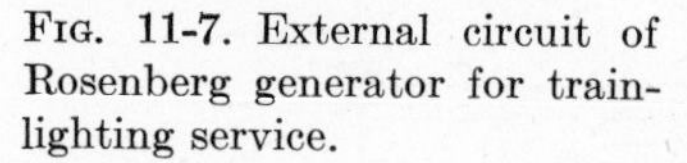
Fig. 11-7. External circuit of Rosenberg generator for train-lighting service.

One practical example of this type of machine is offered by the *Rosenberg generator*, intended for train-lighting service. The machine of Fig. 11-5 is driven from the car axle and connected to the circuit of Fig. 11-7, in which the battery furnishes the power when the train is stationary or operating below a certain minimum speed and also supplies the generator field excitation. The rectifying element prevents the battery from ever discharging through the low-resistance armature. The particular advantages for this service are that the polarity of the generator is independent of the direction of rotation and hence of which way the car is going, and that the current output of the generator is definitely limited regardless of how high the speed becomes. The former fact can be seen mathematically from the dependence of E_d on the square of the speed in Eq. 11-19 or physically by noting that reversal of rotation causes I_q and its flux wave to reverse, and the simultaneous reversal of the rotation and the flux generating E_d leaves its polarity unchanged. The output current as a function of speed is of the form shown in Fig. 11-8, which is simply a plot of Eq. 11-20 with Φ_f constant and E_d equal to V_b, the battery voltage. The generator does not pick up load until the second term on the right-hand side of the equation becomes less than the first.

Commutation in the Rosenberg generator offers no serious problems. Brushes d_1 and d_2, although electrically at the center of the stator poles, are in a region of relatively low flux density because the solid and dotted waves of Fig. 11-6 are in opposition; the flux density in this commutating zone is still further reduced by the slots in the stator pole faces shown in Figs. 11-5 and 11-6. Since the Rosenberg generator is constructed as a salient-pole machine, the interpolar space is the equivalent of these slots in depressing the flux density corresponding to the dashed wave in the commutating zone for brushes q_1 and q_2. If it were necessary, commutating poles could be installed for both sets of brushes, but resistance commutation in conjunction with these slots gives satisfactory results.

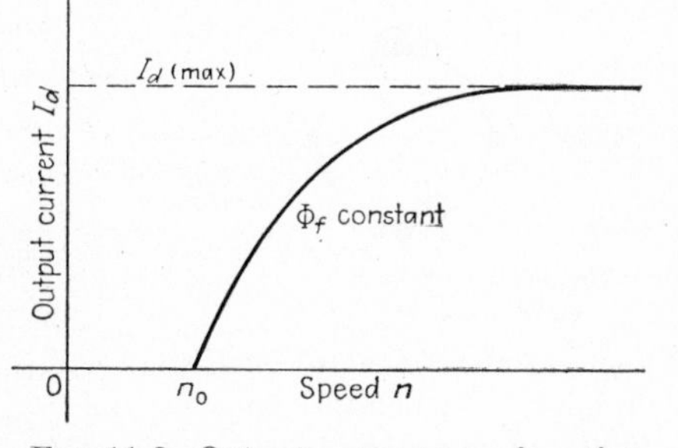

FIG. 11-8. Output current as a function of speed for Rosenberg generator.

c. Armature and Field Excitation with Compensation: The Amplidyne. In the Rosenberg generator, the nature of the output characteristics is dictated to a very considerable extent by the magnetic effect of the output current on the air-gap flux under the stator poles—in other words, by the dotted wave in Fig. 11-6. The opposition of the dotted and solid waves gives rise directly to the upper limit of output current and to the essentially constant-current characteristic of Fig. 11-8. Moreover, this opposition causes the excitation of the separately excited field to be appreciably higher for a given value of output current than if the dotted wave were not present. These thoughts suggest investigation of the possibility and effects of an additional stator winding compensating the armature-reaction mmf caused by the output current.

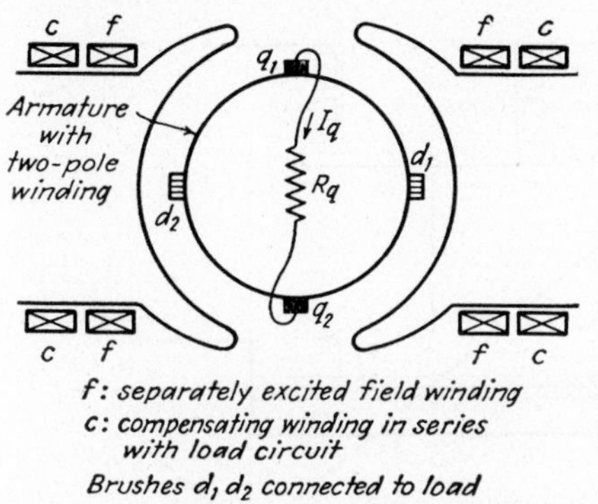

FIG. 11-9. Direct-current machine having armature and field excitation with compensation (Amplidyne generator).

This compensation feature is incorporated in the machine of Fig. 11-9, which in other respects is similar to that of Fig. 11-5. Once again salient stator poles are shown for simplicity and definiteness, although the assumption of a uniform air gap will be adhered to in theory. The winding labeled f is the separately excited winding considered previously. The winding labeled c, however, is a concentrated compensating winding connected in series with the output circuit from brushes d_1 and d_2 and therefore carrying the current I_d. The usual schematic representation of this generator, together with the connections and axial location of the field windings, is shown in Fig. 11-10. The concentrated compensating winding c will not produce the complete point-to-point neutralization of the dotted wave (Fig. 11-6) that would be approached by a distributed pole-face winding like that of Fig. 5-21, but it still may produce a flux neutralizing the voltage-inducing effect of the dotted wave between brushes q_1 and q_2. The compensating coils are wound on the same magnetic axis as the dotted wave, and all that is required is that they have the correct number of turns to produce a component flux per pole

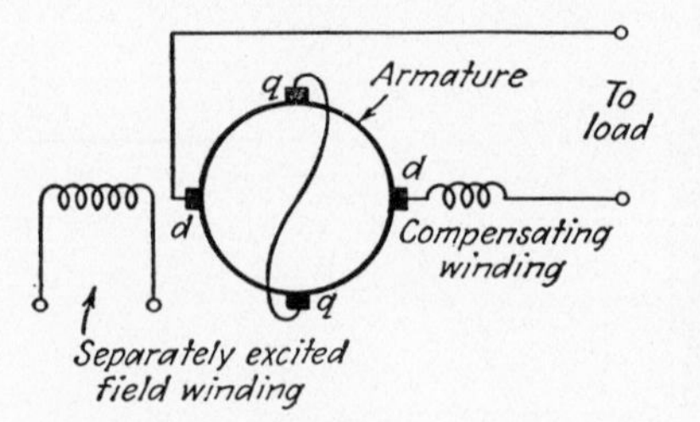

FIG. 11-10. Schematic diagram of Amplidyne generator, showing the minimum essentials.

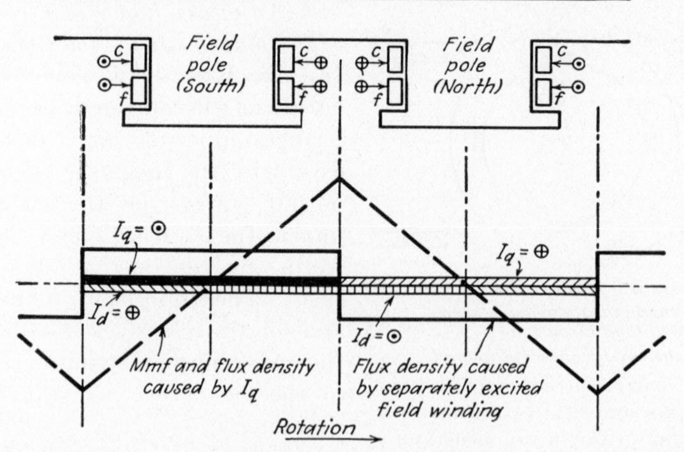

FIG. 11-11. Component mmf and flux-density distribution in machine of Fig. 11-9.

equal and opposite to that corresponding to the dotted wave. Since the winding carries the same current as brushes d_1 and d_2, the compensation naturally adjusts itself to varying values of armature mmf in this axis. Some distortion of the air-gap flux distribution is still present. If the distortion becomes too pronounced, the possibility of distributing the compensating winding in the pole faces still exists, but the design is more economical when the desired results can be obtained with a concentrated winding.

The net results are shown in the developed diagram of Fig. 11-11. Only the flux-density distributions for I_q and the separately excited winding are given here under the assumption that the voltage-inducing effects of I_d and the compensating winding exactly cancel. As in Eq. 11-17 with the I_d term omitted,

$$E_q = k_E \Phi_f n \tag{11-22}$$

The current in brushes q_1 and q_2 is then

$$I_q = \frac{E_q}{R_q} = \frac{n k_E \Phi_f}{R_q} \tag{11-23}$$

and, corresponding to Eq. 11-16, the output voltage is

$$E_d = K_{dq} I_q n = \frac{k_E K_{dq}}{R_q} \Phi_f n^2 \tag{11-24}$$

The commercial version of the machine is known by the trade name *Amplidyne*.[1] It is a common form of control-type generator used where the power requirements of the separately excited field must be held to a minimum because they are supplied from low-power sources, and where at the same time this field must exert complete and approximately proportional control of the generator output over a very wide range of output voltages. Physically the action of the Amplidyne is comparable with that of the two cascaded generators of Fig. 11-12, and it is therefore a two-stage device. The separately excited windings of Figs. 11-10 and 11-12 perform analogous functions. The first stage of Fig. 11-12 is represented by generator A supplying the field excitation for generator B; the second stage is represented by generator B. In Fig. 11-10, the two stages are incorporated in the same machine: the first stage is represented by the generator action giving rise to the current in the short-circuited brushes qq; the air-gap flux created by this current, together with the generator action giving rise to the output voltage across brushes dd, constitutes the second stage. The principal excitation is furnished by the short-circuit current, and the separately excited field must supply only enough flux so that the corresponding generated voltage maintains

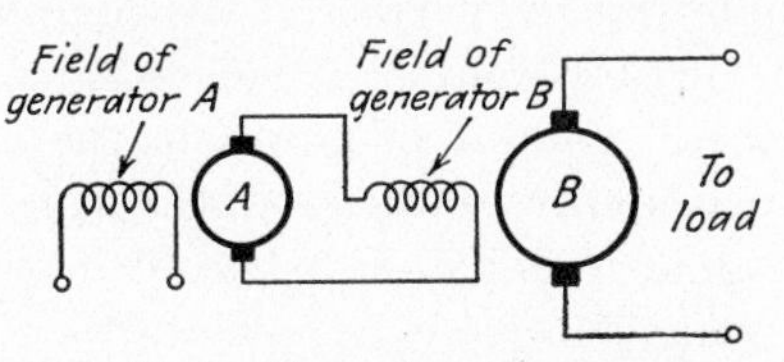

FIG. 11-12. Cascaded d-c generators.

[1] For a more comprehensive theoretical treatment of Amplidyne performance, including methods for the determination of machine constants from open-circuit and short-circuit tests, see T. D. Graybeal, Steady-state Theory of the Amplidyne Generator, *Trans. AIEE*, vol. 61, pp. 750–756, October, 1942.

the current in the low-resistance short-circuited-brush path. The excitation and power expenditure in the field winding are accordingly very much lower than in a conventional generator of similar rating.

Some ideas may now begin to emerge concerning the greater possibilities offered by additional brushes and field windings on d-c machines for obtaining desirable performance features. The full potentialities can be realized only after thorough examinations of a more generalized machine. Such a generalized d-c machine is called a *metadyne* and has been comprehensively investigated by Dr. J. M. Pestarini.[2] The metadyne includes as simple special cases the ordinary d-c machines and the variants discussed in this article.

11-2. The Amplidyne.[3] In the general field of dynamoelectric machines, the most nearly complete and spontaneous control over the mechanical output of a motor is obtained when the motor is a d-c machine supplied with power from a specially designed d-c generator. The generator in turn may be separately excited, and direct control over performance is exerted in the field circuit. Since the generator may have a plurality of field windings in order to produce the desired output characteristics, the field windings in which external control is exerted are referred to specifically as the *control fields*.

Precise control is generally associated with the expenditure of only a small amount of power in the controlling circuitry and with the use of reasonably sensitive measuring equipment to provide the controlling signal. Hence it is highly desirable that the control fields of the foregoing control-type generators take only very small excitation currents and therefore small amounts of control power. That is, the ratio of the armature power being controlled to the control-field power must be appreciably higher than in the conventional d-c generator. Even with high power amplification, electronic amplifiers may often be interposed between the initial control signal and the control fields to provide the necessary over-all gain. The two principal forms of control-type d-c generators are described in this and the following article.

The first of the two forms, the Amplidyne, achieves high power ampli-

[2] J. M. Pestarini, "Metadyne Statics," John Wiley & Sons, Inc., New York, 1952.

[3] Pertinent references on the construction, theory, and applications of the Amplidyne include the following: Alec Fisher, The Design Characteristics of Amplidyne Generators, *Trans. AIEE*, vol. 59, pp. 939–944, 1940; E. F. W. Alexanderson, M. A. Edwards, and K. K. Bowman, Dynamoelectric Amplifier for Power Control, *Trans. AIEE*, vol. 59, pp. 937–939, 1940; D. R. Shoults, M. A. Edwards, and F. E. Crever, Industrial Applications of Amplidyne Generators, *Trans. AIEE*, vol. 59, pp. 944–949, 1940; J. L. Bower, Fundamentals of the Amplidyne Generator, *Trans. AIEE*, vol. 64, pp. 873–880, 1945; J. R. Williams, The Amplidyne, *Elec. Eng.*, vol. 65, No. 5, pp. 208–213, May, 1946; B. Adkins, Amplidyne Regulating Systems, *J. IEE*, vol. 94, Part II*A*, No. 1, pp. 49–60, May, 1947.

fication by being a two-stage device. The minimum essentials are indicated in the schematic diagram of Fig. 11-10. A number of field windings may be present, any or all of which may be used in particular cases to obtain desired performance features. A more complete connection diagram incorporating all of these additional fields is given in Fig. 11-13. A view of a disassembled Amplidyne is given in Fig. 11-14.

The control field, located in the direct axis (also known as the *load axis*), produces a flux which gives rise to a speed voltage across brushes *qq* located in the quadrature axis (also known as the *short-circuit axis*).

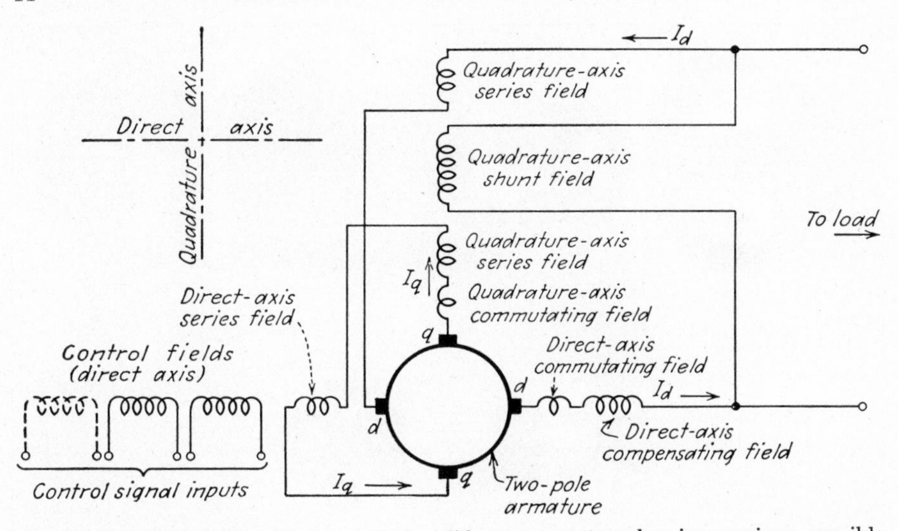

FIG. 11-13. Connection diagram of Amplidyne generator showing various possible auxiliary field windings.

This action corresponds to that in a conventional d-c generator. Brushes *qq* are short-circuited, however, so that a relatively large current may exist in the quadrature-axis brush circuit for a relatively small current in the control field. The quadrature-axis current I_q produces cross-magnetizing armature reaction, again as in a conventional d-c generator, and the armature-reaction flux is stationary in space and centered in the quadrature axis of the machine. This flux accordingly gives rise to a speed voltage across brushes *dd*. These direct-axis brushes supply the load. The direct-axis compensating field is essential to the maintenance of voltage when load current I_d is drawn, however. In the absence of the compensating field, armature-reaction mmf created by I_d would directly oppose the control-field mmf and result in substantial collapse of machine fluxes and voltages. The armature-reaction mmf created by I_d is compensated as exactly as possible by the compensating winding of a normal Amplidyne.

The excitation of the Amplidyne is thus furnished by both the armature and the field. The control field is responsible only for the production of sufficient voltage across the quadrature-axis brushes to force the current I_q through the low-resistance short-circuited path. Relatively high power amplification is thereby achieved. The order of magnitude of the power amplification depends on how much of the available field-winding space is used for the control winding. Thus, according to Adkins,[4] "A typical amplidyne of 2-5 kw would have a power amplification ratio of 20,000:1 if the whole of the field space were used for a

FIG. 11-14. Disassembled view of 5-kw 250-volt 20-amp 1,750-rpm Amplidyne generator. (*Courtesy of General Electric Company.*)

single winding. If, for example, the main field winding occupied 30 per cent of the total space, the amplification ratio when using this winding only would be 6000:1." Much higher amplification can be obtained when needed. The amplification obtained in the first stage of the Amplidyne (*i.e.*, from the control field to the quadrature-axis armature circuit) is significantly higher than that in the second. These ratios may be compared with values of 20 to 100 for conventional generators.

Any of the various auxiliary field windings shown in Fig. 11-13 may be added to provide desirable performance characteristics for specific applications. Such auxiliary windings play roughly the same roles as the commutating fields, stabilizing windings, and series fields of conventional d-c machines in providing the flexibility leading to tailor-made character-

[4] B. Adkins, Amplidyne Regulating Systems, *J. IEE*, vol. 94, Part II*A*, No. 1, pp. 49–60, May, 1947.

istics. The quadrature-axis shunt field, for example, reinforces the air-gap flux produced by the quadrature-axis armature current I_q, thereby increasing the amplification or, for the same amplification, decreasing the required value of I_q. When this field is used, its resistance line must have a greater slope than the second-stage magnetization curve in order that the Amplidyne shall not become self-excited—*i.e.*, in order that the Amplidyne shall not produce an output voltage significantly greater than the residual value when the net control-field excitation is zero. Definite mutual coupling exists between the quadrature-axis armature circuit and the quadrature-axis shunt field. This coupling usually requires corrective steps, such as the use of a high external series inductance in the shunt-field circuit, to minimize transient induced currents in the field.

The flux created by the current I_q may also be reinforced by connection of a quadrature-axis series field in the quadrature-axis brush circuit. This step may result in reduced over-all amplification because of the added impedance of the winding, but it does result in lower values of I_q and better air-gap flux distribution. The quadrature-axis series field in the output circuit may be used to provide compounding action as in a conventional compound generator. A direct-axis series winding in the quadrature-axis armature circuit is sometimes used to compensate for changes in brush-contact resistance. Good commutation is essential to optimum performance. It is obtained by resistance commutation in conjunction with appropriate interpolar spaces, by use of direct-axis commutating poles to provide a commutating voltage at brushes *dd*, or by the further use of quadrature-axis commutating poles. Use of quadrature-axis commutating poles, however, adds to the impedance in the short-circuited path between brushes *qq*. The commutation problems are generally very similar to those in conventional d-c generators.

The control field is usually wound in several sections as indicated in Fig. 11-13. Several signals associated with the controlling process may accordingly be impressed simultaneously and superimposed in the direct-axis magnetic circuit of the machine. The magnetic effect of any one signal may be added to or subtracted from the combined effect of the other signals. One very common connection is to impress on one control field a direct voltage whose magnitude is proportional to the desired value of the quantity being controlled. This field is then called the *reference field*. Another control field, connected so as to buck the reference field, has impressed on it a voltage proportional to the actual value of the quantity being controlled. When the desired and actual values are the same, the output voltage of the Amplidyne is essentially zero. When the two values are different, the output voltage of the Amplidyne is approximately proportional to the difference and is of a polarity tending to correct the difference. A stabilizing signal may be impressed on a third control field to avoid the possibility of hunting, which may be caused by overshooting the desired value.

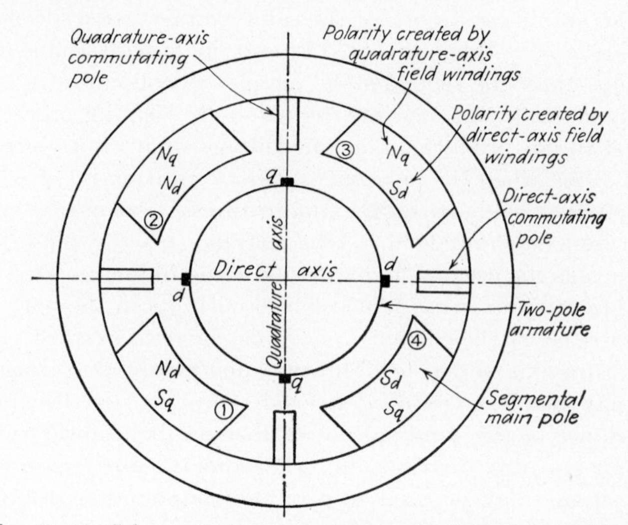

FIG. 11-15. Schematic diagram of structure of 2-pole Amplidyne.

A schematic diagram of the magnetic structure of a 2-pole Amplidyne is given in Fig. 11-15. Commutating poles are shown in both axes. The two main poles are constructed in the form of four segmental poles, or half poles. Segmental poles 1 and 2 form one equivalent direct-axis pole, and segmental poles 3 and 4 form the other; the direct-axis field is thus centered on the horizontal line through the armature. Segmental poles 2 and 3 form one equivalent quadrature-axis pole, and segmental poles 4 and 1 form the other; the quadrature-axis field is thus centered on the vertical line through the armature. Direct-axis field coils are wound around segmental poles 1 and 2 and segmental poles 3 and 4 so that relative magnetic polarities are produced as indicated by the symbols N_d and S_d in Fig. 11-15. Quadrature-axis field coils are wound around segmental poles 2 and 3 and segmental poles 4 and 1 so that relative magnetic polarities are produced as indicated by

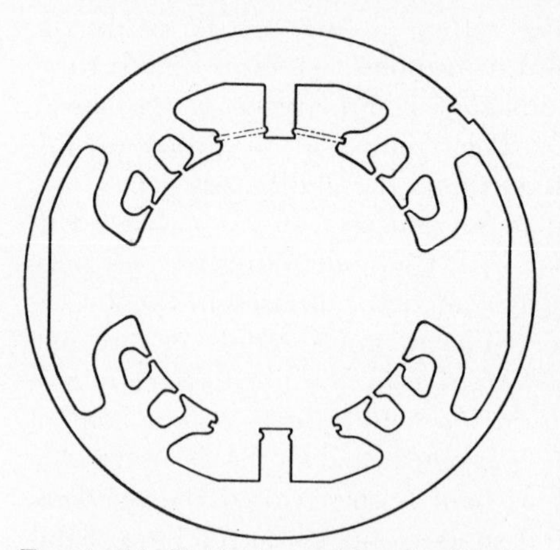

FIG. 11-16. Typical punching for 2-pole Amplidyne with distributed pole-face compensation. (*Courtesy of General Electric Company.*)

the symbols N_q and S_q. The interpolar spaces between segmental poles aid in the production of good commutation even in the absence of commutating poles. The outline of a typical punching for the stator of a 2-pole Amplidyne is given in Fig. 11-16.

To minimize eddy currents and their influence in slowing down the rate of growth or decay of flux, the entire magnetic circuit is laminated. Residual magnetism and hysteresis effects must also be minimized. These effects tend to be larger than in a conventional d-c generator

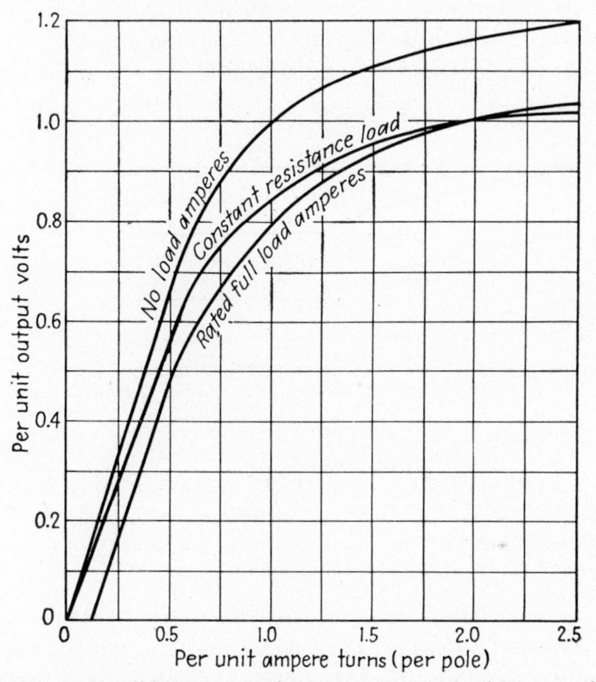

FIG. 11-17. Average Amplidyne saturation curves plotted with per-unit coordinates. Unit voltage equals rated voltage. (*Replotted from curves furnished by General Electric Company.*)

because those produced in the first stage are amplified in the second stage. Occasionally a so-called *killer winding* with a small a-c excitation may be used to minimize residual effects. The air gap is smaller and the flux densities in the iron are generally lower than in normal d-c machines. The rated output for a given frame size is somewhat lower in an Amplidyne than in the conventional generator, but the efficiency may be somewhat higher.

The steady-state characteristics of an Amplidyne generator are illustrated by Figs. 11-17 and 11-18. Figure 11-17 gives the no-load and full-load saturation curves in terms of the output voltage as a function of control-field excitation, as well as the curve followed for a constant-resistance load. Figure 11-18 shows the general nature of the external characteristics for a series of fixed values of control-field excitation. The saturation curves usually bend somewhat more than in the usual generator, largely because of the effect of armature-tooth saturation on the small control-field flux. The Amplidyne generally operates on the substantially linear portion of the saturation curve except when the controlling process calls for a sudden change in operating conditions. Then the control-field excitation may be very high until at least partial readjustment has taken place, a process known as *forcing*.

The transient response of the Amplidyne is of even greater importance than the steady-state performance, for an Amplidyne in a precise regulat-

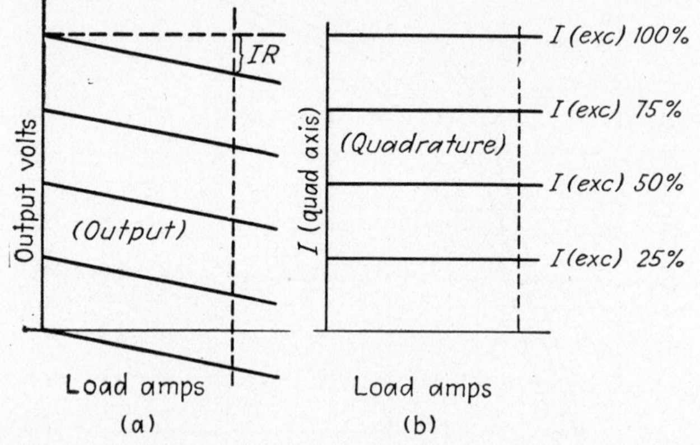

FIG. 11-18. External characteristics of Amplidyne generator. Quadrature-axis armature current (*b*) is substantially independent of load.

ing circuit is rarely called upon to operate under steady conditions for long periods of time. Rather, it is called upon to respond as rapidly as possible to sudden changes in control-field voltage caused by the need for rapid readjustment in the quantity being controlled. Ideally, the response of the Amplidyne and the bringing about of the required readjustment would be instantaneous. Actually, the Amplidyne, as well as the other elements in the over-all control equipment, inserts time delays when the amount of stored energy in electric, magnetic, or mechanical fields must change. In the Amplidyne, time delays are caused by the winding inductances and eddy-current paths; the time constant is in the range from 0.02 to 0.25 sec.

A dynamoelectric power amplifier must be judged in terms of both amplification and speed of response, for an increase in amplification is accompanied by an increase in time lag in the response—by an increase in the time constant of the machine, in other words. "An increase in control-field copper weight or a reduction in air gap results in an increase of both time constant and amplification. A longer time constant indicates slower response, but with equal volt-amperes input, the time to reach a predetermined voltage is much less for a given amplidyne generator with the higher time constant and amplification."[5]

Both the amplification and speed of response are functions of the load constants as well as those of the Amplidyne itself. Accordingly, final over-all judgment must be based on the dynamic performance of the system as a whole in the general manner indicated in Chap. 13. A simplified example of such a control system is given in Fig. 11-19. Here the object is to keep the speed of a d-c motor constant at a preset value. The under-

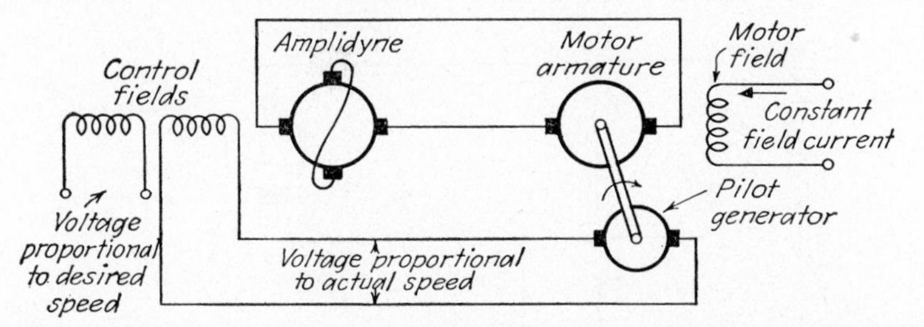

FIG. 11-19. Simplified circuit for speed control of d-c motor supplied from Amplidyne generator.

lying basis of control is the armature-voltage-control or Ward Leonard method with the conventional generator replaced by an Amplidyne. The actual speed of the motor is measured by a small pilot generator or d-c tachometer on the motor shaft. The pilot generator thus impresses on the right-hand control field, or speed-control field, a voltage proportional to the actual motor speed. At the same time and from a separate source, a voltage is impressed on the left-hand control field, or *reference field*, whose magnitude is an expression of the desired speed. The two control fields produce opposing mmfs. When the motor speed is correct, the reference-field mmf exceeds that of the speed-control field by a sufficient amount to generate the appropriate armature terminal voltage to maintain rotation at the correct speed. When the motor speed is too high, the net Amplidyne excitation is decreased by an increase in the opposing speed-control-field mmf; this action causes a decrease in armature terminal voltage and hence in motor speed. When the motor speed is too low, the net Amplidyne excitation is increased by a decrease in the opposing speed-control-field mmf; this action causes an increase in armature terminal voltage and hence in motor speed. Thus, the motor speed may be made independent of changes of load or of other surrounding conditions.

[5] Quoted from Alec Fisher, The Design Characteristics of Amplidyne Generators, *Trans. AIEE*, vol. 59, pp. 939–944, 1940.

The desired speed is preset by impressing the appropriate voltage magnitude on the reference field.

When the control-signal source is too feeble to supply the requisite control-field excitation, electronic amplifiers are inserted between the control equipment and the Amplidyne control field. Also, when the motor being controlled is a large one, the Amplidyne usually controls the field excitation of a conventional generator rather than supplying the motor directly. Another example, shown schematically in Fig. 11-20, illustrates the latter case and shows some of the uses of additional control fields. The main generator and motor in Fig. 11-20 are connected as in the usual Ward Leonard drive, but an Amplidyne replaces the conventional generator

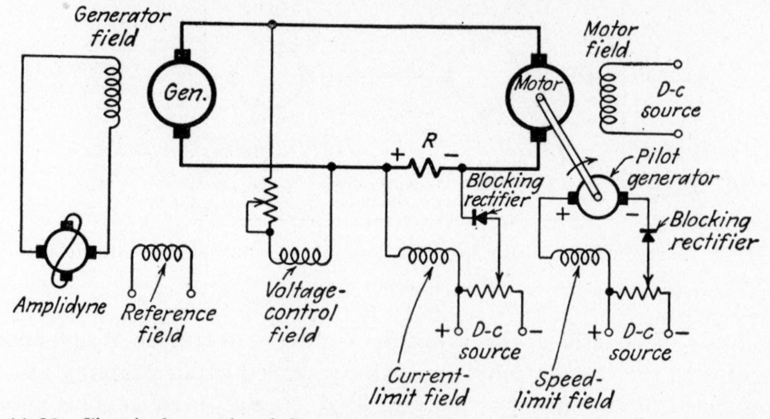

FIG. 11-20. Circuit for maintaining constant motor impressed voltage and limiting motor armature current and speed to predetermined values.

exciter. The objects are to maintain the motor terminal voltage constant at a preset value and at the same time to limit both the motor armature current and speed to predetermined, safe values. Four control fields are required in the Amplidyne. The reference field and the voltage-control field, connected to produce opposing mmfs, maintain constant generator output voltage in the same general manner that the two corresponding fields of Fig. 11-19 maintain constant speed; the value of the generator voltage is adjusted by means of the rheostat in the voltage-control field. Current limitation is provided by connecting the current-limit field so that its mmf opposes the reference-field mmf when the current in the motor armature is excessive, an action which lowers the generator voltage and so restores the current to safe values. Armature current is measured in terms of the voltage drop across a low resistance R (such as an ammeter shunt) in the armature circuit. If this voltage is greater than the opposing voltage picked off a d-c source, a current appears in the current-limit field. If this voltage is smaller, however, no current appears because of the presence of the blocking rectifier (a selenium or copper oxide rectifier); thus the current-limit field cannot aid the reference field and increase the armature current. Speed limitation is provided by the speed-limit field in an essentially identical manner, the measurement of speed being made by a pilot generator connected to the motor shaft. The values of current limit and speed limit may be set by the drop-wire rheostats across the d-c sources in the respective control-field circuits. The entire drive is thereby

FIG. 11-21. Paper winder equipped with Amplidyne side-register control. (*Courtesy of General Electric Company.*)

protected against severe electrical and mechanical strains, while at the same time changes in operating conditions may be brought about as rapidly as these limits permit.

A final example of the use of an Amplidyne for industrial control purposes is illustrated pictorially in Fig. 11-21. The associated diagram of Fig. 11-22 outlines the operating principles.

11-3. The Rototrol and Regulex.[6] The second principal form of control-type d-c generator is, in its most common version, a single-stage device wherein the control-field signals directly determine the output

[6] Pertinent references describing these devices include W. H. Formhals, Rototrol—A Versatile Electrical Regulator, *Westinghouse Eng.*, vol. 2, p. 51, May, 1942; T. B. Montgomery, Regulex—Instability in Harness, *Allis-Chalmers Elec. Rev.*, vol. 11, Nos. 2 and 3, pp. 5–9, second and third quarter 1946.

voltage of the armature. It is called by the trade name *Rototrol* (coined from *rotating control*) or *Regulex* (coined from *regulating exciter*). It is not an armature-excited machine like the Amplidyne, where the armature mmf provides the excitation for the second stage. Instead, it is a relatively simple modification of a conventional d-c generator in which are installed a series- or shunt-field winding for self-excitation and several separately excited control-field windings. In the steady state, essentially all of the excitation is provided by the self-excited or *self-energizing field*.

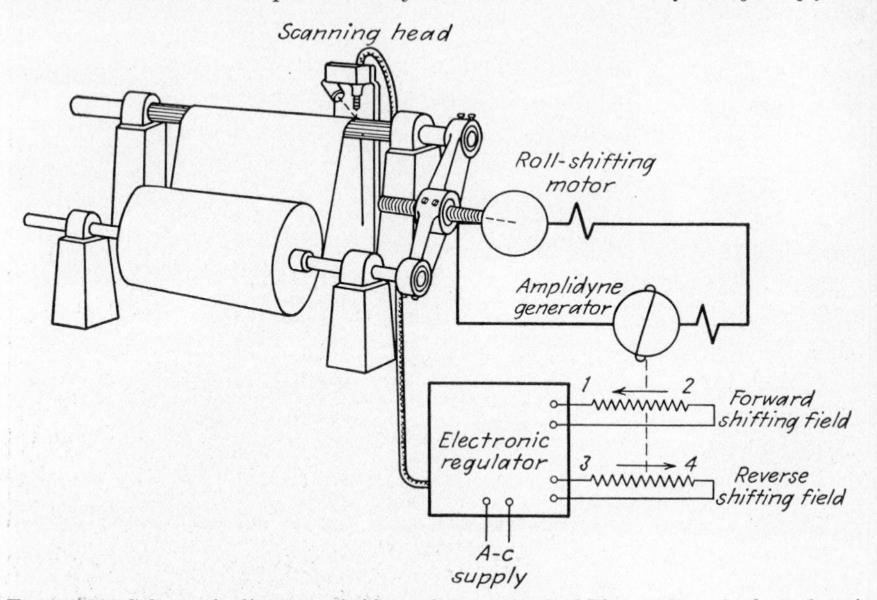

Fig. 11-22. Schematic diagram of side-register control of Fig. 11-21. A photoelectric device "watches" the position of the moving paper edge. The intensity of the reflected light is converted to an electric signal which is amplified and compared with a reference. Any difference causes the Amplidyne to operate the roll-shifting motor. (*Courtesy of General Electric Company.*)

When a change in output voltage is called for, corresponding to a change in operating conditions in the equipment being controlled, the control fields are effective in determining the new operating point. The power level in the control windings is accordingly minimized by calling upon them only to initiate changes or to stabilize steady operating conditions.

As indicated in Fig. 11-23, the self-energizing field of the Rototrol or Regulex may be either a series or a shunt winding. The outstanding feature of the machine is that the resistance of the self-energizing field circuit is adjusted so that its field-resistance line coincides with the linear part of the magnetization curve. The machine is then said to be a *tuned generator*, and the adjusting resistor R (Fig. 11-23) is called a *tuning resistor*. The function of the control fields is then to stabilize operation at the appropriate point on the air-gap line of the magnetization curve or to shift the operating point to a new position in accordance with signals from the controlling equipment. As in the Amplidyne, the control fields usually include a reference field (here sometimes called the *pattern field*) and at least one other field (here sometimes called the *differential field*) connected so that its mmf opposes that of the reference field. Additional control windings may be installed.

Recall from Art. 5-6 that the field-resistance line for a self-excited d-c generator is simply a plot, superimposed on the magnetization curve, of the linear Ohm's law relation between armature terminal voltage and the current in the self-excited field. Recall also that the intersection of the field-resistance line and the magnetization curve determines the no-load

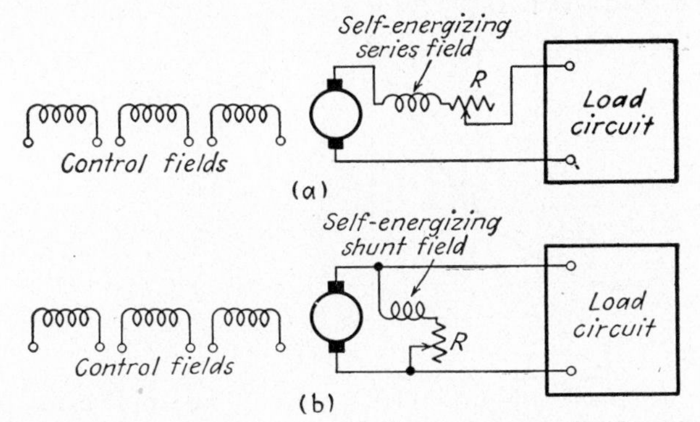

FIG. 11-23. Basic Rototrol or Regulex with (*a*) series and (*b*) shunt self-energizing field.

operating point of a shunt generator. Recognize that substantially the same thought process holds for a series generator when the field-resistance line is based on the entire series-field-circuit resistance, including the load, so that the essential reasoning can be carried out in terms of a shunt field. The effects of residual magnetism and of armature resistance and armature reaction will, in general, be ignored.

With only self-excitation and with the field-resistance line coincident with the air-gap line (See Fig. 11-24), the terminal voltage may lie anywhere between points a and a', with build-up depending on residual magnetism. In general, the voltage may wander between these two points, resulting in voltage instability. When a small amount fg of separate excitation is added, the terminal voltage V_t becomes the definite value $fb = gc$, slightly greater than the value at a. When a small amount $f'g'$ of separate excitation having the opposite polarity is added, the terminal voltage reverses and becomes the opposite value $f'b' = g'c'$. Thus, the terminal voltage tends to change over a wide range when the polarity of a small amount of separate excitation is changed.

This action, together with arranging the over-all control circuitry so that the separate mmf is a function of the departure from the desired value of the quantity being controlled, leads to stabilization of the operating voltage at the appropriate value between points a and a' on the magnetization curve. Figure 11-25 presents an application of the Rototrol or Regulex to the automatic speed control of a d-c motor. The main generator and motor are arranged in a Ward Leonard connection, with the Rototrol furnishing the excitation of the main generator. On one of the Rototrol control fields is impressed a voltage proportional to the desired motor speed. On the other control field is impressed a voltage proportional to the actual motor speed, obtained from a small pilot generator on the motor shaft. These two control fields are connected so that their mmfs oppose. Any separately excited field mmf in the Rototrol is thus proportional to the departure of the motor speed from the desired

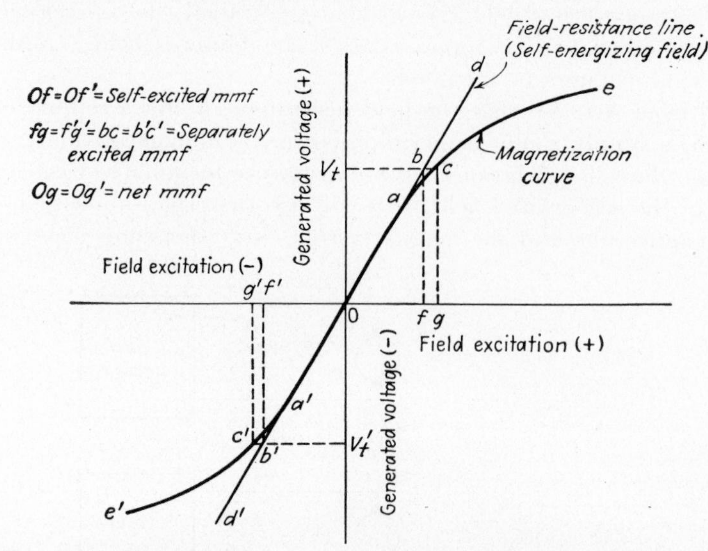

FIG. 11-24. Magnetization curve with field-resistance line tangent to it.

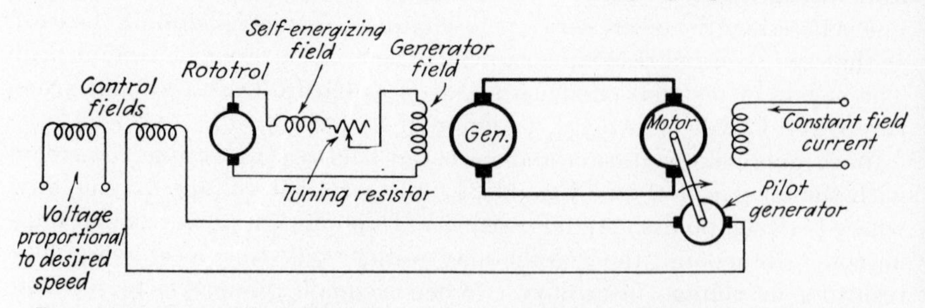

FIG. 11-25. Rototrol or Regulex exciter applied to d-c-motor speed control.

value, and the polarity of the net control-field mmf depends on whether the motor speed is slow or fast.

When the motor speed is slow, the net control-field mmf is of such polarity that the Rototrol output voltage tends to build up to a value somewhat larger than that at point a (Fig. 11-24). This increase in Rototrol voltage is accompanied by increased field current and terminal voltage in the main generator, and hence by an increase in the motor speed. When the motor speed is fast, substantially the reverse actions take place. The net control-field mmf is of such polarity that the Rototrol output voltage tends to build down to a value somewhat below that at point a'.

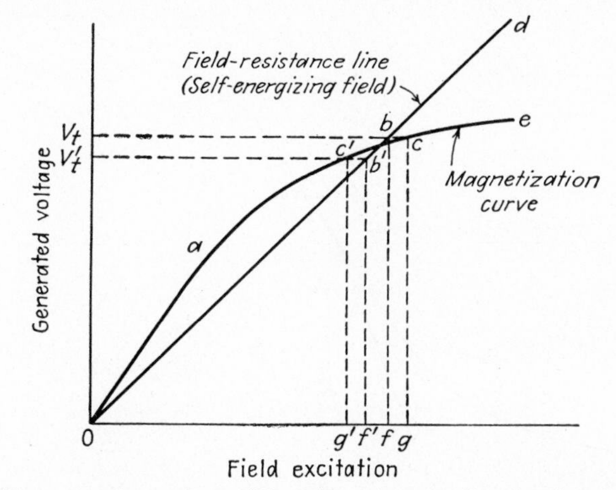

FIG. 11-26. Magnetization curve with field-resistance line having lower than the critical slope.

This decrease is accompanied by decreased field current and terminal voltage in the main generator, and hence by a decrease in the motor speed. When the motor speed is correct, the net control-field mmf is zero. Steady operation then takes place with the Rototrol output voltage at the appropriate value between points O and a. Stabilization of the steady operating voltage may be viewed as the result of a continuous process of differential dither. A differential drift of the Rototrol voltage above the appropriate value means a differential increase in motor speed above the desired value; the increase in turn means the appearance of a differential net control-field mmf of such polarity as to build down the Rototrol voltage to its correct value. Similarly, a differential drift of the Rototrol voltage below its correct value results in a differential restoring mmf from the control field. In the steady state, therefore, the operating point on the magnetization curve is stabilized by the control windings, and the required excitation is furnished by the self-energizing winding.

The advantages of operating with the field-resistance line coincident with the lower part of the magnetization curve may be more fully appreciated by inspection of Figs. 11-26 and 11-27. These figures correspond to Fig. 11-24 except that the field resistance is lower then the critical value in Fig. 11-26 and higher in Fig. 11-27. In both figures (as in Fig. 11-24), fg and $f'g'$ represent small amounts of separately excited mmf of opposite polarities. As this mmf is varied between the values fg and $f'g'$, the terminal voltages vary between V_t and V'_t. The ranges between V_t and V'_t in Figs. 11-26 and 11-27 are seen to be much smaller than in Fig. 11-24. The practical result is that the range of control is much more restricted

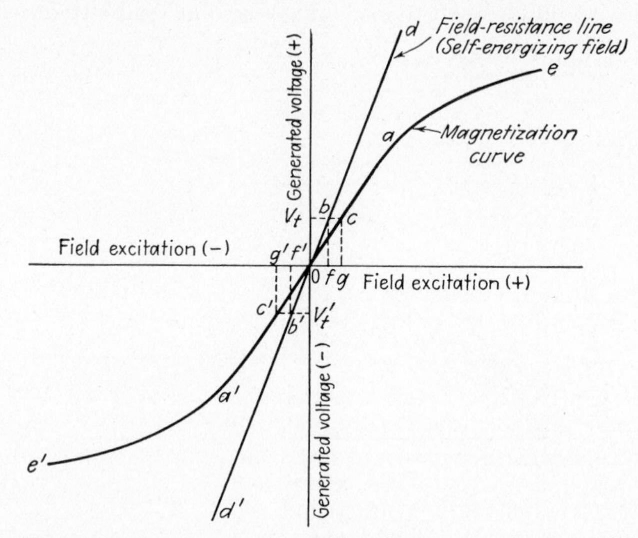

FIG. 11-27. Magnetization curve with field-resistance line having higher than the critical value.

and the response much less spontaneous than when the field resistance is properly adjusted to its critical value.

The general fields of application of the Rototrol and Regulex are substantially the same as for the Amplidyne.[7] When the value of the amplification to be obtained is at a premium, the Rototrol may be constructed as a two-stage or a multistage device by installing additional field windings and special armature-winding and brush arrangements so that proper excitation for the additional fields may be obtained from the armature with the desired number of stages cascaded.[8]

[7] See, for instance, G. A. Caldwell and W. H. Formhals, Electrical Drives for Wide Speed Ranges, *Trans. AIEE*, vol. 61, pp. 54–56, 1942; E. L. Harder and C. E. Valentine, Static Voltage Regulator for Rototrol Exciter, *Trans. AIEE*, vol. 64, pp. 601–606, 1945; W. H. Harris, Industrial Application of Rototrol Regulators, *Trans. AIEE*, vol. 65, pp. 118–123, 1946.

[8] For the details of these special Rototrols, see A. W. Kimball, Two-stage Rototrol for Low-energy Regulating Systems, *Trans. AIEE*, vol. 66, pp. 1507–1511, 1947; and M. Liwschitz, The Multi-stage Rototrol, *Trans. AIEE*, vol. 66, pp. 564–568, 1947.

11-4. Self-synchronous Machines and Systems. Among the more exacting of modern control requirements is that of position control, or causing the angular position of one shaft to follow that of another as closely as possible. A series of devices which have been developed as valuable adjuncts to such control systems may be referred to as *self-synchronous devices*, since the common object is to cause two shafts to run in exact synchronism. They are also known by various trade names, such as *Selsyn*, *Synchro*, and *Autosyn*. In the following discussion, the specific word *Selsyn* will frequently be used in describing the devices.

There are three general types of systems involving Selsyn devices; (1) three-phase power Selsyns for heavy torque transmission, (2) single-phase instrument or indicator Selsyns for only very light torque transmission, and (3) generator-transformer systems for indicating shaft misalignment in terms of a voltage magnitude and polarity. The first of these three types is discussed in Chap. 9. The other two types are described in the present article.

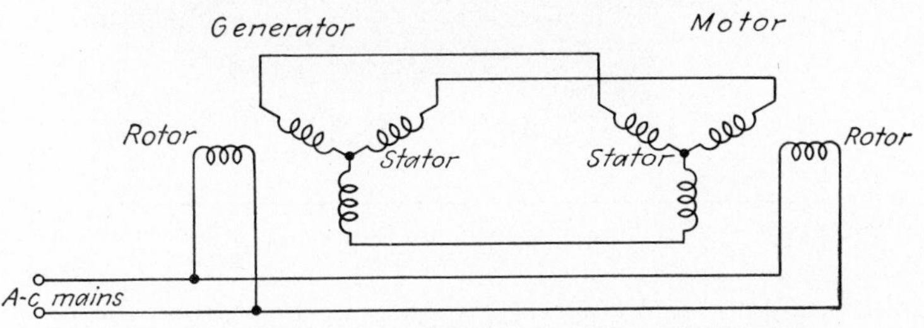

FIG. 11-28. Single-phase Selsyn generator-motor system.

a. Single-phase Generator-motor Systems. In Art. 9-9, it is shown that torque tending to keep two shafts in synchronism is produced by a system of two 3-phase Selsyns whose stator windings are connected in parallel to the same 3-phase source and whose rotor windings have their corresponding terminals connected together (see Fig. 9-25). As illustrated by Fig. 9-27, the torques with the two rotors at standstill are a sinusoidal function of the displacement angle between the shafts, and the torque directions are such as to reduce this angle.

Substantially the same type of action is obtained when the 3-phase system is replaced by the single-phase system shown diagrammatically in Fig. 11-28. In most respects, the construction of the *Selsyn generator* or *transmitter* is similar to that of the *Selsyn motor* or *receiver*. Both have a single-phase winding (usually on the rotor) connected to a common a-c voltage source. On the other member (usually the stator), both have three windings with axes 120° apart and connected in Y; these windings on the generator and motor have their corresponding terminals connected together. When the single-phase rotor windings are excited, voltages are induced by transformer action in the Y-connected stator windings. If the two rotors are in the same space position relative to their stator windings, the generator and motor stator-winding voltages are equal, no current circulates in these windings, and no torque is transmitted. If, however, the two rotor space positions do not correspond, the stator-winding

Fig. 11-29. Typical high-accuracy Selsyn. (*Courtesy of General Electric Company.*)

voltages are unequal and currents circulate in the stator winding. These currents, in conjunction with the air-gap magnetic fields, produce torques tending to bring the two rotor space positions into correspondence.

Mechanically, Selsyns have the same general construction features as small motors. The external appearance of a typical Selsyn is shown in Fig. 11-29. The rotor structure of a Selsyn motor may be seen in Fig.

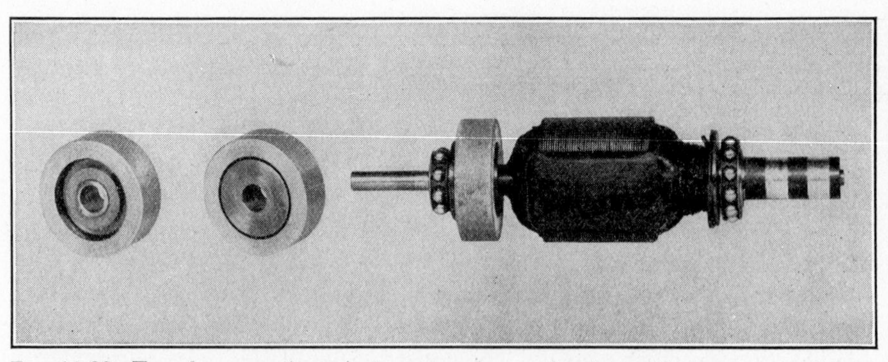

Fig. 11-30. Two dampers (front and rear) and wound rotor, with damper, for Selsyn motor. (*Courtesy of General Electric Company.*)

11-30. The rotor and stator are laminated, and ball bearings are used to minimize friction. Both the generator and motor have 2-pole windings with a salient-pole rotor structure. Analytic evaluation of torque must accordingly recognize saliency in the manner of the two-reaction theory of Chap. 8.[9] As in 3-phase systems, the motor torque at standstill or for slow rotation may be shown to depend closely upon the sine of the relative angular difference in position of the generator and motor shafts. Torque gradients developed by electrically identical generators and motors interconnected as in Fig. 11-28 range from 0.07 in.-oz. per degree for the smaller units to 1.75 in.-oz. per degree for the larger units.[10]

A modification of the Selsyn system of Fig. 11-28 may be introduced by including a *differential Selsyn*, thereby permitting the rotation of a shaft to be a function of the sum or difference of the rotation of two other shafts.

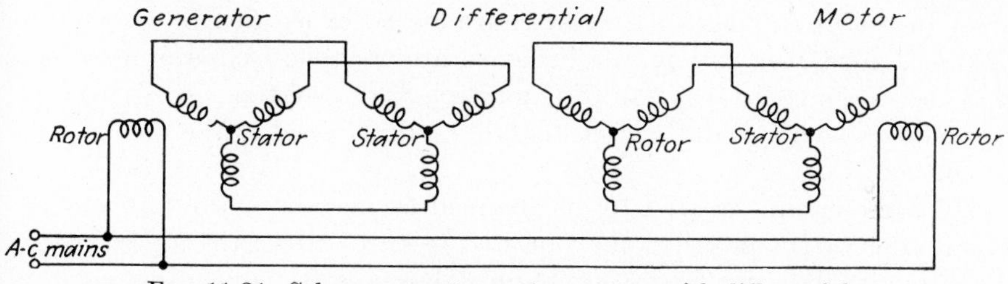

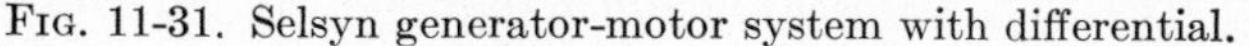

FIG. 11-31. Selsyn generator-motor system with differential.

In Fig. 11-31, the differential Selsyn acts as a differential generator. The voltages impressed on its stator windings induce corresponding voltages in the rotor windings. The relative magnitudes of the three rotor voltages are the same as would exist if the differential were removed and the generator turned through an angle equal to the sum or difference of the generator and differential angles. Such differential generators usually have a bank of three capacitors connected across the primary terminals to improve power factor and hence minimize the possibility of overheating in the system. Alternatively, the differential may be used as a motor supplied from two separate Selsyn generators and producing a rotation dependent upon the sum or difference of the two generator rotations. The connections in this case are the same as in Fig. 11-31 except that the differential is relabeled *Differential motor* and the motor on the right is relabeled *Generator*.

These single-phase Selsyn systems are used primarily for instrumentation and data transmission in cases where the data can be translated into the angular position of a shaft. Remote indication of the height of water in a reservoir or of the position of control surfaces on aircraft are examples.

[9] For quantitative analysis of single-phase Selsyn operation, see T. M. Linville and J. S. Woodward, Selsyn Instruments for Position Systems, *Trans. AIEE*, vol. 53, pp. 953–960, 1934.

[10] These values, together with other orders of magnitude indicated in this article, are taken from T. C. Johnson, Selsyn Design and Application, *Trans. AIEE*, vol. 64, pp. 703–708, 1945.

They may also be used for such purposes as opening or closing a valve to correct discrepancies revealed in terms of the angular position transmitted to the shaft of the receiver Selsyn. One generator may drive several motors, the number depending on the relative size of generator and motor units and on the error which may be tolerated. In instrument systems it may be feasible to incorporate unity-voltage-gain electronic power amplifiers between the generator and motors to increase the power level and permit the use of more motors. The maximum static error for a system consisting of a generator and a single motor of the same size is of the order of 1° and is caused largely by friction in the motor bearings. The error increases as additional Selsyns are added or as the line impedance between generator and motor becomes appreciable. Greater precision may be obtained by the use of a multiple-speed system, involving two complete Selsyn systems geared together as described in the second part of this article.

Dynamic errors, created by mechanical oscillation of the motor shaft about the correct position, may be two or three times the static errors. To minimize dynamic errors, mechanical dampers are built into the rotors of motor units. Dampers are shown in Fig. 11-30. A common form of inertia-friction damper consists of two disks driven by the shaft, one driven directly and the other through a friction pad. When the shaft is running at a steady speed, both disks rotate at the same speed and no damping is produced. When the speed is changing, however, one disk is free to move against the friction pad with respect to the other disk and damping is produced.

When the motor is called upon to supply significant torque, the error increases because of the need of a definite angular displacement between generator and motor shafts for torque transmission. This fact, together with heating of the Selsyn equipment, definitely limits the torque magnitudes.

b. Generator-Transformer Systems. Very commonly the process of controlling with reasonable exactness the instant-by-instant angular position of a shaft calls for the exertion of large torques. When Selsyn equipment must exert these torques directly, a very considerable and intolerable sacrifice in the faithfulness of position reproduction may result. For such control purposes, it is common to apply the self-synchronous principle in such a manner that a voltage is produced whose magnitude is a function of the angular displacement between the positions of two shafts. Such a voltage is an *error voltage,* for its presence indicates a discrepancy in the position of the shaft being controlled. The error voltage may then be fed into other devices to instigate correction of the discrepancy causing it. The Selsyns themselves thus do not have to supply mechanical power. The error voltage may be referred to as an *error-modulated signal*—a carrier wave whose amplitude is proportional to the error and whose instantaneous polarity is determined by the sign of the error.

The basic method of producing the error voltage is shown by the circuit of Fig. 11-32. Two interconnected Selsyns are again involved, one a generator and the other a very similar unit called a *Selsyn* (or *Synchro*) *control transformer*. The rotor of the Selsyn generator is excited from a single-phase source, producing a magnetic field in the generator and voltages in the stator windings of both the generator and the control transformer. If the voltage drops caused by exciting current are neglected, the induced voltages in the two stator windings must be equal. Therefore the distribution of flux about the control-transformer stator must be similar to that about the generator stator. The effect is consequently the same as if the two rotor windings were on the same magnetic

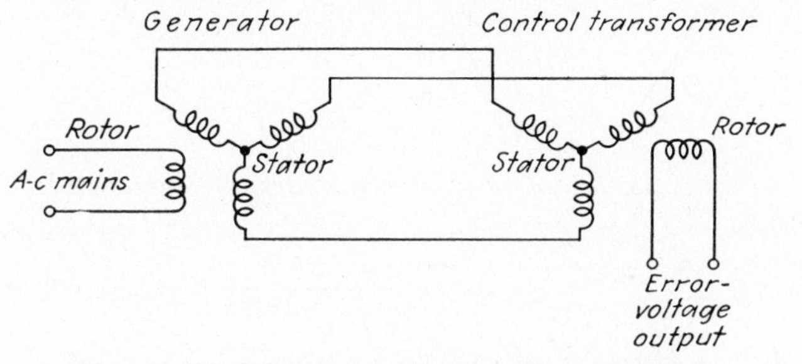

FIG. 11-32. Selsyn generator-transformer system.

circuit and arranged so that their axes could be given any arbitrary displacement angle in space. The arrangement is thus the equivalent of an adjustable mutual inductance between the two rotor windings, but with the added feature that geographical separation of the two windings is possible. When the angle is 90 electrical degrees, corresponding to a 90-electrical-degree displacement of the two shafts, no voltage is induced in the transformer rotor; this displacement is the equilibrium position of the two shafts. When the angle has any value except 90° and 270°, a voltage is induced in the transformer rotor. As shown in Fig. 11-33, the magnitude of the voltage is a function of the angular discrepancy between the two shafts, and the instantaneous polarity depends on the direction of the displacement. The function is essentially a sinusoid. Differential Selsyns may also be incorporated between the generators and control transformers of these systems.

This qualitative picture of the combined operation of generator and control transformer may be made more specific by a brief analysis in outline form for an idealized system as illustrated in Fig. 11-34. Consider that the two Selsyns have cylindrical-rotor structures and that they, together with the interconnecting lines, are lossless. Let E_1 be the rms voltage induced in one leg of the generator stator winding when the axis of that leg coincides with the rotor-winding axis, and assume that the induced voltage varies as the cosine of the angle between the leg and rotor-winding axes. Consider that the rotors are stationary or revolving slowly enough so that speed voltages are negligible. When θ_1 is the angle

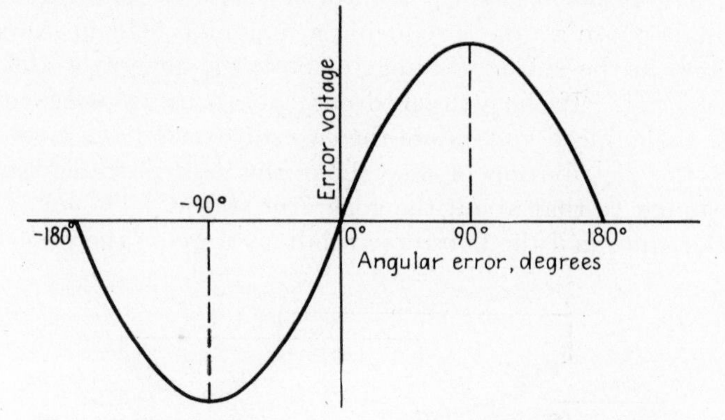

Fig. 11-33. Variation of error voltage with angular error.

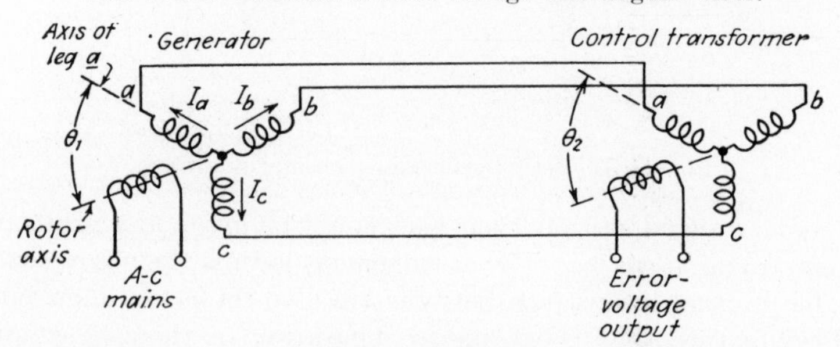

Fig. 11-34. Selsyn generator-transformer system for evaluation of error voltage. (Positive values of θ_1 and θ_2 are measured clockwise from the axis of phase a.)

between the leg-a and rotor-winding axes, the rms voltages in the three legs are

$$E_a = E_1 \cos \theta_1 \tag{11-25}$$

$$E_b = E_1 \cos (\theta_1 - 120°) \tag{11-26}$$

and

$$E_c = E_1 \cos (\theta_1 - 240°) \tag{11-27}$$

Notice that these are single-phase voltages of different magnitudes and do not form a 3-phase system.

Now consider that the iron is unsaturated, so that the self- and mutual inductances of the stator windings are constant. Let L be the total self-inductance of one leg of the generator stator, one leg of the transformer stator, and the interconnecting line. Let M be the sum of the mutual inductance between generator-stator legs plus that between transformer-stator legs. Vector equations involving the three leg currents I_a, I_b, and I_c may then be written by noting that the voltage between stator junctions is the same regardless of the path followed. Accordingly,

$$\begin{aligned} E_1 \cos \theta_1 &- j\omega L I_a - j\omega M(I_b + I_c) \\ &= E_1 \cos(\theta_1 - 120°) - j\omega L I_b - j\omega M(I_a + I_c) \\ &= E_1 \cos(\theta_1 - 240°) - j\omega L I_c - j\omega M(I_a + I_b) \end{aligned} \tag{11-28}$$

Moreover,

$$I_a + I_b + I_c = 0 \tag{11-29}$$

Simultaneous solution of these equations yields

$$j\omega I_a = \frac{E_1}{L - M} \cos \theta_1 \tag{11-30}$$

$$j\omega I_b = \frac{E_1}{L - M} \cos(\theta_1 - 120°) \tag{11-31}$$

and

$$j\omega I_c = \frac{E_1}{L - M} \cos(\theta_1 - 240°) \tag{11-32}$$

Lastly, assume that the mutual inductance between a transformer-stator leg and the transformer-rotor winding has the maximum value M_t and varies as the cosine of the angle between that leg and the rotor axis. When θ_2 is the angle between leg a and the rotor winding, the rms error voltage induced in the rotor is

$$E_e = j\omega I_a M_t \cos \theta_2 + j\omega I_b M_t \cos(\theta_2 - 120°) + j\omega I_c M_t \cos(\theta_2 - 240°) \tag{11-33}$$

Upon substitution of Eqs. 11-30 to 11-32 and reduction to its simplest form, Eq. 11-33 becomes

$$E_e = \frac{3}{2} E_1 \frac{M_t}{L - M} \cos(\theta_2 - \theta_1) \tag{11-34}$$

This result confirms the physical conclusion that the error voltage is zero when the shaft displacement is 90°; it also shows that, under idealized circumstances, the magnitude of the error voltage varies sinusoidally with the departure from this equilibrium displacement.

The Selsyn control transformer has essentially a cylindrical-rotor structure and accordingly conforms quite well with the foregoing assumptions. It also has high-impedance stator windings to minimize the current drain on the generator and its associated effects. As has already been pointed out, the generator has a salient-pole rotor structure, which represents a departure from the idealizing assumptions. The principal static errors are caused by unbalanced reactances and resistances in the stator-winding legs and interconnecting lines, and unbalanced mutual reactances between rotor winding and stator legs. The static error for the generator-transformer system is of the order of $\pm 0.3°$. Velocity errors, caused by the appearance of speed voltages, are introduced when the Selsyns rotate at significant speeds. These errors are of the order of 1° per 320 rpm for 60-cps Selsyns. For a fixed value of rotational speed, velocity errors decrease as the excitation frequency increases, so that the errors are definitely smaller for 400-cps Selsyns.[11]

The precision of the over-all control scheme of which the Selsyn generator and control transformer form a part may be significantly improved by the use of a *two-speed Selsyn system.* Such a system consists of two complete installations after the manner of Fig. 11-32, with the Selsyn units of the second installation mechanically geared up from the first by the ratio N to 1, where N usually ranges from 18 to 36. The second installation, the *high-speed* or *fine system,* then revolves N times for every revolution of the first installation, the *low-speed* or *coarse system.* The high-speed system is caused to take control for small angular errors; because of being geared up, it produces a much higher error voltage per degree error of the shaft being controlled and therefore provides much more sensitive control. The high-speed system has N different equilibrium positions per revolution of the shaft being controlled, however. The low-speed, or 1-to-1, system must therefore take over control for large angle errors; to assure a unique equilibrium position, it must take over before the angle error becomes equal to one-half turn of the high-speed Selsyns. By appropriate use of relays or other expedients, the coarse system may be made to assume control after any prescribed movement of the fine system from the equilibrium position.[12]

The rotor of a Selsyn control transformer normally is connected to the terminals of high-input-impedance electronic equipment, so that the current drain on the transformer is very low. Figure 11-35, for example, illustrates an application to control of the angular position of an output shaft. The object is to cause the output shaft to follow the angular variations of the input shaft. The rotor of the Selsyn generator is mechanically connected to the input shaft. The rotor of the control transformer is mechanically connected to the output shaft and electrically connected to the input of a power amplifier. Mechanical power to

[11] Orders of magnitude cited here are taken from Harold Chestnut, Electrical Accuracy of Selsyn Generator–Control Transformer System, *Trans, AIEE,* vol. 65, pp. 570–576, 1946.

This paper contains quantitative analyses including saliency, resistances, and speed voltages.

[12] Further details on the transfer of control in two-speed systems, as well as on applications, may be found in Raymond Goertz, Synchro Controls for Meters and Servos, *Electronic Industries,* September, 1945.

turn the output shaft and its associated load is furnished by a 2-phase servomotor, described in Chap. 10. The input to the control winding of the servomotor is supplied by the amplifier, which includes phase-splitting capacitors in its circuitry. When the output shaft is in the correct position, the voltage input to the amplifier and hence the power input to the control winding of the motor is zero and the motor does not turn. When

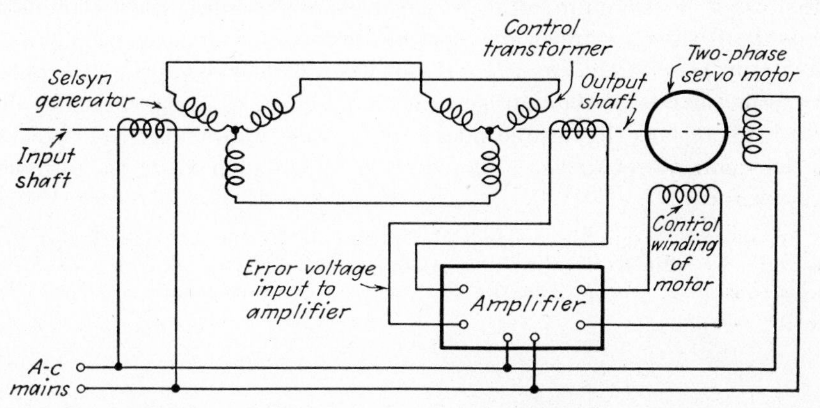

FIG. 11-35. Application of Selsyn generator and transformer to angular-position control.

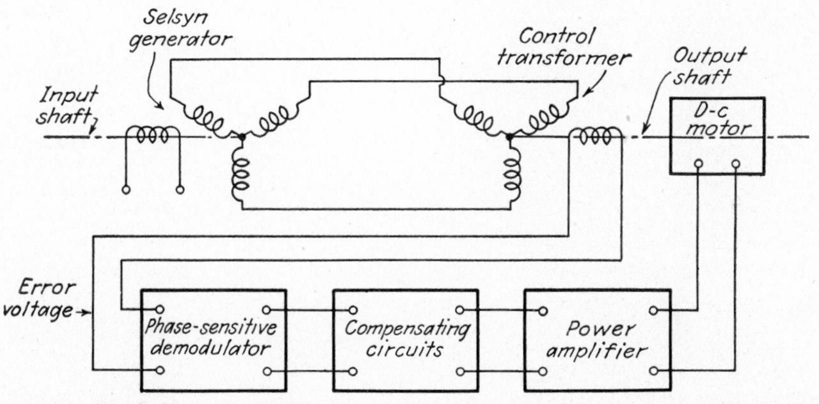

FIG. 11-36. Block diagram of Selsyn control with demodulation of error-voltage signal.

an angular discrepancy exists, a definite error voltage appears at the amplifier input. Its relative polarity is such that the motor is caused to turn in the direction to correct the angular discrepancy.

Two problems commonly appear in applications of this type. First, the output shaft may overshoot and oscillate about the correct position. Appropriate stabilization or damping may thus be necessary. Second, in a continuously rotating system it may be undesirable to operate under a scheme which requires the existence of appreciable angular error to furnish the power for rotation of the output shaft. These potential difficulties may be minimized by making the system sensitive, not only to the error itself, but to the derivative or integral of error, or both. This step involves the equivalent of differentiation or integration of the error voltage, processes which may be executed more readily by electric-circuit elements when the error voltage is in d-c form. The output of the Selsyn transformer is therefore often rectified, or demodulated, in a diode or triode half-wave or full-wave demodulator to produce a proportional direct voltage. Such *demodulation* must be *phase-sensitive; i.e.*, the polarity of the output direct voltage must depend on whether the controller shaft leads or lags the desired position.[13] A d-c motor may then be used for the main power drive. Figure 11-36 shows such a system in block-diagram form.

[13] For several phase-sensitive demodulation circuits, see the reference cited in footnote 12. See also K. E. Schreiner, High-performance Demodulators for Servomechanisms, *Proc. Natl. Electronics Conf.*, vol. 2, pp. 393–403, 1946.

CHAPTER 12

ELECTRICAL TRANSIENTS IN MACHINES AND SYSTEMS OF MACHINES

Energy conversion by electromagnetic methods is, as we have seen, associated with energy storage in magnetic fields. When changes in operating conditions take place, the accompanying changes in stored magnetic energy cannot occur instantaneously. Instead a transient period of readjustment must be interposed between the initial and final operating conditions. Study of this readjustment period is the study of machine transients.

Machine transients are frequently associated with trouble in the system of which the machine is a part. A common effect of an induced or direct lightning stroke on a power system, for example, is a short circuit on one of the lines. The presence of this short circuit must be detected by protective relays and the faulted line cleared from the system by circuit breakers. The high currents accompanying a serious short circuit must not create mechanical stresses which cannot be withstood by the machines, transformers, circuit breakers, and bus bars; the circuit breakers must be capable of interrupting the currents; and the system must in general be able to ride through the disturbance without loss of synchronism. The machines play parts of determining importance during these disturbances. Conversely, when probability and economic considerations indicate that certain disturbances must be provided for, they determine many of the design features of the machines.

Anticipation of trouble is not the only reason for studying machine transients, however. The starting of motors, the build-up and build-down of generator voltage, the response of a machine to a sudden load change, the reactions of a motor which is continually called upon to change its speed and direction of rotation, all are examples of processes involving electrical transients.

Transient considerations in this chapter are limited to d-c and synchronous machines. For d-c machines, transient investigations frequently may require a nonlinear analysis because of saturation. The synchronous-machine treatment is confined to performance following short circuits, and the justifiable neglect of saturation under these conditions permits a linear analysis. Problems which intimately involve dynamic aspects such as the acceleration of masses will be considered in the next chapter; the discussions in this chapter will be limited to electromagnetic aspects. Transient behavior of the machine as a system element, rather than the minute details of performance which can be examined for an isolated machine, is given predominant emphasis. As a result, the treatment, especially for synchronous machines, is presented on a simplified basis, with only aspects which are of primary importance in system transients given any serious consideration. At the same time, an attempt is made to present the simplified approach in such a manner that it leads into the comprehensive theories found in the more advanced literature.

12-1. D-C-machine Transients. Linear Analysis. The most difficult obstacle to overcome in analysis of d-c machines is the appropriate inclusion of saturation. Linear analyses omitting saturation serve two useful purposes, however. First, by virtue of the relatively simple linear differential equations which may then be written, a fuller appreciation of other factors affecting transient performance is made possible, and an approximate picture of the events is gained. Second, for those system problems involving complex combinations of machines and other engineering equipment, over-all dynamic system studies are made possible which otherwise would be practically prohibitive. Of course, it is necessary to take into account the possible influence of machine saturation in engineering interpretation of the results of these studies and to show by experimental comparisons that valid conclusions may be drawn. Often the critical portion of the transient response takes place in substantially the linear region. Not infrequently the degree of accuracy to which other data are known does not warrant precise representation of the machine.

The factors influencing transient performance will be summarized by writing the appropriate equations for several specific cases.

When absence of saturation is postulated for a self-excited generator, it follows logically that either no build-up of voltage takes place or the build-up continues indefinitely (see Art. 5-6). To avoid this unrealistic situation, only machines with an excitation source separate from the armature will be considered in this article. It is also possible to apply essentially the following methods to approximate analysis of self-excited generators by representing the pertinent portion of the magnetization curve by a straight line with a definite vertical intercept or by two straight lines with different slopes. While much of the reasoning applies also to d-c motors, the treatment here will be confined to generators; the mechanical considerations associated with changes in motor speed are thus postponed to Chap. 13. With the brushes in the neutral position, armature reaction is zero, and there is no net mutual effect of the armature circuit on the field circuit.

The field-circuit equation for the separately excited generator of Fig.

12-1 is

$$L_f \frac{di_f}{dt} + r_f i_f = e_f \tag{12-1}$$

where L_f, r_f, e_f, and i_f are the field-circuit self-inductance, resistance, voltage, and current, respectively. Because of the assumed linearity of the magnetization curve, the armature generated voltage e_a is

$$e_a = k_f i_f \tag{12-2}$$

k_f being the proportionality constant. The armature terminal voltage v_t is

$$v_t = e_a - r_a i_a - L_a \frac{di_a}{dt} \tag{12-3}$$

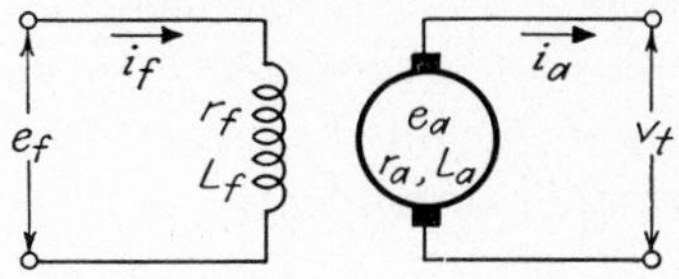

FIG. 12-1. Separately excited d-c generator.

r_a and L_a being the armature-circuit resistance and self-inductance, respectively, and i_a the armature current. An additional relation between v_t and i_a is imposed by the external armature circuit; thus, for a purely resistive load R_L,

$$v_t = R_L i_a \tag{12-4}$$

Simultaneous solution of these four equations yields the desired transient response. The response is not instantaneous because of the finite time required for energy-storage changes in the magnetic fields of the field and armature windings.

When more than one field winding is present on the machine, account must be taken of the added excitation and of the mutual coupling between field windings. With a cumulative series field, as in Fig. 12-2, the mutual inductance M between the two fields causes Eq. 12-1 to be written

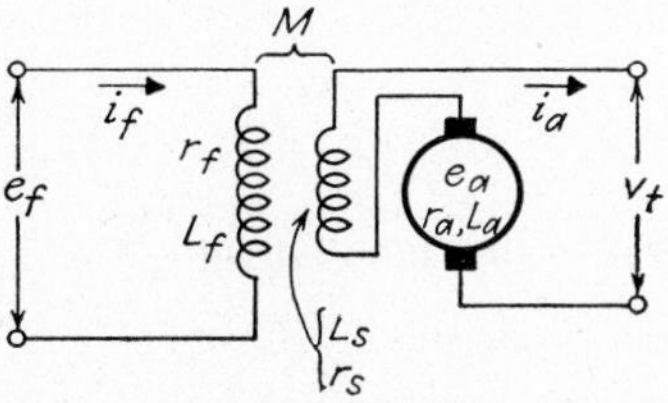

$$L_f \frac{di_f}{dt} + M \frac{di_a}{dt} + r_f i_f = e_f \tag{12-5}$$

FIG. 12-2. Direct-current generator with separate and series excitation.

Equation 12-2 becomes

$$e_a = k_f \left(i_f + \frac{N_s}{N_f} i_a \right) \tag{12-6}$$

where N_s and N_f are the series- and separately excited field turns, respectively, and the constant k_f is evaluated with regard to the separately excited field alone. The effects of resistance r_s and self-inductance L_s of the series winding and of the mutual inductance must be added to Eq. 12-3, giving

$$v_t = e_a - (r_a + r_s)i_a - (L_a + L_s) \frac{di_a}{dt} - M \frac{di_f}{dt} \tag{12-7}$$

Similar methods may be used when other windings are present, as in the control-type generators of Chap. 11.

As more ramifications are added to the machine, the complexity of the constraining equations evidently increases. The reduction of the analysis of these equations to the highly systematic and orderly procedures offered by the methods of operational calculus then becomes of increasing value.[1] Very frequently, too, the numerical orders of magnitude involved may permit the neglect of some factors, particularly in the light of other assumptions being made. Thus, the delay in transient response introduced by armature inductance may well be small in comparison with that caused by the field inductance, indicating that omission of L_a terms may be permissible. In general, when saturation effects are added to those included in Eqs. 12-1 to 12-7, as in the following three articles, further simplification is a necessity if unwieldy methods are to be avoided.

Example 12-1. Consider that the separately excited d-c generator of Fig. 12-1 is a 200-kw 250-volt machine having the following constants:

$$r_f = 33.7 \text{ ohms} \qquad r_a = 0.0125 \text{ ohm}$$
$$L_f = 25 \text{ henrys} \qquad L_a = 0.008 \text{ henry}$$
$$k_f = 38 \text{ volts/field amp}$$

The armature circuit is connected to a purely resistive load $R_L = 0.313$ ohm.

The generator is initially unexcited but rotating at rated speed. A 230-volt d-c source is suddenly connected to the field terminals. As the terminal voltage builds up and the generator takes on load, its speed does not change appreciably.

Compute and plot a curve of terminal voltage as a function of time after connection of the excitation source. Neglect saturation.

Solution. The build-up of field current described by Eq. 12-1 is that of a simple RL circuit transient, or

$$i_f = \frac{E_f}{r_f}(1 - \epsilon^{-r_f t/L_f})$$
$$= \frac{230}{33.7}(1 - \epsilon^{-33.7t/25}) = 6.83(1 - \epsilon^{-1.35t}) \qquad \text{amp}$$

Because e_a and i_f are linearly related, the build-up of armature internal voltage is

$$e_a = 38 \times 6.83(1 - \epsilon^{-1.35t}) = 260(1 - \epsilon^{-1.35t})$$

For the armature circuit, by combination of Eqs. 12-3 and 12-4,

$$\frac{L_a}{R_L}\frac{dv_t}{dt} + \frac{R_L + r_a}{R_L} v_t = e_a$$

Upon substitution of numerical values,

$$0.0255 \frac{dv_t}{dt} + 1.04 v_t = 260 - 260\epsilon^{-1.35t}$$

[1] See V. Bush, "Operational Circuit Analysis," John Wiley & Sons, Inc., New York, 1929, and M. F. Gardner and J. L. Barnes, "Transients in Linear Systems," John Wiley & Sons, Inc., New York, 1942.

This first-order linear differential equation is subject to the boundary condition that v_t must remain zero at the instant the excitation is applied ($t = 0$) because the armature linkages cannot change suddenly. Solution by any of the standard processes yields

$$v_t = 250 - 257\epsilon^{-1.35t} + 7\epsilon^{-40.7t}$$

A plot of this voltage build-up is given by the solid curve of Fig. 12-3.

An idea of the influence of the armature inductance and resistance of this machine, which is typical of d-c generators used for alternator excitation, can readily be gained.

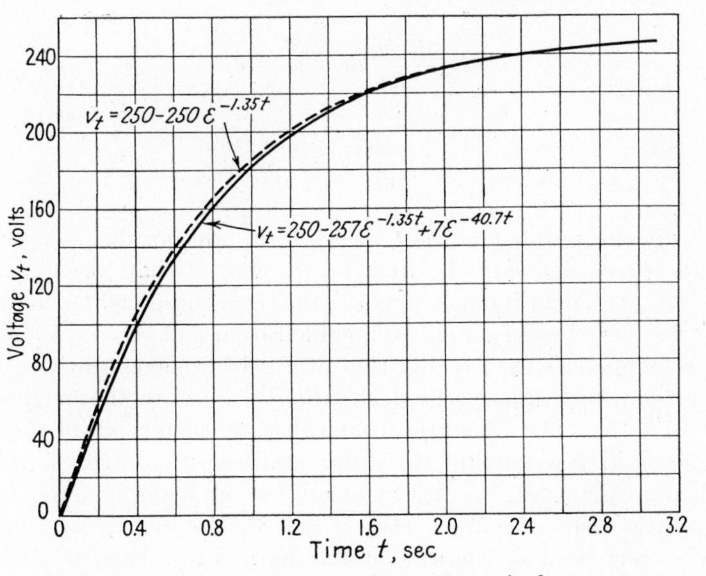

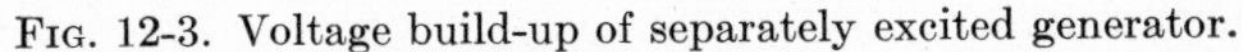
FIG. 12-3. Voltage build-up of separately excited generator.

When armature inductance is ignored, the voltage build-up is given by

$$v_t = 250 - 250\epsilon^{-1.35t}$$

which is shown by the dotted curve of Fig. 12-3. Obviously the influence of armature inductance is very small. The principal effect of r_a is to reduce the final voltage from 260 volts to the 250 volts actually obtained. When this effect is taken into account in interpreting results, it is evidently possible to base many engineering analyses on the assumption of negligible L_a and r_a.

12-2. D-C-machine Transients. Nonlinear Analysis. When saturation is included, the transient equations are no longer readily susceptible to analytical treatment because nonlinearities are introduced. Moreover, it is no longer strictly true that the armature circuit produces no net mutual effect in the field circuit even with the brushes on the neutral: the demagnetizing effect of cross-magnetizing armature reaction, produced in a saturated machine with no compensating winding, provides a coupling medium. This effect, ordinarily small, will be neglected in examining the influence of saturation in modifying the relations for the separately excited generator of Fig. 12-1.

The simple proportionality of Eq. 12-2 no longer holds, and the relation between e_a and i_f becomes that given by the magnetization curve of the machine. Furthermore, the self-inductance L_f in Eq. 12-1 ceases to remain constant but becomes a function of field current i_f. Under these circumstances it is usually more convenient to formulate the relation in terms of field flux linkages; *i.e.*,

$$N_f \frac{d(\sigma\Phi)}{dt} + r_f i_f = e_f \qquad (12\text{-}8)$$

or

$$\sigma N_f \frac{d\Phi}{dt} + r_f i_f = e_f \qquad (12\text{-}9)$$

where N_f is the number of field turns, Φ the air-gap flux per pole, and σ a factor to be defined. It must be recognized that, because of field leakage flux, the field linkages are greater than those created by the air-gap flux Φ. The increase may be included by use of the *coefficient of dispersion* σ, defined as the ratio of the total field linkages to those created by the air-gap flux alone. Typical values of σ are in the neighborhood of 1.10 to 1.15. The assumption of constant coefficient of dispersion, implied in taking σ outside the differentiation symbol in Eq. 12-9, is equivalent to regarding the field leakage flux as being affected by saturation to the same extent as the air-gap flux, which is evidently not entirely correct because the leakage-flux path is to a considerable extent in air.

The flux Φ in Eq. 12-9 can be replaced by the armature voltage e_a by use of Eq. 4-38, which, for constant speed, can be written

$$e_a = k_\varphi \Phi \qquad (12\text{-}10)$$

k_φ being the proportionality constant at the specified speed. Equation 12-9 then becomes

$$\frac{\sigma N_f}{k_\varphi} \frac{de_a}{dt} + r_f i_f = e_f \qquad (12\text{-}11)$$

The equation for the armature circuit is still Eq. 12-3. Equations 12-3 and 12-11, together with the relation between e_a and i_f given in graphical form by the magnetization curve and that between v_t and i_a given by the external armature circuit, constitute the group of simultaneous equations to be analyzed. Further simplifying assumptions are not infrequently made. Either L_a alone or both L_a and r_a are often sufficiently small so that they may be considered zero in Eq. 12-3. These added assumptions must be justified by showing, experimentally or otherwise, that they do not introduce intolerable errors; the discussion at the end of Example 12-1 constitutes partial justification for neglecting L_a and r_a.

The particular aspect of these simultaneous equations which requires further discussion is that the relation between e_a and i_f is usually given in graphical form and is nonlinear. One possibility is to fit an empirical equation to this relation.[2] Another possibility is to express the essential relations in such graphical form that integration may be performed by evaluating areas under a curve. With r_a and L_a assumed to be zero (and in certain other simplified cases), this process leads to expeditious solutions in specific numerical form without the need of approximating the magnetization curve and with no more labor than is involved in the empirical-equation approach. A third method is a step-by-step analysis which, in general, may be applied to any system of linear or nonlinear differential equations.[3]

12-3. Graphical Analysis of Voltage Build-up and Build-down. When armature resistance r_a and inductance L_a are neglected, in addition to the earlier assumptions of negligible armature reaction and mutual effect of the armature on the field, the build-up and build-down of generator terminal voltage is the same under load as at no load. With the field-circuit voltage of the separately excited generator (Fig. 12-4) constant at the value E_f, Eq. 12-11 becomes

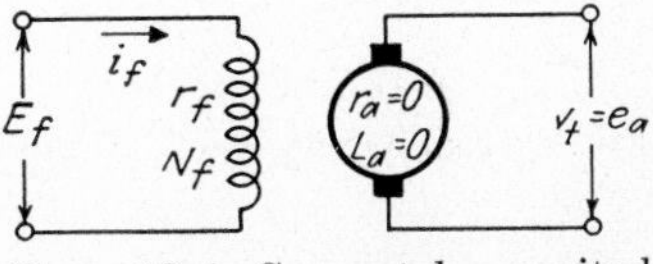

FIG. 12-4. Separately excited generator with negligible armature resistance and inductance.

$$\frac{\sigma N_f}{k_\varphi}\frac{dv_t}{dt} + r_f i_f = E_f \tag{12-12}$$

which may be written

$$dt = \frac{\sigma N_f}{k_\varphi}\frac{dv_t}{E_f - r_f i_f} \tag{12-13}$$

The time required for the voltage to change from the initial value v_{t0} to

[2] For detailed analyses on this basis, as well as by graphical and step-by-step methods, see O. G. C. Dahl, "Electric Power Circuits—Theory and Applications," Vol. II, Power System Stability, Chaps. XV and XVI, McGraw-Hill Book Company, Inc., New York, 1938.

Graphical methods are considered in detail in Reinhold Rüdenberg, "Transient Performance of Electric Power Systems," McGraw-Hill Book Company, Inc., New York, 1950; see especially Chap. 46.

[3] General discussions of graphical and step-by-step integration may be found in R. E. Doherty and E. G. Keller, "Mathematics of Modern Engineering," Vol. I, pp. 163–185, John Wiley & Sons, Inc., New York, 1936.

Specific electrical problems are considered in EE Staff, MIT, "Electric Circuits," Chap. XIII, John Wiley & Sons, Inc., New York, 1940.

the value v_t is then

$$t = \frac{\sigma N_f}{k_\varphi} \int_{v_{t0}}^{v_t} \frac{1}{E_f - r_f i_f} \, dv_t \qquad (12\text{-}14)$$

This integral can be evaluated graphically by finding areas on a plot of the quantity $1/(E_f - r_f i_f)$ as a function of v_t. Thus, consider that the

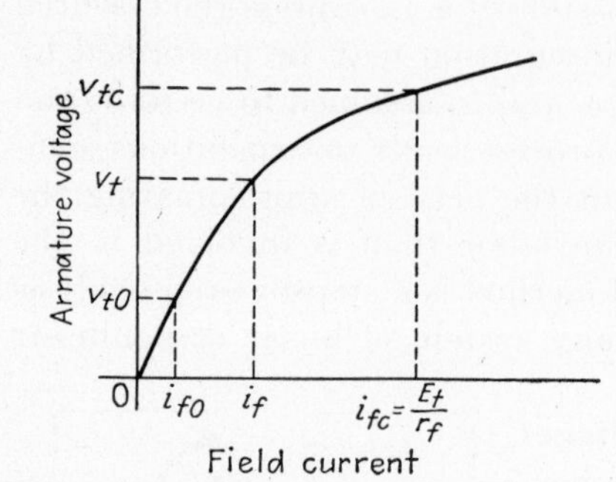

FIG. 12-5. Generator magnetization curve.

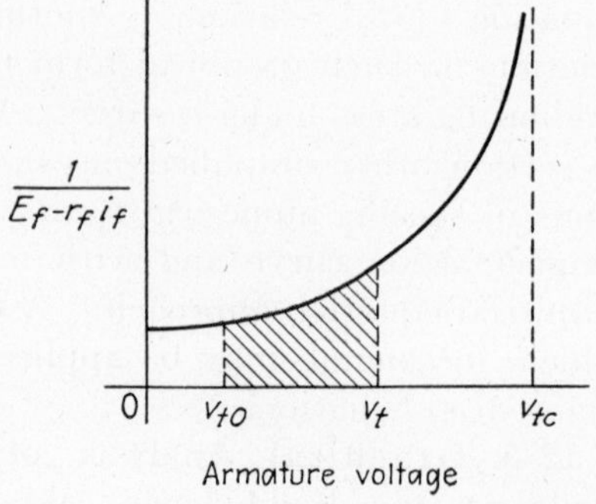

FIG. 12-6. Graphical analysis of voltage build-up.

generator of Fig. 12-4 has the magnetization curve of Fig. 12-5; because of the simplifying assumptions, the ordinates of this curve give v_t directly. Build-up of terminal voltage from the initial value v_{t0} may be caused by the action of a voltage regulator in suddenly decreasing the field-circuit resistance, so that after a sufficient lapse of time the *ceiling voltage* v_{tc} is reached. For each value of v_t, the corresponding value of i_f may be read from the magnetization curve; the associated values of $1/(E_f - r_f i_f)$ may then be computed and plotted against v_t as shown in Fig. 12-6. The crosshatched area may be evaluated by planimeter, by counting little squares on the curve sheet, or by application of the trapezoidal formula or of Simpson's rules. This area, multiplied by $\sigma N_f/k_\varphi$, is the time required for the voltage to build up from v_{t0} to the value v_t. Of course, an infinite time will be required to reach the ceiling voltage. The resulting curve of v_t as a function of time is of the nature indicated in Fig. 12-7.

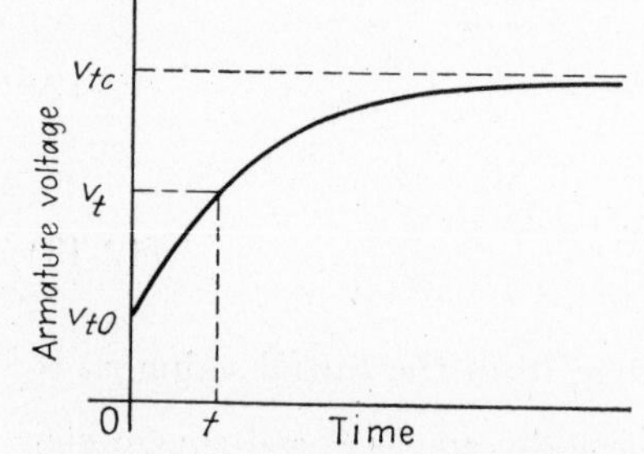

FIG. 12-7. Build-up of terminal voltage from initial value v_{t0} to ceiling value v_{tc}.

The graphical process illustrated by Figs. 12-5 to 12-7 may be applied to many first-order equations where the variables can be separated in this manner. The general procedure is one of trying substantially the above steps or variations of them; if the trials are not successful, the more generally applicable step-by-step method must be used. Only very minor variations are required to adapt the graphical method to self-excited shunt generators or to the computation of voltage build-down.

Example 12-2. The magnetization curve at rated speed for a 200-kw 250-volt separately excited d-c generator is given in Fig. 12-8. For this machine the ratio N_f/k_φ is 0.574, and the coefficient of dispersion σ may be considered constant at 1.15. Armature resistance and inductance and armature reaction may be neglected. The field-circuit resistance r_f is 33.7 ohms.

The generator is initially unexcited but rotating at rated speed. A 230-volt d-c source is suddenly connected to the field terminals. As the terminal voltage builds up and the generator takes on load, its speed does not change appreciably.

a. Compute and plot a curve of terminal voltage as a function of time after connection of the excitation source.

b. Superimpose on this plot the curve of e_a as a function of time obtained in Example 12-1, and compare the two curves. The data in this example are for the same machine. In Example 12-1, both the constant $k_f = 38$ volts per field ampere and the field inductance $L_f = 25$ henrys are evaluated approximately to correspond with the initial slope of the magnetization curve with the residual effect ignored.

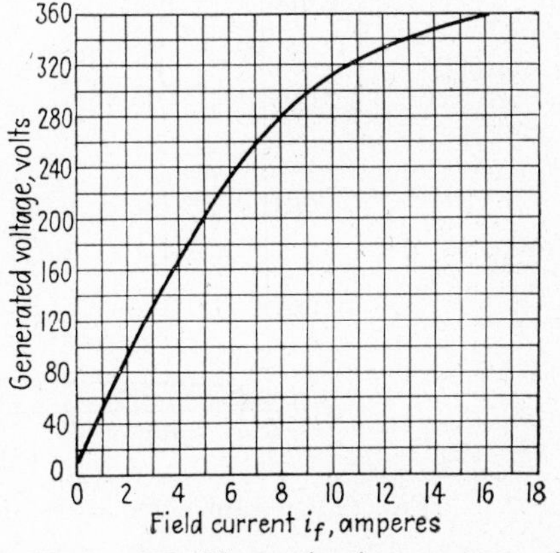

FIG. 12-8. Magnetization curve of 200-kw 250-volt d-c generator, Example 12-2.

Solution. For computing the voltage build-up, Eq. 12-14 becomes

$$t = 1.15 \times 0.574 \int_{10}^{v_t} \frac{1}{230 - 33.7 i_f} \, dv_t$$

Ten volts is used as the lower limit under the assumption that the residual voltage evident in Fig. 12-8 is of the desired polarity.

A curve of $1/(E_f - r_f i_f)$ as a function of v_t is plotted in Fig. 12-9. Computations for this curve are summarized in the first five columns of Table12-1. The integral may be evaluated in terms of the appropriate area between this curve and the horizontal axis; thus, the time to build up to a voltage of 200 volts is proportional to the

TABLE 12-1
COMPUTATION OF VOLTAGE BUILD-UP CURVE, FIG. 12-10

v_t	i_f	$r_f i_f$	$E_f - r_f i_f$	$\dfrac{1}{E_f - r_f i_f}$	Area, volts/volt	Time, sec
10	0	0	230	0.00435	0	0
100	2.24	75.7	154	0.00650	0.479	0.32
200	4.95	167	63	0.0159	1.50	0.99
240	6.28	212	18	0.0540	2.55	1.68
250	6.68	224	5.6	0.1785	3.56	2.34
254	6.83	230	0	∞	∞	∞

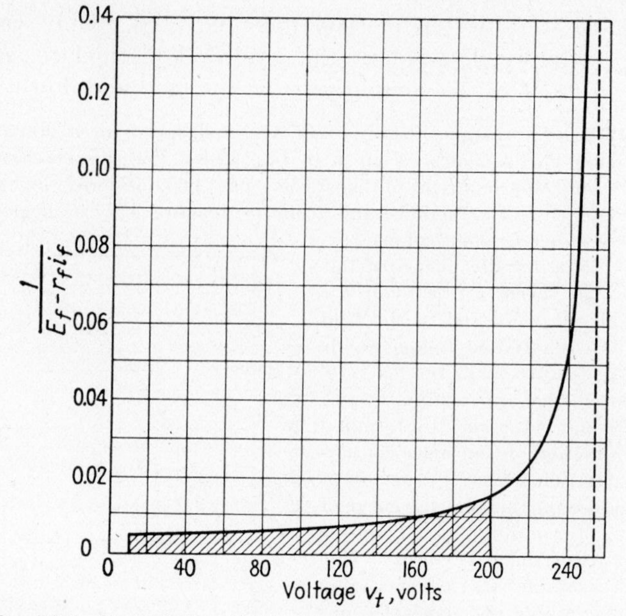

FIG. 12-9. Graphical analysis of voltage build-up, Example 12-2.

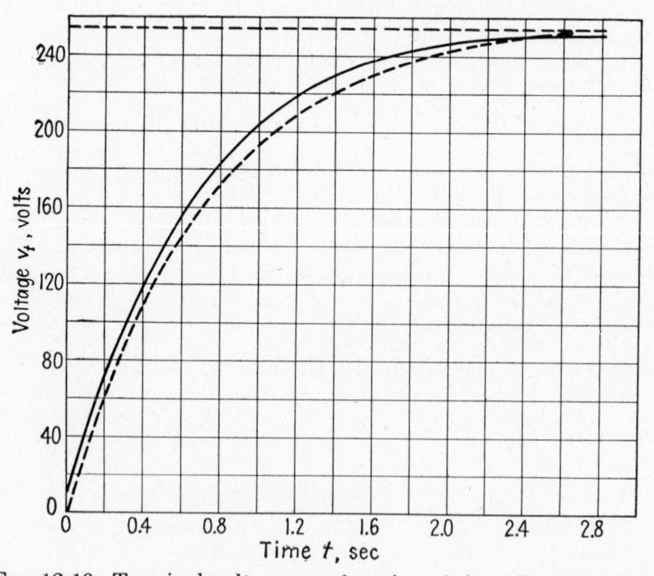

FIG. 12-10. Terminal voltage as a function of time, Example 12-2.

crosshatched area in Fig. 12-9. The resulting curve of v_t as a function of t is plotted in Fig. 12-10.

Also plotted in Fig. 12-10 is a dotted curve of voltage build-up given by the equation

$$e_a = 260 - 260\epsilon^{-1.35t}$$

obtained in Example 12-1 with armature inductance and resistance ignored. The principal differences between the two curves arise from the difference in ceiling voltage caused by using the initial slope of the magnetization curve in Example 12-1, and the fact that build-up is assumed to start from a residual voltage of 10 volts in this example. The rates of voltage rise for the two curves are approximately the same. It should be pointed out that the magnetization curve is that of a typical exciter designed to provide a reasonably high ceiling voltage without undue saturation.

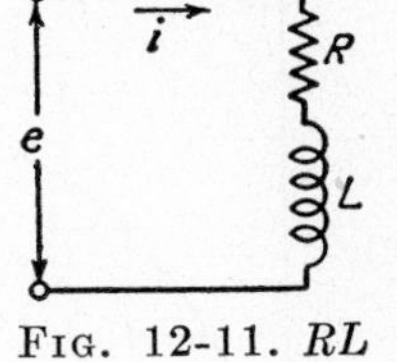

FIG. 12-11. RL circuit.

12-4. Step-by-step Analysis of D-C-machine Transients. When, in addition to saturation, the presence of armature inductance L_a and resistance r_a is to be accounted for, or when the armature load is inductive, it is usually not possible to arrange the differential equations for graphical integration. A step-by-step process of solution must then be used. To illustrate this process, consider the RL circuit of Fig. 12-11 on which is impressed a known time-varying voltage e at $t = 0$ with the circuit at rest. Assume that e is known in graphical form as a function of time, as illustrated by the solid curve of Fig. 12-12, but not in analytical form. The voltage e may be the internal armature voltage of a separately excited generator and may have been obtained by graphical integration of the field-circuit equation, and the resistance and inductance may be those of the generator armature and its load circuit; physically, closure of the armature circuit in this case must be considered to occur at the same instant that build-up of voltage from its initial value e_0 starts.

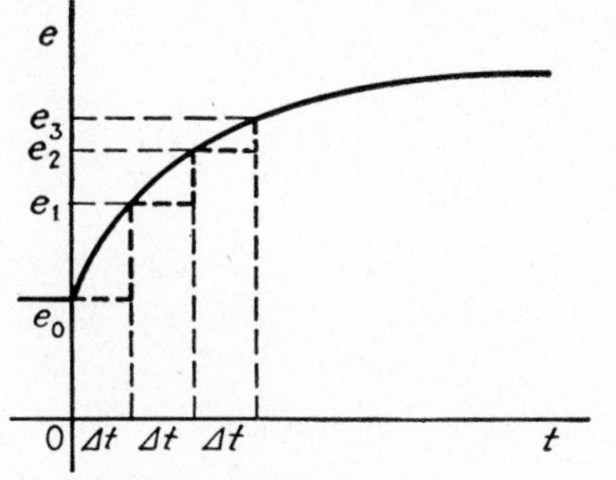

FIG. 12-12. Impressed voltage as a function of time.

The circuit equation is

$$L\frac{di}{dt} + Ri = e(t) \tag{12-15}$$

where the functional notation $e(t)$ is used to emphasize the fact that the voltage is a function of time. Attempts to solve this equation by graphical integration fail, for when it is put in the form previously used,

$$dt = L\frac{di}{e(t) - Ri} \tag{12-16}$$

the right-hand side is seen to be a function of both t and i. The variables cannot be separated, and no significant curve can be plotted as a function of i alone. For a step-by-step solution, Eq. 12-15 is rewritten in the form

$$\frac{di}{dt} = \frac{e(t) - Ri}{L} \tag{12-17}$$

and di/dt is assumed to remain constant for a short interval of time Δt at its value for the beginning of that interval. The increment Δi of current build-up during the interval is

$$\Delta i = \frac{\Delta t}{L} [e(t) - Ri] \tag{12-18}$$

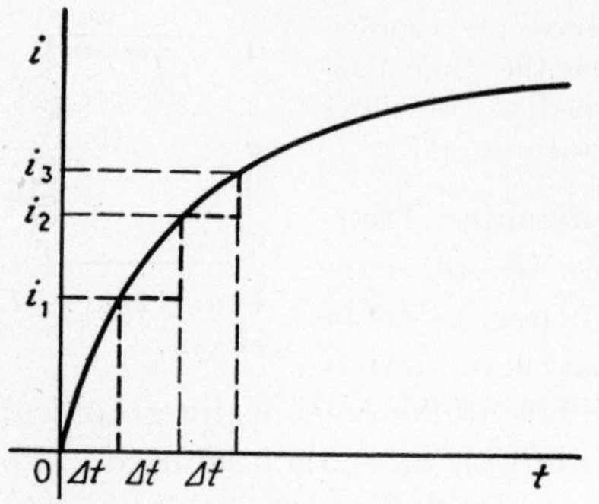

FIG. 12-13. Current response as a function of time.

and the total current at the end of the interval is the sum of this increment and the value at the beginning of the interval.

Thus, at the initial instant the inductance L causes the current to remain zero, and the initial rate of change of current is e_0/L. The current increment Δi_1 during the first interval is Δt times this initial rate, and the current i_1 at the end of the first interval equals the increment Δi_1. At the beginning of the second interval,

$$\left(\frac{di}{dt}\right)_1 = \frac{e_1 - Ri_1}{L} \tag{12-19}$$

and for the second interval,

$$\Delta i_2 = \frac{\Delta t}{L} (e_1 - Ri_1) \tag{12-20}$$

so that the current at the end of the second interval is $i_1 + \Delta i_2$. Continuation of this computational process in the form indicated by Table

TABLE 12-2
COMPUTATIONAL FORM FOR STEP-BY-STEP SOLUTION

(1) Interval n	(2) Time $t = n\,\Delta t$	(3) Current i	(4) e	(5) Ri	(6) $e - Ri$	(7) $\Delta i = \frac{\Delta t}{L}(e - Ri)$
0	0					
1	Δt					
2	$2(\Delta t)$					
3	$3(\Delta t)$					

Column $(3)_n$ = column $(3)_{n-1}$ + column $(7)_{n-1}$.
Column $(3)_0$ from initial conditions.

12-2 yields the complete curve of i as a function of time illustrated in Fig. 12-13.

As indicated in Figs. 12-12 and 12-13, the foregoing process is the equivalent of considering both the voltage and current to remain constant over the interval and to change in step fashion at its end. These assumptions are inherently sources of cumulative error. The length of time interval Δt must be short enough to avoid intolerable errors; on the other hand, it must be recognized that use of an unduly short interval greatly increases the labor involved in the solution. The final choice must be the result of experience and judgment plus a knowledge of the accuracy warranted in a specific problem. For a rough guide, the time constant or period of the transient may be estimated on an approximate linearized basis and an interval of the order of 5 to 10 per cent of the estimated time constant tried.

The step-by-step process in general may be adapted to any differential equation or system of simultaneous differential equations. There are also numerous variations of the process, aimed either at greater facility in a particular problem or at decrease of cumulative error.[4]

12-5. Synchronous-machine Transients: Coupled-circuit Viewpoint. The inherent complexity of synchronous-machine transient phenomena can be appreciated by inspecting the main structural details of the machine with the object of pointing out the significant circuits when transient rather than steady-state conditions prevail. For this purpose, the schematic diagram of Fig. 12-14 is presented. The rotor damping circuits are included because they may be of determining importance. A salient-pole structure is shown to emphasize the differences between the polar, or direct, axis and the interpolar, or quadrature, axis; similar differences exist between the two axes of cylindrical-rotor machines when transients are considered, so that the treatments of the two structural classes become essentially alike.

Under balanced steady-state conditions, the component-mmf wave of the stator winding and the associated component-flux wave revolve at the same speed as the rotor and are of essentially fixed waveform. The flux linkages with the rotor circuits then do not change with time, and no voltages are induced in these circuits. In effect, the main-field winding is the only rotor circuit which need be considered, and its excitation is determined by a simple Ohm's law relationship.

Under transient conditions time-varying currents may exist in all of the rotor circuits. The stator currents will no longer be constant-ampli-

[4] A method of d-c-machine short-circuit analysis based on experimentally determined characteristics and of particular usefulness in aircraft-electric-system analysis is indicated in H. C. Anderson, S. B. Crary, and N. R. Schultz, Present D-c Aircraft Electric Supply Systems, *Trans. AIEE*, vol. 63, p. 265, 1944.

tude sinusoids, and the stator component-mmf and -flux waves will likewise not be constant-amplitude sinusoids in space. Moreover, the possibility of the mechanical speed of the rotor changing with time may have to be considered. As a consequence, the flux linkages with all of the rotor circuits will change with time, and induced currents will exist in all the circuits; the main-field current, for example, is no longer determined by a simple Ohm's law relation. All of these rotor currents are, of course, effective in providing excitation for the machine, for they contribute to the air-gap flux and thus influence the instantaneous values of stator currents.

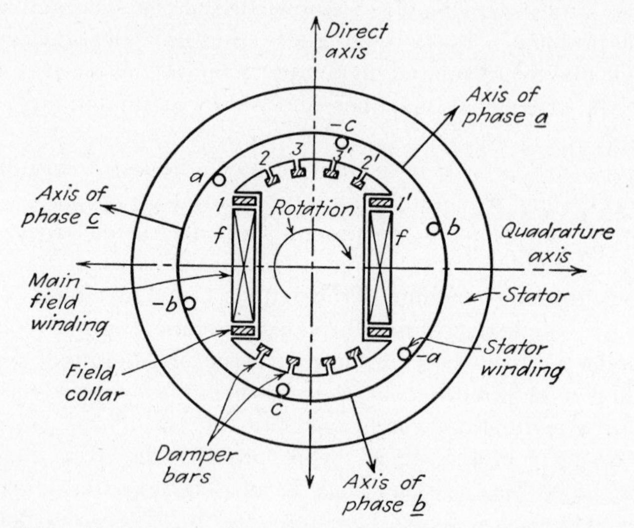

FIG. 12-14. Schematic diagram of synchronous machine showing significant circuits for transients.

In short, the machine must be regarded as an inconveniently large group of mutually coupled circuits in order that a systematic approach to the transient problem may be devised.

In Fig. 12-14 there is a stator circuit for each of the three phases, *a*, *b*, and *c*, and there are rotor circuits corresponding to the field winding and to bars 2-2′ and 3-3′ and to the conducting field collars 1-1′. An additional equivalent rotor circuit may be formed by the bolts and iron of the rotor structure. Cylindrical-rotor machines may likewise have rotor circuits other than the main-field winding, especially in the quadrature axis, where the rotor iron may form an equivalent circuit almost as effective as the main field for induced currents.

All of these circuits have their own resistance and their own self-inductance and mutual inductances with respect to every other circuit. And to make a complex situation still more complicated, the self- and mutual inductances associated with the stator circuits are functions of rotor position, varying periodically as the rotor revolves. Fortunately the self-inductances of the rotor circuits and the mutual inductances between rotor circuits can be considered constant as long as the effect of stator teeth and slots is ignored. In view of this complexity, no attempts have been made to include saturation, hysteresis, or eddy currents in a basic transient analysis of synchronous-machine performance.[5] To reduce the complexity of the problem somewhat, analyses are usually confined to machines having but one effective rotor circuit other than the main field in the direct axis and one effective rotor circuit in the quadrature axis—in other words, one equivalent damper circuit in each axis.[6]

Basic analysis of synchronous-machine transient performance accordingly involves the solution of a set of simultaneous coupled-circuit differential equations. Because of idealization of the machine, the relations between flux linkages and currents are linear, and, because of symmetry of machine geometry, certain of the self- and mutual-inductance coefficients can be recognized as having equal values. Nevertheless, the solution of the equations, even with only one damper circuit in each axis, is a formidable task, not because of any profundity, but because of the complexity of details. The solution is expedited appreciably by a linear transformation of variables in which the three stator phase currents i_a, i_b, and i_c are replaced by three component currents, the *direct-axis component* i_d, the *quadrature-axis component* i_q, and a single-phase component i_0 known as the *zero-sequence component* or *zero-axis component*. Similar transformations are made for voltages and flux linkages. For steady-state balanced operation, i_0 is zero (the significance of i_0 will not be discussed in this chapter because only balanced conditions are discussed in any detail), and the physical significance of the direct- and quadrature-axis components of current is that given in Chap. 8; in fact, the idea of making this transformation of variables arose from an extension of the physical picture corresponding to steady-state two-reaction theory. The changes of variables permit the simultaneous equations to be written in reasonably compact form with each equation relating only variables in the same axis. Furthermore, they enable recognition of certain frequently recurring combinations of machine constants, which become the reactances and time constants discussed in the next four articles. Analyses based on these differential equations are available for problems involv-

[5] For a complete statement of the idealizing assumptions usually made, see R. H. Park, Definition of an Ideal Synchronous Machine, *Gen. Elec. Rev.*, vol. 31, pp. 332–334, June, 1928.

[6] An exception to this statement may be found in investigations of synchronous-motor starting, where the specific configuration of the damper windings is of obvious importance. See T. M. Linville, Starting Performance of Salient-pole Synchronous Motors, *Trans. AIEE*, vol. 49, pp. 531–545, April, 1930.

ing a single machine, a single machine and an infinite bus, and simple two-machine systems.[7]

For engineering application of machine-transient theory, it must be recognized that a single synchronous machine is by no means the only element in the usual system problem. There are in general a goodly number of other such machines with different constants interconnected by a complicated network with each other and with numerous loads. In addition, the main field of each generator is supplied by an exciter in whose field is usually placed an automatic voltage regulator which recognizes the presence of a disturbance and alters conditions in the field. Moreover, action of the prime-mover governors may have a profound influence on system performance. All of these considerations clearly indicate the need for simple methods of characterizing the transient performance of a synchronous machine. Representation of the machine as a system element by means of simple equivalent circuits is desirable—representation not unlike that afforded by synchronous reactance for steady-state performance. The method actually used is to characterize the machine by a relatively few reactances and time constants. The reactances permit the computation of the initial magnitudes of transient currents, and the time constants characterize their decay. The coupled-circuit viewpoint is basic to the method, but because approximations and simplifications are necessary, correlation with test results and with a good physical picture of the phenomena is necessary.

12-6. Synchronous-machine Transients: Approximate Physical Picture. One of the important details in the evolution of a physical picture to interpret transient test data is the handling of circuit resistances. Complete neglect of resistances greatly simplifies the problem. Then, in the absence of capacitance, the total flux linkages with any closed circuit on the rotor cannot change when a disturbance occurs but must remain constant at the initial value. This constancy is caused by the fact that if the linkages with such a circuit did change, an induced *voltage* would necessarily appear in the circuit in violation of Kirchhoff's voltage

[7] An excellent introduction to this approach is offered by B. R. Prentice, Fundamental Concepts of Synchronous Machine Reactances, *Trans. AIEE Suppl.*, vol. 56, pp. 1–20, 1937.

Detailed considerations may be found in R. H. Park, Two-reaction Theory of Synchronous Machines I, *Trans. AIEE*, vol. 48, pp. 716–730, July, 1929; R. H. Park, Two-reaction Theory of Synchronous Machines II, *Trans. AIEE*, vol. 52, p. 352, January, 1933; S. B. Crary and M. L. Waring, The Operational Impedances of a Synchronous Machine, *Gen. Elec. Rev.*, vol. 35, pp. 578–582, November, 1932; A. R. Miller and W. S. Weil, Operational Solution of A-c Machines, *Trans. AIEE*, vol. 55, pp. 1191–1199, November, 1936; A. R. Miller and W. S. Weil, Alternator Short-circuit Currents under Unsymmetrical Terminal Conditions, *Trans. AIEE*, vol. 56, pp. 1268–1276, October, 1937.

law. Any impetus toward a change of linkages, such as might be caused by a rapid increase of stator current following a short circuit, is therefore counteracted by an induced *current* of an appropriate magnitude to maintain constancy of linkages in spite of the impetus. Computation of currents following a disturbance is then simply a matter of finding the various values of flux linkages prior to the disturbance from the specified initial conditions, and solving the coupled-circuit equations which state that these values must remain the same after the disturbance. Algebraic rather than differential equations are involved, and, with zero resistance, the resulting induced currents do not die out with time.

Actually, of course, neither test results nor common sense permits adoption of the notion that the induced currents do not decay with time. The method used practically is justified by the fact that, while all circuits have some resistance so that the flux eventually will be changed through any closed circuit, yet most of the circuits dealt with in synchronous machines have low enough resistance so that the behavior at the first instant after a sudden change is very nearly the same as if the resistances were zero. On this basis the initial currents and flux linkages following a sudden change are determined from a group of reactances set up as if no resistance were present, and the decay of these currents and linkages is handled by means of a group of time constants determined from the resistances as well as the reactances of the circuits.[8] The method is thus approximate in that resistance is only indirectly included in the solution. It is of great practical importance, however, because only by this means can the problems arising in complicated multimachine systems be handled.

This approach leads to a physical picture of happenings inside the machine which ties in directly with the results of experiments. Consider a synchronous generator operating at synchronous speed with a constant d-c slip-ring voltage. One effective rotor circuit in the direct axis in addition to the main-field winding is formed by the amortisseur bars. The machine is operating initially unloaded, and a 3-phase short circuit suddenly appears at its terminals. A symmetrical trace of a short-circuit stator-current wave such as might be obtained oscillographically is given in Fig. 12-15. The wave, whose envelope is shown in Fig. 12-16, may be divided into three periods or time regimes: the *subtransient period*, lasting only for the first few cycles during which the current decrement is very rapid; the *transient period*, covering a relatively longer time during which the current decrement is more moderate; and finally the *steady-state period*, during which the current is determined by the principles of Chaps. 7 and 8. That the three successive periods merge through the medium of

[8] The basis of this approach, sometimes referred to as the *constant-flux-linkage method*, is discussed in R. E. Dohery, A Simplified Method of Analyzing Short-circuit Problems, *Trans. AIEE*, vol. 42, pp. 841–849, 1923.

nearly exponential envelope decays can be shown by appropriate semilog plots. The difference $\Delta i'$ (Fig. 12-16) between the transient envelope and the steady-state amplitude is plotted to a logarithmic scale as a function of time in Fig. 12-17. In similar fashion the difference $\Delta i''$ between the

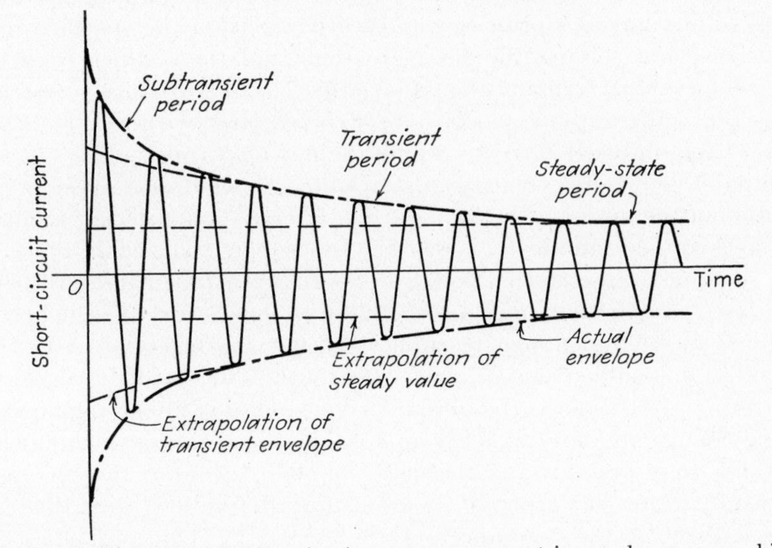

FIG. 12-15. Symmetrical short-circuit armature current in synchronous machine.

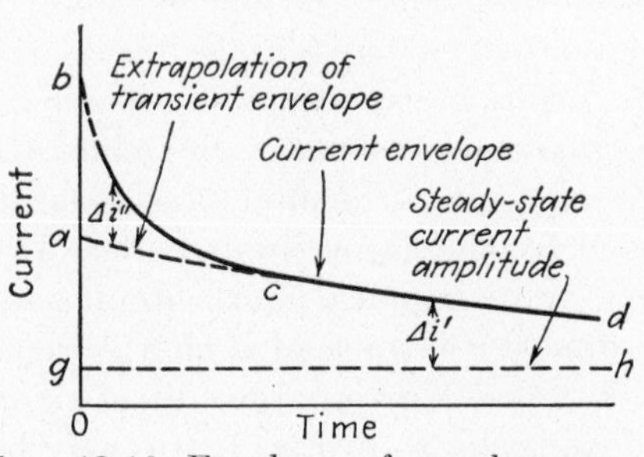

FIG. 12-16. Envelope of synchronous-machine symmetrical short-circuit current.

FIG. 12-17. Current differences plotted to semilog coordinates.

subtransient envelope and an extrapolation of the transient envelope is also plotted in Fig. 12-17. When the work is done carefully, both plots closely approximate straight lines, illustrating the essentially exponential nature of the decrement.[9]

[9] Detailed suggestions for carrying out such oscillogram analysis, together with examples, are given in S. H. Wright, Determination of Synchronous Machine Constants by Test, *Trans. AIEE*, vol. 50, pp. 1331–1351, December, 1931.

A physical picture of the happenings during these periods can be constructed by recognizing that under short-circuit conditions with zero stator-circuit resistance the stator-mmf wave is in the direct axis of the machine. The direct-axis rotor circuits and their flux linkages thus become of determining importance. The flux linkages with the main-field winding must remain constant at their initial value as determined by the field inductance and prefault field current. And this constancy must be maintained in the face of the demagnetizing stator mmf accompanying the short-circuit current of Fig. 12-15. An induced component of field current, like that shown in Fig. 12-18, must therefore appear in order to counteract the demagnetizing mmf. The induced component of field current determines the behavior of stator current during the transient period; it simply represents greater excitation on the machine than is present in the steady state, and consequently the stator currents during the transient period are greater than in the steady state. The induced field current, not being supported by an applied voltage in the field circuit, dies away at a rate determined by the field-circuit resistance and equivalent inductance, and the corresponding increment of stator current dies away at the same rate. The associated transient time constant can be determined from the envelope of Figs. 12-15 to 12-17.

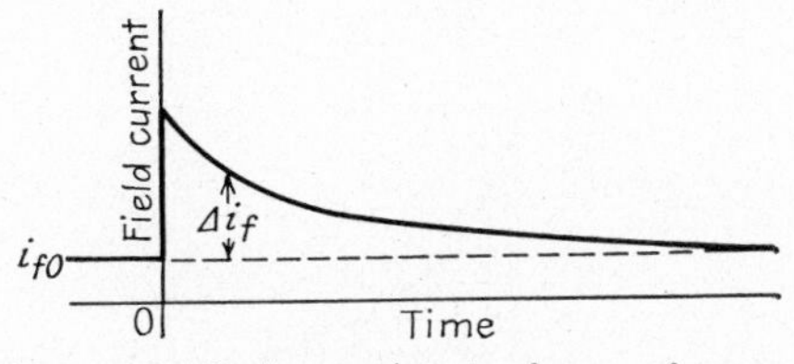

FIG. 12-18. Approximate form of synchronous-machine field current following armature short circuit.

The main field is not the only direct-axis rotor circuit, however. Flux linkages with the damper winding must remain constant at their initial value as determined by the mutual inductance between the field and damper circuits and the prefault field current. And again this constancy must be maintained in the face of the demagnetizing stator mmf accompanying the short-circuit current of Fig. 12-15. A suddenly induced damper current must therefore appear. It determines the behavior of the stator current during the subtransient period; it simply represents a still greater rotor excitation than is present in the transient period, and consequently the stator currents during the subtransient period are greater than in the transient period. The induced damper current dies away at a rate determined by the damper-circuit resistance and equivalent inductance, and the corresponding increment of stator current dies away at the same rate. Because the damper resistance-to-equivalent-inductance ratio is relatively higher than that of the field circuit, the subtransient decrement is much faster than the transient decrement. The associated subtransient time constant can be determined from the envelope of Figs. 12-15 to 12-17.

But the oscillogram of Fig. 12-15 is a special rather than a general case in that a symmetrical current wave is shown. The more usual short-circuit oscillograms have the general appearance illustrated in Fig. 12-19. These traces are not symmetrical about the zero-current axis but exhibit definite d-c components which result in offset waves. A symmetrical

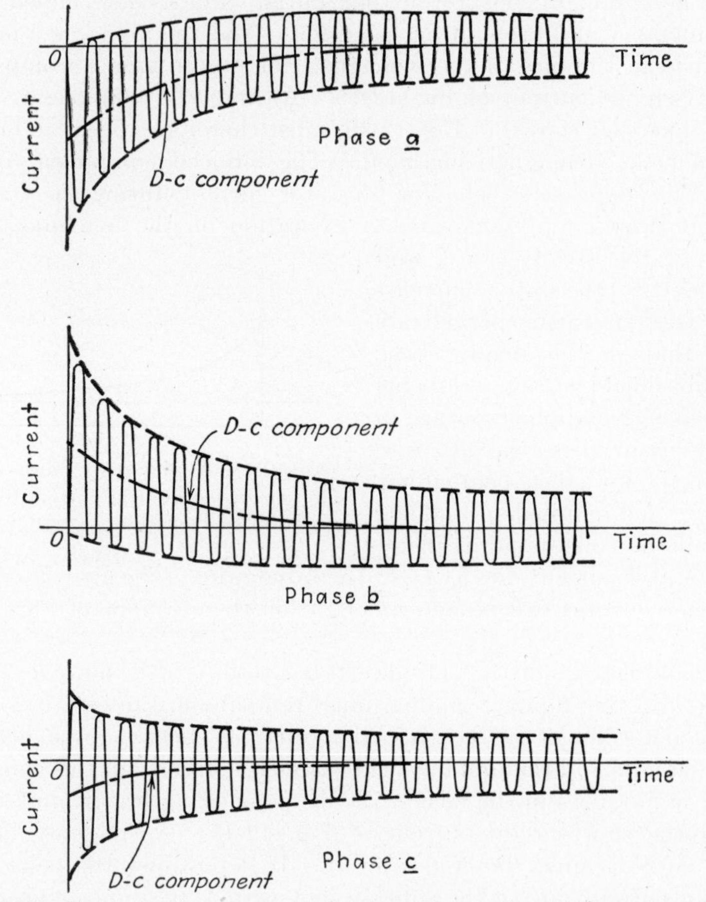

FIG. 12-19. Short-circuit currents in the three phases of a synchronous machine.

wave like that of Fig. 12-15 can be obtained either by replotting the offset waves with the d-c component subtracted or by taking a series of oscillograms until a symmetrical wave is obtained for one of the three phases.

The d-c component of stator current fits into the physical picture when it is recognized that constancy of flux linkages applies as well to each of the three phases of the resistanceless stator. If the short circuit appears at an instant when the linkages with a stator phase are zero, no d-c component is required to maintain them constant at that value and the short-circuit-current wave for that phase is symmetrical. If, however, the short circuit appears at an instant when the phase linkages have a nonzero value, a d-c component must appear in that phase in order to keep the linkages constant. The d-c component, in effect, fills the same need as the d-c component of transient current in a simple RL circuit with a suddenly impressed a-c voltage. As in the RL circuit, the largest possible value of d-c component is equal to the greatest instantaneous value of short-circuit current during the subtransient period. This largest d-c component occurs when the short circuit appears at the instant of maximum linkages for a stator phase, and the corresponding short-circuit-current wave is then fully offset from the zero axis. The d-c component, being unsupported by a voltage in the stator circuit, dies away at a rate determined by the stator-circuit resistance and equivalent inductance.

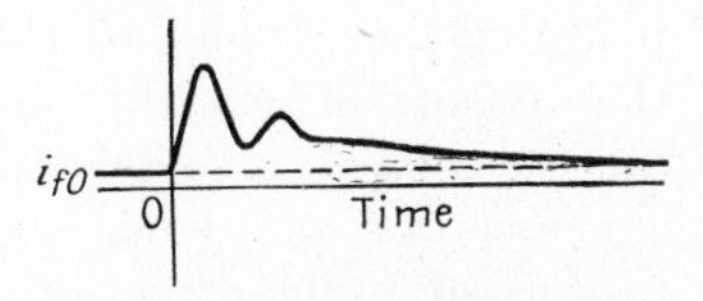

Fig. 12-20. Field current following armature short circuit.

The d-c component of stator current establishes a component field in the air gap which is stationary in space and which therefore induces a fundamental-frequency voltage and current in the synchronously revolving rotor circuits. Figure 12-20 shows the superimposed a-c component in the field current immediately following a 3-phase short circuit at the stator terminals; also illustrated in this figure is the fact that, in contrast to the approximate sketch of Fig. 12-18, the field current cannot change suddenly at the first instant. As shown in Chap. 10, the pulsating fields produced by these single-phase currents can be resolved into oppositely rotating components. One component is stationary with respect to the stator and reacts back upon the d-c component of stator current. The other component travels at twice synchronous speed with respect to the stator winding and induces a second harmonic in it. If the stator circuit is unbalanced (by a line-to-line or line-to-neutral instead of a balanced 3-phase short circuit, for example), higher harmonics may be caused in both the rotor and stator currents by successive reflections back and forth across the air gap. Harmonics are also introduced by the alternating component of stator current under unbalanced conditions. The result is that for an unbalanced short circuit at the machine terminals the waveform may be decidedly different from those given in Figs. 12-15 and 12-18. When short circuits occur at points removed from the machine terminals, the harmonics may be greatly decreased by the intervening reactance. For many engineering purposes, the harmonics are ignored; they will not be included in any subsequent analysis here. Unbalance of the stator circuit will also be omitted from consideration.[10]

[10] For complete details, including harmonics, unbalance, and engineering applications, the following series of papers by R. E. Doherty and C. A. Nickle are regarded

12-7. Synchronous-machine Reactances and Time Constants. On the basis of these physical considerations, it becomes possible to characterize the performance of an unloaded machine following a 3-phase short circuit directly at its terminals by three reactances and three time constants. The direct-axis synchronous reactance x_d determines the steady-state short-circuit current. The *direct-axis transient reactance* x'_d is so defined that it determines the initial value Oa of the symmetrical transient envelope acd (Fig. 12-16); it is equal to the rms value of prefault open-circuit phase voltage divided by $Oa/\sqrt{2}$, the factor $\sqrt{2}$ appearing because acd is the envelope of peak current values. The *direct-axis short-circuit transient time constant* T'_d is so defined that it determines the decay of the transient envelope acd; it is equal to the time required for the envelope to decay to the point where the difference between it and the steady-state envelope gh is $1/\epsilon$, or 0.368 of the initial difference ga. The *direct-axis subtransient reactance* x''_d is so defined that it determines the initial value Ob of the symmetrical subtransient envelope bc (Fig. 12-16); it is equal to the rms value of prefault open-circuit phase voltage divided by $Ob/\sqrt{2}$, the factor $\sqrt{2}$ appearing because bc is the envelope of peak current values. The *direct-axis short-circuit subtransient time constant* T''_d is so defined that it determines the decay of the subtransient envelope bc; it is equal to the time required for the envelope to decay to the point where the difference between it and the transient envelope acd is $1/\epsilon$, or 0.368 of the initial difference ab. The initial value of the d-c component or offset of the current wave, evident in Fig. 12-19, is determined by the point in the cycle at which the fault appears; its largest possible value is equal to the peak amplitude Ob (Fig. 12-16) of the symmetrical subtransient current. The *armature time constant* T_a is so defined that it determines the decay of the d-c component; it is equal to the time required for the d-c component to decay to $1/\epsilon$, or 0.368 of its initial value.

These reactances are appropriate machine constants for use not only for a 3-phase short circuit directly at the terminals of an unloaded machine but also for any application involving a sudden change in direct-axis current. This fact is emphasized by the conventional definitions of the reactances, which are formulated in terms of a suddenly impressed current. These definitions are:[11]

as classical treatments: Synchronous Machines I, An Extension of Blondel's Two-reaction Theory, *Trans. AIEE*, vol. 45, pp. 912–926, 1926; Synchronous Machines II, Steady-state Power-angle Characteristics, *Trans. AIEE*, vol. 45, pp. 927–947, 1926; Synchronous Machines III, Torque-angle Characteristics under Transient Conditions, *Trans. AIEE*, vol. 46, pp. 1–18, 1927; Synchronous Machines IV, Single-phase Phenomena in Three-phase Machines, *Trans. AIEE.*, vol. 47, pp. 457–492, 1928; Synchronous Machines V, Three-phase Short Circuit, *Trans. AIEE*, vol. 49, pp. 700–714, 1930.

[11] AIEE Test Code for Synchronous Machines, No. 503, American Institute of Electrical Engineers, New York, June, 1945.

The *direct-axis transient reactance* is the ratio of the fundamental component of reactive armature voltage, due to the fundamental direct-axis a-c component of the armature current, to this component of current under suddenly applied load conditions and at rated frequency, the value of current to be determined by the extrapolation of the envelope of the a-c component of the current wave to the instant of the sudden application of load, neglecting the high-decrement currents during the first few cycles.

The *direct-axis subtransient reactance* is the ratio of the fundamental component of reactive armature voltage, due to the initial value of the fundamental direct-axis a-c component of armature current, to this component of current under suddenly applied load conditions and at rated frequency.

The time constants T'_d, T''_d, and T_a, on the other hand, can be used only for 3-phase short circuits at the machine terminals. When external impedance is present, the decay of the induced currents is influenced not only by the self- and mutual inductances of the machine itself, but also by the constants of the external circuit. Simple methods are available, however, for the appropriate adjustment of time constants for the presence of external reactance.

Only direct-axis events have been considered up to this point because only direct-axis quantities are involved in 3-phase short circuits on purely reactive networks under the assumptions adopted. When the machine has an active-power loading before the disturbance, quadrature-axis quantities are also involved because changes in quadrature-axis current i_q are to be expected, and constant flux linkages must be maintained with the quadrature-axis rotor circuits in the face of these changes. When these aspects are to be included, the *quadrature-axis transient reactance* x'_q, *subtransient reactance* x''_q, *transient short-circuit time constant* T'_q, and *subtransient short-circuit time constant* T''_q must be considered. These reactances and time constants bear the same relation to quadrature-axis events as the corresponding direct-axis quantities do to direct-axis events. In fact the definitions of x'_q and x''_q are the same as those quoted for x'_d and x''_d, respectively, except that the words *direct axis* are replaced by the words *quadrature axis*.[12]

No field winding exists in the quadrature axis of a normal machine, so that the quadrature-axis rotor circuits must be composed of damper bars or of the rotor iron in the interpolar axis of a cylindrical-rotor machine. If there are no effective rotor circuits in the quadrature axis, $x_q = x'_q = x''_q$. If the quadrature-axis circuit is composed of damper

[12] For a discussion of these reactances in terms of the flux paths involved, see L. P. Shildneck, Synchronous Machine Reactances, a Fundamental and Physical Viewpoint, *Gen. Elec. Rev.*, vol. 35, pp. 560–565, November, 1932.

A more thoroughgoing discussion is presented in R. H. Park and B. L. Robertson, The Reactances of Synchronous Machines, *Trans. AIEE*, vol. 47, pp. 514–536, April, 1928.

bars in a salient-pole machine, the induced currents are of subtransient order and $x'_q = x_q$, with x''_q having a lower value. If the quadrature-axis circuit is formed by the interpolar iron in a solid-cylindrical-rotor machine, the induced currents are usually of transient rather than subtransient order, and x'_q almost equals x''_q, with x_q having a higher value. For a solid-cylindrical-rotor turboalternator, the interpolar iron forms just as effective an induced-current path as the main-field winding in the direct axis, and x'_q is approximately equal to x'_d.

Table 12-3 presents typical values of the constants for different types of synchronous machines. Reactances are given in per unit with the machine rating as a base. Reasonable variation either side of these values may be expected for any particular machine.

TABLE 12-3
TYPICAL VALUES OF MACHINE CONSTANTS
(Reactances are per-unit values based on the machine rating; time constants are in seconds)

Machine constant	Cylindrical-rotor generators		Salient-pole generators	Salient-pole motors (low speed)	Synchronous condensers
	Solid rotor	Laminated rotor			
x_d	1.10	1.10	1.00	1.10	1.60
x'_d	0.20	0.20	0.35	0.50	0.60
x''_d	0.10	0.10	0.23	0.35	0.25
x_q	1.00	1.00	0.65	0.80	1.00
x'_q	0.20	1.00	0.65	0.80	1.00
x''_q	0.15	0.25	0.65	0.40	0.30
T'_d	1.0	1.0	1.8	1.4	2.0
T''_d	0.035	0.035	0.035	0.035	0.035
T_a	0.15	0.15	0.15	0.15	0.15

12-8. Equivalent Circuit for Transient Conditions. By use of the concept of constant flux linkages, coupled-circuit equations can be written corresponding to the conventional definition of direct-axis transient reactance x'_d, and from these equations x'_d may be evaluated in terms of mutual and leakage inductances. From this evaluation, a simple equivalent circuit for x'_d may be obtained, and transient time constants may be interpreted with respect to the equivalent circuit. On the basis of these results, the concepts may readily be extended to apply to a short circuit with external reactance between it and the machine terminals.

To reproduce the conditions for the conventional definition of x'_d, consider an unloaded synchronous machine operating at synchronous speed with zero initial field current but with the slip rings short-circuited so that the field circuit is closed. Neglect of the high decrement during the first few cycles is equivalent to ignoring all direct-axis rotor circuits other than the main field. A direct-axis current is to be suddenly impressed, and the accompanying terminal voltage is to be evaluated.

Let L_f be the leakage inductance of the field winding, L_a the leakage inductance of the armature winding, and M_d the mutual inductance between the armature and the field winding in the direct axis. The terms L_a and M_d correspond to the armature leakage reactance x_a and direct-axis magnetizing reactance $x_{\varphi d}$ for fundamental-frequency steady-state armature currents. Note that $x_{\varphi d}$ and hence M_d include the effect of all three stator phases when the stator currents are balanced. Note also that the symbol x_a is used here for armature leakage reactance, instead of x_l as in Chaps. 7 and 8. This change is made in order that one may distinguish between armature leakage, designated by the subscript a, and field leakage, designated by the subscript f.

At an instant when the field current and direct-axis stator current have the values i_f and i_d, respectively, the flux linkages with the field winding are

$$\lambda_f = (L_f + M_d)i_f - M_d i_d \tag{12-21}$$

The sign convention is that positive values of i_d give rise to linkages in the opposite direction from positive values of i_f. Also, the phenomena are viewed from the stator, and all quantities are referred to the stator winding.

But λ_f is initially zero and, in the absence of resistance, must remain zero at all subsequent instants. Hence when a nonzero value of i_d appears, it must be accompanied by an induced field current given by

$$i_f = \frac{M_d}{L_f + M_d} i_d \tag{12-22}$$

Thus, if i_d varies sinusoidally with time, i_f *as viewed from the stator* must vary sinusoidally with time. This sinusoidally varying i_f corresponds to a direct current in the physical field winding, for a direct field current plus rotation of the rotor looks like an alternating current when viewed from the stator.

In a similar manner, the direct-axis stator linkages are

$$\lambda_d = M_d i_f - (L_a + M_d)i_d \tag{12-23}$$

which, upon substitution of Eq. 12-22, becomes

$$\lambda_d = -\left(L_a + M_d - \frac{M_d^2}{L_f + M_d}\right) i_d \tag{12-24}$$

For sinusoidal variation of i_d with the rms value I_d, the rms linkage magnitude is

$$\Lambda_d = \left(L_a + M_d - \frac{M_d^2}{L_f + M_d}\right) I_d \tag{12-25}$$

and the corresponding rms magnitude of direct-axis voltage is

$$\omega\Lambda_d = \left(\omega L_a + \omega M_d - \frac{\omega^2 M_d^2}{\omega L_f + \omega M_d}\right) I_d \tag{12-26}$$

From the conventional definition, x_d' is then

$$x_d' = \frac{\omega\Lambda_d}{I_d} = \omega L_a + \omega M_d - \frac{\omega^2 M_d^2}{\omega L_f + \omega M_d} \tag{12-27}$$

$$= x_a + x_{\varphi d} - \frac{x_{\varphi d}^2}{x_f + x_{\varphi d}} \tag{12-28}$$

$$= x_d - \frac{x_{\varphi d}^2}{x_f + x_{\varphi d}} \tag{12-29}$$

where $x_f = \omega L_f$ is the field leakage reactance referred to the stator.

Equation 12-28 can be put in alternate form by algebraic modification. Thus,

$$x_d' = \frac{x_a x_f + x_a x_{\varphi d} + x_{\varphi d} x_f + x_{\varphi d}^2 - x_{\varphi d}^2}{x_f + x_{\varphi d}}$$

$$= x_a + \frac{x_{\varphi d} x_f}{x_{\varphi d} + x_f} \tag{12-30}$$

Equation 12-30 shows that x_d' is composed of armature leakage reactance plus modified field leakage reactance. It is the general form commonly used for computation of x_d' from design data.[13]

With x_d' evaluated in terms of mutual and leakage reactances, it can now be shown that it is the reactance which determines the initial value of short-circuit current for a machine with no amortisseur winding. Under prefault conditions with the machine unloaded and having the field current i_{f0}, the field linkages are, from Eq. 12-21, with $i_d = 0$,

$$\lambda_{f0} = (L_f + M_d) i_{f0} \tag{12-31}$$

When the short circuit appears, the field linkages must remain at this value, so that

$$(L_f + M_d) i_f - M_d i_d = (L_f + M_d) i_{f0} \tag{12-32}$$

or

$$i_f = i_{f0} + \frac{M_d}{L_f + M_d} i_d \tag{12-33}$$

The second term on the right-hand side of Eq. 12-33 is the induced component of field current required to maintain constant field linkages.

[13] See L. A. Kilgore, Calculation of Synchronous Machine Constants, *Trans. AIEE*, vol. 50, pp. 1201–1214, December, 1931.

Substitution of Eq. 12-33 in 12-23 gives for direct-axis linkages

$$\lambda_d = M_d i_{f0} - \left(L_a + M_d - \frac{M_d^2}{L_f + M_d}\right) i_d \tag{12-34}$$

Under short-circuit conditions with the d-c component and all harmonics ignored, λ_d must be zero in order that the terminal voltage may be zero. Equation 12-34 then yields

$$i_d = \frac{M_d i_{f0}}{L_a + M_d - \left(\dfrac{M_d^2}{L_f + M_d}\right)} = \frac{x_{\varphi d} i_{f0}}{x_d'} \tag{12-35}$$

But the rms value of $x_{\varphi d} i_{f0}$ is also the rms value of the prefault terminal voltage E_i', as can be seen by multiplying Eq. 12-34 by ω, putting $i_d = 0$, and writing it for rms values. Accordingly, the rms short-circuit current is

$$I_d = \frac{E_i'}{x_d'} \tag{12-36}$$

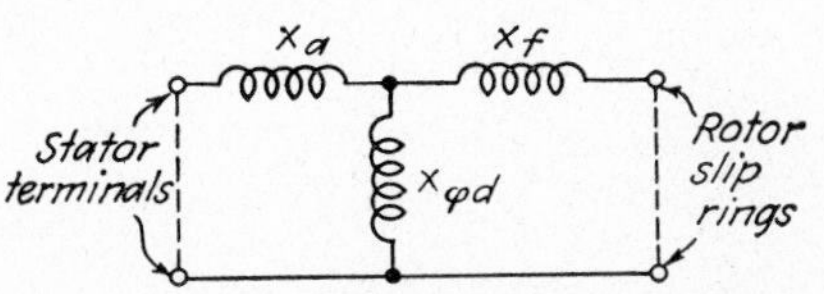

FIG. 12-21. Transformer-type equivalent circuit for synchronous machine.

and its value is limited by the direct-axis transient reactance x_d'.

From Eq. 12-30 for transient reactance x_d' and by recalling that synchronous reactance x_d is the sum of x_a and $x_{\varphi d}$, it may be recognized that the transformer-type equivalent circuit of Fig. 12-21 will serve as an equivalent circuit for both x_d and x_d'. With the machine operating balanced and in the steady state, the stator current has no effect in the rotor circuit, the rotor terminals are regarded as open-circuited, and the reactance viewed from the stator terminals is the synchronous reactance x_d. With the machine in the transient state, the change in stator current is accompanied by an induced current in the field, the rotor terminals are regarded as short-circuited, and the reactance viewed from the stator terminals is the transient reactance x_d'.

The factors influencing the transient time constant may be investigated with the aid of Fig. 12-21. First consider a machine with a closed field circuit but an open armature circuit; the time constant T_{do}' describing the decay of a field transient under these conditions is known as the *direct-axis open-circuit transient time constant.* The stator terminals (Fig. 12-21) are open-circuited, and the field terminals are short-circuited. The field transient is then affected by the self-inductance of the field, $(x_f + x_{\varphi d})/2\pi f$. If r_f is the field resistance, the time constant is

$$T_{do}' = \frac{x_f + x_{\varphi d}}{2\pi f r_f} = \frac{L_f + M_d}{r_f} \tag{12-37}$$

This time constant is a characteristic of the field circuit alone and is simply the usual self-inductance-to-resistance ratio which normally constitutes a time constant for a simple series circuit.

For short-circuit conditions, both the stator and rotor terminals are short-circuited. The equivalent field inductance affecting the decay of a field transient is then that of x_f plus $x_{\varphi d}$ and x_a in parallel, or

$$\text{Equivalent field inductance} = \frac{1}{2\pi f}\left(x_f + \frac{x_a x_{\varphi d}}{x_a + x_{\varphi d}}\right) \tag{12-38}$$

$$= \frac{x_f + x_{\varphi d}}{2\pi f} \frac{x_a + \dfrac{x_{\varphi d} x_f}{x_{\varphi d} + x_f}}{x_a + x_{\varphi d}}$$

$$= \frac{x_f + x_{\varphi d}}{2\pi f} \frac{x'_d}{x_d}$$

The short-circuit time constant is therefore

$$T'_d = \frac{x_f + x_{\varphi d}}{2\pi f r_f} \frac{x'_d}{x_d} = T'_{do} \frac{x'_d}{x_d} \tag{12-39}$$

The reactance and time constant characterizing the transient-current component for a 3-phase short circuit with external reactance x_e between it and the machine terminals can now be indicated. As far as the internal phenomena of the machine are concerned, external reactance is equivalent to increasing the armature leakage reactance from x_a to $x_a + x_e$, and the *direct-axis short-circuit transient time constant adjusted for external reactance*, T'_{de}, becomes

$$T'_{de} = T'_{do} \frac{x'_d + x_e}{x_d + x_e} = T'_d \frac{x_d}{x'_d} \frac{x'_d + x_e}{x_d + x_e} \tag{12-40}$$

The reactance determining the initial magnitude of transient alternating current is, of course, $x'_d + x_e$.

12-9. Application to System Transients. When the machine constants x_d, x'_d, x''_d, T'_d, T''_d, and T_a are known, the stator currents can be predicted with reasonable accuracy for a 3-phase short circuit separated from the terminals of an initially unloaded machine by the external reactance x_e. Thus, if the internal prefault machine voltages behind synchronous reactance, transient reactance, and subtransient reactance are E_i, E'_i, and E''_i, respectively, then the symmetrical, or a-c, component of short-circuit current is

$$I_{ac} = \frac{E_i}{x_d + x_e} + \left(\frac{E'_i}{x'_d + x_e} - \frac{E_i}{x_d + x_e}\right)\epsilon^{-t/T_{de}'} + \left(\frac{E''_i}{x''_d + x_e} - \frac{E'_i}{x'_d + x_e}\right)\epsilon^{-t/T_{de}''} \tag{12-41}$$

T'_{de} and T''_{de} being the appropriate transient and subtransient time constants. Very commonly, rms values of voltage are used in this expression and an rms value of current obtained. Accordingly, the approximate viewpoint adopted is that of the quasi-steady state in which rms values change exponentially with time. Instantaneous values can, of course, readily be obtained when the point in the cycle at which the fault occurs is known.

Superimposed on the symmetrical component of current in each phase is a d-c component given by

$$I_{dc} = I_{dc0}\epsilon^{-t/T_{ae}} \tag{12-42}$$

where I_{dc0} is the initial value, equal and opposite to the instantaneous value of I_{ac} for that phase at $t = 0$, and T_{ae} is the appropriately adjusted armature time constant. The maximum possible d-c component, corresponding to a completely offset wave, is

$$I_{dcm} = \sqrt{2}\,\frac{E''_i}{x''_d + x_e}\,\epsilon^{-t/T_{ae}} \tag{12-43}$$

The total rms value of the dissymmetrical wave at any instant is

$$I_{sc} = \sqrt{I_{ac}^2 + I_{dc}^2} \tag{12-44}$$

when the rms value is used for I_{ac}. On the basis of conservatism, the condition to be studied is commonly taken as that corresponding to the largest d-c component. By a process generally similar to that leading to Eq. 12-40, it can be shown that an approximate but sufficiently accurate value of T''_{de} is[14]

$$T''_{de} = T''_d\,\frac{x'_d}{x''_d}\,\frac{x''_d + x_e}{x'_d + x_e} \tag{12-45}$$

The armature time constant T_a with a 3-phase short circuit directly at the terminals depends on the armature resistance r_a and the equivalent inductance of the armature circuit to direct current. This equivalent inductance depends not only on the armature circuit but also on both the field and damper circuits, for the d-c component induces fundamental-frequency currents in both of these closed circuits. As the rotor revolves, the stationary mmf distribution which the d-c component creates in space reacts on direct-axis rotor circuits to one extent and on quadrature-axis rotor circuits to another because of the different permeances and different rotor circuits in the two axes. It is reasonable on an intuitive basis, therefore, to conclude that the equivalent armature inductance is somewhere between the inductance corresponding to x''_d and the inductance

[14] See S. B. Crary and M. L. Waring, The Operational Impedances of a Synchronous Machine, *Gen. Elec. Rev.*, vol. 35, pp. 578–582, November, 1932.

corresponding to x''_q; usually it is taken as the arithmetic mean of the two. The corresponding armature time constant is

$$T_a = \frac{1}{2\pi f r_a} \frac{x''_d + x''_q}{2} \tag{12-46}$$

The reasoning leading up to Eq. 12-40 may be used to adjust the time constant for external reactance, but it is important in this case to include also the external resistance r_e between the machine terminals and the fault. The adjusted time constant is

$$T_{ae} = \frac{1}{2\pi f(r_a + r_e)} \left(\frac{x''_d + x''_q}{2} + x_e \right) \tag{12-47}$$

For many engineering applications, the subtransient component may be ignored because of its rapid decrement. The third term in Eq. 12-41 is then omitted. Not infrequently, however, the possibility of a large d-c component must be accounted for, especially for fault-current values shortly after the fault has occurred. At least the initial value of subtransient current must be found to permit determination of the maximum possible d-c component.

This summary leads up to the representation of the machine as a system element in system-transient problems. When the highly decremented response during the first few cycles can be ignored, the machine is commonly represented by its direct-axis transient reactance x'_d. To correspond approximately to constant flux linkages with the main-field winding, the voltage behind transient reactance may be kept constant. Flux-linkage decrement may be included by decrementing the machine currents in accordance with the appropriate time constant. Such representation of each individual machine by a single constant reactance makes it possible to perform transient analyses almost as expeditiously as steady-state analyses and at the same time yields results to engineering accuracy for many problems. For computation of power-network short-circuit currents, such as are required for determining circuit-breaker rupturing duties, protective-relay settings, and bus-bar stresses, the power-system loads are usually ignored except in so far as they affect the prefault internal machine voltages. Also, it is common to assume all machine internal emfs to be in phase.[15]

For studies involving machine torques and power outputs under transient conditions, such as are required for investigating maintenance of synchronism during disturbances, the d-c component of fault current is usually ignored because it has negligible influence on synchronous power

[15] For comprehensive discussions of short-circuit-current computations, including unbalanced faults, see C. F. Wagner and R. D. Evans, "Symmetrical Components," McGraw-Hill Book Company, Inc., New York, 1933.

and torque. Also, the voltages behind transient reactance may frequently be considered constant for periods up to about 1 sec after fault occurrence, an assumption which is equivalent to ignoring field-flux-linkage decrement or to implying that the machine exciters, acted upon by the voltage regulators, build up field current at a rate approximately sufficient to compensate the demagnetizing influence of the stator short-circuit currents. There are, of course, numerous problems not susceptible to such simplified treatment and requiring inclusion of quadrature-axis events and external system resistance. To mention one example, studies of the terminal-voltage dip of an alternator following sudden load application rather obviously do not permit neglect of either the load or its resistive component. Such studies demand more comprehensive methods of analysis.[16]

Example 12-3. A hydroelectric station furnishes power to a large metropolitan area over a double-circuit transmission line with transformer banks at the sending and receiving ends, as shown in Fig. 12-22. Because of the large generating capacity

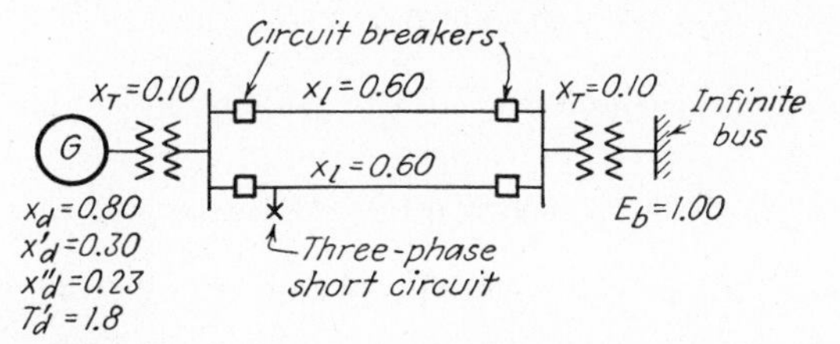

FIG. 12-22. Simplified power system for Example 12-3.

within the metropolitan area, the receiving-end low-tension bus may be considered infinite. The system constants indicated in Fig. 12-22 are per-unit values based on the kva rating of the hydrogenerators. Except for their influence on time constants, resistances are to be neglected.

The receiving-end low-tension bus voltage E_b has its normal 100 per cent value. The generators are initially so loaded that the power delivered is 80 per cent of their kva rating, and the receiving-end low-tension power factor is unity. A solid 3-phase short circuit occurs on one transmission circuit just outside the sending-end high-tension bus.

a. Find the rms total current in one phase of the fault just after its occurrence. Consider that the d-c components contributed by both the hydrogenerators and the infinite bus to this phase have their largest possible values.

b. The sending-end circuit breaker on the faulted circuit opens after 0.10 sec. Find the current which one phase of this breaker may have to interrupt in clearing the 3-phase fault. For this purpose, consider that both the d-c and subtransient components have reached negligible proportions in 0.1 sec.

Solution. *a.* The prefault voltage behind x''_d is

$$E''_i = 1.00 + j0.80(0.50 + 0.23) = 1.16\underline{/30.3°}$$

[16] For studies of the transient voltage-regulation problem, see H. C. Anderson, Voltage Variation of Suddenly Loaded Generators, *Gen. Elec. Rev.*, vol. 48, pp. 25–33, August, 1945.

The initial symmetrical current from the generators is then

$$\frac{1.16}{0.23 + 0.10} = 3.52$$

and from the infinite bus is

$$\frac{1.00}{0.10 + 0.30} = 2.50$$

making the initial symmetrical fault current 3.52 + 2.50 = 6.02.

The d-c component from the generators is, for a completely offset wave, $\sqrt{2}$ (3.52) = 4.97, and from the infinite bus is $\sqrt{2}$ (2.50) = 3.53, making the d-c component in the fault 4.97 + 3.53 = 8.50.

The largest rms total fault current is therefore

$$\sqrt{(6.02)^2 + (8.50)^2} = 10.4$$

b. The prefault voltage behind x_d' is

$$E_i' = 1.00 + j0.80(0.50 + 0.30) = 1.19\underline{/32.6°}$$

and behind x_d

$$E_i = 1.00 + j0.80(0.50 + 0.80) = 1.44\underline{/46.1°}$$

The initial symmetrical generator current with the subtransient ignored is

$$\frac{1.19}{0.30 + 0.10} = 2.97$$

and the final steady-state generator current when the fault remains on the system is

$$\frac{1.44}{0.80 + 0.10} = 1.60$$

The symmetrical generator current passes from the first of these values to the second exponentially with a time constant (Eq. 12-40) equal to

$$T_{de}' = 1.8 \frac{0.80}{0.30} \frac{0.30 + 0.10}{0.80 + 0.10} = 2.13 \text{ sec}$$

The value of this current at t = 0.10 sec is accordingly

$$1.60 + (2.97 - 1.60)\epsilon^{-0.10/2.13} = 2.91$$

Only half of the infinite-bus current, or 1.25, passes through the breaker, so that the symmetrical breaker current is

$$2.91 + 1.25 = 4.16$$

12-10. Résumé. The study of electrical transients in d-c and synchronous machines is necessarily a compromise between the detailed analyses which may be made when only conditions within a single machine are of concern and the more rough-and-ready artifices which must be adopted for simplified representation of the machine as one element in a complex system. The basic problem for both machine types is essentially that of transients in nonlinear coupled circuits, and the most important question from the systems viewpoint is that of deciding on admissible approximations.

For d-c machines, saturation, causing nonconstancy of the field-circuit inductance and nonlinearity of the relation between armature generated voltage and field current, is the principal obstacle to analysis. When facility of analysis is important, one of two steps can be taken: saturation may be ignored, permitting the use of linear differential equations with constant coefficients; or the armature constants may be ignored, a step which usually makes possible a simple graphical analysis. Numerical comparison shows that linearizing of the machine gives results of reasonable accuracy for operation up to about the rated-voltage point on a normal magnetization curve. Such linearization is essential to characterization of the machine as an element in complex systems like the automatic-control schemes of the next chapter, for otherwise over-all analysis of the system may become so obscured in details that significant conclusions may be overlooked.

Graphical solutions, based on numerical evaluation of an integral by finding the area under the curve described by the integrand, are readily applicable to first-order equations whose variables can be separated. Although they do not yield results in literal form, they do give a fair picture of the influence of the various constants, both because one has specific curves and areas as aids to speculation, and because evaluation for a series of conditions is seldom unduly burdensome. Graphical solutions are important for studying the response of machines, especially exciters, at high saturation, and for indicating the order of magnitude of error arising from neglect of saturation.

Saturation is immediately ruled out of consideration in synchronous-machine transients on the basis that we are primarily interested in short-circuit conditions and that short circuits of reasonable severity are usually accompanied by low air-gap densities in the important machines. The principal obstacle is then the complexity of the coupled circuits within the machine. From the partially intuitive and empirical viewpoint adopted in this chapter, the study of synchronous-machine transients may be surveyed by considering the following questions: How may test data in the form of oscillograms for 3-phase short circuits at the machine terminals be used to compute the effects of short circuits at other points in the external network or for other voltage conditions in the machines? How may these test data be correlated with a physical picture of the phenomena based on previous experience with machines and with electric-circuit transients?

The typical oscillogram is found to consist of a decaying d-c component superimposed on a decreasing a-c component. When the d-c component is subtracted, the a-c component is divisible into three time periods, or regimes. The first, or subtransient, period lasts only a few cycles and is one of high decrement; the events in it are largely determined by induced currents in the rotor damper circuits. The second, or transient, period is one of more moderate decrement; the events in it are largely determined by induced currents in the main-field winding. The third is the steady-state period in which events are determined by the principles of Chaps. 7 and 8. The d-c component fills the conventional role of a d-c component in an a-c transient: it makes possible conformity with the physical fact that flux linkages cannot change suddenly by bridging the gap between the prefault armature current and the initial value of the a-c component alone. From previous experience with electric transients, it is expected that the d-c component, the difference between the subtransient and transient current, and the difference between the transient and steady-state current will all decay at close to exponential rates. This expectation is borne out by semilog plots of the various currents. Subtransient and transient reactance are defined so that they make possible simple computation of the initial magnitudes of subtransient and transient currents, respectively, when the initial voltages behind these reactances are known. Subtransient, transient, and d-c time constants are defined so that they specify the exponential decay of the current components.

For most system problems, the subtransient period is over so quickly that it may be ignored; if subtransient currents are computed at all, they are computed only in order to find the initial magnitude of the d-c component. Accordingly, the machine often may be represented as a system element by its direct-axis transient reactance behind which a constant or easily computed voltage exists. System short-circuit studies are thus greatly simplified, and a convenient approach to many engineering problems is made available.

It is once more apparent in retrospect that one of our major preoccupations in the study of specific machines is the devising of appropriate equivalent circuits. To be correct, these equivalents must satisfy only the requirement that the instantaneous currents and voltages at their terminals be the same as at the actual machine terminals. Academically speaking, therefore, a synchronous machine—or any other a-c machine, for that matter—may be represented by a wide variety of reactances provided that the appropriate voltage is placed back of the reactance; or, alternatively and under the same proviso, any synchronous machine may be represented by a constant reactance of, say, 1 ohm. To be useful in engineering, however, these equivalent circuits must simplify rather than complicate the analysis. Hence we demand that an equivalent reactance be chosen so that the voltage behind it may be assumed constant or, at least, be easily computed. Herein lies the reason for using transient reactance in the transient state: for many problems the voltage back of it may be assumed constant. Herein also lies the reason for using synchronous reactance to determine steady-state short-circuit currents: the voltage back of it is readily determined from the field current and remains constant for constant excitation.

PROBLEMS

12-1. In an idealized Amplidyne generator, only one control winding is being used. This winding has the resistance r_f and self-inductance L_f. The internal generated voltage in the quadrature, or short-circuited, armature axis is k_f volts/amp in the control winding. The quadrature-axis armature resistance and inductance are r_q and L_q. The generated voltage E_g in the direct-axis armature circuit is k_q volts/amp in the short-circuited brushes. The effects of any other Amplidyne auxiliaries are to be ignored.

With the Amplidyne unloaded and initially unexcited, show definitely how you would compute the build-up of direct-axis terminal voltage following the sudden appearance of a voltage E_i at the terminals of the control winding.

12-2. Solve Prob. 12-1 for an Amplidyne loaded by the resistance r_d in series with a constant inductance L_d. These values include the direct-axis armature and compensating-field resistance and inductance of the Amplidyne itself. The compensating field causes the mutual effect of the direct-axis armature circuit on the control field to be negligible.

12-3. An approximate and readily obtainable measure of the response of a d-c generator is offered by the initial rate of change of voltage immediately after build-up is initiated. This initial build-up rate may be used, for example, in rough comparisons of the response rates of self- and separately excited generators.

Consider that the generator of Example 12-2 is operating at an armature voltage of 190 volts and is under the control of a voltage regulator which alters the value of external field-circuit resistance in order to maintain the appropriate terminal voltage. When the external resistance is all cut out by the voltage regulator, the field-circuit resistance is reduced to that of the field winding alone, 24.2 ohms. Armature resistance and inductance and armature reaction are to be ignored.

a. Determine the minimum voltage of the excitation source when the ceiling voltage for separate excitation is to be the same as that for self-excitation.

b. Compute and compare the initial build-up rates for self- and separate excitation when the voltage regulator suddenly calls for build-up from 190 volts to the ceiling voltage by short-circuiting the external field resistance. The conditions of *a* obtain for separate excitation.

12-4. Discuss the effect on the time of build-up of a self-excited d-c machine of making the following basic changes. In each case, all other factors are assumed to remain the same. Accompany your discussion with sketches, and state and prove conclusions concisely.

a. Increasing the field resistance
b. Increasing the speed
c. Increasing the number of shunt-field turns, with the same field resistance
d. Increasing the field resistance and number of shunt-field turns in the same ratio
e. Lengthening the air gap by 20 per cent

12-5. A 6-pole 150-kw 250-volt 1,200-rpm exciter is separately excited from a flat-compounded 125-volt pilot exciter. Each of the six shunt-field coils has an external resistor R connected in series with it. Contacts C are connected across each resistor

R so that, when they close, R is short-circuited and the exciter builds up to a higher voltage. All six of these shunt-field circuits are connected in parallel to the pilot-exciter terminals.

The constants of the exciter are as follows:

Turns per pole = 750
Armature flux per pole = 14,140 lines per armature volt
Coefficient of dispersion = 1.15
Ceiling voltage (contacts C closed) = 335 volts
Minimum voltage (contacts C open) = 50 volts
Normal operating armature voltage = 188 volts

Data for the no-load saturation curve at 1,200 rpm are:

I_f, amp per pole	0.8	2.0	3.0	4.0	6.0	8.0	10.0
E_a, volts	50	127	188	233	289	317	335

Armature resistance and inductance and armature reaction may be ignored.

a. Consider that the exciter is operating at minimum voltage, corresponding to contacts C open. Determine the initial build-up rate when the contacts C close.

b. Consider that the exciter is operating at ceiling voltage, corresponding to contacts C closed. Determine the initial build-down rate with the contacts C open.

c. Consider that the resistances R are readjusted so that the exciter is operating at its normal armature voltage with contacts C open. Determine the initial build-up rate when the contacts C close.

d. Will the initial build-up rate at the normal operating voltage as obtained in *c* differ from the build-up rate which would occur at this voltage if build-up were started from minimum voltage as in *a*? Justify your answer.

12-6. This problem is intended to illustrate the general nature of the transient short-circuit current of a self-excited d-c machine and of the factors influencing this current. At the same time, it illustrates the numerical application of a step-by-step approach.

Consider that the generator of Examples 12-1 and 12-2 ($r_a = 0.0125$ ohm, $L_a = 0.008$ henry, $\sigma = 1.15$, $N_f/k_\varphi = 0.574$, magnetization curve given by Fig. 12-8) is operating at rated speed, unloaded, and with a terminal voltage of 250 volts when a short circuit occurs directly at its terminals. Compute and plot a curve of short-circuit current as a function of time. Include armature resistance and inductance and the nonlinearity of the magnetization curve, but ignore the effects of armature reaction. There is no voltage regulator, so that the field-circuit resistance remains constant at the initial value.

This analysis will have a relatively low order of accuracy. The weak points are the assumptions that the armature resistance remains constant at the static value in spite of the rapidly changing current, and that armature reaction remains negligible up to very high currents.

12-7. To illustrate the effects of armature inductance on d-c-machine short-circuit currents, solve Prob. 12-6 with armature inductance ignored, and compare the results.

12-8. The following are the constants of a 35,000-kva 13.8-kv 60-cps water-wheel generator: $x_d = 1.00$, $x'_d = 0.35$, $x''_d = 0.25$, $T'_{do} = 5.0$ sec, $T''_{do} = 0.05$ sec. Reactances are in per unit on the generator rating as a base. This generator supplies a load over a line whose reactance is 0.50 per unit and whose resistance is negligible. Under normal conditions, the generator is fully loaded with a terminal power factor of 0.80 lagging and rated terminal voltage. A 3-phase short circuit is considered to occur at the receiving end of the line.

a. Compute the prefault values of the voltages behind synchronous and transient reactances.

b. Compute the largest possible initial value of the d-c component of short-circuit current in the machine.

c. Give the numerical equation for the generator rms short-circuit current as a function of time after fault occurrence. Ignore the d-c component.

d. The fault is cleared after 0.15 sec. From the results of *c*, give the rms value of generator short-circuit current just before clearing.

12-9. A low-speed salient-pole synchronous motor has constants which are indicated in Table 12-3 as typical for such a machine. It is connected to an infinite bus through a transformer whose reactance is 0.07 on the rated kva input of the motor as a base (the motor reactances are on the same base). The infinite-bus voltage is unity. The motor excitation is so adjusted that, with no shaft load, the transformer takes 0.50 per unit of leading reactive power from the bus at the transformer input. Motor losses are negligible.

a. For purposes of analyzing the response of the motor to a suddenly applied shaft load, the motor would usually be represented by its direct-axis transient reactance with a constant voltage back of that reactance equal to the value before the load was applied. Give the numerical equation for the power-angle curve with respect to the infinite bus under these conditions. Sketch this curve approximately to scale.

b. When the load is applied very slowly, the pertinent power-angle curve is determined by the steady-state principles of Chaps. 7 and 8. Consider that cylindrical-rotor theory is to be used, as in Chap. 7, with the motor represented by its direct-axis synchronous reactance. As an approximate adjustment for saturation, the unsaturated value from Table 12-3 is to be multiplied by 0.8 and assumed to be constant at this value. Give the numerical equation for the power-angle curve under these conditions, and sketch it on the same plot as in *a*.

c. Repeat *b*, but use salient-pole theory as in Chap. 8. Consider that the quadrature-axis synchronous reactance is unaffected by saturation.

d. Compute the initial symmetrical value of per-unit short-circuit current in the transformer for a 3-phase short circuit at its input terminals.

12-10. While an alternator is undergoing a standard short-circuit test on a factory test floor, the short circuit is suddenly removed. Prior to this removal, rated steady-state short-circuit current was flowing. The machine constants are $x_d = 1.20$, $x_q = 0.80$, $x_d' = 0.40$, $x_q' = 0.80$, $T_{do}' = 5$ sec, $T_d' = 1.67$ sec. There are no effective damper circuits in either the direct or the quadrature axis, and the resistance and inductance of the exciter may be assumed negligible.

Give the numerical expression for the per-unit field current as a function of time after removal of the short circuit.

CHAPTER 13

DYNAMICS OF ELECTROMECHANICALLY COUPLED SYSTEMS

Almost all of the discussions of machine performance in Chaps. 3 to 10 are based on static conditions in the machine and the system of which it is a part. A wide range of possible steady-state values is considered, but the transition from one set of values to another is assumed to take place so slowly that the electrical and mechanical equability of the system is completely undisturbed. Such a state of affairs is, of course, desirable while attention is being focused entirely on the machine in an effort to master its workings; such a state of affairs, moreover, is representative of that which is found in many of the more routine machine applications.

As the service requirements become more exacting, however, increasing emphasis must be placed on the dynamic considerations involved in the transition from one steady state to another or involved because the system, when operating, is rarely called upon to settle down to a static state. *Electromechanical transients,* rather than simply *electric transients,* are involved; electrodynamic considerations including in the general case the effects of inertia, friction, and elastic compliance, as well as of resistance, inductance, and capacitance, become determining. An equivalent statement is that energy storage and energy flow into and out of moving masses, and in some cases elastic compliances, must be given equal prominence with energy considerations in magnetic and electric fields.

Because the general subject is so broad, this chapter can provide only an introduction to the dynamics of electromechanical systems. Dynamic analysis of such systems will be illustrated by a series of specific examples drawn largely from electric-machine applications. In all cases the object is to build up a general philosophy of analysis rather than to present specialized techniques which are of only limited application.

13-1. Motional Transients in Simple Systems—Motor Starting. When the duty cycle of a motor requires frequent starting or reversing, energy storage in the rotating mass of both the rotor and the driven equipment becomes a significant factor in over-all performance, especially when the load has high inertia or when the allowable time for starting or reversing is very limited. In fact, even for a motor driving a load characterized by inertia alone, there is a definite limit to the number of starts or reversals per unit of time if the motor is not to be overloaded; existence of this limit often dictates the motor characteristics or rating required for a specific application.

Such problems relating to the starting, stopping, or reversing of motors are among the simplest involving motional transients. In many studies the mains to which the motor is connected may be considered an infinite bus, so that the characteristics of the supply system enter only in the simple form of a constant impressed voltage. The mechanical power available at the motor shaft as a result of energy conversion in the motor serves two functions during the starting period. At any instant, part of the power maintains rotation at the speed then attained, and the remainder accelerates the inertia of the rotor and its connected load. The latter portion of the power may be equated to the time rate of energy storage in the rotating mass. The motor thus does not reach operating speed until the system has had time to convert and store the corresponding amount of energy in that mass. Similarly, the stopping or braking of a motor demands that opportunity be provided for complete dissipation of the stored mechanical energy, either through friction in mechanical braking or through conversion to electrical energy in dynamic braking. Likewise, reversing of the rotor demands complete dissipation of the stored mechanical energy, followed by re-storage corresponding to rotation in the opposite direction.

Analytical details will be illustrated by two examples, the first concerning a d-c motor, the second an induction motor. The simplifying assumptions made in the first example result in a linear system and are typical of those made in dynamic studies of d-c machines.

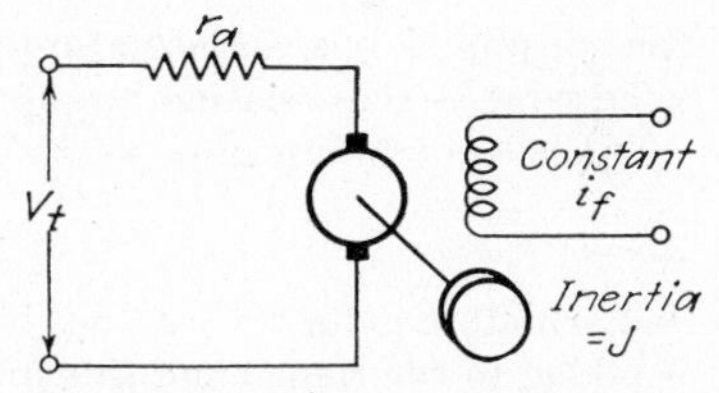

FIG. 13-1. Direct-current motor with pure-inertia load.

Example 13-1. A small d-c motor is directly coupled mechanically to a pure-inertia load as indicated schematically in Fig. 13-1 and is operated with constant field excitation. The motor has the armature-circuit resistance r_a ohms and negligible armature inductance and armature reaction. The effect of rotational losses in the motor is to be ignored. The combined inertia of the armature and load is J.

With the motor at rest, the constant direct voltage V_t is suddenly impressed on its armature terminals.

a. Obtain an expression for the armature current as a function of time.

b. Obtain an expression for the angular velocity of the shaft as a function of time.

c. Normalize the results obtained in *a* and *b*, and discuss their similarity to transients in a purely electrical circuit.

d. Show that the energy dissipated as armature-circuit copper loss during the starting period equals that finally stored in the rotating mass.

e. Consider that the resistance r_a is 34 ohms, the Wk^2 of the armature and load (weight times square of the radius of gyration) is 0.20 in.²-lb, the electromagnetic torque of the motor is 46.4 in.-oz/amp, and the armature generated voltage is 2.06 volts/rev/sec. Determine the time for the motor to come to within approximately 2 per cent of its final speed.

f. Indicate the changes which would be made in the results of *a*, *b*, *c*, and *d* if the load were coupled to the motor shaft through gears stepping down the speed by the factor k_G. The motor armature inertia should now be taken as J_m and the load inertia as J_L. The friction and inertia of the gears themselves should be neglected.

Solution. The equations describing the behavior of the motor and its load will first be written. All quantities will be expressed in mks units. The instantaneous angular velocity of the motor shaft is designated by ω_o and measured in mechanical radians per second. (In this chapter, the symbol ω denotes the mechanical angular velocity of a shaft only when either the subscript *o* for output or *i* for input is attached. When no subscript appears or when *o* or *i* is not part of the subscript, ω refers, as usual in electrical work, to the angular frequency of a sinusoid or of a damped sinusoid. The symbol ω_o is used rather than *n* to distinguish between angular velocity in radians per second and speed in rpm.) At any instant the electromagnetic torque resulting from energy conversion in the motor is, from Eq. 4-56,

$$T = \frac{p}{2\pi}\frac{Z}{a}\Phi i_a = ki_a \tag{13-1}$$

where

$$k = \frac{p}{2\pi}\frac{Z}{a}\Phi \tag{13-2}$$

is the torque per unit of armature current under the specified conditions, i_a is the instantaneous armature current, and other symbols are as in Eq. 4-56.

Similarly, the counter emf of the motor, in accordance with Eq. 4-38, is at any instant

$$e_a = p\Phi\frac{Z}{a}\frac{\omega_o}{2\pi} = k\omega_o \tag{13-3}$$

The constant *k* relating armature generated voltage and speed in radians per second is the same as that relating torque and armature current.

The last constraint imposed by the motor is that

$$V_t = e_a + r_a i_a = k\omega_o + r_a i_a \tag{13-4}$$

Had armature inductance L_a not been regarded as negligible, the term $L_a\, di_a/dt$ would be added to the right-hand side of this equation.

Since rotational losses are ignored and the load requires no power to maintain rotation, all of the electromagnetic torque is available to accelerate the rotating inertia. Accordingly,

$$T = ki_a = J\frac{d\omega_o}{dt} \tag{13-5}$$

a. To obtain the armature current, Eqs. 13-4 and 13-5 are combined, with ω_o eliminated, yielding

$$\frac{Jr_a}{k^2}\frac{di_a}{dt} + i_a = 0 \tag{13-6}$$

When it is recognized that at $t = 0$, both ω_o and e_a are zero, and $i_{ao} = V_t/r_a$, the solution of Eq. 13-6 becomes

$$i_a = \frac{V_t}{r_a}\epsilon^{-(k^2/Jr_a)t} \tag{13-7}$$

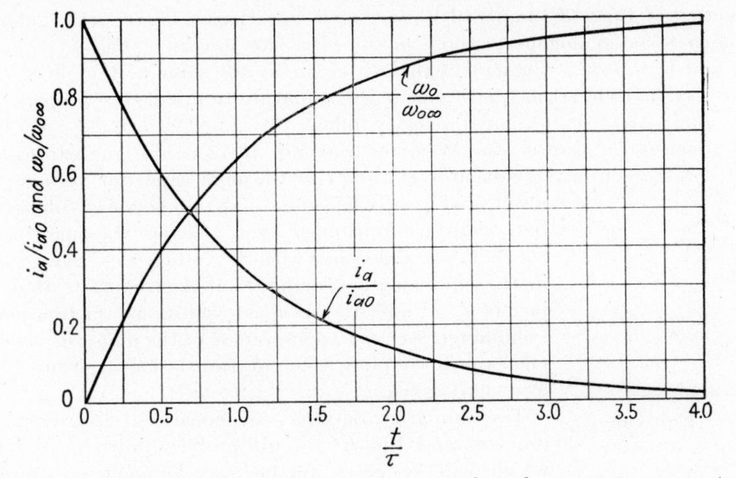

FIG. 13-2. Normalized curves of d-c-motor speed and armature current during starting.

b. To obtain the angular velocity of the shaft, Eqs. 13-4 and 13-5 are again combined but with i_a eliminated, yielding

$$\frac{Jr_a}{k^2}\frac{d\omega_o}{dt} + \omega_o = \frac{V_t}{k} \tag{13-8}$$

the solution of which, for zero angular velocity at $t = 0$, is

$$\omega_o = \frac{V_t}{k}\,(1 - \epsilon^{-(k^2/Jr_a)t}) \tag{13-9}$$

c. To normalize Eq.13-9, notice that

$$\frac{V_t}{k} = \omega_{o\infty} \tag{13-10}$$

is the final steady-state angular velocity. Notice also that

$$\frac{Jr_a}{k^2} = \tau \tag{13-11}$$

is a time constant in the usual meaning of the term for an electric circuit. Equation 13-9 may therefore be most conveniently expressed in the form

$$\frac{\omega_o}{\omega_{o\infty}} = 1 - \epsilon^{-t/\tau} \tag{13-12}$$

The corresponding curve with coordinates in nondimensional terms is given in Fig. 13-2.

In a similar fashion, Eq. 13-7 may be written

$$\frac{i_a}{i_{a0}} = \epsilon^{-t/\tau} \tag{13-13}$$

This curve is also plotted to nondimensional coordinates in Fig. 13-2.

Inspection of Eqs. 13-12 and 13-13 or their counterparts, 13-9 and 13-7, shows the phenomena to be analogous to those in the series RC circuit of Fig. 13-3, in which $R = r_a$ and $C = J/k^2$. Current in the RC circuit is the same as that in the motor armature, so that electrical conditions at the armature terminals are properly reproduced. Build-up of shaft angular velocity follows the same law as build-up of voltage across capacitor C. Notice, for example, that Eq. 13-12 is also the expression for ratio of voltage across the capacitor at time t to the final capacitor voltage; notice also that Eq. 13-9 becomes a relation between voltages when both sides are multiplied by k, and that the quantity $k\omega_o$ in this relation is identical with the voltage e_a. Energy storage in the equivalent capacitor C is then equal to that in the inertia J. Under the specified conditions, the time constant τ characterizes the responsiveness of the motor as an electromechanical coupling element translating armature voltage into shaft speed.

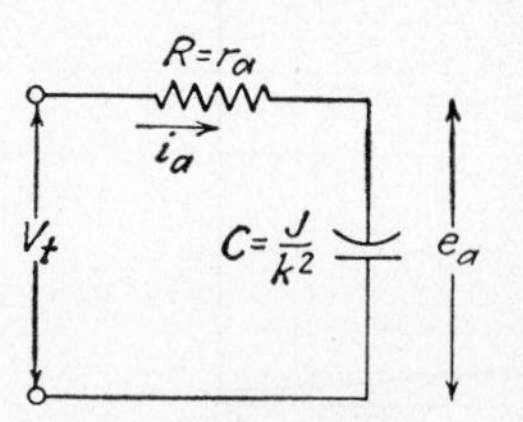

FIG. 13-3. Equivalent circuit of d-c motor.

The similarity between the linearized electromechanical problem and the RC-circuit problem introduces a theme which will be given further development in subsequent articles of this chapter. It leads to two expectations: first, that many of the techniques of electric-circuit analysis may be applied to the study of electromechanical-system dynamics; and second, that actual experiments on the equivalent electric circuits may provide valuable methods for the study of complex dynamic problems. Thus, the concept of machines as circuit elements in the broader sense of the word *circuit*, first mentioned in Art. 4-13, begins to be more tangible.

d. In terms of the electric-circuit analogy, it is immediately evident that the energy dissipated in r_a equals that stored in the rotating mass, for we know that the energy loss in charging a capacitor from a constant-voltage source equals that ultimately stored in the capacitor. To check the conclusion for the electromechanical system, recognize from Eq. 13-4 that

$$r_a i_a = V_t - k\omega_o \tag{13-14}$$

and from Eq. 13-5 that

$$i_a = \frac{J}{k}\frac{d\omega_o}{dt} \tag{13-15}$$

Multiplication of corresponding sides of Eqs. 13-14 and 13-15 gives

$$r_a i_a^2 = J\frac{V_t}{k}\frac{d\omega_o}{dt} - J\omega_o\frac{d\omega_o}{dt} \tag{13-16}$$

which, upon rearrangement and use of Eq. 13-10, becomes

$$r_a i_a^2\,dt = J\omega_{o\infty}\,d\omega_o - J\omega_o\,d\omega_o \tag{13-17}$$

The energy dissipated as copper loss is then

$$\begin{aligned} W_{cu} = r_a \int_0^\infty i_a^2\,dt &= J\omega_{o\infty}\int_0^{\omega_{o\infty}} d\omega_o - J\int_0^{\omega_{o\infty}} \omega_o\,d\omega_o \\ &= \tfrac{1}{2}J\omega_{o\infty}^2 \end{aligned} \tag{13-18}$$

a result which is immediately seen to equal the stored energy in the rotating mass.

e. The numerical data must first be converted to the appropriate mks units. Inertia J is obtained by dividing the Wk^2 by the acceleration of gravity and changing the units. The numerical value of the constant k may be obtained from either the torque constant or the generated-voltage constant. The results are

$$J = 5.85 \times 10^{-5} \text{ mks unit}$$

and

$$k = 0.328 \text{ volt/rad/sec or newton-m/amp}$$

From Eq. 13-11, the time constant is

$$\tau = \frac{5.85 \times 10^{-5} \times 34}{(0.328)^2} = 0.0185 \text{ sec}$$

Now, a simple exponential will decay to 0.0183 or approximately 2 per cent of its initial value in a time equal to four time constants. For the motor to come up to speed in this case then requires 4 × 0.0185, or 0.074 sec.

f. The previous results may be used for the geared drive by simple reinterpretation if the load inertia J_L is referred to the motor shaft in the same way that an impedance is referred from the secondary to the primary of a transformer. Thus, refer to the simple gear train of Fig. 13-4, and recall the basic relations for ideal gears:

$$\omega_{o1} = k_G \omega_{o2} \tag{13-19}$$

and

$$T_1 = \frac{1}{k_G} T_2 \tag{13-20}$$

To accelerate inertia J_2 requires the torque

$$T_2 = J_2 \frac{d\omega_{o2}}{dt} \tag{13-21}$$

on shaft 2, and hence the corresponding torque

$$T_1 = \frac{J_2}{k_G}\frac{d\omega_{o2}}{dt} = \frac{J_2}{k_G^2}\frac{d\omega_{o1}}{dt} \tag{13-22}$$

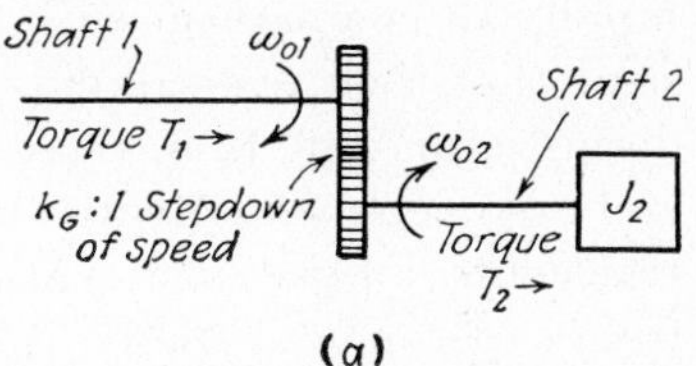

Shaft 1
Torque T_1→
J_1
(b)

FIG. 13-4. (*a*) Two shafts coupled by gears, and (*b*) the equivalent system as viewed from the first shaft.

on shaft 1. Consequently the system of Fig. 13-4*a* may be replaced by that of Fig. 13-4*b* without changing conditions at shaft 1 provided

$$J_1 = \frac{J_2}{k_G^2} \tag{13-23}$$

Accordingly, in reinterpreting the previous results the inertia J should be regarded as

$$J = J_m + \frac{J_L}{k_G^2} \tag{13-24}$$

Insertion of the gear train is evidently equivalent to insertion of an ideal transformer in the analogous electric circuit.

The second example, dealing with the starting of an induction motor, illustrates a possible procedure when significant nonlinearities are unavoidable and when, at the same time, the system being analyzed is not unduly complex. Both the torque produced by the motor and the torque required to turn the load are considered to be nonlinear functions for which data are given in the form of curves as a function of speed. The associated electromechanical transient is of such form that graphical integration, first introduced in Art. 12-3 for purely electrical transients, may be used. At the same time the need for a rather drastic simplifying assumption appears: when voltage is suddenly impressed on the terminals of an induction motor, a complicated electrical transient follows and the performance of the motor, strictly speaking, cannot be predicted during this transient period from the steady-state theory previously developed. Yet it is common in studying the dynamics of induction-motor action to assume that the electrical aspects of motor performance at any instant are the same as if the motor were electrically in the steady state for the particular speed or slip at that instant. This assumption is the equivalent of saying that the purely electrical transients die out so rapidly in comparison with the duration of the electromechanical transient that their over-all effect is insignificant. In terms of the concepts discussed in Art. 12-6, these electrical effects are of a subtransient order and are decremented with the comparative rapidity associated with subtransients. Final justification for such an assumption can come only from experimental comparison of results, and from detailed studies based on more comprehensive theories and applied to the comparison of results in special cases. Such comparisons do justify application of the assumption in engineering studies of the type undertaken in this chapter.[1]

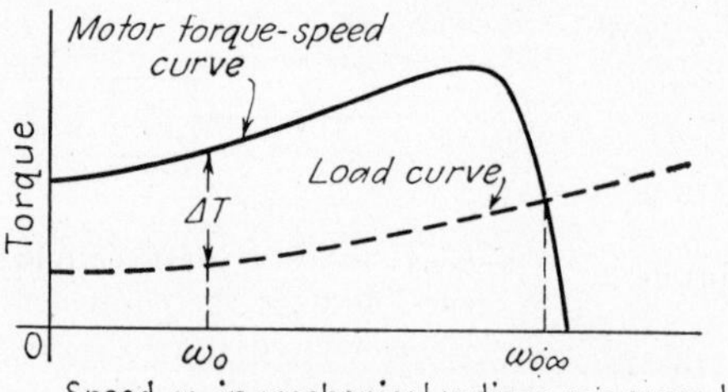

Fig. 13-5. Induction-motor torque-speed curve and curve of load torque.

Example 13-2. A polyphase induction motor has the torque-speed curve for rated impressed voltage shown in Fig. 13-5. A curve of the torque required to maintain rotation of the load is also given in Fig. 13-5. The inertia of the load and rotor is J mks units.

Consider that across-the-line starting at rated voltage is used and that the steady-state torque-speed curve represents the performance under transient conditions with sufficient accuracy. Show how a curve of speed as a function of time may be obtained.

Solution. At any motor speed ω_o mechanical radians per second, the torque differential ΔT between that produced by the motor and that required to turn the load is available to accelerate the rotating mass. Consequently,

$$J \frac{d\omega_o}{dt} = \Delta T \tag{13-25}$$

The time required to attain the speed ω_o is therefore

$$t = J \int_0^{\omega_o} \frac{1}{\Delta T} \, d\omega_o \tag{13-26}$$

[1] For a survey of the considerations involved, see O. G. C. Dahl, "Electric Power Circuits—Theory and Applications," Vol. II, Power System Stability, Chap. XIX, McGraw-Hill Book Company, Inc., New York, 1938; T. M. Linville, Starting Performance of Salient-pole Synchronous Motors, *Trans. AIEE*, p. 531, April, 1930.

The integral in Eq. 13-26 can be evaluated graphically by plotting a curve of $1/\Delta T$ as a function of ω_o and finding the area between the curve and the ω_o axis up to the value corresponding to the upper limit of the integral, a procedure illustrated in Fig. 13-6. The area can be found by planimeter, by counting small squares on the curve sheet, or by dividing it into uniform segments and using the average ordinate for each section. This area in units of radians per second per newton-meter times the inertia J in mks units gives the time t in seconds. The computations can be carried out conveniently in tabular form to yield a result of the type shown in Fig. 13-7.

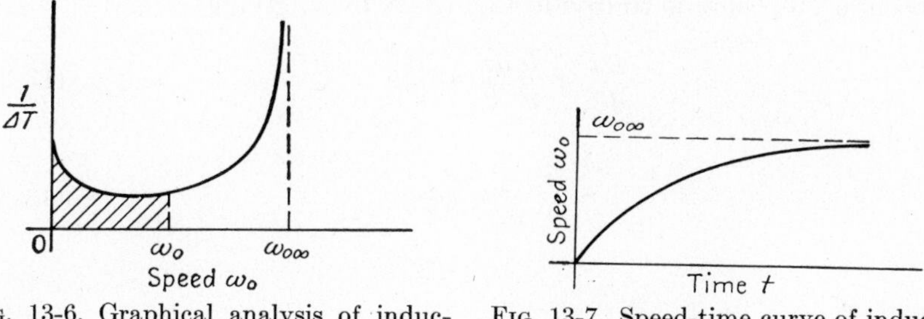

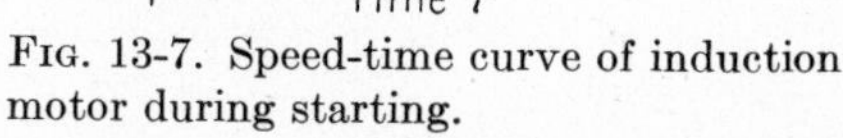

FIG. 13-6. Graphical analysis of induction-motor starting.

FIG. 13-7. Speed-time curve of induction motor during starting.

13-2. Nondimensionalized Solutions for Linear Differential Equations. From part *c* of Example 13-1 it can be seen that definite advantages accrue from expressing the solution of the simple first-order differential equation in nondimensionalized form. So-called *universal curves* like those of Fig. 13-2 graphically depict the general nature of the response and make available numerical results which are very easily applied to all other problems characterized by the same literal equation. Before proceeding to other dynamic studies, therefore, it will be helpful to investigate the nondimensionalizing of solutions to other linear differential equations.

a. Second-order Equations. The form of second-order equation frequently encountered is

$$a\frac{d^2x}{dt^2} + b\frac{dx}{dt} + cx = f(t) \tag{13-27}$$

where a, b, and c are constants, x is the dependent variable, and t is the independent variable. To cite a simple example, it may be the equation for charge in a series RLC circuit on which a voltage which is an arbitrary function $f(t)$ of time is impressed. In our work we shall be particularly interested in a system initially at rest ($x = 0$ and $dx/dt = 0$ at $t = 0$) and on which is impressed a forcing function $f(t)$ which is zero until $t = 0$ and which assumes the constant value d thereafter. The equation is then

$$a\frac{d^2x}{dt^2} + b\frac{dx}{dt} + cx = d \tag{13-28}$$

As in Art. 9-4, the normalizing process is based on reduction of the number of quantities in the equation and its solution by using ratios of quantities and ultimately plotting the results to dimensionless coordinates. For greatest usefulness, it is highly desirable that new quantities replacing ratios of old quantities have definite physical significance. For this reason, judicious choice of new quantities is to a considerable extent based on knowledge of the solution of the equation in its ordinary form.

The first step here is to divide Eq. 13-28 by a, giving

$$\frac{d^2x}{dt^2} + \frac{b}{a}\frac{dx}{dt} + \frac{c}{a}x = \frac{d}{a} \tag{13-29}$$

Then let

$$\frac{c}{a} = \omega_n^2 \tag{13-30}$$

and

$$\frac{b}{2\sqrt{ac}} = \zeta \tag{13-31}$$

whereupon Eq. 13-29 becomes

$$\frac{d^2x}{dt^2} + 2\zeta\omega_n\frac{dx}{dt} + \omega_n^2 x = \frac{d}{a} \tag{13-32}$$

As will be seen below, ω_n is the *undamped natural angular frequency* of the system. The quantity ζ is called the *damping ratio* of the system; it has a physical significance which will also become apparent.

The steady-state solution, or *particular integral*, of Eq. 13-32 is

$$x_\infty = \frac{d}{a\omega_n^2} \tag{13-33}$$

The force-free equation, which yields the transient portion of the solution, or so-called *complementary function*, is

$$\frac{d^2x}{dt^2} + 2\zeta\omega_n\frac{dx}{dt} + \omega_n^2 x = 0 \tag{13-34}$$

The solution is of the form

$$x = A\epsilon^{mt} \tag{13-35}$$

where m can be found by substitution of Eq. 13-35 in Eq. 13-34. When the trivial possibility that $A\epsilon^{mt} = 0$ is discarded, this procedure yields

$$m^2 + 2\zeta\omega_n m + \omega_n^2 = 0 \tag{13-36}$$

as the *characteristic equation*. The roots are

$$m_1, m_2 = -\zeta\omega_n \pm \omega_n\sqrt{\zeta^2 - 1} \tag{13-37}$$

The complete solution of Eq. 13-32 is then

$$x = x_\infty + A_1\epsilon^{m_1t} + A_2\epsilon^{m_2t} \tag{13-38}$$

in which the constants A_1 and A_2 can be found from the initial conditions that at $t = 0$ both x and dx/dt must be zero.

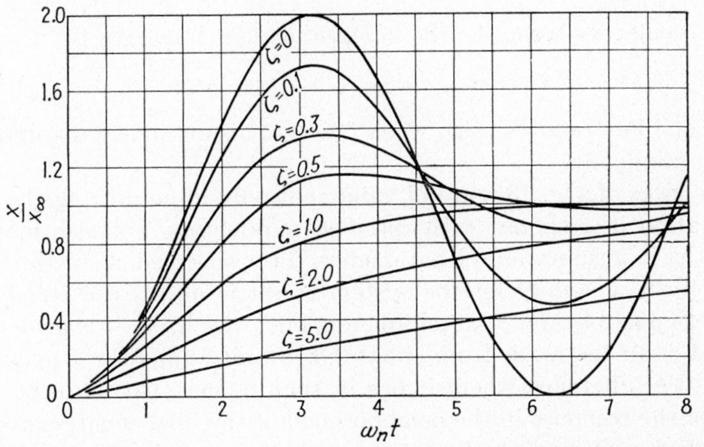

FIG. 13-8. Normalized solutions of the second-order linear differential equation, 13-28. The quantities ω_n, ζ, and x_∞ are given by Eqs. 13-30, 13-31, and 13-33, respectively. These solutions apply only for initial-rest conditions.

The final form of Eq. 13-38 with A_1 and A_2 evaluated depends on whether ζ is less than, equal to, or greater than unity. When $\zeta < 1$,

$$\frac{x}{x_\infty} = 1 - \frac{1}{\sqrt{1 - \zeta^2}} \epsilon^{-\zeta\omega_nt} \sin\left(\sqrt{1 - \zeta^2}\, \omega_nt + \phi\right) \tag{13-39}$$

where

$$\phi = \tan^{-1} \frac{\sqrt{1 - \zeta^2}}{\zeta} \tag{13-40}$$

When $\zeta = 1$,

$$\frac{x}{x_\infty} = 1 - \epsilon^{-\omega_nt}(1 + \omega_nt) \tag{13-41}$$

When $\zeta > 1$,

$$\frac{x}{x_\infty} = 1 - \frac{1}{2\sqrt{\zeta^2 - 1}} \left(\frac{\epsilon^{(-\zeta + \sqrt{\zeta^2 - 1})\omega_nt}}{\zeta - \sqrt{\zeta^2 - 1}} - \frac{\epsilon^{(-\zeta - \sqrt{\zeta^2 - 1})\omega_nt}}{\zeta + \sqrt{\zeta^2 - 1}} \right) \tag{13-42}$$

These results are plotted to the dimensionless coordinates x/x_∞ and ω_nt in the curves of Fig. 13-8 for a series of values of ζ. They are then universal curves depicting the solution of the second-order equation, 13-28, *for initial-rest conditions.* Inspection of Fig. 13-8 and Eqs. 13-39 to 13-42 shows that the numerical value of damping ratio determines whether the response is oscillatory or overdamped, with $\zeta = 1$ representing the critically damped response which is the border line between the other two. Since $\zeta = 1$ for critical damping, ζ in general has the significance

$$\zeta = \frac{\text{actual damping}}{\text{damping for critical response}} \tag{13-43}$$

For an oscillatory response, the *damped angular frequency* is

$$\omega_d = \omega_n \sqrt{1 - \zeta^2} \tag{13-44}$$

Since Eq. 13-44 reduces to ω_n when $\zeta = 0$, ω_n is obviously the undamped angular frequency.

The curves of Fig. 13-8 are of value, not only in permitting the simple computation of response with specified parameters, but also in greatly aiding the determination of parameters for a specified response. Thus, if the object is simply for the system to settle down to a steady state as soon as possible and if all parameters but ζ are fixed, it is evident that ζ should lie in the range from about 0.5 to unity but that it makes relatively little difference where it lies in that range. On the other hand, values of the response in the neighborhood of the final steady-state value are reached earlier for the lower end of this range.[2]

b. Higher-order Equations. Systems with more ramifications—in effect, systems with more than two independent energy storage elements—give rise to differential equations of higher than the second order, the analysis of which is made burdensome by the necessity of solving a characteristic equation of higher order than a quadratic. Literal solutions exist for cubic and quartic equations, but they are of relatively little use. A systematic method of finding the roots, both real and complex, of a higher-order algebraic equation in numerical form is the Graeffe root-squaring method.[3]

For a third-order linear differential equation, the characteristic equation resulting from assuming $A\epsilon^{mt}$ as a solution is of the form

$$m^3 + am^2 + bm + c = 0 \tag{13-45}$$

[2] An indication of the value of the foregoing normalizing procedure is given by its wide usage. For varied examples, see R. H. Frazier, "Elementary Electric-circuit Theory," pp. 378–383, McGraw-Hill Book Company, Inc., New York, 1945; R. H. Park and E. H. Bancker, System Stability as a Design Problem, *Trans. AIEE*, vol. 48, p. 170, 1929; H. E. Edgerton and F. J. Zak, The Pulling into Step of a Synchronous Induction Motor, *J. IEE*, vol. 68, p. 1205, September, 1930; C. S. Draper and G. V. Schliestett, General Principles of Instrument Analysis, *Instruments*, vol. 12, pp. 137–142, 1939; G. S. Brown and A. C. Hall, Dynamic Behavior and Design of Servomechanisms, *Trans. ASME*, July, 1946, pp. 503–522.

The notation used here is substantially that of Draper, Brown, and Frazier.

[3] See, for instance, R. E. Doherty and E. G. Keller, "Mathematics of Modern Engineering," Vol. I, pp. 98–128, John Wiley & Sons, Inc., New York, 1936.

A real root can be found by trial or by successive approximations, and the equation reduced to a quadratic. If the response is oscillatory, the quadratic then contributes the oscillatory component. One method[4] of systematizing the solution is to write Eq. 13-45 in the form

$$(m + \xi\omega_{nq})(m^2 + 2\zeta_q\omega_{nq}m + \omega_{nq}^2) = 0 \tag{13-46}$$

as the product of a real root and a quadratic factor. The quantities ζ_q and ω_{nq} now bear the same relation to the quadratic factor or oscillatory component as they do to the solution of Eq. 13-36, and systematization not unlike that of Fig. 13-8 may be attained.

In many systems containing more than two energy-storage elements, two principal ones can be segregated. The problem can then be reduced approximately to a quadratic.

13-3. Motional Transients in Simple Systems—Synchronous-machine Oscillations. Important dynamic problems arise in synchronous-machine systems because successful operation of the machines demands equality of the mechanical speed of the rotor and the speed of the stator field, and because synchronizing forces tending to maintain this equality are brought into play whenever the relationship is disturbed. If the instantaneous speed of a synchronous machine in a system containing other synchronous equipment should decrease slightly, the decrease would be associated with a decrease in torque angle if the machine were a generator or an increase if it were a motor. In either case, as long as the torque angle did not exceed the optimum value, the result would be an excess of power input over power output to the load, and the power difference would accelerate the rotating mass, tending to restore equilibrium conditions. For example, if a large load is suddenly applied to the shaft of a synchronous motor, the motor must slow down at least momentarily in order that the torque angle may assume the increased value necessary to supply the added load. In fact, until the new angle is reached, an appreciable portion of the energy furnished to the load comes from stored energy in the rotating mass as it slows down. When the newly required value of angle is first reached, equilibrium is not yet attained, for the mechanical speed is then below synchronous speed. The angle must momentarily increase further in order to permit replacing the deficit of stored energy in the rotating mass below that corresponding to synchronous speed. Restoration of equilibrium may be unattainable. In any case the ensuing processes involve a series of oscillations about the final position even when equilibrium is ultimately restored. Exact description of such events can be given only in terms of the associated electromechani-

[4] Discussed and applied by G. S. Brown and A. C. Hall, Dynamic Behavior and Design of Servomechanisms, *Trans. ASME*, July, 1946, pp. 503–522.

cal differential equation, and decisions on restoration of equilibrium can be based only on the solution of the equation.

Similar oscillations or hunting, with the accompanying power and current pulsations, may be particularly troublesome in synchronous motors driving loads whose torque requirements vary cyclically at a fairly rapid frequency, as in motors driving reciprocating air or ammonia compressors. If the natural frequency of mechanical oscillation of the synchronous motor approximates the frequency of an important torque harmonic in the compressor cycle, intolerable oscillations result. Similar dynamic problems are involved in the pulling into step of synchronous motors, and as a result maximum load inertias are specified in the ASA performance standards relating to pull-in torque. Electrodynamic transients of a very complicated form but of the same basic nature occur in electric power systems covering over 100,000 square miles of territory. Unless they are carefully investigated during system planning, they may result in complete shutdowns over wide areas.

a. The Basic Electromechanical Equation. As in all other types of machines, the electromechanical equation for a synchronous machine follows from recognition of the three classes of torque acting on the rotating members; an inertia torque, an electromagnetic torque T_e resulting from energy conversion, and a mechanical shaft torque T_{sh} representing input from the prime mover or output to turn the load. In writing the equation, it is most convenient to specify the angular position of the shaft at any instant as the electrical angle δ between a point on it and a synchronously rotating reference. This convenience arises from the fact that electromagnetic torque may be readily expressed in terms of such an angle; in fact, in many simple problems the angle δ is so chosen as to be identical with the torque angle. Since the inertia torque is given by the product of the moment of inertia and the angular acceleration, it becomes

$$T_{\text{inertia}} = J \frac{2}{p} \frac{\pi}{180} \frac{d^2\delta}{dt^2} \qquad \text{newton-m} \tag{13-47}$$

where p is the number of poles and the factor $2\pi/180p$ converts electrical degrees to mechanical radians. The electromechanical equation for the machine is

$$J \frac{2}{p} \frac{\pi}{180} \frac{d^2\delta}{dt^2} + T_e = T_{sh} \tag{13-48}$$

Equation 13-48 is written specifically for a generator. The same equation may be applied to motor action by following an appropriate sign convention. The convention used will be stated below when the contribution from energy conversion is considered. Machine losses do not appear explicitly in Eq. 13-48. Appropriate account of losses may be taken in evaluating the torque terms T_e and T_{sh}, but most commonly they are ignored entirely.

Evaluation of the energy-conversion contribution can be most readily accomplished from the equivalent circuit of the machine and its associated network. When so evaluated, it appears directly in terms of power, rather than torque, and it is therefore convenient to rewrite Eq. 13-48 as a relation between powers. Such rewriting can be done when it is assumed that only negligible departures from synchronous speed will occur during the electromechanical oscillations, an assumption which is justified by the fact that angular oscillations become intolerable well before appreciable inaccuracy is introduced. Accordingly, when both sides of Eq. 13-48 are multiplied by synchronous angular velocity,

$$J \frac{2}{p} \frac{\pi}{180} \frac{2\pi n}{60} \frac{d^2\delta}{dt^2} + P_e = P_{sh} \tag{13-49}$$

where n is synchronous speed in rpm, P_e is the electromagnetic power in watts, and P_{sh} the mechanical shaft power in watts. The entire coefficient of the first term is an inertia constant and will be given the symbol M and expressed in watts per electrical degree per second squared; *i.e.*,

$$M = J \frac{2}{p} \frac{\pi}{180} \frac{2\pi n}{60} = 0.00365J \frac{n}{p} \tag{13-50}$$

or, in terms of system frequency f,

$$M = 0.438J \frac{f}{p^2} \tag{13-51}$$

Alternatively, when the weight times the square of the radius of gyration is given as Wk^2 lb-ft^2, the constant M is

$$M = 0.0185Wk^2 \frac{f}{p^2} \tag{13-52}$$

When the synchronous machine is operating with a time-varying rotor angle δ, two components enter into the electromagnetic power P_e. One component, commonly called *damping power*, arises from induction-machine action and is a function of slip or the departure $d\delta/dt$ from synchronous speed; it is often considered to vary linearly with $d\delta/dt$, an assumption which corresponds to linearity of the torque-slip curve of an induction machine for small slips.[5] The second component, commonly called *synchronous power*, is a function of δ, since synchronous-machine action is directly dependent on torque angle. The electromechanical

[5] For more comprehensive treatment of damping power, see O. G. C. Dahl, "Electric Power Circuit—Theory and Applications," Vol. II, Power System Stability, Chap. XIX, McGraw-Hill Book Co., Inc., New York, 1938.

equation, 13-49, then becomes

$$M \frac{d^2\delta}{dt^2} + P_d \frac{d\delta}{dt} + P(\delta) = P_{sh} \tag{13-53}$$

where P_d is the damping power in watts per electrical degree per second and the term $P(\delta)$ indicates that synchronous power is a function of angle δ.

The specific nature of the external network must be known before the function $P(\delta)$ can be identified. When consideration is restricted to one machine connected directly to the terminals of a very large system (see Art. 7-8), the function is $P_m \sin \delta$, where P_m is the amplitude of the sinusoidal power-angle curve. Equation 13-53 becomes

$$M \frac{d^2\delta}{dt^2} + P_d \frac{d\delta}{dt} + P_m \sin \delta = P_{sh} \tag{13-54}$$

Positive values of δ denote generator action and therefore energy conversion from mechanical to electrical form, positive values of P_{sh} denote mechanical power input to the shaft, positive values of $d\delta/dt$ denote speeds above synchronous speed, and positive values of $d^2\delta/dt^2$ denote acceleration. Alternatively, the reverse convention may be used. That is, positive values of δ may denote motor action, positive values of P_{sh} mechanical power output from the shaft, positive values of $d\delta/dt$ speeds below synchronous speed, and positive values of $d^2\delta/dt^2$ deceleration.

Because of the presence of the term $P_m \sin \delta$, Eq. 13-54 is nonlinear and not susceptible to formal solution in the manner of Eq. 13-27. Two different techniques of analysis are available. The first involves an approximation which permits linearization and which is discussed below in further detail. The second makes use of the techniques of nonlinear analysis introduced in Chap. 12; a full discussion of these techniques as applied to Eq. 13-54 is beyond the scope of this book.

b. Linearized Analysis for Single Machine Connected to Large System. When the rotor angle δ is small, advantage may be taken of the fact that the sine of a small angle is closely equal to the angle in radians; *i.e.*, if δ varies between about $+30°$ and $-30°$,

$$\sin \delta = \frac{\pi}{180} \delta \tag{13-55}$$

The term $P_m \sin \delta$ in Eq. 13-54 may then be replaced by the term $P_s\delta$, where P_s is the *synchronizing power*, or slope of the power-angle curve in watts per electrical degree. Equation 13-54 becomes

$$M \frac{d^2\delta}{dt^2} + P_d \frac{d\delta}{dt} + P_s\delta = P_{sh} \tag{13-56}$$

ing from electromechanical energy conversion. Now recall from the thought process leading from Eq. 13-48 to Eq. 13-53 that both P_{sh} and $P_m \sin \delta$ are proportional to the corresponding torques. Recall also that the integral $\int T\, d\delta$ of torque with respect to angle is energy. The area OAB in Fig. 13-10 is then seen to be proportional to the energy abstracted from the rotating mass during the initial period when electromagnetic energy conversion is insufficient to supply the shaft load. When point B is reached on the first excursion, therefore, the rotor has a momentum in the direction of deceleration. Acting under this momentum, the rotor must swing past point B until an equal amount of energy is recovered by the rotating mass. The result is that the rotor swings to point C and the angle δ_{max}, at which point

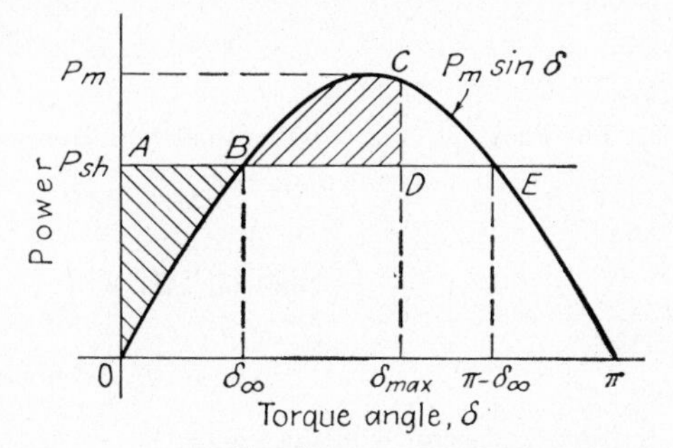

FIG. 13-10. Synchronous-motor power-angle curve and power required by load.

$$\text{Area } BCD = \text{area } OAB \tag{13-57}$$

Thereafter, in the absence of damping, the rotor continues to oscillate between points O and C at its natural frequency. The damping present in any physical machine causes successive oscillations to be of decreasing amplitude and finally results in dynamic equilibrium at point B. The analogy to the oscillations of a pendulum may be noted.

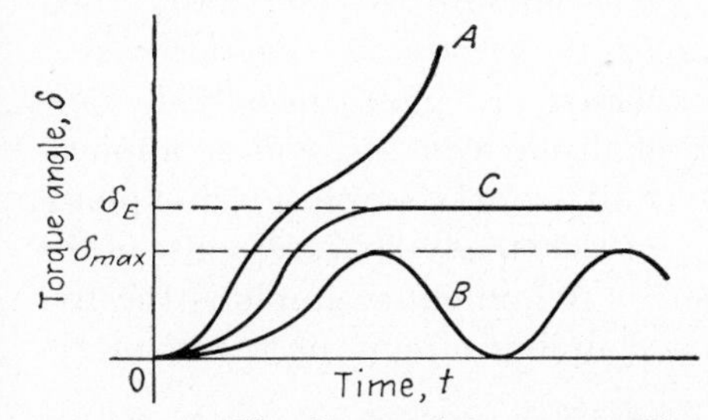

FIG. 13-11. Simple synchronous-machine swing curves showing instability (curve A), stability (curve B), and marginal or critical case (curve C).

This *equal-area method* provides a ready means of finding the maximum angle of swing. It also provides a simple indication of whether synchronism is maintained and a rough measure of the margin of stability. Thus, if area $BCED$ in Fig. 13-10 is less than area OAB, the decelerating momentum can never be overcome, the angle-time curve follows the course of curve A in Fig. 13-11, and synchronism is lost. On the other hand, if area $BCED$ is greater than area OAB, synchronism is maintained with a margin indicated by the difference in areas and the angle-time curve follows curve B of Fig. 13-11. Equality of areas $BCED$ and OAB yields a borderline solution of unstable equilibrium for which curve C is followed.

Example 13-4. Determine the maximum shaft load which may be suddenly applied to the motor of Example 13-3 when it is initially operating unloaded. The synchronizing power of 11.0 kw per electrical degree quoted in that example is the initial slope of the power-angle curve followed under these conditions. Damping is to be ignored.

Solution. The initial slope of the sinusoidal power-angle curve expressed in kilowatts per radian is equal to the amplitude of the curve in kilowatts. Hence

$$P_m = 11.0 \times \frac{180}{\pi} = 630 \text{ kw}$$

The load P_{sh} (Fig. 13-12) must be adjusted so that

$$\text{Area } OAB = \text{area } BCD$$

or

$$P_{sh}\delta_\infty - \int_0^{\delta_\infty} 630 \sin \delta \, d\delta = \int_{\delta_\infty}^{\pi - \delta_\infty} 630 \sin \delta \, d\delta - P_{sh}(\pi - 2\delta_\infty)$$

Also

$$P_{sh} = 630 \sin \delta_\infty$$

Trial-and-error solution yields

$$P_{sh} = 455 \text{ kw} = 610 \text{ hp}$$

Notice that the result is independent of inertia when damping is neglected. Under these circumstances, inertia determines the period of oscillation but does not influence its amplitude.

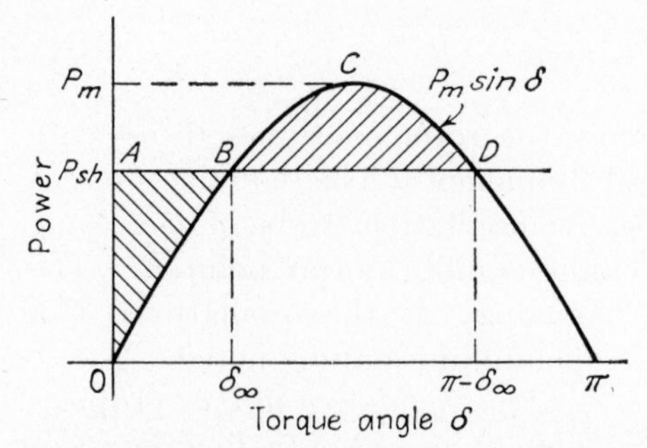

FIG. 13-12. Graphical application of equal-area criterion.

13-4. Frequency Response of Simple Systems.

A valuable and widely used means of summarizing important properties of electric circuits is offered by their *frequency-response characteristics*, which are plots, usually in normalized form for widest applicability, of the amplitude and phase of the steady-state response of the circuit to a sinusoidal driving function. A familiar example is the frequency-response characteristic of the coupling circuit of a resistance-capacitance-coupled amplifier.

Such characteristics are of value in circuit theory because, by virtue of Fourier series, they enable one to picture the response to an arbitrary forcing function. Realization of the full power of frequency-response methods demands recognition of a definite correlation between the frequency-response characteristic and the transient response of the circuit. Thus, peaks in the amplitude-frequency response in general occur at approximately the natural frequencies of the transient response, and the relative magnitudes of the peaks are an inverse indication of the relative damping of the natural frequencies. In other words, the steady-state response to a sinusoidal function tells much about the transient response of the circuit as well.

Since this approach has been highly developed in circuit theory, we naturally wish to take advantage of it in dynamic analysis of linear systems, where the problems are essentially the same even though points of difference exist in the vocabulary and symbolism. Two simple introductory examples will be presented in this article, and the general theme will be developed further in discussing closed-cycle systems.

Example 13-5. The speed of the small d-c motor in Example 13-1 is to be controlled by varying the impressed armature voltage. For this service, ideal performance is represented by a shaft speed which is at all times directly proportional to the impressed armature voltage. Direction of rotation as well as speed is to be controlled, so that the polarity of the impressed voltage will change. In general, the impressed voltage may vary in a more or less random manner in accordance with the dictates of the speed requirements. In order to study the responsiveness of the motor, however, the voltage is considered to vary from a maximum positive value $+V_{tm}$ to a maximum negative value $-V_{tm}$ sinusoidally with time.

a. Show how well the motor speed variation is able to follow the voltage variation as the frequency of the latter is increased. Comment on the results obtained.

b. For the numerical values given in Example 13-1*e*, determine the frequency for which the amplitude of speed variation becomes $1/\sqrt{2}$ of that for ideal performance.

Solution. *a.* The differential equation controlling motor performance under these circumstances is, by adaptation of Eq. 13-8,

$$\frac{Jr_a}{k^2}\frac{d\omega_o}{dt} + \omega_o = \frac{V_{tm}}{k}\sin\omega t \tag{13-58}$$

or

$$\tau\frac{d\omega_o}{dt} + \omega_o = \frac{V_{tm}}{k}\sin\omega t \tag{13-59}$$

where ω is the angular frequency of the voltage variation and τ is the motor time constant given by Eq. 13-11.

We are interested here in only the steady-state solution of Eq. 13-59. We know from circuit theory that the steady-state solution of an equation such as Eq. 13-59 can be obtained by replacing the differential operator d/dt by $(j\omega)$, d^2/dt^2 by $(j\omega)^2$, and $\int dt$ by $1/j\omega$, and then interpreting the dependent and independent variables as time-vector quantities having a magnitude and phase angle. Accordingly,

$$\tau(j\omega)\Omega_o + \Omega_o = \frac{V_{tm}}{k} \tag{13-60}$$

or

$$\Omega_o = \frac{V_{tm}}{k(1 + j\omega\tau)} \tag{13-61}$$

is the relation between the vector amplitude Ω_o of the sinusoidal speed variation and the vector amplitude V_{tm} of the sinusoidal voltage variation. As is customary in circuit theory, the lower-case symbol ω_0 denoting an instantaneous value is replaced by the capital symbol Ω_o when the amplitude of the sinusoidal variation is to be indicated; for simplicity, however, the subscript m is not added to the angle-amplitude symbol since only the peak value has significance. Equation 13-61 is written as a relation between amplitudes rather than between rms values, for the latter are of no especial interest in electromechanical problems.

Inspection of Eq. 13-61 shows that Ω_o will be directly proportional to V_{tm} only when $\omega = 0$; that is,

$$(\Omega_o)_{\omega=0} = \frac{V_{tm}}{k} \tag{13-62}$$

corresponding to very slow variation. This fact suggests a method of nondimensionalizing the result: division of Eq. 13-61 by 13-62 yields

$$\frac{\Omega_o}{(\Omega_o)_{\omega=0}} = \frac{1}{1 + j\omega\tau} \tag{13-63}$$

The ratio of magnitudes is

$$\left| \frac{\Omega_o}{(\Omega_o)_{\omega=0}} \right| = \frac{1}{\sqrt{1 + (\omega\tau)^2}} \tag{13-64}$$

The phase angle by which the speed variation lags the voltage variation is

$$\gamma = \tan^{-1} \omega\tau \tag{13-65}$$

The results given by Eqs. 13-64 and 13-65 are plotted in Fig. 13-13. As is naturally to be expected, the curves show rapid departure from ideal performance as the fre-

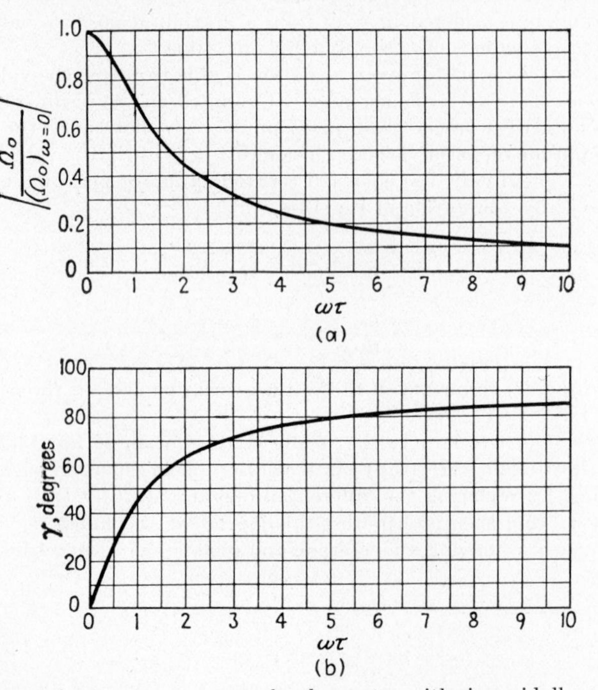

FIG. 13-13. Normalized response curves for d-c motor with sinusoidally varying armature voltage. (*a*) Amplitude-response ratio. (*b*) Phase lag angle.

quency of variation is increased. Because of its inertia and the consequent need of energy storage in the rotating mass, the motor is incapable of faithfully following rapidly varying voltage signals.

Reference to the electric-circuit analogue of Fig. 13-3 will show that the foregoing process is the equivalent of studying the variation of voltage across capacitor C as a function of the impressed circuit voltage.

b. From either the curves of Fig. 13-13 or by substituting $1/\sqrt{2}$ for the ratio in Eq. 13-64,

$$\omega\tau = 1$$

Since, from Example 13-1, $\tau = 0.0185$ sec,

$$\omega = \frac{1}{0.0185} = 54.0 \text{ rad/sec}$$

and the corresponding frequency is

$$f = \frac{54.0}{2\pi} = 8.6 \text{ cps}$$

In the preceding example it is desired that the output variation follow the input variation as faithfully as possible. In the following example, on the other hand, it is desired to suppress the variations as much as practicable.

Example 13-6. Reciprocating air and ammonia compressors require a torque which fluctuates periodically about a steady average value. For a 2-cycle unit, the torque harmonics have frequencies in cycles per second which are multiples of the speed in revolutions per second. When, as is commonly the case, the compressors are driven by synchronous motors, the torque harmonics cause periodic fluctuation of the torque angle δ and may result in undesirably high pulsations of power and current to the motor. It is therefore essential that, for the significant harmonics, the electrodynamic response of the motor be held to a minimum.

a. Investigate the response of the motor of Example 13-3 to torque harmonics, covering the frequency range for which the response is appreciable.

b. For a particular compressor, the first-order torque harmonic has an amplitude of 580 lb-ft. The Wk^2 of 10,500 lb-ft² given in Example 13-3 includes the inertia of the compressor. Determine the maximum deviation in torque angle caused by this harmonic and the corresponding pulsation of synchronous power.

c. Consider that a flywheel is added to bring the total Wk^2 up to 16,500 lb-ft². Repeat the computation of *b*, and compare the results.[6]

Solution. *a*. Because the absolute values of torque angle involved are small, linearized analysis may be used. From Eq. 13-56, the differential equation concerned is

$$M\frac{d^2\delta}{dt^2} + P_d\frac{d\delta}{dt} + P_s\delta = P_{shm}\sin\omega t \tag{13-66}$$

where P_{shm} corresponds to the amplitude of the harmonic-torque pulsation whose angular frequency is ω, and δ is now the component of the rotor angle contributed by this harmonic. When changed to the form typified by Eq. 13-32, Eq. 13-66 becomes

$$\frac{d^2\delta}{dt^2} + 2\zeta\omega_n\frac{d\delta}{dt} + \omega_n^2\delta = \frac{P_{shm}}{M}\sin\omega t \tag{13-67}$$

[6] Values used in this example are adapted from data in R. E. Doherty and R. F. Franklin, Design of Flywheels for Reciprocating Machinery Connected to Synchronous Generators and Motors, *Trans. ASME*, vol. 42, pp. 523–560, 1920. Another important paper on this subject is H. R. Goss and H. V. Putman, Calculation of Flywheels for Air Compressors, *Trans. ASME*, vol. 51, pp. 117–130, 1929.

in which

$$\omega_n = \sqrt{\frac{P_s}{M}} \tag{13-68}$$

$$\zeta = \frac{P_d}{2\sqrt{P_s M}} \tag{13-69}$$

By following the procedure of Example 13-5, the vector form of Eq. 13-67, from which the steady-state solution may be obtained, is

$$(j\omega)^2\Delta + 2\zeta\omega_n(j\omega)\Delta + \omega_n^2\Delta = \frac{P_{shm}}{M} \tag{13-70}$$

Here, Δ is the amplitude of the sinusoidal time variation of the angle δ. The vector expression for Δ is

$$\Delta = \frac{P_{shm}/M}{(\omega_n^2 - \omega^2) + j2\zeta\omega_n\omega} \tag{13-71}$$

At the natural frequency of the motor and compressor, $\omega = \omega_n$, and the response becomes

$$\Delta_n = \frac{P_{sh}/M}{j2\zeta\omega_n^2} \tag{13-72}$$

A method of nondimensionalizing Eq. 13-71 now suggests itself. By dividing Eq. 13-71 by Eq. 13-72 and writing an expression for magnitude only, one obtains

$$\left|\frac{\Delta}{\Delta_n}\right| = \frac{2\zeta\omega_n^2}{\sqrt{(\omega_n^2 - \omega^2)^2 + (2\zeta\omega_n\omega)^2}} \tag{13-73}$$

which reduces algebraically to

$$\left|\frac{\Delta}{\Delta_n}\right| = \frac{1}{\sqrt{(\omega/\omega_n)^2 + (1/2\zeta)^2[1 - (\omega/\omega_n)^2]^2}} \tag{13-74}$$

For the particular motor and load involved here, the damping ratio $\zeta = 0.1$ (see Example 13-3). A nondimensionalized plot based on Eq. 13-74 for this value of ζ is given in Fig. 13-14. From this plot it is evident that the relative pulsations in angle decrease rapidly as the harmonic-torque frequencies increase above the natural frequency. At twice natural frequency, for example, the angle amplitude is only 6.6 per cent of that at the natural frequency. Since, for this machine and load, $\omega_n = 27$, twice natural frequency is $(2 \times 27)/2\pi$, of 8.6 cps.

It may be noted in passing that the foregoing investigation is analogous to one which might be conducted for the charge on or voltage across the capacitor in a series *RLC* circuit on which an alternating voltage is impressed.

b. From Example 13-3,

$$M = 14.9 \qquad P_d = 80.6 \qquad P_s = 11{,}000 \qquad \omega_n = 27.0 \qquad \zeta = 0.1$$

For a speed of 257 rpm, the frequency and angular frequency of the first-order torque harmonic are, respectively,

$$f = {}^{257}\!/\!_{60} = 4.3 \text{ cps}$$

and

$$\omega = 2\pi \times 4.3 = 27.0 \text{ rad/sec}$$

The harmonic frequency is thus seen to be equal to the undamped natural frequency of the motor and compressor.

The torque amplitude in terms of power at synchronous speed is

$$P_{shm} = \frac{2\pi \times 257 \times 580}{33,000} \times 746 = 21,200 \text{ watts}$$

Hence, from Eq. 13-72, the amplitude of the angle pulsation is

$$|\Delta_n| = \frac{21,200}{14.9 \times 2 \times 0.1 \times (27.0)^2} = 9.8 \text{ elec deg}$$

The associated pulsation in synchronous power has the amplitude

$$P_s|\Delta_n| = 11,000 \times 9.8 = 108 \text{ kw}$$

The seriousness of such a power pulsation can be appreciated when it is recognized that a fully loaded 200-hp motor under normal conditions draws a power of about

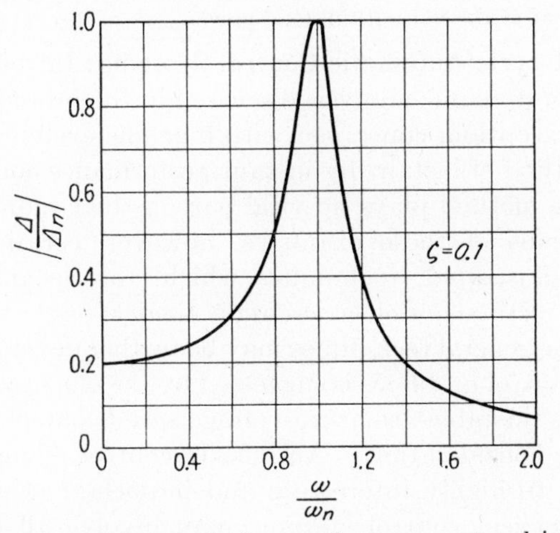

FIG. 13-14. Amplitude-response ratio for synchronous motor driving a compressor, Example 13-6.

160 kw from the a-c mains. The departure from normal caused by the power pulsation is ±67.5 per cent.

c. The natural angular velocity and damping ratio must be recomputed for the new inertia when the flywheel is added. From Eqs. 13-52, 13-68, and 13-69, respectively,

$$M = 0.0185 \times 16,500 \times \frac{60}{(28)^2} = 23.4$$

$$\omega_n = \sqrt{\frac{11,000}{23.4}} = 21.7$$

and

$$\zeta = \frac{80.6}{2\sqrt{23.4 \times 11,000}} = 0.0795$$

The amplitude of the angle pulsation at the natural frequency is, from Eq. 13-72,

$$|\Delta_n| = \frac{21,200}{23.4 \times 2 \times 0.0795 \times (21.7)^2} = 12.1 \text{ elec deg}$$

Since

$$\frac{\omega}{\omega_n} = \frac{27.0}{21.7} = 1.244$$

it follows from Eq. 13-74 that

$$\left|\frac{\Delta}{\Delta_n}\right| = \frac{1}{\sqrt{(1.244)^2 + \left(\frac{1}{2 \times 0.0795}\right)^2 [1 - (1.244)^2]^2}} = 0.273$$

The amplitude of the angle pulsation is accordingly

$$|\Delta| = 0.273 \times 12.1 = 3.3 \text{ elec deg}$$

and the associated pulsation in synchronous power has the amplitude

$$P_s|\Delta| = 11{,}000 \times 3.3 = 36.4 \text{ kw}$$

Addition of the flywheel has thus reduced the deviation of synchronous power to about ± 23 per cent of the normal full-load power.

13-5. Closed-cycle Automatic Control Systems: Introductory Aspects. The examples of dynamic analysis discussed in the preceding four articles are, with one exception, concerned with machine systems in which there is no direct method of instant-by-instant performance control or, at least, in which such a method plays no vital part in the circumstances investigated. By means of these examples, however, certain techniques of approach are illustrated, techniques which, for linear problems, lean heavily on the methods of electric-circuit theory.

That the same general techniques may be further developed and applied to automatic-control problems is suggested by the one exception (Example 13-5) in which adjustable-armature-voltage speed control of a d-c motor is the motivating consideration. Automatic control of machine performance gives rise to highly interesting and important dynamic problems. In general, electrical control systems may involve all of the elements normally studied in an electrical engineering curriculum—circuits, electronic devices, machines, and the details of applied mechanics, to mention but a few. The general background of machine-output control will be discussed in this article.

Machine output, in the control sense, refers to more than simply the mechanical power delivered by the shaft of a motor or the electrical power delivered by a generator, although the power output is controlled at least incidentally in accomplishing other desired results. Among the more significant machine quantities over which control may be exercised are:

1. *Speed.* Accurate control of speed over a wide range (and sometimes coordination with the speed of other motors) is a common requirement. Paper-making machines and some steel-mill drives are examples.

2. *Torque.* An example of need for control of torque is the winding and unwinding of continuous material on reels, where a constant winding tension is required.

3. *Position.* Automatic positioning of a machine cutting tool for the next cut is an example of controlling the angular position of a shaft or the linear position of an object geared to it. The tracking of aircraft by radar and the automatic positioning of antiaircraft artillery in accordance with the directions received from the radar signals, mentioned in Chap. 1, is another example.

4. *Acceleration.* Controlled acceleration may be required during the transition from one speed to another in a coordinated drive.

5. *Voltage.* Maintenance of a constant generator terminal voltage is an obvious example.

6. *Frequency.* The necessity of turbine-governor control to maintain constant frequency in electric supply systems is also an obvious one.

A certain degree of control over performance is, of course, inherent in the basic machine characteristics when the most suitable type of machine is chosen. A synchronous motor, for example, produces a single constant speed regardless of load without the use of external regulating devices. Or when the degree of compounding is appropriately adjusted, a d-c compound motor is capable of producing inherently a wide range of speed decreases with load. When the desired behavior becomes more complex and the performance standards more exacting, however, sufficient versatility is not provided by the machine characteristics alone: a control system must be added. Even with external control, judicious appraisal of machine characteristics is essential to minimize the duty on the controlling mechanism and to make the desired response as spontaneous as possible.

In devising an electrical control scheme, an electrical quantity must be selected whose value is a measure of the actual performance feature to be controlled, and this quantity or its deviation from an established ideal must actuate the controlling mechanism in a prescribed fashion. The type of control and its degree of reliance on inherent motor characteristics depend on the precision required. Two types of control are recognized: *open-cycle control*, in which actuation of the control mechanism is substantially independent of the actual performance of the controlled device; and *closed-cycle control*, in which actuation of the control mechanism is affected by the performance of the controlled device.

Suppose, for example, that it is desired to maintain constant speed at any preset value and that a d-c shunt motor with fixed field excitation and adjustable armature voltage is selected. If the inherent speed regulation of a shunt motor constitutes satisfactory fulfillment of the requirements, the problem is simply one of maintaining the armature terminal voltage constant at any preset value, for this voltage is a reasonably close measure of speed at constant field current. If the inherent regulation of the motor is not good enough, armature-resistance-drop compensation may be added to the voltage regulator, an addition which means making the regulator responsive to armature current to the extent that it increases the voltage enough to compensate the increased armature-resistance drop with load. The armature induced emf is thereby kept substantially constant, resulting in closer speed regulation. So far as motor speed is concerned, however, both methods are open-cycle control schemes, for the actual motor speed is not measured, and the controller is presented with no direct information indicating whether it is performing its function properly. Accurate attainment of the specified set speed demands that the characteristics of all equipment interposed between the setting dial and the final motor shaft remain absolutely fixed at the values for which the control scheme is designed or adjusted. The effects of such disturbances as temperature changes, hysteresis, armature reaction, changing tube characteristics (if an electronic method is used), and supply voltages all may cause significant inaccuracies.

When these extraneous influences are to be circumvented and precise control of motor speed obtained, the actual speed may be measured in terms of the voltage of a pilot generator coupled to the motor shaft and the difference between this voltage and one proportional to the desired speed may be used to actuate the controller in such fashion as to tend to eliminate the error. Closed-cycle control is thereby achieved.

The broad general features of closed-cycle control may be seen from the schematic diagram of Fig. 13-15. The output quantity to be controlled is designated as θ_o. The input signal θ_i presents data specifying the desired performance. The feedback link and error detector enable comparison of actual performance θ_o with desired performance θ_i; if an error $\mathcal{E}$ exists, the controller acts accordingly to correct the discrepancy. These general features may be recognized as having much in common with feedback amplifiers, and many of the analytical details will be found to be identical. Closed-cycle control systems are sometimes subdivided into two classes. When the input signal θ_i remains substantially constant or is subjected to only relatively slow changes, the system is classed as a *regulator;* the main object of a regulator is to prevent extraneous effects from influencing the output quantity θ_o. A generator voltage regulator is an example. When the input signal θ_i changes rapidly, the system is classed as a *servomechanism;* the main object of a servomechanism is to cause the output quantity θ_o to follow θ_i as faithfully as possible.

The controlling signal usually results from a low-power-level electrical-measurements process. Position, for instance, may be indicated by the voltage of a Selsyn transformer, by the output of a phototube scanning the driven object, or by arranging a resistance, inductance, or capacitance to be affected by position. Because of the low power level of both θ_i and the value of θ_o fed back, amplification is one essential function of the controller. Such amplification is obtained by electronic or electromagnetic means or by both in cascade. The chain of events starting with measurement of actual performance and passing through the entire cycle of amplification and control in any particular case can be followed by superimposing the characteristics of each element. This superposition must be one of dynamic characteristics, however, for stability of operation, speed of response, and freedom from hunting are closely related dynamic problems of determining importance.

13-6. Illustrations of Closed-cycle Systems. In order to illustrate the application of closed-cycle control to electric machines, a series of examples of regulators and servomechanisms is presented in Figs. 13-16 to 13-26. Block diagrams of the style of Fig. 13-15 and indicating only

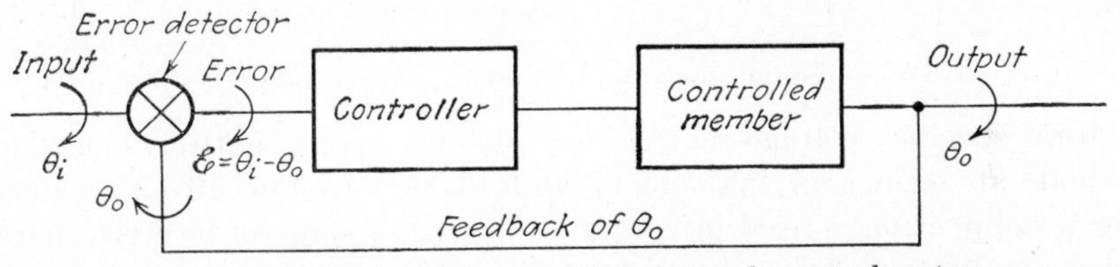

FIG. 13-15. Schematic diagram of closed-cycle control system.

the principal elements are used in most of the illustrations so that the main features stand out. For any specific application, a variety of possibilities exists, although only enough examples are given to indicate qualitatively the general thought process. Simple examples of stabilizing arrangements are shown in a few figures, and their presence is indicated symbolically in a few others. Such arrangements are essential in all cases and may involve additional loops in the systems, making them appreciably more complicated than shown here. Additional refinements may be necessary to achieve the desired rapidity of dynamic response with minimum error, the general philosophy being to obtain the appropriate over-all frequency-response characteristics for the system. Likewise, detailed auxiliaries such as the compensating and commutating fields of Amplidynes are omitted for greater clarity. It should be emphasized that the object of this article is simply to provide a coordinated over-all glimpse of some qualitative high lights as a prelude to the analysis of very simple systems.

a. Generator Regulators. Regulation of generator voltage is the process of controlling the voltage so that it remains at or near a particular set value. A general closed-loop diagram for automatic voltage regulation is given in Fig. 13-16. As in all other closed-loop diagrams, the output quantity, in this case the voltage to be regulated, is designated as θ_o; the input, or reference, quantity specifying the value to be maintained is designated as θ_i. This reference, or datum, may be of an electrical nature, such as a constant voltage obtained from an independent source or the balance point of a voltage-sensitive bridge, or it may be of a mechanical nature, such as the tension of a spring or the balance point of a lever. The values of θ_o and θ_i are compared to determine the error $\mathcal{E}$, which is amplified and made to determine the excitation of the generator so that θ_o is a sufficiently faithful reproduction of θ_i.

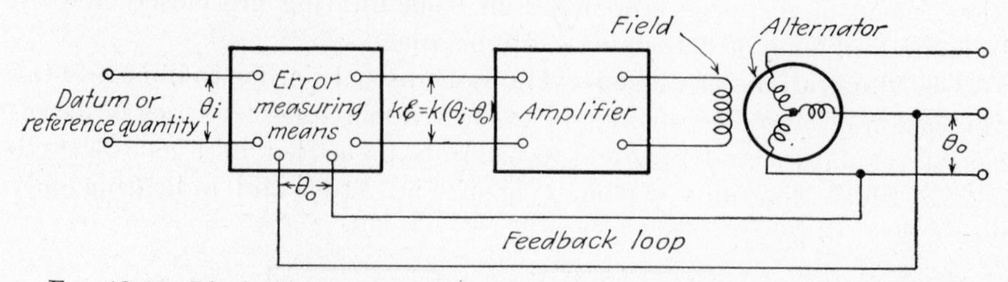

FIG. 13-16. Block diagram for automatic voltage regulation of an alternator.

More specific voltage-regulating schemes using entirely electrical methods are shown in Figs. 13-17 and 13-18. In Fig. 13-17, vacuum-tube amplification is used in conjunction with a stage of electrodynamic power amplification; the vacuum-tube amplifier supplies the exciter field, and the exciter in turn furnishes excitation for the generator main field. In Fig. 13-18, the amplification is entirely electrodynamic, with a control-type generator or Amplidyne supplying the generator excitation. As described in Art. 11-2, the mmfs of the control and reference fields of the Amplidyne oppose each other, so that the magnetic circuit is also the error-measuring device. Both figures show a d-c generator as the

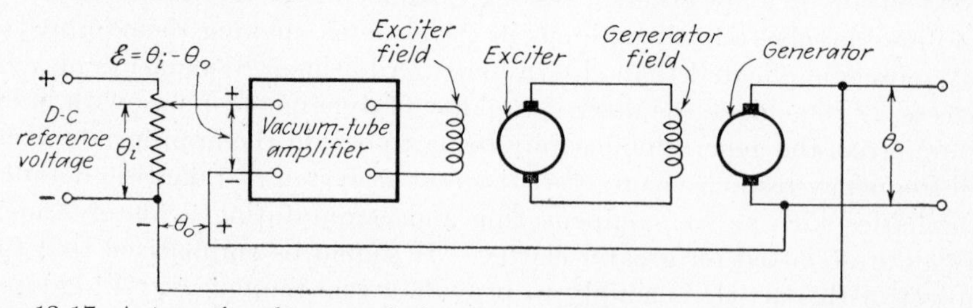

FIG. 13-17. Automatic voltage regulation of a d-c generator. Electronic amplification is used.

machine whose voltage is being regulated, but the same basic methods may be used for alternators by adding a rectifier and smoothing filter and, for high-voltage machines, a potential transformer to the feedback loop. For regulation of a 3-phase generator, the voltage fed back is usually a composite for all three phases.

Two problems, already mentioned at the end of Art. 11-4, arise in the control schemes of Figs. 13-17 and 13-18, as well as in all of the later simplified examples. The first is the apparent need of a nonzero steady-state error in order that the generator be continuously excited. This error can be circumvented or minimized in several ways. In an Amplidyne, as stated in Art. 11-2, the steady-state reference-field mmf may be made to exceed the control-field mmf by a sufficient amount to furnish the required excitation with approximately zero error. The steady excitation for the Rototrol or Regulex is furnished by the self-energizing field, with the reference and control fields furnishing only stabilizing action. More generally, the control circuit may be made responsive, not only to the error itself, but also to its integral in order to minimize long-time errors.

The second problem is hunting. Serious hunting may be inherent in all of these systems because of time lags in the response caused princi-

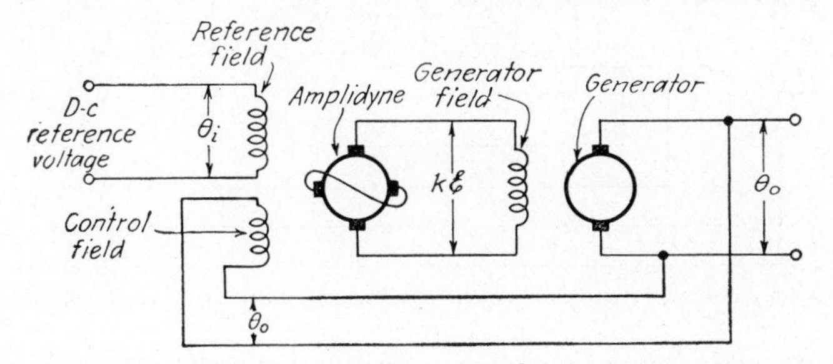

FIG. 13-18. Automatic voltage regulation of a d-c generator with an Amplidyne exciter.

pally by energy storage in the circuit inductances, especially in the field-winding inductances. Thus, a sudden change in load on the main generator will cause a deviation in voltage from its set value, and correction of the voltage cannot take place without the lapse of a definite time to permit readjustment of the stored energies. This time lag between impetus and response may result in successive overshooting and undershooting of the correct voltage, representing serious oscillations about the final position as in some of the examples discussed in previous articles of this chapter. To allay these disturbances, stabilizing or antihunt arrangements are necessary.

An example of such stabilization is shown in Fig. 13-19, which, except for the addition of the stabilizing loop, is a reproduction of Fig. 13-17. A voltage which is approximately the derivative of the generator-field voltage is fed back to the system input so that its effect is in series with the error actuating the controller and of such relative polarity that it opposes rapid changes of output voltage. The general effect is not unlike that of amortisseur windings in damping synchronous-machine oscillations. A voltage derivative is obtained in Fig. 13-19 because in a simple

RC circuit the voltage across the resistor closely approximates the derivative of the applied voltage when the drop across the capacitor predominates. The stabilizing voltage is, of course, zero under steady-state conditions. Optimum stabilization results in the response being changed from one like that for damping ratios of zero to 0.1 in Fig. 13-8 to one like that for damping ratios somewhat under 1.0.

b. D-C-motor Speed Regulators. Regulation of motor speed is the process of controlling the speed so that it remains at or near a particular set value. Where versatility of control is concerned, as in motor operation over a wide range of preset speeds, it is natural that d-c motors

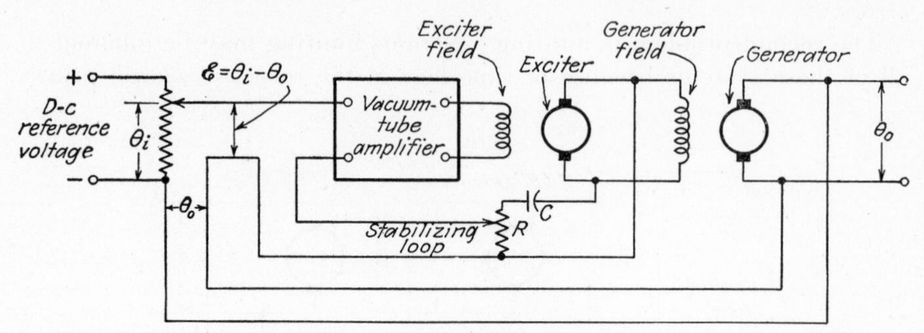

FIG. 13-19. Voltage-regulator circuit of Fig. 13-17 with stabilization added.

should be the most common choice. The motor performance is controlled when the voltage of either the field supply or the armature supply is changed. Three general possibilities therefore exist.

1. CONTROLLED FIELD EXCITATION, CONSTANT ARMATURE VOLTAGE OR CURRENT. The armature circuit is supplied directly from the d-c mains or through constant-voltage or constant-current rectifiers or motor-generators from the a-c mains. The field is supplied from a vacuum-tube amplifier (for a small fractional-horsepower motor), thyratrons, or an Amplidyne (sometimes in conjunction with a vacuum-tube amplifier to supply the Amplidyne excitation) whose voltage is controlled in accordance with the desired operations. Only very small or negligible control power is required in any case. When rotation in both directions is involved, a split control field in the motor or Amplidyne, if one is used, may offer attractive possibilities.

2. CONTROLLED ARMATURE VOLTAGE, CONSTANT FIELD EXCITATION. This possibility is the long-used adjustable-armature-voltage, or Ward Leonard, method arranged in the most suitable form for the desired automatic control. The armature- and field-supply possibilities of (1) are simply interchanged here. For large motors, the tubes or Amplidyne operate in the field of a separately excited d-c generator supplying the motor armature power. The power handled by the control device is

thereby decreased greatly, but the response time is increased because of the time constant of the separately excited generator field.

3. CONTROLLED ARMATURE VOLTAGE, CONTROLLED FIELD EXCITATION. When control of speed over a very wide range is involved, the economical solution is sometimes a combination of the first two methods. Adjustable-speed electronically controlled d-c motors supplied from a-c sources form one application of this combination. Field control covers the upper end of the range, from maximum speed down to about one-third of maximum, and armature control covers the lower end.

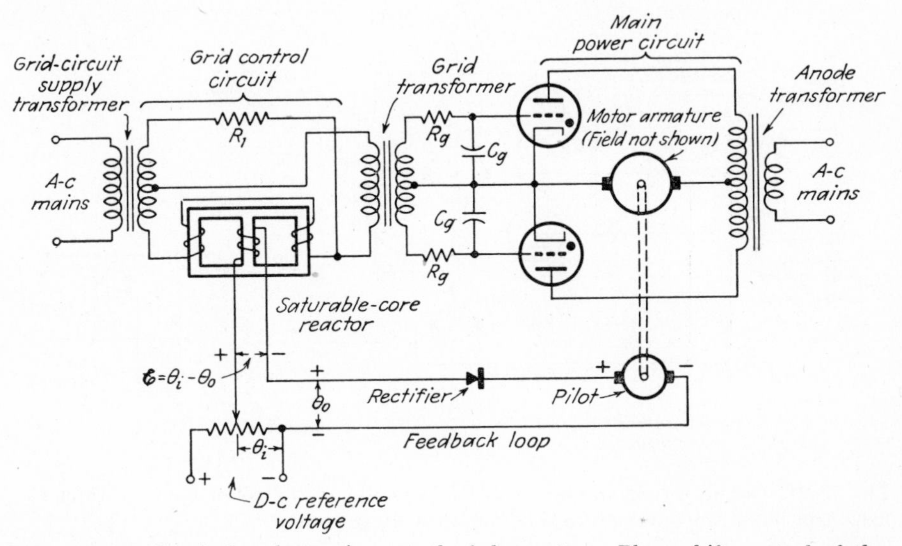

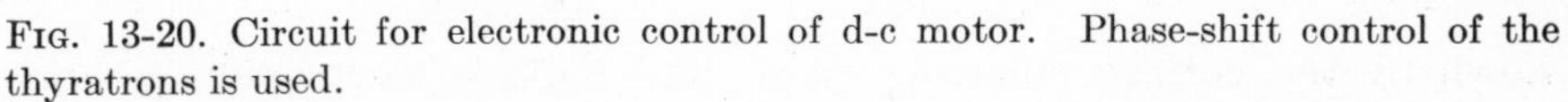

FIG. 13-20. Circuit for electronic control of d-c motor. Phase-shift control of the thyratrons is used.

Application of these general considerations is illustrated by the simplified diagrams of Figs. 13-20 to 13-23, all of which are based on speed control with a small pilot magneto coupled to the motor shaft to measure the actual speed in terms of its generated voltage. The circuits of Figs. 13-20 and 13-21 utilize thyratron control and differ only in the method of varying the thyratron conduction period, the former using phase-shift control secured by means of the resistor R_1 and the variable inductance of the saturable-core reactor, and the latter using a variable d-c grid bias superimposed on a fixed a-c bias. In both cases the speed is preset by the input θ_i picked off the reference voltage. Grid resistor R_g is to prevent excessive grid current, and C_g is a small protective capacitor to absorb voltage surges and so prevent them from affecting thyratron operation.

In Fig. 13-20, the voltage θ_i is opposed by the pilot voltage θ_o in a series circuit including the d-c winding of the saturable-core reactor. When the motor speed is too low, the voltage by which θ_i exceeds θ_o causes a current in the d-c winding of the reactor. The direct current saturates the reactor and advances the phase of the grid voltage, increasing the motor armature voltage and hence the motor speed. For simplicity, the anode transformer and the control-circuit supply transformer are shown separately, although they may be combined.

When the motor of Fig. 13-21*a* is slow, the voltage θ_i across R_1 from the reference source exceeds the voltage θ_o across R_2 from the pilot. As

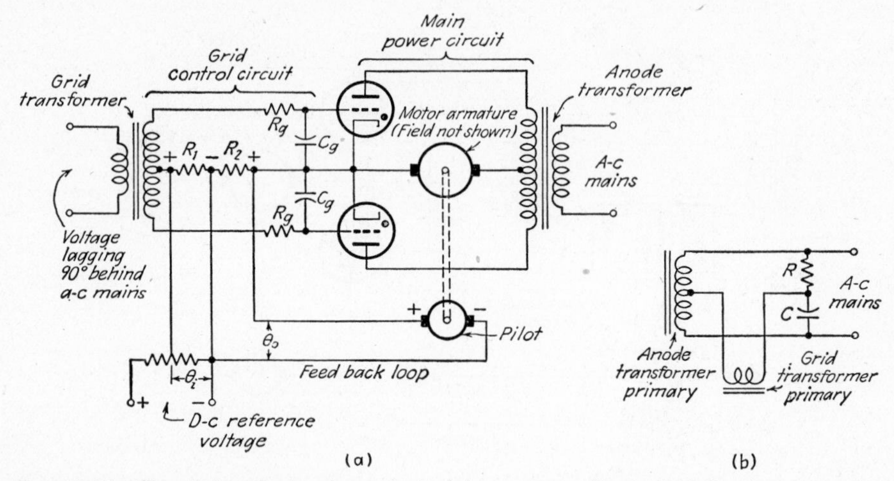

FIG. 13-21. Circuit for electronic control of d-c motor. Control of the thyratrons by fixed grid phase shift and adjustable d-c grid voltage is used.

shown by the voltage polarities on R_1 and R_2, this excess causes a net positive d-c bias on the grids, advancing the conduction angle and increasing the motor voltage. To avoid complicating the diagram, the source of the voltage impressed on the grid transformer is not shown in Fig. 13-21*a* but is indicated separately in Fig. 13-21*b*. As shown, it is obtained from the a-c mains and the anode transformer by choosing R and C to give a 90° phase shift.

Not infrequently in the speed regulation of d-c motors, the reference voltage in Figs. 13-20 and 13-21 is compared with the motor voltage instead of a pilot voltage; compensation for increased armature-resistance drop with load is incorporated by adding a voltage proportional to armature current in the feedback loop. A somewhat similar arrangement may be made to limit the armature current and hence the torque during acceleration. Most integral-horsepower motors so controlled are supplied from polyphase-connected thyratrons instead of the single-phase full-wave connection. The constant reference voltage may be obtained from the a-c mains by a separate rectifier working through a glow-discharge voltage-regulator tube with series ballast resistance. Additions must also be made to ensure stable operation. When part of the speed range is to be covered by field control, the field-supply circuit is basically a duplicate of the armature-control circuit, one being made ineffective while the other is in use. The complete circuit of a motor so controlled may be complicated indeed.[7] When so modified, the motor is often referred to as a *thyratron motor.* Such a modification of the circuit of Fig. 13-20 is known by the trade name *Thymatrol;* a similar modification of the circuit of Fig. 13-21 is known by the trade name *Mototrol.*

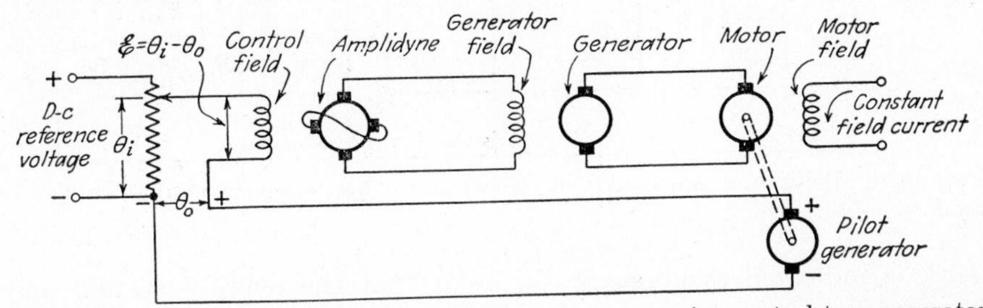

Fig. 13-22. Circuit for speed regulation of large d-c motor using control-type generator as exciter for main generator. Split control fields in the exciter (as in Fig. 13-18) more commonly form the error-measuring means.

A third example (Fig. 13-22) illustrates speed regulation of a large motor by electrodynamic means. Two stages of power amplification of the speed error signal $\mathcal{E}$ appear, one in the control-type generator or Amplidyne and one in the main generator. The operation of this simplified circuit may readily be traced by similarity to several of the preceding examples.

c. Servomechanisms Employing D-C Motors. As examples of servomechanisms with d-c motors driving the output members, two block diagrams for remote position control of the output shaft are presented in Figs. 13-23 and 13-24. In both examples, Selsyn generators and control transformers are used for data transmission in the manner described in Art. 11-4. The input to the controller, indicating quantitatively the discrepancy between the desired and actual positions at any instant, accord-

[7] See for instance, E. E. Moyer and H. L. Palmer, Thyratron Motor Control, *Trans. AIEE*, vol. 62, pp. 706–711, November, 1943.

The following are a selected few from the many references on electronic speed control of motors: G. W. Garman, Thyratron Control of D-c Motors, *Trans. AIEE*, vol. 57, pp. 335–352, 1938; A. J. Williams, Jr., Combined Thyratron and Tachometer Speed Control of Small Motors, *Trans. AIEE*, vol. 57, pp. 565–568, 1938; E. H. Vedder and K. P. Puchlowski, Theory of Rectifier D-c Motor Drives, *Trans. AIEE*, vol. 62, pp. 870–877, 1943; B. J. Dalton, Electronic Motor Control, *Gen. Elec. Rev.*, vol. 48, pp. 12–17, May, 1945.

ingly appears in the form of an error-modulated signal—a carrier wave whose amplitude is proportional to the error and whose instantaneous polarity is determined by the sign of the error.

The system of Fig. 13-23 is based on Ward Leonard control of the d-c motor. The error signal is demodulated and amplified to furnish the generator-field excitation; the generator in turn supplies energy to the motor armature. The presence of a compensating or stabilizing net-

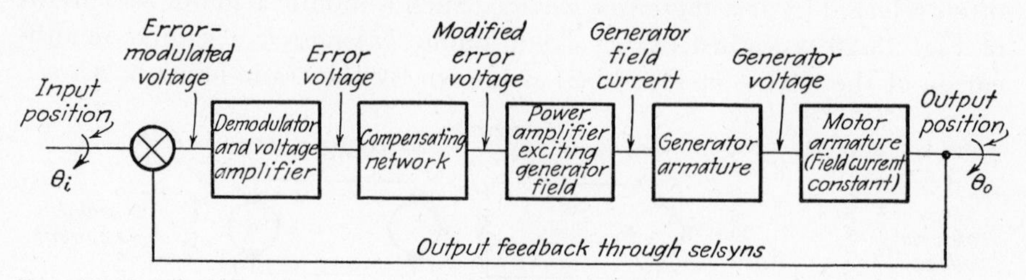

FIG. 13-23. Block diagram of position controller using armature-voltage control of final d-c motor.

work is indicated symbolically in order that the over-all system may have the desired dynamic-response characteristics with the requisite degree of stability.

Figure 13-24 is similar except that it is based on field control of a d-c motor whose armature current is constant and supplied from a separate source. To make these block diagrams more tangible, a typical circuit diagram for the servo amplifier of Fig. 13-24 is given in Fig. 13-25. It includes the elements in the first three of the four rectangular blocks in Fig. 13-24. The demodulator of the error signal must be phase-sensitive

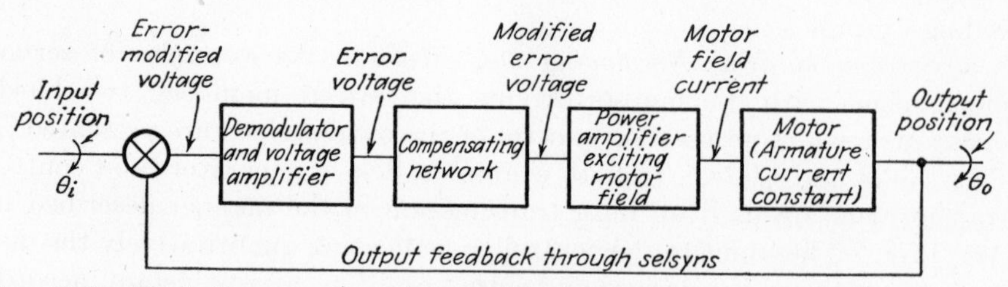

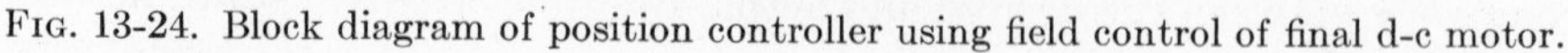
FIG. 13-24. Block diagram of position controller using field control of final d-c motor.

(*i.e.*, the polarity of the output must depend on whether the driven shaft is leading or lagging the input shaft) because the sign of the error is conveyed by the instantaneous polarity of the a-c error voltage relative to a reference voltage of carrier frequency. The reference voltages introduced into the demodulator circuit in Fig. 13-25 are obtained from the same source as the Selsyn excitation voltage. Full-wave demodulation is shown rather than half-wave because less filtering is required and the time lag associated with energy storage in the filter is smaller. The compensating network shown in both sides of the balanced d-c voltage amplifier is of the type shown separately in Fig. 13-26 and known as a *phase-lead network* or *phase-advance network*. By inserting such phase lead in cascade with the controller, appreciable compensation is achieved for

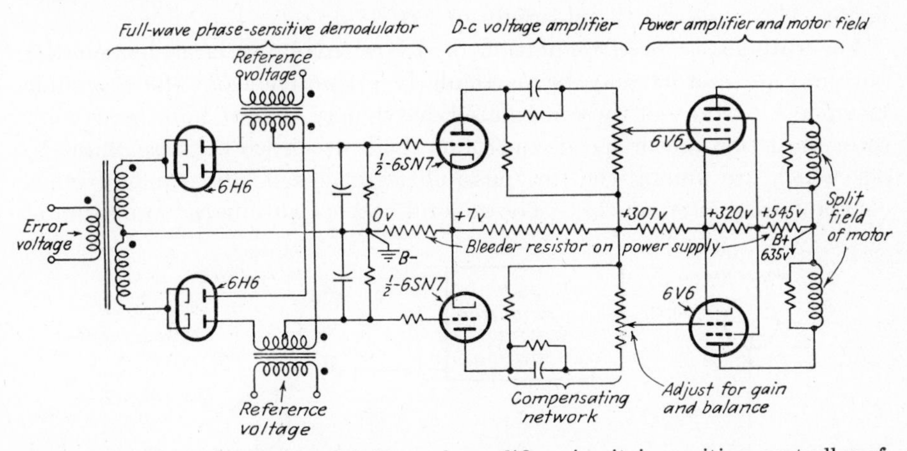

FIG. 13-25. Example of demodulator and amplifier circuit in position controller of Fig. 13-24.

inductive lags associated with energy storage in the servomotor and controller, especially that in the motor field in this case. Or, from another standpoint, a voltage proportional to error is applied to the network, and a voltage proportional to error plus its first derivative is obtained to a known approximation from the network. The end result is that the effective over-all time constant is significantly reduced. The phase-lead network is one of a number of such circuits used for cascade compensation or stabilization; cascaded devices and added feedback loops form two important methods of stabilization and lag compensation.[8]

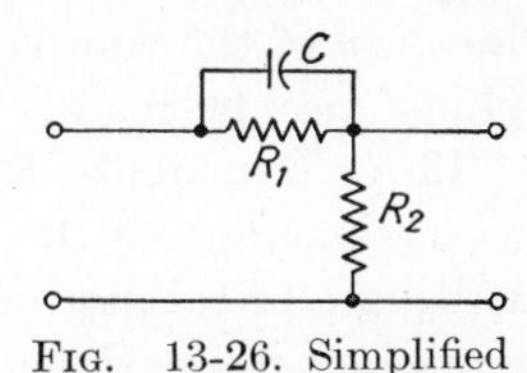

FIG. 13-26. Simplified diagram of compensating network used in circuit of Fig. 13-25.

Many other examples of remote position control can be found, not only electrical examples but also hydraulic, pneumatic, and mechanical ones.

d. Automatic Control of A-C Motors. Most types of a-c motors inherently possess substantially constant-speed characteristics, a fact that limits the possibilities of control of operating performance. Because of the convenience and economy of a-c supplies, however, these possibilities

[8] See A. C. Hall, Application of Circuit Theory to the Design of Servomechanisms, *J. Franklin Inst.*, vol. 242, pp. 279–307, October, 1946, and A. L. Whiteley, Theory of Servo Systems, with Particular Reference to Stabilization, *J. IEE*, vol. 93, Part II, pp. 353–367, August, 1946.

sometimes exhibit over-all advantages. A few of them will be mentioned here.

An obvious candidate for low-power servomechanism usage is the 2-phase induction motor whose characteristics are analyzed in Chap. 10. An a-c servomechanism based on this motor has already been presented in Fig. 11-35 and discussed briefly in Art. 11-4.

For automatic speed regulation of drives involving large horsepower outputs, a-c motors may be particularly attractive from the economic viewpoint. Many of these regulated drives may be based on the wound-rotor-induction-motor speed-control methods described in Chap. 9, methods which are among the few possibilities of speed adjustment from a constant-frequency source. The general basis of automatic regulation of

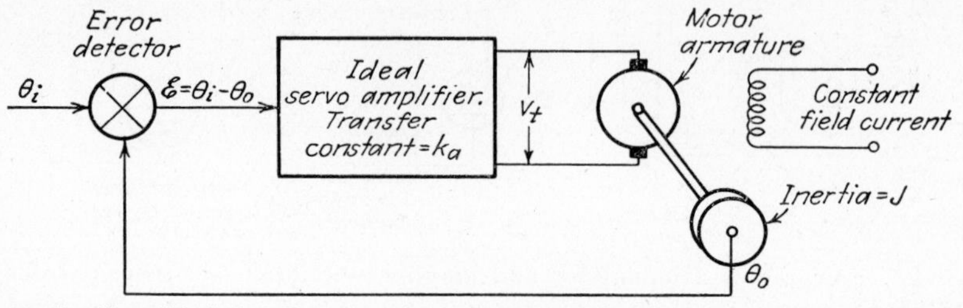

FIG. 13-27. Simplified closed-cycle system for control of d-c motor driving pure-inertia load.

such drives can be visualized from the examples already given for d-c motors. One other speed-control method worth noting is the possibility of inserting an adjustable-speed coupling (an eddy-current clutch or a hydraulic coupling, for example) in the shaft of a constant-speed motor. Because of the comparatively low control-power requirements, such couplings may be readily adapted to closed-cycle control.

13-7. Transient Response of Closed-cycle Systems.[9] Transient analysis of any of the closed-cycle systems of the last article involves the writing and solving of the appropriate linear electrodynamic differential equations in the same general manner as for the somewhat simpler Examples 13-1 and 13-3. To illustrate the procedure, the simplified closed-cycle system of Fig. 13-27 will be considered. Here the objective is to cause the angular position θ_o of the d-c-motor shaft to follow the angular position θ_i of a remote shaft. As in Example 13-1, the motor is directly coupled to a pure-inertia load, and the combined inertia of the armature and load is J. The motor has the armature-circuit resistance r_a ohms and negligible armature inductance and armature reaction. The effect

[9] For comprehensive treatments of the transient method of analysis, see G. S. Brown and D. P. Campbell, "Principles of Servomechanisms," John Wiley & Sons, Inc., New York, 1948, and G. S. Brown and A. C. Hall, Dynamic Behavior and Design of Servomechanisms, *Trans. ASME*, July, 1946, pp. 503–522.

of rotational losses in the motor is to be ignored. With the angles θ_o and θ_i measured in mechanical radians, the constant k relates both torque T and armature current i_a, and counter emf e_a and angular velocity $d\theta_o/dt$. The servo amplifier supplying energy to the motor armature is considered ideal (*i.e.*, contains no significant energy-storage elements, such as inductance and capacitance, and inserts no energy dissipation) and hence may be characterized completely by the transfer constant k_a expressing the ratio of the output voltage v_t to the input error $\mathcal{E}$. The error detector is similarly idealized. Any conversion constant associated with the error detector to convert angular difference in mechanical radians to a voltage is considered to be part of the constant k_a, so that the error $\theta_i - \theta_o$ at the output of the error detector and input of the amplifier may be treated as if it were a voltage.

a. The Differential Equations. The equation relating specifically to the motor and load are evidently the same as those in Example 13-1; *i.e.*,

$$T = ki_a = J\frac{d^2\theta_o}{dt^2} \tag{13-75}$$

and

$$e_a = k\omega_o = k\frac{d\theta_o}{dt} = v_t - r_a i_a \tag{13-76}$$

One new equation appears in order to express the presence of the feedback loop and servo amplifier:

$$v_t = k_a\mathcal{E} = k_a(\theta_i - \theta_o) \tag{13-77}$$

Algebraic combination of these relations yields as the equation for θ_o

$$J\frac{d^2\theta_o}{dt^2} + \frac{k^2}{r_a}\frac{d\theta_o}{dt} + \frac{kk_a}{r_a}\theta_o = \frac{kk_a}{r_a}\theta_i \tag{13-78}$$

When normalized in the manner of Eq. 13-32, this equation becomes

$$\frac{d^2\theta_o}{dt^2} + 2\zeta\omega_n\frac{d\theta_o}{dt} + \omega_n^2\theta_o = \omega_n^2\theta_i \tag{13-79}$$

where

$$\omega_n = \sqrt{\frac{kk_a}{Jr_a}} = \sqrt{\frac{k_a}{k}\frac{1}{\tau}} \tag{13-80}$$

and

$$\zeta = \frac{k^2/r_a}{2\sqrt{J(kk_a/r_a)}} = \frac{1}{2}\sqrt{\frac{k}{k_a}\frac{k^2}{Jr_a}} = \frac{1}{2}\sqrt{\frac{k}{k_a}\frac{1}{\tau}} \tag{13-81}$$

In Eqs. 13-80 and 13-81, τ is the time constant of the motor and, as in Example 13-1, is given by

$$\tau = \frac{Jr_a}{k^2} \tag{13-82}$$

The solution of Eq. 13-79 may follow the general pattern established in Art. 13-2 for Eq. 13-32 to yield results in nondimensionalized form. In the light of this previous experience, it is evident from Eqs. 13-80 and 13-81 that both the natural frequency and the damping ratio become lower as the motor time constant τ becomes larger. Also evident is the fact that increasing the amplification or transfer constant k_a increases the natural frequency but lowers the damping ratio; too high an amplification will therefore result in an undesirable succession of overshooting and undershooting of the correct angular position.

As an alternate to the response of output angle θ_o to a specified disturbance, it may also be desirable to express the response for error $\mathcal{E}$. The differential equation for error, corresponding to Eq. 13-79, may be found to be

$$\frac{d^2\mathcal{E}}{dt^2} + 2\zeta\omega_n \frac{d\mathcal{E}}{dt} + \omega_n^2\mathcal{E} = \frac{d^2\theta_i}{dt^2} + 2\zeta\omega_n \frac{d\theta_i}{dt} \tag{13-83}$$

which may also be solved in nondimensionalized form.

b. Solution for Constant Displacement. The response of the closed-cycle system to a suddenly applied constant angular displacement θ_i at the input—to a so-called *step function*, in other words—is a significant indication of the ability of the system to follow abrupt random changes in its input. The system is considered to be initially at rest with zero values for both θ_o and $d\theta_o/dt$ at zero time. Under these conditions, the solution of Eq. 13-79 is of the same form as that of Eq. 13-32. The steady-state solution is

$$\theta_o = \theta_i \tag{13-84}$$

and the complete solution for the dimensionless ratio θ_o/θ_i is the same as that given by Eqs. 13-39 to 13-42 for the ratio x/x_∞. Thus, for the underdamped or oscillatory case ($\zeta < 1$), corresponding to Eq. 13-39,

$$\frac{\theta_o}{\theta_i} = 1 - \frac{1}{\sqrt{1-\zeta^2}} \epsilon^{-\zeta\omega_n t} \sin\left(\sqrt{1-\zeta^2}\,\omega_n t + \phi\right) \tag{13-85}$$

where

$$\phi = \tan^{-1} \frac{\sqrt{1-\zeta^2}}{\zeta} \tag{13-86}$$

The curves of Fig. 13-8 are therefore plots of θ_o/θ_i as a function of $\omega_n t$ for a series of values of ζ.

The steady-state error $\mathcal{E}$ is evidently zero. The error response or time variation of error can be obtained readily from the solution for θ_o/θ_i by recognizing that

$$\frac{\mathcal{E}}{\theta_i} = 1 - \frac{\theta_o}{\theta_i} \tag{13-87}$$

Thus, the curves of Fig. 13-8 may be used as plots of $\mathcal{E}/\theta_i$ as a function of $\omega_n t$ by changing the numbers on the ordinate scale so that they become 1 minus the present numbers.

c. Solution for Constant Velocity. A second disturbance which is important for analysis consists of a step function in the form of a suddenly applied constant velocity ω_i at the input. The system is again considered to be at rest initially. Here a solution in terms of error response is of most significance. For this purpose, Eq. 13-83 can be rewritten as

$$\frac{d^2\mathcal{E}}{dt^2} + 2\zeta\omega_n \frac{d\mathcal{E}}{dt} + \omega_n^2\mathcal{E} = \frac{d\omega_i}{dt} + 2\zeta\omega_n\omega_i \tag{13-88}$$

Note that $\mathcal{E}$ is still an error in angle, $\theta_i - \theta_o$, not an error in velocity.

The steady-state solution of Eq. 13-88 is

$$\mathcal{E}_\infty = \frac{2\zeta\omega_i}{\omega_n} \tag{13-89}$$

A constant steady-state error $\mathcal{E}_\infty$ must exist for operation of the motor at constant velocity in order that the counter emf e_a of the motor may be compensated by an equal terminal voltage v_t at the output of the amplifier. The actual situation can be seen by replacing ζ and ω_n in Eq. 13-89 by their values from Eqs. 13-80 and 13-81, a process which yields

$$\mathcal{E}_\infty = \frac{k}{k_a}\omega_i \tag{13-90}$$

or

$$k_a\mathcal{E}_\infty = v_t = k\omega_i = e_a \tag{13-91}$$

The complete solution for error in the nondimensional form $\mathcal{E}/\mathcal{E}_\infty$ as a function of $\omega_n t$ may be obtained by the methods of Art. 13-2. Inspection of Eqs. 13-80, 13-81, and 13-90 shows that increasing the constant k_a increases the natural angular frequency ω_n and decreases the steady-state error, both of which are desirable; because of the accompanying decrease of damping ratio ζ, however, too great an increase of sensitivity leads to intolerable overshoot and tendency to hunt.

Example 13-7. The small d-c motor and inertia load of Example 13-1 ($r_a = 34$ ohms, $J = 5.85 \times 10^{-5}$ mks unit, $k = 0.328$, $\tau = 0.0185$ sec) are used in the system of Fig. 13-27 with the object of controlling the angular position of the load shaft. The assumption of an idealized error detector and servo amplifier are to be followed.

a. With the system adjusted for critical damping, determine the values of the transfer constant k_a, the undamped natural frequency, the effective duration of the transient following a sudden displacement of the input shaft, and the steady-state error for a constant velocity input of 20°/sec.

b. Consider now that the system is to be adjusted so that the steady-state error for a constant velocity input of 20°/sec is not to exceed 0.5°. Determine the corresponding values of the transfer constant k_a, the undamped natural frequency, the damping ratio, and the effective duration of the transient following a sudden displacement of the input shaft.

c. In addition to the motor, the system consists of a Selsyn data-transmission system having a sensitivity of 0.5 volt rms per degree displacement, a phase-sensitive demodulator having a sensitivity of 0.8 volt output per volt rms input, and power amplification to supply the armature. For the conditions of *b*, determine the required voltage sensitivity of the power amplification—*i.e.*, the ratio of the armature terminal voltage to the demodulator output voltage.

Solution. *a.* From Eq. 13-81,

$$1 = \frac{1}{2}\sqrt{\frac{0.328}{k_a}\frac{1}{0.0185}}$$

or

$$k_a = 4.43$$

From Eq. 13-80,

$$\omega_n = \sqrt{\frac{4.43}{0.328}\frac{1}{0.0185}} = 27.0 \text{ rad/sec}$$

and

$$f_n = \frac{27.0}{2\pi} = 4.3 \text{ cps}$$

From Fig. 13-8, the transient is seen to subside to within about 2 per cent when $\omega_n t$ is about 7.0. The effective duration of the transient is accordingly 7.0/27.0, or 0.26 sec. The steady-state error, from Eq. 13-90, is

$$\mathcal{E}_\infty = \frac{0.328}{4.43} \times 20 = 1.5°$$

b. For the error to be held to 0.5°, from Eq. 13-90,

$$0.5 = \frac{0.328}{k_a} \times 20$$

or

$$k_a = 13.1$$

Then

$$\omega_n = \sqrt{\frac{13.1}{0.328}\frac{1}{0.0185}} = 46.5 \text{ rad/sec}$$

$$f_n = \frac{46.5}{2\pi} = 7.4 \text{ cps}$$

and

$$\zeta = \frac{1}{2}\sqrt{\frac{0.328}{13.1}\frac{1}{0.0185}} = 0.58$$

From Fig. 13-8, it is again seen that the transient has effectively subsided when $\omega_n t$ is about 7.0. The effective duration of the transient is accordingly 7.0/46.5, or 0.15 sec. The performance of this system is evidently better all round than that in *a*.

c. The Selsyns, demodulator, and power amplifier are considered to be noninteracting—*i.e.*, the presence of any one does not affect the performance of the others. For elements in noninteracting cascade, the over-all transfer constant is the product of the individual transfer constants. The voltage sensitivity k_{pa} of the power amplification is accordingly given by

$$13.1 = \left(0.5\,\frac{180}{\pi}\right) \times 0.8k_{pa}$$

or

$$k_{pa} = 0.57 \text{ volt output per volt input}$$

More elaborate closed-cycle systems with a greater number of independent energy-storage elements will, of course, give rise to higher-order differential equations and require much more laborious analyses. The broad principles are the same as those illustrated here, however. The possibility of nondimensionalizing the solutions of third-order equations is mentioned in Art. 13-2*b*; as the order of the equation grows higher, it becomes increasingly difficult to isolate the effect of any one system constant. As the control systems and the differential equations grow more complicated, the value of highly systematizing the methods of solving the equations greatly increases.[10]

13-8. Frequency Response of Closed-cycle Systems.[11] As mentioned in Art. 13-4, dynamic analysis of linear systems by frequency-response methods forms an important complement to transient analysis of the systems. Study of the amplitude and phase response of systems for varying frequency of sinusoidal disturbance amounts, in effect, to the application of circuit theory to analysis of the systems. A brief introduction to such studies of closed-cycle systems is presented in this article.

a. Second-order Systems. The most direct correlation between system frequency response and transient analysis occurs in systems whose performance is characterized by a second-order differential equation. To bring out this correlation, the simple system of Fig. 13-27, whose transient behavior is studied in the preceding article, will be subjected to frequency-response analysis here. The forcing function for this analysis is sinusoidal variation with time of the input θ_i; the response to be determined is the steady-state amplitude and phase of the output θ_o over the significant frequency range.

The basic differential equation, 13-79, is

$$\frac{d^2\theta_o}{dt^2} + 2\zeta\omega_n \frac{d\theta_o}{dt} + \omega_n^2\theta_o = \omega_n^2\theta_i \tag{13-92}$$

with the undamped natural frequency ω_n and damping ratio ζ given by Eqs. 13-80 and 13-81, respectively. As in Art. 13-4, Eq. 13-92 can be transformed into a vector relation between the variables by replacing

[10] See M. F. Gardner and J. L. Barnes, "Transients in Linear Systems," Vol. I, John Wiley & Sons, Inc., New York, 1942, for treatment of the Laplace-transform approach.

[11] For comprehensive treatments of the frequency-response method of servomechanism analysis, see G. S. Brown and D. P. Campbell, "Principles of Servomechanisms," John Wiley & Sons, Inc., New York, 1948, and A. C. Hall, Application of Circuit Theory to the Design of Servomechanisms, *J. Franklin Inst.*, vol. 242, pp. 279–307, October, 1946.

d/dt by $(j\omega)$ and d^2/dt^2 by $(j\omega)^2$ and substituting the vector amplitudes of the dependent and independent variables. The result is

$$(j\omega)^2\Theta_o + 2\zeta\omega_n(j\omega)\Theta_o + \omega_n^2\Theta_o = \omega_n^2\Theta_i \tag{13-93}$$

The symbol Θ denotes the amplitude or peak value of the quantity θ.

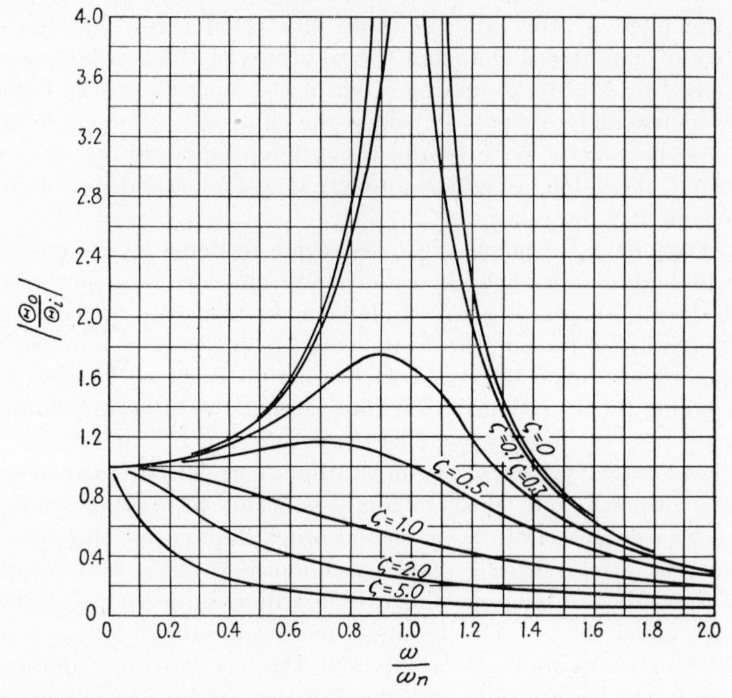

FIG. 13-28. Normalized curves of amplitude response as a function of frequency of the input control signal for the second-order system of Fig. 13-27.

Equation 13-93 yields for the vector ratio of output to input

$$\frac{\Theta_o}{\Theta_i} = \frac{1}{\left(1 - \frac{\omega^2}{\omega_n^2}\right) + j2\zeta\frac{\omega}{\omega_n}} \tag{13-94}$$

The amplitude-response ratio is accordingly

$$\left|\frac{\Theta_o}{\Theta_i}\right| = \frac{1}{\sqrt{\left(1 - \frac{\omega^2}{\omega_n^2}\right)^2 + \left(2\zeta\frac{\omega}{\omega_n}\right)^2}} \tag{13-95}$$

and the phase angle measured from Θ_i to Θ_o is

$$\Psi = -\tan^{-1}\frac{2\zeta(\omega/\omega_n)}{1 - (\omega^2/\omega_n^2)} \tag{13-96}$$

Curves of amplitude-response ratio and phase angle are plotted as a function of the dimensionless variable ω/ω_n for a series of values of ζ in Figs. 13-28 and 13-29. As in many other analyses involving frequency-response characteristics, the ideal characteristic would be a perfectly flat amplitude response and zero phase shift for all frequencies. Comparison of Figs. 13-28 and 13-8 gives clear evidence of correlation between frequency response and transient response of second-order systems. High

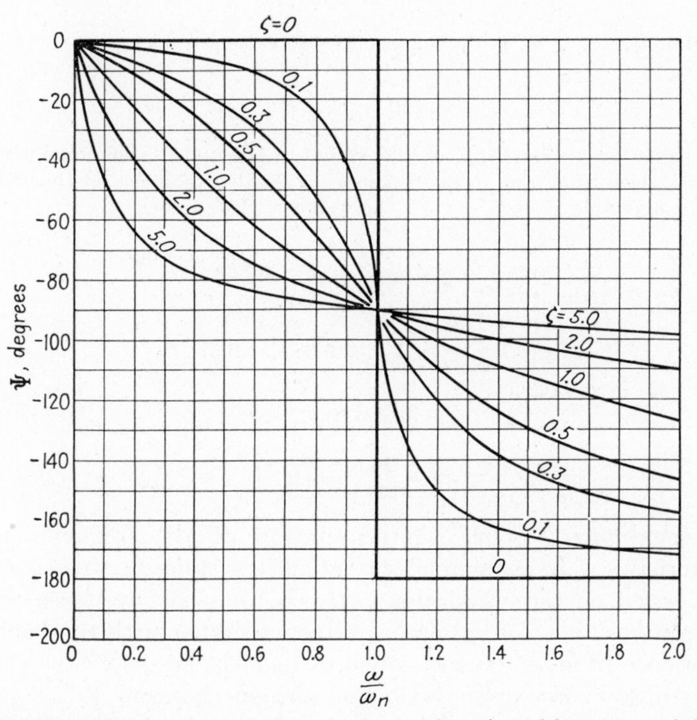

FIG. 13-29. Normalized curves of phase angle as a function of frequency of the input signal for the second-order system of Fig. 13-27. Negative angles are angles of lag of output behind input.

peaks in the amplitude-response curve evidently correspond to undesirable overshooting and undershooting in the transient response. On the other hand, a rapid falling off of the amplitude response as frequency increases corresponds to sluggish transient response. From the nature of both figures and of the quantities plotted on the horizontal axis, it is evident that a relatively high natural frequency corresponds to a relatively low effective duration of the transient following a disturbance.

Example 13-8. *a.* For a closed-cycle system characterized by a second-order differential equation, determine the value of the peak of the amplitude-response curve and the angular frequency at which it occurs. Both quantities are to be expressed as functions of the damping ratio ζ.

b. Compute the numerical values of these quantities for the system of Example 13-7*b*.

Solution. a. The solution consists in differentiating Eq. 13-95 with respect to the variable ω/ω_n and equating the derivative to zero. The amplitude response is then found to have a mathematical maximum at zero frequency, and at

$$\frac{\omega}{\omega_n} = \sqrt{1 - 2\zeta^2} \tag{13-97}$$

Substitution of Eq. 13-97 in 13-95 gives for the response peak

$$\left|\frac{\Theta_o}{\Theta_i}\right|_{\max} = \frac{1}{2\zeta\sqrt{1 - \zeta^2}} \tag{13-98}$$

It will be noted from Eqs. 13-97 and 13-98 that, for damping ratios equal to or greater than 0.707, there is no peak in the response curve other than that at the origin.

b. From Example 13-7*b*, $\zeta = 0.58$; the response peak is then

$$\left|\frac{\Theta_o}{\Theta_i}\right|_{\max} = \frac{1}{2 \times 0.58\sqrt{1 - (0.58)^2}} = 1.06$$

It occurs when

$$\frac{\omega}{\omega_n} = \sqrt{1 - 2(0.58)^2} = 0.57$$

or since $\omega_n = 46.5$ rad/sec,

$$\omega = 46.5 \times 0.57 = 26.5$$

and

$$f = \frac{26.5}{2\pi} = 4.2 \text{ cps}$$

b. Higher-order Systems. Interpretation of the frequency-response characteristics of more complex closed-cycle systems is, to a considerable extent, based on the correlation between frequency response and transient response for a second-order system, together with the background of experience from which one skilled in such studies views the characteristics. In the words of one writer on servomechanisms:[12]

A general design rule based on the system frequency response is summarized as follows. If the peaks in the amplitude response are limited to values of approximately one and one-third to one and one-half, and if the predominant peak (generally the first) occurs at a frequency at least three times the inverse of the period allowed for a transient to disappear, the system will be satisfactory for the application.

For example, if a system is required to respond to sudden inputs with such a rapidity that the error must not be more than a few per cent of its initial value within one second, the lowest natural frequency of the system should be at least three cycles per second. The designer can then feel confident that the system will meet its requirements.

[12] A. C. Hall, Application of Circuit Theory to the Design of Servomechanisms, *J. Franklin Inst.*, vol. 242, pp. 279–307, October, 1946.

The response-peak values of $1\frac{1}{3}$ to $1\frac{1}{2}$ mentioned in this quotation correspond to damping ratios of 0.41 to 0.36 in a second-order system. Of course, such a general rule is by no means made the sole basis of design, but it does establish perspective and presents a valuable checking procedure for a proposed design Moreover, plots of the appropriate frequency loci furnish definite indications of what must be done to a proposed system in the way of design changes and compensating networks to achieve the desired performance. Consideration of these design techniques and refinements is beyond the scope of the present discussion, however; little more will be attempted in the remainder of this article

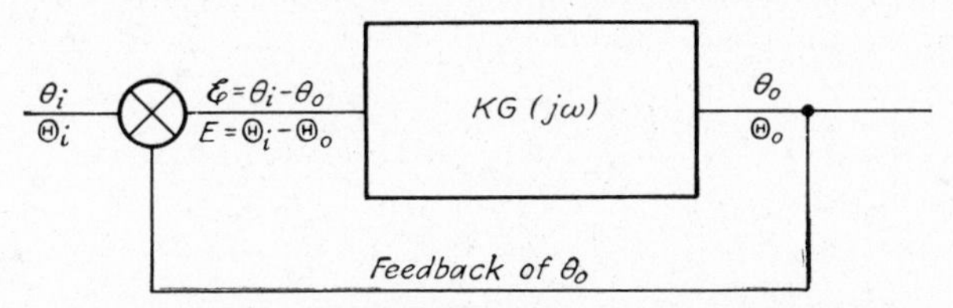

FIG. 13-30. Schematic representation of closed-cycle system.

than to systematize the process of obtaining frequency-response characteristics for somewhat more complicated systems.

Any closed-cycle system, such as those of Figs. 13-15 to 13-27, is susceptible to the simple schematic representation of Fig. 13-30, in which the single block contains everything but the idealized feedback path closing the loop. For a linear system, the performance of this single block may be characterized by the *transfer function* $KG(j\omega)$, defined as the vector ratio of output Θ_o to the block input E or

$$KG(j\omega) = \frac{\Theta_o}{E} \tag{13-99}$$

The symbol E designates the vector amplitude of the error $\mathcal{E}$ for a sinusoidal time variation. In the symbol $KG(j\omega)$, the parenthetical $(j\omega)$ is not a multiplying factor but denotes that the transfer function is a function of angular frequency ω; the portion of this function designated by K is the *static sensitivity*, or part which is independent of ω; the portion $G(j\omega)$ is the frequency-dependent part. The transfer function is simply a vector ratio of an effect to a cause and is not unlike many transfer parameters used in circuit theory. Once $KG(j\omega)$ has been found, other pertinent performance ratios may be obtained. Thus, since the vector relation for error is

$$E = \Theta_i - \Theta_o \tag{13-100}$$

the following vector relations may also be obtained:

$$\frac{\Theta_o}{\Theta_i} = \frac{KG(j\omega)}{1 + KG(j\omega)} \tag{13-101}$$

and

$$\frac{E}{\Theta_i} = \frac{1}{1 + KG(j\omega)} \tag{13-102}$$

The performance features of the system may then be readily investigated.

Example 13-9. Determine the transfer function $KG(j\omega)$ of the system shown in Fig. 13-27 and described in the opening paragraph of Art. 13-7. Normalize the transfer function to give $KG\left(j\frac{\omega}{\omega_n}\right)$, and show that Eq. 13-94 for the vector ratio Θ_o/Θ_i may be obtained from the result.

Solution. Equations 13-75 to 13-77, written at the beginning of Art. 13-7*a* and expressing the performance of the motor and servo amplifier, may be written in vector form and solved for the vector ratio Θ_o/E to yield

$$KG(j\omega) = \frac{\Theta_o}{E} = \frac{k_a/k}{j\omega(1 + j\tau\omega)} \tag{13-103}$$

where, as in Eq. 13-82,

$$\tau = \frac{Jr_a}{k^2} \tag{13-104}$$

Equation 13-103 shows that the static sensitivity K is

$$K = \frac{k_a}{k} \tag{13-105}$$

and the frequency-dependent portion of the transfer function is

$$G(j\omega) = \frac{1}{j\omega(1 + j\tau\omega)} \tag{13-106}$$

By expanding the denominator of Eq. 13-103 and multiplying both numerator and denominator by k/k_a, one obtains

$$KG(j\omega) = \frac{1}{-(k/k_a)\tau\omega^2 + j(k/k_a)\omega} \tag{13-107}$$

After use of the change of variable given by Eqs. 13-80 and 13-81, this expression becomes

$$KG\left(j\frac{\omega}{\omega_n}\right) = \frac{1}{-(\omega^2/\omega_n^2) + j2\zeta(\omega/\omega_n)} \tag{13-108}$$

which is the normalized form of the transfer function.

Substitution of Eq. 13-108 in 13-101 yields, after some algebraic simplification,

$$\frac{\Theta_o}{\Theta_i} = \frac{1}{1 - (\omega^2/\omega_n^2) + j2\zeta(\omega/\omega_n)} \tag{13-109}$$

which is the same as Eq. 13-94.

c. Sustained Oscillations. As in any system involving feedback from the output to the input, there is always a possibility of self-excited operation of any practical closed-cycle control system—*i.e.*, the system may undergo sustained oscillations even with no input θ_i. Examination of this possibility involves substantially the line of thought used in studying vacuum-tube oscillators or in examining the possibility of oscillation in vacuum-tube amplifiers. A brief qualitative description is given here.

In the system of Fig. 13-30, a sufficient number of energy-storage elements, with their associated time lags and phase shifts between output and input, will cause the output Θ_o to be 180° out of phase with error E at some finite frequency. In other words, the transfer function $KG(j\omega)$ will be a negative real number at this frequency. If that number is unity, self-excitation may take place; *i.e.*, even with $\theta_i = 0$, feedback of the output around the closed loop supplies the proper input, and the system oscillates steadily at the frequency corresponding to the 180° phase shift. If that number is greater than unity, oscillations may take place at an amplitude which increases until it is limited by nonlinearities in the system, a process not unlike the build-up of a shunt generator described in Art. 5-6. The system will not undergo sustained oscillations if the magnitude of the transfer function is less than unity at the frequency producing a 180° phase shift.

It should be noted that these conditions furnish a criterion for absolute stability. The normal closed-cycle system operates well within these limits.

13-9. Electric-circuit Analogues of Electromechanical Systems. One dominating thought in the parts of the foregoing articles dealing with linear systems involving electromechanical coupling is that the dynamics of these systems may be thoroughly investigated by the methods of linear-circuit theory. This statement, of course, is merely the equivalent of saying that study of both the circuit problems and the dynamic problems is synonymous with the study of linear differential equations with constant coefficients. The similarity of the problems may be emphasized by a brief discussion of electric circuits which are analogous to electromechanical-energy-conversion or -coupling devices. At the same time, a method of experimentally simulating the performance of these devices is obtained.

Analogous electric circuits must be the mathematical equivalents of the prototype systems. They are therefore based on term-by-term identity of the respective differential equations.

Example 13-10. Figure 13-27 shows schematically a closed-cycle electromechanically coupled system in which the coupling element is a d-c motor with constant field current. As described in Example 13-1, this motor has the armature-circuit resistance r_a, combined inertia of armature and load J, torque per unit armature current and voltage per unit angular velocity k, and negligible armature inductance, armature reaction, and rotational losses.

a. Obtain two circuits which are the mathematical equivalent of the motor and its pure-inertia load as far as dynamic performance is concerned.

b. Compare and discuss these two circuits.

c. Consider that the circuit analogue is to be part of an *analogue-type computer* or *simulator* for the study of the over-all performance of the closed-cycle system by oscillographic observations in the equivalent network. Discuss the freedom of choice in numerical values of circuit constants so that the analogue may be easily realizable and readily operated physically.

d. Show a possible circuit analogue for the entire system of Fig. 13-27.

Solution. (*a*) The equations specifying the behavior of the motor and load are Eqs. 13-1, 13-3, 13-4, and 13-5. From these equations may be obtained relations for output angle θ_o and armature current i_a, both in terms of armature terminal voltage v_t, which must now be regarded as a variable; *i.e.*,

$$\frac{Jr_a}{k}\frac{d^2\theta_o}{dt^2} + k\frac{d\theta_o}{dt} = v_t \tag{13-110}$$

and

$$r_a i_a + \frac{k^2}{J}\int i_a\,dt = v_t \tag{13-111}$$

Equation 13-110 is the current-voltage relation for the *RL* circuit of Fig. 13-31 when current is considered analogous to angular velocity; this circuit is therefore an

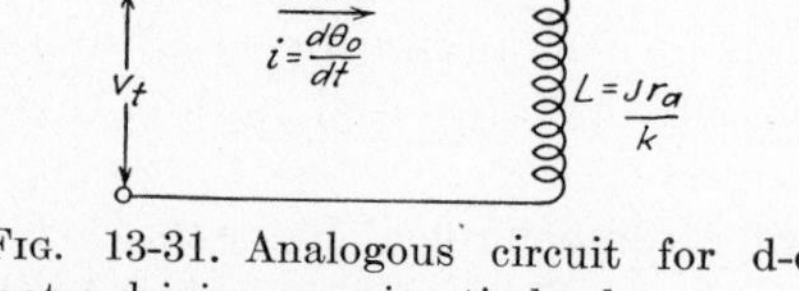

FIG. 13-31. Analogous circuit for d-c motor driving pure-inertia load.

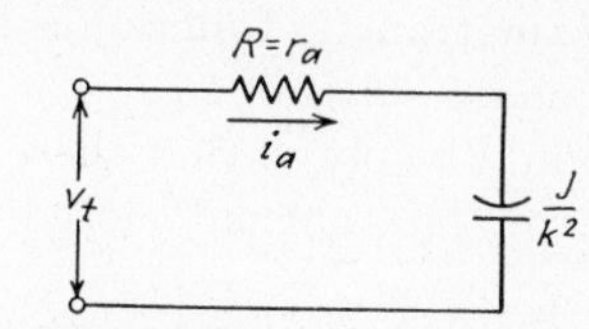

FIG. 13-32. Equivalent circuit for d-c motor driving pure-inertia load.

analogue. Likewise, Eq. 13-111 is the current-voltage relation for the *RC* circuit of Fig. 13-32 with the current directly equal to the motor armature current; this circuit is therefore also an analogue.

b. The *RL* circuit of Fig. 13-31 is a mathematical analogue in which velocity and current are analogous quantities and torque and voltage are also analogous quantities. Specifically, the output angular velocity is proportional to the circuit current, and the shaft torque is proportional to the voltage across the inductance. The circuit current obviously bears no simple relation to the current actually drawn by the motor. The circuit therefore cannot be connected to the output terminals of the physical amplifier with the expectation that it will correctly represent the drain of the motor on the amplifier; in other words, it is an *analogous circuit* but not an *equivalent circuit* in the sense that it maintains the correct physical voltage and current at its terminals. As a mathematical analogue, however, it may form part of a valuable computing device when the amplifier and other associated equipment are represented by corresponding analogues. As discussed in part *c* below, the scale factors or proportionality constants in the velocity-current and torque-voltage relations may be altered in order to increase greatly the convenience of physical reproduction of the circuits.

The *RC* circuit of Fig. 13-32 is likewise a mathematical analogue, but it is also an *equivalent circuit* in that the identity of the physical voltage and current at the motor terminals is maintained. The circuit may therefore be connected to the terminals of the amplifier with the expectation that it will completely represent the effect of the motor on the amplifier performance. Here, velocity and voltage are analogous quantities, and torque and current are also analogous quantities. Specifically, the output angular velocity is proportional to the voltage across the capacitor, and the shaft torque is proportional to the circuit current. As discussed in part c, the scale factors or proportionality constants in the velocity-voltage and torque-current relations may not be altered in the interest of convenient physical reproducibility unless the equivalent-circuit properties are to be abandoned and the circuit regarded as simply an alternative mathematical analogue.

c. Oscillographic observation of transient performance in a circuit like that of Fig. 13-31 usually involves creating a repetitive transient by means of a synchronously operated switch and observing this repetitive transient on the screen of an oscilloscope either visually or photographically. The duration of the transient must therefore be such that it will occupy only part of the switching cycle, and means for varying the time scale accordingly must be available.

For the circuit of Fig. 13-31, the differential equation, 13-110, may be rewritten

$$\frac{1}{a^2}\frac{Jr_a}{k}\frac{d^2\theta_o}{d\lambda^2} + \frac{1}{a}k\frac{d\theta_o}{d\lambda} = v_t \qquad (13\text{-}112)$$

where the new time variable λ is

$$\lambda = \frac{t}{a} \qquad (13\text{-}113)$$

Thus, by changing the inductance by the factor $1/a^2$ and the resistance by the factor $1/a$, the time scale may be changed by the factor $1/a$.

Another change of scale may be required in order that physical circuit elements be easily obtained and the resulting current and voltage magnitudes be easily measurable. Inductance and resistance may be scaled up by the factor b by multiplying both sides of Eq. 13-112 by this factor, giving

$$\frac{b}{a^2}\frac{Jr_a}{k}\frac{d^2\theta_o}{d\lambda^2} + \frac{b}{a}k\frac{d\theta_o}{d\lambda} = bv_t \qquad (13\text{-}114)$$

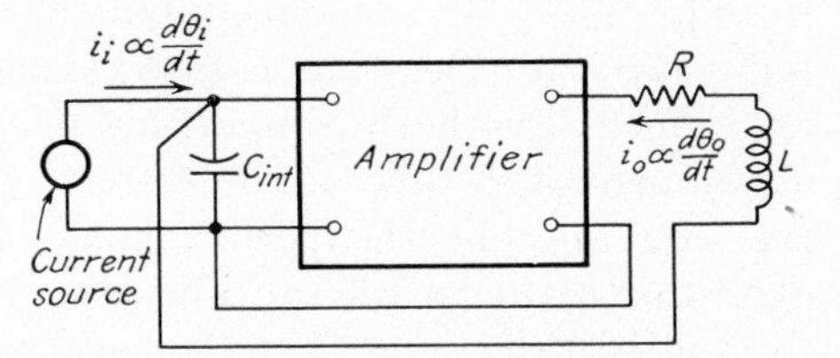

FIG. 13-33. Analogue for circuit of Fig. 13-27.

Alternatively, if it is undesirable for the scale factor b to be associated with the voltage v_t, Eq. 13-114 may be written

$$\frac{b}{a^2}\frac{Jr_a}{k}\frac{d^2(\theta_o/b)}{d\lambda^2} + \frac{b}{a}k\frac{d(\theta_o/b)}{d\lambda} = v_t \qquad (13\text{-}115)$$

As a third possibility, part of the factor b may be associated with θ_o and part with v_t.

The numerical values quoted in Example 13-1 ($k = 0.328$, $r_a = 34$, $J = 5.85 \times 10^{-5}$) may be used in an illustration. The corresponding resistance and inductance in Fig. 13-31 are $R = 0.328$ ohm and $L = 6.06$ mh. Suppose, however, that the estimated duration of the system transient is 1.0 sec and that the switch goes through 10 switching cycles per second. A value of a of 100 might be chosen to adapt the time scale, changing R and L to 3.28 milliohms and 0.606 μh. Choice of a factor b of 10^6 would change R and L to the more convenient values of 3,280 ohms and 0.606 henry.

Neither of these two scale changes can be made in Fig. 13-32 if its equivalent-circuit properties are to be retained; for the numerical values of Example 13-1, R must be 34 ohms, and C must be 544 μf. If these properties are abandoned and the circuit is regarded as simply a mathematical analogue, the degrees of freedom are the same as in Fig. 13-31.

d. An analogue for the entire system, based on the circuit of Fig. 13-31, is shown in Fig. 13-33. The source at the left is a current source rather than the more familiar voltage source. The capacitor C_{int} serves as an integrating medium: the current in it is $i_i - i_o$ and is therefore proportional to $d(\theta_i - \theta_o)/dt$. The voltage across it is proportional to $\theta_i - \theta_o$, the positional error. Its capacitance must be sufficiently large so that it has negligible influence on the currents i_i and i_o in the input and output circuits.[13]

The equivalent circuit of Fig. 13-32 is one of a type which is common to all electromagnetic-energy-conversion devices having linear relationships between torque or force and current and between angular or linear velocity and induced voltage. These circuits may be used for the study of a number of electromagnetic devices, among them being D'Arsonval, ballistic, and vibration galvanometers, bifilar oscillographs, moving-coil loudspeakers, and moving-coil microphones.[14]

13-10. Résumé. Dynamic problems are inherently system problems rather than single-machine problems. Machine loads become more than simply vague devices absorbing specified or computed amounts of power: their dynamic characteristics must be delineated with the same degree of care required for the machine itself. Electric power sources must be similarly delineated in many problems. System components may thus include not only machines but electronic amplifiers and controlled rectifiers, static electrical networks, and combinations of purely mechanical elements, with all components playing equally important roles in the attainment of the over-all objectives. Many of the analyses are based on the premise that the performance of the system components can be expressed by linear relations between the variables. Examples are given to illustrate the type of steps necessary to include significant nonlinearities, however. The linear analyses are the most important ones conceptually for our purposes, and the following discussions pertain only to them unless nonlinearities are explicitly mentioned.

Dynamic analyses of both the simple and the more complicated systems reduce essentially to the study of linear differential equations with constant coefficients. So far as the electric-motor components are concerned, the appropriate equations are written by recognizing that the torque resulting from electromagnetic energy conversion must be equal to that furnished to the mechanical system, rotational losses being neglected or

[13] Discussions of servomechanism analogues of this type and of results obtained from them are given in G. D. McCann, S. W. Herwald, and H. S. Kirschbaum, Electrical Analogy Methods Applied to Servomechanism Problems, *Trans. AIEE*, vol. 65, pp. 91–96, February, 1946; S. W. Herwald and G. D. McCann, Dimensionless Analysis of Servomechanisms by Electrical Analogy, *Trans. AIEE*, vol. 65, pp. 636–639, October, 1946.

[14] Further general considerations of electromechanical equivalence may be found in F. A. Firestone, The Mobility Method of Computing the Vibration of Linear Mechanical and Electrical Systems, *J. Applied Phys.*, vol. 9, pp. 373–387, 1938; M. F. Gardner and J. L. Barnes, "Transients in Linear Systems," John Wiley & Sons, Inc., New York, pp. 50–85, 1942.

included approximately as part of the load friction. Additional equations express the dynamic performance of other system components and the constraints imposed by their interconnection. The relationship for the desired variable as a function of time, obtained by combination of these equations, is a linear differential equation whose order depends on the number of independent energy-storage elements in the system. The desired variable on which principal interest is focused is often one describing the behavior of an output shaft; the specific differential equation is then dependent also on whether it is the angular position, velocity, or acceleration of the shaft that constitutes the dependent variable.

The principal theme running through the chapter, that the study of system dynamics involves reasoning and methods identical with those of electric-circuit analysis, follows from the fact that both problems become the study of the same differential equations. Investigation of the equations of machine dynamics is accordingly based on both the transient-analysis method and the frequency-response method. Transient analyses have the advantage of more direct and tangible interpretation: a time plot showing a succession of violent overshootings and undershootings of a desired position, for example, can leave little doubt of the worth of the system dynamically. Transient analyses have the disadvantages that much laborious computation is required in all but the simpler systems and that it becomes difficult to suggest corrective measures when the transient response is unsatisfactory. Both disadvantages may be lessened appreciably, but not abolished, by expressing the equations and solutions in nondimensional or normalized form.

Physical interpretation of frequency-response analyses is not so immediately obvious and tangible as is that of transient analyses, and experience gained from experimental and theoretical comparisons is of great help. Simple, direct mathematical correlation can be achieved between transient response and frequency response for systems characterized by second-order equations and is illustrated by comparison of Figs. 13-8 and 13-28. For more complex systems, however, the correlation is neither direct nor simple. Basically, it rests on the fact that when the steady-state response of a linear system is known for all frequencies, the transient response for any analytic forcing function can be obtained. For our purposes, interpretation and application of frequency-response techniques for high-order systems must be patterned empirically on the correlation for a second-order system. This pattern is summarized by the quotation in Art. 13-8 arbitrarily placing the limit of about $1\frac{1}{3}$ to $1\frac{1}{2}$ on the peak ratio of output to input, and indicating that the frequency at this peak should be at least three times the inverse of the period allowed for a transient to disappear. Such empirical guides, combined with experience, ultimately enable us to draw conclusions from the frequency-response characteristic of a closed-cycle electromechanical system with the same spirit displayed in interpreting similar characteristics for an electrical coupling network, filter, amplifier, microphone, or loud-speaker.

As a matter of fact, a certain degree of empiricism or need for engineering judgment similarly enters into application of transient analyses, for one or more specific disturbances must be postulated. To a certain extent, the applicability of the analysis depends on the faithfulness with which service conditions are simulated by the assumed disturbances. Moreover, when a variety of disturbances are considered, optimum design for one disturbance may not correspond to that for another, and hence judgment and experience are required in arriving at the over-all optimum.

Determination of the frequency-response characteristics of a system is accomplished in an organized fashion by combining the transfer functions of system components to form the over-all transfer function. These transfer functions are vector ratios of the output quantity to the input quantity expressed as functions of the angular frequency of the sinusoidally varying input quantity. They express the attenuation (or gain) and phase shift which take place across the component. They resemble the transfer constants and parameters used in linear-circuit theory. The similarity which becomes evident in the study of automatic regulators, servomechanisms, and feedback amplifiers is most helpful in the study of all three devices.

The concepts of transfer functions and frequency response applied to such system components as static compensating circuits and electronic amplifiers appear perfectly normal from the very outset and gives rise to little or no confusion in physical interpretation. When applied to such components as d-c motors and generators, however, the concepts, with their implications of a-c input and output quantities, may appear initially confusing. We know, for instance, that a normal, practical d-c motor with constant d-c field excitation cannot be expected to operate successfully with a 60-cps a-c voltage impressed on its armature. But we also know that the speed of such a motor will faithfully follow slow variations, including reversal, of the armature impressed voltage—of the order of a small fraction of a cycle per second, say, to pick a safe extreme. To present a quantitative measure of the ability of the motor to follow variations as their rates of change are increased from very low values is exactly the object of both the transfer functions and the frequency-response characteristics. In accordance with the foregoing statements, we expect the output-input amplitude ratio for the system including this motor to be close to unity at very low frequencies and to be practically zero at 60 cps. Inspection of the transfer function and frequency-response characteristic not only shows the motor to be an inappropriate energy-conversion device if rates of change comparable with those of a 60-cps frequency are important but also enables us to draw an approximate line of frequency demarcation above which the system is unsuitable. When the transfer-function concept is applied, the machine truly becomes a circuit element in the broader sense described in the latter part of Art. 4-13. The idea of alleviating some of the shortcomings of a machine by means of cascaded compensating circuits consisting of static networks becomes a more natural and easily applied one when both the machine, with its electrical and mechanical elements, and the networks are placed in the same category.

As is also anticipated in Art. 4-13, representation of machines as circuit elements in the electromechanical sense is based on relatively bare simplicity of the machinery theory involved. This simplicity is dictated by the fact that many systems consist of complicated arrays of components, necessitating for each component the simplest possible representation consistent with reasonable accuracy. Neglect of such effects as saturation and armature reaction has, of course, a bearing on the accuracy of the results. From the point of view of stability or freedom from hunting, neglect of saturation is usually a conservative approximation, for the system then has a greater sensitivity, and increased sensitivity is often accompanied by increased hunting. In general, the order of magnitude of error introduced by assumptions and approximations may be expected to be about 10 per cent even with careful measurement or computation of the system constants, which in itself is a difficult task. Final adjustments for the precise attainment of specified objectives must be made experimentally after the system is constructed.

Of course, many problems will inevitably arise in which nonlinearities cannot be ignored. Solution by graphical integration illustrates one of the common methods of nonlinear analysis; use of computing machines offers another possibility. These analyses obviously become very complicated for all but simple systems, but many of the problems are of such great economic and engineering importance that these complications must be tolerated, and detailed studies must be made. The electromechanical oscillations which may occur in electric power systems are an example.

In spite of the fact that, by virtue of assumptions and approximations, only relatively simple machine theory is applied in most of the analyses presented, one cannot proceed confidently and authoritatively without the more detailed theoretical background gained from a comprehensive study of machine performance. The more detailed knowledge and experience enable one to evaluate and appraise results, to be sure that no major omissions have been made, and to estimate the limits within which the results are meaningful. Moreover, complete theoretical details are essential to the optimum design of the machine from the dynamic viewpoint. Since not infrequently the machine is the weakest dynamic link in the system, the need for detailed improvements becomes doubly important.

The existence of electromechanical equivalent circuits for system problems characterized by linear differential equations with constant coefficients emphasizes the broad applicability of the techniques of circuit analysis. Our study of electric machinery, having opened with considerations of the aspects common to all energy-conversion devices, accordingly closes on the same general note of broad similarity.

PROBLEMS

13-1. This problem is concerned with the starting of a d-c shunt motor as investigated in Example 13-1.

a. An external starting resistance is to be connected in series with the armature and cut out in steps as the motor comes up to speed. Discuss the effects on (1) the energy dissipated in the armature circuit during the starting period and (2) the time required to reach substantially final speed.

b. Discuss the effect of the installation of a cumulative series field on (1) the energy dissipated in the armature circuit during the starting period and (2) the time required to reach substantially final speed.

13-2. A d-c generator and a d-c motor have their armatures directly connected electrically to form a Ward Leonard system. The generator is driven by a constant-speed prime mover, and the motor field is excited by a constant current. The motor drives a pure-inertia load. Linearized analysis of motor and generator performance is to be used.

The motor is rated at 3 hp and has the following characteristics:

Armature resistance = 0.75 ohm
Wk^2 (including load) = 40 lb-ft^2
Torque per unit armature current = 1.25 newton-m/amp
Armature inductance is negligible

The generator is of a size consistent with supplying the 3-hp motor and has the following characteristics:

Armature resistance = 0.25 ohm
Field resistance = 200 ohms
Field inductance = 10 henrys
Armature generated voltage per unit field current = 1,500 volts/amp
Armature inductance is negligible

Armature reaction and all rotational losses are to be ignored.

At an instant when the generator is unexcited and the motor armature is stationary, a constant voltage of 36.6 volts is impressed on the generator field.

a. Give the numerical equation for motor speed in rpm as a function of time.

b. Sketch the curve of speed as a function of time.

c. Determine the time for the speed to attain 98 per cent of its final value.

13-3. A mill-type d-c motor used for driving auxiliaries in steel mills has the steady-state characteristics given in Table 13-1. The speed curve is based on a terminal voltage of 230 volts. The total hot resistance of the armature, series field, and commutating field is 0.033 ohm. Assume a brush drop of 1 volt per brush at all loads. Full-load current of the motor is 350 amp. The Wk^2 of the motor armature is 335 lb-ft², and the Wk^2 of the magnetic brake used with the motor is 106 lb-ft².

TABLE 13-1

Armature current, amp	Speed, rpm	Torque, lb-ft
100	640	300
200	560	600
300	480	900
400	460	1,300
500	430	1,700
600	410	2,100
700	390	2,500

This motor with brake is to be used for driving a rack which moves a side guard from side to side across a roll table. To prevent stripping the gears when the side guard strikes the guard on the opposite side of the table, the motor operates with a permanent resistance in series with the armature, which limits the current at standstill to twice the full-load current. No accelerating contactors are used. The friction torque of the rack and gearing is 250 lb-ft at the motor. This torque can be assumed constant at all speeds. The equivalent Wk^2 of the rack and gearing at the motor shaft is 200 lb-ft².

a. Plot the speed of the motor against armature current from standstill to friction load speed.

b. Plot motor speed and armature current against time for the motor starting from rest and accelerating to friction-load speed.

c. Plot travel of the rack in inches against time from standstill to friction-load speed, assuming that the rack moves 6 in. per revolution of the motor.

13-4. Figure 13-34 shows a d-c generator and motor in a Ward Leonard connection with the generator excitation furnished by a push-pull Class A amplifier. It is part of a scheme for obtaining automatic speed control of the motor. The motor drives a pure-inertia load. Linearized analysis of motor and generator performance is to be used. Armature reaction and all rotational losses are to be ignored.

The motor is rated at 3 hp and has the following characteristics:

Armature resistance = 0.75 ohm
Wk^2 (including load) = 40 lb-ft²
Torque per unit armature current = 1.25 newton-m/amp
Armature inductance is negligible

The generator is of a size consistent with supplying the 3-hp motor and has the following characteristics:

Armature resistance = 0.25 ohm
Field resistance = 200 ohms (each section)
Field inductance = 10 henrys (each section)
Coefficient of coupling between field sections = 1.0
Generated voltage = 1,500 volts per ampere difference in the split fields
Armature inductance is negligible

The two tubes are identical and have an amplification factor $\mu = 10$ and plate resistance $r_p = 800$ ohms.

At an instant when the generator has zero net excitation and the motor is stationary, a contant voltage $E_i = 15.3$ volts is impressed at the amplifier input.

a. Give the numerical equation for motor speed in rpm as a function of time.

b. Sketch the curve of speed as a function of time.

c. Determine the time required for the speed to attain 98 per cent of its final value.

13-5. A d-c shunt motor is driving a pure-inertia load. The armature and field are supplied from a source of constant direct voltage. The motor is initially operating in the steady state. Neglect all rotational losses and armature reaction. Assume the flux is directly proportional to the field current and that armature inductance is negligible.

The field rheostat is suddenly shorted out. Develop the differential equation for the speed of the motor following this disturbance, using the ordinary symbols for the

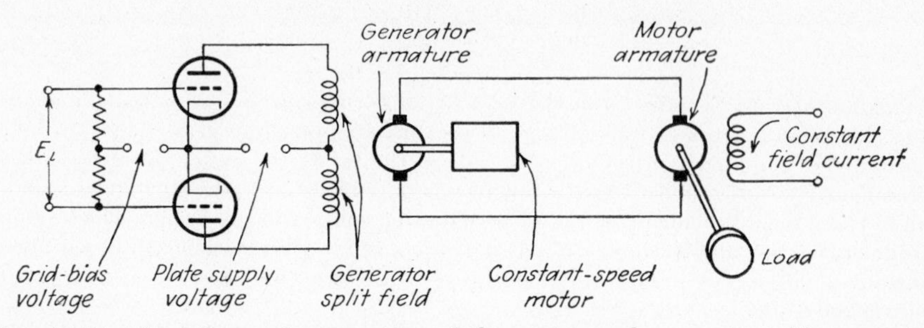

Fig. 13-34. Ward Leonard connection of d-c motor and generator with generator excitation furnished by vacuum-tube amplifier, Prob. 13-4.

various quantities. Indicate all initial conditions. It is not necessary to solve the equation.

13-6. In modern continuous rolling mills the stands, or rolls, through which the bar passes in the rolling process are arranged in tandem, with the majority of the stands driven by separate motors. It is common to use d-c motors supplied with power from one or several generators. The transient changes of the motor speed under suddenly applied loads as the bar enters one stand after another may seriously affect the quality of the product. In particular, the *impact speed drop* which occurs at the maximum of the transient oscillation is of major importance.

Consider a single motor M supplied by a generator G, each with separate and constant field excitation. The internal voltage E of the generator may be considered constant, and the armature reaction of both machines may be considered negligible. With the motor running without external load and the system in the steady state, a bar enters the stand at $t = 0$, causing the load torque to be increased suddenly from zero to T. The following numerical values apply:

Internal voltage of G	$E = 387$ volts
Motor plus generator armature inductance	$L = 0.00768$ henry
Motor plus generator armature resistance	$R = 0.0353$ ohm
Moment of inertia of motor armature and connected rolls, all referred to motor speed	$J = 42.2$ kg-m^2
Electromechanical conversion constant for motor	$k = 4.23$ newton-m/amp
No-load armature current	$i_o = 35$ amp
Suddenly applied torque	$T = 2{,}040$ newton-m

Determine the following quantities:

a. The undamped angular frequency of the transient speed oscillations

b. The damping ratio of the system

c. The time constant of the system, in seconds

d. The initial speed, in rpm

e. The initial acceleration, in rpm per second

f. The ultimate speed drop, in rpm

g. The impact speed drop, in rpm

13-7. A polyphase induction motor has negligible rotor rotational losses and is driving a pure-inertia load. The moment of inertia of the rotor plus load is J mks units.

a. Obtain an expression for the rotor energy loss during starting. Express the result in terms of J and the synchronous angular velocity ω_s.

b. Obtain an expression for the rotor energy loss associated with reversal from full speed forward by reversing the phase sequence of the voltage supply (a process known as *plugging*). Express the result in terms of J and ω_s.

c. State and discuss the degree of dependence of the results in *a* and *b* on the current-limiting scheme which may be used during starting and reversal.

d. A 5-hp 3-phase 4-pole 60-cps squirrel-cage induction motor has a full-load efficiency of 85.0 per cent. The total Wk^2 of rotor plus load is 1.5 lb-ft^2. The total motor losses for a reversal may be assumed to be 2.25 times the rotor losses. The impairment of ventilation arising from the lower average speed during reversing is to be ignored.

Using the result in *b*, compute the number of times per minute that the motor can be reversed without its allowable temperature rise being exceeded.

e. Discuss the optimism or pessimism of the result in *d*.

13-8. Following are points on the torque-speed curve of a 3-phase squirrel-cage induction motor with balanced rated voltage impressed:

Torque, per unit	0	1.00	2.00	3.00	3.50	3.25	3.00
Speed, per unit	1.00	0.97	0.93	0.80	0.47	0.20	0

Unit speed is synchronous speed; unit torque is rated torque. The motor is coupled to a machine tool which requires rated torque regardless of speed. The inertia of the motor plus load is such that it requires 1.2 sec to bring them to rated speed with a constant *accelerating* torque equal to rated torque.

With the motor driving the load under normal steady conditions, the voltage at its terminals suddenly drops to 50 per cent of rated value because of a short circuit in the neighborhood. It remains at this reduced value for 0.6 sec and is then restored to its full value by clearing of the short circuit. The undervoltage release on the motor does not operate. Will the motor stop? If not, what is its lowest speed? Neglect any effects of secondary importance.

13-9. A 230-volt 3-phase Y-connected 6-pole 60-cps wound-rotor induction motor has a stator-plus-rotor leakage reactance of 0.50 ohm per phase referred to the stator, a rotor-plus-load moment of inertia of 1.0 kg-m^2, negligible losses (except for rotor copper loss), and negligible exciting current. It is connected to a balanced 230-volt source and drives a pure-inertia load. Across-the-line starting is used, and the rotor-circuit resistance is to be adjusted so that the motor brings its load from rest to one-half synchronous speed in the shortest possible time.

Determine the value of the rotor resistance referred to the stator and the minimum time to reach one-half of synchronous speed.

13-10. The quotation below is taken from ASA Standards C50-1943, Rotating Electrical Machinery, published by the American Standards Association, New York, 1943. It gives an expression for the natural frequency of a synchronous motor connected directly to an infinite bus.

Prove that the expression is correct.

"The expression for undamped natural frequency of oscillation of an infinite system is as follows.

$$f_n = \frac{35{,}200}{n}\sqrt{\frac{P_r \times f}{Wk^2}}$$

where f_n = natural frequency in cycles per minute
n = revolutions per minute
P_r = synchronizing power defined in (*d*)
f = frequency of circuit in cycles per second
W = weight of all revolving parts in pounds
k = radius of gyration in feet"

"(*d*) The synchronizing coefficient P_r is determined by dividing the shaft power by the corresponding angular displacement of the rotor. It is expressed in kw per electrical radian. Unless otherwise stated, the values given will be for rated voltage, load, power factor, and frequency."

13-11. The ideal conditions for synchronizing an alternator with an electric power system are that the alternator voltage be the same as that of the system bus in magnitude, phase, and frequency. Departure from these conditions results in undesirable current and power surges accompanying electromechanical oscillation of the alternator rotor. As long as the oscillations are not too violent, they may be investigated by a linearized analysis.

Consider that a 2,500-kw 0.80-power-factor 25-cps 26-pole oil-engine-driven alternator is to be synchronized with a 25-cps system large enough to be considered an infinite bus. The Wk^2 of the alternator, engine, and associated flywheel is 750,000 lb-ft². The damping-power coefficient P_d is 3,600 watts per electrical degree per second, and the synchronizing-power coefficient P_s is 1.21×10^5 watts per electrical degree. Both P_d and P_s may be assumed to remain constant. In all cases below, the terminal voltage is adjusted to its correct magnitude. The engine governor is sufficiently insensitive so that it does not act during the synchronizing period.

a. Consider that the alternator is initially adjusted to the correct speed but that it is synchronized out of phase by 20 electrical degrees, with the alternator leading the bus. Obtain a numerical expression for the ensuing electromechanical oscillations. Also give the largest value of torque exerted on the rotor during the synchronizing period. Ignore losses, and express this torque as a percentage of that corresponding to the nameplate rating.

b. Repeat *a* with the alternator synchronized at the proper angle but with its speed initially adjusted 1.0 cps fast.

c. Repeat *a* with the alternator initially leading the bus by 20 electrical degrees and its speed initially adjusted 1.0 cps fast.

13-12. *a.* A polyphase synchronous motor is initially operating at no load. A mechanical load requiring rated torque is suddenly applied to the shaft. Sketch the curve of instantaneous speed as a function of time immediately after load application.

b. Repeat *a* with the synchronous motor replaced by a polyphase induction motor.

c. If your two curves in *a* and *b* are different in any respect, give basic reasons for these differences.

13-13. A synchronous motor whose input under rated operating conditions is 10,000 kva is connected to an infinite bus over a short feeder whose impedance is purely reactive. The motor is rated at 60 cps, 600 rpm, and has a total Wk^2 of 500,000 lb-ft² (including the shaft load). The power-angle curve under transient conditions is 2.00 sin δ, where the amplitude is in per unit on a 10,000-kva base.

a. With the motor operating initially unloaded, a 10,000-kw shaft load is suddenly applied. Does the motor remain in synchronism?

b. How large a shaft load may be suddenly applied without loss of synchronism?

c. Consider now that the suddenly applied load is on for only 0.2 sec, after which a comparatively long time elapses before any load is again applied. Determine the maximum value of such a load which will still allow synchronism to be maintained. Use the equal-area criterion as an aid in the process. For purposes of computing the angle δ at 0.2 sec, ignore damping, and use a linearized analysis in which the power-angle curve is approximated by a straight line through the origin and the 60° point.

d. As an alternate to the approximate, linearized analysis for determining values of δ at 0.2 sec in part *c*, refer to I. H. Summers and J. B. McClure, Progress in the Study

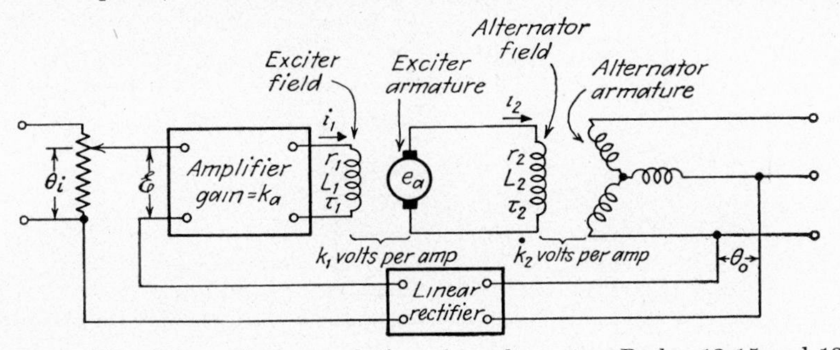

Fig. 13-35. Circuit for voltage regulation of an alternator, Probs. 13-15 and 13-25.

of System Stability, *Trans. AIEE*, vol. 49, p. 132, 1930. Use the precalculated swing curves presented in this paper. Compare the result with that in part *c*.

13-14. This problem relates to the simplified closed-cycle control system of Fig. 13-27, described in Art. 13-7.

a. The transient response of the system to a sudden angular displacement θ_i at the input is known to be of the form

$$\theta_o = \theta_i(1 + A\epsilon^{-60t} - B\epsilon^{-10t})$$

where A and B are numerical constants.

Find the damping ratio ζ, undamped natural angular velocity ω_n, undamped natural frequency f_n, and the time constant τ of the motor and its inertia load.

b. Consider that the damping ratio of the system is to be reduced to $\zeta = 0.5$ by changing only the amplifier gain k_a. Write the numerical equation describing the transient response of the modified system to a sudden angular displacement θ_i at its input.

c. By using the curves of Fig. 13-8, find the times t in seconds required for the systems of *a* and *b* to reach 95 per cent of their new angular position following a sudden displacement of their input.

d. Consider that the systems must also follow a constant-velocity input $\omega_i = 20$ degrees/sec. Determine the corresponding steady-state angle errors under conditions of *a* and *b*.

13-15. A proposed scheme for regulating the output voltage of a 500-kva alternator is shown diagrammatically in Fig. 13-35. In addition to the alternator, the system includes a d-c exciter whose field excitation is obtained from the output of a vacuum-tube amplifier. The input to the amplifier is the difference between the set value of voltage θ_i and the actual output voltage θ_o. The resistance and inductance of the exciter-field circuit (including the output impedance of the amplifier) are r_1 and L_1. The generated voltage of the exciter is k_1 volts/amp in its field. The resistance and inductance of the alternator-field circuit (including the exciter armature) are r_2 and L_2. The alternator voltage is k_2 volts/amp in its field. For simplicity, the linear rectifier required to change the alternating voltage θ_o to a direct voltage for comparison with θ_o may be assumed to produce 1.0 volt d-c output per volt a-c input. (Alternatively, θ_o may be considered the output voltage of the rectifier, and any transfer constant associated with the rectifier may be considered as part of the constant k_2.)

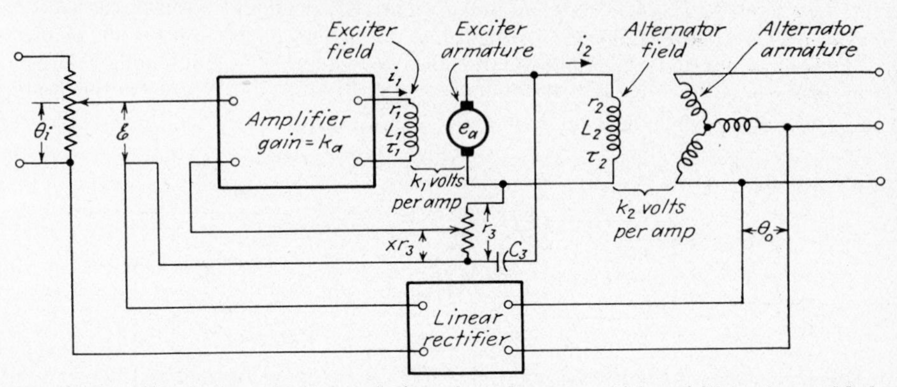

FIG. 13-36. Circuit for voltage regulation of an alternator with stabilizing loop added, Probs. 13-16 and 13-26.

To examine the stability of the system, consider that the alternator and exciter are rotating at rated speed, but that initially their fields are unexcited, and $\theta_i = 0$.

a. Show that the response of the system to a suddenly impressed value of θ_i is characterized by the differential equation

$$\tau_1\tau_2 \frac{d^2\theta_o}{dt^2} + (\tau_1 + \tau_2) \frac{d\theta_o}{dt} + (1 + K)\theta_o = K\theta_i$$

Identify the time constants τ_1 and τ_2 and the static sensitivity K in terms of the system constants.

b. For a particular alternator and its excitation system, $\tau_1 = 0.4$ sec, and $\tau_2 = 1.0$ sec. The system is to regulate within 0.5 per cent; *i.e.*, the steady-state error in θ_o is not to exceed 0.5 per cent of the set value θ_i. Determine the damping constant ζ, the undamped natural angular frequency ω_n, and sketch the curve of the response θ_o/θ_i as a function of time.

c. Indicate whether or not the performance of the system is satisfactory.

This same study is made by frequency-response techniques in Prob. 13-25; improvement in the stability of this system is the subject of Probs. 13-16 and 13-26.

13-16. Because insufficient damping is found to be present in the voltage-regulating system of Fig. 13-35, Prob. 13-15, an additional feedback loop is to be introduced to improve system performance. As shown in Fig. 13-36, a circuit r_3-C_3 is connected across the exciter output, and the fraction x of the voltage across r_3 is fed back in series with the error $\mathcal{E}$ to the input of the amplifier. For purposes of analysis, the voltage across r_3-C_3 is to be taken as e_a, so that the resistance and inductance of the exciter armature are neglected in this respect. Otherwise the system is as described in Prob. 13-15.

a. Explain physically why this addition may be expected to improve the dynamic performance of the system. Is the steady-state performance affected?

b. To analyze the dynamic response of the system to a suddenly impressed value of θ_i under initial-rest conditions (the exciter and alternator are, of course, rotating at rated speed), write the differential equations of the system in operator form with the differential operator d/dt replaced by p and the integral operator $\int dt$ replaced by $1/p$. Then by treating the resulting equations as though they were algebraic equations, show that the response to a suddenly impressed value of θ_i is characterized by the equation

$$\theta_o = \frac{K\theta_i}{(1 + \tau_1 p)(1 + \tau_2 p) + \dfrac{(1 + \tau_2 p)p}{1 + \tau_3 p} K \dfrac{r_2}{k_2} x\tau_3 + K}$$

Identify the time constants τ_1, τ_2, and τ_3 and the static sensitivity K in terms of the system constants.

c. For the special case of $\tau_3 = \tau_2$ and with initial rest conditions, it is permissible to cancel $1 + \tau_2 p$ and $1 + \tau_3 p$ in the middle term of the denominator of the equation in (*b*). Equality of τ_3 and τ_2 does not imply optimum operating conditions; it merely permits evaluation of the effect of the added loop without analyzing anything more than a simple second-order equation. Show that this equation becomes

$$\tau_1\tau_2 \frac{d^2\theta_o}{dt^2} + \left(\tau_1 + \tau_2 + K \frac{r_2}{k_2} \tau_2 x\right) \frac{d\theta_o}{dt} + (1 + K)\theta_o = K\theta_i$$

Compare this equation with that given in part *a* of Prob. 13-15.

d. As in Prob. 13-15, take $\tau_1 = 0.4$ sec and $\tau_2 = \tau_3 = 1.0$ sec, and consider that the system is to regulate within 0.5 per cent. In addition consider that $k_2/r_2 = 20$ and $x = 0.75$. Determine the damping constant ζ, the undamped natural angular frequency ω_n, and sketch the curve of the response θ_o/θ_i as a function of time. Compare the results with those of part *b* of Prob. 13-15.

This same study is made by frequency-response techniques in Prob. 13-26.

13-17. In the d-c generator-motor system described in Prob. 13-2, the field of the generator is to be excited by a sinusoidal voltage having a 75-volt amplitude and a 1.0-cps frequency. Compute the maximum value in rpm of the sinusoidally varying motor speed.

13-18. In the system of Fig. 13-34, Prob. 13-4, a sinusoidal voltage having a 10-volt amplitude and a 1.0-cps frequency is to be impressed at the amplifier input. Compute the maximum value in rpm of the sinusoidally varying motor speed.

13-19. A d-c motor is driving a pure-inertia load and has its armature supplied from a constant-voltage d-c source. Rotational losses, armature reaction, and armature inductance are negligible. The air-gap flux is directly proportional to the field current.

Develop the expression for the vector amplitude of the sinusoidal speed variation when the field voltage is varied sinusoidally. Use the ordinary symbols for the quantities involved.

13-20. For the servomechanism shown in block-diagram form in Fig. 13-30, consider that the transfer function is of the simple form

$$KG(j\omega) = \frac{K}{j\omega(1 + j\omega\tau)}$$

The undamped natural frequency is 10 cps, and the damping ratio is 0.70.

a. Write the transfer function in numerical form with only ω appearing as a literal symbol.

b. Determine the steady-state angle error accompanying a constant velocity input of 20°/sec.

13-21. A 3-hp d-c motor to be used in the simplified closed-cycle system of Fig. 13-27 has the following constants:

Wk^2 (including load) $= 40$ lb-ft²
$r_a = 0.75$ ohm
$k = 1.25$ newton-m/amp

It is desired that the system follow a constant input angular velocity ω_i of 120 rpm with a steady-state angle error of no more than one-quarter of a revolution.

a. Find the damping factor ζ and undamped angular frequency ω_n corresponding to these conditions. Using the curves of Fig. 13-8 as a guide, indicate whether or not

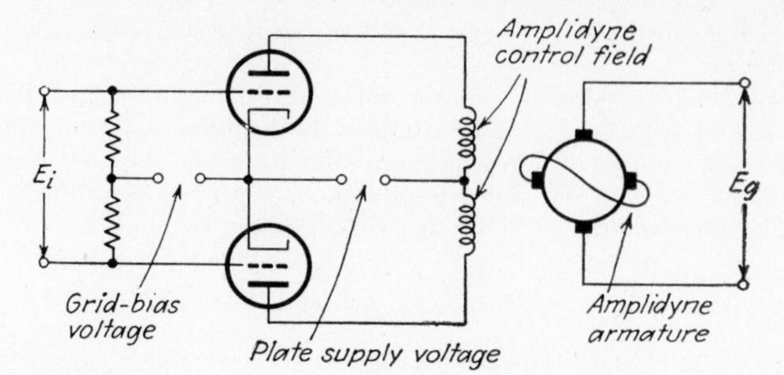

FIG. 13-37. Amplidyne generator with excitation furnished by vacuum-tube amplifier, Prob. 13-22.

you feel that the transient response of the system is satisfactory without the addition of any stabilizing circuits.

b. The response of the system to a sinusoidal variation of the input θ_i is now to be considered. Specifically, the steady-state amplitude-response ratio Θ_o/Θ_i is not to exceed $1\frac{1}{3}$ at its peak. Values of r_a, k, and the allowable steady-state angle error for constant input angular velocity remain as in *a*. Find the largest allowable value of the Wk^2 of the motor plus its load.

c. Using the curves of Fig. 13-8, estimate the time required for the system of *b* to settle down to within 5 per cent of the final angle after a sudden angular displacement at the input.

13-22. Figure 13-37 shows a portion of an automatic control system consisting of a push-pull Class A amplifier supplying the control field of an Amplidyne. The tubes are identical and have the amplification factor μ and plate resistance r_p. Each section of the split control field has the resistance r_f and self-inductance L_f. The coefficient of coupling between the two sections may be taken as unity.

For simplicity, the Amplidyne is to be treated on the following basis: The internal generated voltage in the quadrature, or short-circuited, armature axis is k_f volts per ampere difference in the split control fields. The quadrature-axis armature resistance and inductance are r_q and L_q. The generated voltage E_g in the direct-axis armature circuit is k_q volts/amp in the short-circuited brushes. The direct-axis armature resistance and inductance are not to be included here because they would logically be combined with the constants of the Amplidyne output circuit. The Amplidyne compensating field (not shown) causes the mutual effect of the direct-axis armature circuit on the control field to be negligible. For present purposes, the effects of any other Amplidyne auxiliaries are to be ignored.

Show that the transfer function $KG(j\omega) = E_g/E_i$ may be expressed in the form

$$\frac{K}{(1 + j\omega\tau_f)(1 + j\omega\tau_q)}$$

where K is the static sensitivity and τ_f and τ_q are time constants of the amplifier plus control field and of the quadrature-axis armature circuit, respectively. Identify K, τ_f, and τ_q in terms of the amplifier and Amplidyne constants.

13-23. A closed-cycle system of the general form of Fig. 13-23 but without the compensating network consists of a d-c motor and generator in a Ward Leonard connection with the angular position of the motor shaft fed back to the input through a Selsyn data-transmission system. The resulting error voltage is supplied to a phase-sensitive demodulator and power amplifier to excite the generator field.

The motor and load are those of Example 13-1 ($J = 5.85 \times 10^{-5}$ mks unit, $k = 0.328$, armature resistance $= 34$ ohms). The generator has an armature resistance of 26 ohms, field resistance of 1,150 ohms, field inductance of 16 henrys and generates an emf of 1.5 volts per milliampere of field current. The output circuit of the power amplifier may be represented by an internal voltage E in series with a pure resistance of 1,700 ohms. The constants of the error detector, demodulator, and amplifier are such that this internal voltage is k_1 volts per radian of error with no associated phase shift. Rotational losses, armature reaction, and armature inductance in the motor and generator are to be ignored.

a. Determine the transfer function $KG(j\omega)$.

b. Determine the vector ratio Θ_o/Θ_i of output to input.

c. For $k_1 = 20$, plot the amplitude response Θ_o/Θ_i as a function of frequency.

13-24. Consider that, in the system of Prob. 13-23, the constant k_1 is increased by advancing the amplifier gain control. For what value of k_1 will the system oscillate? What is the corresponding frequency?

13-25. The scheme shown in Fig. 13-35 and described in Prob. 13-15 for regulating the output voltage of an alternator is to be analyzed by frequency-response techniques.

a. Obtain a literal expression for the system transfer function $KG(j\omega)$ in terms of the system constants defined in Prob. 13-15.

b. Using the numerical values given in part *b* of Prob. 13-15, obtain a numerical expression for the vector ratio Θ_o/Θ_i of output to input as a function of frequency. Sketch the curve of the amplitude of this ratio as a function of frequency, and evaluate the maximum amplitude.

c. Compare the conclusions reached from this study with those indicated by the transient study of Prob. 13-15.

Improvement in the frequency response of this system is the subject of Prob. 13-26.

13-26. Because the frequency response of the voltage-regulating system of Prob. 13-25, Fig. 13-35, is found to be unsatisfactory, an additional feedback loop is to be introduced to improve system performance. The revised system is shown in Fig. 13-36 and described in Prob. 13-16.

a. Obtain a literal expression for the system transfer function $KG(j\omega)$ in terms of the system constants defined in Probs. 13-15 and 13-16.

b. Reduce the expression in *a* to its appropriate form for the special case of $\tau_3 = \tau_2$.

c. Using the numerical values given in part *d* of Prob. 13-16, obtain a numerical expression for the vector ratio Θ_o/Θ_i of output to input as a function of frequency. Sketch the curve of the amplitude of this ratio as a function of frequency, and evaluate the maximum amplitude.

d. Compare the conclusions reached from this study with those indicated by the transient study of Prob. 13-16.

APPENDIX A

BASIC THEORY OF TRANSFORMERS

The transformer is one of the principal reasons for the widespread use of a-c power systems, for it makes possible electric generation at the most economical generator voltage, power transfer at the most economical transmission voltage, and power utilization at the most economical and efficacious voltage for the particular utilization device. The transformer is also widely used in low-power low-current electronic and control circuits for performing such functions as matching the impedances of a source and its load for maximum power transfer, insulating one circuit from another, or isolating direct current while maintaining a-c continuity between two circuits.

Moreover, the transformer is one of the simpler devices comprising two or more electric circuits coupled by a common magnetic circuit, and its analysis involves many of the principles, stratagems, and artifices essential to the study of more complicated electrical machines. The concepts of transformer behavior thus have the added feature of serving as a prelude to the study of a-c rotating machines. The purpose of the following treatment is to present the basic theory with particular emphasis on its similarities to a-c machine theory.

A-1. Transformer Construction. Essentially, a transformer consists of two or more windings interlinked by a mutual magnetic field. If one of these windings, the *primary*, is connected to an alternating-voltage source, an alternating flux will be produced whose amplitude will depend on the primary voltage and number of turns. The mutual flux will link the other winding, the *secondary*, and will induce a voltage in it whose value will depend on the number of secondary turns. By properly proportioning the numbers of primary and secondary turns, almost any desired voltage ratio or *ratio of transformation* can be obtained.

Transformer action evidently demands only the existence of alternating mutual flux linking the two windings and is simply utilization of the mutual-inductance concept. Such action will be obtained if an air core is used, but it will be obtained much more effectively with a core of iron or other ferromagnetic material, because most of the flux is then confined to a definite path linking both windings and having a much higher permeability than that of air. Such a transformer is commonly called an *iron-*

core transformer. The majority of transformers are of this type, the outstanding exception being air-core transformers for use at high frequencies beyond the audio range. The following discussion will be concerned almost wholly with iron-core transformers.

In order to reduce the losses caused by eddy currents in the core, the magnetic circuit usually consists of a stack of thin laminations, two common types of construction being shown in Fig. A-1. In the *core type* (Fig. A-1*a*) the windings are wound around two legs of a rectangular magnetic core, while in the *shell type* (Fig. A-1*b*) the windings are wound around the center leg of a three-legged core. Silicon-steel laminations 0.014 in. thick are generally used for transformers operating at frequencies

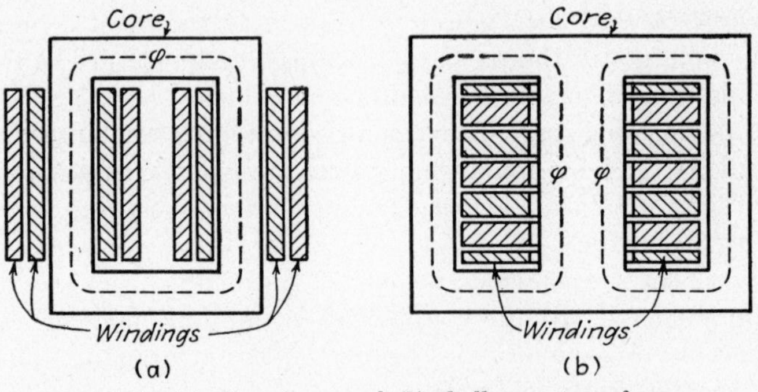

Fig. A-1. (*a*) Core-type and (*b*) shell-type transformer.

below a few hundred cycles per second. Silicon steel has the desirable properties of low cost, low core loss, and high permeability at high flux densities (65 to 90 kilolines/in.^{2}). The cores of small transformers used in communication circuits at high frequencies and low energy levels are sometimes made of compressed powdered ferromagnetic alloys such as permalloy.

Most of the flux is confined to the core and therefore links both windings. Although leakage flux which links one winding without linking the other is a small fraction of the total flux, it has an important effect on the behavior of the transformer. Leakage is reduced by subdividing the windings into sections placed as close together as possible. In the core-type construction, each winding consists of two sections, one section on each of the two legs of the core, the primary and secondary windings being concentric coils. In the shell-type construction, variations of the concentric-winding arrangement may be used, or the windings may consist of a number of thin "pancake" coils assembled in a stack with primary and secondary coils interleaved.

Figure A-2 illustrates the internal construction of a *distribution transformer* such as is used in public-utility systems to provide the appropriate utilization voltage at the consumer's premises. The external appearance of this transformer is shown in Fig. A-3. The particular transformer in Fig. A-2 has a core made of two continuous ribbons of cold-rolled silicon steel, wound around the preformed coils by an ingenious manufacturing

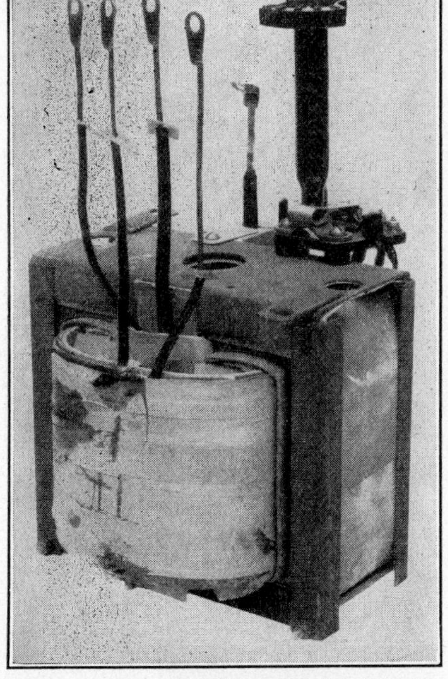

FIG. A-2. Assembled core and coils of a 5-kva distribution transformer for use on a 7,200-volt rural line. The transformer has two 120-volt secondaries which may be connected either in parallel, or in series (with a grounded conductor connected to the mid-point) for 120/240-volt three-wire supply to residential and small-power loads. (*Courtesy of General Electric Company.*)

FIG. A-3. External appearance of the rural-line transformer of Fig. A-2. Only one high-voltage insulator is needed, because one side of the 7,200-volt primary line and one end of the primary winding are grounded. (*Courtesy of General Electric Company.*)

process, drawn tight, and spot-welded. This method of construction minimizes air gaps and takes advantage of the superior magnetic properties of cold-rolled steels when the flux is in the direction of rolling of the steel.

Figure A-4 shows the external appearance of a large *power transformer* of the type found at the sending or receiving end of a long high-voltage power-transmission line.

Transformers like those of Figs. A-2 to A-4 commonly have their wind-

FIG. A-4. External appearance of a large three-phase oil-immersed power transformer showing 115-kv bushings. On both sides of the main tank are radiators through which the oil circulates. The fans mounted on the radiators aid in cooling. The rating is 50,000 kva self-cooled by natural convection and 66,667 kva forced-air cooled with fans running. (*Courtesy of Westinghouse Electric Corporation.*)

FIG. A-5. Pulse transformer removed from its case. This transformer has voltage ratings of 22:5.5 kv and a peak power rating of 600 kw. It is capable of handling a minimum pulse width of 0.25 μsec at 4,000 pulses per second, or a maximum pulse width of 2.5 μsec at 400 pulses per second. (*Courtesy of General Electric Company.*)

ings and cores *oil-immersed* for cooling and insulation. The entire unit may be *self-cooled, water-cooled,* or *forced-air-cooled,* depending on the means used to cool the oil. In small transformers, such as Fig. A-3, the tank has sufficient surface area to cool the oil by radiation and natural convection. The difficulty of cooling electrical apparatus in general increases with size, because the losses increase roughly as the cube of the dimensions, while the surface area increases only as the square of the dimensions. Elaborate means must therefore be provided for cooling large apparatus, as illustrated in Fig. A-4. In transformers for indoor use when fire hazard is to be minimized, oil may be replaced by a non-inflammable liquid insulation (known by various trade names such as *Pyranol* or *Inerteen*), or the transformer may be *air-immersed.*

A *pulse transformer* of the type used in radar circuits and for similar applications is shown in Fig. A-5. In a typical radar application, a pulse transformer changes the voltage of a series of pulses of about 1 μsec duration at a repetition rate of about 1,000 pulses per second. Its construction is similar to that of a power transformer. The main difference is that thinner core laminations and fewer turns of wire are used.

A-2. No-load Conditions. Consider the behavior of the transformer shown in Fig. A-6 with its secondary circuit open and an alternating voltage v_1 applied to its primary terminals. A small steady-state current i_φ, called the *exciting current,* exists in the primary and establishes an alternating flux in the magnetic circuit. This flux induces an emf in the primary equal to

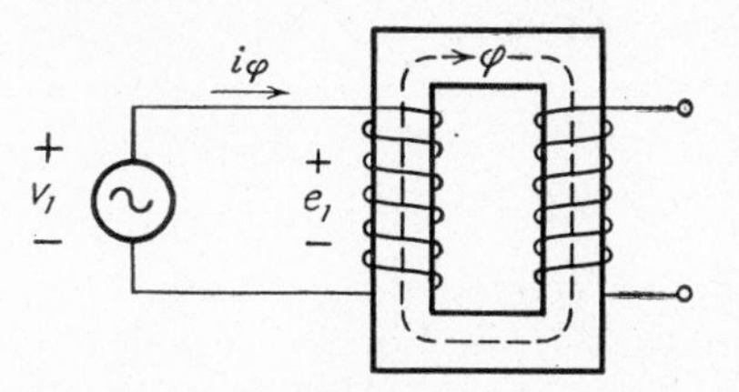

FIG. A-6. Transformer with open secondary.

$$e_1 = \frac{d\lambda_1}{dt} = N_1 \frac{d\varphi}{dt} \tag{A-1}$$

where λ_1 is the flux linkage with the primary, φ the flux (here assumed all confined to the core), and N_1 the number of turns in the primary winding. The voltage e_1 is in volts when φ is in webers. Lenz' law shows it to be a counter emf having the polarity relative to v_1 shown by the + and − signs in Fig. A-6. This counter emf together with the drop in the primary resistance r_1 must balance the applied voltage v_1; thus

$$v_1 = r_1 i_\varphi + e_1 \tag{A-2}$$

In most power apparatus the no-load resistance drop is very small indeed, and the induced emf e_1 very nearly equals the applied voltage v_1. Furthermore the waveforms of voltage and flux are very nearly sinusoidal. The analysis can then be greatly simplified. Thus if the instantaneous flux is

$$\varphi = \phi_{max} \sin \omega t \tag{A-3}$$

the induced voltage is

$$e_1 = N_1 \frac{d\varphi}{dt} = \omega N_1 \phi_{\max} \cos \omega t \tag{A-4}$$

where $\phi_{\max}$ is the maximum value of the flux and $\omega = 2\pi f$, the frequency being f cps. For the positive directions shown in Fig. A-6, the induced emf leads the flux by 90°. The rms value of the induced emf is

$$E_1 = \frac{2\pi}{\sqrt{2}} f N_1 \phi_{\max} = 4.44 f N_1 \phi_{\max} \tag{A-5}$$

If the resistance drop is negligible, the counter emf equals the applied voltage. Under these conditions, if a sinusoidal voltage is applied to a winding, a sinusoidally varying core flux must be established whose maxi-

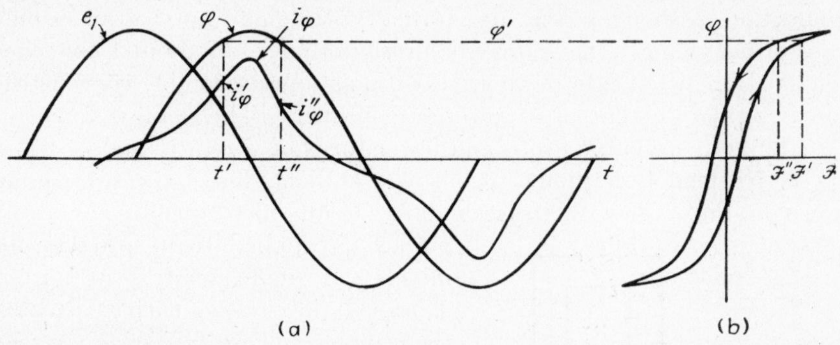

FIG. A-7. Excitation phenomena. (*a*) Voltage, flux, and exciting-current waveforms, and (*b*) corresponding flux-mmf loop.

mum value $\phi_{\max}$ satisfies the requirement that E_1 in Eq. A-5 equals the rms value V_1 of the applied voltage; thus

$$\phi_{\max} = \frac{V_1}{4.44 f N_1} \tag{A-6}$$

The flux is determined solely by the applied voltage, its frequency, and the number of turns in the winding. This important relation applies not only to transformers but also to any device operated with sinusoidal alternating impressed voltage, so long as the resistance drop is negligible. The magnetic properties of the core determine the exciting current. It must adjust itself so as to produce the mmf required to create the flux demanded by Eq. A-6.

Because of the nonlinear magnetic properties of iron, the waveform of the exciting current differs from the waveform of the flux. A curve of the exciting current as a function of time can be found graphically from the magnetic characteristics of the core material in the manner illustrated in Fig. A-7. Sine waves of voltage e_1 and flux φ in accordance with Eqs. A-3 to A-6 are shown in Fig. A-7*a*. The corresponding flux-mmf loop for the core is shown in Fig. A-7*b*. Values of the mmf corresponding to various values of the flux can be found from this hysteresis loop. For example, at time t' the instantaneous flux is φ' and the flux is increasing; the corresponding value of the mmf is $\mathfrak{F}'$ read from the increasing-flux portion of the hysteresis loop. The corresponding value i'_φ of the exciting current is plotted at time t' in Fig. A-7*a*. At time t'' the flux also has the instantaneous value φ', but it is decreasing, and the corresponding values of mmf and current are $\mathfrak{F}''$ and i''_φ. In this manner the complete curve of exciting current i_φ can be plotted, as shown in Fig. A-7*a*.

If the exciting current is analyzed by Fourier-series methods, it will be found to comprise a fundamental and a family of odd harmonics. The fundamental can, in turn, be resolved into two components, one in phase with the counter emf and the other lagging the counter emf by 90°. The fundamental inphase component accounts for the power absorbed by hysteresis and eddy-current losses in the core. It is called the *core-loss component* of the exciting current. When the core-loss component is subtracted from the total exciting current, the remainder is called the *magnetizing current*. It comprises a fundamental component lagging the counter emf by 90°, together with all the harmonics. The principal harmonic is the third. For typical power transformers, the third harmonic usually is about 40 per cent of the exciting current.

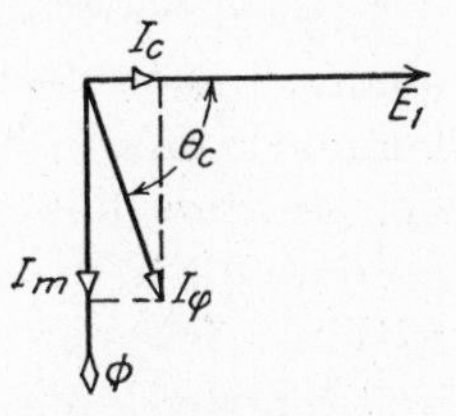

FIG. A-8. No-load vector diagram.

Except in problems concerned directly with the effects of harmonics, the peculiarities of the exciting-current waveform usually need not be taken into account, because the exciting current itself is small. For example, the exciting current of a typical power transformer is about 5 per cent of full-load current. Consequently the effects of the harmonics usually are swamped out by the sinusoidal-current requirements of other linear elements in the circuit. The exciting current may then be represented by its *equivalent sine wave*, which has the same effective value and frequency, and produces the same average power as the actual wave. Such representation is essential to the construction of a vector diagram. In Fig. A-8, the vectors E_1 and ϕ, respectively, represent the induced emf and the flux. The vector I_φ represents the equivalent sinusoidal exciting current. It lags the induced emf E_1 by a phase angle θ_c such that

$$P_c = E_1 I_\varphi \cos \theta_c \tag{A-7}$$

where P_c is the core loss. The component I_c in phase with E_1 represents the core-loss current. The component I_m in phase with the flux represents an equivalent sine wave having the same rms value as the magnetizing current.

Note that the magnetizing current contributes nothing to the active power, because its fundamental component is in quadrature with the induced voltage. The volt-ampere input corresponding to the magnetizing current is entirely reactive. Any electromagnetic device which draws all or part of the excitation for its magnetic circuit from an a-c system therefore may be expected to operate at a lagging power factor, and this is the reason why the majority of industrial loads operate lagging. The lagging reactive power drawn from the system serves the purpose of establishing the working flux, while the active power supplies the losses and takes care of the work performed.

Typical core-loss and exciting volt-ampere characteristics of a high-quality silicon steel used primarily for power and distribution transformer laminations are shown in Fig. A-9. The volt-ampere curve shows the volt-ampere input per pound of core corresponding to the rms exciting current for a sine-wave flux at 60 cps. As an approximation accurate within a few per cent over most of the range in Fig. A-9, the exciting volt-ampere input at constant flux density can be assumed proportional to the frequency for a range from 25 to 60 cps.

The core-loss curves are given for the common range of power frequencies. Core loss comprises hysteresis and eddy-current losses. The hysteresis loss is proportional to the area enclosed by a hysteresis loop and the number of loops traced out per second. The hysteresis loss per pound of core may be approximated empirically by the expression

$$p_h = k_h f B_{\max}^n \tag{A-8}$$

k_h being a characteristic constant of the material and $B_{\max}$ the maximum flux density, while n, called the *Steinmetz exponent,* may vary from about 1.5 to over 2.0 and is often taken as 1.6. At power-system frequencies, the eddy-current loss per pound is given approximately by

$$p_e = k_e f^2 B_{\max}^2 \tag{A-9}$$

when the flux varies sinusoidally, k_e being a characteristic constant for the core material and lamination thickness. The eddy-current loss in a given core can also be expressed in terms of the rms voltage E induced in the N-turn exciting winding, as follows:

$$P_e = K_e \left(\frac{E}{N}\right)^2 \tag{A-10}$$

regardless of waveform and frequency. The constants k_e and K_e vary approximately as the square of the lamination thickness. Eddy currents also have a magnetic effect, tending to make the flux density at the center of a lamination lower than at its surface. This screening effect is small in properly laminated cores at power-system frequencies but may be of great importance at higher frequencies.

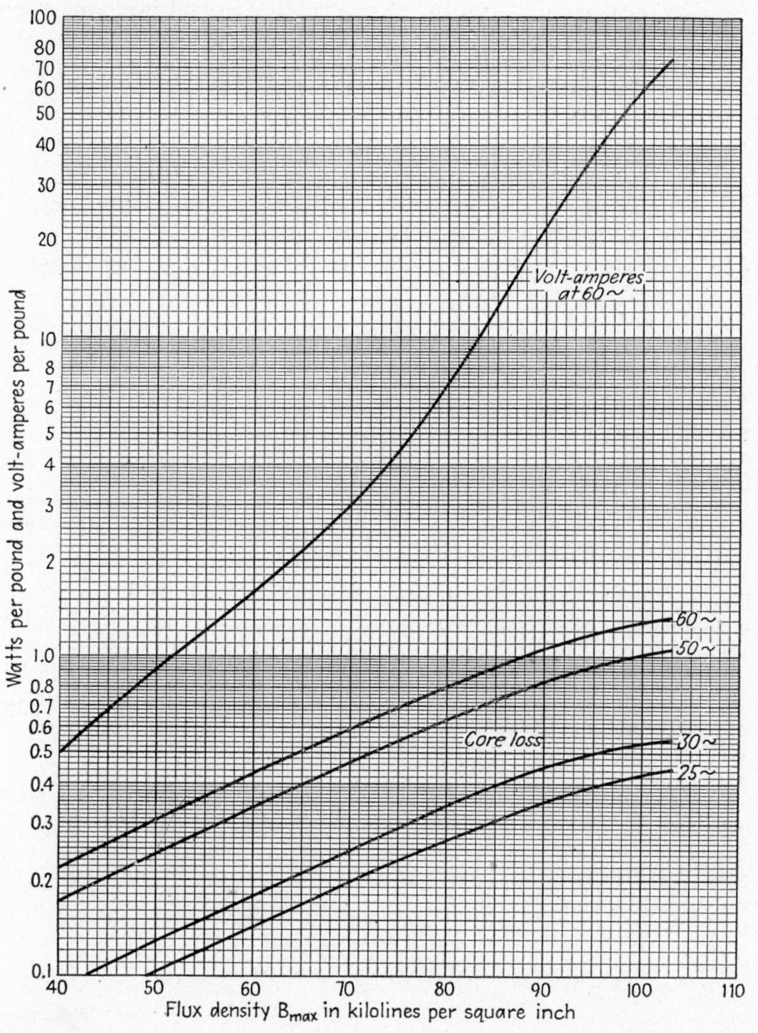

FIG. A-9. Core-loss and exciting volt-ampere characteristics of USS Transformer 52 silicon steel, 14-mil laminations. Density = 0.272 lb/in.^{3} (*Courtesy of United States Steel Company.*)

Example A-1. The net cross-sectional area of steel in the core of a 500-kva core-type transformer is 80 in.^{2}, and the mean length of the flux paths in the core is 130 in. The magnetic characteristics of the core material are shown in Fig. A-9. The maximum flux density in the core at rated voltage and frequency is not to exceed 80 kilolines/in.^{2}

a. Find the number of turns in the primary winding for a sinusoidal primary voltage of 12,000 volts rms at 60 cps.

b. Compute the corresponding core loss, exciting volt-amperes, and no-load power factor.

c. Compute the exciting current and its core-loss and magnetizing components.

d. If the frequency is reduced to 50 cps, the applied voltage remaining at 12,000 volts, find the corresponding values of core loss and exciting volt-amperes.

Solution. *a.* The core flux ϕ_{max} must not exceed $80 \times 80 = 6{,}400$ kilolines, or 0.064 weber. From Eq. A-6, the number of primary-winding turns must be not less than

$$N_1 = \frac{V_1}{4.44 f \phi_{max}} = \frac{12{,}000}{4.44 \times 60 \times 0.064} = 705$$

b. From Fig. A-9, at 80 kilolines/in.² and 60 cps

Core loss = 0.80 watt/lb
Excitation = 7.1 va/lb

The core volume is $80 \times 130 = 10{,}400$ in.³, and from the density data given with Fig. A-9, the core weight is $10{,}400 \times 0.272 = 2{,}830$ lb. Therefore

Core loss: $$P_c = 2{,}830 \times 0.80 = 2{,}260 \text{ watts}$$
$$EI_\varphi = 2{,}830 \times 7.1 = 20{,}100 \text{ va}$$

Power factor: $$\cos\theta_c = \frac{P_c}{EI_\varphi} = 0.113$$
$$\sin\theta_c = 0.994$$

c. Rms exciting current: $$I_\varphi = \frac{20{,}100}{12{,}000} = 1.68 \text{ amp}$$

Core-loss current: $I_c = I_\varphi \cos\theta_c = 0.190$ amp
Rms magnetizing current: $I_m = I_\varphi \sin\theta_c = 1.67$ amp

d. If the frequency is reduced to 50 cps with constant applied voltage, the flux must increase in accordance with Eq. A-6. The flux density for 50 cps and 12,000 volts therefore is

$$B_{max} = 80 \times {}^{60}\!/_{50} = 96 \text{ kilolines/in.}^2$$

In Fig. A-9, the corresponding core loss at 50 cps is 0.95 watt/lb. The excitation read from the 60-cps volt-ampere curve is 41 va/lb. On the assumption that the exciting volt-ampere input at constant flux density is proportional to the frequency, the 50-cps excitation is $\frac{5}{6} \times 41 = 34.2$ va/lb. Multiplying by the core weight gives, at 50 cps and 12,000 volts,

$$P_c = 2{,}830 \times 0.95 = 2{,}690 \text{ watts}$$
$$EI_\varphi = 2{,}830 \times 34.2 = 96{,}700 \text{ va}$$

Note the rapid increase in the excitation resulting from the increase in flux required by the same applied voltage at the lower frequency. Largely because of this effect on excitation, the combined variations of impressed voltage and frequency from the rated values for an a-c machine should not be allowed to exceed 10 per cent.

A-3. Effect of Secondary Current. Ideal Transformer. As a first approximation to a quantitative theory, consider a transformer with a primary winding of N_1 turns and a secondary winding of N_2 turns, as shown schematically in Fig. A-10. Let the properties of this transformer be idealized in that the winding resistances are negligible, all of the flux is confined to the core and links both windings, core losses are negligible, and the permeability of the core is so high that only a negligible exciting current is required to establish the flux. These properties are closely approached but never actually attained in practical transformers. A hypothetical transformer having these properties is often called an *ideal transformer*.

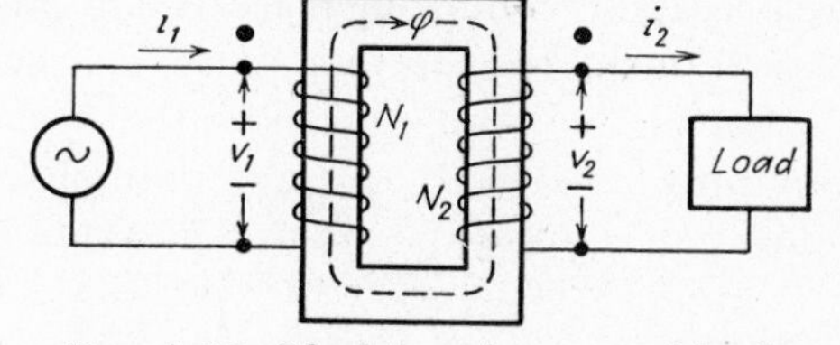

FIG. A-10. Ideal transformer and load.

When a time-varying voltage v_1 is impressed on the primary terminals, a core flux φ must be established such that the counter emf e_1 equals the impressed voltage when winding resistance is negligible. Thus

$$v_1 = e_1 = N_1 \frac{d\varphi}{dt} \tag{A-11}$$

The core flux also links the secondary and produces an induced emf e_2 and an equal secondary terminal voltage v_2 given by

$$v_2 = e_2 = N_2 \frac{d\varphi}{dt} \tag{A-12}$$

From the ratio of Eqs. A-11 and A-12,

$$\frac{v_1}{v_2} = \frac{N_1}{N_2} \tag{A-13}$$

Thus an ideal transformer changes voltages in the direct ratio of the turns in its windings.

Now let a load be connected to the secondary. A current i_2 and an mmf $N_2 i_2$ are then present in the secondary. Unless this secondary mmf is counteracted in the primary, the core flux will be radically changed and the balance between impressed voltage and counter emf in the primary will be disturbed. Hence a compensating primary mmf and current i_1 must be called into being such that

$$N_1 i_1 = N_2 i_2 \tag{A-14}$$

This is the means by which the primary knows of the presence of current in the secondary. Note that for the positive directions shown in Fig. A-10 the mmfs of i_1 and i_2 are in opposite directions and therefore compensate. The net mmf acting on the core therefore is zero, in accordance with the assumption that the exciting current of an ideal transformer is zero. From Eq. A-14,

$$\frac{i_1}{i_2} = \frac{N_2}{N_1} \tag{A-15}$$

Thus an ideal transformer changes currents in the inverse ratio of the turns in its windings. Also notice from Eqs. A-13 and A-15 that

$$v_1 i_1 = v_2 i_2 \tag{A-16}$$

that is, instantaneous power input equals instantaneous power output, a necessary condition because all causes of active- and reactive-power losses in the transformer have been neglected.

For further study, consider the case of a sinusoidal applied voltage and an impedance load. Vector symbolism can then be used. The circuit is shown in simplified form in Fig. A-11*a*, in which the dot-marked terminals

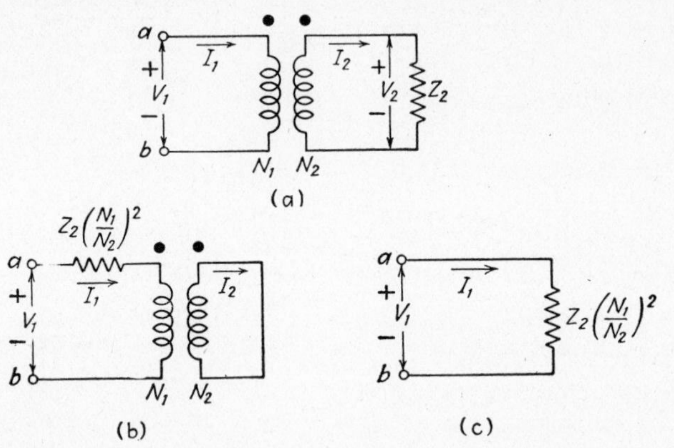

Fig. A-11. Three circuits which are identical at terminals *ab* when the transformer is ideal.

of the transformer correspond to the similarly marked terminals in Fig. A-10. The dot markings indicate terminals of corresponding polarity; *i.e.*, if one follows through the primary and secondary windings of Fig. A-10 beginning at their dot-marked terminals, one will find that both windings encircle the core in the same direction with respect to the flux. Therefore if one compares the voltages of the two windings, the voltages from a dot-marked to an unmarked terminal will be of the same instantaneous polarity for primary and secondary. In other words, the voltages V_1 and V_2 in Fig. A-11*a* are in phase. Also the currents I_1 and I_2 are in phase. The fact that their mmfs must balance is accounted for by their being in opposite directions through the windings.

In vector form, Eqs. A-13 and A-15 can be expressed as

$$V_1 = \frac{N_1}{N_2} V_2 \quad \text{and} \quad V_2 = \frac{N_2}{N_1} V_1 \tag{A-17}$$

$$I_1 = \frac{N_2}{N_1} I_2 \quad \text{and} \quad I_2 = \frac{N_1}{N_2} I_1 \tag{A-18}$$

From these equations,

$$\frac{V_1}{I_1} = \left(\frac{N_1}{N_2}\right)^2 \frac{V_2}{I_2} = \left(\frac{N_1}{N_2}\right)^2 Z_2 \tag{A-19}$$

where Z_2 is the complex impedance of the load. Consequently, as far as its effect is concerned, an impedance Z_2 in the secondary circuit may be replaced by an equivalent impedance Z_1 in the primary circuit, provided that

$$Z_1 = \left(\frac{N_1}{N_2}\right)^2 Z_2 \tag{A-20}$$

Thus the three circuits of Fig. A-11 are indistinguishable as far as their performance viewed from terminals *ab* is concerned. Transferring an impedance from one side of a transformer to the other in this fashion is called *referring the impedance* to the other side. In a similar manner, voltages and currents may be *referred* to one side or the other by using Eqs. A-17 and A-18 to evaluate the equivalent voltage and current on that side.

To sum up, *in an ideal transformer voltages are transformed in the direct ratio of turns, currents in the inverse ratio, and impedances in the direct ratio squared; and power and volt-amperes are unchanged.*

A-4. Transformer Reactances and Equivalent Circuits. The departures in an actual transformer from the ideal properties assumed in Art. A-3 must be included to a greater or lesser degree in most analyses of transformer performance. A more complete theory must take into account the effects of winding resistances, magnetic leakage, and exciting current. Sometimes the capacitances of the windings also have important effects, notably in problems involving transformer behavior at frequencies above the audio range or during rapidly changing transient conditions such as those encountered in the pulse transformers of radar circuits and in power-system transformers as a result of voltage surges caused by lightning or switching transients. The analysis of these high-frequency problems is beyond the scope of the present treatment, however, and accordingly the capacitances of the windings are neglected in the following analyses.

Two methods of analysis by which the departures from the ideal can be taken into account are (1) an equivalent-circuit technique based on physical reasoning and (2) a mathematical attack based on the classical theory of magnetically coupled circuits. Both methods are in everyday use, and both have very close parallels in the theories of rotating machines. Because it offers an excellent example of the thought process involved in translating physical concepts into a quantitative theory, the equivalent-circuit technique is presented here.

a. Leakage Reactances and an Equivalent Circuit. The total flux linking the primary winding may be divided into two components: the resultant mutual flux, confined essentially to the iron core and produced by the combined effect of the primary and secondary currents; and the primary leakage flux, which links only the primary. These components are identified in the elementary transformer shown in Fig. A-12, where for simplicity the primary and secondary windings are shown on opposite legs of the core. In an actual transformer with interleaved windings, the details of the flux map are more complicated, but the essential features remain the same. Because the leakage path is largely in air, the leakage flux and the voltage induced by it vary linearly with primary current I_1. The effect on the primary circuit is the same as that of flux linkages anywhere in the circuit leading up to the transformer primary and may be simulated by assigning to the primary a *leakage inductance* (equal to the leakage-flux linkages with the primary per unit of primary current) or *leakage reactance* x_{l1} (equal to $2\pi f$ times leakage inductance). In addition there will be a voltage drop in the primary effective resistance r_1.

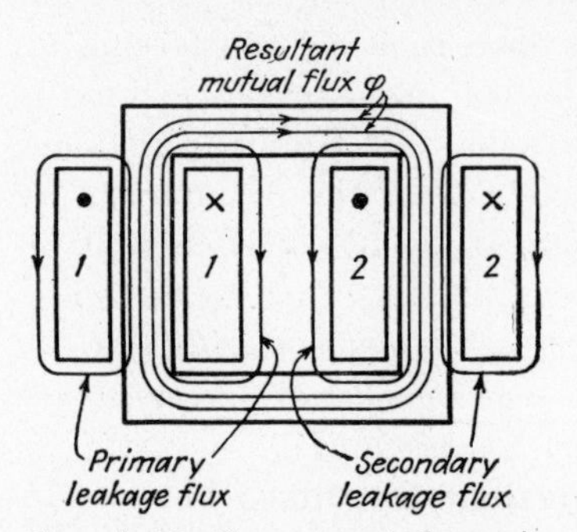

Fig. A-12. Component fluxes in a transformer.

The impressed voltage V_1 is then opposed by three vector voltages: the I_1r_1 drop in the primary resistance, the I_1x_{l1} drop arising from primary leakage flux, and the counter emf E_1 induced in the primary by the resultant mutual flux. All these voltages are appropriately included in the equivalent circuit of Fig. A-13*a*.

The resultant mutual flux links both the primary and secondary windings and is created by their combined mmfs. It is convenient to treat these mmfs by considering that the primary current must meet two requirements of the magnetic circuit: it must not only (1) counteract the demagnetizing effect of the secondary current but also (2) produce sufficient mmf to create the resultant mutual flux. According to this physical picture, it is convenient to resolve the primary current into two components, a load component and an exciting component. The *load component* I_2' is defined as the component current in the primary which would exactly counteract the mmf of the secondary current I_2. Thus for opposing currents,

$$I_2' = \frac{N_2}{N_1} I_2 \tag{A-21}$$

It equals the secondary current referred to the primary as in an ideal transformer. The *exciting component* i_φ is defined as the additional primary current required to produce the resultant mutual flux. It is a nonsinusoidal current of the nature described in Art. A-2.

The exciting current can be treated as an equivalent sinusoidal current I_φ, in the manner described in Art. A-2, and can be resolved into a core-loss component I_c in phase with the counter emf E_1 and a magnetizing component I_m lagging E_1 by 90°. In the equivalent circuit (Fig. A-13*b*) the equivalent sinusoidal exciting current is accounted for by means of a shunt branch connected across E_1, comprising a noninductive resistance whose conductance is g_c in parallel with a lossless inductance whose sus-

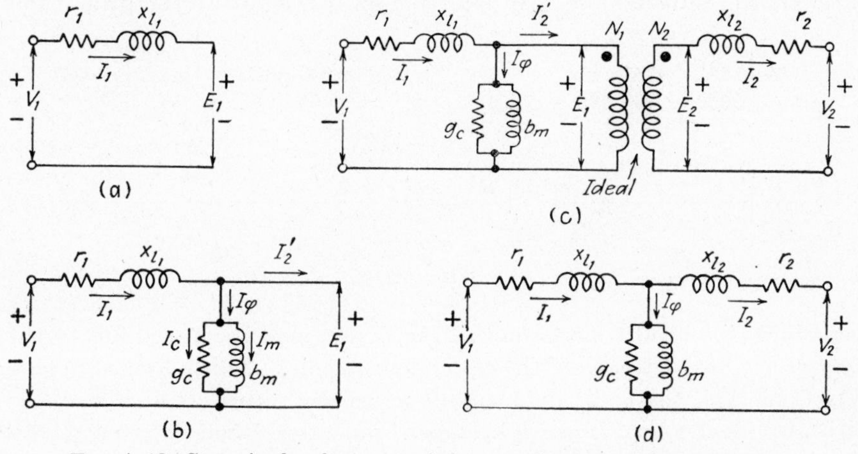

FIG. A-13. Steps in development of the transformer equivalent circuit.

ceptance is b_m. Alternatively a series combination of resistance and reactance can be connected across E_1. In the parallel combination (Fig. A-13*b*) the power $E_1^2 g_c$ accounts for the core loss due to the resultant mutual flux. When g_c is assumed constant, the core loss is thereby assumed to vary as E_1^2 or (for sine waves) as $\phi_{\max}^2 f^2$, where $\phi_{\max}$ is the maximum value of the resultant mutual flux. The magnetizing susceptance b_m varies with the saturation of the iron. When the inductance corresponding to b_m is assumed constant, the magnetizing current is thereby assumed to be independent of frequency and directly proportional to the resultant mutual flux. Both g_c and b_m are usually determined at rated voltage and frequency; they are then assumed to remain constant for the small departures from rated values associated with normal operation.

The resultant mutual flux φ induces an emf E_2 in the secondary, and since this flux links both windings, the induced-voltage ratio is

$$\frac{E_1}{E_2} = \frac{N_1}{N_2} \tag{A-22}$$

just as in an ideal transformer. This voltage transformation and the current transformation of Eq. A-21 can be accounted for by introducing an ideal transformer in the equivalent circuit, as in Fig. A-13*c*. The emf E_2 is not the secondary terminal voltage, however, because of the secondary resistance and because the secondary current I_2 creates *secondary leakage flux* (see Fig. A-12). The secondary terminal voltage V_2 differs from the induced voltage E_2 by the voltage drops due to secondary resistance r_2 and *secondary leakage reactance* x_{l2}, as in the portion of the equivalent circuit (Fig. A-13*c*) to the right of E_2.

The actual transformer therefore is equivalent to an ideal transformer plus external impedances. By referring all quantities to the primary or

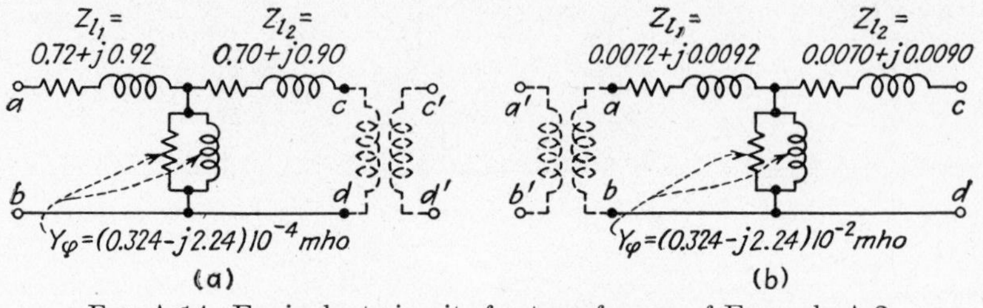

Fig. A-14. Equivalent circuits for transformer of Example A-2.

secondary, the ideal transformer in Fig. A-13*c* may be moved out to the right or left, respectively, of the equivalent circuit. This is almost invariably done, and the equivalent circuit is usually drawn as in Fig. A-13*d* with the ideal transformer not shown and all voltages, currents, and impedances referred to the same side. In order to avoid a complicated notation, the same symbols have been used for the *referred* values in Fig. A-13*d* as were used for the *actual* values in Fig. A-13*c*. In what follows we shall almost always deal with the referred values. One simply keeps in mind the side of the transformer to which all quantities have been referred. The circuit of Fig. A-13*d* is often called the *T circuit* for a transformer.

Example A-2. A 50-kva 2,400:240-volt 60-cps distribution transformer has a leakage impedance of $0.72 + j0.92$ ohm in the high-voltage winding and $0.0070 + j0.0090$ ohm in the low-voltage winding. At rated voltage and frequency the admittance Y_φ of the shunt branch accounting for the exciting current is $(0.324 - j2.24) \times 10^{-2}$ mho when viewed from the low-voltage side.

Draw the equivalent circuit (*a*) referred to the high-voltage side and (*b*) referred to the low-voltage side, and label the impedances numerically.

Solution. The circuits are given in Fig. A-14*a* and *b*, respectively, with the high-voltage side numbered 1 and the low-voltage side numbered 2. The voltages given on the nameplate of a power-system transformer are based on the turns ratio and neglect the small leakage-impedance voltage drops under load. Since this is a 10 to 1 transformer, impedances are referred by multiplying or dividing by 100. The value of an impedance referred to the high-voltage side is greater than its value referred to the low-voltage side. Since admittance is the reciprocal of impedance, an admittance is referred from one side to the other by use of the reciprocal of the referring factor for impedance. The value of an admittance referred to the high-voltage side is smaller than its value referred to the low-voltage side.

The ideal transformer may be explicitly drawn, as shown dotted in Fig. A-14, or it may be omitted in the diagram and remembered mentally, making the unprimed letters the terminals.

b. Approximate Equivalent Circuits. Various approximations of the equivalent circuit are commonly used in transformer computations. For comparison, these are summarized in Fig. A-15. All quantities in these circuits are referred to either the primary or the secondary, and the ideal transformer is not shown.

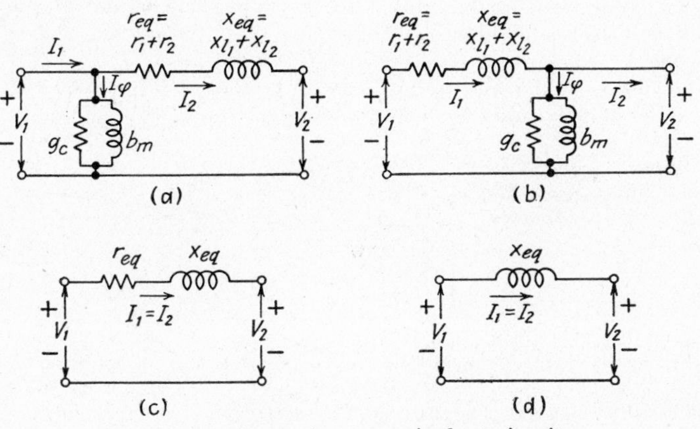

FIG. A-15. Approximate equivalent circuits.

The computational labor involved often can be appreciably reduced by moving the shunt branch representing the exciting current out from the middle of the T circuit to either the primary or the secondary terminals, as in Figs. A-15*a* and *b*. These are *cantilever circuits*. The series branch is the combined resistance and leakage reactance referred to the same side. This impedance is sometimes called the *equivalent impedance* and its components the *equivalent resistance* r_{eq} and *equivalent reactance* x_{eq}, as shown in Fig. A-15*a* and *b*. Error is introduced by neglect of the voltage drop in the primary or secondary leakage impedance caused by the exciting current, but this error is insignificant in most problems involving power-system transformers.

Further simplification results from neglecting the exciting current entirely, as in Fig. A-15*c*, in which the transformer is represented as an equivalent series impedance. If the transformer is large (several hundred kva or over), the equivalent resistance r_{eq} is small compared with the equivalent reactance x_{eq} and may frequently be neglected, giving Fig. A-15*d*. The circuits of Fig. A-15*c* and *d* are sufficiently accurate for most ordinary power-system problems. Finally, in situations where the currents and voltages are determined almost wholly by the circuits external to the transformer or when a high degree of accuracy is not required, the entire transformer impedance may be neglected and the transformer may be considered to be ideal as in Art. A-3.

The circuits of Fig. A-15 have the additional advantage that the total equivalent resistance r_{eq} and equivalent reactance x_{eq} can be found from a very simple test, as shown in Art. A-5, whereas measurement of the values of the component leakage reactances x_{l1} and x_{l2} is a difficult experimental task.

Example A-3. The 50-kva 2,400:240-volt transformer whose constants are given in Example A-2 is used to step down the voltage at the load end of a feeder whose impedance is $0.30 + j1.60$ ohms. The voltage V_s at the sending end of the feeder is 2,400 volts.

Find the voltage at the secondary terminals of the transformer when the load connected to its secondary draws rated current from the transformer and the power factor

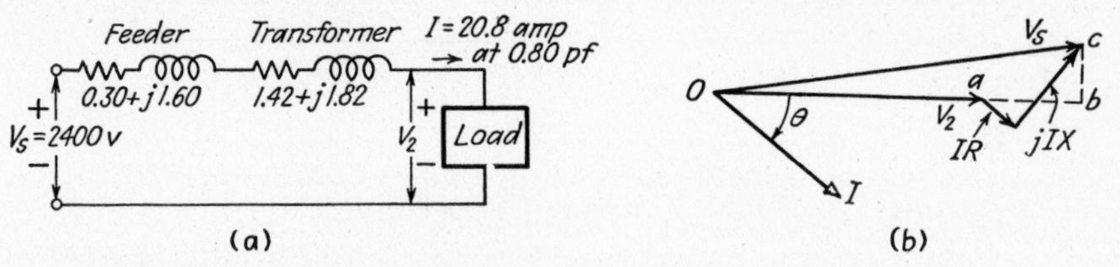

FIG. A-16. Equivalent circuit and vector diagram for Example A-3.

of the load is 0.80 lagging. Neglect the voltage drops in the transformer and feeder caused by the exciting current.

Solution. The circuit with all quantities referred to the high-voltage (primary) side of the transformer is shown in Fig. A-16*a*, wherein the transformer is represented by its equivalent impedance, as in Fig. A-15*c*. From Fig. A-14*a*, the value of the equivalent impedance is $Z_{eq} = 1.42 + j1.82$ ohms, and the combined impedance of the feeder and transformer in series is $Z = 1.72 + j3.42$ ohms. From the transformer rating, the load current referred to the high-voltage side is $I = 50{,}000/2{,}400 = 20.8$ amp.

The vector diagram referred to the high-voltage side is shown in Fig. A-16*b*, from which,

$$Ob = \sqrt{V_s^2 - (bc)^2} \tag{A-23}$$

and

$$V_2 = Ob - ab \tag{A-24}$$

Note that

$$bc = IX \cos \theta - IR \sin \theta \tag{A-25}$$
$$ab = IR \cos \theta + IX \sin \theta \tag{A-26}$$

where R and X are the combined resistance and reactance, respectively. Thus

$$bc = (20.8)(3.42)(0.80) - (20.8)(1.72)(0.60) = 35.5 \text{ volts}$$
$$ab = (20.8)(1.72)(0.80) + (20.8)(3.42)(0.60) = 71.4 \text{ volts}$$

Substitution of numerical values in Eq. A-23 shows that Ob very nearly equals V_s, or 2,400 volts. Substitution of numerical values in Eq. A-24 then gives $V_2 = 2{,}329$

volts referred to the high-voltage side. The actual voltage at the secondary terminals is 2,329/10, or

$$V_2 = 233 \text{ volts}$$

A-5. Short-circuit and Open-circuit Tests. Two very simple tests serve to determine the constants of the equivalent circuits of Fig. A-15 and the power losses in a transformer. These consist in measuring the input voltage, current, and power to the primary, first with the secondary short-circuited, and then with the secondary open-circuited.

With the secondary short-circuited, a primary voltage of only 2 to 12 per cent of the rated value need be impressed to obtain full-load current. For convenience, the high-voltage side is usually taken as the primary in this test. If V_{sc}, I_{sc}, and P_{sc} are the impressed voltage, primary current, and power input, the short-circuit impedance Z_{sc} and its resistance and reactance components R_{sc} and X_{sc} referred to the primary are

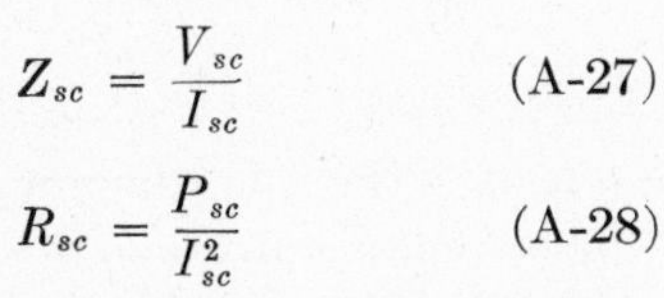

$$Z_{sc} = \frac{V_{sc}}{I_{sc}} \qquad \text{(A-27)}$$

$$R_{sc} = \frac{P_{sc}}{I_{sc}^2} \qquad \text{(A-28)}$$

$$X_{sc} = \sqrt{Z_{sc}^2 - R_{sc}^2} \qquad \text{(A-29)}$$

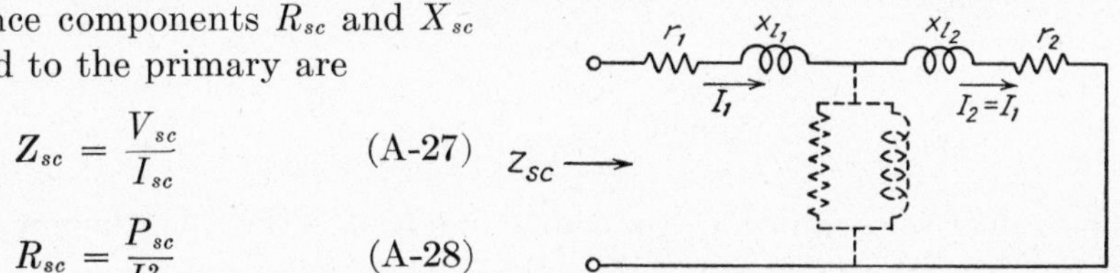

FIG. A-17. Equivalent circuit with short-circuited secondary.

The equivalent circuit with the secondary terminals short-circuited is shown in Fig. A-17. The voltage induced in the secondary by the resultant core flux equals the secondary leakage-impedance voltage drop, and at rated current this voltage is only about 1 to 6 per cent of rated voltage. At the correspondingly low value of core flux, the exciting current and core losses are entirely negligible. The exciting admittance, shown dotted in Fig. A-17, then can be omitted, and the primary and secondary currents are very nearly equal when referred to the same side. The power input very nearly equals the total copper loss in the primary and secondary windings, and the impressed voltage equals the drop in the combined primary and secondary leakage impedance Z_{eq}. The equivalent resistance and reactance referred to the primary very nearly equal the short-circuit resistance and reactance of Eqs. A-28 and A-29, respectively. The equivalent impedance can, of course, be referred from one side to the other in the usual manner. On the rare occasions when the equivalent T circuit of Fig. A-13*d* must be resorted to, approximate values of the individual primary and secondary resistances and leakage reactances can be obtained by assuming that $r_1 = r_2 = 0.5r_{eq}$, and $x_{l1} = x_{l2} = 0.5x_{eq}$ when all impedances are referred to the same side.

With the secondary open-circuited and rated voltage impressed on the primary, an exciting current of only 2 to 6 per cent of full-load current is obtained. If the transformer is to be used at other than its rated voltage, the test should be taken at that voltage. For convenience, the low-voltage side is usually taken as the primary in this test. The voltage drop in the primary leakage impedance caused by the small exciting current is entirely negligible, and the primary impressed voltage V_1 very nearly equals the emf E_1 induced by the resultant core flux. Also the primary copper loss caused by the exciting current is entirely negligible so that the power input P_1 very nearly equals the core loss P_c. Thus the exciting admittance $Y_\varphi = g_c - jb_m$ in Fig. A-13*d* very nearly equals the open-circuit admittance $Y_{oc} = g_{oc} - jb_{oc}$ determined from the impressed voltage V_1, exciting current I_φ, and power input P_1 measured in the primary with the secondary open-circuited; thus the exciting admittance and its conductance and susceptance components are very nearly

$$Y_\varphi = Y_{oc} = \frac{I_\varphi}{V_1} \tag{A-30}$$

$$g_c = g_{oc} = \frac{P_1}{V_1^2} \tag{A-31}$$

$$b_m = b_{oc} = \sqrt{Y_{oc}^2 - g_{oc}^2} \tag{A-32}$$

The values so obtained are, of course, referred to the side which was used as the primary in this test. When the approximate equivalent circuits of Fig. A-15*c* and *d* are used, the open-circuit test is used only to obtain core loss for efficiency computations and to check the magnitude of the exciting current. Sometimes the voltage at the terminals of the open-circuited secondary is measured as a check on the turns ratio.

Example A-4. With the instruments located in the high-voltage side and the low-voltage side short-circuited, the short-circuit-test readings for the 50-kva 2,400:240-volt transformer of Example A-2 are 48 volts, 20.8 amp, and 617 watts. Find the equivalent resistance and equivalent reactance referred to the high-voltage side.

Solution. The subscript H will be added to denote that these constants are referred to the high-voltage side.

$$Z_{eqH} = \frac{48}{20.8} = 2.31 \text{ ohms}$$

$$r_{eqH} = \frac{617}{(20.8)^2} = 1.42 \text{ ohms}$$

$$x_{eqH} = \sqrt{(2.31)^2 - (1.42)^2} = 1.82 \text{ ohms}$$

A-6. Efficiency and Voltage Regulation. The efficiency of a transformer, like that of all apparatus dealing with power and energy, is the ratio of power output to power input; thus

$$\text{Efficiency} = \frac{\text{output}}{\text{input}} = \frac{\text{input} - \text{losses}}{\text{input}} \tag{A-33}$$

$$= 1 - \frac{\text{losses}}{\text{input}} \tag{A-34}$$

Formulations in terms of losses are particularly useful for electric machinery, for it is usually more convenient, economical, and accurate to determine efficiency by measuring the losses than by input-output measurements. Because the efficiency is high (usually 97 per cent or higher at normal loads for transformers of 10 kva rating and larger), approximations which result in a few per cent error in the losses have very little effect on the efficiency.

As a basis for comparison among competing transformers, test procedures and methods of calculation involving small approximations have been standardized by the ASA.[1] The philosophy of these standard methods is the same as that for rotating machines, as explained in Art. 4-11. According to the ASA Standards, the core loss under load at rated voltage and frequency is assumed to equal the no-load loss measured in an open-circuit test at rated voltage and frequency with a sinusoidal impressed voltage. The core loss is then assumed to be constant as long as the operating voltage and frequency remain constant. The loss due to the load current, known as the *load loss*, equals the I^2r losses in the windings plus stray losses due to the leakage fluxes. Since the stray losses vary approximately as the square of the load current, the total load loss varies as I_2^2, just as if it were a true copper loss. In fact, the load loss is often referred to as the copper loss. Thus the load loss, or copper loss, equals $I_2^2 r_{eq}$ where the equivalent resistance r_{eq} is obtainable from a short-circuit test. According to the ASA Standards, the equivalent resistance should be corrected to an assumed operating temperature of 75°C, but we shall omit this refinement here.

The load on a transformer rarely remains constant at the rating of the transformer. In selecting a transformer for a given application it is often economical to choose a rating which will be overloaded occasionally for periods of short duration. [The ASA Standards (footnote 1) give recommendations for permissible overloads.] The average load over a daily or seasonal period, however, generally is appreciably lower than the transformer rating. Hence the maximum efficiency should occur at less than rated load, depending on the load curve of the intended service. It can readily be shown that, for any device whose losses consist of a constant component plus a component which varies as the square of the load, maximum efficiency occurs at the load for which the variable loss equals the constant loss. Economic comparison of competing transformers should be based on the efficiency at all loads encountered in the load cycle, and not on just the full-load efficiency. If the transformer is energized continuously, the core loss is present for 24 hr per day; but the copper loss is present only when the transformer is delivering useful output. Consequently the core loss is considerably more important than the full-load copper loss in determining the operating costs of the transformer. Modern

[1] ASA Standards, Transformers, Regulators, and Reactors, *Bull.* C57, American Standards Association, New York, 1948.

distribution transformers are designed so that the core loss is only about one-third of the full-load copper loss.

Cost studies may be made by evaluating the costs of losses over the entire load cycle and taking due account of fixed charges and of other operating costs for the transformer. When all factors except the transformer efficiencies are the same, a comparison between competing transformers can be made very simply in terms of the energy efficiencies. *Energy efficiency* is the ratio of the total energy delivered by the transformer to that supplied to the transformer, both energies being evaluated over the period of time for a complete load cycle. When this period is 24 hr, the result is called the *all-day efficiency.*

Voltage regulation, a figure of merit sometimes used for power and distribution transformers, is the change in secondary terminal voltage from no load to full load and is usually expressed as a percentage of the full-load value, the latter being taken as the rated secondary voltage; *i.e.*,

$$\text{Per cent regulation} = \frac{E_{oc2} - V_2}{V_2}(100) \tag{A-35}$$

where V_2 is the full-load secondary terminal voltage and E_{oc2} is the no-load secondary voltage with the primary terminal voltage held constant as the load is removed. Regulation can be computed very simply from the equivalent circuit, that of Fig. A-15*c* ordinarily being used. It depends on the power factor of the load and may become negative if this power factor is sufficiently leading.

Notice that regulation here applies to the transformer alone, whereas in actual service the change of voltage will also be affected by voltage drops in the transmission and distribution feeders. To avoid the possibility of unduly low or high voltages at the load, most power transformers have extra taps on the high-tension or low-tension windings (or both) by which the turns ratio can be changed somewhat, in accordance with the demands of a particular installation.

Example A-5. An open-circuit test on the 50-kva 2,400:240-volt transformer of Example A-4 with the low-voltage side energized gives instrument readings on the low-voltage side of 240 volts, 5.41 amp, and 186 watts. Using the results of Example A-4, compute the efficiency and regulation at full load, 0.80 power factor lagging.

Solution. Full-load high-tension current is

$$I_H = \frac{50{,}000}{2{,}400} = 20.8 \text{ amp}$$

$$\begin{aligned}
&\text{Copper loss} = I_H^2 r_{eqH} = (20.8)^2(1.42) &&= 617 \text{ watts}\\
&\text{Core loss} &&= \underline{186}\\
&\text{Total losses at full load} &&= 803\\
&\text{Output} = (50{,}000)(0.80) &&= \underline{40{,}000}\\
&\text{Input} &&= 40{,}803
\end{aligned}$$

$$\frac{\text{Losses}}{\text{Input}} = \frac{803}{40{,}803} = 0.0197$$

By Eq. A-34,

$$\text{Efficiency} = 1 - 0.0197 = 0.980$$

To compute the regulation, the equivalent circuit of Fig. A-15*c* will be used with everything referred to the high-voltage side, as indicated by the subscript H. The primary voltage is assumed to be adjusted so that the secondary terminal voltage has its rated value at full load, or $V_{2H} = 2{,}400$ volts referred to the high-voltage side. The required value of the primary voltage V_{1H} can be computed from the equivalent circuit (Fig. A-15*c*). The corresponding vector diagram with V_{2H} as the reference vector is shown in Fig. A-18, whence (in complex notation)

$$\begin{aligned} V_{1H} &= V_{2H} + I_H(r_{eqH} + jx_{eqH}) \qquad \text{(A-36)} \\ &= 2{,}400 + (20.8)(0.80 - j0.60)(1.42 + j1.82) \\ &= 2{,}446 + j13 \end{aligned}$$

The magnitude of V_{1H} is 2,446 volts. If this voltage were held constant and the load removed, the secondary voltage on open circuit would rise to 2,446 volts referred to the high-voltage side. From Eq. A-35,

$$\text{Regulation} = \frac{2{,}446 - 2{,}400}{2{,}400}(100) = 1.92\%$$

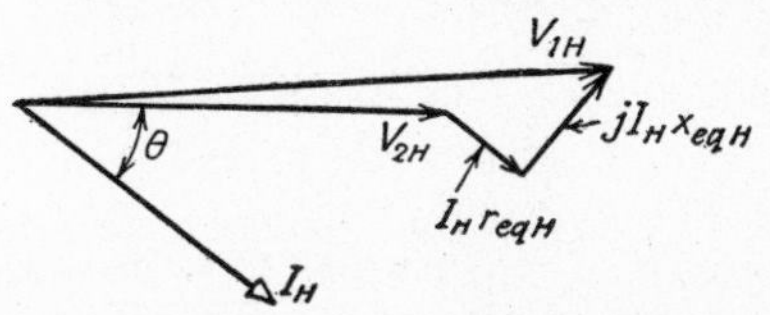

FIG. A-18. Vector diagram at full load, 0.80 power factor lagging, Example A-5.

A-7. The Problems of Variable-frequency Transformers. Small iron-core transformers operating in the audio-frequency range (hence called *audio-frequency transformers*) are often used as coupling devices in electronic circuits for communications, measurements, and control. Their principal functions are either to step up voltage, thereby contributing to the over-all voltage gain in amplifiers, or to act as impedance-transforming devices bringing about the optimum relation between the apparent impedance of a load and the impedance of a source. They may also serve other auxiliary functions, such as providing a path for direct current through the primary while at the same time keeping it out of the secondary circuit.

Application of transformers for impedance matching makes direct use of the impedance-transforming property shown in Eq. A-20. Vacuum-tube oscillators and amplifiers, for example, give optimum performance when working into a definite order of magnitude of load impedance, and transformer coupling may be used to change the apparent impedance of the actual load to this optimum. A transformer so used is called an *output transformer*.

When the frequency varies over a wide range, as for example in an audio-frequency amplifier for the reproduction of music, it is important that the output voltage be as closely as possible instantaneously proportional to the input voltage. Ideally this means that voltages should be amplified equally and phase shift should be zero for all frequencies in the audio range. The *amplitude-frequency characteristic* (often abbreviated to *frequency characteristic*) is a curve of the ratio of the load voltage on the secondary side to the internal source voltage on the primary side plotted as a function of frequency, a flat characteristic being the most desirable. The *phase characteristic* is a curve of the phase angle of the load voltage relative to the source voltage plotted as a function of frequency, a small phase angle being desirable. These characteristics are dependent not only on the transformer but also on the constants of the entire primary and secondary circuits.

As an example of these characteristics and an excellent example of an engineering analysis which makes use of approximations based on physical

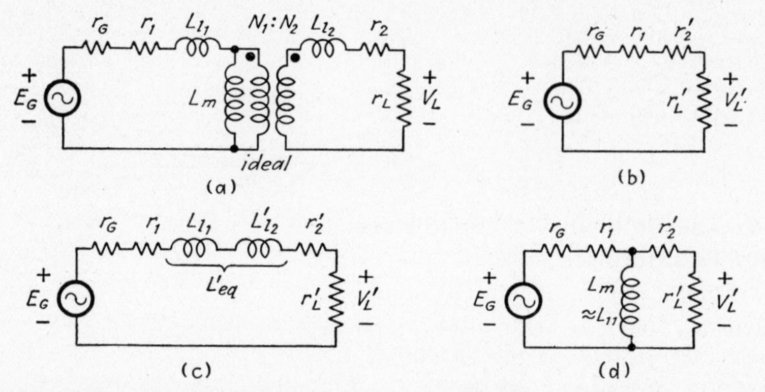

Fig. A-19. Equivalent circuits of an output transformer. (*a*) Complete equivalent circuit. (*b*) Approximate equivalent in the middle range of audio frequencies. (*c*) High-frequency equivalent. (*d*) Low-frequency equivalent.

reasoning, consider an audio-frequency amplifier coupled to a loud-speaker through an output transformer. The amplifier is considered as equivalent to a source of voltage E_G in series with an internal resistance r_G, and the loud-speaker is considered approximately as a resistance load r_L, as shown in Fig. A-19*a*, wherein the transformer is represented by the equivalent circuit of Fig. A-13*c*, with core loss neglected. Sometimes the stray capacitances of the windings must be taken into account at high audio frequencies, especially when the source impedance is higher than a few thousand ohms. Experience has shown, however, that when the source is a triode vacuum-tube amplifier the effects of the capacitances are small.

The analysis of a properly designed circuit breaks down into three frequency ranges.

1. At intermediate frequencies (around 500 cps) none of the inductances are important, and the equivalent circuit reduces to a network of resistances, as shown in Fig. A-19*b*, wherein all quantities have been referred to the primary, as indicated by the prime superscripts. Analysis of this

circuit shows that the ratio of load voltage V_L to source voltage E_G is

$$\frac{V_L}{E_G} = \frac{N_2}{N_1}\frac{r'_L}{R'_{se}} \tag{A-37}$$

where

$$R'_{se} = r_G + r_1 + r'_2 + r'_L \tag{A-38}$$

In this middle range (which usually extends over several octaves) the voltage ratio is very nearly constant; *i.e.*, the amplitude characteristic is flat, and the phase shift is zero.

2. As the frequency is increased, however, the leakage reactances of the transformer become increasingly important. The equivalent circuit in the high audio range is shown in Fig. A-19*c*. Analysis of this circuit shows that at high frequencies

$$\frac{V_L}{E_G} = \frac{N_2}{N_1}\frac{r'_L}{R'_{se}}\frac{1}{\sqrt{1 + (\omega L'_{eq}/R'_{se})^2}} \tag{A-39}$$

where L'_{eq} is the equivalent leakage inductance. The voltage ratio relative to its mid-range value is

$$\text{Relative voltage ratio} = \frac{1}{\sqrt{1 + (\omega L'_{eq}/R'_{se})^2}} \tag{A-40}$$

The phase angle by which the load voltage lags the source voltage is

$$\theta = \tan^{-1}\frac{\omega L'_{eq}}{R'_{se}} \tag{A-41}$$

Curves of the relative voltage ratio and phase angle as functions of the reactance-to-resistance ratio $\omega L'_{eq}/R'_{se}$ are shown in the right-hand half of Fig. A-20.

3. At low frequencies, the leakage reactances are negligible, but the shunting effect of the magnetizing branch becomes increasingly important as its reactance decreases. The inductance of the magnetizing branch very nearly equals the self-inductance L_{11} of the primary. The equivalent circuit at low frequencies is shown in Fig. A-19*d*, from which

$$\frac{V_L}{E_G} = \frac{N_2}{N_1}\frac{r'_L}{R'_{se}}\frac{1}{\sqrt{1 + (R'_{par}/\omega L_{11})^2}} \tag{A-42}$$

where

$$R'_{par} = \frac{(r_G + r_1)(r'_2 + r'_L)}{r_G + r_1 + r'_2 + r'_L} \tag{A-43}$$

The voltage ratio relative to its mid-range value is

$$\text{Relative voltage ratio} = \frac{1}{\sqrt{1 + (R'_{par}/\omega L_{11})^2}} \tag{A-44}$$

and the phase angle by which the load voltage leads the source voltage is

$$\theta = \tan^{-1} \frac{R'_{\text{par}}}{\omega L_{11}} \tag{A-45}$$

Curves of the relative voltage ratio and phase angle as functions of the reactance-to-resistance ratio $\omega L_{11}/R'_{\text{par}}$ are shown in the left-hand half of Fig. A-20.

The points at which the relative voltage ratio is 0.707 are called the *half-power points*. From Eq. A-40, the upper half-power point occurs at

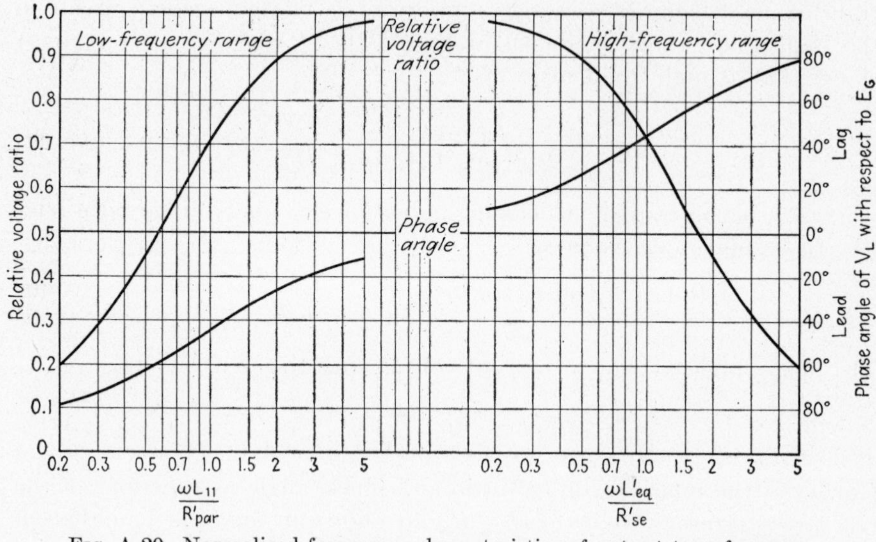

Fig. A-20. Normalized frequency characteristics of output transformers.

a frequency f_h for which the equivalent leakage reactance $\omega_h L'_{eq}$ equals the series resistance R'_{se}, or

$$f_h = \frac{R'_{se}}{2\pi L'_{eq}} \tag{A-46}$$

and from Eq. A-44, the lower half-power point occurs at a frequency f_l for which the self-reactance ωL_{11} equals the parallel resistance R'_{par}, or

$$f_l = \frac{R'_{\text{par}}}{2\pi L_{11}} \tag{A-47}$$

The band width is describable in terms of the ratio

$$\frac{f_h}{f_l} = \frac{R'_{se}}{R'_{\text{par}}} \frac{L_{11}}{L'_{eq}} \tag{A-48}$$

A broad band width requires a high ratio of self-inductance to leakage inductance, or a coefficient of coupling as close as possible to unity.

A-8. Autotransformers. Instrument Transformers. Viewed from the terminals, substantially the same transformation effect on voltages, currents, and impedances can be obtained with the connections of Fig. A-21*a* as in the normal transformer with two separate windings shown in Fig. A-21*b*. In Fig. A-21*a*, the winding *bc* is common to both the primary and secondary circuits. This type of transformer is called an *autotransformer*. It is really nothing but a normal transformer connected in a special way. The only difference structurally is that winding *ab* must be provided with extra insulation. The performance of an autotransformer is governed by the same fundamental considerations already discussed for transformers having two separate windings. Autotransformers have lower leakage reactances, lower losses, smaller exciting current, and cost less than two-winding transformers when the voltage ratio does not differ too greatly from 1-to-1. A disadvantage is the direct copper connection between the high- and low-voltage sides.

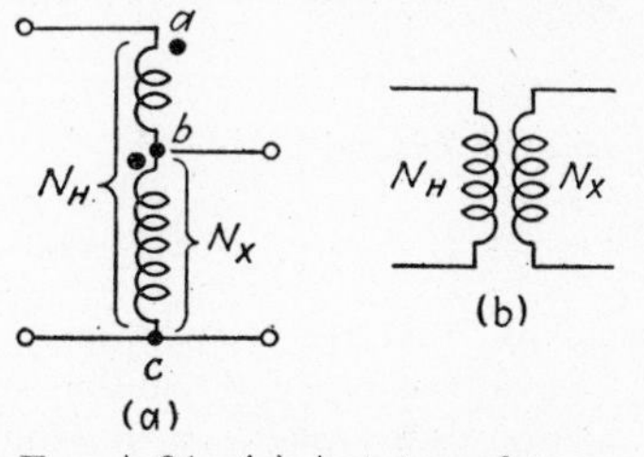

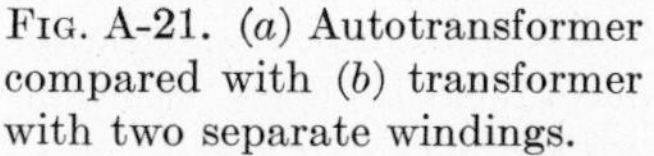

FIG. A-21. (*a*) Autotransformer compared with (*b*) transformer with two separate windings.

Example A-6. The 2,400:240-volt 50-kva transformer of Examples A-4 and A-5 is connected as an autotransformer as shown in Fig. A-22 in which *ab* is the 240-volt winding and *bc* is the 2,400-volt winding. (It is assumed that the 240-volt winding has sufficient insulation so that it can withstand a voltage of 2,640 volts to ground.)

a. Compute the voltage ratings V_H and V_X of the high-tension and low-tension sides, respectively, when the transformer is connected as an autotransformer.

b. Compute the kva rating as an autotransformer.

c. Data with respect to the losses are given in Examples A-4 and A-5. Compute the full-load efficiency as an autotransformer at 0.80 power factor.

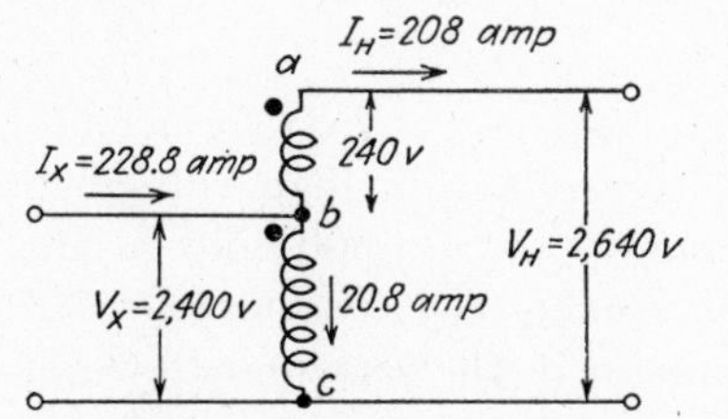

FIG. A-22. Autotransformer of Example A-6.

Solution. *a*. Since the 2,400-volt winding *bc* is connected to the low-tension circuit, $V_X = 2{,}400$ volts.

When $V_{bc} = 2{,}400$ volts, a voltage $V_{ab} = 240$ volts in phase with V_{bc} will be induced in winding *ab* (leakage-impedance voltage drops being neglected). The voltage of the high-tension side therefore is

$$V_H = V_{ab} + V_{bc} = 2{,}640 \text{ volts}$$

b. From the rating of 50 kva as a normal two-winding transformer, the rated current of the 240-volt winding is 50,000/240, or 208 amp. Since the 240-volt winding is in series with the high-tension circuit, the rated current of this winding is the rated current I_H on the high-tension side as an autotransformer. The kva rating as an autotransformer therefore is

$$\frac{V_H I_H}{1{,}000} = \frac{(2{,}640)(208)}{1{,}000} = 550 \text{ kva}$$

The rating can also be computed on the low-tension side in a manner which highlights the current-transforming properties. Thus if the current in the 240-volt winding has its rated value of 208 amp, the current in the 2,400-volt winding must produce an equal and opposite mmf (exciting current being neglected) and therefore must be 20.8 amp in the arrow direction, Fig. A-22. The current I_X on the low-tension side as an autotransformer therefore is

$$I_X = 208 + 20.8 = 228.8 \text{ amp}$$

and the kva rating is

$$\frac{V_X I_X}{1{,}000} = \frac{(2{,}400)(228.8)}{1{,}000} = 550 \text{ kva}$$

Note that this transformer, whose rating as a normal two-winding transformer is 50 kva, is capable of handling 550 kva as an autotransformer. The higher rating as an autotransformer is a consequence of the fact that all of the 550 kva does not have to be transformed by electromagnetic induction. In fact, all that the transformer has to do is to boost a current of 208 amp through a potential rise of 240 volts, corresponding to a rating of 50 kva.

c. When connected as an autotransformer with the currents and voltages shown in Fig. A-22, the losses are the same as in Example A-5, namely, 803 watts. But the output as an autotransformer at 0.80 power factor is (0.80)(550,000) = 440,000 watts. The efficiency therefore is

$$1 - \frac{803}{440{,}803} = 0.9982$$

The efficiency is so high because the losses are those incident to transforming only 50 kva.

Among special-purpose transformers are *instrument transformers* for inserting instruments, meters, and protective relays in high-voltage or high-current circuits. Voltage measurements in a 4,600-volt circuit, for instance, are made by inserting a *potential transformer* of ratio 4,600:120 volts and using a standard 150-volt instrument in the secondary. Similarly, current measurements are made by connecting a *current transformer* of the appropriate ratio with its primary in series with the circuit and its secondary connected to a 5-amp ammeter. The secondary of a current transformer should never be open-circuited while its primary carries current. A dangerously high voltage may be induced in the open-circuited secondary. Instrument transformers insulate the metering or relaying circuit and permit greater standardization of meters, instruments, and relays. Such transformers must be designed for accurate voltage or current ratio and minimum phase displacement between input voltages or currents and the corresponding output quantities.

A-9. Transformers in Polyphase Circuits. Three aspects of the application of transformers in polyphase systems are considered in this article. Primary emphasis is given to 3-phase systems, because of their predominant importance.

a. Three-phase Connections. Three single-phase transformers may be connected to form a 3-phase bank in any of the four ways shown in Fig. A-23. In all four parts of this figure, the windings at the left are the primaries, those at the right are the secondaries, and any primary winding is mated in one transformer with the secondary winding drawn parallel to it. Also shown are the voltages and currents resulting from balanced

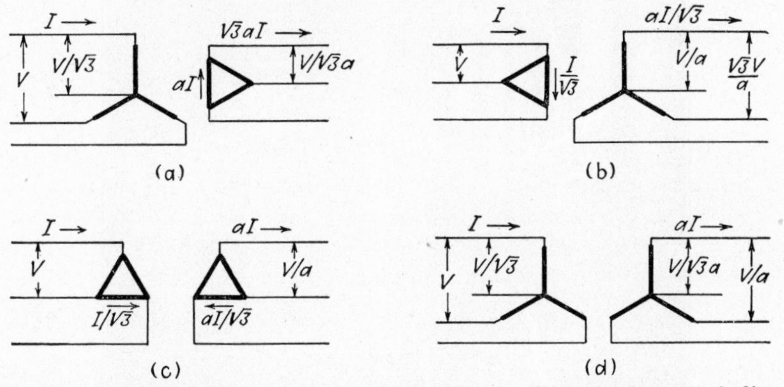

FIG. A-23. Common 3-phase transformer connections. The transformer windings are indicated by the heavy lines.

impressed primary line-to-line voltages V and line currents I when the ratio of primary to secondary turns N_1/N_2 is a and ideal transformers are assumed. It will be noted that for fixed line-to-line voltages and total kva, the kva rating of each transformer is one-third of the kva rating of the bank, regardless of the connections used, but the voltage and current ratings of the individual transformers depend on the connections.

The Y-Δ connection is commonly used in stepping down from a high voltage to a medium or low voltage. One of the reasons is that a neutral is thereby provided for grounding on the high-voltage side, a procedure which may be shown to be desirable in most cases. Conversely, the Δ-Y connection is commonly used for stepping up to a high voltage. The Δ-Δ connection has the advantage that one transformer may be removed for repair or maintenance while the remaining two continue to function as a 3-phase bank with, however, the rating reduced to 58 per cent of that of the original bank; this is known as the *open-delta*, or *V*, *connection*. The Y-Y connection is seldom used, because of difficulties with exciting-current phenomena, some of which are described in part *b* of this article.

Instead of three single-phase transformers, a 3-phase bank may consist of one 3-phase transformer having all six windings on a common core and contained within a common tank. The internal construction of a typical large 3-phase transformer is shown in Fig. A-24. Advantages of 3-phase transformers are that they cost less, weigh less, require less floor space, and have somewhat higher efficiency. Disadvantages are the

FIG. A-24. Core and coils of a 3-phase core-type transformer rated 7,500 kva self-cooled, 10,000 kva forced-air cooled, 66 kv Δ : 12.5 kv Y. Taps on the windings permit changing the ratio under load through a range of ± 10 per cent. (*Courtesy of Allis-Chalmers Manufacturing Company.*)

greater cost of stand-by units and the increased cost and inconvenience of repairs.

Circuit computations involving 3-phase transformer banks under balanced conditions can be made by dealing with only one of the transformers or phases and recognizing that conditions are the same in the other two transformers except for the phase displacements associated with a 3-phase system. It is usually convenient to carry out the computations on a per-phase-Y line-to-neutral basis, since transformer impedances can then be added directly in series with transmission-line impedances. The impedances of transmission lines can be referred from one side of the transformer bank to the other by use of the square of the ideal line-to-line voltage ratio of the bank. In dealing with Y-Δ or Δ-Y banks all quantities can be referred to the Y-connected side. In dealing with Δ-Δ banks in series with transmission lines, it is convenient to replace the Δ-connected impedances of the transformers by equivalent Y-connected impedances. It is well known that a balanced Δ-connected circuit of Z_Δ ohms per phase is equivalent to a balanced Y-connected circuit of Z_Y ohms per phase if

$$Z_Y = \tfrac{1}{3} Z_\Delta \tag{A-49}$$

Example A-7. Three single-phase 50-kva 2,400:240-volt transformers identical with that of Example A-4 are connected Y-Δ in a 3-phase 150-kva bank to step down the voltage at the load end of a feeder whose impedance is $0.15 + j1.00$ ohm per phase. The voltage at the sending end of the feeder is 4,160 volts, line to line. On their secondary sides the transformers supply a balanced 3-phase load through a feeder whose impedance is $0.0005 + j0.0020$ ohm per phase.

Find the line-to-line voltage at the load when the load draws rated current from the transformers at a power factor of 0.80 lagging.

Solution. The computations can be made on a per-phase-Y basis by referring everything to the high-voltage Y-connected side of the transformer bank. The voltage at the sending end of the feeder is equivalent to a source voltage V_s of

$$V_s = \frac{4{,}160}{\sqrt{3}} = 2{,}400 \text{ volts to neutral}$$

From the transformer rating, the rated current on the high-voltage side is 20.8 amp per phase Y. The low-voltage feeder impedance referred to the high-voltage side by means of the square of the ideal line-to-line voltage ratio of the bank is

$$\left(\frac{4{,}160}{240}\right)^2 (0.0005 + j0.0020) = 0.15 + j0.60 \text{ ohm}$$

and the combined series impedance of the high-voltage and low-voltage feeders referred to the high-voltage side is

$$Z_{\text{feeder}} = 0.30 + j1.60 \text{ ohms per phase Y}$$

From Example A-4, the equivalent impedance of the transformer bank referred to its high-voltage Y-connected side is

$$Z_{eqH} = 1.42 + j1.82 \text{ ohms per phase Y}$$

The equivalent circuit for one phase referred to the Y-connected primary side then is exactly the same as Fig. A-16*a*, and the solution on a per-phase basis is exactly the same as the solution of Example A-3, whence the load voltage referred to the high-voltage side is 2,329 volts to neutral. The actual load voltage is

$$V_{\text{load}} = 233 \text{ volts, line to line}$$

This is the line-to-line voltage because the secondaries are Δ-connected.

Example A-8. The three transformers of Example A-7 are connected Δ-Δ and supplied with power from a 2,400-volt (line-to-line) 3-phase bus through a feeder whose impedance is $0.20 + j0.80$ ohm per phase. The equivalent impedance of each transformer referred to its high-voltage side is $Z_{eqH} = 1.42 + j\,1.82$ ohms. The secondaries supply power to a load through a 240-volt feeder whose impedance is $0.0010 + j0.0020$ ohms per phase.

Compute the steady-state short-circuit currents in the primary and secondary feeder wires and in the primary and secondary windings of the transformers resulting from a 3-phase short circuit at the load terminals.

Solution. The computations will be made on an equivalent per-phase-Y basis, with everything referred to the high-voltage side. The source voltage is

$$V_s = \frac{2{,}400}{\sqrt{3}} = 1{,}385 \text{ volts to neutral}$$

The high-voltage feeder impedance Z_H is $0.20 + j0.80$ ohm per phase Y. The low-voltage feeder impedance Z_X referred to the high-voltage side by the square of the ideal line-to-line voltage ratio is

$$Z_X = \left(\frac{2{,}400}{240}\right)^2 (0.0010 + j0.0020) = 0.10 + j0.20 \text{ ohm per phase Y}$$

From Eq. A-49 and the transformer data in Example A-7, the equivalent Y value of the transformer impedance is

$$Z_{eqY} = \tfrac{1}{3}(1.42 + j1.82) = 0.473 + j0.607 \text{ ohm per phase Y}$$

The total series impedance is

$$Z = 0.773 + j1.607, \text{ or } 1.78 \text{ ohm per phase Y}$$

The short-circuit current in the high-voltage feeder wires is

$$\frac{V_s}{Z} = \frac{1{,}385}{1.78} = 778 \text{ amp}$$

The current in the low-voltage feeder wires is

$$\frac{2{,}400}{240}(778) = 7{,}780 \text{ amp}$$

The current in the high-voltage Δ-connected primary windings is

$$\frac{778}{\sqrt{3}} = 449 \text{ amp}$$

and the current in the low-voltage Δ-connected secondaries is

$$\frac{2{,}400}{240}(449) = 4{,}490 \text{ amp}$$

b. Third-harmonic Phenomena in Three-phase Circuits. As shown in Art. A-2, the exciting current for sine-wave flux must have a fairly large third-harmonic component, because of the nonlinear magnetic characteristics of the core. This third harmonic may have a significant effect on the behavior of 3-phase transformer banks.

Figure A-25 shows three identical waveforms differing in phase by one-third of a cycle, each comprising a fundamental and a third-harmonic component. These waveforms may represent currents or voltages in a balanced 3-phase system. Note that, while the fundamentals differ in phase by 120°, the third harmonics are in phase. This latter fact is the basis for all the peculiarities of the third-harmonic behavior.

Suppose that the waves represent the three line currents i_a, i_b, and i_c in a balanced Y-connected system whose neutrals are interconnected, as in Fig. A-26*a*. The current i_n returning to the source in the neutral conductor is

$$i_n = i_a + i_b + i_c \qquad \text{(A-50)}$$

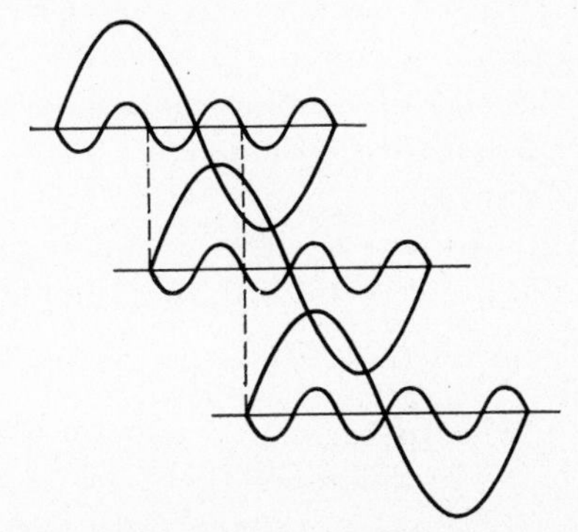

FIG. A-25. Balanced 3-phase waveforms with third harmonics.

The instantaneous sum of the fundamental components of the three line currents is zero, for they are three equal sine waves differing in phase by 120°. Therefore there is no fundamental current in the neutral wire under balanced conditions. The third harmonics, however, are in phase. Consequently their instantaneous sum is three times the instantaneous value i_3 of any one of them. The neutral wire provides the return path for the three third-harmonic currents. If the neutral wire is disconnected, $i_n = 0$ and therefore third-harmonic currents cannot exist.

Now consider the voltages in a Y-connected system such as that of Fig. A-26*a*. Let the three waves in Fig. A-25 be the instantaneous voltages to neutral v_{an}, v_{bn}, v_{cn}, respectively, where the voltages are falls in

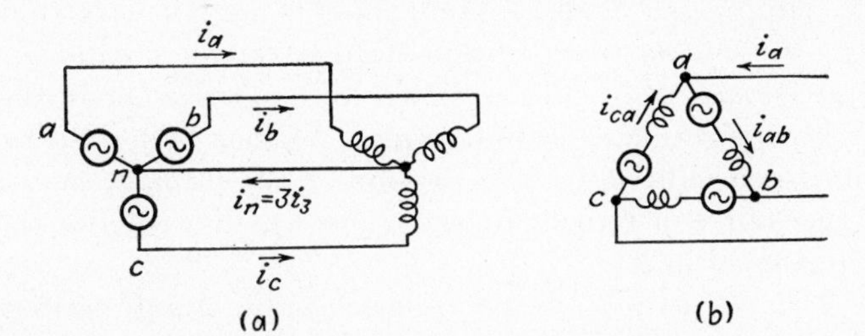

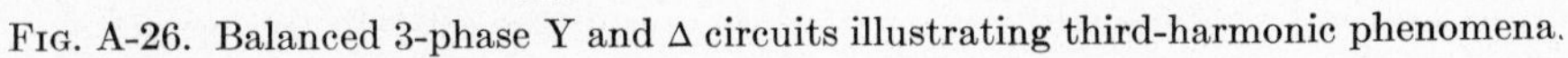

FIG. A-26. Balanced 3-phase Y and Δ circuits illustrating third-harmonic phenomena.

potential in the direction from the first to the second subscript. The instantaneous line-to-line voltage v_{ab} is

$$v_{ab} = v_{an} - v_{bn} \qquad \text{(A-51)}$$

The third-harmonic components of the line-to-neutral voltages cancel, and therefore there are no third-harmonic components in the line-to-line voltages even though such harmonics may be present in the line-to-neutral voltages.

Now consider the circuit of Fig. A-26*b*, which may represent the Δ-connected windings of a generator or a transformer bank. Let the three waves in Fig. A-25 be the emfs e_{ab}, e_{bc}, and e_{ca} generated in the three phases. The third-harmonic components E_3 are in phase and therefore produce a resultant emf $3E_3$ acting around the Δ. The emf $3E_3$ gives rise to a third-harmonic current I_3 which circulates within the Δ. The third-harmonic emf is consumed by the impedance drop in each phase, and the third-harmonic voltage between line terminals is zero. Only the fundamental components of the generated emfs appear between line terminals.

Now let the three waves in Fig. A-25 be the currents i_{ab}, i_{bc}, and i_{ca} in the Δ-connected windings of Fig. A-26*b*. The line current i_a is

$$i_a = i_{ab} - i_{ca} \tag{A-52}$$

The third-harmonic components on the right-hand side of Eq. A-52 cancel, and therefore there are no third-harmonic components in the line currents, even though third-harmonic currents caused by third-harmonic emfs generated internally in the Δ may circulate within the Δ.

Since the exciting current of a transformer for sine-wave flux must contain a third-harmonic component, the following conclusions can be drawn with respect to 3-phase connections of single-phase transformers:

1. If either the primary or the secondary windings (or both) are connected in Δ, the third-harmonic exciting currents will flow therein and the voltages will be sinusoidal.

2. In the Y-Y connection with isolated neutrals the third-harmonic currents are suppressed, and therefore the flux cannot vary sinusoidally. The voltages to neutral then contain third-harmonic components which may be large enough to become troublesome. This is one of the reasons why the Y-Y connection is seldom used. When it is desired to use this connection, it is usually advisable to connect the primary neutral to the neutral of the source or to provide the transformers with a tertiary set of windings connected in Δ.

c. Phase Transformation. A polyphase system of any desired number of phases can be derived from any other polyphase system by means of a bank of transformers. The general principles are rather simple. Figure A-27*a* shows two transformers whose primaries are supplied with voltages V_a and V_b obtained from two different phases of a polyphase system and represented vectorially in Fig. A-27*b*. The transformers have ratios of transformation N_1/N_2 of a_1 and a_2, respectively. The secondary voltages are V_a/a_1 and V_b/a_2, ideal transformers being assumed. If the secondaries are connected in series with the relative polarities indicated by the dot markings in Fig. A-27a, the resultant voltage V_2 is, vectorially,

$$V_2 = \frac{V_a}{a_1} + \frac{V_b}{a_2} \tag{A-53}$$

Note that by proper choice of the transformation ratios a_1 and a_2, the vector V_2 can be made to lie anywhere within the angle between the two secondary voltage vectors. By reversal of one or both of the transformer

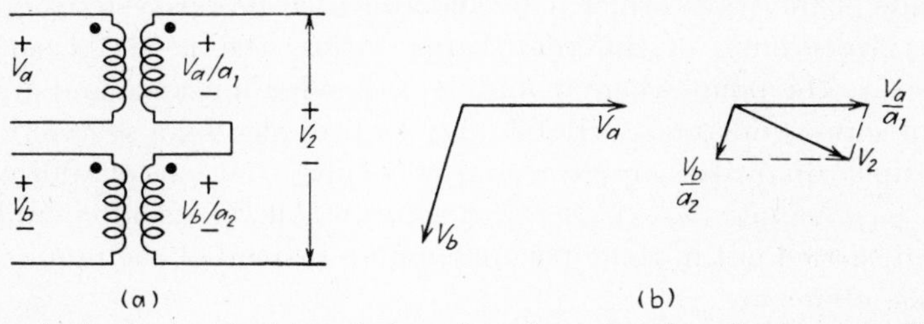

FIG. A-27. Basic principles of phase transformation in polyphase circuits.

secondaries, V_2 can be made to lie at any desired angle throughout the entire 360°. Thus a secondary voltage having any desired phase with respect to the primary voltages can be obtained. The problem is merely one of the geometry of the vector diagram.

Now suppose each of the transformers had several independent secondaries. By suitable interconnections among these secondaries, a number of secondary voltages having any desired magnitudes and phase relations

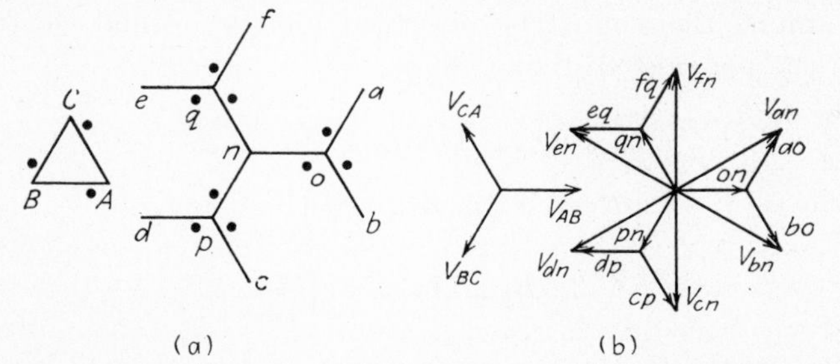

FIG. A-28. (a) 3-phase-Δ to 6-phase-forked-Y transformer connections. (b) Voltage vector diagram.

among themselves can be obtained. All that is necessary is that we start with two primary voltages which are out of phase. Through use of this principle, a balanced polyphase system of voltages having any desired number of phases can be derived from any other polyphase system.

As an example, the 3-phase-Δ to 6-*phase-forked*-Y, or *double-zigzag*, connection sometimes used to supply 6-phase power to rectifiers is shown in Fig. A-28a. Each transformer has a primary and three independent secondaries, the latter having the same number of turns. The primary and secondary windings drawn parallel to one another are on the same transformer; for example, the secondary windings *on*, *pd*, and *qe* are mated with the primary winding AB. The vector diagram of voltages is shown in Fig. A-28*b*, from which it can be seen that balanced 6-phase voltages to neutral are obtained.

A-10. The Per-unit System. In the preceding discussions and examples, considerable care must be taken to have all quantities referred to the same side of the transformer. For complicated power systems involving many transformers of different turns ratios, the need for such care increases to the point where it may be a decided nuisance and a possible cause of serious mistakes. Relief may be provided by a system in which all pertinent quantities are expressed as decimal fractions of appropriately chosen base values—*i.e.*, in *per-unit values*. All the usual computations are then carried out in these per-unit values instead of the familiar volts, amperes, ohms, etc.

Quantities such as voltage V, current I, power P, reactive power Q, volt-amperes VA, resistance R, reactance X, impedance Z, conductance G, susceptance B, and admittance Y can be translated to and from per-unit form as follows:

$$\text{Quantity in per unit} = \frac{\text{actual quantity}}{\text{base value of quantity}} \tag{A-54}$$

where *actual quantity* refers to the value in volts, amperes, ohms, etc. To a certain extent, base values may be chosen arbitrarily, but certain relations among them must be observed for the normal electrical laws to hold in the per-unit system. Thus,

$$P_{\text{base}},\ Q_{\text{base}},\ VA_{\text{base}} = V_{\text{base}} I_{\text{base}} \tag{A-55}$$

$$R_{\text{base}},\ X_{\text{base}},\ Z_{\text{base}} = \frac{V_{\text{base}}}{I_{\text{base}}} \tag{A-56}$$

$$G_{\text{base}},\ B_{\text{base}},\ Y_{\text{base}} = \frac{I_{\text{base}}}{V_{\text{base}}} \tag{A-57}$$

In normal usage, values of VA_{base} and V_{base} are chosen first; values of I_{base} and all other quantities in Eqs. A-55 to A-57 are thereby established.

The value of VA_{base} must be the same over the entire system concerned. When a transformer is encountered, the values of V_{base} are different on each side and must be in the same ratio as are the turns on the transformer. Usually the rated or nominal voltages of the respective sides are chosen. The process of referring quantities to one side of the transformer is then taken care of automatically by the use of Eqs. A-54 to A-57 in finding and interpreting per-unit values. The procedure thus becomes one of translating all quantities to per-unit values, using these values in all the customary circuit-analysis techniques, and translating the end results back to the more usual forms.

When only one electrical device, such as a transformer, is involved, the device's own rating is generally used for the volt-ampere base. When expressed in per unit on the rating as a base, the characteristics of power and distribution transformers do not vary much over a wide range of ratings. For example, the exciting current usually is between 0.02 and 0.06 per unit, the equivalent resistance usually is between 0.005 and 0.02 per unit (the smaller values applying to large transformers), and the equivalent reactance usually is between 0.015 and 0.10 per unit (the larger values applying to large high-voltage transformers). Similarly, the per-unit values of synchronous- and induction-machine constants fall within a relatively narrow range. When several devices are involved, however, an arbitrary choice of volt-ampere base must usually be made in order that the same base be used for the over-all system. Per-unit values may be changed from one volt-ampere base to another with the same voltage base by the relations

$$(P,Q,VA,G,B,Y)_{\text{pu on base 2}} = (P,Q,VA,G,B,Y)_{\text{pu on base 1}} \frac{(VA)_{\text{base 1}}}{(VA)_{\text{base 2}}} \qquad \text{(A-58)}$$

$$(R,X,Z)_{\text{pu on base 2}} = (R,X,Z)_{\text{pu on base 1}} \frac{(VA)_{\text{base 2}}}{(VA)_{\text{base 1}}} \qquad \text{(A-59)}$$

Example A-9. The exciting current measured on the low-voltage side of the 50-kva 2,400:240-volt transformer of Examples A-4 and A-5 is 5.41 amp. Its equivalent impedance referred to the high-voltage side is $1.42 + j1.82$ ohms. Take the transformer rating as a base.

a. Express the exciting current in per unit on the low-voltage side and also on the high-voltage side.

b. Express the equivalent impedance in per unit on the high-voltage side and also on the low-voltage side.

Solution. The base values of voltages and currents are

$$V_{\text{base } H} = 2{,}400 \text{ volts} \qquad V_{\text{base } X} = 240 \text{ volts}$$
$$I_{\text{base } H} = 20.8 \text{ amp} \qquad I_{\text{base } X} = 208 \text{ amp}$$

where subscripts H and X indicate the high- and low-voltage sides, respectively. From Eq. A-56,

$$Z_{\text{base } H} = \frac{2{,}400}{20.8} = 115.2 \text{ ohms}$$

$$Z_{\text{base } X} = \frac{240}{208} = 1.152 \text{ ohms}$$

a. From Eq. A-54,

$$I_{\varphi X} = \frac{5.41}{208} = 0.0260 \text{ per unit}$$

The exciting current referred to the high-voltage side is 0.541 amp. Its per unit value is

$$I_{\varphi H} = \frac{0.541}{20.8} = 0.0260 \text{ per unit}$$

The per-unit values are the same referred to either side. The turns ratios required to refer currents in amperes from one side of the transformer to the other (as in Eq. A-18) are taken care of in the per-unit system by the base values for currents on the two sides when the volt-ampere base is the same on both sides and the voltage bases are in the ratio of the turns.

b. From Eq. A-54 and the value for $Z_{\text{base } H}$,

$$Z_{eqH} = \frac{1.42 + j1.82}{115.2} = 0.0123 + j0.0158 \text{ per unit}$$

The equivalent impedance referred to the low-voltage side is $0.0142 + j0.0182$ ohm. Its per-unit value is

$$Z_{eqX} = \frac{0.0142 + j0.0182}{1.152} = 0.0123 + j0.0158 \text{ per unit}$$

The per-unit values are the same, the referring factors being taken care of in per unit by the base values.

When applied to 3-phase problems, the base values for the per-unit system are chosen so that the relations for a balanced 3-phase system hold among them:

$$(P_{\text{base}}, Q_{\text{base}}, VA_{\text{base}}) \text{ 3-phase} = 3VA_{\text{base per phase}} \tag{A-60}$$

$$V_{\text{base (line to line)}} = \sqrt{3}\, V_{\text{base (line to neutral)}} \tag{A-61}$$

$$I_{\text{base (per phase }\Delta)} = \frac{1}{\sqrt{3}} I_{\text{base (per phase Y)}} \tag{A-62}$$

In dealing with 3-phase systems the 3-phase kva base and the line-to-line voltage base are usually chosen first. The base values for phase voltages and currents then follow from Eqs. A-60, A-61, and A-62. Equations A-55, A-56, and A-57 still apply to the base values per phase. For example, the base value for Y-connected impedances is given by Eq. A-56 with V_{base} taken as the base voltage to neutral and I_{base} taken as the base current per phase Y; the base value for Δ-connected impedances is also given by Eq. A-56 but with V_{base} taken as the base line-to-line voltage and I_{base} taken as the base current per phase Δ. Division of Eq. A-61 by Eq. A-62 shows that

$$Z_{\text{base (per phase }\Delta)} = 3Z_{\text{base (per phase Y)}} \tag{A-63}$$

The factors of $\sqrt{3}$ and 3 relating Δ and Y quantities in volts, amperes, and ohms in a balanced 3-phase system are thus automatically taken care of in per unit by the base values. Such 3-phase problems can be solved in per unit as if they were single-phase problems, without paying any attention to the details of the transformer connections except in translating volt-ampere-ohm values into and out of the per-unit system.

Example A-10. Solve Example A-8 in per unit on the transformer-bank rating as a base.

Solution. The base values on a 150-kva 3-phase base are shown in Table A-1.

TABLE A-1
BASE VALUES FOR EXAMPLE A-10

	V_{base}, volts	I_{base}, amp	Z_{base}, ohms
Transformers, per phase Δ, H	2,400	20.8	115.2
Transformers, per phase Δ, X	240	208	1.152
Feeder, per phase Y, H	1,385	36.0	38.4
Feeder, per phase Y, X	138.5	360	0.384

Converting the impedances given in Example A-8 to per unit gives

$$Z_{\text{feeder } H} = \frac{0.20 + j0.80}{38.4} = 0.0052 + j0.0208 \text{ per unit}$$

$$Z_{\text{feeder } X} = \frac{0.0010 + j0.0020}{0.384} = 0.0026 + j0.0052 \text{ per unit}$$

and for the transformers,

$$Z_{eq} = \frac{1.42 + j1.82}{115.2} = 0.0123 + j0.0158 \text{ per unit}$$

$$\text{Total impedance } Z = \text{sum} = \overline{0.0201 + j0.0418 \text{ per unit}}$$

The magnitude of Z is 0.0468 per unit. The source voltage is 1.00 per unit. The short-circuit current is

$$I = \frac{1.00}{0.0468} = 21.4 \text{ per unit}$$

The ampere values of the short-circuit currents in the various parts of the system are 21.4 times their base values. For example, the current in the low-voltage feeder wires is (21.4)(360) = 7,700 amp.

Note that the same per-unit value for the Δ-connected transformer impedances is obtained by converting their value to an equivalent Y value in ohms (Eq. A-49), and then converting this ohmic value to per unit by use of the per-phase-Y base impedance; thus

$$Z_{eq} = \frac{1.42 + j1.82}{3 \times 38.4} = 0.0123 + j0.0158 \text{ per unit}$$

When expressed in per unit by use of the appropriate base for each component, the relations between Δ and Y quantities are taken into account by the base values, and the system can be treated as an equivalent Y-connected system.

A-11. Multicircuit Transformers. Transformers having three or more windings, known as *multicircuit* or *multiwinding transformers*, are often used to interconnect three or more circuits which may have different voltages. For these purposes a multicircuit transformer costs less and is more efficient than an equivalent number of two-circuit transformers. A transformer having a primary and two secondaries is generally used to supply power to electronic circuits. One secondary supplies power at a few volts to heat the cathodes of the electron tubes, and the other supplies power at a few hundred volts to the plate circuits. The distribution transformers used to supply power for domestic purposes usually have two 120-volt secondaries connected in series. Lighting circuits are connected across each of the 120-volt windings, while electric ranges, domestic hot-water heaters, and other similar loads are supplied with 240-volt power from the series-connected secondaries. A large distribution system may be supplied through a 3-phase bank of multicircuit transformers from two or more transmission systems having different voltages. The 3-phase transformer banks used to interconnect two transmission systems of different voltages often have a third, or *tertiary*, set of windings to provide voltage for auxiliary power purposes in the substation or to supply a local distribution system. Static capacitors, or synchronous condensers, may be connected to the tertiary windings for purposes of power-factor correction or voltage regulation. Sometimes Δ-connected tertiary windings are put on 3-phase banks to provide a circuit for the third harmonics of the exciting current.

Some of the problems arising in the use of multicircuit transformers concern the effects of leakage impedances on voltage regulation, short-circuit currents, and division of load among circuits. These problems can be solved by an equivalent-circuit technique similar to that used in dealing with two-circuit transformers. The equivalent circuits are more complicated, however, because they must take into account the leakage impedances associated with each pair of windings. For example, the leakage-impedance voltage drops in a three-circuit transformer can be represented by three impedances, but a four-circuit transformer requires six. In these equivalent circuits all quantities are referred to a common base, either by use of the appropriate turns ratios as referring factors or by expressing all quantities in per unit. The exciting current usually is neglected.

The following discussion will be confined to three-circuit transformers.[2] A three-circuit transformer is shown schematically in Fig. A-29*a*, in which 1-1′ is the primary winding. Secondary and tertiary quantities are referred to the primary, and windings 2-2′ and 3-3′ indicate the equivalent secondary and tertiary on the basis of a 1-to-1-to-1 turns ratio. Terminals 1′, 2′, and 3′ are of like polarity. These terminals can be considered to be connected together to a common terminal 0, as shown by the dotted lines. The three external circuits can then be considered to be connected between terminals 1, 2, and 3, respectively, and the common

[2] For discussion of the general theory of multicircuit transformers see, for example, L. F. Blume, editor, "Transformer Engineering," 2d ed., Chap. V, John Wiley & Sons, Inc., New York, 1951; EE Staff, MIT, "Magnetic Circuits and Transformers," John Wiley & Sons, Inc., Chap. XXVII, New York, 1943.

terminal 0. If the exciting current is neglected, the vector sum of the currents I_1, I_2, and I_3 is zero. The current in the connection between terminal 0 and the junction of terminals 1′, 2′, 3′ therefore is zero, and this connection can be omitted without disturbing the currents. The transformer then is equivalent to the arrangement shown in Fig. A-29*b*, in which the box is a network with three terminals and contains impedances accounting for the leakage-impedance voltage drops. In so far as its effects on the external circuits are concerned such a three-terminal network is equivalent to three impedances connected either in Δ or in Y. The Y arrangement usually is more convenient. The transformer there-

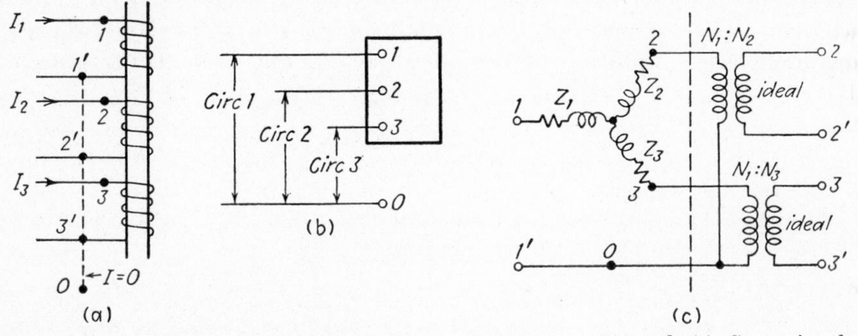

FIG. A-29. (*a*) Elementary three-winding transformer. (*b*) and (*c*) Steps in the development of its equivalent circuit.

fore is equivalent to the circuit shown to the left of the dotted line in Fig. A-29*c*, in which the impedances Z_1, Z_2, and Z_3 account for the effects of the leakage impedances among the three pairs of windings. If desired the factors referring all quantities to, say, the primary can be shown explicitly by means of ideal transformers as shown to the right of the dotted line in Fig. A-29*c*. The terminals 2-2′ and 3-3′ to the right of these ideal transformers then are equivalent to the actual secondary and tertiary terminals. When the ideal transformers are included, the equivalent circuit does not require a conductive connection among the three circuits. Usually the ideal transformers can be omitted, however, and the external circuits can be considered to be connected between the common point 0 and terminals 1, 2, and 3, respectively, to the left of the dotted line. One then simply remembers that all quantities are referred to a common base.

This equivalent circuit represents the impedance phenomena associated with three windings on a common magnetic core. It applies equally well to the external behavior of autotransformers and of transformers having separate windings, although the internal phenomena differ. It also applies on a per-phase basis to polyphase connections except the more complicated ones involving cross connections among the various phases (as, for example, in the double-zigzag secondary circuits of Fig. A-28*a*).

The impedances of Fig. A-29c can readily be determined from the results of three simple short-circuit tests. Thus if Z_{12} is the short-circuit impedance of circuits 1 and 2 with circuit 3 open, inspection of the equivalent circuit (Fig. A-29c) shows that

$$Z_{12} = Z_1 + Z_2 \tag{A-64}$$

Similarly

$$Z_{13} = Z_1 + Z_3 \tag{A-65}$$
$$Z_{23} = Z_2 + Z_3 \tag{A-66}$$

where Z_{13} is the short-circuit impedance of circuits 1 and 3 with circuit 2 open and Z_{23} is the short-circuit impedance of circuits 2 and 3 with circuit 1 open. These short-circuit impedances are the values referred to a common base. Solution of Eqs. A-64, A-65, and A-66 then gives

$$Z_1 = \tfrac{1}{2}(Z_{12} + Z_{13} - Z_{23}) \tag{A-67}$$
$$Z_2 = \tfrac{1}{2}(Z_{23} + Z_{12} - Z_{13}) \tag{A-68}$$
$$Z_3 = \tfrac{1}{2}(Z_{13} + Z_{23} - Z_{12}) \tag{A-69}$$

Example A-11. The results of three short-circuit tests on a 7,960:2,400:600-volt 60-cps single-phase transformer are as follows:

Test	Winding excited	Winding short-circuited	Applied voltage, volts	Current in excited winding, amp
1	1	2	252	62.7
2	1	3	770	62.7
3	2	3	217	208

Resistances may be neglected. The rating of the 7,960-volt primary winding is 1,000 kva, of the 2,400-volt secondary is 500 kva, and of the 600-volt tertiary is 500 kva.

a. Compute the per-unit values of the equivalent-circuit impedances of this transformer on a 1,000-kva rated-voltage base.

b. Three of these transformers are used in a 3,000-kva Y-Δ-Δ 3-phase bank to supply 2,400-volt and 600-volt auxiliary power circuits in a generating station. The Y-connected primaries are connected to the 13,800-volt main bus. Compute the per-unit values of the steady-state short-circuit currents and of the voltage at the terminals of the secondary windings if a 3-phase short circuit occurs at the terminals of the tertiary windings with 13,800 volts maintained at the primary line terminals. Use a 3,000-kva 3-phase rated-voltage base.

Solution. *a.* First convert the short-circuit data to per unit on 1,000 kva per phase. For primary,

$$V_{\text{base}} = 7{,}960 \text{ volts}$$
$$I_{\text{base}} = \frac{1{,}000}{7.96} = 125.4 \text{ amp}$$

For secondary,

$$V_{\text{base}} = 2{,}400 \text{ volts}$$
$$I_{\text{base}} = \frac{1{,}000}{2.4} = 416 \text{ amp}$$

Conversion of the test data to per unit then gives

Test	Windings	V	I
1	1 and 2	0.0316	0.500
2	1 and 3	0.0967	0.500
3	2 and 3	0.0905	0.500

From Test 1, the short-circuit impedance Z_{12} is

$$Z_{12} = \frac{0.0316}{0.500} = 0.0632 \text{ per unit}$$

Similarly, from Tests 2 and 3,

$$Z_{13} = \frac{0.0967}{0.500} = 0.1934 \text{ per unit}$$

$$Z_{23} = \frac{0.0905}{0.500} = 0.1910 \text{ per unit}$$

From Eqs. A-67, A-68, and A-69, the equivalent-circuit constants are

$$Z_1 = jX_1 = j0.0378 \text{ per unit}$$
$$Z_2 = jX_2 = j0.0254 \text{ per unit}$$
$$Z_3 = jX_3 = j0.1556 \text{ per unit}$$

b. Base line-to-line voltage for the Y-connected primaries is $\sqrt{3}$ (7,960) = 13,800 volts, or the bus voltage is 1.00 per unit. From the equivalent circuit with a short circuit on the tertiaries,

$$I_{sc} = \frac{V_1}{Z_1 + Z_3} = \frac{V_1}{Z_{13}} = \frac{1.00}{0.1934} = 5.18 \text{ per unit}$$

(Note, however, that this current is 10.36 per unit on the rating of the tertiaries.) If the voltage drops caused by the secondary load current are neglected in comparison with those due to the short-circuit current, the secondary terminal voltage equals the voltage at the junction of the three impedances Z_1, Z_2, and Z_3 in Fig. A-29*c*, whence

$$V_2 = I_{sc}Z_3 = (5.18)(0.1556) = 0.805 \text{ per unit}$$

A-12. Résumé. Although no electromechanical energy conversion is involved in a static transformer, the theory of its performance has many points of similarity with the basic theory of the electrical behavior of a-c rotating machines. Both transformers and rotating machines comprise two or more windings on a common magnetic circuit. From the viewpoint of these windings essentially the same electromagnetic phenomena take place. For the reader who has not yet studied rotating-machine theory, this discussion should serve not only as a brief résumé of transformer theory but also as a preview of some of the similar problems to be encountered later in the analysis of rotating machines. For the reader who is already familiar with basic a-c rotating-machine theory, this discussion should strengthen the statements made at numerous points in this text regarding the basic sameness of the electromagnetic phenomena involved in a wide variety of electromagnetic devices.

In both transformers and rotating machines, a magnetic field is created by the combined action of the currents in the windings. In an iron-core transformer most of this flux is confined to the core and links all the windings. This resultant mutual flux induces voltages in the windings proportional to their numbers of turns and provides the voltage-changing property. In rotating machines most of the flux crosses the air gap and, like the core flux in a transformer, links all the windings on both stator and rotor. The voltages induced in the windings by this resultant mutual air-gap flux are similar to those induced by the resultant core flux in a transformer. The difference is that mechanical motion together with electromechanical energy conversion is involved in rotating machines. The torque associated with this energy-conversion process is created by the interaction of the air-gap flux with the magnetic field of the rotor currents.

In addition to the useful mutual fluxes, in both transformers and rotating machines there are leakage fluxes which link one winding without linking the other. Although the detailed picture of the leakage fluxes in rotating machines is more complicated than in transformers (see Art. 4-9), their effects are essentially the same. In both, the leakage fluxes induce voltages in a-c windings which are accounted for as leakage-reactance voltage drops. In both, the leakage-flux paths are mostly in air, and the leakage fluxes are very nearly linearly proportional to the currents producing them. The leakage reactances therefore are assumed to be constant, independent of the degree of saturation of the main magnetic circuit.

In a transformer, the time-varying core flux induces voltages in the windings in accordance with Faraday's law. For sinusoidal variations, the relation between the rms value of the induced voltage and the maximum value of the flux is given by Eq. A-5. In polyphase a-c machines of the synchronous or induction type, the resultant air-gap flux consists of a constant-amplitude wave sinusoidally distributed around the air gap and rotating at constant speed. A concentrated full-pitch winding (such as that in Fig. 3-11*a*, for example) then is subjected to a sinusoidal time variation in flux linkages caused by relative motion of the field and the windings, and the voltage induced in it is given by Eq. 3-36, which is of exactly the same form as the transformer equation, A-5. The fact that rotating-machine windings are distributed in a number of slots modifies the voltage equation by introducing correction factors for pitch and breadth, as in Eq. 4-14. From the viewpoint of the winding, however, the induced-voltage phenomena in transformers and rotating machines are essentially the same, although the internal phenomena causing the time variations in flux linkages are different. In a rotating machine the time variation in flux linkages is caused by relative motion of the field and the winding, and the induced voltage is sometimes referred to as a *speed voltage*. Speed voltages accompanied by mechanical motion are a necessary counterpart of electromechanical energy conversion. In a static transformer, however, the time variation of flux linkages is caused by the growth and decay of a stationary magnetic field, no mechanical motion is involved, and no electromechanical energy conversion takes place.

The resultant core flux in a transformer induces a counter emf in the primary which together with the primary resistance and leakage-reactance voltage drops must balance the applied voltage. Since the resistance and leakage-reactance voltage drops usually are small, the counter emf must approximately equal the applied voltage and the core flux must adjust itself accordingly, as in Eq. A-6. Exactly similar phenomena must take place in the armature windings of an a-c motor—the resultant air-gap flux wave must adjust itself to generate a counter emf approximately equal to the applied voltage. In both transformers and rotating machines, the net mmf of all the currents must accordingly adjust itself to create the resultant flux required by this voltage balance. This basic concept is emphasized in numerous places throughout the text. In any a-c electromagnetic device in which the resistance and leakage-reactance voltage drops are small, the resultant flux is very nearly determined by the applied voltage and frequency, and the currents must adjust themselves accordingly so as to produce the mmf required to create this flux.

In a transformer, the secondary current is determined by the voltage induced in its secondary, the secondary leakage impedance, and the electrical load. In an induction motor, the secondary (rotor) current is determined by the voltage induced in its secondary, the secondary leakage impedance, and the mechanical load on its shaft. Essentially the same phenomena take place in the primary winding of the transformer and in the armature (stator) windings of induction and synchronous motors. In all three, the primary, or armature, current must adjust itself so that the combined mmf of all the currents creates the flux required by the applied voltage. In transformers and induction motors it is convenient to treat this mmf balance by resolving the primary current into two components: a load component whose mmf balances that of the secondary current, and an exciting component which sets up the flux and accounts for the power input corresponding to the core loss. The exciting current lags the applied voltage by nearly 90°. When all the excitation is supplied to a-c windings, lagging reactive kva input is required to create the flux, as shown in Art. A-2. With synchronous machines, however, a controllable amount of excitation is supplied by the d-c field winding. The reactive kva input to the armature then adjusts itself so that the combined excitation furnished by it and by the d-c field excitation creates the air-gap flux required by the applied voltage. In so far as electromagnetic phenomena are concerned, however, there is no basic difference between the behavior of transformers, induction machines, and synchronous machines.

The analysis of many electrical devices is greatly facilitated by representing them by equivalent electric circuits comprising R, L, and C circuit parameters and voltage sources connected so that the electrical behavior of the circuit is essentially the same as that of the device which it represents. Such representation immediately permits the well-known techniques of circuit theory to be applied to the solution of the problem in hand. Often the solution suggests itself from inspection of the equivalent circuit. Thus a two-winding transformer is equivalent to the simple T circuit of Fig. A-13*d*, or the cantilever circuits of Fig. A-15*a* and *b*, if the exciting current is treated as an equivalent sine wave and if the effects of winding capacitances are negligible. This equivalent-circuit technique is also used as an aid to the analysis of rotating machines. For example, a synchronous machine operating under steady-state conditions is representable by an emf proportional to its field current in series with an inductive impedance. In so far as electrical phenomena in its primary circuits are concerned, a polyphase induction motor is equivalent to a transformer with a resistive load connected to its secondary terminals. Thus the equivalent-circuit technique is another example of the similarities in the thought processes involved in the analysis of transformers and of rotating machines.

Further examples of these basic similarities can be cited. Except for friction and windage, the losses in transformers and rotating machines are essentially the same. Tests for determining the losses and equivalent-circuit constants are essentially the same: an open-circuit or no-load test gives information regarding the excitation requirements and core losses (and friction and windage in rotating machines), while a short-circuit test together with d-c resistance measurements gives information regarding leakage reactances and copper losses. The handling of the effects of magnetic saturation is another example: in both transformers and a-c rotating machines, the leakage reactances are assumed to be unaffected by saturation, and the saturation of the main magnetic circuit is assumed to be determined by the resultant mutual or air-gap flux.

PROBLEMS

A-1. A square voltage wave having a fundamental frequency of 60 cps and equal positive and negative half-cycles of amplitude E volts is impressed on a resistanceless winding of 1,000 turns surrounding a closed iron core of 10^{-3} m^2 cross section.

a. Sketch curves of voltage and flux as functions of time.

b. Find the maximum permissible value of E if the maximum flux density is not to exceed 1.00 weber/m^2.

c. For a sinusoidal 60-cps voltage of 100 volts rms, the eddy-current loss in the core is 1.00 watt/kg. Find the eddy-current loss for the square voltage wave of amplitude 200 volts.

A-2. A 5-kva transformer has a 550-volt 60-cps primary winding with 210 turns. The net cross-sectional area of steel in the core is 11.7 in.^{2} Magnetic characteristics of the core material are given in Fig. A-9. The core weighs 100 lb. For operation at rated voltage and frequency, compute:

a. The maximum core flux, in webers
b. The maximum flux density, in kilolines per square inch
c. The core loss, in watts
d. The excitation volt-amperes
e. The exciting current, in amperes, and its core-loss and magnetizing components.

A-3. A 500-kva 60-cps transformer with an 11,000-volt primary winding takes 3.35 amp and 2,960 watts at no load, rated voltage and frequency. Another transformer has a core with all its linear dimensions $\sqrt{2}$ times as large as the corresponding dimensions of the first transformer. Core material and lamination thickness are the same in both transformers.

If the primary windings of both transformers have the same number of turns, what no-load current and power will the second transformer take with 22,000 volts at 60 cps impressed on its primary?

A-4. The flux density and core loss of a transformer operating on a voltage of 6,600 volts at 60 cps are, respectively, 70 kilolines/in.^{2} and 2,500 watts. Suppose that all the linear dimensions of the transformer core are doubled, the numbers of turns in the primary and secondary windings are halved, and the new transformer is operated on a voltage of 13,200 volts at 60 cps. The same grade of iron and the same thickness of laminations are used for both transformers.

What are the values of flux density and core loss for the new transformer?

A-5. A voltage of 200 volts rms applied to the primary winding of a small transformer results in a core flux

$$\varphi = 900 \cos \omega t \text{ kilolines}$$

and an exciting current

$$i_\varphi = \sqrt{2}\,(1.00 \sin \omega t + 0.50 \sin 3\omega t + 5.00 \cos \omega t + 2.00 \cos 3\omega t)$$

Find:

a. The core loss P_c
b. The reactive volt-amperes input
c. The effective value of the exciting current

A-6. The resistances and leakage reactances of a 10-kva 60-cps 2,400:240-volt distribution transformer are as follows:

$$r_1 = 4.20 \text{ ohms} \qquad r_2 = 0.0420 \text{ ohm}$$
$$x_{l1} = 5.50 \qquad x_{l2} = 0.0550$$

where subscript 1 denotes the 2,400-volt winding, and subscript 2 the 240-volt winding. Each quantity is referred to its own side of the transformer.

a. Find the equivalent impedance referred to the high-voltage side and referred to the low-voltage side.

b. Consider the transformer to deliver its rated kva at 0.80 power factor lagging to a load on the low-tension side with 240 volts across the load. Find the high-tension terminal voltage.

c. Repeat *b* for a power factor of 0.80 leading.

d. Consider the core loss to be 70 watts. Find the efficiency under the conditions of *b*.

e. Will the efficiency be different under *c*?

f. Suppose that the load in *b* should accidentally become short-circuited. Find the steady-state current in the high-voltage lines, assuming the voltage impressed on the transformer to remain the same as in *b*.

g. The exciting current of the transformer is 2.9 per cent of full-load current. If the transformer is given an open-circuit test at rated voltage and a short-circuit test at rated current, what will be the readings of the wattmeter, voltmeter, and ammeter in each case? Give results for instruments and impressed voltage (1) on the high-voltage side and (2) on the low-voltage side.

A-7. A 1-to-1-ratio transformer has a primary leakage reactance x_{l1} of 1.00 ohm, a secondary leakage reactance x_{l2} of 1.00 ohm, and a magnetizing susceptance b_m of 0.010 mho. Neglect the effects of resistances and core losses.

a. The windings are connected in series with their mmfs aiding, and an alternating voltage of 100 volts is impressed on the series combination. Find the current and the voltages across each winding.

b. Repeat *a* if one of the windings is reversed.

A-8. When a 50-kva 2,300:230-volt 60-cps transformer is operated at no load on rated voltage, the input is 200 watts at 0.15 power factor. When it is operating at rated load, the voltage drops in the total resistance and leakage reactance are, respectively, 1.2 and 1.8 per cent of rated voltage.

Determine the input power and power factor when the transformer delivers 30 kw at 0.80 power factor lagging and 230 volts to a load on the low-voltage side.

A-9. When operated at rated frequency and rated secondary voltage (240 volts) with the primary winding open-circuited, a 10-kva 60-cps 2,400:240-volt distribution transformer takes 63.3 watts and 0.533 amp. When operated at rated frequency and rated primary current with the secondary winding short-circuited, it takes 142 watts at 57.7 volts.

a. Compute the voltage regulation of this transformer for an inductive load of 8 kw at rated secondary voltage and 0.8 power factor.

b. Compute the efficiency of the transformer when supplying the load specified in *a*. Neglect changes in load loss with temperature.

A-10. The following data were obtained for a 20-kva 60-cps 2,400:240-volt distribution transformer tested at 60 cps:

	Voltage, volts	Current, amp	Power, watts
With high-voltage winding open-circuited	240	1.066	126.6
With low-voltage terminals short-circuited	57.5	8.34	284

a. Compute the efficiency at full-load current and rated terminal voltage at 0.8 power factor.

b. Assume that the load power factor is varied while the load current and secondary terminal voltage are held constant. By means of a vector diagram, determine the load power factor for which the regulation is greatest. What is this regulation?

A-11. *a.* Show that the maximum efficiency of a transformer operating at a constant output voltage and power factor occurs at that kva load for which the copper losses equal the core losses. In doing so, recall that the core losses remain constant, while the copper losses vary as the square of the kva load.

b. For the transformer of Prob. A-10, determine the kva output at maximum efficiency.

A-12. Find the load power factor for which the efficiency of the transformer of Prob. A-10 at rated kva load is 0.960.

A-13. A single-phase load is supplied through a 33,000-volt feeder whose impedance is $105 + j360$ ohms and a 33,000:2,400-volt transformer whose equivalent impedance is $0.26 + j1.08$ ohms referred to its low-voltage side. The load is 180 kw at 0.85 leading power factor and 2,250 volts.

a. Compute the voltage at the sending end of the feeder.

b. Compute the voltage at the primary terminals of the transformer.

c. Compute the power and reactive-power input at the sending end of the feeder.

A-14. The daily variation of load on a distribution feeder is approximately as follows:

	Kw	Reactive kva
8:00 A.M. to 1:00 P.M.	65	45
1:00 P.M. to 6:00 P.M.	80	50
6:00 P.M. to 12:00 M.	30	30
12:00 M to 8:00 A.M.	No load	

The feeder is supplied from a 100-kva transformer having a no-load core loss of 370 watts and a full-load copper loss of 1,200 watts.

Determine the all-day efficiency of the transformer.

A-15. A source which may be represented by a constant voltage of 5 volts rms in series with an internal resistance of 2,000 ohms is connected to a 50-ohm load resistance through an ideal transformer. Plot the power in milliwatts supplied to the load as a function of the transformer ratio, covering ratios ranging from 0.1 to 10.0

A-16. An audio-frequency output transformer has a primary-to-secondary turns ratio of 31.6. Its primary inductance measured with the secondary open is 19.6 henrys and measured with the secondary short-circuited is 0.207 henry. The winding resistances are negligible.

This transformer is used to connect an 8-ohm resistance load to a source which may be represented by a variable-frequency internal emf in series with an internal impedance of 5,000 ohms resistance. Compute the following that relate to the frequency characteristics of the circuit:

a. The upper half-power frequency

b. The lower half-power frequency

c. The geometric mean of these frequencies

d. The ratio of load voltage to source voltage at the frequency of *c*

A-17. An audio-frequency output transformer, having a turns ratio of 17.32, is to be used to match a source, having an internal resistance of 3,000 ohms, to a resistance load of 10 ohms. The upper and lower half-power frequencies are to be 50 and 10,000 cps. Neglect core loss and winding resistances. Specify:

a. The primary self-inductance

b. The equivalent leakage inductance referred to the primary

A-18. What will be the half-power frequencies of the circuit of Prob. A-17 if the transformer is replaced by one identical in all respects except that both the primary and secondary of the new transformer are wound with twice as many turns of wire having half the cross-sectional area? Neglect the transformer winding resistances.

A-19. A 480:120-volt 5-kva 2-winding transformer is to be used as an autotransformer to supply a 480-volt circuit from a 600-volt source. When tested as a 2-winding transformer at rated load, 0.80 power factor lagging, its efficiency is 0.965.

a. Show a diagram of connections as an autotransformer.

b. Determine its kva rating as an autotransformer.

c. Find its efficiency as an autotransformer at full load, 0.80 power factor lagging.

A-20. Figure A-30 shows a 3-winding autotransformer supplying two loads L_1 and L_2. Voltage drops and exciting current may be neglected. Find the currents in the 3 windings *ab*, *bc*, and *cd* for the following load conditions:

a. $L_1 = 360$ kva, $L_2 = 0$

b. $L_1 = 0$, $L_2 = 120$ kva

c. $L_1 = 360$ kva, $L_2 = 120$ kva at same power factor

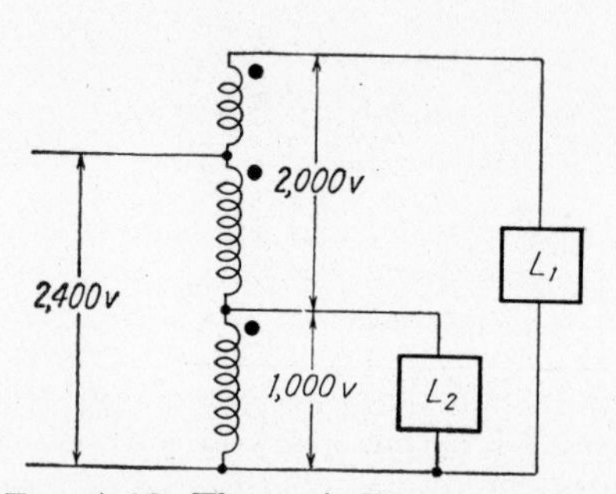

Fig. A-30. Three-winding autotransformer, Prob. A-20.

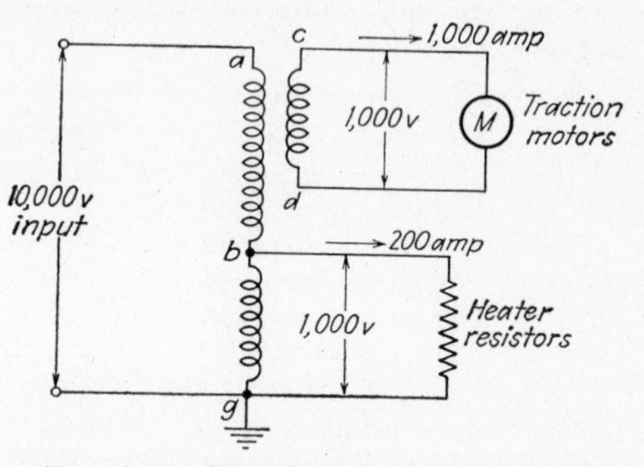

Fig. A-31. Transformer for Prob. A-21.

A-21. Figure A-31 shows a transformer in a multiple-unit motor car on an electrified suburban railroad. Show that winding *bg* will run hotter when the traction motors are shut off than when they are running. Determine the current ratings for windings *ab*, *bg*, and *cd*.

A-22. The high-voltage terminals of a 3-phase bank of three single-phase transformers are connected to a 3-wire 3-phase 13,800-volt (line to line) system. The low-voltage terminals are connected to a 3-wire 3-phase substation load rated at 1,500 kva and 2,300 volts line to line.

Specify the voltage, current, and kva ratings of each transformer (both high- and low-voltage windings) for the following connections:

a. High-voltage windings Y, low-voltage windings Δ

b. High-voltage windings Δ, low-voltage windings Y

c. High-voltage windings Y, low-voltage windings Y

d. High-voltage windings Δ, low-voltage windings Δ

A-23. In the single-line diagram of a balanced 3-phase system shown in Fig. A-32, load *A* is 200 kva of induction motors operating at 0.707 power factor; load *B* is 200 kw of lamps at 1.00 power factor.

a. Compute the kva load on each transformer in each bank.

b. Compute the line currents in the 600-volt line to the left of load *A*.

A-24. Figure A-33 shows a Δ-Δ bank of 2,400:240-volt transformers. The secondaries *ab*, *bc*, *ca* have center taps *p*, *q*, *r*. Neglect leakage-impedance voltage drops, and assume rated primary impressed voltage. With secondary voltage V_{ab} as reference vector, draw a vector diagram showing voltages *ab*, *bc*, *ca*, *pq*, *qr*, *rp*, *ap*, *bp*, *cp*. Find the magnitudes of these voltages.

A-25. A Δ-Y-connected bank of three identical 100-kva 2,400:120-volt 60-cps transformers is supplied with power through a feeder whose impedance is $0.80 + j0.30$ ohm per phase. The voltage at the sending end of the feeder is held constant at 2,400 volts line to line. The results of a single-phase short-circuit test on one of the transformers with its low-voltage terminals short-circuited are

$V_H = 52.0$ volts $f = 60$ cps
$I_H = 41.6$ amp $P = 950$ watts

a. Determine the secondary line-to-line voltage when the bank delivers rated current to a balanced 3-phase 1.00-power-factor load.

b. Compute the currents in the transformer primary and secondary windings and in the feeder wires if a solid 3-phase short circuit occurs at the secondary line terminals.

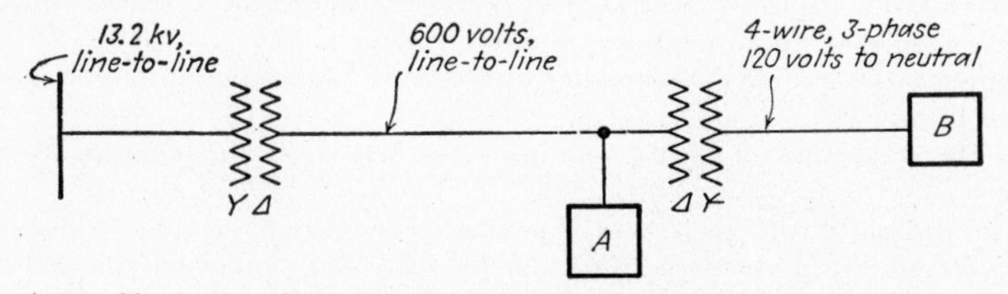

FIG. A-32. Single-line diagram of a 3-phase distribution system, Prob. A-23.

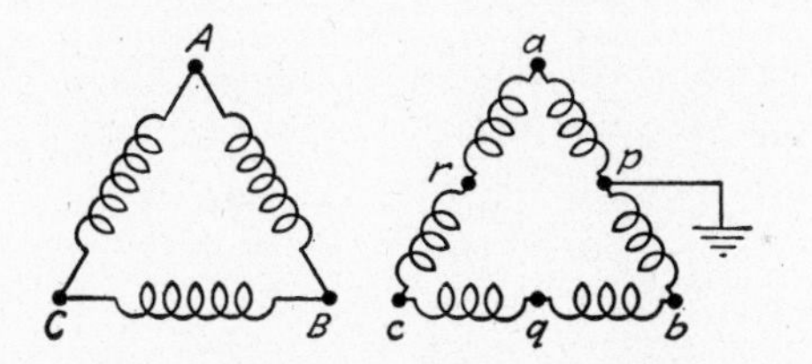

FIG. A-33. Transformer bank for Prob. A-24.

A-26. In the system of Fig. A-32 (Prob. A-23), the transformer bank supplying the lighting load *B* consists of three 75-kva 600:120-volt single-phase transformers having an impedance of $0.012 + j0.014$ per unit on their rating as a base; the sending-end bank is a 450-kva 3-phase transformer having an impedance of $0.008 + j0.021$ on its rating as a base; the 600-volt feeder has an impedance of $0.032 + j0.016$ ohm per phase.

a. For the loads specified in Prob. A-23, compute the voltage at the sending-end bus for a voltage of 115 volts to neutral at the lighting load *B*.

b. Compute the voltage at the lighting load if the induction-motor load *A* is disconnected and the sending-end voltage is held at the value found in part *a*. Consider that for small changes in voltage the lighting load *B* behaves as a constant resistance.

A-27. Consider that all windings in the Δ-double-zigzag connection (Fig. A-28) have the same number of turns. Neglect exciting current and leakage-impedance voltage drops.

a. Find the 6-phase voltage to neutral for a 3-phase impressed voltage of 100 volts.

b. Find the primary line currents for sinusoidal 6-phase line currents of 100 amp.

A-28. A 3-phase bank consisting of three single-phase 3-winding transformers is used to step down the voltage of a 3-phase 110-kv transmission line. The following data apply to one of the transformers:

Ratings:

Primary 1: 10,000 kva, 63,500 volts
Secondary 2: 5,000 kva, 11,000 volts
Tertiary 3: 5,000 kva, 7,580 volts

Short-circuit Reactances on 5,000-kva Base:

$X_{12} = 0.071$ per unit
$X_{23} = 0.054$ per unit
$X_{13} = 0.092$ per unit

Resistances are negligible.

The transformers are connected Y-Δ-Y. The Δ-connected secondaries supply their rated current to a balanced load at 0.80 power factor. The tertiaries supply their rated current to a balanced load at 1.00 power factor.

a. Compute the primary line-to-line voltage to maintain rated voltage at the secondary terminals.

b. For the conditions of part *a*, compute the line-to-line voltage at the tertiary terminals.

c. If the primary voltage is held constant as in part *a*, to what value will the tertiary voltage rise if the secondary load is removed? Consider that the tertiary load behaves as a constant resistance.

TABLE OF CONSTANTS AND CONVERSION FACTORS FOR RATIONALIZED MKS UNITS

Constants

Permeability of free space, $\mu_0 = 4\pi \times 10^{-7}$ weber/amp-turn m
Permittivity (capacitivity) of free space, $\epsilon_0 = 8.854 \times 10^{-12}$ coulomb²/newton-m²
Acceleration of gravity, $g = 9.807$ m/sec²

Conversion Factors

Length:	1 m = 3.281 ft
	= 39.37 in.
Mass:	1 kg = 0.0685 slug
	= 2.205 lb (mass)
Force:	1 newton = 0.225 lb
	= 7.23 poundals
Torque:	1 newton-m = 0.738 lb-ft
Energy:	1 joule (watt-sec) = 0.738 ft-lb
Power:	1 watt = 1.341×10^{-3} hp
Moment of inertia:	1 kg-m² = 0.738 slug-ft²
	= 23.7 lb-ft²
Magnetic flux:	1 weber = 10^8 maxwells (lines)
Magnetic flux density:	1 weber/m² = 10,000 gauss
	= 64.5 kilolines/in².
Magnetizing force:	1 amp-turn/m = 0.0254 amp-turn/in.

INDEX

I